STANDARD SEAMANSHIP

FOR THE

MERCHANT SERVICE

BY

FELIX RIESENBERG, C.E.

Master Mariner in Sail and Steam;
Lieutenant Commander, U. S. N. R. (Ret.)
Commanding Schoolship Newport, 1917-1918-1919; 1923-1924.
Member, American Society of Naval Architects and Marine Engineers.
Author of "Under Sail," "The Men on Deck," "Bob Graham at Sea," "Vignettes of the Sea," "Shipmates," "Log of the Sea," "Mother Sea," etc.

625 ILLUSTRATIONS

SECOND EDITION—SIXTH PRINTING

NEW YORK
D. VAN NOSTRAND COMPANY, INC.
250 FOURTH AVENUE

Printed in the United States of America

LANCASTER PRESS, INC., LANCASTER, PA.

Robert C. Kraet - 1st class Pilot and Master
24 Ketcham ave.,
Amityville, N. Y.

120

The S. S. Lewis Luckenbach

Length, 527′; Breadth, 40′; Depth, 28′; Tonnage, 14,400 D.W.; I.H.P., 5,000; Speed, 15 knots

This model represents an American freighter of ample tonnage and speed. The hold divisions are clearly shown and the economy in engine and boiler space is apparent. The vessel is an oil burner with twin screws driven by geared turbines. Cargo is handled by two sets of pair masts, connected by substantial mast bridges and by four groups of king posts. The steel bridge between the fore masts serves as a lookout station. Permanent cargo light reflectors are fitted to the pair masts under the bridges. Hatch covers are painted green on starboard side and red on port side and correct placing is assured by white diagonal lines. At the forward end of each hatch half length hatch covers are fitted for convenience in opening to enter holds, or to ventilate. Clear decks, clean lines and shipshape gear throughout distinguish this type of cargo carrier.

To my sailor son

MIDSHIPMAN WILLIAM P. RIESENBERG

United States Navy

The seaman carries on in open competition with the world. Only the most able and efficient nations prosper in the constant commercial struggle waged upon the sea. The ocean cargoes of the world always move through channels of the least resistance—of lowest total transportation cost.

The owner, underwriter, seafarer and the maritime nations they represent, measure their prosperity by the standard of ability, energy and integrity engaged in the management of shipping.

PREFACE

When the sea and men and ships were brought together at the beginning of the ancient craft of seamanship, the range of man's vision extended with his conquest on the sea. The dreadful superstitions of land-locked people gradually gave way before the enlightenment and freedom of the seas—the seaman moves forward in the very vanguard of human progress.

Without the sailor, and without the heroic heritage with which he has endowed the world, men today would live in dark and hopeless isolation. In the old days the boldest sought the sea—the most daring men were those who voyaged far beyond the blue horizon. And today, when everything at sea seems safe, sailors handle mighty vessels thousands of times as great and more difficult to manage than those with which the art of seamanship began.

The work of the sailor, as his name implies, started with the use of the winds, the spreading and management of sails. Propulsion by means of oars continued for many years after sails came into use. The Phœnician galleys and the long ships of the Vikings combined both oars and sails. The long voyages of the world, however, were first made possible by sail. The *nef* and the *caravel* and the larger and more able craft that followed, on to the time of the *Great Republic* and the ships of her day, carried the art of sailing to a high state of perfection. Then came a third transition in motive power at sea. Boilers and engines were placed in the hulls of ships and seamanship combined the art of sailing with the art of handling vessels by their own power applied through paddle wheels or screws. For centuries the sailor had managed his craft alone, after the passing of the oarsman, and then he was joined by a new seafarer, the ocean engineer.

Always the old processes of seamanship have undergone their changes. Oars—oars and sail—sail—sail and steam— and today we have steam and motor vessels covering the seas and able sailing craft still holding on and improving their opportunities in the world-wide lanes of trade. As fuel increases in cost sail comes back wherever voyages are long and freights too low to tempt the power carrier.

In the great field of power driven steel construction a vast economic struggle is in progress between the engines of Watt and Fulton, the turbines of Parsons and Curtis, and the motor of Diesel. And aside from this there is the competition of coal and oil fuel for the generation of steam. Overshadowing the giant struggle is the spirit of Faraday picking and choosing a prime mover for the final dynamo sprung from his discoveries.

As motive forces and materials of construction have improved the tonnage of vessels has increased until a point is near where limiting factors, both economic and material, tend to put an end to further growth in size. The thousand foot liner and the twenty thousand ton dead weight carrier are about the largest craft for trans-ocean service or for world-wide cargo trade. Sailing craft of seven to eight thousand dead weight tons are all that men may safely handle even with the most scientific sailing gear.

These larger faster craft have brought with them great demands upon the ancient art of seamanship. New and better gear is required. Steel and fiber ropes of superior make and of unprecedented size and strength are now employed. Tackle of all kinds is heavier, stronger. Anchor cables have reached an enormous size; anchors are being forged to as great a weight as fifteen tons. Boats have multiplied until the larger passenger carriers are covered with flotillas of small craft nested in twos and threes under huge mechanical davits with steam and electric hoists for their management. Forces have multiplied in every direction while crews, composed of able seamen, are smaller and often less able than before. And with all of this has come a tremendous increase in the value of property at sea, while thousands of lives are entrusted to the safety of a single ship.

In considering these matters we must always remember that the sea is no respecter of ships or persons. The sea is always ready, at the first sign of failure, to rush in and destroy the very craft it so readily supports upon the surface of the water. The sea is only safe and harmless so long as the ship is safe and seaworthy and ably handled. The great liner, with a gash in her side, becomes a very charnel house of death. In a few moments the safe and comfortable ship is a horrible trap. The great powerful craft rushing through the sea at express speed turns her power and her momentum into a dreadful cause of destruction when she piles upon a reef, rams an iceberg, or cuts down another vessel.

No matter how important a man at sea may consider himself, unless he is fundamentally worthy the sea will some day find him out. If a wrong move is made at sea, in a critical moment, death may be the penalty for the most simple failure—not only death to one but to many. Incompetence may prevail upon the shore but at sea it sooner or later is ruthlessly uncovered and utter disaster often follows in its wake. The strong feeling among seafaring men that disaster is disgrace has its origin in this ancient law of the sea. The master going down with his ship signifies the inward feeling of the man who has lost all when he has lost his shield of honor. His seamanship has failed in the great emergency, or, lulled by false security, he has neglected some precaution and many lives, other than his own, are the price of his neglect. To live longer under such a burden would be too much so he pays the price of failure with his life.

This tradition of the master's responsibility is further emphasized by the fact that, no matter why his vessel founders, he must be the last to leave his sinking ship. These basic things, grown out of actual and constant contact with danger, place the art of seamanship upon the very highest plane of responsible employment.

An understanding of the points of seamanship is of great importance to all who contribute toward the construction and equipment of vessels. The naval architect and the designing engineer and builder should at least have a sound working knowledge of seamanship. This has not always been the case and the opinion of seaman, in the merchant marine at least, is too seldom considered by those who plan the structures the seaman must later on manage at sea.

With the increase in the use of power has come a feeling of segregation between the sailormen and engineers. The great engines are a mystery to most of those who work on deck, the ground tackle, cargo gear and boats are strange to those who work below. In the very old days the men who rowed were chained to their benches at the galley oars. Today men are held by rules and customs that chain them to their special jobs. Some day, many, many years from now, perhaps, seamen and engineers will be one crew performing their duties in rotation, ready at all times for the call of "all hands" to do a job of sailorizing or of engineering as the case may be. Officers will alternate between the bridge and the engine room and the master and chief engineer will be one. Those below will get a breath of fresh air and a wider outlook, those on deck, and on the bridge, will be more able and better men. Sticking too close to one grindstone, as we do today, makes us clever on the one hand and blind on the other. In the meantime ocean going engineers should know as much as possible about the launching and handling of small boats and should be familiar with the use and purposes of ground tackle and cargo gear. Everywhere on board ship the functions of the seaman and the engineer interlock and combine and their duties bring with them the necessity for intelligent cooperation.

In 1757 the French *savant* Pierre Bouguer, distinguished as a profound mathematician and geodesist, noted the lack of treatises on seamanship compared with the abundance of books on navigation. To a certain extent this lack of writing on the art of seamanship exists today and always will so long as men must write from first hand knowledge. Seamen, since the beginning, have handed down much of their knowledge by word of mouth and through hard experience. Old men become clever in the lore of the sea by actual physical contact with its forces. In every age the most useful things survive and are passed onward and in seamanship we still employ many ancient knots and tools. Seamen of today follow customs and use many phrases once current on the exploring, fighting and trading ships of the distant past.

The outstanding books on seamanship have been so few that the list is worthy of recording. In 1777 William Hutchinson wrote *A Treatise on Practical Seamanship.* D'Arcy Lever's

Young Officer's Sheet Anchor appeared in 1835. In 1841 Richard Dana of *Two Years Before the Mast* fame, published his *Seamen's Friend,* a manual containing valuable data on the seamanship of his day. In 1845 Tinmouth published his interesting *Inquiry Relative To Various Points on Seamanship.* Brady's *Kedge Anchor,* Stevens' *On Stowage,* Luce's *Seamanship,* and the seamanships of Nares and Alston followed in due course, all of them exclusively the seamanship of sail. Stevens, in his later editions, shows the stowage of steamers.

Late in the last century Captains Todd and Whall published their *Practical Seamanship for The Merchant Service,* a work to first take up the problems growing out of steam, though still devoted, in large part, to the sailing craft of the time. This excellent book has been revised and while out of date on many points contains much valuable information and is still in large demand. Then we have the naval seamanships of Knight and Henderson and the *Manual of Seamanship* of the British Admiralty. Admiral Knight's excellent *Modern Seamanship* is the official text book of the United States Navy. All of these latter books are mainly devoted to the seamanship of steam, and none of them treat of modern merchant service developments. Stowage, the tanker, cargo gear, winches, the preparation of cargo holds and the special problems incident to the carriage of live stock, or passengers, are not included in the naval books.

For some years it has been evident that a new work on seamanship is needed by the merchant seaman. Great progress has been made in ship construction and handling and many special safety devices and appliances have come into general use. The great increase in the number of persons carried afloat, the added danger and responsibility, seems to call for a comprehensive presentation of the art as it stands today.

The author has been engaged in the preparation of this book during the greater part of the last four years, having begun preliminary work on the seamanship soon after taking command of the Schoolship *Newport* in the summer of 1917, and continuing since his retirement from that post in the spring of 1919. Generous and valuable assistance has been rendered him from many sources and he has attempted to fully acknowledge this in the foreword and in the text.

Standard Seamanship is offered to those serving at sea and is also modestly suggested as of value to those who design build, own and insure ships. It is the hope of the author that the book may aid in the attainment of a broad and sound foundation in seamanship among the younger members of a most useful, and important profession.

Felix Riesenberg

New York,
January 2, 1922

PREFACE TO THE SECOND EDITION

This new edition of Standard Seamanship finds the work still held in esteem by seamen after fifteen years of use at sea. Our Merchant Service Schoolships have largely adopted it as a text, and it has even found a place on board the Belgian Schoolship *Mercator*. Naval designers, shipbuilders and shipping operators have made use of it. Many seamen have written me. Their criticisms have been kindly and constructive and of value in keeping the book up to date. I wish to here, publicly, thank the many friends of the book.

The fundamentals of seamanship remain as they always were and always will be. The art must be acquired at sea, thoroughly from the keel up. There is nothing in the idea that seamanship is being displaced by engineering. Seamanship is one of the earliest forms of engineering. It employed the principle of the airfoil centuries before men learned to fly. Every act of seamanship is dependent upon some application of mechanics and it is a growing part of seamanship that it will soon require those who handle the ship as a whole, her rudder, propellors, anchors, masts, booms, and boats, to also be familiar with her machinery below decks.

Weather knowledge is as important now as it was in former times—for a while this truth was neglected. Visual signals, in the Merchant Service, have become subordinate to radio. This is unfortunate for visual signalling is at its peak in the Navy. In time of war ships will have to rely largely upon flags, semaphores and lights for their communications.

The newer seamen, deprived by circumstances of the benefits of rigorous training in sail, are evidencing renewed interest in the many points of seamanship to be acquired on board modern vessels. The rigging of cargo gear, the purchasing of heavy weights, the management of boats carried high above the water, calls for great skill. Their responsibilities have increased with the growth in size and the higher speeds of vessels.

Felix Riesenberg

San Francisco,
June 6, 1936

CONTENTS

CHAPTER I

TYPES OF VESSELS

I

Steam and Motor Vessels

Steamers and other vessels depending upon mechanical propulsion now form the bulk of overseas carriers and may be roughly divided into two classes—*Liners*, and *Tramps.*

Liners may be considered to include all vessels plying between definite ports and running on a more or less well defined schedule, whether carrying passengers, cargo, or both.

Tramps are generally understood to be vessels engaged in cargo carrying, their movements governed by the freights that offer. Tramps are usually of moderate tonnage and draft, designed to enter many ports, and of slow speed and low fuel consumption. Economy of operation and adaptability as cargo carriers are the factors kept foremost in their design.

The above division is one based on use rather than design, but in either case we have vessels of marked characteristics only fitted for certain services. The large mail steamer, of great tonnage and speed, only able to enter deepwater ports, with special terminal facilities, must necessarily be a liner. Ranging down from this we have a great variety of ocean craft.

The many kinds of vessels met with at sea, and seen in the ports of the world, have been called into existence through balancing of the wide range of requirements and restrictions governing the building and operating of steamers. A few of the things entering into the design of ocean craft are given for the consideration of the seafaring man for whom this book is being written.

Depth of water in harbors likely to be used.
Dock dimensions at terminals.
Length of runs to be made. } *Direct factors in figuring bunker*
Speed desired. } *spaces, horsepower and tonnage.*

Classes of passenger trade.
Possible service as cruisers, or transports.
Weather conditions and sea conditions to be met on contemplated routes.
Kinds of fuel available.
Most economical materials of construction.
Labor costs of fabrication.*
Kinds of cargo to be carried:

General, Grain, Coal, Oil, Molasses, Cotton, Livestock, Lumber, Combustible materials, Acids, Explosives, Perishable, such as frozen meats, fruits, Fertilizer, Heavy machinery, Ore, Sulphur, etc.

Size of vessel will also depend somewhat on the amount of cargo generally available. The type of cargo handling gear will depend upon kind of cargo, condition of lading and discharging, whether at wharves, or into lighters, and the pumps, refrigerating machines, winches, masts, booms, and king posts, are also largely a result of existing conditions, all gradually being improved through experience. For instance, winches on deck, close to the hatch coamings, have often proven in the way, and now many vessels are fitted with *winch platforms*, lifting this machinery clear of the deck, and clear of the washing of the sea in all but the heaviest weather. The winchmen have a better view of their work, if well placed, and greater efficiency results from improved design.

The sea officer and engineer should constantly study his vessel with such considerations in mind and many suggestions of value will be carried ashore to the ship architect and designer.

The result of growing experience is standardization, and now certain recognized types of vessels are being evolved as best fitted for particular trades. The development of better engines, the use of oil fuel, either under boilers or direct, are large factors in the changing design of ocean craft.

* The general design of cargo ships is also determined by considerations of first cost and operating cost.

Limiting size will be determined, therefore, by the amount of money the owners may desire to put in a single ship, in combination with other factors.

Types of Vessels

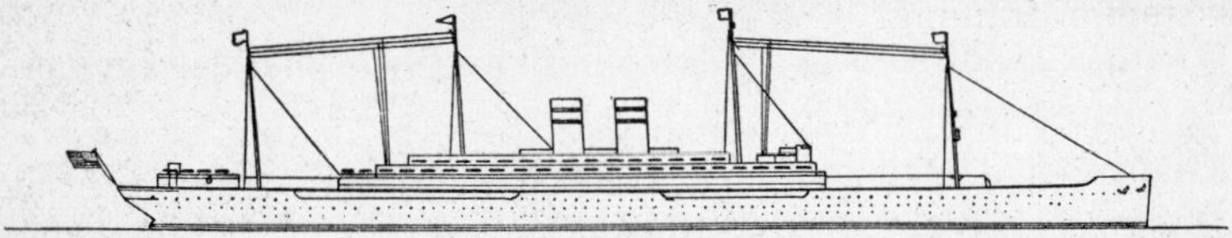

Fast Transatlantic and Transpacific Express. Oil burning, turbine engines geared direct, or electric drive. Loaded displacement 30,000 to 60,000 tons. High speed, large passenger accommodation, mail and special cargo only.

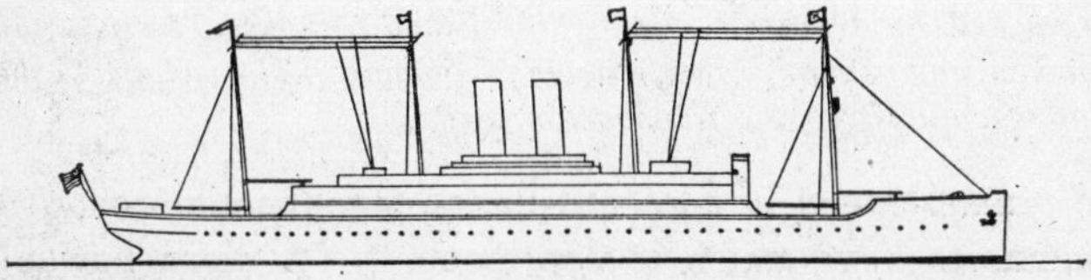

Slower, passenger and mails. Vessel designed for service to South American ports, Africa, The Mediterranean Ports, and for tourist cruising. Moderate cargo holds. Oil or coal burning reciprocating or turbine engines. 10,000 to 30,000 tons loaded displacement.

The two types illustrated are capable of a large range of variation but both show the characteristics of such large passenger craft. Harbor depths, wharves and length of run are limiting factors.

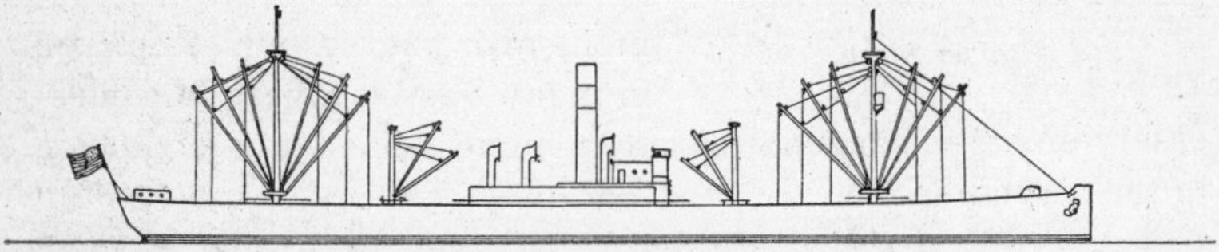

The S. S. Texan, 18,000 tons loaded displacement. A typical American cargo carrier. Reciprocating engines.

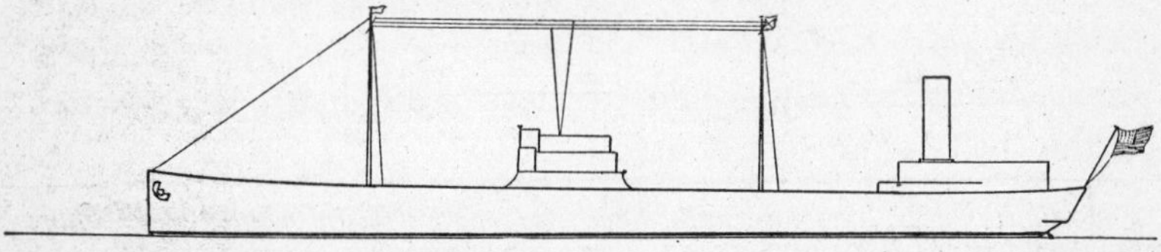

A steam tanker. Wide range of tonnage. The motor tanker fitted with Diesel type engines is entering this field. Most tankers have their power plant aft and bridge amidships.

The tanker is being largely constructed on the longitudinal system of framing.*

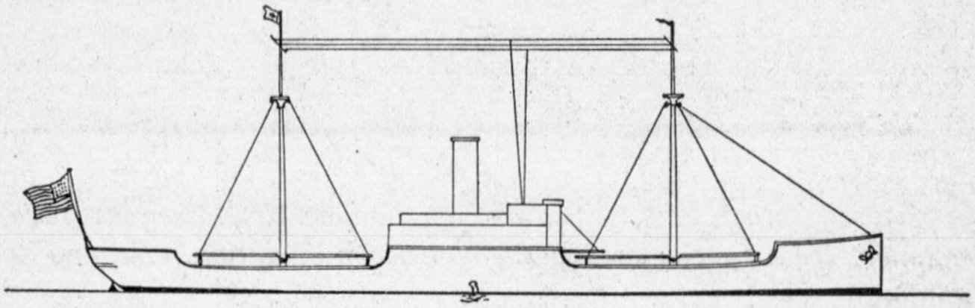

Well decked cargo carrier, the " three island " type. This is a favorite tramp model, and is built in a wide range of tonnage. The well decks, housed over, are often used for the transport of cattle.

The *cruiser stern* is a recent development in merchant craft and seems to have much to commend it. A stern hawse pipe fitted with a large stern anchor of the stockless type, is a handy arrangement from the point of seamanship, and the stern windlass engine can operate the poop capstans.

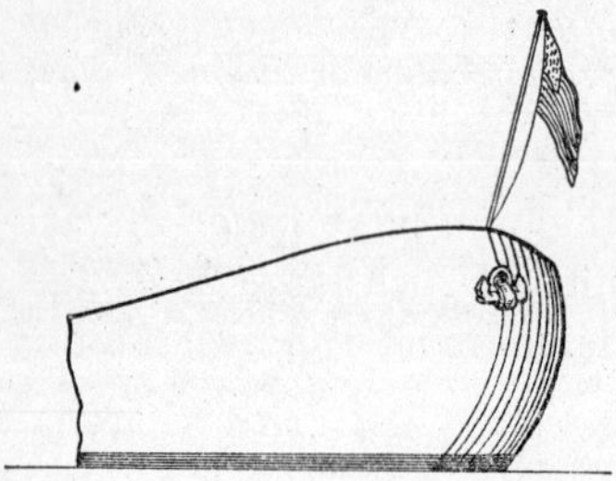

Cruiser Stern

Having the stern anchor handy, to be let go in an instant, or lowered in a boat, is an improvement over the system employed in many vessels where this necessary emergency anchor is often found lashed to a stanchion in the 'tween deck.

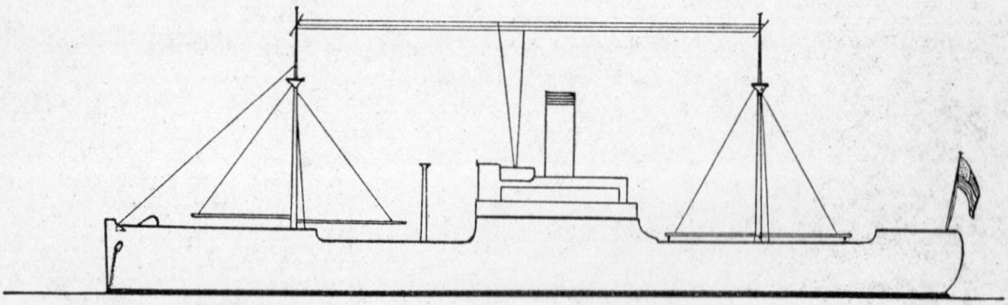

Freighter with long forecastle head, fore hatch on forecastle head, short forward well deck, and long after well deck. Cruiser stern. Wide range of tonnage.

* The Isherwood and the Gatewood systems of longitudinal framing are most used.

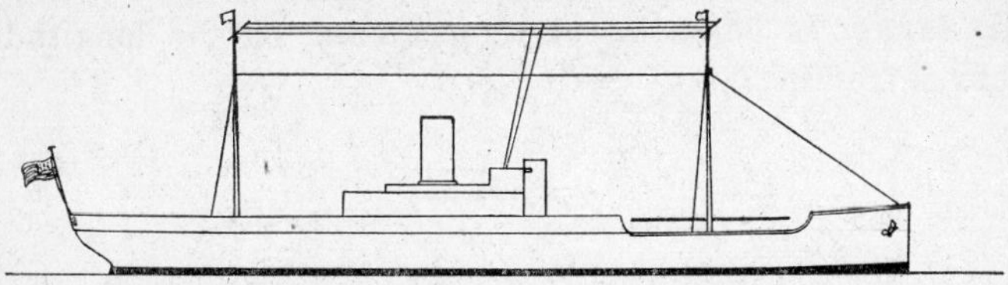

Well deck forward, topgallant forecastle, and long poop. Passenger carrier in limited trades, cargo and passengers from port to port in coast line service. Tonnage range from 2,000 to 10,000.

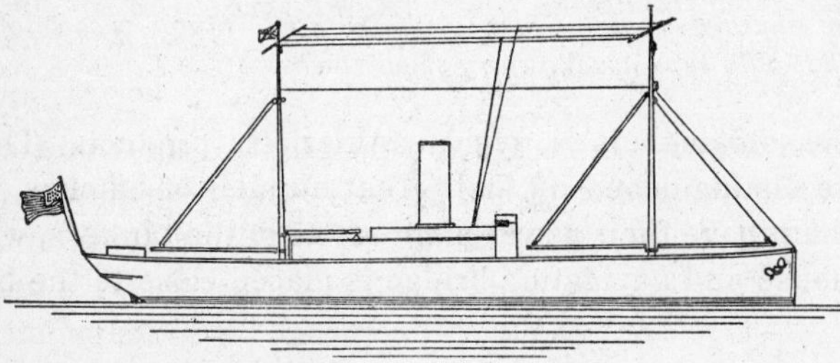

Flush deck. Awning decked construction. Coastwise, cargo and possibly small passenger accommodation. 1,000 to 6,000 tons approximate range of displacement. Fruit steamers are generally of this type and are usually painted white.

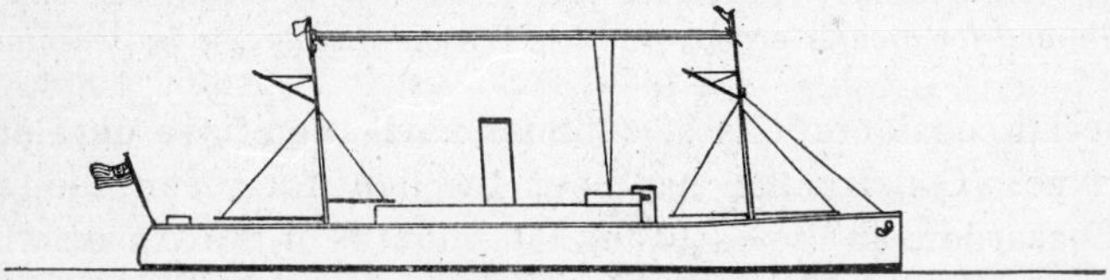

Spar decked, cruiser stern, cargo and small passenger accommodation. Moderate tonnage.

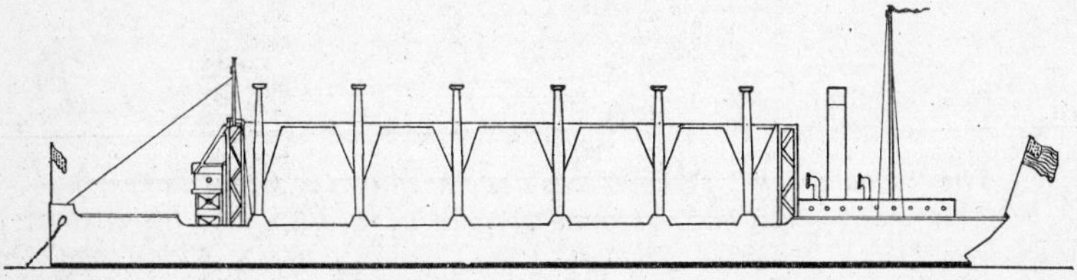

A United States naval collier. A highly specialized type of craft for quick coaling operations at sea, or in port, from ship to ship.

The motor vessel. The passing of the funnel, comes to us with almost as great a shock as the passing of sail. Something has gone and there is nothing to take its place. The motor ship, as it is generally styled, comes with as wide a variety of design as does the steamer. When the stack goes a great deal of dirt and waste of fuel will go with it. Motor vessels of the Diesel and hot-bulb type usually carry small stacks.

The lake steamer is a typical American product. These vessels are distinguished by their great number of hatches, and many of them have their power plant aft as in the tankers, while the pilot house and navigating bridge is placed close to the bow.

The "lake steamer," developed for the carriage of grain, coal, and ore in bulk, and for greater economy in loading and discharging by machinery.

Special considerations of summer navigation have developed this type. Construction has been too light for ocean use, and even hazardous in the early and late months of the season when the great inland lakes are often swept by heavy storms.

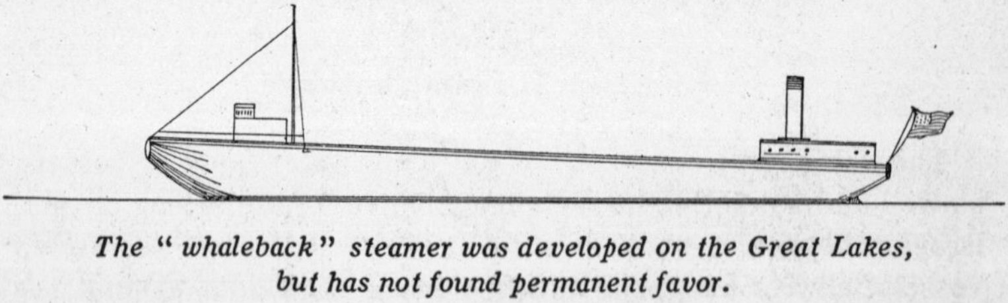

The " whaleback " steamer was developed on the Great Lakes, but has not found permanent favor.

A number of other special types of seagoing craft have been designed and some have achieved considerable use.

Holms, in his standard work, "Practical Shipbuilding" describes the turret deck steamer as follows:

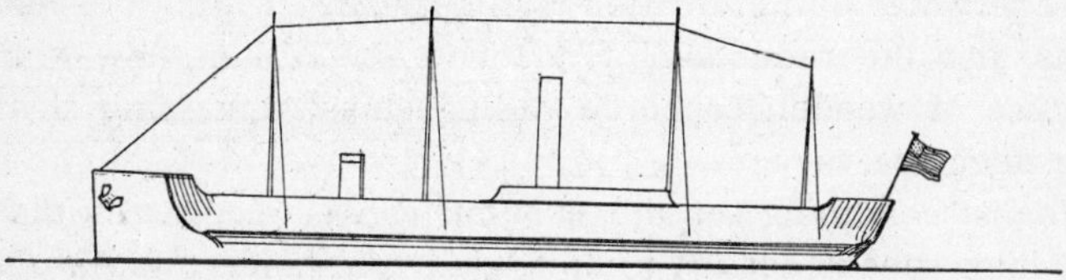

The "turret deck" steamer has been very popular with the British, and presents certain advantages from a measurement standpoint.

"The Turret-deck type, now practically obsolete, may be regarded as a development of the American whale-back; the only resemblance, however, is in the rounded gunwale and the absence of sheer; under water the hull is of normal form. Its peculiarity lies in the fore-and-aft superstructure, which resembles a continuous high-coaminged hatchway, decked over, however, except in the way of the hatchway openings; it is termed the 'turret deck.' Several advantages are claimed for this design, particularly its suitability for carrying grain in bulk."

In the sketches of vessels relative size is partly indicated by the proportion of the upper works.

Extreme size in vesel construction seems to have been reached. The pre-war competition between Great Britain and Germany in the Transatlantic Trade was bringing forth such monsters as the *Leviathan* (formerly the *Vaterland*), the *Imperator,* and the *Bismarck,* while the British came back with ships like the *Aquitania.* Then, in 1935 and 1936, followed the French Liner *Normandie* and the Cunard-White Star Liner *Queen Mary.**

Advances in Naval Architecture

The value of streamlining of the underwater body of vessels, so well understood in the high development of the sailing clipper, is again becoming a major factor in the design of power driven vessels, always balancing the fine block coefficient against the ability to carry cargo.

* The largest ships of the world are listed. Figures from Lloyd's Register:

Maierform hulls, bulbous bows, the Oertz Rudder, the contra propellor, all are an indication of the studies and improvement here and to come.

Underwater hull protection and surfacing, leading to smoother skins and the reduction of friction, are also in line with the practice of wooden coppered sailing ships, remaining clean on long deep sea voyages.

The streamlining, of the superstructure, recognizes the fact that high speeds set up greater wind resistances, and as in the automobile ashore, these studies are being carried on at sea. The *Normandie* is an outstanding example of this type of design.

Propulsion is going toward higher steam pressures and superheat of a high degree, steam through turbines, and probably the final use of mechanical reduction gearing between the prime movers and the shafts.

Oil firing takes the place of coal, with a trend toward the combined use of colloidal fuel. (See footnote, page 32.)

The status of the large motor vessel, driven by Diesel engines, seems, for the time, to be in the balance. Engineers agree that there is a limitation as to the size of efficient Diesel motors. But in smaller craft, rapid advances are being made. The gasoline driven launch and lifeboat seems at an end of its use, largely because of fire hazard, Diesel power taking its place.

Name.	Registered Tonnage.	L'gth Bet. Per-p'dic.	Breadth.	Name.	Registered Tonnage.	L'gth Bet. Per-p'dic.	Breadth.
		Ft. In.	*Ft. In.*			*Ft. In.*	*Ft. In.*
Queen Mary, Br....	80,772	1,004 0	118 0	Columbus, Ger.....	32,565	749 6	83 1
Normandie, Fr......	80,000	981 4	117 9	*Augustus, It.......	30,418	710 9	82 8
Majestic, Br........	56,599	915 5	100 1	Statendam, Holl....	28,291	674 2	81 3
Berengaria, Br......	52,101	883 6	98 3	Champlain, Fr......	28,124	606 5	83 0
Bremen, Ger........	51,656	898 7	101 9	*Georgic, Br........	27,759	683 6	82 4
Rex, It............	51,062	879 9	97 0	Cap Arcona, Ger....	27,561	643 6	84 6
Europa, Ger........	49,746	890 2	102 1	*Britannic, Br......	26,943	683 6	82 4
Leviathan, U. S.....	48,943	907 6	100 3	Empress of			
Conte di Savoia, It..	48,502	814 6	96 1	Japan, Br........	26,032	644 0	83 8
Aquitania, Br.......	45,647	868 7	97 0	Conte Grande, It....	25,661	652 2	78 3
Ile de France, Fr....	43,450	763 7	92 0	*Lafayette, Fr......	25,178	577 2	77 6
Empress of				Columbia, U. S.....	24,578	670 4	78 4
Britain, Br.......	42,348	733 3	97 8	Conte Biancamano,			
Paris, Fr..........	34,569	735 4	85 3	It............	24,416	650 9	76 1
Homeric, Br........	34,351	751 0	83 3	Manhattan, U. S....	24,289	668 4	86 3
Roma, It...........	32,583	705 6	82 8	Washington, U. S...	24,289	668 4	86 3

II

Sailing Craft

Sailing craft have always been an important part of the merchant marine of the United States and, at the present time, 1921, nearly a million and a half gross tons of our shipping are propelled by sail alone, or by sail and motor. The high cost of fuel, frequent delays in bunkering, and the added cost of the engineering crew, make the sailer an economic factor in the carriage of cargo overseas. Bulk cargoes, lumber, and, in fact all non-perishable goods are easily transported by sail over the long routes where trade wind conditions make for speed almost equal to that of the slow tramp. Sailing craft have increased in size and today we have the five masted bark *France*, the largest sailing craft afloat. She flys the French flag and is the logical outcome of the many years of consistent development of long voyage sailing ships and *sailors*, by the French Government. The *France* displaces 10,500 tons and carries a deadweight of 7,500 tons. She is 430 feet over all and 55.8 feet beam, and spreads 75,000 square feet of sail. The *France* has averaged 17 knots for a day's run; her crew consists of fifty-five men.*

* The American clipper ship *Sovereign of the Seas*, as recorded by Captain Arthur H. Clark in his *Clipper Ship Era,* is supposed to have attained bursts of speed up to 19 knots, making an average days run of 17⅔ knots on March 18, 1853. She did this with a sprung foretopmast, *fished* by the crew. Her complement was 105 men and boys, *eighty of these were able seamen*, not counting the officers, a Master and four Mates, two boatswains, two carpenters, and two sailmakers. She carried under three thousand tons dead weight.

Other fast runs under sail, all of them in excess of the above, and all made by American built ships, are the following:

Ship *James Baines*, Black Ball Line, January, 1855, when running the easting down, bound out to Melbourne, day's run—420 knots.

Ship *Donald McKay*, Black Ball Line, Feb. 27, 1855, Boston to Liverpool, on her maiden voyage, day's run—421 knots.

Ship *Lightning*, Black Ball Line, March 19, 1857 when running the easting down bound out to Melbourne, day's run—430 knots.

This same ship, on her maiden voyage, Boston to Liverpool, logged the world's record day's run on March 1, 1855—436 knots.

The ship *James Baines* hung up the world's record for hourly speed. The following is from her log book:

" June 17th. (1856), Lat. 44, S., Long. 106, E., ship going 21 knots with main skysail set." The *James Baines* sailed under British colors.

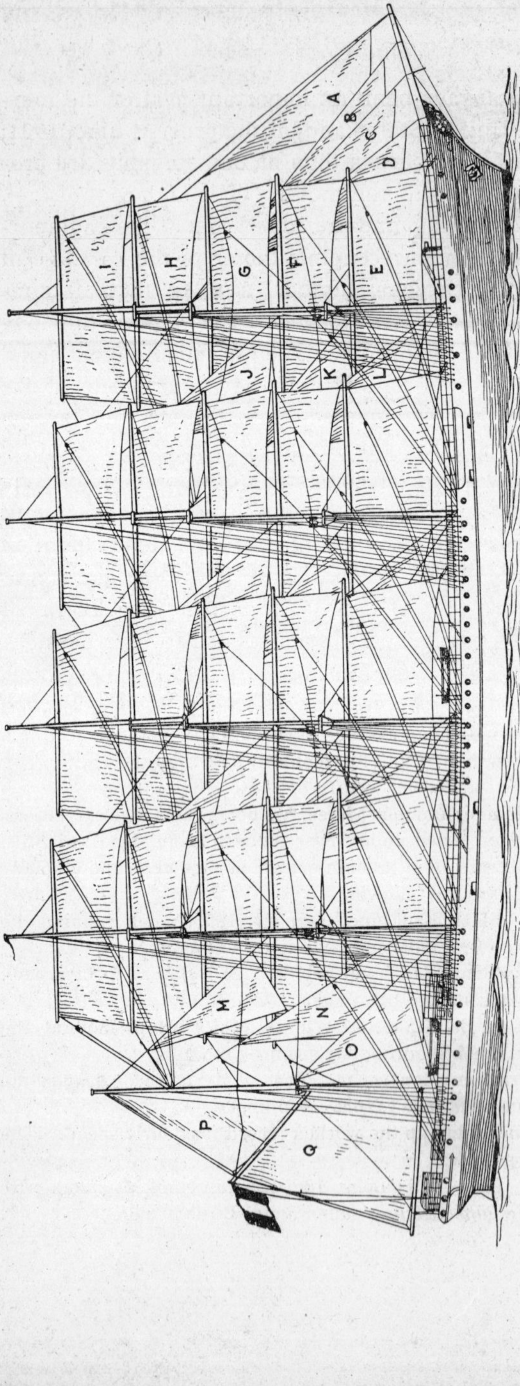

The Five Masted Bark France, A steel vessel with lower and topmasts of steel and in one piece.

A—Flying jib. B—Outer jib. C—Jib. D—Fore topmast staysail. E—Fore sail. F—Fore lower topsail. G—Fore upper topsail. H—Fore lower topgallant sail. I—Fore upper topgallant sail. The other square sails have the same names with the mast prefix changed. The masts are Fore, Main, Mizzen, Jigger and Spanker. J—Main topgallant staysail. K—Main topmast staysail. L—Lower main topmast staysail. The other stay-sails not lettered being named the same way with the proper mast prefix. M—Spanker topmasts staysail. N—Lower spanker topmast staysail. O—Spanker staysail. P—Spanker topsail. Q—Spanker.

At the present time the rig coming into favor with Americans is the four and five masted barkentine, a good rig for working to windward and reasonably able in going before the wind. These craft are generally fitted with twin screw motors.

The problem of the present day of *large* ships and *small* crews is set forth by a very able sailor, Captain C. T. Larsen of Seattle, quoted in an excellent article by Mr. Fred. B. Jacobs, in the *Marine Review* of Aug., 1920, on the economic status of sailing craft. Captain Larsen's observations follow:

"In a very large sailing ship, the sails and rigging are too heavy for economical operation. The larger the sail is, the more difficult it is to take in during a gale and it often blows away. Again, it is much easier to get charters for the smaller vessels. Where a large steamer will take a cargo for half a dozen different ports, this procedure would not pay with a sailing ship on account of the extra expense and loss of time in moving from port to port.

"I do not think it would prove economical to carry the enormous spread of canvas that the old-time clipper ships did. A vessel would be compelled to carry an abnormally large crew and the extra sails and gear would be comparatively expensive, making the extra cost of operation more than offset the gain in speed.

Too much canvas expensive

"For certain trades it is more economical to operate sailing vessels than steamers. The lumber trade from the Pacific coast to Australia furnishes a good illustration because the prevailing winds are such that a sailing vessel can make good time. Some of the schooners and barkentines on the Pacific make excellent running time, up to 14 knots an hour. In the barkentine, *Koko Head*, while I was master, we made 336 miles one day and on the following day 305 miles. We also made the passage from Cape Flattery to Delagoa bay in 85 days, from Delagoa Bay to Newcastle, N. S. W., in 30 days and from Newcastle to Kahului, T. H., in 36 days.

Sailers economical

Speed

"Aside from the cannery ships operating on the Pacific coast, going to Alaska in the spring and coming back in the fall to lay up all winter at San Francisco, there are not many square-rigged ships or barks operated on the Pacific. There are, however, quite a number of barkentines and, in my opinion, the barkentine is the best rig of all. It offers a large spread of canvas to run with when the wind is aft and it also has the advantage of fore-and-aft sails when the wind is abeam, or forward of the beam.

The Barkentine

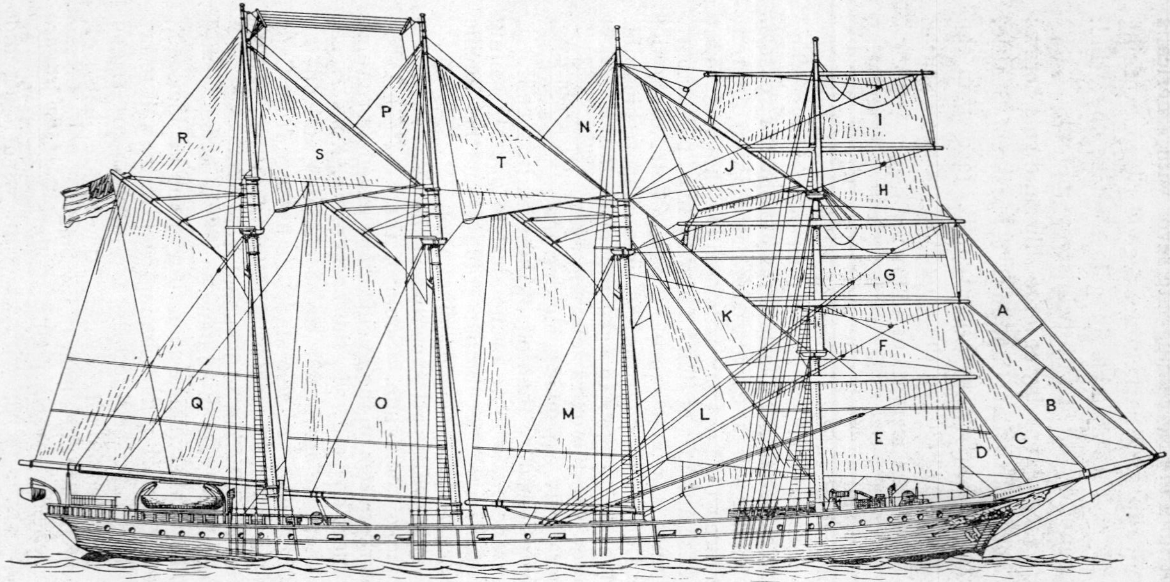

Four Masted Barkentine

Four and five masted barkentines are becoming numerous in the American Merchant Marine. Many of them are handsome models with full sail power and many carry auxiliary motors.

A—Flying jib. B—Outer jib. C—Jib. D—Fore topmast staysail. E—Foresail. F—Fore lower topsail. G—Fore upper topsail. H—Fore lower topgallant sail. I—Fore upper topgallant sail. J—Main topmast staysail. K—Upper main staysail. L—Main staysail. M—Mainsail. N—Main topsail. O—Mizzen. P—Mizzen topsail. Q—Spanker. R—Spanker topsail. S—Spanker topmast staysail. T—Mizzen topmast staysail.

"The large number of sails and yards on a square rigger make her difficult to handle in coming about as all the yards must be hauled. With the helm alee and the head of the ship within about a point and a half of the wind, if the order 'mainsail haul' is given and carried out just at the right moment, the yards will swing of themselves, as any deep water sailor knows. And if a good run is made with the braces, they can be run nearly sharp up on the other tack on one run. With an inexperienced crew, if the run is left until the ship's head is in the wind, the sail is becalmed and before it can be got sharp up, the wind on the other bow will cause a dead haul. This looks easy on paper but with the small crews allotted to modern square riggers it is a man's job.

Large number of sails

Difficulty of tacking

"Sometimes, when the wind shifts suddenly, a square rigger is caught all aback, that is, the wind is bearing on the forward part of the sails. Then the ship must be boxed off which calls for good judgment. Sometimes she refuses to box off in which case the officer on watch must proceed as if he were staying ship.

Ship taken aback

"Just imagine for a moment what it means to handle a square rigger on a night as dark as a 'score of black cats' and it is readily seen where seamanship of the highest order is required. Modern square riggers are not as easily handled as the shorter clippers of half a century ago. These ships could be brought about in heavy weather when under doubled reefed topsails and courses; that is, if the sea was not running too high. Present-day ships will not come about when under shortened sail and for this reason it is necessary to wear them around.

Long ships hard to handle

Modern ships must wear in heavy weather

"About the only advantage possessed by a bark over a ship, assuming that in both cases the vessel is a 3-master, is that the bark can be handled by a smaller crew. The spanker and the gaff topsail, being fore-and-aft sails, take care of themselves in tacking. The barkentine possesses a decided advantage in the opinion of many seamen over a bark or a ship in that it is easily handled, owing to the absence of a large number of square sails. Again, a barkentine possesses practically all the advantages of a schooner for working to windward with the added value of square sails for running free.

The bark needs smaller crew

"The principal advantage of a fore-and-aft rigged vessel is that it is quite easy to handle in tacking ship. With the fore-and-aft rigged craft, she is in her safest position with her head near the wind. There is no danger of being caught aback in tacking or

Advantages of fore and after

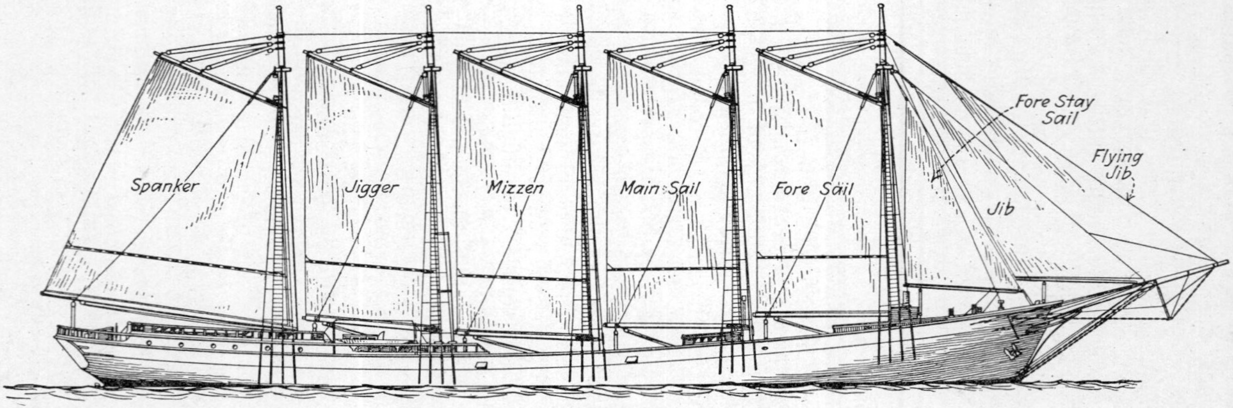

Five Masted Baldheaded Schooner

The baldheaded schooner is a rig found on many auxiliary craft. It is sometimes found on barges. The lower sails may be made somewhat larger and are generally fitted with special reef bands. Considerable labor is saved when the topsails are dispensed with. For a motor schooner it seems to be a success. For sailing alone the regular schooner appears the better rig. Most fore and aft sailors name the aftermast sail the spanker. The following method of naming the masts of a five master is coming into favor: Fore, Main, Middle, Mizzen, Spanker.

III

Tonnage

The tonnage measurement of vessels is determined in a number of ways depending upon the manner in which the measurement is intended to be applied. The different tonnage measurements are tabulated as follows:

Gross Tonnage
Net Registered Tonnage
Under Deck Tonnage
Deadweight Capacity
Displacement
Power-tonnage
Equipment-tonnage

Gross Tonnage, is the internal capacity of the vessel, expressed in units of 100 cubic feet. This unit is based on Moorsom's system of ship measurement in which the "ton" is arbitrarily figured at 100 cubic feet.

Net Registered Tonnage, sometimes referred to as *Registered Tonnage,* or the *Net Tonnage,* is arrived at by deducting from the gross tonnage the spaces taken by boilers, engines, shaft alleys, steering apparatus, chain lockers, chart house, officer's quarters, crew forecastle, and other spaces not available for the carriage of passengers or cargo.*

Net tonnage is used in computing harbor and port dues, canal tolls, and other tolls, except pilotage, where the draft is usually the unit of measurement in computing charges.

Under Deck Tonnage is somewhere between the Gross and Net tonnage measurement. It is the tonnage, by 100 cubic feet increments, measured below the second deck from below, that is

* A great part of the ancient commerce between France and England consisted of cargoes of wine carried in great casks, or *tuns.* The carrying capacity of different vessels was expressed in this unit, ultimately corrupted to *ton.* The weight of a tun of wine was approximately 2,000 lbs.

An exceedingly interesting paper, "*Rules for the Calculation of Tonnage and Their History,*" by Lieut. Commander Carl H. Hermance, U. S. N. R. F. may be found in the *Proceedings* of the U. S. Naval Institute, March, 1920. And, by the way, *all* Naval Reserve Officers should belong to the U. S. Naval Institute. The dues are $3.00 per year. The *Proceedings* are published monthly and are of exceptional professional interest. Address, the Secretary, Annapolis, Maryland.

tonnage below the *tonnage deck.* This deck is the upper deck in vessels having not more than two decks, and the second deck from below in vessels having three or more decks.

The U. S. Navigation Laws require that all spaces deducted from the gross tonnage be marked certifying to their use, such as, "Certified for steering gear;" "Certified for engine space;" "Certified for accommodation of Master;" "Certified for stowage of sails," etc.*

Certification legends must be permanently cut in a beam over the door leading to the respective places.†

Deadweight capacity is the actual carrying capacity of the vessel. It is the most sensible means of comparing cargo ships. It is simply the weight of the cargo the vessel can carry. In passenger craft, the deadweight carrying capacity varies through wide limits, depending upon the proportion of the vessel given over to cargo holds. Weight of fresh water, bunker fuel, stores and crew is included in figuring deadweight tonnage.‡

* The rules for the measurement of ships, to obtain the gross and net registered tonnage are lengthy and without the scope of a work devoted to seamanship. The reader who wishes to follow the subject of ship measurement further is referred to the following:

Measurement of Vessels, Department of Commerce, Washington, D. C. The charge for this is ten cents—it is very complete.

Instructions Relating to the Measurement of Ships, British Board of Trade, London.

Reglement de Navigation dans le Canal Maritime de Suez.

Simpson's *The Naval Constructor* gives concise rules governing the measurements for register tonnage, deductions for engine room, etc., and the subdivisions for measuring tonnage sections.

White's *Manual of Naval Architecture*, also gives detailed information on tonnage laws and measurements. This is an important subject and plays a large part in the ultimate design of merchant vessels.

† "Every documented vessel of the United States must have the figures denoting her tonnage deeply carved, or otherwise permanently marked, on the main beam. If the number cease to be so marked she shall be subject to a fine of thirty dollars on every arrival in a port of the United States while left unmarked." R. S. 4153, Sec. 5.

‡ Though 100 cubic feet of space are allotted to the ton in computing tonnage, in ascertaining freight charges based upon the bulk of the cargo, forty cubic feet only are allowed. This is the space occupied by a ton of good, close stowed steaming coal, and is not far from that required for a ton of average cargo.

A cargo ton is estimated either by weight or by measurement.

Displacement is the actual weight of the entire vessel and all that is in her. Displacement varies with the draft. This tonnage is figured in long tons (2,240 lbs.).*

Light displacement is the weight of the vessel with holds and bunkers empty.

Heavy displacement is the displacement when a vessel is completely loaded, cargo and bunker spaces filled, and vessel down to her deepest mark.

The tonnage of men of war is generally given in terms of displacement with normal coal and ammunition and other supplies on board.

Displacement in salt and fresh water varies, that is the amount of water displaced is more in fresh than in salt water. Thirty-five cubic feet of salt water weigh one long ton, and thirty-six cubic feet of fresh water also weigh one long ton. This gives rise to the greater draft of vessels in fresh water. A vessel loaded to her marks in fresh water will lift clear when coming into salt water, that is she can actually carry more cargo on a salt water voyage when loaded to the same draft.

The following rule is useful in this connection and should be remembered. Consider river water as weighing 63 lbs. per cubic foot, while salt water weighs 64 lbs. per cubic foot.

Therefore a vessel can be loaded to her marks in river water, and one sixty-fourth (by weight) added to her cargo. This will submerge her marks, but on entering salt water she will lift to her marks due to its greater density. That is, if 6,400 tons have been put on board, and the vessel is down to her marks,

* The weight ton in the United States and in British countries is the English long or gross ton of 2,240 pounds. In France and other countries having the metric system a weight ton is 2,204.6 pounds.

A measurement ton is usually 40 cubic feet, but in some instances a larger number of cubic feet is taken for a ton. Most ocean package freight is taken at weight or measurement (W/M), ship's option. Roughly speaking, the tons of cargo that can be carried by a freight steamer can be obtained by multiplying the net tonnage by 2.5.

For a modern freight steamer the following relative tonnage figures would ordinarily be approximately correct: *net tonnage, 4,000; gross tonnage, 6,000; deadweight carrying capacity, 10,000; displacement loaded, about 13,350.*

—*U. S. Shipping Board Bulletin.*

Displacement Tons	Draft	Dead Weight Tons	Free Board
	19		1
	18		2
	17		3
	16		4
2100	15	1410	5
1870	14	1180	6
1650	13	960	7
1440	12	750	8
1250	11	560	9
1075	10	385	10
925	9	235	11
800	8	110	12
690	7	0	13
	6		
	5		
	4		
	3		
	2		
	1		

Displacement and Dead Weight Scale

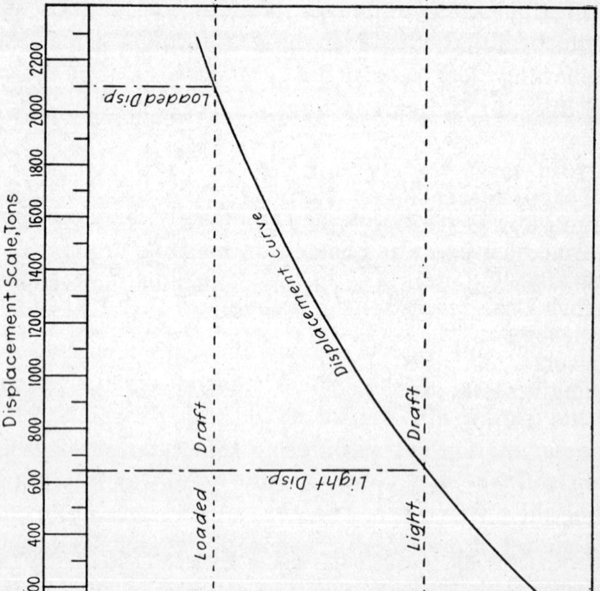

Displacement scale for a 2,100 ton vessel

100 tons more can be added if she is to go from fresh to salt water.*

The displacement measurement is most useful in the loading and trimming of vessels through the use of the *Displacement curve* and the *Tons per Inch* scale. All modern steamers are supplied with this curve and scale and from it the weight of the vessel can be taken by reading the draft, fore and aft, taking the mean, and setting it off on the scale.

To arrive at the displacement of a merchant vessel with a fair degree of accuracy estimate the *block coefficient* (if not known) that is the ratio of the volume of the ship under water to the volume of a block having length, breadth, and depth, equal to the length, beam, and draft of the vessel under consideration.

The following block coefficients or coefficients of fineness, are given by Biles, in *Design and Construction of Ships:*

Very full cargo vessels up to 8 knots	.85 to 9
Full cargo vessels up to 12 knots	.8 to 85
Large cargo vessels up to 12 to 14 knots	.76 to 82
Intermediate cargo and coastwise vessels	.65 to 7
Fast Atlantic Liners	.6 to 65
English Channel passenger steamers	.5 to 6
Battleships	.6 to 65
Cruisers	.48 to 55
Sailing vessels	.6 to 72
Yachts (sailing)	.3 to 52

Walton in *Know Your Own Ship* puts it this way with regard to estimating the coefficient of fineness, and, as estimating is more or less a matter of intelligent guess work, we give his directions:

* *Example:* A ship having 1,200 tons displacement, 12′ 6″ mean draft in sea water, and 6 tons per inch immersion at this draft; what would be her draft in fresh water?

First find volume displacement in fresh water, which is $1{,}200 \times 36 = 43{,}200$ cu. ft. From this, subtract volume displacement in sea water, which is $1{,}200 \times 35 = 42{,}000$ cu. ft. $43{,}200 - 42{,}000 = 1{,}200$ cu. ft., which is volume of layer or water plane between fresh and sea water drafts.

As the tons per inch immersion at this draft are 6; then the change in draft in inches $= \frac{1}{6} \times 1{,}200 \div 36 = 5.5$ in.; $5.5'' + 12'\ 6'' = 12'\ 11.5''$ draft in fresh water.

—From *The Naval Artificer's Manual, U. S. Naval Institute.*

.8 (coef. fineness), would be a very full vessel.
.7 to .75, an average cargo steamer.
.65, a moderately fine cargo steamer.
.6, a fine passenger steamer.
.5, an exceedingly fine steamer, but an average for steam yachts.
.4, a very fine steam yacht.

Let us figure the displacement tonnage of a vessel, taking our dimensions as follows.—Just to make it easy:

Length	600 feet
Beam	60 "
Draft	30 "

Our vessel is a large craft carrying passengers and cargo and we will assume her block coefficient to be .7.

Then we have the following calculation:

$$.7 \times \frac{600 \times 60 \times 30}{35} = 21{,}600 + \text{(approx.) tons displacement,}$$

35 being the cubic feet of sea water to a ton.

Power-tonnage is the sum of the gross tonnage and the indicated horsepower of the engines. This measurement was devised to provide a comparison between vessels for the purpose of determining their importance. It is sometimes used in allotting salary schedules for American Merchant Marine officers. A vessel of ten thousand gross tons and five thousand I.H.P. would be rated as of 15,000 *power-tons.* Also a craft of five thousand gross tons and ten thousand I.H.P. would be a 15,000 *power-tons* craft, the commands being considered of equal importance and entitled to the same rate of pay.*

* (Figures are inclusive)

Classes	Single Screws	Twin Screws
A	Over 20,001	Over 15,001
B	12,001 to 20,000	9,001 to 15,000
C	7,501 to 12,000	5,501 to 9,000
D	5,001 to 7,500	3,501 to 5,500
E	Below 5,001	Below 3,501

Vessels are classed according to their "power-tonnage," represented by gross tonnage plus indicated horsepower as given in the latest "List of Merchant Vessels of the United States," compiled by the Commissioner of Navigation.

Equipment tonnage. The Equipment Tonnage of a ship is that tonnage arrived at from certain dimensions given in the Classification Society Rules which take into consideration the exposed surfaces both above and below water, and is used primarily to determine the size of anchors, chains, and hawsers.

Equipment tonnage very closely approximates the gross tonnage in most ships of ordinary construction.

IV

Linear Dimensions

Other ship dimensions are often subject to confusion through careless use of terms. The following principal measurements are defined:

Length over all
Length between perpendiculars
Length, registered
Length for tonnage
Length by A.B.S. Rules*
Length on load water line
Floodable length
Depth moulded
Depth by A.B.S. Rules
Depth registered or *Depth of Hold*
Breadth moulded
Breadth registered
Draft—Freeboard—Load Line

Length over all is the distance between the forward and after extremities of the hull.

Length between perpendiculars is the distance from the forward side of the stem to the after part of the rudder post. When the stem or rudder post are raked, the measurement is taken through the intersection of the upper deck, or in the case of an awning decked vessel, or one with a shelter deck, the intersection of the second deck with the fore part of the stem and the after part of the rudder post.

When the stem is bent, as in a clipper bow, the straight middle part is extended up to meet the line of the deck from which the measurements are taken.

* A.B.S. American Bureau of Shipping.

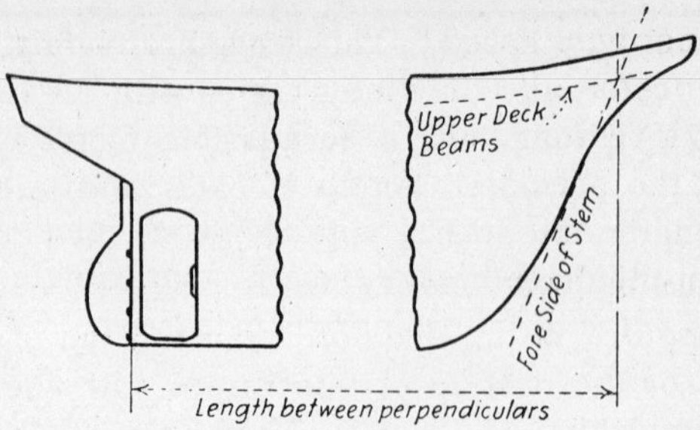

Length registered is the distance from the fore part of the stem, under the bowsprit, if any, to the after side of the head of the sternpost.

Length for tonnage is measured in a straight line along the tonnage deck from the inside of the inner plate at the bow to the inside of the inner plate at the stern, making allowance for the rake, if any, which the midship bow and stern members may have in the actual deck.

Length by A.B.S. Rules. The length is the distance in feet on the estimated summer load line, from the fore side of the stem to the after side of the rudder post; where there is no rudder post the length is to be measured to the center of the rudder stock.

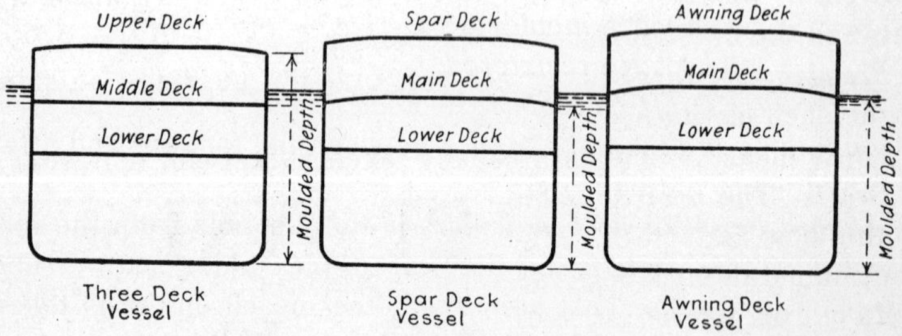

Length on load water line is the distance from the front of the stem to the after part of the rudder post, on the load water line.

Floodable length is the extreme length of compartment that can be flooded and the vessel still remain afloat with decks almost awash. Under the rules for bulkhead spacing a margin of safety must be allowed. This margin of safety is called the *permissible factor,* and the factor varies with the length of ship. A vessel 571 ft. long, has a permissible factor of 0.5, which means that the permitted length of each hold is only half the floodable length. In such a ship there are two compartments watertight in the floodable length.

Depth moulded is the distance from the top of the keel, or intersection of the outside of the frames with the center line, measured amidships, to the level of the top of the upper deck beam at the gunwale, or of the second deck in the case of awning and shelter deck vessels.

Depth by A.B.S. Rules, (D) is the molded depth in feet, measured at the middle of the vessel's length on the estimated summer load line, from the top of the keel to the top of the deck beams at side from which the freeboard is estimated. In cases where watertight bulkheads are carried to a deck above the freeboard deck and it is desired to have them recorded in the register as effective, D is to be taken to the bulkhead deck.

Depth registered, *or Depth of hold* is distance amidships from top of double bottom, or top of floors, or from a point 2.5 inches above these points where ceiling plankings if fitted, amidships, no matter what its thickness, to the top of the upper deck beams, or second deck beams in awning or shelter deck vessels.

Breadth moulded is the greatest breadth of hull measured between the outer surfaces of the frames.

Breadth registered is the greatest breadth measured outside of the shell plating.

These measurements are usually taken in feet and tenths.

Draft. The draft is taken at the bow and stern. The draft numerals must be *accurately cut* or painted on *both* sides of stem and stern post. Numerals are 6 inches high. The base of the numeral resting on the even foot. Inches are estimated by eye. Roman numerals are better marks, but ordinary arabic numerals are less easily mistaken.

Draft by A.B.S. Rules, (d) is the molded draft in feet from the top of the keel to the center of disc or summer load line. The draft to be used with the tables is not to be less than .66 the depth (D)

Freeboard and Load Line. The freeboard of a vessel is the height of the side above water level, measured at the middle of the vessel's length, that is at amidships from the top of the freeboard deck; the distance being determined in accordance with the Freeboard Tables. Under the British Regulations, the measurement is actually made from a line called "statutory deck-line," which is placed above the top of the freeboard deck, this modification being required by the British Merchant Shipping Acts.* As, however, the correction for the amount of statutory

* "The subject of loading of vessels is closely connected with the name of Samuel Plimsoll, who, as a member of Parliament, conducted in the early seventies of the last century a strong campaign for the fixing of load lines on vessels under the British flag. In Plimsoll's opinion the unusual number of disasters at sea that had been occurring for years were due chiefly to the overloading of vessels, and he contended that Parliament should establish a load line for every vessel.

"A royal commission, appointed to investigate the question, reported to Parliament in 1874 that the establishment of load lines could not be successfully accomplished by law, since no rule of universal application could be applied without injury to British shipping.

"Parliament, however, did not accept the recommendations of this commission and passed an act known as the merchant shipping act of 1876, which provided that a circular disk, with a line drawn through the center, should be painted amidships on both sides of every British vessel, except those under 80 tons register engaged in the coasting trade. This mark, which came to be known as Plimsoll mark, was to indicate the greatest draft to which vessels should be loaded. The fixing of the load line was in the first instance determined by the shipowner, but it was the duty of the Board of Trade to see that no overloaded vessel cleared from any British port.

"This indefinite method of procedure led to many disputes which were, in the course of time, settled by the general acceptance by the Board of Trade and shipowners of load-line marks fixed according to the reserve buoyancy tables of Lloyd's Register.

"No further action was taken in regard to this subject until 1890, when it was decided that the matter of load lines should be placed upon a more definite and scientific basis. Accordingly, in that year the load-lines act was passed. This act provided that the load lines should be marked in accordance with regulations provided by the Board of Trade, and that the position of the disk should conform with the tables fixed by the load-line committee. This act was deck-line is added on to the freeboard, as calculated from the table, the general definition given above is correct in practice.

The method of marking directly from the deck is used by the American Bureau of Shipping, which has officially adopted the British Freeboard Tables as the basis of its freeboard assignments. Further, as this particular requirement of the Merchant Shipping Acts in regard to the statutory deck-line has no application in this country, the American Bureau has been left free to adopt this somewhat simpler method of marking.

The *loadline* of a vessel is the draft to which the vessel is immersed when weighted down to the various markings on the sides, placed there in accordance with the requirements of the Freeboard Tables. The reserve buoyancy of a vessel is measured by the volume of the enclosed, or water-excluding, portions of a ship which come above the load water line. This amount depends upon the form of the upper structure of the ship and varies according to the draft to which the ship is immersed. . . .

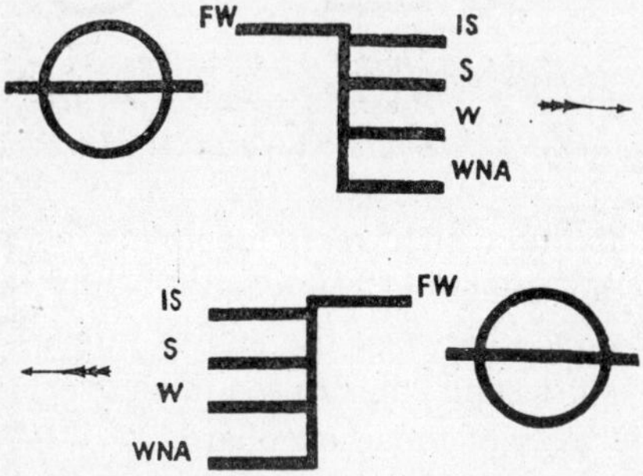

2

Plimsoll Mark for Steamers (arrow points forward)

FW = Fresh Water.

IS = Indian Ocean in Summer.

WNA = North Atlantic in Winter (October to March inclusive).

S = Summer in waters other than the Indian Ocean.

W = Winter in waters other than the North Atlantic.

All except the first of the above symbols indicate the maximum depth in salt water for the corresponding oceans and seasons.

reproduced in the merchant shipping act of 1894, sections 437 to 443, and provision was made for its modification by the Board of Trade without reference to Parliament."—From *Navigation Laws,* Special Agent Series No. 114, Department of Commerce, Washington.

The question of freeboards is primarily a question of safety of life at sea. Safety of ships and cargoes, and protection of the interests of shippers and underwriters are important in themselves; but it is the business of the Government to see that no special interests of one section of the community are served at the expense of any other section. Commercial and political ends must always be made subservient to the bigger considerations involved in the protection of human life and the Government owes it to its citizens to provide adequate legislation for the protection of the lives of those who go to sea.

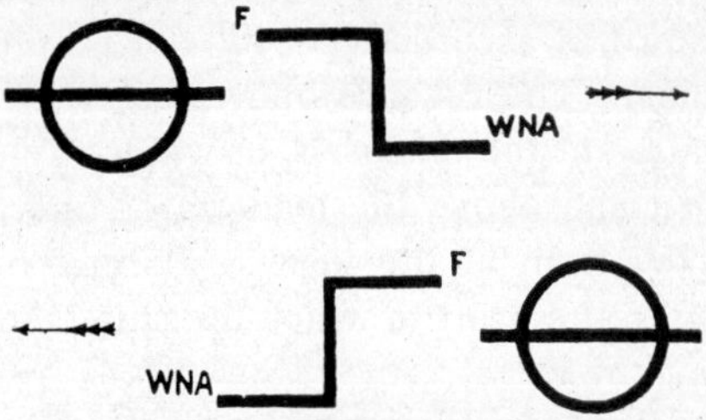

Plimsoll Mark for Sailing Vessels
F = Fresh Water.
WNA = Winter in North Atlantic.

The responsibility which rests upon a Government in this respect cannot be delegated elsewhere. Only the Government can hold the balance between the selfish interests of those who might be tempted to send ships to sea in an overloaded condition, at a risk to the lives of those on board.

The modern cargo ship loads, let us say from 30 to 40 tons per inch of immersion at the load water line. An extra foot of draft will, therefore, mean that the ship carries 360 to 480 additional tons of cargo, unless the owner is prevented from doing so by restrictions imposing on the vessel a definite maximum draft established by an independent and impartial authority.

The freeboard of a vessel depends upon a good many factors, among which are the following: Type of vessel, strength of hull and houses, sheer of deck, trade of vessel, time of year. Freeboard markings are placed on vessels by the American Bureau or Lloyds Register (if desired by the owner in this country), and their ruling should be followed, as a formula based on depth may not take into account the vessel's peculiarity. Associations such as The New York Underwriters' will often limit the draft. For full information about the British Board of Trade freeboard see pamphlet 'Freeboard Tables' published by them. An article by H. A. Everett published in the April, 1917, issue of *Marine Engineering* will be found very interesting. We quote from it as follows:

"The American Bureau *formerly* published a suggested freeboard allowance which in the cases of the ordinary cargo steamer will give a freeboard roughly one foot greater than that assigned by the Board of Trade. An abstract of this table is given below:

Depth of Hold from Top of Ceiling to Underside of Deck (Main Deck), Feet	Freeboard at Lowest Point of Sheer for Each Foot Depth of Hold, Inches
8	1½
12	2¼
16	2½
20	3
24	3¼
28	3½

"'Hurricane deck vessels having no water ports fitted at the second deck, also raised quarter deck vessels, may have less, but suggest that hurricane deck vessels have not less than one-half and quarter deck vessels not less than three-quarters of the freeboard in the table. The depth of hold and freeboard to be measured from the second deck in hurricane deck vessels. . . .'

"The following formula will give approximately the freeboard for an ordinary cargo vessel of over 20 feet depth, having a normal sheer, the freeboard being measured from the weather deck:

$$\text{"Freeboard} = .40 \text{ depth} - 6.0 \text{ (feet)}$$

"Depth = depth from top of keel plate to weather and strength deck (foot units)."

V

Propelling Machinery

The power plant of a mechanically propelled vessel is of such vast importance in the handling of the ship that a work on seamanship must at least enumerate the various kinds of power now being employed at sea. Further study by deck officers is highly desirable and many excellent books are to be had in this field.

Steamers may have their power plants conveniently divided into two components, the steam making apparatus, and the steam using apparatus, or into simply *boilers and engines.* Further classification is of course necessary.

Boilers can be divided as follows:

Fire tube boilers. Water and steam surrounding tubes, fire led through tubes and headers. The principal forms of the fire tube boiler are the following: *Scotch* boiler; *Vertical* boiler; *Locomotive* boiler; *Leg,* or *flue* and *return tube* boiler.

Water tube boilers. Water circulating inside of tubes, fire and hot gasses surrounding these tubes, steam collected in suitable drums, etc. The principle forms under which water tube boilers may be classified are the following: *Large* and *small* tube boilers; *Straight* and *curved* tube boilers. By the position of the tubes, viz., *inclined*, or *horizontal;* by the *arrangement* of the tubes, viz., in *groups*, or as *single tubes;* by the position of the upper ends in regard to water level, viz., into *drowned tube* and *priming tube*, boilers. In the drowned tube the end is below the water level, while the priming tube extends above the water level. By the arrangement of the circulation, as *single tube*, or *double tube* boilers.

The above statement will show that water tube boilers are capable of a great many variations in form. There are many boilers of this variety, combining different parts of the above classification and known by trade names. The water tube boiler roughly consists of steam drum or drums, on top, tubes, and bottom drums to supply the tubes with water. *Surrounding* these tubes and drums are the fires placed on suitable grates, and the hot gasses are made to be more effective by *baffles* and *headers.*

Further classification of the steam making part of the ship's power comes through the use of different fuels, namely coal, and oil, also a combination of coal dust and oil, known as *colloidal fuel*, and the method of burning, viz., *Natural draft* or *Forced draft.**

* The imperative need for increased supplies of liquid fuel, particularly for naval purposes, has prompted American engineers to investigate the prob-

Engines using steam may be classified as follows:

Reciprocating engines. Compound; triple, or quadruple expansion, the steam passing successively through, two, three, or four cylinders, gradually increasing in size before exhausting into the condenser. The *pressure* of the steam is used in high pressure, 1st intermediate, 2d intermediate and low pressure cylinders, in the *quadruple expansion* type.

Turbine engines in which the *velocity* of the steam, issuing from nozzles, and *impinging* against *guides* and *blades*, causes the direct *rotation* of the shaft upon which the turbines are mounted. As in the case of reciprocating engines, the steam is sent from one casing to another, gradually increasing in size, where its expansion is utilized.

Turbines in slow or medium speed vessels are only efficient when rotating more rapidly than is efficient, or possible, for a propeller immersed in water. For this reason the high turbine speeds must be reduced by suitable *reducing gears* attached to the propeller shafts. To go astern special *backing* turbine blades are brought into action, these are mounted on the same shaft as the going ahead blades.

Another power plant that has been tried is the combination of high pressure reciprocating cylinders, the lower pressure steam exhausting through them to low pressure turbines. This utilizes the smaller high pressure cylinders with their direct action against the shaft, and avoids the large low pressure reciprocating parts while using the smaller low pressure turbine principle. This type is no longer used because of the improved design of reducing gears.

Electric drive is used where steam driven turbines turn electric generators or dynamos. The current is then led aft to motor units attached direct to the propellor shafts. The largest

lem of incorporating solid and liquid fuels in such manner that the resultant mixture can be handled and utilized as ordinary oil fuel. The work was carried out under the auspices of the Submarine Defence Association with the assistance of the United States Navy Department, and the results are of importance as they promise not only conservation of oil fuel, but also utilization of low-grade solid fuel. This combination is called *Colloidal Fuel.*

example of electric drive is the French liner *Normandie.* The giant aircraft carriers, *U.S.S. Saratoga* and *U.S.S. Lexington,* are steam powered, turbine driven, electric propelled ships. But the newer navy craft have been designed to be driven by mechanical reduction gearing.

High pressure steam. Higher steam pressures with high degrees of superheat are coming into usage at sea. The Standard Shipping Company's *G. Harrison Smith,* a 20,000 ton tanker, is powered with De Laval turbines of 4,000 S.H.P. with double reduction gears, turning the propellor at 75 R.P.M., her Babcock and Wilcox water tube boilers supplying steam at 375 lbs. pressure and with 725 degrees of total steam heat and 28¼ inches of vacuum. This is a highly efficient plant.

Higher steam pressures, rising over 400 lbs. as on the *R.M.S. Queen Mary,* bring steam, through turbines, to greater economical use at sea. Still higher steam pressures are in the offing.

Motor ships:—The thermal efficiency of the steam engine, no matter how refined we may make it, will always be low, and the work delivered at the propellor per ton of coal, or oil, burned is shamefully small when compared with the theoretical heat energy contained in the fuel.

The internal combustion engine is making its way rapidly because of its greater economy both in space and fuel. Boilers are dispensed with, and the moving parts are less cumbersome per horsepower developed. With the coming of these engines we have the motor ship.

Motor power plants may be simply divided as follows:

Heavy oil engines such as the *Diesel,* and the *hot-bulb* engines depending for ignition on their high compression, the pressure developing heat sufficient to ignite the charge. Such engines can operate on practically any kind of oil fuel.*

* The mode of compressing air and injecting fuel into it for combustion, peculiar to the Diesel engine, is responsible for a very low fuel consumption, compared to automobile engines on the one hand, and also as compared to steam machinery on the other. This fuel oil consumption is equivalent to nearly 35 per cent. thermal efficiency for the Diesel engine, the actual weight of oil consumed depending somewhat on its quality.

—Dr. C. E. Lucke, Head of the Department of Mechanical Engineering, Columbia University.

Gasolene and *kerosene* engines, with electrical ignition, on the principle of the automobile engine.

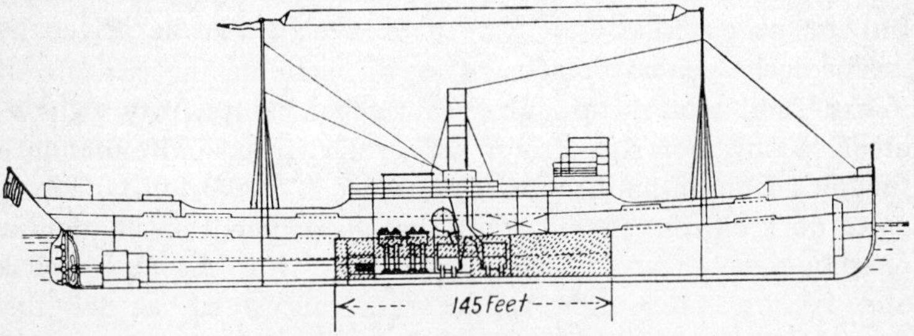

Reciprocating Steam Engine

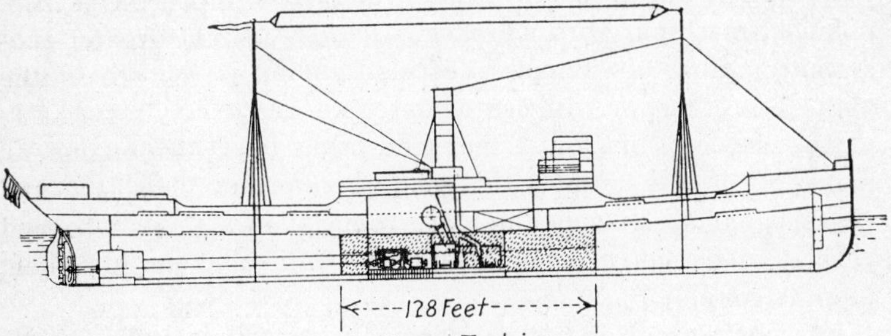

Steam Turbines

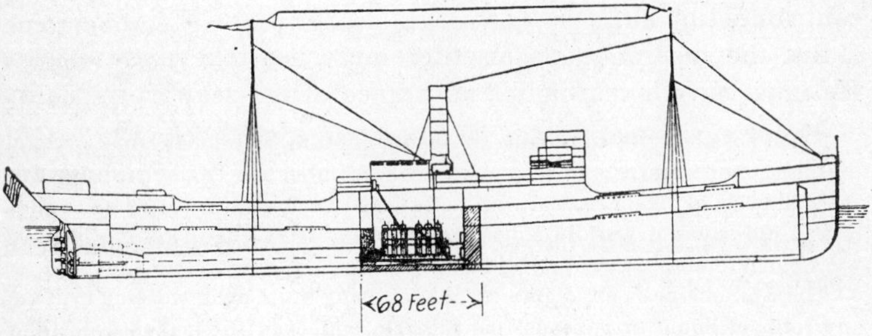

Motor Ship

Sketches show relative space occupied by machinery and bunkers.

Producer gas engines. Gas is generated from coal, or coal dust and the gas so generated is used in an internal combustion engine.

We are in the very beginning of the development of the internal combustion engine. Chemical power, whether released through heat explosion, or by other means, may be the basis for future power at sea.*

The turbo-generator sets, of steam, sending the current aft to the shaft motors through great copper cables, may be soon displaced by motor-generator sets, gas driven, and effecting a further saving in bunker and boiler space.

All deck officers should study the development of ship power plants.

VI

Classification

The whole business of overseas trade is stabilized through the financial machinery of *insurance.* The sea will always claim a certain number of victims. Vessels founder, go ashore, collide with each other, or with ice or derelicts, catch fire, boilers explode, cargoes shift, and a thousand perils beset them on every hand. It is the purpose of good seamanship to so manage vessels that such happenings are reduced to a minimum, that vessels in danger are not abandoned until all hope of saving them is gone.

But when losses do occur, as they always will, insurance steps in and pays the loss to the individual out of the general fund contributed by all.

But the insurance underwriter must not take undue risks. He must have a reasonable assurance of the seaworthy quality

* The possibility of combining in one engine the superior thermal cycle at the high temperatures and pressures of the combustion engine with the low thermal cycle of steam to deal with its rejected heat, and, in the same engine, to add the superior working advantages of the steam engine, is the basis of work carried out by Mr. W. J. Still.

The Still engine is an engine capable of using in its main working cylinder any form of liquid or gaseous fuel hitherto employed; it makes use of the recoverable heat which passes through the surfaces of the combustion cylinder, as well as into the exhaust gases, for the evaporation of steam, which steam is expanded in the combustion cylinder itself on one side of the main piston, the combustion stroke acting on the other side. It increases the power of the engine, and reduces the consumption of the fuel per horsepower developed.—From a paper by Mr. Frank D. Acland, Royal Society of Arts, May 26 1919.

of the vessel he is insuring. The vessel must comply with certain rules of construction, and also, of course, with the navigation laws of the country from which she hails, and in certain respects, with the laws of the countries with which she trades.

Rules of construction, setting down the minimum requirements as to size, strength and position of the various parts of a hull, of the rigging, ground tackle, etc. of modern vessels are formulated by the various classification societies.

The American Bureau of Shipping, recognized by the U. S. Government as the official classification society of the United States, has set up such rules, and inspects and surveys vessels. These rules are based upon long experience and tests under sea conditions, interpreted by scientific methods.

The ratings given vessels by the A.B.S. are a safe guide for the placing of insurance on hull and cargo.

The classification society also is the greatest safeguard against loss of life at sea through faulty construction, or poor equipment.

The following extract from the "Conditions of Classification" of the Rules of The American Bureau of Shipping, are of interest to the seaman:

"(1) Vessels which have been built under the special supervision of the Surveyors to the Bureau, in accordance with Plans approved by the Committee and the requirements of the Rules, or with alternative arrangements equivalent thereto, will receive Certificates of Class. In each case a written application must be made for Classification to the Secretary, or to the Surveyor for the district in which the vessel is to be built, from whom the necessary application forms may be obtained. Vessels which are approved for trade in any part of the world will be distinguished in the Bureau's Record Book by the symbol ✠ A.1., signifying the Highest Classification of the American Bureau of Shipping and Special Survey during construction of the Hull. Vessels intended for trade in any part of the world but which have not been built in accordance with the requirements of the Rules for the Highest Classification, will be distinguished in the Bureau's Record Book by the symbol ✠ A.1. 'With Freeboard,' it being a condition of the Classification of such Vessels that minimum Freeboards will be assigned by the Committee. Vessels intended for a particular trade which have been built to scantlings specially arranged and approved by the Committee for that trade, will be distinguished in the Bureau's Record Book by the symbol ✠ A.1. followed by the necessary limitation of trade: For example 'River Service;' 'Coasting Service;' 'Tug Service;' 'Fishing Service;' 'New York–Boston;' etc.

" Machinery and Boilers which have been built under the special supervision of the Surveyors to the Bureau and in accordance with the requirements of the Rules, will receive a Certificate of Class; such machinery will be distinguished in the Bureau's Record Book by the symbol ✠ A.M.S., signifying the Highest Classification of the American Bureau of Shipping and Special Survey during construction for Machinery and Boilers.

" The letter Ⓔ placed after the symbols of classification, thus: ✠ A.1. Ⓔ will signify that the Equipment of the vessel is in compliance with the requirements of the Rules.

" In cases where the Equipment is not in compliance with the requirements of the Rules, a dash will be substituted for the letter Ⓔ thus: ✠ A.1.—

" (2) Vessels which have not been built under the supervision of the Surveyors to the Bureau but are submitted for Classification will be subjected to a Special Classification Survey, as set forth in Section 46. Certificates of Class will be granted if the Hull, and in case of Steam Vessels, the Machinery and Boilers, are found satisfactory and are approved by the Committee; the symbols in the Record Book will be as described in Paragraph 1, but the mark ✠ signifying Special Survey during construction will be omitted."

From the " Conditions as to Surveys " we take the following:

" The Special Periodical Surveys on Classed Vessels must be carried out at intervals of four years from the date of build, or at such shorter intervals as may be fixed by the Committee in special cases, or from a date six months after launching in the case of a new Vessel, not completed within that period. Such Surveys may, if desired by the Owners, be carried out within twelve months prior to the date when they become due, provided the subsequent interval between Surveys does not exceed four years. . . .

" Owners will receive notice of the dates when the Special Periodical Surveys become due, but it must be understood that the responsibility for non-compliance with such notice rests with the Owners, or their Representatives."

The *Record of American and Foreign Shipping,* is published by the A.B.S. on the first of January of each year and corresponds to the *Register* published by Lloyds.

The oldest of the British societies is Lloyd's, an association of marine underwriters and surveyors taking its name from a coffee house kept by Mr. Edward Lloyd in Tower Street, London, during the seventeenth century, where owners, underwriters and shipmasters came to transact business.*

Without the classification societies merchant shipping would be in an uncertain condition. Seamen who note the condition and performance of their vessels under the severe tests of actual stress, and who make intelligent reports on their behavior, add greatly to the knowledge necessary to the naval architect and designer.

" In practice, the arrangement and massiveness of the various parts are simply that which long *experience* of the strength and endurance, displayed in active service by vessels of different sizes and type, indicates as the minimum compatible with these qualities. . . . It is mainly due to . . . classification societies that this experience, extending over the whole history of wood, iron, and steel shipbuilding, and which otherwise might have been lost, has at all times been carefully recorded, interpreted, and made available to all in the annual publication of their rules of construction and tables of scantlings."—Holms' "*Practical Shipbuilding*."

* The principal classification societies are as follows:

American Bureau of Shipping.
Lloyds Register of British and Foreign Shipping.
Bureau Veritas, Paris.
British Corporation, Glasgow.
Imperial Japanese Maritime Corporation.
Norske Veritas.
Registro Navale Italiano.
Germanischer Lloyd.
Nederlandsche Vereeniging van Assuradeuren.
Veritas Austro-Ungarico.

The societies assigning load line marks identify their marks by two letters over the horizontal line and on each side of the disc (see page 256). The markings used are as follows—A. B.—American Bureau of Shipping; L. R.—Lloyds Register; B. V.—Bureau Veritas; B. C.—British Corporation; N. V.—Norske Veritas; G. L.—Germanischer Lloyd.

CHAPTER II

THE HULL

I

Steel Construction

Steel vessels form the greatest percentage of the world's tonnage. The names and purposes of the component parts of a steel hull should be familiar to the seaman who is charged with the use of the structure as a whole, when maneuvering the ship, and with its parts, while working cargo, handling ground tackle, etc. He should therefore have a very precise knowledge of the *formation, use, location* and *names* of the various members entering into the construction of the ship.

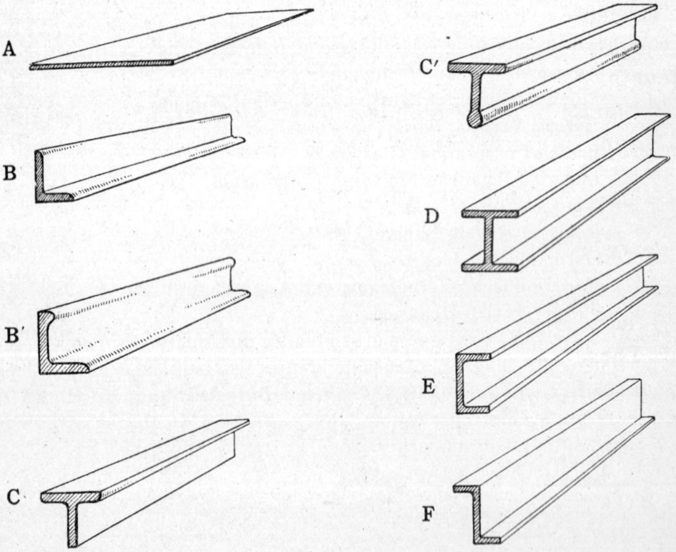

Within the last quarter century great advances have been made in ship construction. Mild steel is now used in the majority of seagoing vessels and the various shapes of this material have practically become standard. Differences in design are brought about by different combinations of the standard shapes. The standard shapes are also varied in a great number of sizes and weights. These are illustrated by typical sections that can easily be identified by inspecting the construction of a modern steel vessel.

These shapes are

A, the plate, of many sizes and weights.
B, the angle, plain and bulb, (B′) with legs of various length, and of many weights.
C, the T bar.
C′, the T bar with bulb.
D, the I beam.
E, the channel.
F, the Z bar.

In the construction of vessels of extreme size, steel of high tensile strength is introduced where necessary in order to keep down weight, as in the sheer strakes, amidships, in liners of great length.

In addition to the above standard forms of construction certain special forms of material are often employed, such as *half*

Special forms

rounds, rods, angle bars, columns, hatch ledges, and some others. These rolled shapes, together with special *forgings* and *castings* form the component parts of a steel hull.

Built up sections of standard forms.

Many combinations of these standard forms are possible and special columns, beams, frames, boxes, and the like are formed.

The *angle bar* is generally employed in the construction of the framing of a vessel, as shown in the illustration. The outer angle is the *frame*, the inside angle, riveted to it, is the

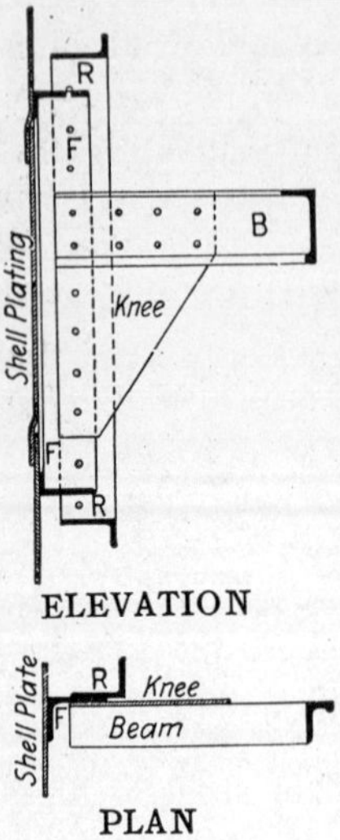

Joint of Deck Beam and Frame

reverse frame. The shell plating is riveted to the outboard flange of the frame.

The *shell plating* constitutes the outer plating of the hull and corresponds to the planking on a wooden vessel. It is placed on the hull in long strips, called *strakes*, and these are combined in various ways, overlapping, edge to edge, and in single and double layers. The principle forms of shell plating are illustrated in the sketch.

The strakes on the bilge taper in breadth, being wider as the hull widens out amidships. The *topside strakes* are usually parallel, or nearly so. To avoid narrowing, certain strakes are discontinued at some distance from the ends of the vessel. A strake, so discontinued is called a *drop strake*, and the strake taking the place of two drop strakes and continuing them is called a *stealer*.

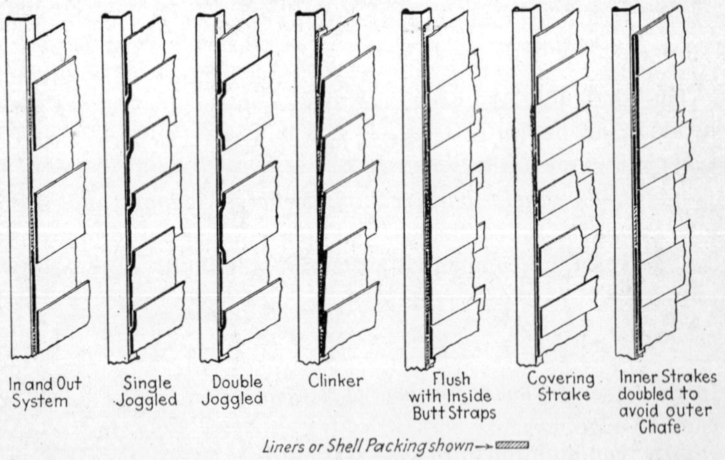

Types of shell plating

The various forms of material constituting the hull are generally fastened together by means of rivets, though some progress

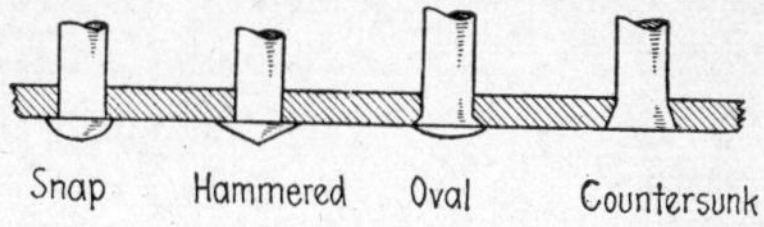

has been made in fastening steel parts together by the process of electric welding. Riveting, however, is still the standard form of fastening, the rivets being heated red and driven while workable through heat. The standard shapes of rivets are shown. The *swell neck* form is best for ship work as it fills the holes better. The *head* of the rivet is formed on it before driving, the *point* is formed in the process of driving, which may be by hand, or by some form of power hammer.

Tap rivets are really screws worked in where rivets cannot be driven.

The distance between the centers of rivets is known as the *pitch*. In fastening together parts of a ship the strength of joint desired, the thickness of material, and the shearing strength of the rivets is considered in determining the pitch. Rivets may be in either *single* or *double shear* as shown in the sketch. The shearing stress on a rivet is, as the name implies, the stress tending to shear the rivet in two, or three parts.

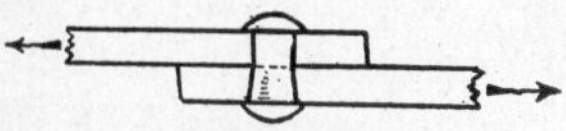

Single Shear

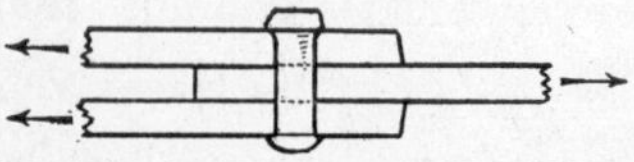

Double Shear

The shell plating, deck plating, hatch coamings, and bulkheads must be watertight, as also must be the tanks, and to secure this desired water tightness *caulking* is resorted to.

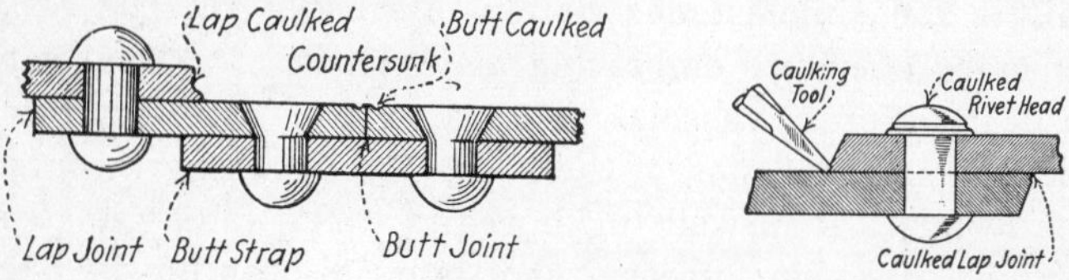

In the case of a steel vessel this consists in bending down one part, or edge, in close contact with its neighbor, as shown in the sketch, rather than in ramming caulking material in between, as oakum is rammed into the seams of a wooden ship. Rivet heads that show leakage are also caulked, but this is not considered good practice, such rivets, if discovered in the course of construction, should be backed out and new ones driven.

Butt joints are caulked as shown in sketch.

II

Transverse Construction

This system follows the ancient method of building up *ribs*, or *frames*, resting *transversely* on a *keel*, and connected, across their tops and middles by *beams*, the whole structure bound together by longitudinals called *stringers*, the ends of the vessel consisting of the *stem* and *sternpost*, generally large forgings. All enclosed by *plating* on the outside of the hull, and *deck plating* over the beams.

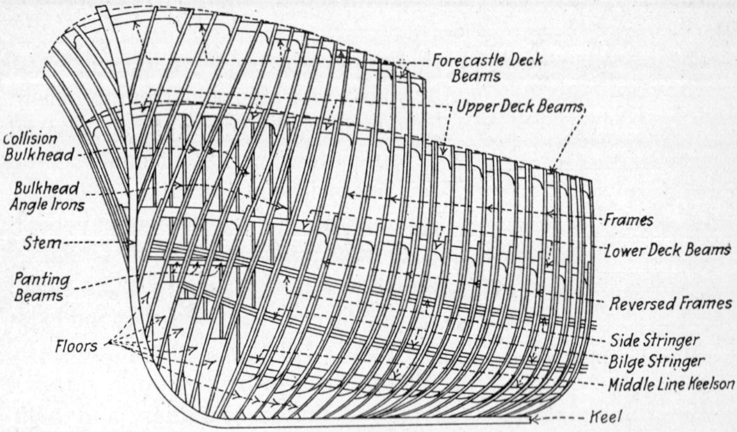

Forward Framing

This is the simplest description of what is, in fact, a very complicated structure embracing many parts, of a great variety of form in different vessels. The parts of a vessel can best be studied by an inspection of the vessel itself, having recourse to the drawings. It is well to know the *exact* name and *use* of every part of a ship; no one who wants to be a finished sailor should content himself with less knowledge than this.

It is best to first study the combination of the parts of the structure, as a whole, noting their relation to each other, and then to learn the construction and use of the many members making up the hull of the vessel.

Transverse section of various types of vessels are helpful in further study of the vessel and its parts.

The location of tanks in the double bottom and the arrangement of beams in the hold of a three-decked vessel is shown in the accompanying illustrations.

III

Parts of Hull

The principal parts and fittings of the hull will now follow with a brief description of each part named, given in alphabetical order.

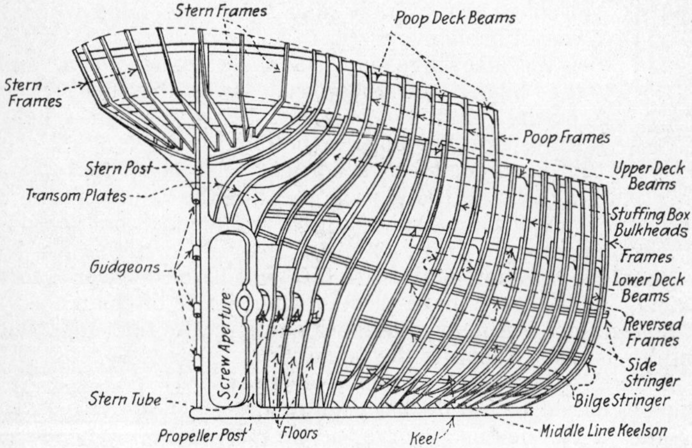

After Framing

Accommodation ladder. A ladder extending down the outside of the hull, steps perpendicular to the side of the vessel. This is usually the gangway ladder for the accommodation of passengers, and is swung from a small *davit*, the upper end being hinged to a *gangway platform*. It is fitted with extensions, when the vessel is light and with middle platforms in vessels of high freeboard.

Awning stanchions. Stanchions at the rail used to support the rope *jackstays* and other devices for the spreading and supporting of the awnings.

Beam. An athwartship member of the framing, supporting the decks. Beams are fastened to the frames by knees, as shown in sketches and are one of the most important elements in the strength of the vessel.

Beam knee. A type of special beam enlarged where it is riveted to the framing.

Belaying pin. A wooden or metal bar slipping in a hole in *pin rail* for belaying gear. A square (oblong section), pin is called a *cavil.*

Belaying Pin

Bent plate washer. A bent plate used in connecting a bar keel to the garboard strake.

Bilge. The rounded portion of the hull—or holds—between the bottom and the sides of the vessel. The bilge is somewhat indefinite, but is used in the naming of many parts of the structure, such as *bilge keels* (on the outside to prevent rolling), *bilge keelsons* (on the inside for added strength) and for the description of dunnage placed in the bilge, to keep cargo clear of *bilge water*, that may lie in the bilge when the vessel heels over.

We also have *bilge stringers; bilge blocks* (under the bilge when the vessel is in dry dock); *bilge pumps;* and a vessel is " *bilged* " when a hole is stove into her bilge or bottom.

Block, or *block coefficient* (also *coefficient of fineness*), is the decimal fraction representing the volume of the underwater body of the vessel, taking her, " Block " that is product of length, beam and draft, as unity.

Bobstay. A short stay from the end of the bowsprit, to the stem. Most vessels have three or four, made of chain.

Boiler stool. A heavy bracket resting on the tank tops, floors and keelsons. Supports the boilers.

Bollard. Cast steel, or iron cylindrical shapes, bolted to the decks, usually also to the deck beams. Serve a similar purpose as the *bitts* fitted in wooden craft. Hawsers led through the *mooring pipes* in the *bullwarks*, are made fast to the *bollards.* Bollards are sometimes cast with a removable cap, screwing up and down, and serve to ventilate compartments below.

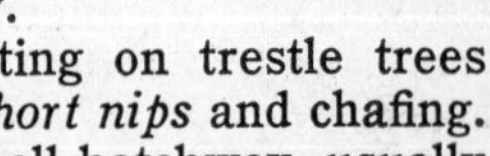

Bollards

Bolsters. Curved pieces of wood, resting on trestle trees over which the shrouds are laid, prevent *short nips* and chafing.

Booby hatch. Wooden cover over a small hatchway, usually aft, fitted with a sliding or hinged cover and used as a companion, or for hoisting in and out small stores.

Boom. General term for the spars used in hoisting cargo, and coal. The term derrick is sometimes used when referring to these spars.

Bosom piece. Short angle or butt strap used in joining the ends of angle bars.

Boss. The central casting of a propellor into which the *tail shaft* is bolted and to which the *blades* are bolted, or cast.

Bossing. Shell plating bent to fit around the propellor shaft, doing away with the need of *struts* in a twin screw vessel.

Boundary plank. Planking built around metal structure which extends above the deck, and against which the wood-decking is laid, usually of hard wood. Teak is often used for this purpose as it is not discolored by rust. Also called *Margin plank.*

Bow frame. The most forward frame in ships not fitted with a bowsprit. When a bowsprit is fitted it is called a *knighthead* frame.

Bow port. Small square port in the bow of a vessel, to allow the stowage of long pieces of timber. Only used in vessels having a single hold, usually in wooden sailing craft.

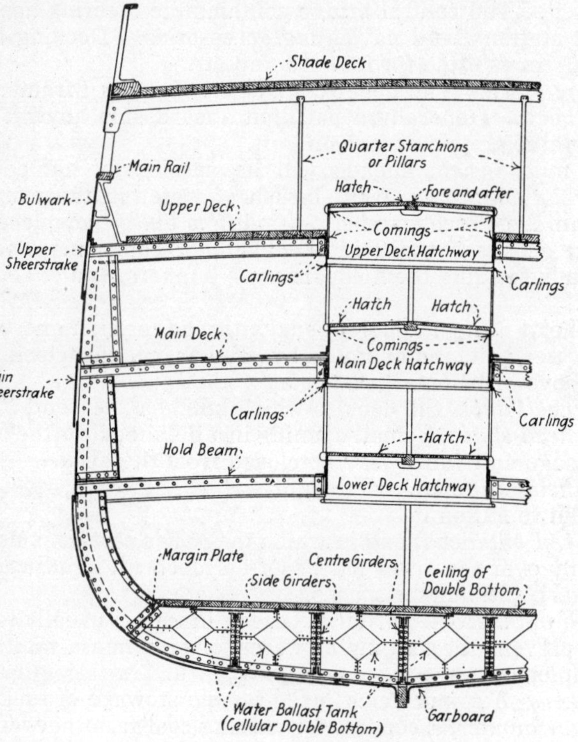

Midship section, heavy construction

Bowsprit. A spar extending forward over the bow. Rests on the stem, to which it is secured by bands or lashings called the *gammoning*, the heel being wedged in the *knightheads*, some distance aft of the stem. It is stayed by the *bobstays*, and *bowsprit shrouds*, and extends and takes the stress of the *fore stays*, hove through *bees* to the stem.

Box beam. A built-up beam in the form of a box girder.

Bracket. A small plate used to connect various parts, such as deck beams to frames, frames to margin plates, etc.

Breaching. The Y-shaped pipe which connects the boilers to the funnel.

Breakwater. Structure built on the forward deck to protect hatchways, and companion ways from the seas.

Breast hook. Horizontal framing fitted in the bow to give strength to the structure and support the shell plating against heavy blows.

Bridge. The structure from which the vessel is managed and navigated. The central bridge contains the steering apparatus, lookout stations, and navigating accessories. Docking bridges are sometimes fitted far forward and aft.

Bridge piece. The upper connection of a stern frame.

Bulkhead. Generally a partition aboard ship anywhere, extending athwartship or fore and aft.

The following bulkheads will be specifically named—*after peak bulkhead;* to prevent inrush of water in the event of a break in the propellor shaft. *Collision bulkhead*, placed well forward as a safeguard in the event of collision. The main bulkheads dividing the holds, reserve bunkers, and engine room spaces.

Bulkhead fittings—*doors*, usually three feet high and two feet wide, watertight, and operated by hand or by quick closing gears from above or below.

Bulkhead deck, the deck to which bulkheads extend.

Bulkhead sluice, a small opening in a bulkhead for the purpose of drainage and which may be closed from the deck.

Bulkhead stiffeners, angles, or webs and angles, riveted to a bulkhead to stiffen it.

Stepped bulkhead, one in which the upper part does not come vertically over the lower part. Often met with in adjusting the machinery and bunker spaces.

Wash bulkhead, a partial bulkhead in tanks, usually fore and aft, to prevent the surging of water, or oil when a tank is only partly filled.

Bunker. A compartment used for the stowage of fuel.

Pocket bunker, a conduit for passing coal from between deck bunkers to the firerooms.

Reserve bunker, usually forward and next after the forward holds, extending athwartship. On short runs can be used for cargo.

Wing bunker, bunkers situated in the wings, abreast of the boilers.

Cabin. General term for living quarters of officers and passengers.

Camber. The rise or crown of a deck above a horizontal line connecting the ends of the beam.

Cant frame. A frame not perpendicular to the fore and aft line of the keel.

Capstan. A vertical revolving drum, spool shaped, and fitted with *pawls. Whelps*, or ridges on the drum prevent wet lines from *surging.* Capstans are power driven but may also be operated by man power by the use of *capstan bars* fitting into *pigeon holes* in the capstan head.

Cargo battens. Planking cleated or bolted to the reverse frames, in the holds and between decks, to protect cargo from contact with the steel plating and frames.

Carlings. Short beams or girders, similar to headers, used to support the end of a deck beam where it is cut for hatch openings, mast holes, etc.

Cat head. A short heavy projecting knee at the bows fitted with sheaves, and used for securing an old fashioned anchor. It also serves as a support for jibbom guys on sailers.

Ceiling. The wooden flooring on the tank tops, also the inside lining of a wooden ship.

Cellular double bottoms. The construction of double bottoms in which *longitudinal* or *intercostal* plates and the transverse floors, subdivide the space into small compartments or cells.

Center girder. The center line girder connecting the keel and keelson of a steel built vessel.

Chain locker. A deep compartment forward, either immediately forward or aft of the collision bulkhead, for the stowage, by gravity, of the anchor chains. The chain locker is usually divided into port and starboard lockers by a wooden bulkhead.

Checkered plate. Used in engine room flooring, ladders, etc.

Cheek plates. The plates riveted at the mast head to form the *hounds*, which support the *trestle trees*, these, in turn supporting the *fid*, which passes through the *heel* of a *fidded topmast.* (See Chapter 6.)

Chocks. Heavy metal fittings through which hawsers, or lines may be led. Also the seats or saddles of boats, of wood or metal. On shipboard a chock may be anything that is used to wedge or *chock up* weights carried on deck or in the holds.

A Chock

Circulating pump. The large pump which circulates the cool sea water through the condenser.

Cleanout door. A door near the bottom of a furnace to allow the cleaning out of cinders and ashes.

Clearing plug. The plug screwed into the bottom of a trap in plumbing fixtures, removed when trap is to be cleared.

A Cleat

Cleat. A ship fitting used for the belaying of ropes.

Coaming. The plating around a hatch or skylight.

Coffer dam. Space between two water tight bulkheads, located close together. (See Chapter 11.)

Collision chocks. Heavy brackets fitted fore and aft of boilers and connected to floors and framing. Intended to take up impact in the event of a head-on collision.

Columns. The vertical pillars in between decks and holds, of various forms, and either stationary or removable.

Companion. The entrance and stairway leading from a weather deck to the cabin space below, or from the topgallant forecastle to the forecastle.

Compartment. A subdivision of space in a ship.

Compensation. The increase in strength of members to make up for ports, and the doubling of plates around hatchways, etc., to compensate for loss of area in deck plating.

Composite vessel. Generally understood to be a vessel built of metal framing and wood planking. The upper plating may be of steel and the underwater body planked and coppered. The Schoolship *Newport* is of this construction.

Cross head. The casting at the rudder head connecting it to the hand steering gear.

Davit. The crane or cranes used in hoisting and lowering ship's boats. Use also is made of an *anchor davit*, in stowing the old fashioned anchor which is brought on board the forecastle head. A davit is used to sling the companion ladder.

Dead eye. A solid circular block, usually of lignum vitae through which *lanyards* are rove. Used in *setting up* stays, shrouds, etc., where turnbuckles are not fitted. Generally restricted to use in wooden vessels. (See Chapter 6.)

Deadrise. The vertical distance between the point where the slope of the vessel's bottom intersects the moulded breadth line and the base line. (See page 62.)

Deck. The plating or planking over the beams, corresponds to the flooring in buildings ashore.

Flush deck, running fore and aft with no breaks.

Forecastle deck, short deck on forecastle.

Poop deck, short deck on poop. Other decks take the names from the structure covered, such as *bridge*, etc. The decks in the body of a vessel are as follows—from the top down:

Bridge deck	*Shelter deck*	*Lower deck*
Boat deck	*Upper deck*	*Orlop deck*
Promenade deck	*Main deck*	*Lower orlop deck*

Decks on most modern passenger craft are now lettered, A Deck being the highest on which passengers are housed, and so on down, B, C, D, E, etc.

The American Bureau of Shipping designates decks as follows: the "Freeboard Deck" then (going down) second deck; third deck, fourth deck, etc.

Deflection. The amount a beam, or column, sags or springs out of line under a load.

Derrick. Alternative term for a cargo boom.

Derrick post. Corresponds to a mast, or king post, except that the derrick post may revolve about its axis.

Diagonal ties. Bands of steel running across from one side of a vessel to an other at an angle to the deck beams. Used to stiffen the decks of sailing craft.

Diamond plates. Diamond shaped plates connecting the web frames to the side stringers. Act as brackets, stiffening the frame of the vessel.

Diaphragm. A web plate placed between two members in the structure of a vessel and used to stiffen them.

Dog. A bent metal fitting with handle used to close doors, manhole covers, etc.

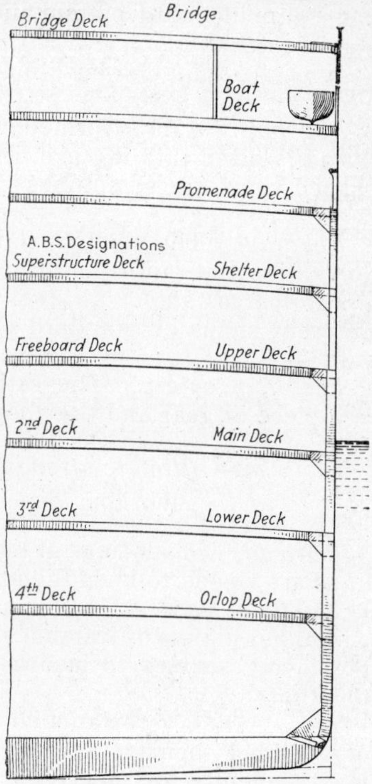

Names of Decks

Donkey boiler. Every seagoing vessel carrying passengers must be fitted with a donkey boiler of sufficient capacity to work the *fire pumps*, wireless if need be, etc. The donkey boiler shall not be placed below the lower decks. The donkey boiler is an emergency boiler and is used in port to supply steam to winches, heating system, etc., when the main boilers are cold.

Edge strip. A narrow strip of metal (buttstrap) placed under the joint in shell plating laid flush.

Escape holes. Small man holes in the deck, remote from hatchways, used for trimmers to get out of bunkers after filling bunker with coal, also used to fill remote corners of bunkers with coal.

Expansion bend. A bent section of piping to allow for expansion and contraction without causing leaky joints. Used in deck steam lines, etc.

Expansion plans. Developments of the shell plating and framing of the ship showing the size and mark of every plate and frame including bottom and sides. This makes the drawing look distorted, being correct in length but expanded in breadth. Very useful things to have on board, in the event of damage to plates or frames while away from home.

Eye bolt. A bolt formed with an eye in the head. When a ring is fitted into the eye, it is known as a *ring bolt.* Heart-shaped rings are sometimes fitted when the bolts are used for passing lashings.

Eyebrow. The semicircular or triangular iron placed over a port to prevent rain from dripping into it. Also called a *wriggle.*

Fabricated ship. A steel ship built or "fabricated" in different shops on standard plans, and assembled in the shipyard.

Factor of safety. The ratio between the ultimate strength of a piece of gear and the allowed working stress.

$$\frac{\textit{Ultimate strength}}{\textit{Working load}} = \textit{Factor of safety}$$

Fairlead. Small rings of lignum vitae or metal through which lines are rigged to keep them clear.

Faying surface. The surface of plates that comes in contact with other plates, or framing. All holes should be punched *from* the faying surface to insure a close fit when the plates come together.

Fid. A heavy rectangular steel pin fitted through the heel of a fidded topmast, or topgallant mast, and upon which the mast depends for support. The ends of the fid rest on the *trestle trees.*

Fiddley. The open grating around the funnels of a steamer. A favorite roost for *soldiers*, during cold weather.

Flaws in steel. Blisters, raised projections on the surface, caused by gases getting under the skin of the metal.

Blow holes, cavities in steel caused by air and gas.

Brittleness, lack of ductility caused by phosphorus.

Crystallization, caused by fatigue (steel gets tired) from repeated overloading, pounding, etc. Must look out for this in cargo hooks, shackles, chains, etc. When such parts fracture the presence of crystallization can often be noted.

Internal stresses, caused by improper working of temperature, and lack of annealing.

Piping, hollow center in steel bars, caused by shrinkage while molten.

Red shortness, ragged appearance on edges of steel plates caused by too much sulphur in the steel.

Vents, same as blow holes.

Floor, the lower portion of a transverse frame. Usually a vertical plate extending from center line of keel to bilge, and from inner to outer bottom plating.

Fore and afters. The longitudinal pieces over a hatchway, supported by the strongbacks (cross beams). The center fore and after is usually of steel, the fore and afters between this and edge of coaming are usually of wood.

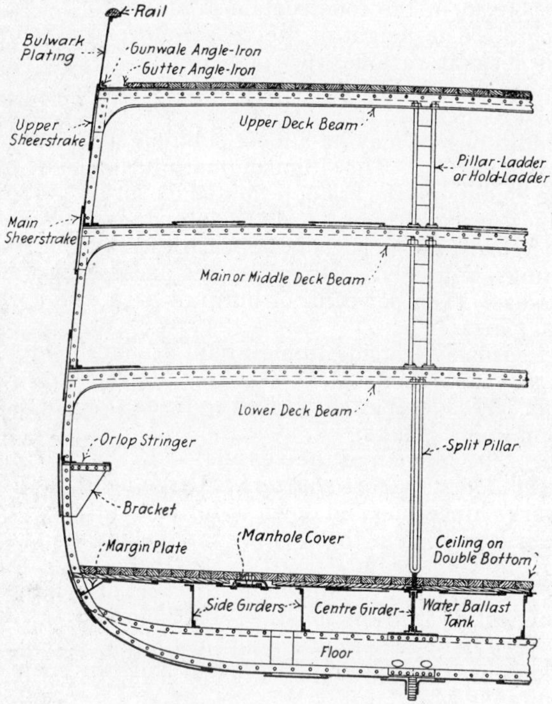

A midship section, light construction

Forecastle. The forwaıd part of the hull, usually raised above the main deck, formerly used as quarters for crew. Pronounced "Fo'c'sle" (Fōk sill).

Fore foot. Point of the stem where the keel rounds up to meet the stem piece. A broad fore foot is called a *club foot. Paravanes*, used to sweep up mines, attach to the fore foot.

Fore peak. The compartment or tank just within the bow and forward of the collision bulkhead.

Foundation plate. Heavy plate upon which the *keelson* rests.

Framing. The skeleton of the vessel.

Frame, knighthead, first frame in bow of a vessel carrying a bowsprit.

Frame liners, filler plates placed between frame and outer strakes in *in and out* plating.

Frame spacing, for and aft distance between frames.

Transverse framing, the usual framing of vessels, as described so far.

Longitudinal framing, *Isherwood System* and *Gatewood System*, much used in the construction of tankers.

Freeboard. The height of the vessel out of water measured to various decks in various types of vessels. Freeboard depends upon the construction of the vessel, for instance, turret vessels are allowed to measure freeboard to the turret deck, while in fact their breadth of hull may be almost submerged. (See page 28.)

Freeboard marks. The Plimsol mark has become standard, and these loading marks are determined by surveys of the underwriters in American ships. (See Chapter I, page 29.)

Freeing port. Large ports in bulwarks, usually on well decks, with gratings, or hinged ports to free the decks from water when shipping seas. Ten per cent. of bulwark area usually taken up by freeing parts.

Funnel casing. Outside funnel, built around inside stack for strength and insulation.

Furring. Wooden battens bolted to frames to hold cabin and store room lining planks.

Galley. The kitchen of the vessel.

Gangway doors, or port shutters. Large doors or shutters in the bulwarks hinged up and down or fore and aft, to admit gangway ladders, or to clear the way for cargo skids.

Girder. A deep beam.

Goose neck. The usual fitting at the heel of a cargo or other boom, connecting it to the mast. (See Chapter 5.)

Grain feeders. Reservoirs built just above grain holds to keep holds filled with grain and prevent shifting. Similar to oil trunks in tankers.

Granulated cork. Used in coating inside steel work to prevent sweating.

Graving piece. A short piece of plank, inserted into damaged plank of an old deck. Does not go down to the beams. Ends of graving piece usually pointed. (See page 922).

Gudgeons. The sockets in the rudder post into which the rudder *pintles* ship.

Gunwale. The upper side of a small boat. Sometimes used in connection with the fitting of vessels. *Gunwale tanks*, etc.

Gutter. The depression at the edge of decks to drain off water to the *scuppers*.

Hatches. The openings in the decks through which cargo, fuel, etc is passed.

Hatch battens, narrow metal bars at the hatch coamings, resting against the tarpaulins and wedged tight by driving *hatch wedges* between the battens and the *hatch cleats* in which they rest.

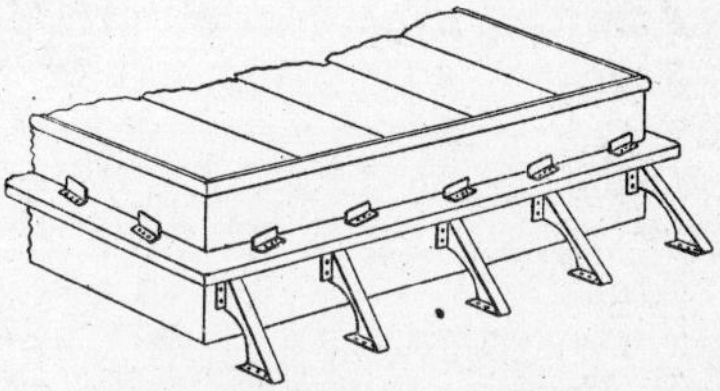

Corner of hatch on a fabricated vessel

Hatch covers, usually of heavy wood, sometimes of steel resting on rubber gaskets.

Hatch tarpaulins, canvas covers extending over hatch and down side of coamings, and held in place by battens as described above. Usually treated to make them waterproof.

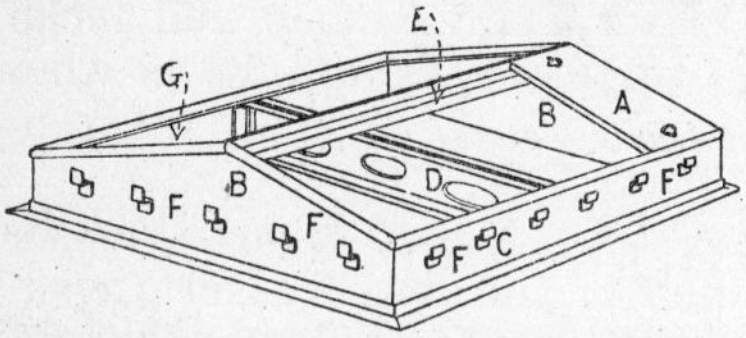

Usual form of hatch construction.
A, wooden hatch covers.
B, forward and after coaming.
C, side coaming.
D, steel strong back.
E, fore and after (steel).
F, wedge cleats.
G, hatch rim.

Hatchway, the vertical opening under a hatch.

Expansion hatch, the hatch over an expansion trunk.

Hawse pipe. The pipes in the bow through which the anchor cables pass, and intowhich the stockless anchors stow.

Hawser. A large rope used in working the ship, towing, tying up to a wharf, etc.

Helm. Generally used with reference to the tiller, also the whole apparatus by which the vessel is steered.

Hold. A cargo carrying compartment in the body of the vessel.

Hold beams. Beams in a hold, similar to deck beams but carrying no deck plating, they generally have no *camber*.

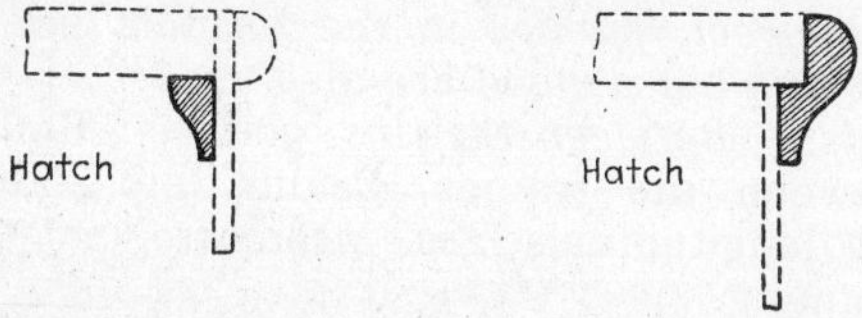

Forms of ledges for hatch covers

Hold-beam system. The placing of hold beams on every tenth frame to provide added strength.

Holding down bolts. Heavy bolts for holding down machinery on its beds. The main engines, plummer blocks, thrust bearings, winches, anchor engines, etc.

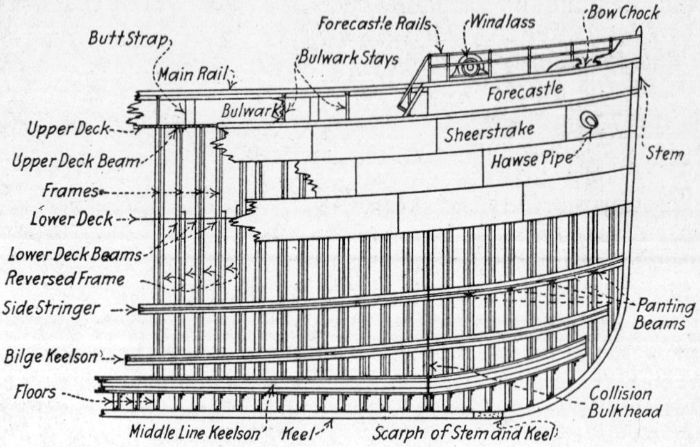

Bow plating frames, etc.

Hull. The body of a vessel.

Hulk. Generally an abandoned or cut down vessel used for storage, etc., such as coal hulks.

Hull efficiency. A decimal obtained by the following calculation.

$$\frac{\text{Ship resistence} \times \text{speed}}{\text{Thrust} \times \text{speed of propellor}} = \text{H. Eff.}$$

Hull number. A number assigned to a ship and with which all material entering the ship is marked to avoid confusion in assembling.

Ice doubling. Extra plates in bow to reinforce against impact with ice.

Insulation. The non-conduction material built into holds and compartments intended for the carriage of frozen or chilled cargo. Insulating materials are *charcoal*, *sawdust*, *silicate of cotton*, or *slagwool*, *pumice* in the form of fine gravel. *Felt* and *cow hair* and balsa wood are also used.

Intercostals. *Between-the-ribs* plates. Built in separate sections between the frames, beams, etc. Floors are continuous and longitudinals are *intercostal* in the transverse system of framing.

Jack staff. Staff at bow for flying jack; jack only used when *not* under way.

Jib boom. Spar extending forward from the bowsprit. Only used in sailing craft.

Joggle. Plates bent to fit over other work, or other plates.

Keel. The backbone of the vessel. Of various forms. Usually flat underneath. Duct keel is a hollow box girder and carries longitudinal pipe system.

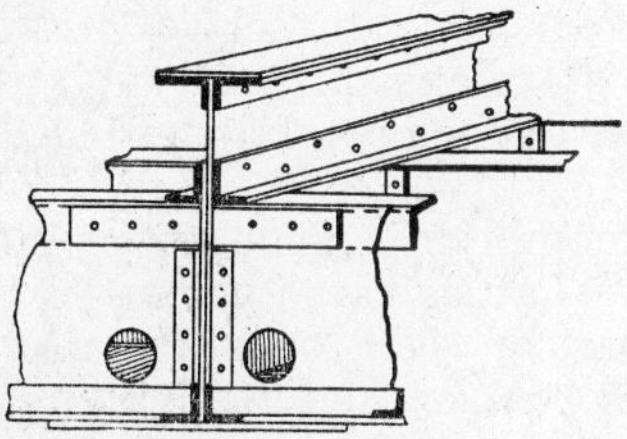

Flat keel and keelson

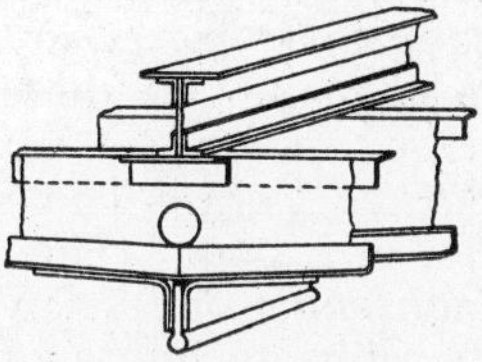

Bar keel

Keel bar, an exterior bar beneath main keel.

Keel blocks, blocks built up under keel to support it while ship is building, or when ship is in dry dock.

False keel, a plate or timber bolted to outside of keel to protect it and take up wear in case of grounding.

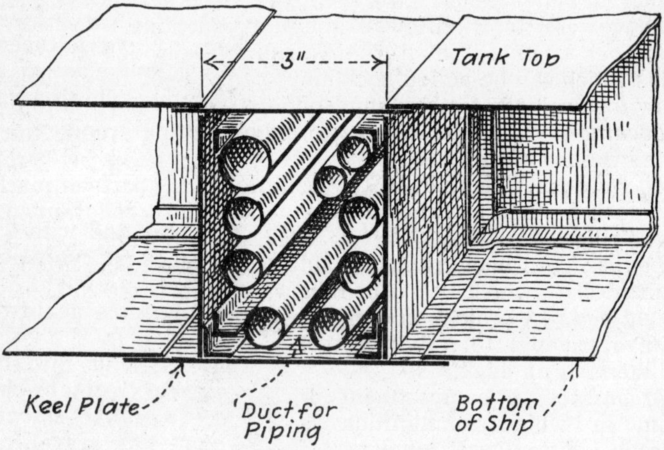

Duct keel

Keelson. An inner keel extending above the keel inside of the vessel. Pronounced *Kelson.*

Side keelson, a stringer between the outer bottom and the tank top and parallel to the keel.

King post. A short steel post generally without stays, supporting minor cargo booms. Sometimes used as a ventilator.

Knee. A triangular or curved bracket connecting deck beams to the frames.

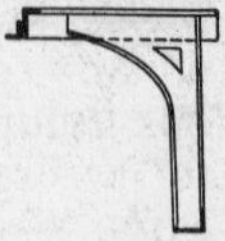

Knee

Knuckle line. The intersecting line between the poop plating and the stern plating in a vessel having an overhanging counter.

Lanyard. The heavy hemp gear rove through *deadeyes*, or *hearts*, in setting up stays and shrouds. Also of manila at the end of boat davit guys, for setting them taut.

Lattice work. The diagonal members in an open or lattice girder or frame. (See Chapter 5—Lattice cargo boom.)

Lightening holes. The circular, or oval, openings in floor plate webs to lighten the weight. Also used to lighten deep hatch strongbacks.

Lignum vitae. A very hard dense wood used for bearing surface in tail shaft bearings, around pintles of rudders and for dead eyes, block sheaves, etc.

Limber board. The line of ceiling next to the keelson or the margin plates in a steamer. This can be lifted and exposes the gutter next the keels, known as *the limbers.*

Limber holes. Holes cut in floor plates close to the keelson, or margin plates, and next to the lower angle bars of the frames, to allow water to drain toward the pump suctions.

Limber chains. Small chains running through the limber holes which can be pulled back and forth to keep them clear and allow for drainage to the pump suctions.

Locking hoop. A collar in two halves, fitting around the top of the rudder stock.

Locking pin. Any pin or key used in locking parts of machinery, such as the steel pin for locking the loose quadrant to the keyed tiller.

Louvre. An opening in the side of a deck house fitted with inclined slats which keep out rain water and serve to ventilate.

Lug pad. A projection carrying an eye, riveted to a bulwark or bulkhead or on deck.

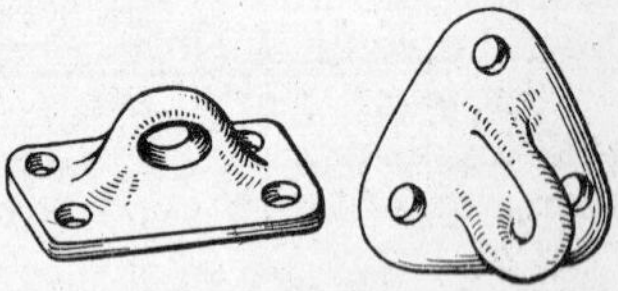

Lug pads

Magazine. A compartment or room in which ammunition is stored. Fitted with means of flooding, and kept away from all fire. (See Chapter 9.)

Manger. A dam built abaft of the hawse pipes to collect water washing into the hawse.

Margin plate. The outer wing of the inner bottom, connecting it with the shell plating at the bilge.

Mast. The main upright spars of a vessel are called the masts. Generally set on the center line and slightly raked aft.

Masts are now generally built up of metal in various sections, usually round. Some craft have square masts, in the shape of a box column. The masts of modern vessels are mainly placed for the support of cargo gear and are stayed against maximum cargo loads. Modern masts also find a use in the erection of radio apparatus, the carrying of the required lights, and as vantage points for lookouts. Very little sail is carried except in case of extreme emergency. A stout trysail and staysail equipment however would be a good insurance in the event of injury to engines, and might be of use in heavy weather under such conditions. Wood masts are solid, or built in sections and hooped.

Mast cap, the massive metal ring fitting over a lower mast head and through which the topmast is secured to it.

Mast coat, canvas coat fitted around base of mast where it passes through the weather deck to make the mast hole water tight.

Mast doubling, the point where the lower and top mast parallel each other, also the top and topgallant masts. Also refers to the extra plating in built-up steel masts.

Fore mast, the forward masts, lower, top, topgallant royal and skysail. The highest mast carried by a steamer is usually a topmast.

Mast hole, the openings in a deck through which the masts pass.

Main mast, the second mast from forward, with upper masts as on the fore.

Mizzen mast, the third mast from forward, etc. Other masts in the order of their number from forward are, *Jigger*, *driver*, *spanker*. Or, *Fore*, *Main*, *Middle*, *Jigger*, etc.

Mast partners, carlings and extra framing around the mast holes.

Mast pedestal, a frame work strongly braced, built over a deck on which a mast is stepped, when the mast cannot be extended down between decks. Also called a *tabernacle*.

Pole mast, a mast made in one piece throughout, that is lower and topmast in one. Also the wooden pole topmast erected over a steel lower mast to carry radio antenna, lights, etc.

Mast step, the structural frame into which the heel of the mast rests. Over the keelson in small vessel, otherwise in one of the between decks, or over the shaft tunnel in the case of a single or triple screw vessel of moderate tonnage.

Mast wedges, the wooden wedges driven between the mast and the partners, to hold the mast rigid to the hull of the vessel.

(For details of masts see Chapters V and VI.)

Messenger. A chain or rope, used to transmit power from an engine to some windlass or capstan a distance away, or not otherwise directly connected.

Mooring pipes. The eliptical openings in the bulwarks, fitted with rounded edges for the use of mooring lines.

Oil tight. Riveted and caulked to prevent oil leakage. Oil will go through joints where water is kept out.

Outreach. The distance a cargo boom can reach out beyond the mast.

Overhang. Portion of the hull extending beyond the water line fore and aft.

Oxter plate. The shell plate of very sharp curvature connecting to the sternpost.

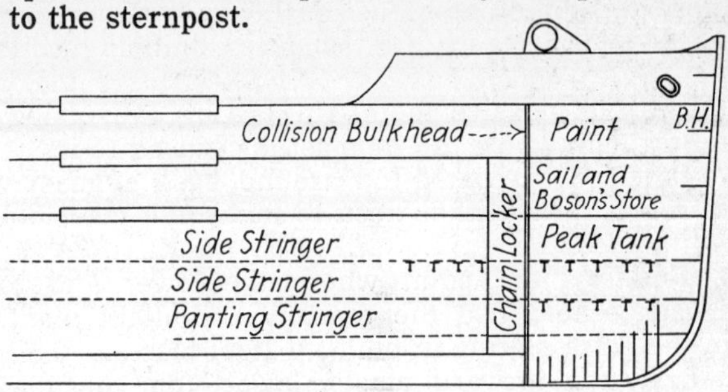

Panting beams shown in cross section

Panting beam, panting stringer. The beams and stringers reinforcing the frames forward, to take up the *panting stresses,* due to wave action.

Parrall. A hoop, or tub, riding up and down the topmast, to support the upper topsail yard. Also fitted on other yards that hoist.

Plummer block. The heavy structural supports carrying the shaft journals.

Poop. The after elevated deck of a ship with a well deck aft. Usually carries the steering gear, and living quarters, for crew.

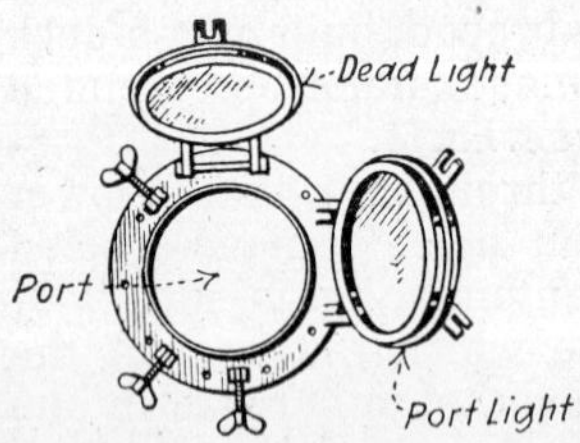

Parts of a port

Port. The left hand side of the vessel looking forward. Also openings in the hull or deck houses to admit air, cargo, or coal.

Blind port, a port fitted with a steel door closing flush with the side.

Port light, the heavy circular glass closure framed with metal, that screws against the port openings in cabins and between decks.

Note: All ports, leading to housing spaces, should be amply large enough to permit the passage of a full grown adult person.

Dead lights, the steel discs that screw down over the port lights, securing against breakage of the glass, and shutting out light when necessary.

Propeller. The screw that propells the vessel.

Propeller arch, the arched part of the hull formed by the stern frame and under which the propeller is situated.

Propeller post, forms the forward part of the *stern frame.* The after part of the stern frame is the *rudder post.* Above is the propeller arch, or *bridge piece*, and below is the *sole piece*, connecting the two posts and extending the keel to the foot of the rudder.

Propeller shaft, or *shaft*, the heavy steel shaft that transmits the power from the engine to the propeller.

Quadrant. The quadrantal shaped casting, keyed to the rudder head and to which the steering chains are attached. Sometimes the quadrant is toothed and the motion of the steering engine is transmitted to it by a worm gear, or by pinions. Many combinations of steering machinery are used but the quadrant is found in most of them.

Quarter deck. Deck on a sailing ship aft of the mainmast.

Quarter pillars. The pillars and stanchions half way between the center line and the side of the ship.

Rabbet. The score in the stem and stern posts into which the shell plating butts. In wooden vessels the fore and aft *hood ends* of planking butt into rabbet in stem and stern post.

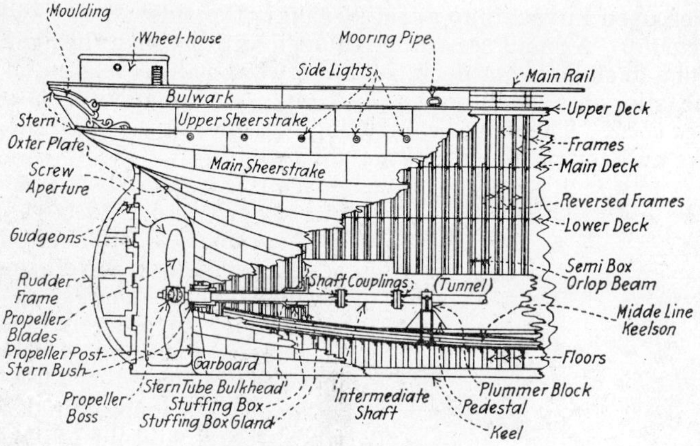

After plating and framing

Rake. The inclination of spars and funnels from the vertical. The inclination of a bowsprit from the horizontal is called the *stave* or *steeve* of the bowsprit.

Rake bunkers. Bunkers in which one side is sloped.

Rider plate. The foundation plate between a pillar and the center keelson.

Rolling chocks. Heavy brackets under the boilers and engines to take up the extra stress of rolling.

Rose box. Also called *strainer*, or *strum box*, perforated boxes over the ends of the bilge suction pipes.

Roundhouse. An erection from 6 to 8 feet in height on or above the upper deck but not extending from side to side of the vessel, as is the case with a bridge, a forecastle, a poop, or raised quarter-deck. For descriptive purposes on vessel documents, spaces not extending from side to side of the vessel, of less height, such as cabin heads or trunks, and closed-in spaces over the holds of motor boats, etc., may be classed as roundhouses.

Rudder. The steering blade under the stern.

Rudder arms, heavy steel arms running from the *rudder stock* across the sides of the *rudder plate.*

Balanced rudder, a rudder pivoted so that the forward part balances the force of water against the after part when the helm is put over.

Bow rudder, a rudder in a recess on the stem sometimes fitted to ferry boats and other craft.

Samson post. Same as *king post.* Supports cargo booms.

Scuppers. The drainage holes in the waterways on a deck, or on top of a deck house. *Blind scuppers*, drainage pipes led down inside the shell plating and out *below* the water line. A device used in yachts to avoid streaking the sides.

Scuttle. A small square hatch used as a passage through the top of a deck house or deck, as the forward scuttle, leading to the forecastle, on a small craft.

Sea cock. The valves controlling the flow of sea water into the tanks and compartments of the ship.

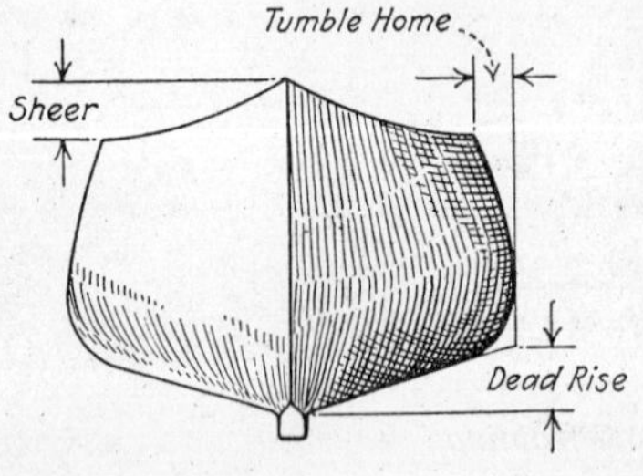

Seam. A joint between two planks, or two plates.

Sheathing. Copper or composition nailed on the outside of a wooden vessel on her underwater body to prevent fouling; also means any kind of sheathing, as in holds, etc.

Sheer. The longitudinal curve from stem to stern.

Shifting board. Board partitions placed fore and aft to prevent shifting of loose cargoes, such as grain.

Shoulder. The projection made on a plate when caulked.

Shovelling flat. Flat part of coal bunker bottom.

Shrouds. The stays from the mast top to the sides of a vessel, in the case of a lower mast. From mast top to lower mast top rim, in the case of a topmast. Shrouds are *side* stays.

Side stringers. Plate girders with horizontal webs framing in between the web frames.

Sole piece. The bottom connection of a stern frame.

Sounding pipe. The vertical pipe in a hold, leading to tanks, double bottoms, bilges and oil tanks, the sounding rods, chalked, are lowered through these pipes to get the depth of liquid at the bottom. An extra plate should be placed on tank or bilge bottom immediately *under* the sounding pipes, for the sounding rod to strike on.

Spring buffer. The heavy coiled spring inserted in the steering apparatus to take up shock.

Stanchion. Same as pillar, or column.

Starboard. The right hand side of a vessel when looking forward.

Steel. Iron cast from the molten state into a mass containing a small percentage of carbon and sometimes some other particular element to give it special properties. We quote the

Ship Steel*

Elements	Analysis Mild Steel	Analysis Malleable Iron
Iron	99.185	99.090
Carbon	0.180	0.111
Silica	trace	0.088
Sulphur	0.045	0.094
Phosphorus	0.045	0.117
Manganese	0.500	0.000
Copper	0.045	0.000
Slag, etc.	0.000	0.500
	100.000	100.000

* Percentage of Carbon in Various Grades of Steel.

Carbon Per cent.	Uses
0.05—0.10	Wire, tubing, nails, etc.
0.10—0.15	Rivets, screws and parts to be hardened.
0.15—0.20	Ordinary forgings, and as for 0.10—0.15.
0.20—0.25	Boiler plate, structural steel, ordinary forging, etc.
0.25—0.35	Forgings, structural steel, etc.
0.35—0.45	Shafts, axes, strong forgings, gears, etc.
0.45—0.55	Crank pins and other parts subject to shocks.
0.60—0.70	Forging dies, set screws, etc.
0.70—0.80	Chisels, smith hammers, wrenches, etc.
0.80—0.90	Punches, dies, rock drills, circular saws, etc.
0.90—1.00	Mch. hammers, punches and dies, springs, etc.
1.00—1.10	Springs, slow speed mch. tools, taps, etc.

following from *Holms' Practical Shipbuilding*. "As is, of course, well known, it is the element *carbon* which transforms pure iron into steel, and within a certain limit, the greater its proportion the harder and stronger the steel. From the analysis given it will be observed that carbon is also present in malleable iron, but as it exists here merely as an entangled impurity, it does not confer hardness and strength. The *softest mild steel* differs little from a chemically pure iron; it contains less than one tenth of one per cent. of carbon, its strength is about 20 tons per square inch, and it stretches more than 30 per cent. of its length before breaking. In passing from this material to a hard, *high carbon steel*, the qualities of mildness and ductility gradually disappear. The *hardest steel*, such as used for razors, etc., contains about 1.4 per cent. of carbon, its tensile strength is about 100 tons per square inch, it cannot be welded, and, of course, it is extremely brittle. Between these two extremes (of very mild, low-carbon steel, and a very hard high-carbon one) steel of any required strength may readily be produced, the ductility and general mildness, however, being in inverse proportion to the strength."

The tensile strength of ship steel runs from about 28 to 32 tons per square inch.

It is well for the sea officer to understand something of the resistance of the materials with which he works. Assuming the tensile strength of the steel in a chain, or hook, to be twenty tons per square inch, for a straight pull (tension), he can get a very reasonable idea of what it will safely hold by simply figuring its cross sectional area. In the design of the many parts of a ship technical data of a highly scientific nature is employed. Compressive strength, shearing strength, and torsional strength are considered in designing the vessel and its parts. However it is all a matter of theory based upon practice; of *empirical formulae*. The sea officer who takes the time to study his ship may add greatly to the imperfect knowledge with which naval architects have to work. As ships get larger, theory is stretched to meet conditions still unknown. The *factor of safety* is the figure that represents the number of times the ultimate resistance of material exceeds the working load for which it is designed. This is usually at least five, and when figuring constructions liable to sudden stresses such as a ship receives, ten and twelve times the estimates stresses are provided for in the design.

1.10—1.20	Thread cutting dies, ball bearing races, wood working machine knives, slow speed metal cutting, etc.
1.20—1.30	Files and similar tools.
1.30—1.40	Wire-drawing dies, engravers' tools, etc.
1.40—1.50	Ditto.
1.50—1.60	Metal-cutting saws, etc.

Cold bending test, to bend a piece of steel 180 degrees around a pin of a radius equal to one and a half times the thickness of the piece being tested.

Cold flanging, to turn the edge of a plate while the metal is cold. As the garboard plates, for instance.

Cold rolling, to continue rolling of plates after they have cooled below a red heat. This increases the strength of the plates.

Alloy steels. Alloy steel are those steels containing certain extra elements by the addition of which remarkable new properties have been given to the metal. These wlll be briefly enumerated.

Chrome steel, containing from 1.5 to 2.5 per cent. of chromium, having very high elastic limit and withstanding shocks very well. Used for tools, gears, armor plate, etc.

Manganese steel, containing from 11 to 14 per cent. of manganese; so hard that no other steel will cut it. Used for castings, machinery, etc.

Nickel steel, contains from 2.25 to 4.5 per cent. of nickel; very strong and tough and hard, and has a low coefficient of expansion. Used for armor plate, steel castings, shafting, etc.

Tungsten steel, contains from 3 to 10 per cent. of tungsten, having remarkable hardness. Used in "high speed" tools because it does not loose its temper when hot and can cut at high speed. This steel retains magnetism better than any other steel.

Vanadium steel, contains from 0.1 to 0.15 per cent. of vanadium, is very strong and tough and stands impact well. Eliminates blow holes and bubbles. Used in castings, forgings, machines, etc.

Combinations of the different alloys, and other alloys, such as *molybdenum, aluminum,* and *copper*, are used in the manufacture of special alloy steel. Copper is said to increase the resistance of steel to corrosion. The discovery of a perfect non-corrosive steel of good resistance would be an unlimited benefit to man in his great works of construction where rust is constantly eating away the metal in every unprotected part. Seamen who are constantly chipping and painting realize this defect in ship steel.

The manufacture of steel is carried on by different processes; only the briefest mention of these may be included here and the following summary is taken from the Mechanical Engineer's Hand Book.

"*Open-hearth Process* (Siemens-Martin Process). Steel made by this process is called either acid or basic. In either process the product is low in carbon and must be recarbonized by means of proper agents. The process may be carried on in stationary or tilting furnaces. From 15 to 80 tons are made in one heat, and some special furnaces have a capacity up to 200 tons. The duration of the heat is from 6 to 12 hours.

" *Acid open-hearth steel.* The charge consists of pig iron and ore or pig iron and scrap having a low phosphorus content, and is melted in an open-hearth furnace with an acid or siliceous lining. The process consists in removing the impurities in the pig iron to a great extent by means of an oxydizing flame brought about by the union of producer gas with preheated air in a reverberatory furnace. The process is similar to the puddling process for making wrought iron, but is carried on at a much higher temperature, the products, both metal and slag, being molten.

" *Basic open-hearth process.* The charge of either melted or solid pig iron, or a mixture of pig iron and low carbon scrap is heated in a furnace similar to the acid furnace. The lining in this case is of dolomite, lime, magnesite or other basic material. Ore may or may not be used.

" *The Bessemer Process* may be either acid or basic, but no basic Bessemer steel is made in the United States. The production of acid Bessemer steel is rapidly diminishing, giving way to open-hearth, electric, and duplex. From 8 to 20 tons of steel are made in one heat which lasts from 10 to 15 minutes. The furnace or converter is pear shaped and mounted on trunions so it can be tilted easily for charging and pouring."

Electric steel is made in an electric furnace of which there are many of the induction or arc type.

Those who must work with steel may profitably study this fascinating subject. We are still to see many improvements in the manufacture and combination of alloys.

Stem. The forging or casting forming the forward end of the framing and extending from the keel to the forecastle.

Stern frame. The large casting forming the after end of the framing of the underwater body of the vessel.

Stern tube. The tube through which the *tail shaft* passes outside of the hull. It is fitted with the *stern gland*, lined with lignum vitae and lubricated by water from the sea.

Stoke hold. Generally called the *fire room* in American practice. The space before the fires where the furnaces are stoked, or fired.

Strake book. A book containing the lists of plates in the vessel, their marks and dimensions.

Stress. A force acting on a structure. Vessels may be subjected to many stresses, *bending, buckling, compression, hogging, panting, pounding, racking, sagging, shear, tension, torsion.* All of these are understandable to the seaman. Panting is the stress caused by the waves beating against the bow and sides.

Pounding is a similar stress caused by sea action. Racking is the force tending to distort the shape of a section through the vessel. Sagging is caused when a vessel is lifted on her ends, the middle sagging down. Hogging is the reverse of sagging.

In this connection it may be well to correct a common error in the use of words. *Stress* is a force, while *strain* is a permanent distortion due to some stress. A vessel that has hogged, or sagged, has been *strained*.

Stringer. A continuous fore and aft member used to give longitudinal strength to a vessel, named according to location. Panting stringers, side stringers, bilge stringers.

Strongback. Heavy removable hatch beam; usually steel girders, fitting into slots on inside of the hatch coamings.

Strut. Support for the propeller end in twin screw vessels.

Stud. The short steel cross bar in heavy anchor chain.

Thrust block. The heavy bearing and its supporting block constituting the thrust bearing and block. This takes the push of the propeller and transfers it to the body of the vessel.

Tom. Term for a shore. Used in tomming and shoring up sagging floors, decks, etc., and in strengthening against extra heavy loads.

Transom. The last main frame of a ship attached to the stern framework. Transom beam is the beam across this frame.

Trim. This is the difference in draft forward and aft. For instance, a vessel may *trim* one foot by the head, or two feet by the stern. In the first case she is a foot deeper forward than aft. In the second case she is two feet deeper aft.

Tuck plate. A flat plate fitted over the bridge piece of the stern frame, when the body of the hull is some distance above the arch.

Tumble home. The sloping inboard of the vessel's side above the level of the greatest beam. See sketch, p. 62.

Tunnel well. A well in the double bottom under the shaft tunnel to collect any water that may get into the tunnel.

Uptake. The breaching in the smoke flue which connects the boiler to the funnel.

Vang. A stay or *guy* fitted to standing gaffs and booms, to steady them in any desired position.

Wash plate. Plates or baffles placed in tanks to prevent excessive surging of contents when partly filled.

Wash port. Also called freeing port. Opening in bulwarks to allow for quick overflow of water when seas are shipped.

Waterway. The narrow gutters along the sides of the deck to take care of run off during rain or washdown.

Weather deck. An upper deck exposed to the weather.

Wildcat. The large toothed sprocket wheel that catches the anchor chain and carries it over the windlass.

IV

Longitudinal Construction

The *Gatewood* and the *Isherwood* systems of construction* are the methods generally employed in the construction of vessels on the longitudinal system. The numerous frames of a transverse vessel are omitted and heavy transverse web frames are spaced ten to twelve feet apart, and a system of longitudinal framings is used between them, doing away with the heavy side stringers of the usual construction.

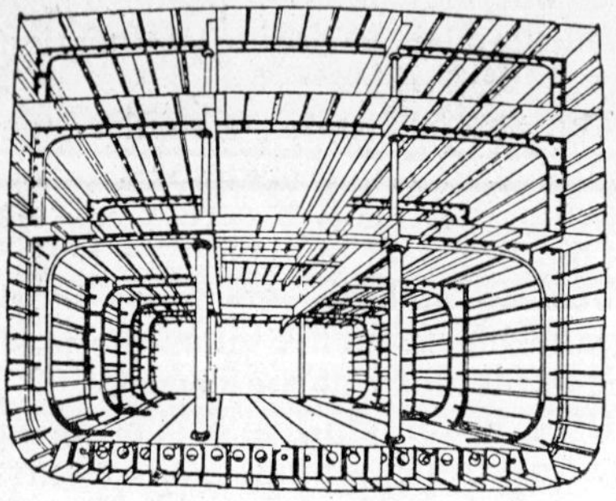

Longitudinal framing, Isherwood system

This system of shipbuilding is finding much favor in the construction of tank vessels. It increases the longitudinal strength of the hull and also results in a considerable reduction in weight. But recent progress in transverse construction has cut down this advantage to a considerable extent. The illustration shows the disposition of web frames and longitudinals. The beams, coamings, stanchions, tanks, and bulkheads are named as in the transverse system.

V

Methods of Construction

Methods of construction are changing with advanced knowledge of shipbuilding.

We are now well started on *standard ship* construction that is, vessels of a certain type and tonnage built one after another from the same plans. This is a necessary development because of the demand for greater efficiency in production.

The standard ship has been followed, through war efforts, by the *fabricated ship*, a plan adopted with enthusiasm during the

* The Gatewood system has been developed by Mr. William Gatewood, naval architect of the Newport News Shipbuilding and Dry Dock Co. The Isherwood system is the development of an English naval architect, Mr. J. W. Isherwood. The *Arcform* design, an Isherwood development, is specially suited for tanker construction.

days of war. The fabricated ship is necessarily a standard vessel, and in the case of many vessels is constructed of structural steel, instead of the special ship steel generally used. The fabricated ship is built in parts made strictly to size at shops scattered over the country where the various shapes are rolled. The finished materials are shipped to the yard at tide water, for assembly and launching. This system saves the shipment of all waste material, and does away with much of the expensive machinery of the usual shipyard. Such vessels can be taken to distant points and assembled without much trouble. The fabricating of steel strictly to size was in successful practice in bridge and other engineering works for many years, and has proven entirely practical in the construction of ships. The first fabricated ships were specially designed to make use of the special bridge and structural shapes already being rolled. Heavier steel was required but this has proven an advantage in many ways. The fabricated vessels, built of structural steel, rust out less quickly and have proven seaworthy and strong.

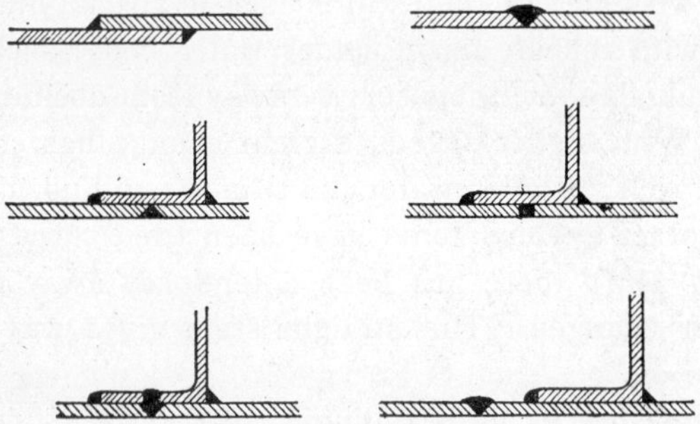

Welded connections

Welded ships are being tried and for many connections the process of welding can be advantageously employed.*

* The merits of rivetless vessels have been much discussed, and English builders not long ago launched a 500-ton rivetless steamer. It remains for American engineers to declare the welding system, which does away with rivets, is practical for large ships.

J. S. Dudley, research engineer, and L. L. Holladay, electrical engineer of the Merchant Shipbuilding Corporation, owners of yards at Harriman and Chester, on the Delaware, announce that they have completed designs for an

In 1936–7 welded plating has taken a definite place in naval construction.

The *cast steel ship* is being seriously considered. A cast steel ship of 10,000 D.W. tons is said to have only 2,000 major parts to its hull, against 20,000 such parts in a vessel of ordinary construction. The special cast parts are welded together by a special process. The claim is made that the cast steel ship has twenty per cent. less metal in her hull and is stronger than a riveted ship. Such a ship is supposed to carry from five to six tons of cargo for each ton of steel in the hull.

The *concrete ship* was pushed to the fore during war emergency times and some successful applications of this form of construction were launched. But the general opinion seems to be against concrete, or rather *ferro-concrete* for such craft are heavily reinforced by steel. No doubt concrete, in special cases, and in smaller craft, will have a useful application, but it does not seem to be the best material for deep sea service.

The *composite type* of construction—metal frames and topsides and wooden planking, still is used in special hulls. When sheathed with copper, on the under water body, such craft are specially valuable for tropic service away from docking facilities.

Form. With higher speeds a great change has come in the form of vessels. Under water the *Maierform* hull, the bulbous bow, and other developments have been tried successfully. In the *Queen Mary* there has been a tendency away from these underwater changes. The straight stem gives way to clipper bows.

Wind resistance. Streamlining of ship's superstructure seems to have come to stay. Bridges, forward houses, and funnels are adapted to the better reduction of head wind resistances.

Rolling control. Anti-rolling tanks, bilge blisters, and gyrostabilizers have been used to reduce and almost eliminate the rolling motion of steamers.

8,800-ton Emergency Fleet type freighter, to be built without rivets. The hull will be 401 feet long and 54 feet molded breadth, with a displacement of 12,231 tons. Mr. Holladay describes the ship as follows:

"The hull is electric welded throughout and therefore wholly without

VI

Wooden Construction

Shipbuilding undoubtedly began with wood, at least with wooden framing and probably hide or bark stretched over this. Down through the ages wood has remained with us as an excellent material for the construction of ships. The art of planking and caulking was known to the ancients. "*Pitch it within and without with pitch*"* is part of the oldest specification remaining on record. Not long back the writer remembers reading (in a Sunday supplement) of the discovery of the timbers of the *Ark* on top of Mount Ararat, giving *gopher wood* the record for endurance.

rivets in its construction. In addition to certain beams, keel, keelsons, etc., running longitudinally, the bottom shell plating, sheer strakes and deck plating run longitudinally; however, the side shell plating, top plates to double bottom and bulkhead plates run transversely or vertically. All plates are abutted without lapping straps or angles and then are welded with a joint 95 to 100 per cent. as strong as the abutting steel members; which results in the elimination of all overlapping steel in plating, liners, angle irons for joining structural parts, stapling and rivets.

"As this material was added originally only incidentally or unavoidably, and for no purposes of strength or stiffness, therefore, none or only minor compensation need be made for its removal. We may, therefore, expect a saving of steel due to elimination about as follows:

Overlapping of plates at joints	5½% or 160 tons
Angle-irons uniting structural parts, stapling, etc.	7 % or 203 tons
Liners	1 % or 29 tons
Rivet heads	2 % or 58 tons
Total	15½% or 450 tons

"To sum up, the electric welded ship will contain about 15 per cent. less steel, will take 40 per cent. less labor, will take 25 per cent. less time for construction, will take 2 per cent. less power for propulsion, will be cheaper to maintain, and be of 5 per cent. greater capacity.

"The outstanding and unquestionable net gain of such a welded ship over its counterpart assembled by riveting is the increase in cargo-carrying capacity of more than 500 tons, which, when translated into earnings, represents little less than a revolution in shipbuilding and ship transportation."

—From *Marine Journal*, N. Y.

* *Genesis, 6–14.*

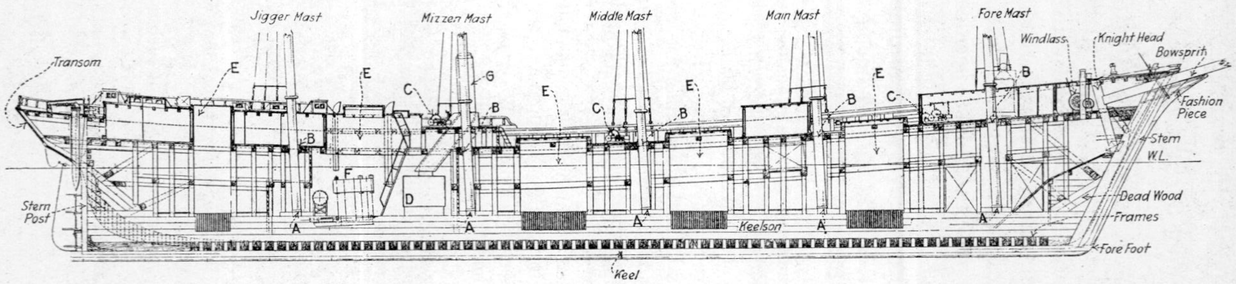

Longitudinal section of a wooden five-masted schooner with steam auxiliary engines

A—Mast steps. B—Mast partners. C—Winches. D—Boilers. E—Hatch openings. F—Engines. G—Smoke stacks.

The masts here are named Fore, Main, Middle, Mizzen and Jigger.

This is simply another way of naming the masts on a five-mast schooner

Wood construction brought with it the use of sails, and this combination of wood and canvas and wind has stood the test of ages at sea under all conditions.

Where wood is abundant and of the right kind, it will always find a use in shipbuilding.

Oak framing and long leaf yellow pine planking, decks and floors, is a combination that stands stress of weather and is particularly fitted for the construction of the good-sized schooners and barkentines now coming into more active service since the war.

The section and elevation shown are typical of this form of construction. Grown knees are not used as much as in previous times, heavy ledges taking their place and adding a large measure of longitudinal strength to the hull. Steel straps in the wake of rigging and across the beams, add greatly to the resistance of the hull to sailing stresses.

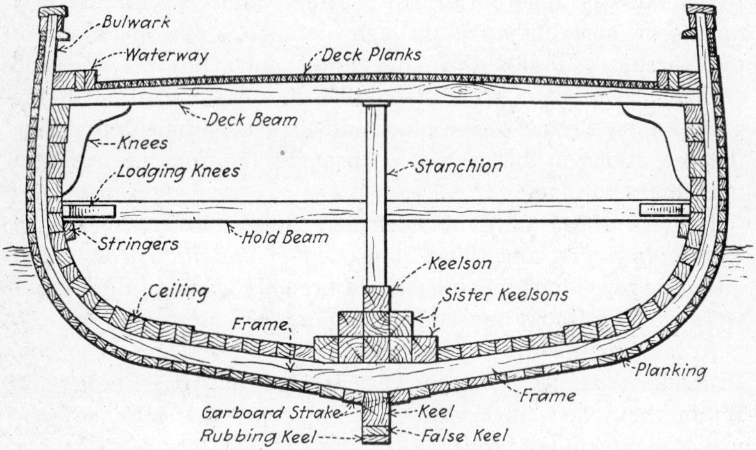

Cross section of a wooden vessel

High keelsons, forming a center girder, prevent hogging. The working of ship timber to size by means of machinery permits of better joints and the use of larger members.

Seamen who wish to gain a better understanding of the construction of modern American wooden vessels are advised to consult " How Wooden Ships Are Built " by E. Cole Estep. This is a simple practical treatise exceptionally well illustrated by photographs showing the best practice.

CHAPTER III

ROPES—KNOTS—SPLICES

I

Rope

The use of rope, one of man's most valuable tools, reaches back through the ages beyond the earliest records of history. No doubt our monkey ancestors were the first to grasp, both mentally and physically, the utility of the natural ropes, the great vines festooned from branch to branch of the primeval forest. By the use of rope early man provided himself with the first means of applying force through distance. The discovery of the purchase, doubling, trebling and quadrupling his man and animal power was a great step forward. The invention of the great knots, the use of the block and sheave, perhaps antedating the invention of the wheel, all brought the rope into greater usefulness to man.

Modern ropes may be classified into those composed of *vegetable fibers*, and those composed of *metallic wires. Hair* and *hide* ropes have been used; in the old days hide tiller ropes were rove but today these ancient things are no more.

At sea, under sail, rope, and rope craft of all kinds, are supreme. In modern steam and motor vessels rope and rope fittings still retain their vast importance. Cargo gear calls into play the use of many kinds of rope, as *standing rigging, lifts, guys, whips,* and *falls.* Boat falls, perhaps the most important of all ropes, are generally of manila. The *hawser*, of manila or wire for towing, warping, and securing vessels in their berths, has grown larger and more important than ever before. *Small stuff, signal halyards, lead* and *log lines*, and the like, are more numerous than ever and finer and better gear is being made.

Wherever forces are to be transmitted over a distance, ships moved, or weights lifted, the modern seaman must use and understand the properties of ropes; it is a fascinating subject.

The vegetable fibers used in rope making are mainly as follows:

Manila fibre is secured from the wild banana plant which grows exclusively in the Philippines, a most important product to our seafaring community. The fibre is stripped from the leaf stems contained in the trunk and is prepared by hand labor. Climatic and soil conditions, as well as the human element determine the grade of the manila fibre.

Undoubtedly manila is the most important rope making material now in use so far as vegetable fibres are concerned.

Sisal hemp, from Yucatan, is used to a great extent in the manufacture of cheaper grades of rope. Sisal, as a fibre, is a substitute for manila but is not so strong or durable. It may be of interest to compare the physical properties of these two kinds of rope.

	Tensile strength	Color
Manila	30,000 lbs. per sq. in.	Light straw, silky.
Sisal	23,000 " " " "	Yellow-white, *sometimes tinge of green.*

Manila is glossy, with a brilliant sheen, smooth and pliable. Fibre, round, easily separated, very light. Length of fibre six to ten feet.

Sisal lacks gloss, is stiff and harsh, and is easily injured by exposure to the weather. Length of fibre two to four feet.

Rope is also made from hemp fibre grown in the United States, Russia and Italy. The best Italian hemp cordage, untarred, is manufactured in Norway. It is very costly and is sometimes used on yachts for reeving the main sheet purchase, and other purchases requiring great strength, flexibility when wet, and good handling properties. This rope is a flat white in color something like cotton.

Coir rope is useful for running *guess warps*. It is very buoyant, does not become water logged. Coir hawsers are specially useful on coal and cargo lighters knocking about a harbor. It is about one half as strong as manila. Coir rope is of a reddish brown color, stretches before parting and is always left-handed.

Other hemp used in rope making is the *Phormium* hemp of New Zealand, and *Sunn* hemp of the East Indies. Many other special fibres are used, but the commercial manufacture of rope is generally confined to the above.

It will not be necessary to go into the detail of rope making, nor would space permit, but in a brief way it will be understood that the primary object in twisting fibres together in a rope is that, by mutual friction, they may be held together when under stress applied to the rope as a whole. Hard twisting increases this friction and has the further advantage of compacting the fibres and making the rope less liable to take up moisture. But, as the twist is increased, the yield of rope from a given length of yarn diminishes. The proper degree of twist given to ropes is generally such that the rope is from three fourths to two thirds the length of the yarn composing it.

A rope test should develop its *working value*. It should be an endurance test rather than a simple breaking test on new rope. This suggestion was first published by the author in an article in *The Seafarer* of January 1921.

Many of the definitions given below are from "Plymouth Rope and The Merchant Marine" issued by the Plymouth Cordage Company and are inserted here with their permission.

Yarn (or thread). A number of fibers twisted together. This twist is usually right hand, but can be left hand if the use of the rope requires it.

Strand. Two or more yarns twisted together. This twist is in the opposite direction to the twist in the yarns.

Note. The whole principle of rope making depends upon this opposing of twists. The yarn tends to unlay, but as it is layed up on an opposite twist in the strand the two tendencies counteract. The strand is given an extra twist and the strands composing the rope are laid up with an opposite twist to the strands.

For instance—Yarns right handed.
Strands left handed.
Rope right handed.

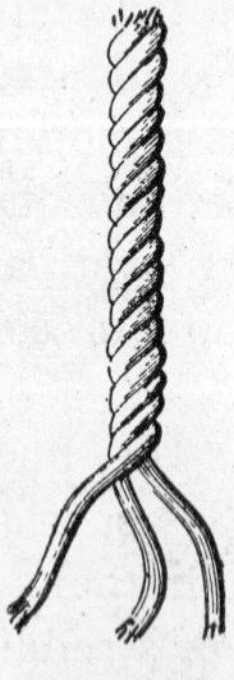

Plain laid

Plain-laid rope. Three, four, or six strands twisted together in the opposite direction to the twist in the strands, so that one twist offsets the other, making the strands hold together, as explained above.

Cable or Water-laid Rope. Three, sometimes four, plain-laid three stranded ropes twisted together in the opposite direction to the lay of the ropes composing the cable. This rope has a somewhat less tensile strength than a plain-laid rope of equal diameter but is more elastic, strands stand greater surface wear, and the rope is therefore superior for special work, wrecking jobs, towing, etc.*

Cable laid

Cord. A term indicating two or three yarns twisted together, additional twist being put in the yarns during the process in an opposite direction to the turn in the cord.

Lay. This term is used to designate the amount (and kind, *i.e.*, right or left), of twist put into a rope; *i.e.*, the angle of the strands in the rope and the threads in the strands. Usually expressed as *hard-laid; common* or *regular-laid, soft-laid, bolt rope, sailmaker's lay.* Other variations are often made in rope required for special work. Generally speaking the softer the lay, the stronger the rope. A hard-laid rope has greater firmness and resistance to abbraisive wear. In soft laid rope the wearing qualities are sacrified to ease in handling, whereas in hard-laid rope strength is often sacrificed to utility. In all cases the use of a rope should govern the lay. The amount of twist which is put into the strands when they are laid into the rope is sometimes referred to as "long jaw," meaning a soft-laid rope—"short jaw" meaning a hard-laid rope. The "jaw" is the distance between two points on the same strand, and measures along the length of the rope in a direct line.

Four stranded. Plain laid—with heart

Right-laid rope. Rope in which the strands are twisted together in the opposite direction to the movement of a clock's hands, that is strands are *left*, rope is *right-laid.*

Left-laid rope. Opposite to above.

An easy way to tell the lay of a rope by simply looking at it as follows: Right-handed rope, strands run *upward* to the *right.* Left-handed rope, strands run *upward* to the *left.*

Hawser. Any rope 5 inches in circumference, and above, that is used for towing is designated as a *hawser.* It may be plain-laid or hawser-laid.

The term *hawser-laid* is used to describe left-handed rope.

A *cable* is designated as being *hawser-laid*, being made from three right-laid ropes. It is always long-laid (soft).

* *Water-laid* rope is made by wetting the fibres in spinning, instead of using oil or tallow. Such rope is seldom made, and is always *cable-laid.*

Coil. Standard length, unless otherwise designated, 200 fathoms, or 1,200 feet. Half coils are also used, being half of above.

Yardage (of rope). Is the length per unit of weight.

Bolt-rope. A special word may be said of *bolt rope.* This is the name now given to rope of superior quality made from long selected fibers. Bolt rope was originally used for the roping of sails. The necessity for an exceptionally strong and serviceable rope that would lay dead ahead of the sailmaker was the cause of its development. Bolt rope is made from manila fiber and from tarred Russian, Italian and American hemp. Hemp bolt rope is used largely on sailing yachts (Russian hemp being given the preference as it will retain the tar better than the American hemp, although the latter is somewhat stronger). For general purposes manila bolt rope is superior and is most commonly used. Wire bolt rope is used on the leeches and foot of large square sails.

Tarred fittings or *small stuff* or *seizing stuff.* Names generally given to marline, houseline, two and three strand spunyarn, roundline and hambroline. All tarred fittings with the exception of hambroline are made from yarns spun right-handed and the angle of the individual yarns is left. The yarn for hambroline is spun left-handed and the yarn in the cord is right.

Note: Small stuff is also designated by the number of threads as 6-thread, 15-thread, 18-thread or 21-thread stuff.

Marline. Is made from yarns spun from double dressed American hemp and tarred. It is a cord made of two yarns and is used for worming, serving, and small seizing, and for general use on shipboard. Marline is ordered by weight and runs as follows:

Common marline	222	feet to the pound
Medium "	360	"
Yacht "	520	"

Houseline. Is made of the same material and in the same manner as marline except that the cord has three instead of two yarns. It is used for the same purpose as marline. Sometimes both marline and houseline are made untarred. Houseline runs about 160 feet to the pound.

Roundline. Roundline is a cord made in the same manner as houseline but of larger size, and is used for the same purpose. It is used for worming larger ropes where the cuntline to be filled is larger. Roundline runs about 92 feet to the pound.

Hambroline. Hambroline is a cord of three yarns approximately the same size as and yardage as roundline. It differs from roundline in having an opposite twist.

Spunyarn. While spunyarn is made of the same materials as the other tarred fittings its method of manufacture is somewhat different. In a corded product the yarns are first spun and then an additional twist is given them in the opposite direction to the twist of the product. In spunyarn the yarns are twisted together with no additional twist being put into them. Spunyarn lies smooth under the serving mallet and gives a close covering to the rope being served and keeps out the water. It is also used for general work on shipboard. It has two, three, and sometimes four yarns.

Ratline. Is generally made from tarred American hemp. It is an especial part of the boatswain's store for general use on shipboard. Except perhaps in sailing craft, ratline stuff is seldom used for its original purpose, namely the " ratlines " forming the rope ladder supported by the shrouds. It is three stranded, and the strands are given a medium twist while the rope is rounded up with afterturn so the eyesplice may be easily tucked and held by the afterturn of the rope when it is employed as ratlines.

On steamers ratline is used for heavy serving, as lashings for spars, anchors, and boats, and to a large extent as heaving lines.

Tarred hemp lanyard. Lanyards are still used occasionally. It is four stranded and seldom over four and a half inches in circumference.

Quartermaster's stores. These are generally the log lines, signal halyards, lead lines, hand and deep-sea, so far as the rope equipment of the vessel is concerned.

Signal halyards. Three-strand plain-laid, untarred hemp is generally used. It runs in the following sizes.

3/4″ in hanks.	30 fathoms each
1″ in coils................	120 "
1 1/8″ in coils..............	120 "

Signal halyards are also very often rove from braided cord, the sizes most often used being those below:

No. 7....................	7/32″ in diameter
" 8....................	1/4″ "
" 9....................	9/32″ "
" 10....................	5/16″ "

It can be had up to 1 1/8″ in diameter.

*Samson cord** (braided cotton) is very largely used.

Lead lines, log lines. These will be found under the chapter on Compass, Log Lead.

The use of manila rope. Three strand manila, common-lay, is used for all work not calling for extra strength. Cargo slings, cargo hoists, falls, working tackles, boom tackles, painters,

* *Trade name.*

whips, gantlines, scaffold slings, etc. It is generally right-handed, untarred. Sizes from six-thread to 10 inch.

Four strand manila, yarns tallow treated, with fiber heart. Much used for life boat falls. Comes in sizes from $2\frac{1}{2}$ to 6 inches in circumference

(Note: rope sizes, as used at sea, refer to the circumference, unless otherwise stated.)

Towing lines. Should be made of the best bolt rope stock. These lines come in five-inch sizes and upwards in standard coils of two hundred fathoms.

Any rope larger than ten inches may be furnished in coils of two hundred and fifty fathoms.

Manila handling lines. These lines used in docking and in tieing up and often called "working lines" come in the regular sizes above five-inch. They should be of the best quality.

Wrecking cable. Hawser laid, averaging from 14 to 16 inches in circumference.

Fishermen's cables. The fishing boat, riding to a long scope in deep water, still holds to the fiber cable. These ropes are hawser-laid, and of great strength, usually tarred. The sizes range from four to twelve inches in circumference. Coils run 60, 75, 90, 100 and 120 fathoms.

Basis. Manufacturers in quoting the price of rope make use of a basis size. Generally for manila and sisal cordage, rope $2\frac{1}{4}$ inch (circum.) is taken as the basis. This figure is then used in working out costs as follows:

3-strand rope $2\frac{1}{4}$ inch and larger, basis price.
3-strand rope, 2 inch, $\frac{1}{2}$ cent over basis.
3-strand rope, $1\frac{3}{4}$, $1\frac{1}{2}$ and $1\frac{1}{4}$ inch, one cent over basis.
3-strand rope, $1\frac{1}{8}$ inch, $1\frac{1}{2}$ cents over basis.
3-strand rope, 1 and $\frac{3}{4}$ inch, 2 cents over basis.
3-strand rope, 9/16 inch, $2\frac{1}{2}$ cents over basis
3-strand rope, $\frac{1}{2}$ inch, 3 cents over basis.
4-strand rope 1 cent per lb. more than 3 strand.

From this it will be seen that all ropes of the basis size or *larger* are figured at a certain price per pound. The smaller sizes running to a higher figure per pound, and four stranded rope more per pound than three stranded.

Oakum was formerly a byproduct, picked from junk aboard the long voyage sailer, and is now manufactured ashore. It comes under rope lore and should be of good quality as it is used for caulking seams of wooden vessels and wooden decks and in some cases hatch covers are caulked before battening down the tarpaulins on wet runs through stormy weather with cargoes subject to damage by water.

Oakum is sold in fifty-pound bales, gross weight. Rope oakum comes in coils of about fifty pounds.

The navy specifications contain the following requirements as to quality:

Material. Oakum shall be made from Italian, Russian or American hemp (Canabis sativa), line or tow, or from any No. 1 grade Sunn, or No. 2 grade Benaries, or North Bengal Sunn, or from any combination of these fibers; and shall be thoroughly carded and finished, free from excessive lumps, dirt, or other extraneous matter.

Spinning. Oakum shall be spun by machine into slivers or threads in the form of balls or hanks not exceeding 5 pounds each; it shall be soft and uniform in texture, strong and sufficiently twisted to be suitable in all respects for calking seams of vessels. The slivers or threads shall contain not less than 43 feet to the pound and not more than 75 feet to the pound, unless otherwise required.

Impregnation. The fibers shall be thoroughly impregnated with pine tar to an amount not to exceed 30 per cent. of the total weight of the fiber and tar.

Packing. Oakum shall be baled in regular packages containing about 50 pounds each. Bales shall be compressed no more than necessary and shall be securely bound with laths and strong tarred sisal yarns. Old timers picking oakum under the foc's'le head during heavy weather, knew nothing about these requirements.

II

Notes on the Care of Rope

To open a coil of rope, loosen the burlap cover, lay the coil on the flat side *with the inside end nearest the deck.* Then reach *down* through the center of the coil and draw the rope *up* and out of the coil. Do not uncoil from the outside as extra turns are put in the rope and kinks are apt to form.

To thoroughfoot a rope, coil down against the lay, bring lower end up through center of coil and coil down with the lay. This will take out the kinks and extra turns. If many turns in rope, coil small; if few turns, coil large.

So far we are all right when we have *both* ends of our rope free. When taking the turns out of the hauling part of a boom guy, or a topping lift, or a brace, coil down *left*-handed (for right-handed rope) that is, against the hands of a clock, beginning at the pin or cleat, and *dip* the end *down* through the coil, pulling it out, *capsize* the coil and proceed as before. These are definite directions on the method of *thoroughfooting* a rope.

Use on capstan and windlass. The principle of the contrary turn in rope making must be considered in the care of rope used on a capstan or windlass. If the rope is thrown on always in the same direction the " afterturn " will be continually thrown out, and the rope will be injured. When using rope on winch heads at each end of a shaft, care must be taken when the winch is running and no strain on either one of the ropes, that the turns on the idle head do not chafe.

Taut dry ropes should be immediately slacked off when wet by rain. This is specially important with long ropes rove as running rigging. The contraction of untarred rope, manila in particular, when wet, is well understood. Signal halyards should belay in such fashion that they will give enough to allow for this when doused by rain.

Lashings, as for rafts, and at shear heads, or when lashing the garland on a heavy mast or spar, are hove taught dry. When wet, by being put overboard or by dashing water over them, great tightness is obtained.

Acid is very detrimental to the life of a rope and dangerous to those using it. Great care must always be taken to keep rope away from any possible contact with acid, or with strong acid fumes. Damp rope will absorb such fumes and will be acted upon very rapidly.

Although a *wet rope* gives an increased breaking strength if the rope is new, and though manila rope deteriorates very little from wetting, rope should never be put away while wet or damp. After use, rope should be cleaned and dried, and coiled down in a loose coil. Small ropes and tackles should be hung up, large ropes should be coiled, or faked, on gratings raised from the deck to insure the circulation of air and freedom from wet by water running on the deck.

Rope should be stored in dry, well-ventilated places. The fore and after peak storerooms of the average vessel are far from ideal. Whenever possible these places should be cleaned out and all rope stores *roused* up on deck and given a sun bath. Dry rot in rope is little understood, but it is the source of a great deal of loss in the life and strength of rope.

Boat falls and running rigging, always under some tension, dry out quickly. Care should be taken of the *hauling parts* of boat falls. These are coiled in tubs, to conform with the regulations of the United States Steamboat-Inspection Service. These ends, generally not properly ventilated, deteriorate rapidly. Many officers turn boat falls *end-for-end*, placing the partly rotted, but *larger looking* rope at the davit heads and the long-jawed well-preserved stuff in the tubs. Boat falls should never be turned. When no longer A1, these ropes should be shifted to less important use, and new ones rove.

Hawser and mooring lines should be hoisted clear of the deck in loose coils and thoroughly dried out before stowing below. When wet with *salt water*, it is advisable to get them up in a good rain and wash out the salt, or use a hose if fresh water is available. The salt crystals make the rope highly hygroscopic and if stowed below for a time it will become damp.

Sand or grit of any kind cuts away the fibres of a rope and causes rapid deterioration. Ropes brought on deck, especially handling lines coiled aft under the cinders from the funnel, should be covered with tarpaulins when not in use. The ends of all mooring lines should be similarly protected when possible. Generally vessels in port take little care of these important lines.*

Large ropes do not rot out as rapidly as small ones.

Water proofing. The protection of rope fibre against moisture has made great studies in recent years. A number of satisfactory processes having been developed such as the Whitlock. *Water Flex* process, etc.

The working loads for various sizes and kinds of rope will be found in the Rope Tables at the end of this chapter.

* In a paper presented in 1917 before the Engineers Society of Western Pennsylvania, J. Melville Alison, of Manchester, England, dwelt upon the long life of rope used in the driving of machinery. Among many cases cited by Mr. Alison the following may be of interest to seamen:

"A remarkable case of longevity may be mentioned of 24 cotton ropes 1¾ in. in diameter, employed to transmit 820 hp. in a Lancashire cotton mill and running at a velocity of 4,396 ft. per minute directly from the engine flywheel, which is 28 ft. in diameter. These were fixed in September, 1878, and are still running in 24 hours a day service, a period of over 38 years. Another set has been working 28 years on an average of 20 hours per day and appears little the worse for wear."

Undoubtedly intelligent care of the ropes of a ship, whether a sailer or a steamer, must in the long run pay a handsome return in economy.

Before closing the section on rope mention should be made of *re-made rope.* Certain manufacturers buy up old junk and taking out the best parts re-make it into surprisingly good looking rope. This rope is made up of strands spun with the old cover yarns placed in the heart and the clean inside yarns outside. A re-made rope can be detected by opening up the strands, revealing the soiled or uneven inside strands. It is also liable to have a very " bilgy " smell, due to former voyaging in the fore or after peaks. It is about half as strong as new rope.

In purchasing rope from unknown dealers test it carefully to be certain that it is genuine *manila.* Manila rope, because of certain natural oils inherent to the manila fibre, will not suffer from wetting by salt water. All sisal yarns are weakened by being wet. To test fibre immerse the yarns in a bucket of salt water for about two days. Pure manila will come out fine and strong. Sisal will be stringy and will comb apart. Some kinds of sisal when dry is as strong and even stronger than manila and much of it looks very fine in a new rope. Wetting at once causes it to deteriorate.

Ropes were formerly all made in a *rope walk*, now the very best kind of rope is also made by machinery. Some old timers, however, seem to prefer the walk-laid rope because of their belief that the strands of such rope will all be of absolutely the same length throughout. When the rope is under stress all strands should bear an equal part of the load, so the wear will be even. Much of the re-made rope on the market is due to the fact that often two strands of a rope will wear out while a third strand seems to be almost perfect showing that the rope, in the first place, was not properly made, or was grossly mishandled. The " good " strand is used to form the basis for the inferior rope resulting from re-making.

In purchasing rope the reputation and standing of the maker is a safeguard. Owing to the fact that safety of life often depends upon the integrity of rope the Government will not permit a rope maker to brand his product as " Manila Rope " unless it is the genuine article made from new yarns.

The largest cable-laid rope made up to the present time is a 24″ hawser laid rope.

Plain-laid, three stranded rope, has been made as large as 25″. Twelve inch, plain-laid three stranded rope is about the largest size in general use.

III

Knots, Hitches, Bends; etc.

A great many knots have come down to us from our seafaring ancestors and in most instances their origin is lost in the dim distance of the unrecorded past. But with the modern seaman most of these formations now only possess an academic interest. The *sheep-shank*, for instance, is used about as often as the crossbow. In Standard Seamanship we will picture many knots, bends, and hitches, and explain the formation and use of those employed on board ship.

Sheepshank

The bowline. King of knots. Nothing can jamb it; it will *never* slip *if* properly made. The bowline, with gear of moderate size, is made as follows. Take the bight of the rope in the left hand, the end in the right hand both palms up. Standing part and end leading *away* from body. Place the *end* over the *bight*, above the index finger of the left hand. Place the index finger of the right hand on top of this end, crossing

Bowline with loop passed over bight forming a running bowline.

Bowline
Back view of a bowline. Knots very often look quite different when viewed from different sides.

the bight, and the *thumb* of the *right* hand *under* the *bight;* turn the right wrist, outboard (*i.e.*, to the right) and you will form a loop in the bight of the line and will have placed the end of the rope through this loop in one motion. This loop is the *goose neck.* Now finish the knot by carrying the end *back* around the standing part of the rope, on the right side, and *down* around standing part on the left side, back again through the goose neck. This is the sailor's way of *casting* a bowline in a piece of gear of moderate size. You may have to get someone to show you how it is done, for the art of knotting and splicing can not be learned entirely from books.

The bowline is useful in many ways. If you wish to attach a painter to a ring, pass end through and form the bowline, and you are safe from everything but chafe or parting under too great a stress. It is used in sending men over the side, in forming temporary eyes in large ropes and in small ones. It has a thousand applications.

French bowline. When sending a man over the side on hazardous work, into a smoke-filled hold, or anywhere where he may become unconscious, or loose his grip, and where he may have to use *both hands*, make use of the *French bowline.* The writer has not seen this form of the bowline illustrated in any work on seamanship. It was brought to his attention in 1897 by Victor Mathes, of Dunkirk, able seaman on the American three skysail yarder *A. J. Fuller*, when on a voyage around the Horn.* Seaman Mathes saw it used in the French Navy. The bowline is formed in the same fashion as the regular bowline, except that the end (D), instead of going about the standing part (E)

* "Our work under the fo's'sle head got all hands started and during many a dismal wet dog watch we practiced the forming of every knot from the *bowline* down, Peter, the boy, and myself trying to outdo each other in the variety of our achievements. Frenchy taught us a new way to form that 'king of knots' the *bowline*, in which the loop is passed through the goose-neck twice, forming a double loop, a most useful knot employed in the French navy. When a man is to be lowered over side, he sits in one of the loops and the other is passed under his arm pits, the gooseneck coming against his chest. His weight tautens the part under his arms. It is impossible for a man to drop out of this bowline, even though he becomes unconscious."

—*Under Sail,* page 125.

First publication of this knot was made by the author in the "Outing" Magazine of August, 1913.

at once, is given a round turn about the bight of the goose neck (A), and then the knot is finished off as before.

This leaves two loops that are loosely connected through the goose neck. The loops are made so that a man can sit in one (B) while the other (C) goes under his arm pits, the knot being at his breast. The weight of the man hauls the arm pit loop taut, he is safe against falling out and is held upright if unconscious.

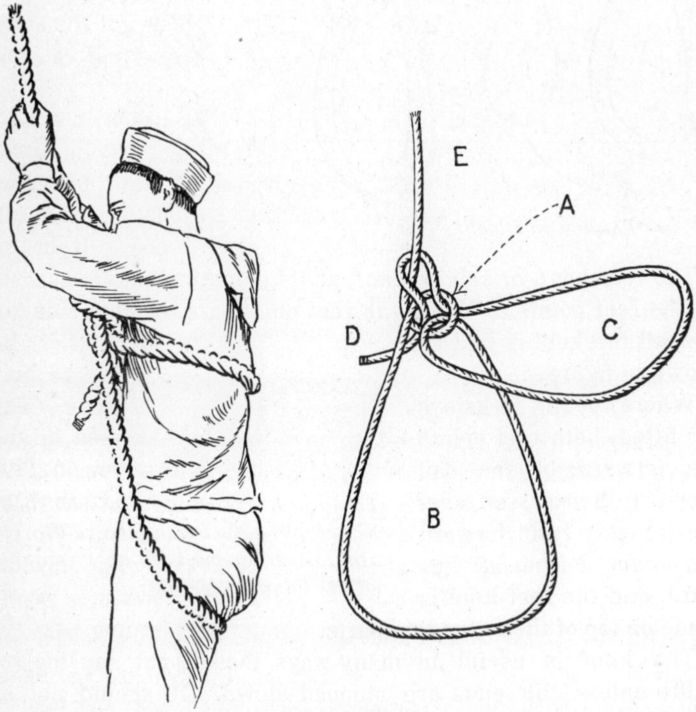

French bowline

This little-known knot is perhaps one of the most useful applications of the bowline.

The *bowline on a bight*, is well known, though of slight utility. It is formed as in the ordinary way, using the bight instead of the end, the parts being double. When the bight is up through the goose neck, it is passed around the standing part by dipping it down and lifting the loop through it. The drawings show this better than words.

Spanish bowline. Not much use for this.

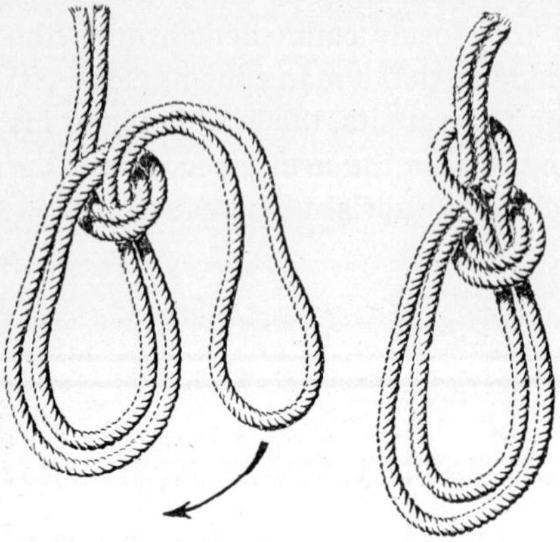

Bowline on a bight

Spanish bowline

The *reef knot*, or *square knot*, as its name implies, is used to tie the reef points. Where the reef points are on both sides of the sail the knot is tied as shown in figure.

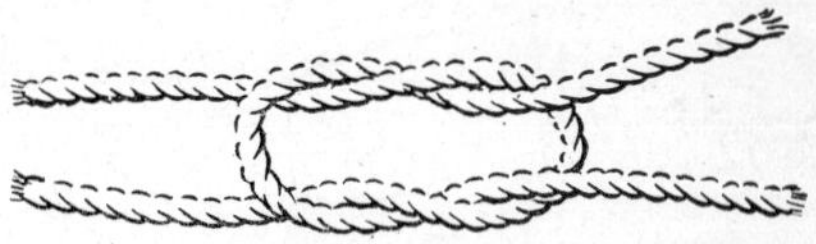

Reef or Square Knot. The knot is shown open. It should be hauled tight, the lower ends go around the yard. The artist, never having been on a yard, did not get this exactly right.

Where reefing jackstays are fitted, both reef points are forward of the sail they are then passed *over* the jackstay from forward aft, *under* it from aft forward, and the reef knot is made on top of their standing parts.

The knot is useful in many ways though not any too reliable unless the ends are stopped down. It should not be used to bend together ropes for hauling. It is a good knot for tying up things, packages and the like. When the reef knot is made correctly both parts come up together at each side of the knot, otherwise, when one is up and the other down we have the *granny*. Youngsters will always remember how easy it is to make a granny.

Granny knot—one end up, one end down

A study of this knot will show that it is closely allied to the *overhand knot* of classic uselessness. The *double overhand knot* is also seldom used.

Overhand knot

Double overhand

The *figure-of-eight* knot fits in about here and brings forth memories of "pieces of eight." Sometimes it is useful to prevent the end of an extended fall from running out through the hauling block. Sailors regard it with tolerance and tailors find it useful in decorating ladies dresses and military uniforms, as Keats wrote "*A thing of beauty is a joy forever*," so the figure-of-eight knot has a valid reason for its being.

Figure-of-eight knot

Bag knot

But when we get into the realm of these complications we find the *bag knot* or the *hackamore* to confuse us. Any able seaman should be *able* to make it.

Half hitch

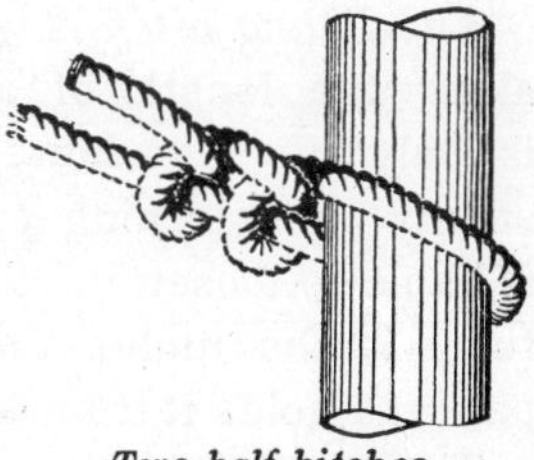

Two half hitches

The *half hitch* and *two half hitches* are very useful knots and are often employed to make fast lines of moderate size.

A round turn and two half hitches, are very much used on board ship. The latter with the end stopped down is used in securing mooring lines to posts where no eye is fitted.

Round turn and two half hitches

The *clove hitch* is really two half hitches about a spar, or rail, or the standing part of another rope. The clove hitch is very useful. It is used in hitching ratlines to the shrouds other than the swifter and after leg.

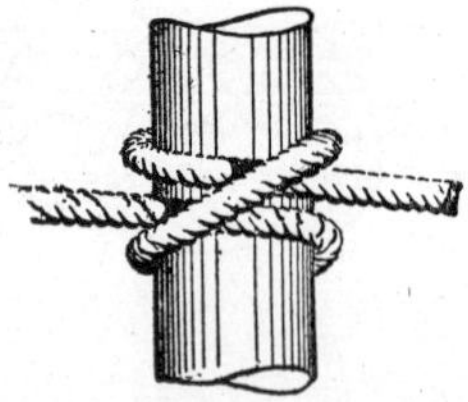

Clove hitch

Rolling hitch

Sheet bend

The *rolling hitch* is very effective when a pull is to be resisted along the length of a spar. It is only effective however for a steady pull, slacking and jerking is liable to loosen it. The double turn jambs under the hauling part and holds it from slipping.

The *timber hitch*, and *timber and half hitch* are useful when towing spars.

Timber hitch

The *sheet bend*, sometimes called *becket* or *signal halyard bend* is used as the name implies, in bending flags where snap hooks are not fitted. It is also used in securing the standing part of small tackles to the becket in one of the blocks.

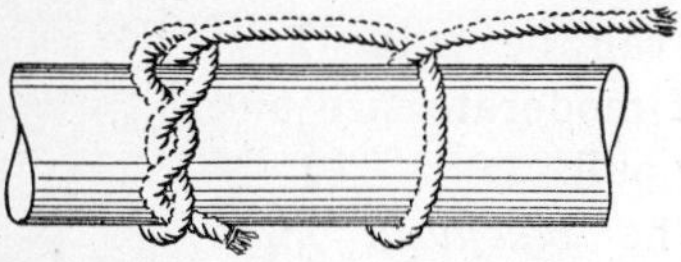

Timber and half hitch

The *double sheet bend* is more secure and serves very well for bending ropes together when they are not too large. If the ends are stopped to the standing parts it is very reliable.

Open carrick bend

The *carrick bend* and *double carrick bend* are used in bending together hawsers. The last gives an easy connection distributing the stress along the fibres of the rope.

Double sheet bend

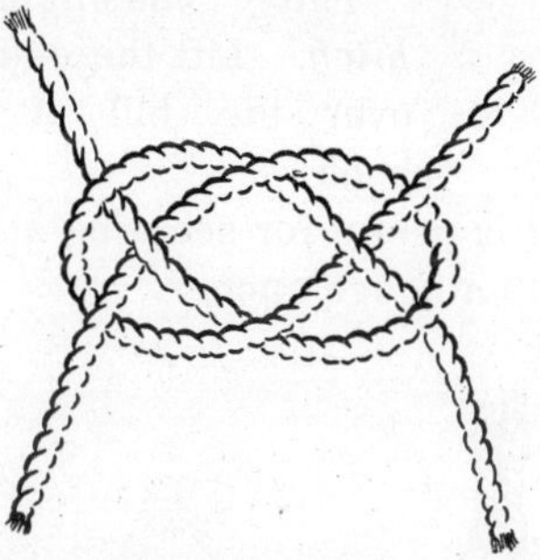

Double carrick bend

Carrick bend

The open carrick bend. A good bend for heavy lines.

Note: Ends are always lashed to standing parts of carrick bends.

The *reeving line bend* is useful where the lines must be payed out through a hawse pipe or a small towing chock. It is not as elastic as the carrick bend. Two bowlines are sometimes used in connecting hawsers, the short nip at the loops is a disadvantage under heavy and continuous stress.

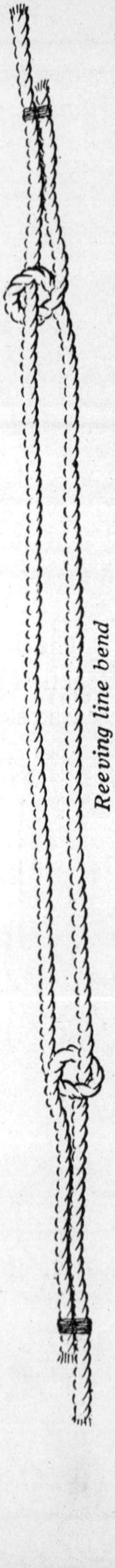

Reeving line bend

The *cat's paw* is used when it is necessary to clap a tackle on a rope, or a handy billy on the hauling part of a larger purchase. It can be made anywhere on the bight of a rope of moderate size and affords a sure hold for a steady pull.

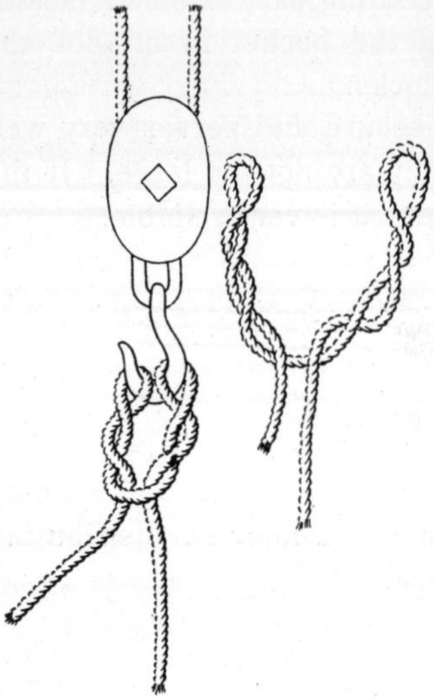

Cat's paw

The *blackwall hitch* and *double blackwall* hitch are seldom used. Their purpose is to secure a rope to the hook of a block. It is generally better to form a bowline and hook into the loop, unless there is very little end when the above hitches come into play. Teach these to the ship's boys for few of them nowadays know how to make them.

The *midshipman's hitch.* Lift the end out over the bill of the hook.

The *fishermen's bend* is useful for securing a rope to a buoy, or a hawser to a kedge anchor.

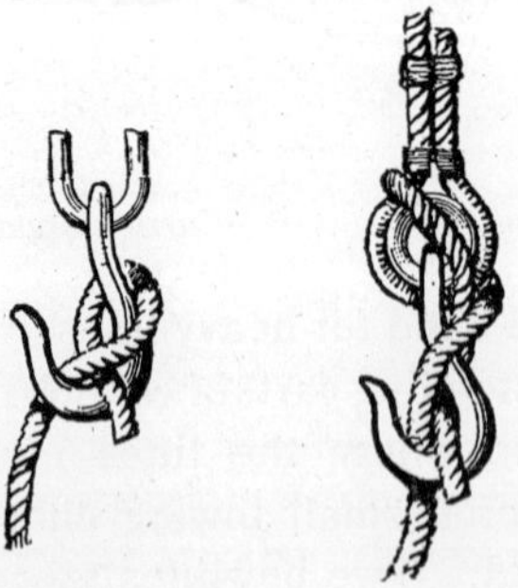

Single *Double*

Blackwall hitches

Midshipman's hitch

The *stuns'le tack bend* is very handy *when* you set the *stuns'ls.* So is the *stuns'le halyard bend.*

Fishermen's bend

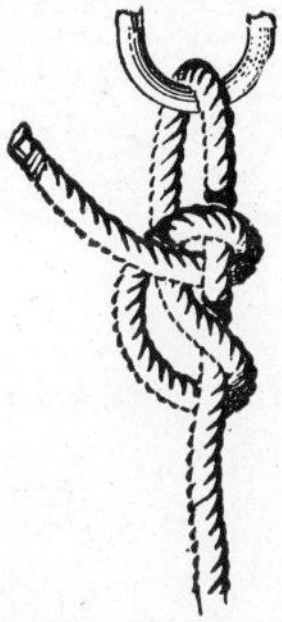

Stuns'le tack bend

Stuns'le halyard bend

The *stevedore's knot.* Used to prevent a fall from running through the large swallow of a cargo block.

Stevedore's knot. Upper, commenced;

lower, (almost) jambed

Crabber's eye knot. A running eye with extra friction.

Masthead knot. A knot that can be formed at the head of a jury mast. The knot is formed on the middle of a rope, the two ends lead aft as backstays, the forward loop provides for the hooking or bending of a fore stay, and the side loops for shrouds. When the knot is formed and set up, these loops are supposed to lie close to the mast head.

Japanese knot. Another fancy one.

Crabber's eye knot

Marling hitch. Used in lashing hammocks. Use *seven* hitches between the ends. The marling hitch is specially useful. It is used for marling the wire bolt ropes to large sails, and for making selvagee strops. Note that the parts come out from *under* the hitch, in that way helping to *jamb* the turns. Used with *marling spike* to heave taut turns of a lashing or in clapping on seizings.

Mast head knot

Japanese knot

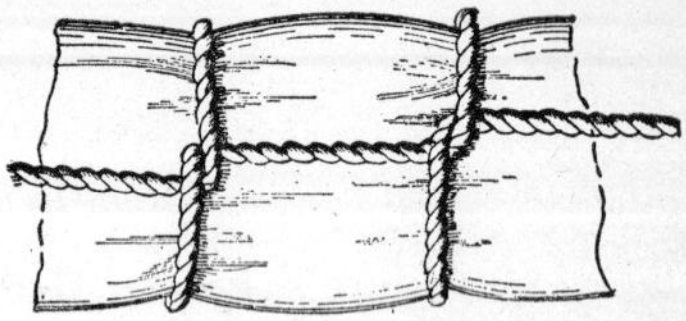

Marling hitch

Selvagee strop. This is a strop made of many turns of spun yarn, rope yarn, or other small stuff. Where a large strop is made sixteen to twenty-one thread stuff may be used. It is

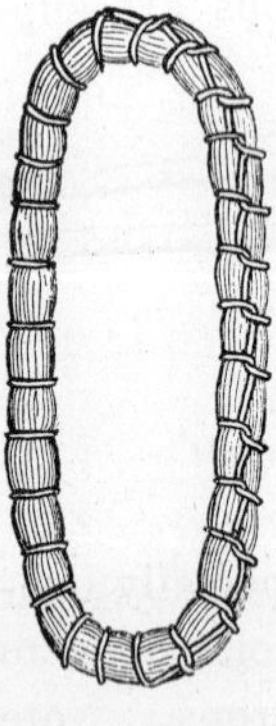

Selvagee strop

Hooking a "Handy Billy" on a large rope

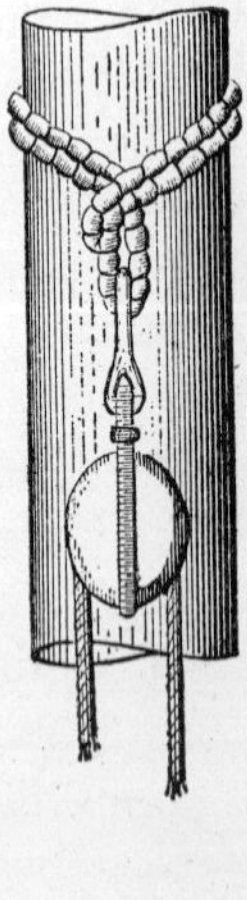

Hooking on a spar

formed by passing the parts, with equal tension, around two large spikes on a board, and then *marling* the parts together, with *marline*. It is one of the safest strops for hooking a tackle to a stay, or spar. The illustrations show several methods of using this strop.

Knotting a rope yarn. Very many men at sea nowadays do not know how to knot a rope yarn. In making a selvagee strop

Knotting a rope yarn

this must be done, where rope yarn is used. The parts shown in the drawing are hauled tight. The rope yarn will then be secured without *give.*

Lashings are a particularly necessary and useful part of seamanship on any vessel. They are *passed* and *hove taut*, and the ends are often *frapped* about the standing parts. Frapping turns are the turns at right angles to the main turns of a lashing and serve to bring the parts together and to make the lashing still more secure. To heave a lashing tight, form a marling hitch, and heave on it with the point of a spike, or if you have a large lashing, use a small heaver, or a bar.

The *Marling hitch* gives the marling spike its name (often called *marline* spike). The marling hitch is formed by crossing the bight over the point of the spike and sticking spike through as shown. A twist of the wrist does it. Someone must *show* you this.

Rose lashing. Useful in securing the foot rope to a yard.

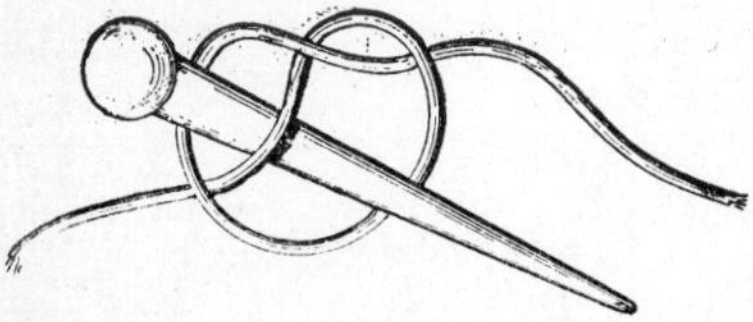

Marling hitch

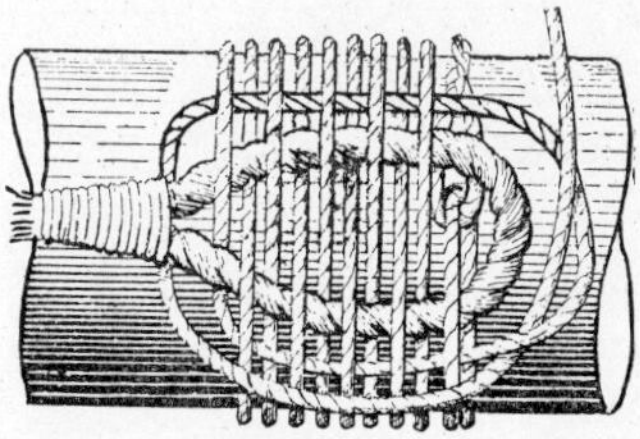

Rose lashing

Seizings are of great importance in the rigging on board ships Care should be taken in *clapping on* seizings, as the method of procedure is very clearly laid down. Seizings, of course, are used in many places on board steamers, and are often very poorly done.

Stopper with a hook

Racking seizing. Used to rack, or hold together two parts of a fall, or rigging when being *set up.* If you wish to shift the hauling part of a heavy boom topping lift from one cleat to another on the mast table, boom topped up, rack the fall to the one next to it, cast off and shift. Where this is done often, have a *stopper with a hook,* and use this, if falls are too far apart for racking.

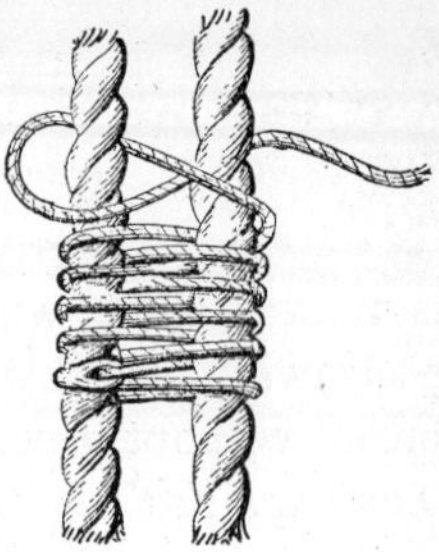

Racking seizing

Plain or round seizing. The drawing shows the beginning, the turns passed, end under last turn, and the frapping turns, which are knotted.

Middle seizing. This is a round seizing passed about the bights of two pieces of gear that are required to lie close to each

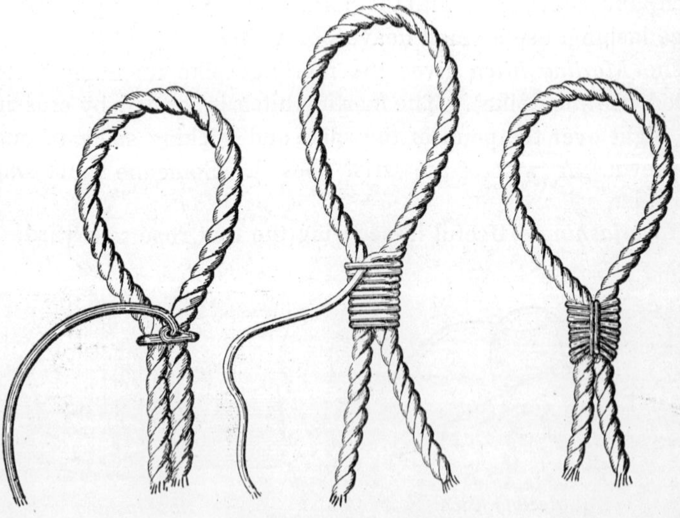

Plain or round seizing

other. The drawing shows the manner of knotting the frapping turns. Where stays are turned up around dead eyes or thimbles, the upper seizings are of this kind.

Eye seizings are those formed at the neck of an eye, and are usually found under a *thimble* (a round or pear-shaped ring of metal fitting in an eye to take the chafe).

Riding turns, are the turns put over the first turns in a seizing, or lashing. These should not be hove too taut. They *ride* in the spaces between the parts underneath.

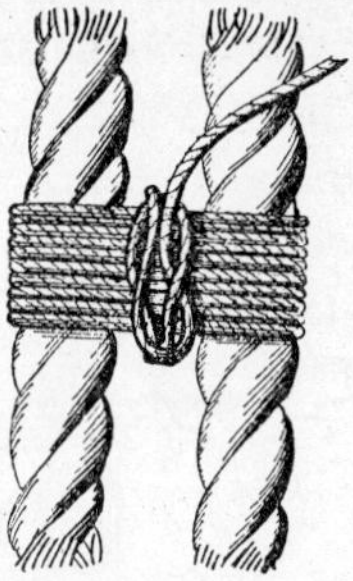

Middle seizing

Seizing with riding turns

A study of seizings will show that they are simply small lashings.

Another method of making an eye or throat seizing

The *Spanish windlass* is a combination of a bar, a rope and two heavers. Used to apply power for bringing the parts of a rope together. The heavy *throat seizing* at the eyes of the rigging, is often passed after the shrouds have been brought together by a Spanish windlass. This method of applying power dates back beyond the caravels of Columbus. It is still a very useful thing.

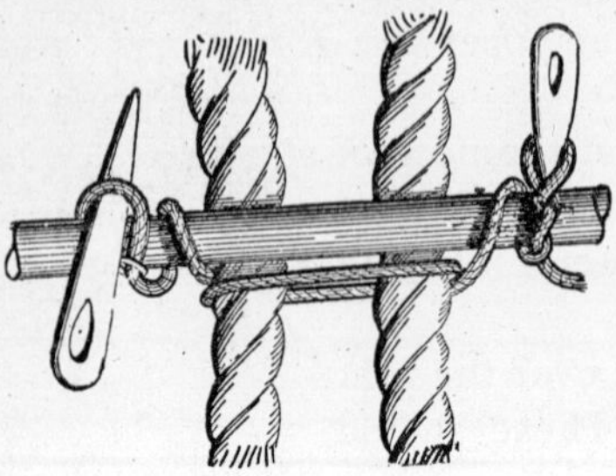

Spanish windlass

Throat seizings, aside from the throat seizings under the eyes of the rigging, the seizings made where two ropes cross are

Throat seizings

also called by that name. The drawings show two methods of forming this seizing.

Clinches are formed by seizing an eye in the bight of a rope near the end, the eye passing around the standing part of the rope forming a running eye, the bight or standing part running through the loop formed by the clinch. When the eye of the clinch is formed so that the end of the rope is next to the running loop, it is called an *inside clinch.* When the end is away from it it is called an *outside clinch.* Clinches are used to secure the buntlines to the foot of a sail when they are not rigged as spilling lines.

Outside clinch

Inside clinch

To bend a rope cable to an anchor use an inside clinch. See *ground tackle.*

Shroud knot. Used in joining a rope stay that has been carried away when there is very little end left for splicing or knotting. Come up on the lanyard, and unlay the strands for a short distance back from the break. Bring the rope together,

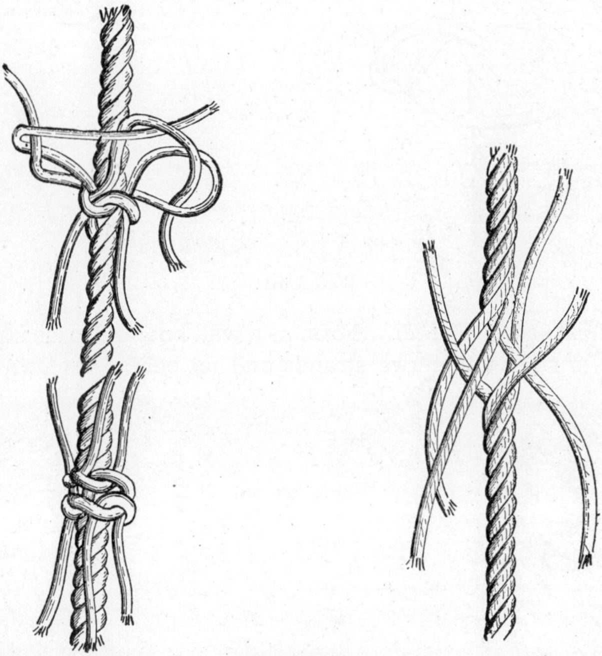

Shroud knot

forking the strands. Form a wall knot on each rope with the strands of the other. Ends may be fayed down and served on each side of knot.

Wall knot. Unlay rope, pass the strands around from left to right up underneath of the strand next to the right, as shown in illustration, then form the knot and pull the strands through taut.

Double wall. Follow around the strands of a single wall, opening up the lay of the knot with a spike, the three strands again coming up through the center. Also called a *stopper knot.*

A *Crown* is formed by bending the strands of a rope over each other, tucking the third one as shown in the *Single Mathew Walker* and crown.

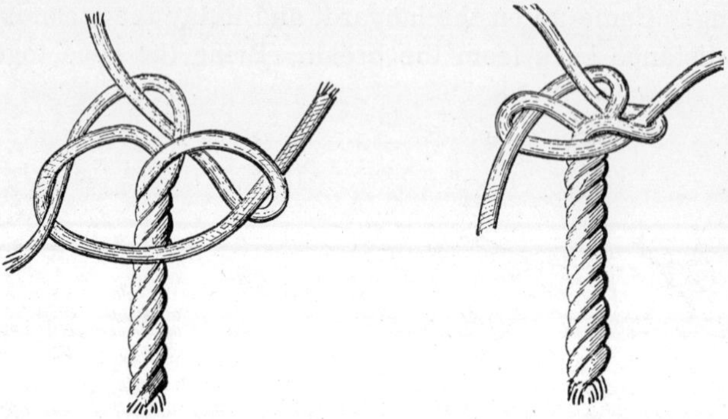

Wall knot

Single Mathew Walker. Form as a wall knot but pass strands around to right under two strands and up behind its own part.

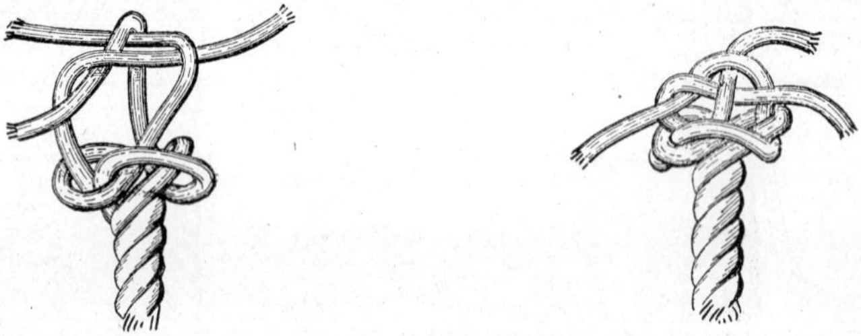

Single Mathew Walker and crown

Double Matthew Walker. Pass strands around from left to right *under all* parts and *up through its own bight.*

Manrope knot. Form a wall, and crown it. Then follow strands of wall around again and then form the crown. A very good knot at the end of manropes leading down the side ladders. If someone should slip overboard in a tideway there is something to catch hold of.

Many of the knots shown may seem useless. In fact they are mainly ornamental. On the other hand they are amusing and when sailors busy themselves with these things they are gaining the fine points of a handicraft that has its origin in the remotest times. Also, many men are going to sea nowadays

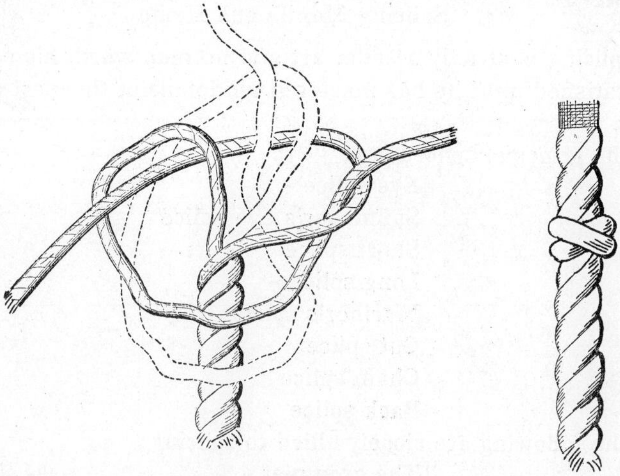

Double Mathew Walker

who would profit by a closer attention to the fundamental things in seamanship. Sailors have been getting soft. Riggers do their work while the vessel is in port, and when disaster comes,

Manrope knot

all they can do is to sit around and wait for someone to pick them up. Jury rigs call for the highest skill in seamanship and many a craft has been saved through the skill and seamanship of her crew in lashing, knotting and splicing.

IV

Splices

Splicing Manila and Hemp

Splicing is strictly a sailor art and no man worth his salt will be satisfied until he has mastered all details of this part of rope lore.

The principal splices are:

Eye splice
Sailmaker's eye splice
Short splice
Long splice
Mariner's splice
Cut splice
Chain splice
Back splice

The following are closely allied to splicing:

The grommet
The cringle

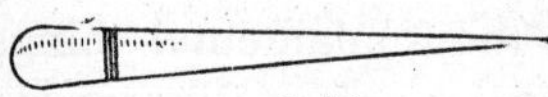

A fid

In splicing manila and hemp ropes, a *fid* is used. This is a pointed wooden spike, larger than a marling spike. Made of *lignum-vitae*, *hickory* or other hard wood.

We will now attempt to describe the manner of making the above splices, etc. The young seaman must understand however that the art can only be mastered by practice and by observation, watching seamen and riggers at work and picking up the little wrinkles necessary to completeness and finish.

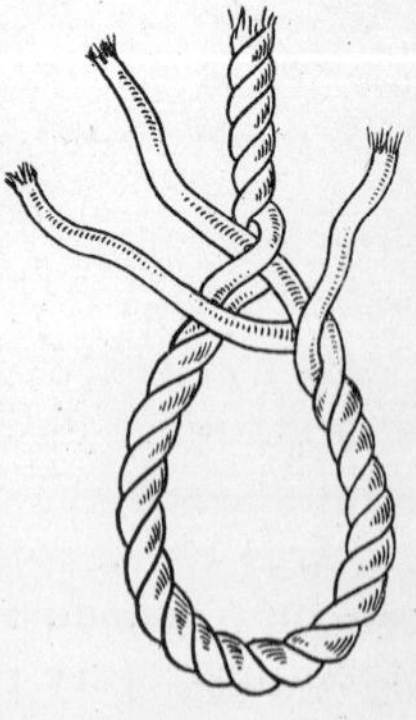

Fig. A

Eye splice. Unlay the rope for a sufficient distance, depending upon its size, and leave end enough in the strands to tuck three times. In a large rope it is well to whip the ends of the strands, though a careful workman will not have to do this.

Decide upon the size of the eye required, then bring down the crotch of the strands (also whipped, if a large rope) and lay them in this fashion. Middle strand up, and strands lying on either side. Have the bight of the rope away from you, the eye toward the body. Tuck as follows (Fig. A):

Middle strand under strand immediately below it.

Left-hand strand, over the strand under which the first strand was tucked and under the next (Fig. B).

Then turn the splice over, give the last strand an extra twist with the lay, and tuck it under the remaining strand in the bight of the rope. All strands are tucked from right to left (in a right-handed rope) (Fig. C).

Then tuck over and under twice more. If splice is to be finished off and served, cut out a third of the strands, underneath, at the last two tucks.

Note: The strands in figures are loose to show method of tucking.

Fig. B

Fig. C

Sailmaker's eye splice. Tuck as in the ordinary eye splice, then instead of tucking over and under, let each strand follow round and round the strands of the bight. This preserves the lay of the rope and makes it easier to rope a sail, as the roping twine and canvas can follow the lay of the rope.

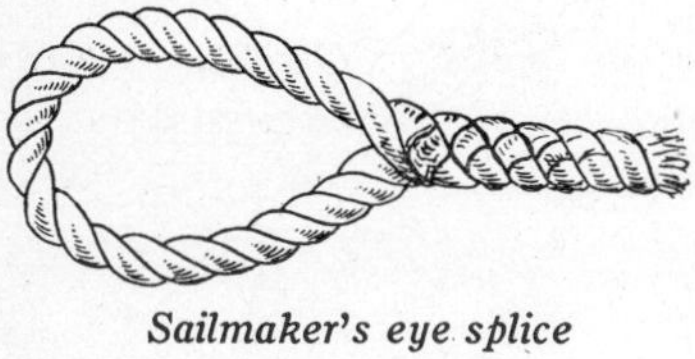

Sailmaker's eye splice

Where two ropes of unequal size are spliced together, the splice is called a *sailmaker's splice.* This is seldom done at present.

An *eye splice in four stranded rope* is made by tucking left strand under two next (to right) under one, and remaining strands each under one. All tucks from right to left.

Short splice. Unlay the strands at the end of the ropes to be joined. Crotch the ends. In a large rope stop down the ends on one side against the bight and tuck the others over and under, then turn around and tuck the other ends over and under, from

Eye splice in four stranded rope

right to left (with right-handed rope). Tuck whole twice, then cut out strands for neatness if required and tuck twice again on each side.

Some sailors make this splice very handily by first taking half turns with the strands as they are crotched. It will be found that one tuck is put in this way and the ropes are kept close together. In splicing ropes of moderate size this is always done as it saves time.

The long splice. The long splice, next to the eye splice, is the most important of the splices. It should be carefully made, and will not increase the diameter of the rope, nor mar its strength to any great extent. In the illustration the unlaying of one strand and following it with another strand from the rope to be ioined to it is clearly shown.

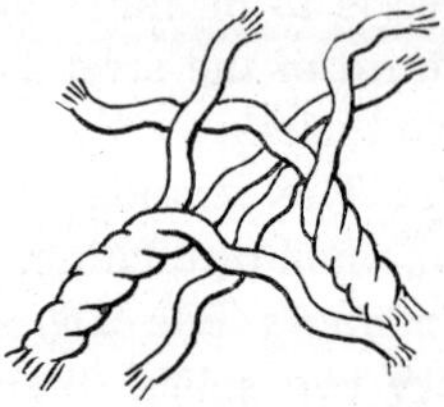

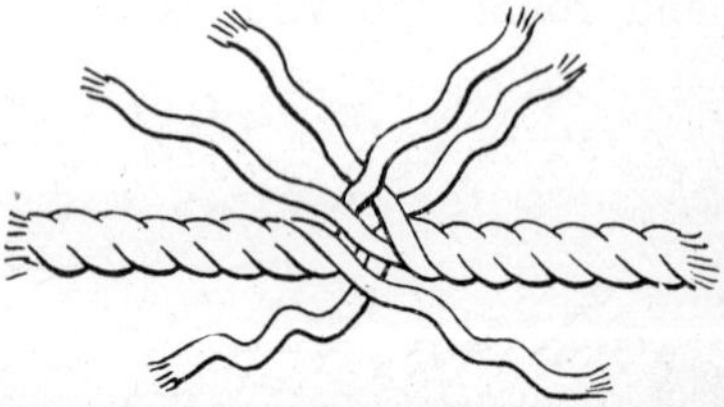

To begin the splice carefully unlay at least six times the circumference of the rope (if the rope is to run over a shieve double this). Crotch the strands, hold them in close contact and carefully unlay a strand back from the crotch, following it with a strand of the rope to be joined. The two strands remaining at the crotch are of course ready for tucking.

A short splice

Tuck once and then cut out from under the strands and tuck as in a sailmaker's eye splice. The tucks should be whipped with sail twine.

The mariner's splice. This is a splice in cable-laid rope.

Proceed as in a long splice. Then instead of tucking the " strands " these are in turn spliced as above. It is a regular sailor's job to long splice a cable-laid rope.

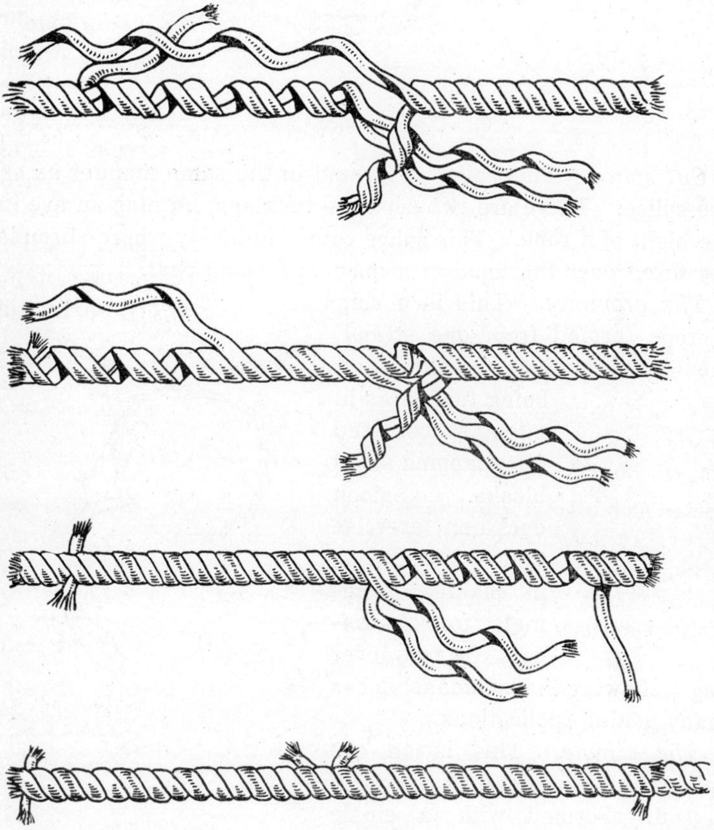

Long splice

Chain splice. This is used where a rope tail is to be spliced into a chain. Used where chain sheets are fitted to lower topsails.

Chain splice

Back splice

Back splice. Crown the strands and splice back into the lay of the rope, as in a short splice. Useful at the end of falls, when a whipping cannot be put on.

Cut splice

Cut splice. This splice is formed in the same manner as an eye splice. There are two separate tuckings, forming an eye in the bight of a rope. This splice comes in handy where shrouds are fitted over the head of a mast in a small boat.

The grommet. This is a ring of rope formed from one strand, the ends coming together and being tucked as in a long splice. Used for strapping small blocks. Saloon deckmen exercise their seamanship in making grommets for passengers to toss over pegs, showing that seamanship has many useful applications.

Finished grommet

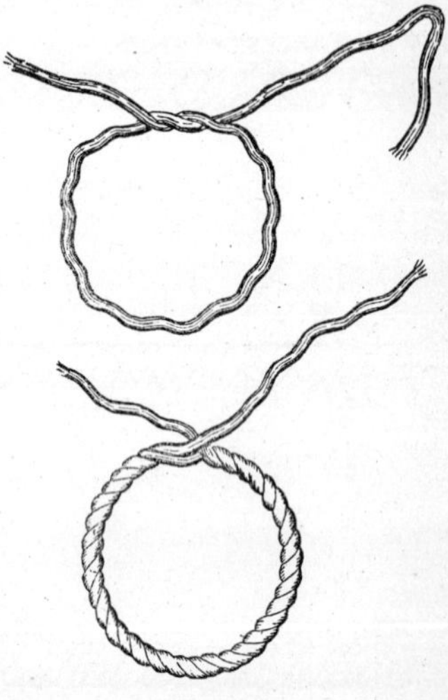

Grommet

The cringle. This is an eye spliced into the head or leech of a sail. Formed with a single strand as the grommet is formed. The illustration are self-explanatory. To *turn in* a cringle in stiff four-stranded hemp bolt rope is a real test of a man's seamanship.

Turning in a cringle on the leech of a sail.

Turning in a cringle on the bight of another rope. Used on nets, etc. Usually worked over a round thimble

Aside from knotting and splicing many things are to be met with in handling rope.

Worming is the laying of a smaller rope, or *worm* along the lay of a larger rope to bring the surface of the rope more nearly round for the purpose of serving.

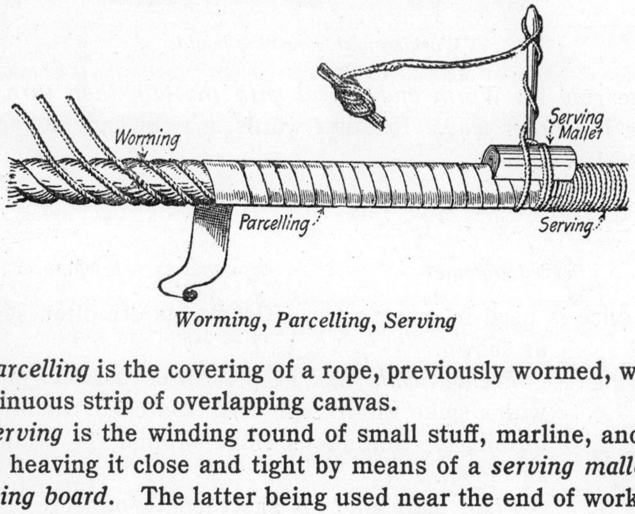

Worming, Parcelling, Serving

Parcelling is the covering of a rope, previously wormed, with a continuous strip of overlapping canvas.

Serving is the winding round of small stuff, marline, and the like, heaving it close and tight by means of a *serving mallet* or *serving board.* The latter being used near the end of work and on eye splices where the larger tool cannot be used unless the

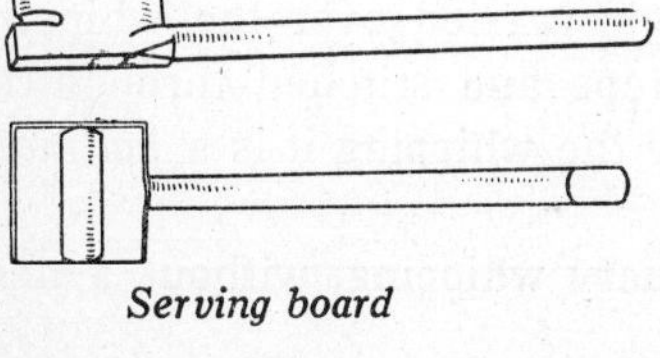

Serving board

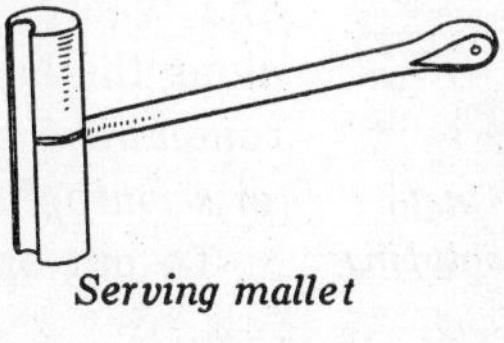

Serving mallet

service is led over the end of the mallet (you must see this done; any rigger will show you).

Working with a serving board

The rule is: *Worm and parcel with the lay, then turn and serve the other way.* In other words, a right-handed rope is served left-handed.

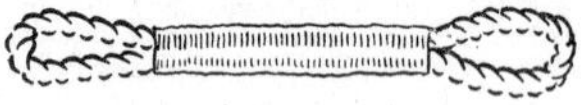

Served grommet

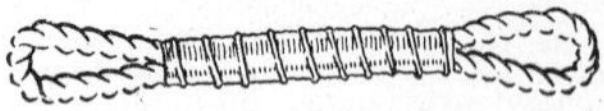

Grommet French-whipped

Service is used in many ways. Grommets are often served as shown.

Plain whipping

French whipping, is a form of service, put on with a spike where each turn is hitched, the hitches forming a continuous ridge around the whipping as shown.

Plain whipping. A short length of service, or a short end seizing at the end of a rope to prevent it from unlaying. This is usually made with twine and where the twine is carried over the whipping along the lay of the rope and stitched through the rope above and below the whipping it is a *sailmaker's whipping.*

To put on an ordinary whipping, without a needle, heave all turns taut over the end, leave a few turns loose, tuck the finishing end back under these, then heave them taut and pull the end up under them cutting it off. If both beginning end and finishing end are brought up between the same turns, the whipping can be made very secure by square knotting them and pushing the knot under the turns.

In making knots, hitches, bends, splices, etc., know just what the knot or splice is expected to do. A rolling hitch is only satisfactory when the pull is one particular way. Many other rope formations are the same. Use rope with knowledge and understanding as to its limitations and strength. A few years on a sailer are of great educational value in this respect.

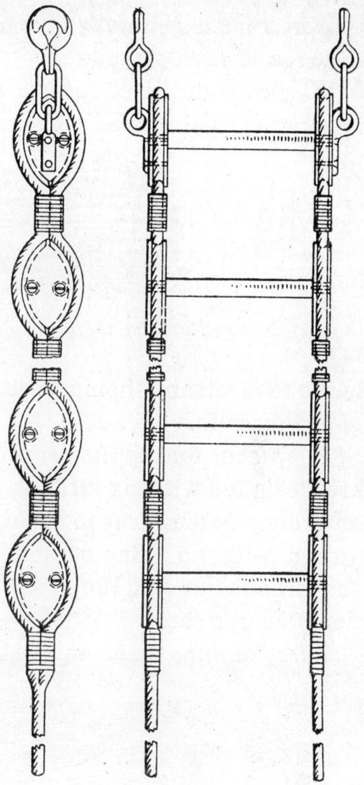

A Jacob's Ladder

V

Wire Rope

Many kinds of wire rope are now being manufactured, the art having reached a high state of perfection.* On shipboard wire rope is used in many places, all standing rigging is of wire, many mooring lines and hawsers are of wire, and the use of hemp clad flexible wire rope for cargo whips has become standard practice. Definite knowledge of the construction and uses of wire rope should be a part of the equipment of the seaman who is up in his profession.

* Stranded bronze-wire ropes were found in the Pompeian ruins. Modern wire ropes are a development of the nineteenth century.

Wire rope is generally of six strands and differs in the number of wires in each strand.

Wire rope designed for use as *standing rigging* is less flexible, is generally galvanized and consists of larger wires.

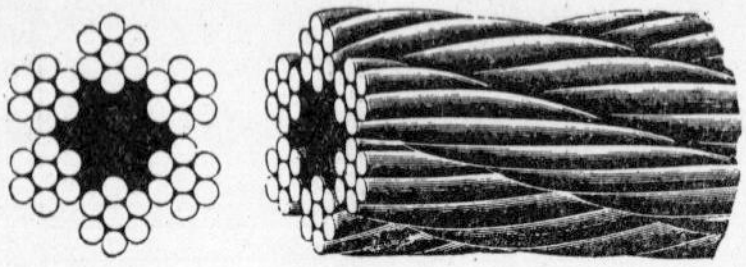

Standing rigging

Six strands, seven to twelve wires to a strand, and hemp core, is the usual construction.

Wire rope used for *hawsers* and *mooring lines* is six stranded, twelve or more wires to a strand, hemp core in each strand and in the center of the strands.

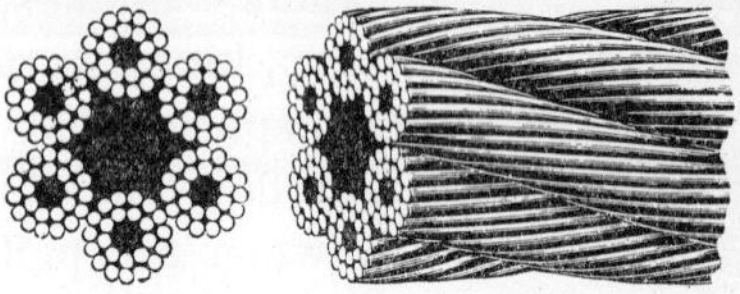

Hawsers and mooring lines

Deep sea towing hawsers are designed with six strands and thirty seven wires to each strand with no hemp core in the strands but with the usual hemp center core.

Wire running rope is designed with the usual number of strands, each strand consisting of a circle of twelve wires about a large hemp core, and with a large hemp core in the center.

Deep sea towing hawsers

Very many special types of wire rope are made but the principle of flexibility through looser construction, or strength through the reverse where wire is to be stationary, is seen in all of them. Only a few typical sections of wire rope can be shown.

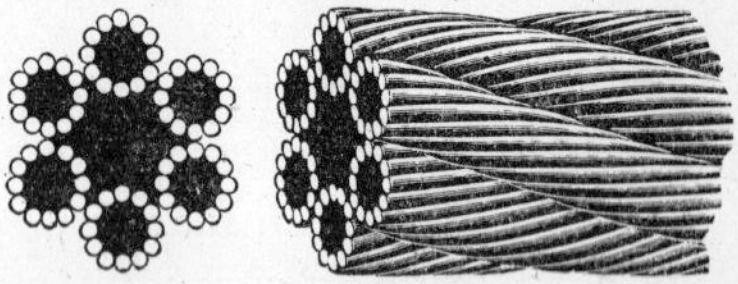

Wire running rope

Armored wire rope consists of flat wire wound around the individual strands. It is used extensively in wrecking and other similar operations.

Special types of wire rope with metal heart wires of flat or triangular section are used, but these types do not specially commend themselves to use on board ship. Some of these are five stranded.

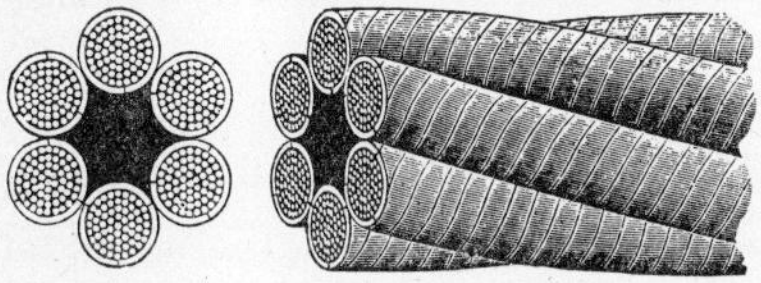

Armored wire rope

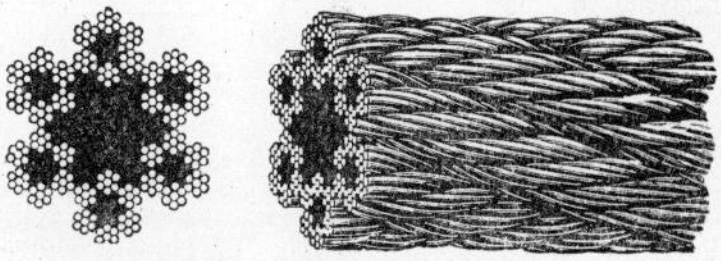

Tiller or hand rope

Wire rope is made of the following materials:

Wrought iron	relative	strength	1
Crucible steel	"	"	2
Plow steel	"	"	2.5
Monitor steel	"	"	3

Wire rope, because of its great strength, and lack of stretching power, is to be used with great care. When mooring with wire it is very essential that all parts of the rope bear an equal stress. The writer has in mind the case of an eighteen thousand ton (displacement) steamer moored to a wharf in San Francisco some years back. At the full strength of the tide, running ebb, with stern sticking some hundred feet out beyond the bulkhead, the ship was pulled off from her wharf. The breast lines aft were under high tension—the parts leading back around the posts on the wharf were not taking their full load, and the standing part snapped. Then the rest of the breast lines snapped or unshipped, the stress was taken up by the springs, they snapped, and in less than five minutes the ship, seemingly secure with heavy wires, was cross ways in the slip, her starboard quarter against the cluster piles on the next wharf—luckily there was nothing in between to be crushed. What happened when we breasted her back, against the tide, using a ten-inch manila line, and a drunken fireman, returning at midnight, insisted upon boarding the ship upon this line, stretching some fifty feet to the wharf, is another story and finds no place in a book on "seamanship."

Wire hawsers are excellent things however when handled with care and understanding. The first thing to beware of in handling lines is the constant danger of kinks. In uncoiling a wire great care must be taken in this respect. Also when hauling on a line, and then slacking up, to shift the end, a large bight may

Correct way to uncoil a wire rope

run out, drop on a string piece and kink before the winches or capstans are started again. Always look out for this when using wires.

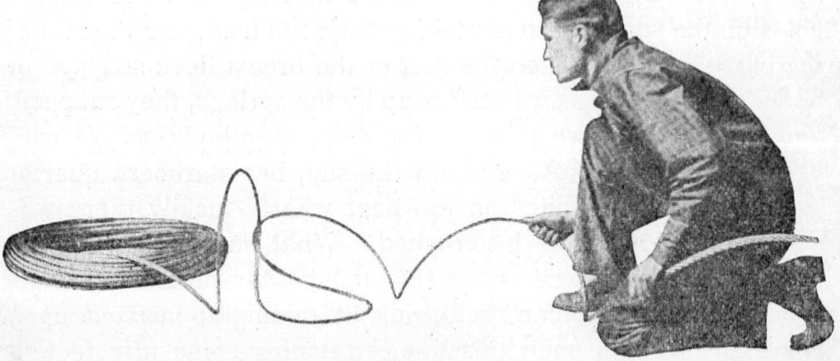

Wrong way to uncoil a wire rope

Wire ropes for deck use are generally stowed on stationary reels fitted with handles and gears for winding. This is the only way to properly take care of such ropes. The wires should be oiled and protected from the wet by waterproof tarpaulin covers. Galvanizing is the best method of protection, however, and even such ropes should be coated when dry with a certain amount of raw linseed oil. Greasy oils are worse than useless on ship ropes. *Do not grease your lines;* we all know they are hard enough to handle as it is. Linseed oil dries and gives a better hold, and also protects.

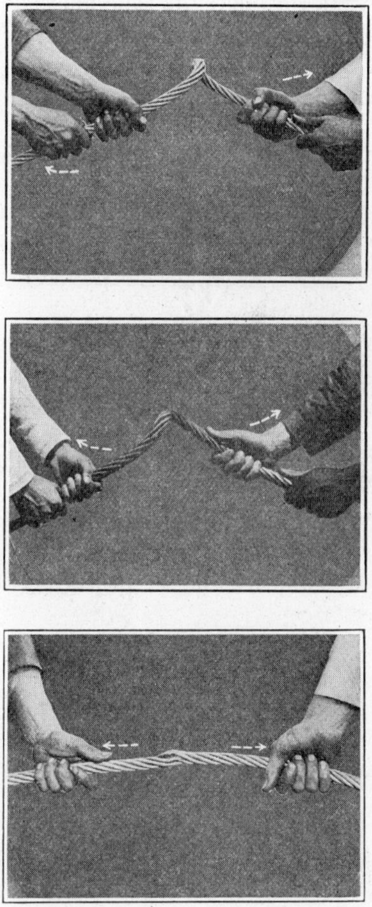

Wrong way to take out a kink

The hemp core in wire ropes serves as a reservoir for oil and helps in the lubrication.

Wire rope on shipboard is seldom used over sheaves, except in the case of heavy purchases where the falls are of wire. Care should be taken to use large blocks, and where possible avoid all short nips in the rope.

In using wire rope falls for heavy weights go very slowly, also the hauling part of the rope should be taken around the drum of a heavy winch *and end secured.* Never lead such hauling parts to a capstan unless the end of the rope is in turn secured to a stout *new* manila messenger and this, in turn, led to a second winch or capstan *always under stress.* If no second winch can be used take in the slack around a heavy bollard, keeping a sufficient number of turns at all times.

The Correct Way to Remove Kinks from Wire Rope

Here is the way to straighten out a kink that has not been made permanent by pulling it into the rope, or "pulling the kink through," as rope users sometimes call it.

As soon as a loop—always the beginning of a kink—is noticed, it should be "taken in hand" *at once*. By all means prevent tension on the rope, or the result will be permanent injury to the rope.

Having secured your kink while still in the formative stage, reverse the process that produced it. To do this, uncross the ends by *pushing them apart,* as shown in photographs. The small arrows show the directions in which the hands should move.

Now turn the rope over and place the bent portion above the knee, then push downward until the rope appears as in last cut.

From this point it is comparatively easy to straighten out the remaining bend by laying the rope on a board and pounding with a wooden mallet, or anything else handy that won't injure the wires.

With a very stiff rope, or one of large diameter, it may be necessary to do the first part of the operation on something more substantial than the human leg. Two people, even, may be required to do the work. But the small amount of energy and time expended in removing a kink *properly* will invariably pay in lengthening the life—and final cost—of wire rope.

Hemp covered wire rope. This type of wire rope is of such special use in the handling of cargo and has proven so durable and effective that some additional mention should be made of it in a book on merchant service seamanship.

It has many of the advantages of manila, is much smaller and easier to handle about a hatch, does not suffer damage readily when drafts of cargo are hauled out of a between deck, the fall scraping under the hatch coaming.

It is from three to five times as strong as manila of equal size, and is half as heavy as manila of equal strength.

It resists rust because of the tar and oil in the hemp service covering the strands.

When wires break and stick through the hemp covering, discard the fall at once.

Boat falls are being rove off with hemp-covered rope. This latter practice is to be looked upon with some consideration. On a very cold night this is not the easiest stuff in the world to handle.

The following rules for the use of wire rope are given by the Navy Department:

Operation of wire rope. The principal causes of deterioration of wire rope are heavy abrasion, overstrain, bending, and corrosion. Evidence of abrasion is shown by the outside wires wearing thin in a short time. If the wires are little worn, break off squarely, sticking out all over the rope, there is evidence of an overload or severe bending.

Size of sheave. The diameter of the sheave should be greater than fifteen times the diameter of the rope, and for inflexible rope a still larger diameter of sheave must be used. Ordinary commercial practice allows 1 foot diameter of sheave for ¾-inch diameter of the rope.

Factor of safety. A factor of safety of five is recommended. For cranes and falls upon which there is sudden and repeated stress, it is safer to figure a factor of safety upon the elastic limit of the material rather than upon the tensile strength.

Wire rope is generally designated by its diameter* and this should be measured as shown in the sketch, but seamen usually speak of wire rope by its circumference, as in the case of fibre ropes. Running wire rope should be discarded when the outside wires are reduced one half of their original diameter.

Wire rope consists of wires running the full length of the rope, each one carefully inspected before use. It is one of the most reliable forms of rope, and barring kinks, and mishandling, is not liable to fail in an emergency.

In ordering wire rope from the manufacturer, or in specifying it for ship's use, state clearly what use is to be made of it. Standing rigging, mooring lines, or towing, etc.

When wire rope is cut, a whipping should be clapped on each side of the place where the division is to be made, to prevent the rope from unlaying. Use a sharp hacksaw to make the cut.

* It may be of interest to note the size of the great wire rope cables in use on the following bridges over the East River, New York. Each bridge is suspended on four cables.

	Brooklyn Bridge	Williamsburg Bridge	Manhattan Bridge
Diameter of cable	15.5″	18.75″	20.75″
Number of wires	5,358	7,696	9,472
Length of cable	3,577′	2,900	3,234
Weight of each cable	818 tons	1,086 tons	1,527 tons
River span	1,595.5′	1,600′	1,470′
Width of bridge	85′	118′	120′

All of these cables were made by the John A. Roebling's Sons Co. of Trenton, N. J. The wires are not twisted, but are held together by steel bands, and heavy service.

VI

Splicing Wire Rope

The most important splice used aboard ship when working wire is the eye splice. The short splice may be used when wire is to remain standing and only a moderate amount is to be expended in making the splice. The long splice is not made very often, except perhaps in piecing out wire ridge ropes, and the like. Large handling lines are seldom spliced. The long splice finds its greatest application in the joining of ends in wire transmission lines ashore and the instructions for making this splice given by many of the wire rope manufacturers have this use in mind.

Wire splicing is an art that calls for a great deal of gumption. The successful splicer of wire uses his head first and his " beef " afterwards. One of the best sailor men the writer ever was shipmates with, a slight young chap, walked on board his ship not long ago after many years had passed. He was in charge of the wire rope department of a large manufacturing plant, having gained the job through his ability to splice wire.

1—" T " shaped splicing pins. 2—Round splicing pins. 3—Taper spike. 4—Knife. 5—Wire cutters. 6—Wooden mallets. 7—Hemp rope strap. 8—Hickory stick.

Tools shown in the picture are used by the John A. Roebling's Sons Co. in splicing wire.

The tools used in wire splicing are important and should be rightly handled. In splicing stiff rope a rigging screw is needed, or better still a vise. A sharp cold chisel, a hammer and a wooden mallet, several marline spikes and a special flat-pointed marline spike are useful.

The tools shown in the illustration are used as follows: The " T " shaped splicing pins for opening the lay of rope. The round splicing pins for working in between strands. The taper spike for opening the strands and taking out the hemp center. Knife for cutting the hemp core. Wire cutters for cutting off ends of strands. Wooden mallets to hammer down any uneven surfaces. In addition to these the hemp rope strap and hickory stick is used to untwist the strands, as shown in the illustration.

Many rope splicers prefer the " T " shaped splicing pin to the taper spike for opening strands.

Seizing wire, marline, and at least two small handy billy tackles to use as jiggers, in rousing through strands when tucking, are useful. A small steel chain and hook, to use as a strap, is also handy. Where possible it is easier to work the wire on a rigger's or machine bench. Also have some slush to lubricate the strands when pulling through.

Never cut wire until a good stout whipping is on it at both sides of the cut. When unlaying for a splice have the rope whipped where it is to join. In the case of a long splice this whipping is removed when following through the strands. In making an eye splice it can remain in place while the splice is being tucked. If a thimble is to be fitted the whipping will cut out when the thimble is hammered into the eye, that is if the job is a neat close splice.

The eye splice is most often used on board ship. Expert riggers favor the following method of turning in this splice.

1st. Clap on a stout whipping from one to four feet from end of wire rope, depending upon its size.

2d. Whip the end of each strand with strong sail twine. Unlay the strands and cut out heart of rope (not of strands).

3d. Place rope in splicing box or vise in position shown by illustration, eye away from you, bight of rope under your right arm.

4th. Untwist rope, using heaver as shown in by cut on page 121.

The eye is lying flat, and the strands to be tucked lie against the bight on the right side, that is, on the side away from you.

5th. Open a way through the middle of the bight, spike horizontal, pointing away from you. This is easy when enough turn has been taken out of the bight by the heaver.

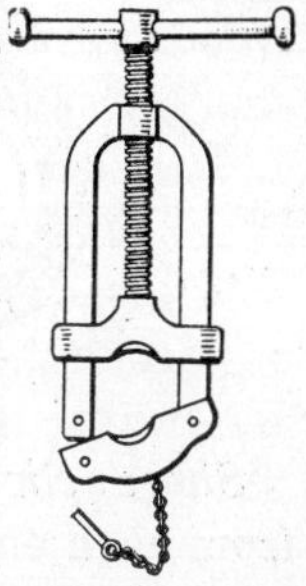

A rigging screw

6th. Take top one of strands to be tucked, and shove it through the middle of rope, following the spike which may be withdrawn as tucking strand goes through. When through, tuck this strand, around the strand of bight lying above it.

7th. Take next strand, down through middle, having opened the way again, but only under two strands, and around the strand lying just above it.

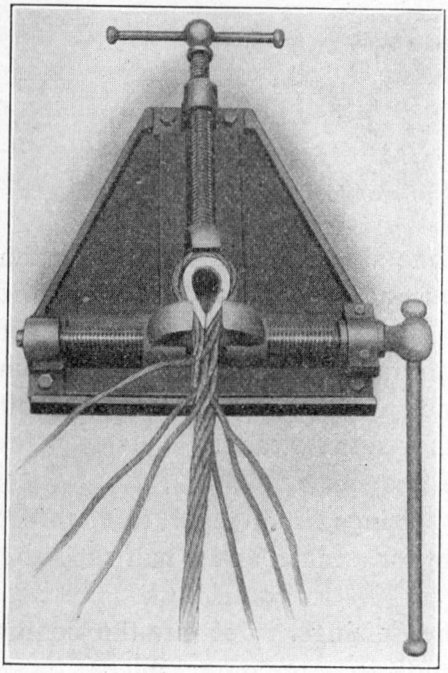

A rigger's vise, which is of great service in splicing eyes, etc.

8th. Take next strand, down through middle opening, but only under and around one strand.

9th. Now take next strand, (fourth), and tuck it over and around the next strand to right.

10th. Take next one over and around the next.

11th. Take last strand over and around the last untouched strand on the bight.

Note: All strands are tucked around in the same direction that the wires run in the strand. Strands are then tucked once more, around and around, sailmaker fashion, then heart is taken out of strands and half of the wires are cut out and the splice is tucked twice more.

Finish the splice by parcelling with tarred canvas and serve over all with hambroline. The thimble is usually pounded into the eye after it is formed, sometimes after the first tuck is made, the strands being hauled close with a jigger, or by use of the pipe heaver.

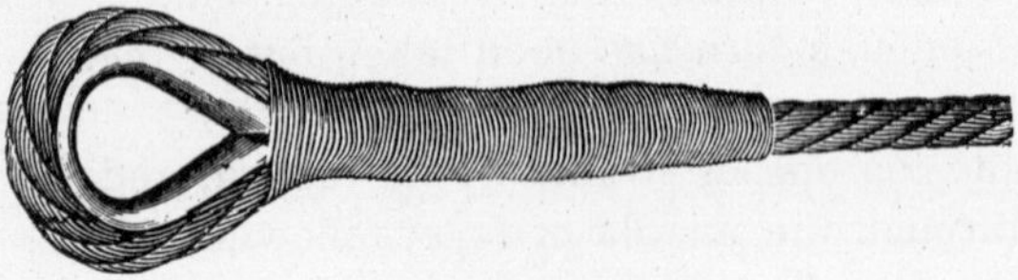

Eye splice served

Short splice. 1st. Clap on a good seizing two or three feet from each end.

2d. Unlay the strands and take out the hemp heart.

3d. Marry the ends, interlocking the twelve strands.

Eye formed with clamps
Always have nuts on side of standing part, as shown

4th. Stop down the ends on one side and proceed to tuck the other into the rope over one and under two strands opening the rope with the flat-ended spike. Push spike in far enough to get the strands through before withdrawing it. Tuck twice whole strand, once one half, and once one quarter. Then take off the stop and repeat with the other set of strands.

It is well to parcel and serve this splice.

Long splice. 1st. Clap on seizings from eight to ten feet from the end of each rope, eight for an inch and a half rope and longer for larger sizes.

2d. Unlay the strands to the seizings. Cut out the center heart (*not* the heart of the strands as in the other splices).

3d. Marry the ropes, interlocking the strands. Follow the strands along to each side of the joint, stopping them in place at about four foot intervals, and cut off the strands about a foot and a half from the rope.

4th. Starting with the left-hand pair, unlay the rope with the heaving stick applied as shown, pick out the hemp heart for a

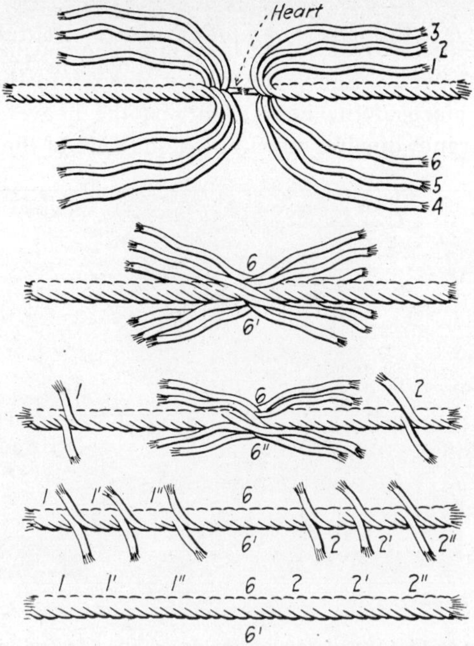

Method of making long splice

Opening strands before tucking

Wrap the endless piece of manila rope around the wire rope as shown in plate and insert stick in loop. Pull the end of the stick so that the wire rope will be untwisted between the vise and the stick.

foot each way, cutting it with a sharp knife. Measure the strand to be tucked and cut off leaving a length equal to half of the heart removed. Shove the strand down into the center of the rope in place of the heart; untwist the heavers. Do this with each strand, dipping down one along side of the other.

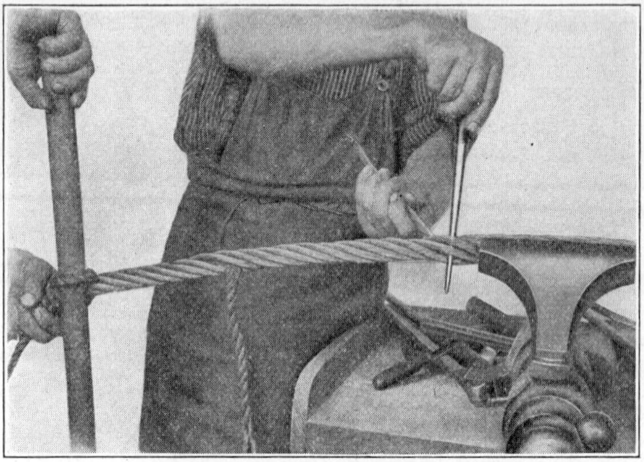

To tuck strand

Insert spike so that it will be over the projecting end and under the next two strands of the rope. Pull the spike toward yourself. This will cause it to travel along the rope, leaving an opening in front. While one hand is employed in moving the spike, the other hand holding the end of the strand should lay this end in the opening, as indicated in the picture.

5th. Repeat this operation with each of the six pairs of strands.

This completes the splice. It can hardly been seen. The lay of the rope, when under pressure grips the strands lodged in the center in place of the heart and the splice is practically as strong as the rope itself. It is a mistake to make the splice too short.

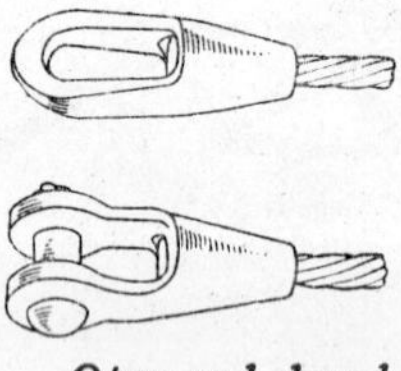

Open and closed sockets

Tucking the strands as in a rope splice is not recommended as it tends to weaken the rope on account of the nip.

It is very good practice to let the youngsters on board ship try a hand, at wire splicing. Very often the ability to turn in a neat and strong splice in wire is of the utmost utility.

Sockets are secured by passing end of rope through socket after wires have been cleaned. The best practice is to *tin* the wires. Molten *zinc* is then poured into the head of the socket, the lower end being stopped with clay.

Bad practice is to turn over the ends of the wires (not tinned) and to use babbit metal which melts at a lower temperature than zinc.

Before pouring *zinc* heat socket and wires with a blow torch.

VII

Rope Tables

Approximate Weight and Strength Best Manila Rope

Diameter, Inches	Circumference in Inches	No. of Feet in 1 Lb.	Weight of 1,000 Feet, Lbs.	Coils		Strength of New Manila Rope, Lbs.
				Length, Feet	Weight, Lbs.	
$\frac{3}{16}$	6 thd.fine	75 feet	14	2,280	30	500
$\frac{1}{4}$	6 "	55 "	20	2,600	50	620
$\frac{5}{16}$	9 "	41 "	30	1,870	55	1,000
$\frac{3}{8}$	12 "	26 "	42	1,690	65	1,275
$\frac{7}{16}$	$1\frac{3}{8}$	19 "	50	1,500	75	1,875
$\frac{1}{2}$	$1\frac{1}{2}$	$13\frac{1}{2}$ "	75	1,350	90	2,400
$\frac{9}{16}$	$1\frac{3}{4}$	10 "	105	1,200	125	3,300
$\frac{5}{8}$	2	$7\frac{1}{2}$ "	130	1,200	155	4,000
$\frac{3}{4}$	$2\frac{1}{4}$	6 "	159	1,200	190	4,700
$\frac{13}{16}$	$2\frac{1}{2}$	5 "	196	1,200	235	5,600
$\frac{7}{8}$	$2\frac{3}{4}$	4 "	225	1,200	272	6,500
1	3	$3\frac{1}{3}$ "	297	1,200	325	7,500
$1\frac{1}{16}$	$3\frac{1}{4}$	$2\frac{7}{8}$ "	317	1,200	380	8,900
$1\frac{1}{8}$	$3\frac{1}{2}$	$2\frac{1}{2}$ "	363	1,200	435	10,500
$1\frac{1}{4}$	$3\frac{3}{4}$	$2\frac{1}{6}$ "	421	1,200	505	12,500
$1\frac{3}{8}$	4	$1\frac{9}{10}$ "	475	1,200	570	14,000
$1\frac{1}{2}$	$4\frac{1}{2}$	$1\frac{1}{2}$ "	596	1,200	715	17,000
$1\frac{5}{8}$	5	$1\frac{1}{5}$ "	738	1,200	885	20,000
$1\frac{3}{4}$	$5\frac{1}{2}$	1 "	888	1,200	1,065	25,000
2	6	10 inches	1,063	1,200	1,275	30,000
$2\frac{1}{8}$	$6\frac{1}{2}$	$8\frac{3}{5}$ "	1,250	1,200	1,500	33,000
$2\frac{1}{4}$	7	$7\frac{2}{5}$ "	1,455	1,200	1,745	37,000
$2\frac{1}{2}$	$7\frac{1}{2}$	$6\frac{1}{2}$ "	1,667	1,200	2,000	43,000
$2\frac{5}{8}$	8	$5\frac{2}{3}$ "	1,900	1,200	2,280	50,000
$2\frac{7}{8}$	$8\frac{1}{2}$	5 "	2,142	1,200	2,570	56,000
3	9	$4\frac{1}{2}$ "	2,405	1,200	2,885	62,000
$3\frac{1}{8}$	$9\frac{1}{2}$	4 "	2,671	1,200	3,205	68,000
$3\frac{1}{4}$	10	$3\frac{5}{8}$ "	2,984	1,200	3,580	75,000

The relative strength of Manila to Sisal is about as 7 is to 5. Manila, Sisal and Jute ropes weigh (about) alike. Tarred Hemp Cordage will weigh (about) one fourth more.

Comparison of Strength between Wire Rope and Manila Rope

Approximate Breaking Stress Calculated in Tons of 2,000 Pounds

Diameter in Inches	Wire Transmission Rope. One Hemp Core Surrounded by Six Strands of Seven Wires Each				Wire Hoisting Rope. One Hemp Core Surrounded by Six Strands of Nineteen Wires Each				Average Quality New Manila Rope
	Iron	Crucible Cast Steel	Extra Strong Crucible Cast Steel	Plow Steel	Iron	Crucible Cast Steel	Extra Strong Crucible Cast Steel	Plow Steel	
	Tons	Tons	Tons	Tons	Tons	Tons	Tons	Tons	Tons
2¾	......	......	......	......	111	211	243	275	26
2½	......	......	......	......	92	170	200	229	21½
2¼	......	......	......	......	72	133	160	186	18½
2	......	......	......	......	55	106	123	140	15
1¾	......	......	......	......	44	85	99	112	12½
1⅝	......	......	......	......	38	72	83	94	10
1½	32	63	73	82	33	64	73	82	8½
1⅜	28	53	63	72	28	56	64	72	7½
1¼	23	46	54	60	22.8	47	53	58	6¼
1⅛	19	37	43	47	18.6	38	43	47	5¼
1	15	31	35	38	14.5	30	34	38	4
⅞	12	24	28	31	11.8	23	26	29	3¼
¾	8.8	18.6	21	23	8.5	17.5	20.2	23	2¼
⅝	6	13	14.5	16	6	12.5	14	15.5	2
9/16	4.8	10	11	12	4.7	10	11.2	12.3	1¼
½	3.7	7.7	8.85	10	3.9	8.4	9.2	10	1–
7/16	2.6	5.5	6.25	7	2.9	6.5	7.25	8	¾
⅜	2.2	4.6	5.25	5.9	2.4	4.8	5.30	5.75	½
5/16	1.7	3.5	3.95	4.4	1.5	3.1	3.50	3.8	⅜
9/32	1.2	2.5	2.95	3.4	......	......	......	......	3/10
¼	......	......	......	......	1.1	2.2	2.43	2.65	¼

—Waterbury Co.

Stowage Space Required For Rope of Various Sizes

Coils of 1,200 Feet or 200 Fathoms 365.76 Meters

Size	Coil Dimensions	Cubic Feet	Size	Coil Dimensions	Cubic Feet
6thd. fine	8″ × 11″ × 11″	.56	4¼ in.	27″ × 37″ × 37″	21.39
6thd.	9″ × 12″ × 12″	.75	4½ "	29″ × 38″ × 38″	24.23
9thd.	10″ × 14″ × 14″	1.13	4¾ "	30″ × 41″ × 41″	29.18
12thd.	11″ × 15″ × 15″	1.43	5 "	30″ × 43″ × 43″	32.10
15thd.	12″ × 16″ × 16″	1.77	5¼ "	31″ × 45″ × 45″	36.32
18thd.	13″ × 17″ × 17″	2.17	5½ "	33″ × 47″ × 47″	42.18
1½ in.	15″ × 18″ × 18″	2.81	5¾ "	32″ × 48″ × 48″	42.66
1¾ "	15″ × 21″ × 21″	3.82	6 "	33″ × 48″ × 48″	44.
2 "	17″ × 22″ × 22″	4.76	6½ "	33″ × 53″ × 53″	53.64
2¼ "	17″ × 26″ × 26″	6.65	7 "	35″ × 55″ × 55″	61.27
2½ "	19″ × 25″ × 25″	6.87	7½ "	36″ × 59″ × 59″	72.52
2¾ "	20″ × 29″ × 29″	9.73	8 "	37″ × 61″ × 61″	79.67
3 "	22″ × 30″ × 30″	11.46	8½ "	48″ × 59″ × 59″	96.69
3¼ "	24″ × 31″ × 31″	13.34	9 "	45″ × 62″ × 62″	100.10
3½ "	25″ × 34″ × 34″	16.72	9½ "	46″ × 64″ × 64″	109.03
3¾ "	25″ × 35″ × 35″	17.72	10 "	46″ × 67″ × 67″	119.50
4 "	27″ × 36″ × 36″	20.25			

—Plymouth Cordage Co.

Approximate Comparison of Strength

(Manila and Hemp Covered Wire)

Manila Rope			Crescent Hemp Clad Wire Rope—Diameter			
Circumference	Diameter	Approximate Breaking Strain	Iron	Crucible Steel	Extra Strong Crucible Steel	Plougt Steel
$1\frac{3}{4}$	$\frac{9}{16}$	2,250	$\frac{1}{4}$	....	....	....
2	$\frac{5}{8}$	3,000	....	....	....	....
$2\frac{1}{4}$	$\frac{3}{4}$	4,000	$\frac{3}{8}$	$\frac{1}{4}$	....	....
$2\frac{1}{2}$	$\frac{13}{16}$	5,000	....	....	$\frac{1}{4}$	....
$2\frac{3}{4}$	$\frac{7}{8}$	5,800	....	$\frac{5}{16}$	....	$\frac{1}{4}$
3	1	7,000	....	....	$\frac{5}{16}$	....
$3\frac{1}{4}$	$1\frac{1}{16}$	8,000	$\frac{1}{2}$	....	....	$\frac{5}{16}$
$3\frac{1}{2}$	$1\frac{1}{8}$	9,200	....	$\frac{3}{8}$	....	....
$3\frac{3}{4}$	$1\frac{1}{4}$	11,000	....	....	$\frac{3}{8}$	....
4	$1\frac{5}{16}$	12,000	$\frac{5}{8}$	....	....	$\frac{3}{8}$
$4\frac{1}{4}$	$1\frac{3}{8}$	13,500	....	$\frac{7}{16}$	....	....
$4\frac{1}{2}$	$1\frac{1}{2}$	15,500	....	....	$\frac{7}{16}$	....
$4\frac{3}{4}$	$1\frac{9}{16}$	17,000	$\frac{3}{4}$	$\frac{1}{2}$	....	$\frac{7}{16}$
5	$1\frac{5}{8}$	19,000	....	$\frac{9}{16}$	$\frac{1}{2}$	....
$5\frac{1}{2}$	$1\frac{3}{4}$	23,500	$\frac{7}{8}$	....	$\frac{9}{16}$	$\frac{1}{2}$
6	2	27,000	....	$\frac{5}{8}$	....	....
$6\frac{1}{2}$	$2\frac{1}{8}$	31,500	1	....	$\frac{5}{8}$	$\frac{5}{8}$
7	$2\frac{1}{4}$	37,000	$1\frac{1}{8}$	$\frac{3}{4}$	....	....
$7\frac{1}{2}$	$2\frac{1}{2}$	42,000	....	....	$\frac{3}{4}$	....
8	$2\frac{5}{8}$	48,000	$1\frac{1}{4}$	$\frac{7}{8}$	....	$\frac{3}{4}$
$8\frac{1}{2}$	$2\frac{7}{8}$	54,000	....	....	$\frac{7}{8}$	....
9	3	61,000	$1\frac{3}{8}$	1	....	$\frac{7}{8}$
$9\frac{1}{2}$	$3\frac{1}{8}$	67,000	$1\frac{1}{2}$	....	1	....
10	$3\frac{3}{8}$	75,000	....	$1\frac{1}{8}$	....	1

—Geo. C. Moon Co., Inc.

Wire Rope Tables (U. S. Navy)

Navy Standard Mooring Hawsers

Composed of 6 strands with a hemp core, each strand consisting of 14 wires and a center of hemp or jute yarn. Large eye splicefitted at one end and thimble in opposite end to attach to reel.

Diameter	Approximate Circumference	Weight per Fathom	Weight per Coil, 100 Fms.	Breaking Stress	Use
			Pounds	*Pounds*	
$\frac{13}{16}$-inch	$2\frac{1}{2}$-inch	....	447	28,400	Note that Navy standard mooring hawsers may be made in the following lengths: $1\frac{1}{8}$-inch, 640 fathoms; $1\frac{1}{4}$-inch, 490 fathoms; $1\frac{7}{16}$-inch, 375 fathoms; $1\frac{5}{8}$-inch, 300 fathoms.
1 -inch	3 -inch	....	644	41,500	
$1\frac{1}{8}$-inch	$3\frac{1}{2}$-inch	....	830	53,740	
$1\frac{1}{4}$-inch	4 -inch	....	1,080	69,380	
$1\frac{7}{16}$-inch	$4\frac{1}{2}$-inch	....	1,377	87,000	
$1\frac{5}{8}$-inch	5 -inch	....	1,750	113,700	

Wire Rope Tables (U. S. Navy)

Galvanized Steel Wire Rope.

Composed of 6 strands, with a hemp core, 19 wires to a strand; or 18 wires with a center of jute, cotton, or hemp twine.

Diameter	Approximate Circumference	Weight per Fathom	Weight per Coil, 100 Fms.	Breaking Stress	Use
Inches	*Inches*	*Pounds*	*Pounds*	*Pounds*	
$\frac{5}{16}$	1	0.90	90	6,170	Standing rigging.
$\frac{3}{8}$	$1\frac{1}{8}$	1.27	127	8,740	Guys.
$\frac{7}{16}$	$1\frac{1}{4}$	1.71	171	11,760	Boat slings, running rigging $\frac{7}{16}$-inch and less.
$\frac{1}{2}$	$1\frac{1}{2}$	2.23	223	15,230	Topping lifts.
$\frac{9}{16}$	$1\frac{3}{4}$	2.80	280	19,150	(For coaling booms.)
$\frac{5}{8}$	2	3.60	360	24,680	
$\frac{3}{4}$	$2\frac{1}{4}$	5.07	507	34,980	Wheel ropes.
$\frac{13}{16}$	$2\frac{1}{2}$	5.94	594	40,800	($\frac{7}{16}$-inch and under.)
$\frac{7}{8}$	$2\frac{3}{4}$	6.88	688	47,040	
1	3	9.00	900	60,960	
$1\frac{1}{16}$	$3\frac{1}{4}$	10.80	1,080	70,550	
$1\frac{1}{8}$	$3\frac{1}{2}$	11.60	1,160	78,730	
$1\frac{3}{16}$	$3\frac{3}{4}$	13.00	1,300	87,320	
$1\frac{1}{4}$	4	14.48	1,448	98,720	
$1\frac{3}{8}$	$4\frac{1}{4}$	17.30	1,730	118,450	
$1\frac{7}{16}$	$4\frac{1}{2}$	18.80	1,880	128,980	
$1\frac{1}{2}$	$4\frac{3}{4}$	20.38	2,038	139,960	
$1\frac{5}{8}$	5	23.23	2,323	160,230	

Galvanized Steel Wire Rope.

Composed of 6 strands, with a hemp core, each strand consisting of 37 wires, or 36 wires with a hemp, jute, or cotton center.

Diameter	Approximate Circumference	Weight per Fathom	Weight per Coil, 100 Fms.	Breaking Stress	Use
		Pounds	*Pounds*	*Pounds*	
$\frac{3}{8}$-inch	$1\frac{1}{8}$-inch	1.32	132	8,460	
$\frac{7}{16}$-inch	$1\frac{1}{4}$-inch	1.80	180	11,520	
$\frac{1}{2}$-inch	$1\frac{1}{2}$-inch	2.34	234	16,330	
$\frac{9}{16}$-inch	$1\frac{3}{4}$-inch	3.00	300	19,040	
$\frac{5}{8}$-inch	2 -inch	3.72	372	23,520	Towing hawsers; crane falls; bridles, large and small; tiller ropes; tiller ropes on ships' boats; cat and fish pendants; clear hawse pendants; dip ropes; torpedo slings, and slings for general hoisting.
$\frac{3}{4}$-inch	$2\frac{1}{4}$-inch	5.34	534	35,730	
$\frac{7}{8}$-inch	$2\frac{3}{4}$-inch	7.20	720	46,150	
1 -inch	3 -inch	9.48	948	60,170	
$1\frac{1}{8}$-inch	$3\frac{1}{2}$-inch	12.00	1,200	76,200	
$1\frac{1}{4}$-inch	4 -inch	14.70	1,470	94,000	
$1\frac{3}{8}$-inch	$4\frac{1}{4}$-inch	18.00	1,800	113,800	
$1\frac{1}{2}$-inch	$4\frac{3}{4}$-inch	21.30	2,130	131,690	
$1\frac{5}{8}$-inch	5 -inch	24.90	2,490	154,880	
$1\frac{3}{4}$-inch	$5\frac{1}{2}$-inch	29.10	2,910	184,300	
2 -inch	$6\frac{1}{4}$-inch	37.80	3,780	240,760	
$2\frac{1}{4}$-inch	$7\frac{1}{8}$-inch	48.00	4,800	299,100	

Wire Rope Tables (U. S. Navy)

Plow Steel Wire Rope.

Composed of 6 strands, with a hemp core, 19 wires to a strand; or 18 wires, with a center of jute, cotton, or hemp twine.

Diameter	Approximate Circumference	Weight per Fathom	Weight per Coil, 100 Fms.	Breaking Stress	Use
Inches	*Inches*	*Pounds*	*Pounds*	*Pounds*	
$\frac{3}{8}$	$1\frac{1}{8}$	1.27	127	10,340	
$\frac{1}{2}$	$1\frac{1}{2}$	2.23	223	18,000	
$\frac{5}{8}$	2	3.60	360	29,160	
$\frac{3}{4}$	$2\frac{1}{4}$	5.07	507	41,350	
$\frac{7}{8}$	$2\frac{3}{4}$	6.88	688	55,640	
1	3	9.00	900	72,040	
$1\frac{1}{8}$	$3\frac{1}{2}$	11.60	1,160	93,040	
$1\frac{1}{4}$	4	14.48	1,448	116,690	
$1\frac{7}{16}$	$4\frac{1}{2}$	18.80	1,880	152,430	

Composed of 6 strands, with a hemp core, each strand consisting of 37 wires, or 36 wires with a hemp, jute, or cotton center.

Diameter	Approximate Circumference	Weight per Fathom	Weight per Coil, 100 Fms.	Breaking Stress	Use
		Pounds	*Pounds*	*Pounds*	
$\frac{3}{8}$-inch	$1\frac{1}{8}$-inch	1.32	132	10,000	
$\frac{1}{2}$-inch	$1\frac{1}{2}$-inch	2.34	234	19,300	Transmission rope for steering gear; boat crane falls; crane falls, afloat and ashore; hawsers, where great strength is required, relieving tackles.
$\frac{5}{8}$-inch	2 -inch	3.72	372	27,790	
$\frac{3}{4}$-inch	$2\frac{1}{4}$-inch	5.34	534	40,000	
$\frac{7}{8}$-inch	$2\frac{3}{4}$-inch	7.20	720	54,400	
1 -inch	3 -inch	9.48	948	71,100	
$1\frac{1}{8}$-inch	$3\frac{1}{2}$-inch	12.00	1,200	90,000	
$1\frac{5}{8}$-inch	5 -inch	24.90	2,490	183,000	
2 -inch	$6\frac{1}{4}$-inch	37.80	3,780	284,500	

Rough Rules for Getting the Strength of Ropes

An officer may want to make a quick lift and not have tables handy. It is well to memorize these rules.

To get size of manila rope suitable for a given load. Multiply load in tons by 7. The square root of this will be the size of the rope in inches (circumference).

A. Five ton load.

$$5 \times 7 = 35.$$
$$\sqrt{35} = 5.9, \text{ say } 6''.$$

The table gives six-inch manila as having a strength of 30,000 lbs.; this would give us a factor of safety of 3.

B. Two ton load.

$$2 \times 7 = 14.$$
$$\sqrt{14} = 3.7, \text{ say } 3\tfrac{3}{4}''.$$

The table gives three and three quarter inch manila a strength of 12,500 lbs., or a little better than 3 for a factor of safety.

To work the rule backward the safe working load for any rope is found by squaring the circumference and dividing by seven.

For working purposes wire rope may be considered three times the strength of manila rope, of the same size.

When tables are handy the safe working load of rope may be taken as about one sixth of the tabulated ultimate strength. Manila rope may be stressed to a greater degree, say one third of its ultimate strength when the load is only to be applied for a short period and *without jerks*.

These are very loose rules. Never overestimate the strength of a piece of gear. Err on the safe side, but of course use judgment, and this comes with familiarity in using rope.

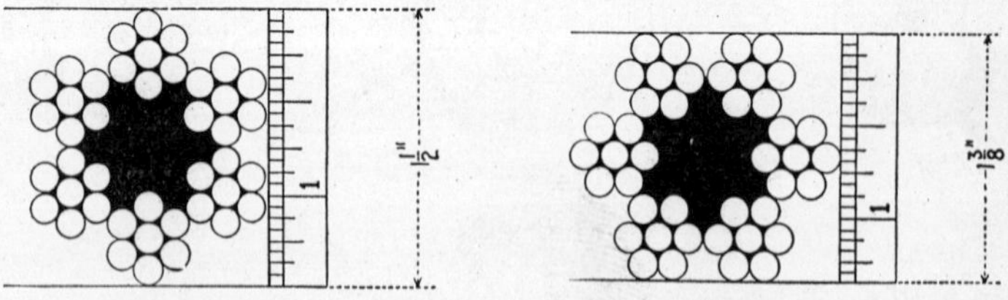

Right *Wrong*

How to measure wire rope

CHAPTER IV

BLOCKS AND TACKLES

I

Blocks

Blocks are among the most important fittings on board ship and their construction and use should be understood by all seamen. The blocks used on lifeboat davits, and the blocks at the lower end of lifeboat falls are of the utmost importance. These will be specially treated in the chapter devoted to lifeboats.

Blocks are usually *single, double, treble*, or *fourfold, etc.* The number of *sheaves* indicating the name of the block.

A block primarily consists of the *shell*, the *strap*, the *sheave*, or *sheaves*, and the *pin*, the *hook* or *shackle*, and some are fitted with a *becket* for attaching a stationary part of the fall.

Blocks are usually strapped with steel, or have interior straps, leading down from the hook. Formerly blocks were strapped with rope.

Sheaves are *bushed* with metal and are sometimes fitted with rollers or self-lubricating bearings, special metal filled with graphite plugs.

Bushings are the bearing a sheave has upon the pin. The three styles shown are those most commonly used.

Plain

Roller

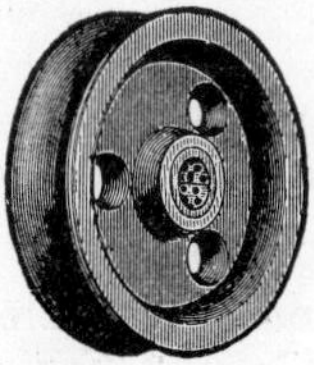

Self-lubricating

Bushings

In a *Plain Bushed* sheave the bearing is simply a hole drilled in cast iron. These, are most commonly used.

Roller Bushed sheaves bear on rollers that in turn bear on the pin. These run with less friction than the common sheave, and on this account are generally the favorite where hand power is used for hoisting. Also referred to as *Patent* bushings.

Self-lubricating sheaves are made with a perforated bronze bushing, the holes being filled with a special lubricant. As the bearing wears, the lubricant is distributed, thus the name "self-lubricating." On account of their construction, these sheaves are the most durable, and are generally used in *wire rope blocks.*

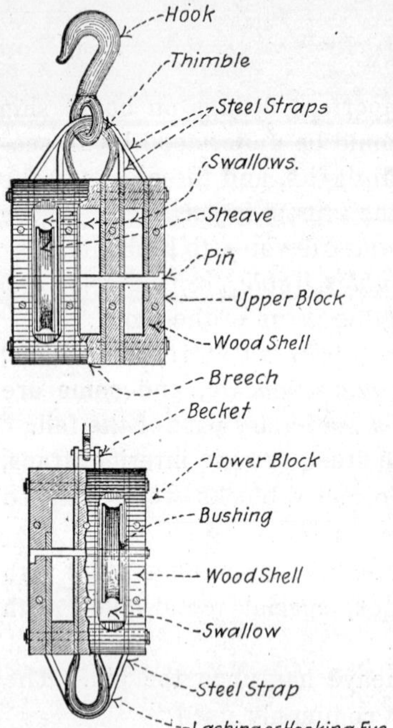

Parts of a block

Use no oil on self-lubricating sheaves.

Sheaves are made of metal or of lignum vitae.

The parts of a block are best shown by a drawing.

Special blocks. Blocks often take their names from the position and use to which they are put. This is specially so in sailing craft.

Cargo blocks. Usually the block at the boom end. Large metal blocks, often with wooden cheeks. Wide swallow, and mounted with swivel neck, and shackle, or moused hook.*

A whip is rove through the cargo block.

Snatch blocks. Blocks fitted with hinged shell, or hook so that a rope may be *snatched* on the bight. Used as lead blocks in warping, and in leading boat falls to winches, or in leading topping lifts to winches. Snatch blocks are among the most useful of the loose blocks carried by a vessel. In hooking a snatch block do so with the point of the hook up, so that when the load comes off the block it will not unhook as it slams down on the deck.

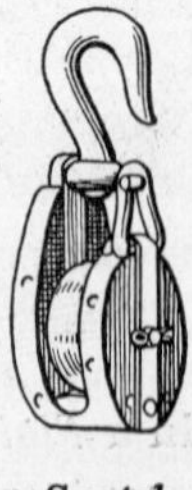

Snatch block

* All blocks should be overhauled at least once a year, pins examined, bushings oiled, and straps red leaded. Many steamship men think a block will last forever, if kept painted on the outside.

Lead blocks. Blocks slung to the mast table under the booms, and giving a fair lead to the cargo whips from the cargo block down to the drum of the winch. Of course there are many other blocks that may be styled lead blocks.

Gin blocks. Metal blocks with open metal shell or frame. Usually the shell merely consists of a guard to keep the rope from running off the score of the sheave.

Gin block

Fish block. The lower block of a fish tackle, fitted with a fish hook, used in fishing an old fashioned anchor. See Chapter on ground tackle (Chap. 17).

Cat block. Used where anchors are *catted*, the upper sheaves of the *cat fall* being rove through the cat head, the lower through the cat block, fitted with the cat hook. Ancient lore but still in service at sea on many craft.

Fish and cat blocks are always double and sometimes treble blocks.

Sister blocks. Two sheaves one above other in same shell fitted to lead their falls in opposite directions.

A secret block, is a single block with closed shell, two holes in lower part admit passage of fall. Used to prevent fouling by other gear, or sails. Used on *bunt jigger.*

Fiddle block, a double block, sheaves in same position with relation to each other as in a sister block but falls lead the same way. Used under the eyes of the rigging where a double block may be needed but there is only room for a single width of shell.

Clump block. A small egg-shaped block with rounded shell. Very strong. Used at the end of staysail pendants for hauling easily over the stays next aft.

Cheek block. A half shell covering a sheave on the side of a mast or other spar. Used on gaffs and booms.

Jeer blocks are large blocks used in sending up and down lower yards. Jeer blocks are often a permanent part of the slings, a slip hook being fitted between them.

Dasher block. The small signal halyard block at the end of the spanker or monkey gaff. (Monkey gaff is the small signal gaff sometimes fitted on the after mast of sailing craft; it carries no sail and is supported by an eye under the topgallant mast head, and is steadied by vangs to the horns of the cross trees.)

Tye blocks. Large steel blocks on the topsail and topgallant yards. The topsail tye reeves through the former, and topgallant tye through the latter. Only used with heavy yards.

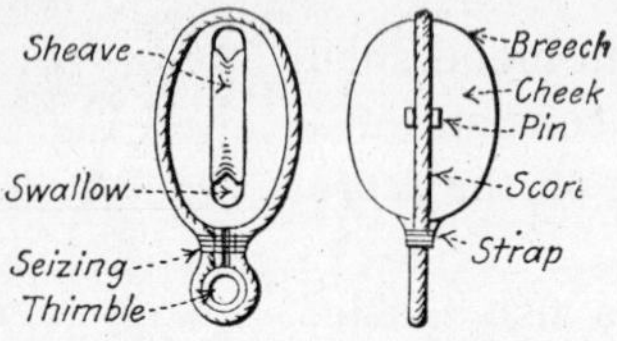

Rope. Strapped block

Tail block. Handy block fitted with a tail for clapping on gear, etc. A small tail snatch block is handy for hauling in the deep sea lead line when this is used.

Quarter blocks, clew line blocks, hanging blocks, sheet blocks, halyard blocks, brace blocks, brail blocks, gantline blocks, downhaul blocks, etc., take their names from the gear that is rove through them, from their position, etc. These will be easily identified by a study of the rigging.

Blocks are *hooked* or *shackled.* Hooks should always be *moused* when there is danger of them unhooking. Mousing a hook with serving wire or with a small shackle strengthens it to a considerable extent.

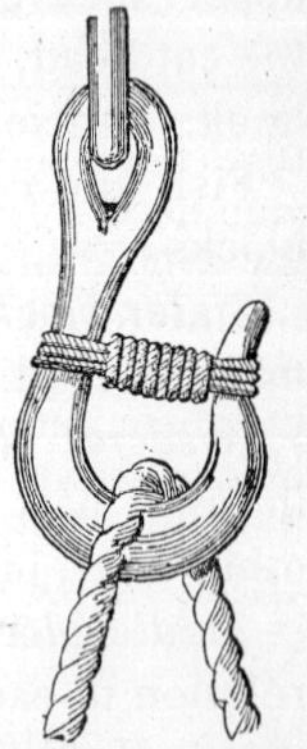
Hook moused with wire or marline, etc.

Lead blocks are sometimes fitted with swivel connections, and various other devices, such as ball and sockets. These fancy things are usually to be found on yachts rather than commercial vessels.

Extra heavy blocks for wire rope. Sheaves from 16 to 30 inches diameter. Capacity from 20 to 100 tons.

Weighted blocks for wire rope. These blocks are made with *overhauling* weights running from 100 to 500 pounds.

*Standardizing Tackle Blocks**

Heavy steel blocks for lifting large weights are of special interest. The following notes on the design of heavy metal blocks may be of interest to those who like to go deeper into the subject of blocks.

* Data supplied by the Engineering Department of the Parish Supply and Manufacturing Company, Chicago, Ill.

For some time, naval architects, engineers and draftsmen, as well as the owners and operators of various types of ships, have recognized the fact that there has been a sad lack of data in regard to the tackle blocks used in their rigging equipments. This has been especially true of the malleable iron shell and steel shell blocks used for heavy loads.

It is true that tackle-block manufacturers have had certain standards of construction, and that it has been possible in some cases to secure from them dimensions of various parts and fittings. How these dimensions were arrived at, however, could not be determined, and it has been only through the wasteful process of repeated failure in actual service that tackle-block users have determined what sizes and types of blocks might be used for specific purposes.

Hook moused with a shackle

Because of these conditions, the Emergency Fleet Corporation was placed at a great disadvantage during the war. Efforts were made to obtain adequate data from the block manufacturers, but because of their inability to secure the complete information required it was necessary for their draftsmen to do the best they could with the material available. The extreme wastefulness of this method has been amply proven in the breaking and binding of the specification blocks when the ships were loading, and in the heartbreaking delays, due to the necessity of securing blocks for replacement.

This state of affairs is known to all shipbuilders, and has often been deplored. To a lesser extent they, too, have had to learn by bitter experience, and the standards arrived at in their specifications are based almost entirely on observation and a knowledge of working conditions.

An effort has been made by block manufacturers to remedy this lack of information, and tackle block users may now secure scientifically determined data in regard to every detail and specification. Engineers have completed numerous experiments and tests, which have proved that in the design of a tackle block the stresses in various parts of the block, resulting from the load carried, may be determined with a considerable degree of accuracy. This information may be used in properly designing the various parts.

Typical Calculations for Tackle Block Design

As a typical example of the methods employed, a triple, heavy-pattern, diamond-shell block, Fig. 1 may be taken. This block has 12-inch sheaves designed to carry a load of 7 tons. The hook for the hoist is a number 13 Williams-Vulcan hook with a shank diameter of $1\frac{3}{4}$ inches.

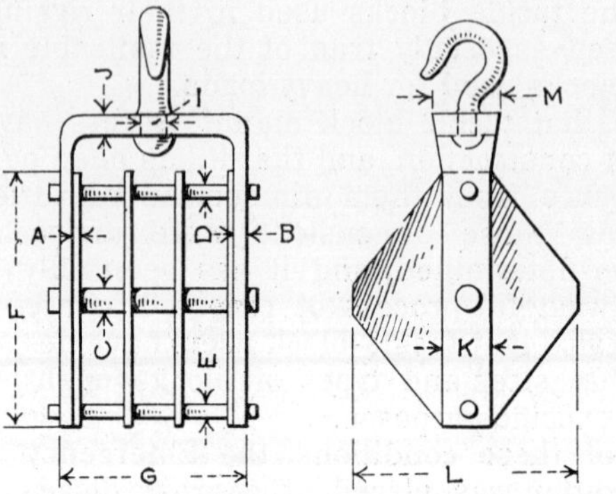

Fig. 1

The strap is shown in Fig. 2. The center pin has a diameter of $d = 1\frac{1}{2}$ inches. The important factor in the design of the pin is the bearing pressure of the bronze bushings in the hubs of the sheaves, per square inch of projected area. This is

$$p = \frac{Q}{Z' \times d} = \frac{14{,}000}{4\frac{7}{8} \times 1\frac{1}{2}} = 7{,}920 \text{ pounds per square inch,}$$

where: Q = total load on block,
Z' = combined length of hubs of sheaves,
d = diameter of pin.

The resultant pressure is comparatively low because the more or less intermittent use of a tackle block permits much higher pressures, especially in the case of a high-grade bronze block. The pin may then be checked for bending stresses, considering it as a beam supported at both ends and carrying a uniformly distributed load of 14,000 pounds. However, the pin receives considerable support from the cheek plates between the sheaves, which reduce the resultant stresses very considerably; the amount of this reduction it is, however, impossible to calculate with any degree of accuracy.

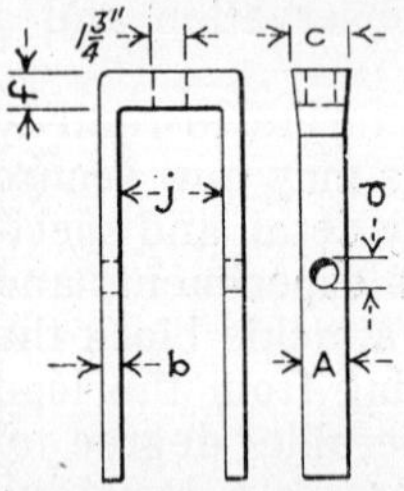

Fig. 2

The sides of the strap are in tension, the weakest section being at the center pin. This section is shown in Fig. 3. The load is $Q/2$, so that we have the equation

$$\frac{Q}{2} = (a - d)\, b\, S_t,$$

in which S_t is the safe tensile stress of the material. A factor of safety of 4 or 5 may be used, which will give a value of 12,000 to 16,000 for mild steel. We can now assume a value for either

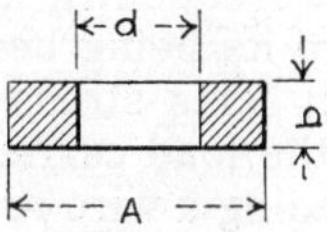

Fig. 3

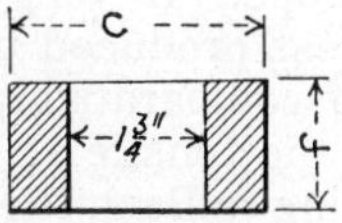

Fig. 4

a or b and calculate the other dimension. Taking b at ⅝ inch, and S_t at 12,000, the equation becomes;

$$\frac{14{,}000}{2} = (a - 1\tfrac{1}{2}) \times \tfrac{5}{8} \times 12{,}000.$$

Solving this for a, the result is $a = 2.44$ inches, which for reasons of construction is increased to 3 inches.

The crown of the strap is treated as a beam supported at the center and carrying a load, $Q/2$ at each end. The dangerous section, Fig. 4, is at the center. The bending moment at this section is;

$$M = \frac{QZ}{4}.$$

We therefore have the equation;

$$\frac{QZ}{4} = S_b Z,$$

in which S_b is the safe bending stress and Z is the section modulus, which for this section is $1/6\,(c - 1\tfrac{3}{4})\,f^2$. The equation thus becomes

$$\frac{QZ}{4} = 1/6\,(c - 1\tfrac{3}{4})\,S_b.$$

A value of c is now assumed, say 4 inches, and S_b is taken at 16,000. Solving the equation for f the result is

$$\frac{14{,}000}{4} \times 7 = 1/6\,(4 - 1\tfrac{3}{4})\,f^2 \times 16{,}000.$$

$$\text{and } f = \sqrt{\frac{6 \times 14{,}000 \times 7}{4\,(4 - 1\tfrac{3}{4}) \times 16{,}000}} = 2 \text{ inches.}$$

The following calculation, from the same source, is most important.

Determining the Stresses in Wire Rope

It may be well to calculate the stress in the wire rope which is ¾-inch diameter, the usual 6 strand, 19 wire per strand hoisting rope. A very important factor, frequently neglected, is the stress produced in wire rope due to its being bent over a sheave of comparatively small diameter. This stress must be added to the tensile stress produced by the load carried.

According to Bach the stress due to bending a wire rope over a sheave is

$$S_b = 3/8\, E \frac{h}{D},$$

in which E is the modulus of elasticity (30,000,000 for steel), h is the diameter of the individual wires of the rope, and D is the sheave diameter. For a pair of triple blocks, each rope will carry 1/6 of the total load of 2,400 pounds. The diameter of the wire is approximately 1/15 of the rope diameter, or 0.05 inch. Then

$$S_b = 3/8 \times 30{,}000{,}000 \times \frac{.05}{12} = 47{,}000 \text{ pounds per square inch.}$$

The stress due to the load S_t is

$$S_t = \frac{Q}{nA},$$

where A is the sectional area of each wire, and n is the number of wires in the rope, so that

$$S_t = \frac{2{,}400}{119 \times 0.00196} = 10{,}300 \text{ pounds per square inch.}$$

The total stress is

$$S = S_b + S_t = 57{,}300 \text{ pounds per square inch.}$$

It is thus seen that the bending stress in this case is by far the most important. For high-grade plow steel rope the factor of safety is about 3, which is not too low for such material.

Ordering Blocks

When ordering blocks from the maker, state the following: Size of block (length in inches), measuring shell, not hook and becket); number of sheaves; kind of connection, *i.e.*, hook, shackle, ring, sister hooks, swivel, stiff, etc.; whether becket is required, or not; kind of shell, ash, lignum vitae, steel; kind of sheave, plain, roller bushed (sailors call them " patent sheaves," or self-lubricating. Also material, *i.e.*, galvanized iron, or composition, or lignum vitae.

It is also well to mention the use that is to be made of the block.

II

Tackles and Purchases

Any mechanical advantage which increases the force as applied through rope and blocks is a purchase. And a tackle, as generally understood, is the same thing. The tackle may be of different kinds and still only have the *same purchase.*

Also, purchases are referred to when we consider the handling, or *purchasing*, of heavy weights.

The following concise table, inserted here by permission of Merriman Brothers, of Boston, sums up the theoretical and actual purchase of certain practical combinations of blocks, rope, and bushings. This is a very valuable table resulting from careful experiments.

Table Showing Theoretical Purchase of Various Combinations of Blocks together with Approximate Efficiency and Actual Purchase

Combination	Movable Block	Bushing	Theoretical Purchase	Efficiency	Actual Purchase
For Manila Rope.			*Times*	*Per Cent.*	*Times*
Two Single, 6 in.	Single, without Becket	Common	2	81	1.62
		Self-Lub.	2	87	1.74
		Patent	2	90	1.8
Single and Double, 6 in.	Single, with Becket	Common	3	60	1.8
		Self-Lub.	3	73	2.19
		Patent	3	78	2.34
Two Double, 6 in.	Double, without Becket	Common	4	48	1.92
		Self-Lub.	4	61	2.44
		Patent	4	70	2.8
Two Double, 8 in.	Double, without Becket	Common	4	58	2.32
		Self-Lub.	4	68	2.72
		Patent	4	75	3
Double and Triple, 6 in.	Double, with Becket	Common	5	41	2.05
		Self-Lub.	5	52	2.6
		Patent	5	64	3.2
Double and Triple, 12 in.	Double, with Becket	Common	5	63	3.15
		Self-Lub.	5	68	3.4
		Patent	5	72	3.6
For Wire Rope.					
Single and Double, 10 in.	Single, with Becket	Self-Lub.	3	91	2.73
Double and Triple, 10 in.	Double, with Becket	Self-Lub.	5	86	4.3

Theoretical and Actual Purchase and Efficiency

Theoretically the purchase of a pair of blocks is equal to the number of parts of rope that go to the movable block. Thus, in the combination of two single blocks, the single without becket being the movable block, the theoretical purchase is two times; in the combination of a double and single block, the single block with becket being the movable block, the theoretical purchase is three times, etc. In practice, however, we find this theoretical purchase considerably reduced by the friction of the sheaves and rope, so that the actual purchase is always materially less than the theoretical purchase.

If N = the number of parts of rope leading to the movable block, then Efficiency $= \frac{\text{Load}}{N \times \text{Pull}} \%$

Experiments in determining the efficiency of various combinations of blocks show considerable variation in result, depending not only upon the accuracy with which the blocks are made, but also upon the size and kind of rope. The results shown in the table may be taken as a fair average.

It will be noticed that with the same number of sheaves in a purchase there is a marked increase in efficiency when large sheaves are used.

It is customary to figure that working hand-over-hand, a man will pull about half his own weight. Given number of men available, weight to be lifted, the amount of purchase can be calculated.

Next to knowing what combination of rope and blocks, to use the most important thing to consider is the size of rope, and the size of block to go with it. The tables following, also prepared by Merriman Brothers, are most useful. Such tables are of great utility to the ship's officer when he is rigging for heavy weights, and are also of great assistance to the designer who lays out cargo and other ship's gear.

Standard blocks will, as a rule, not carry as much weight as the *new* rope that can be used in them. This is specially so of blocks with hook connection. Shackles are much stronger and should always be used for heavy lifts.

Suitable Working Load for Blocks

Regular Tackle Blocks with Loose Hooks

Size Block	Diameter Manila Rope	Two Singles or Single and Double	Two Doubles or Double and Triple	Two Triples
Inches	*Inches*	*Pounds*	*Pounds*	*Pounds*
5	$\frac{9}{16}$	250	350	500
6	$\frac{3}{4}$	400	600	800
7	$\frac{3}{4}$	600	800	1,200
8	$\frac{7}{8}$	800	1,400	2,000
9	$\frac{7}{8}$	1,400	2,000	3,200
10	1	2,000	3,500	5,000
12	$1\frac{1}{8}$	4,000	5,500	7,000
14	$1\frac{1}{4}$	6,000	7,500	9,000

Wide Mortise Tackle Blocks with Loose Hooks

(With shackles one and one-half times the following load may be carried)

Size Block	Diameter Manila Rope	Two Singles or Single and Double	Two Doubles or Double and Triple	Two Triples or Triple and Quadruple
Inches	*Inches*	*Tons*	*Tons*	*Tons*
8	1	$\frac{3}{4}$	$1\frac{1}{2}$	2
10	$1\frac{1}{4}$	2	$2\frac{1}{2}$	$3\frac{1}{2}$
12	$1\frac{5}{16}$	$3\frac{1}{2}$	$4\frac{1}{2}$	6
14	$1\frac{5}{8}$	$4\frac{1}{2}$	6	7
16	$1\frac{3}{4}$	7	8	10

Extra Heavy Wide Mortise Blocks with Lashing Shackles

Size Block	Diameter Manila Rope	Two Doubles or Double and Triple	Two Triples or Triple and Quadruple	Two Quadruples
Inches	*Inches*	*Tons*	*Tons*	*Tons*
18	2	20	25	30
20	$2\frac{1}{4}$	30	35	40
22	$2\frac{1}{2}$	35	45	55
24	3	50	65	75

Wire Rope Blocks with Shackles

(With hooks not more than one-half the following load should be carried)

Diameter Sheave	Diameter Wire Rope	Two Singles or Single and Double	Two Doubles or Double and Triple	Two Triples or Triple and Quadruple
Inches	*Inches*	*Tons*	*Tons*	*Tons*
10	$\frac{1}{2}$ or $\frac{5}{8}$	5	7	9
12	$\frac{5}{8}$ " $\frac{3}{4}$	7	10	12
14	$\frac{3}{4}$ " $\frac{7}{8}$	9	12	15
16	$\frac{7}{8}$	12	17	22
18	1	15	22	30

The relation of the length of shell, diameter of rope to be used and the diameter of the sheave is shown in the following Merriman table of vessel blocks:

Vessel Blocks

Galvanized Iron or Lignum-vitae Sheaves

Size of Sheave	Diameter of Rope	Length of Shell	Size of Sheave	Diameter of Rope	Length of Shell
Inches	*Inches*	*Inches*	*Inches*	*Inches*	*Inches*
$1\frac{3}{4} \times \frac{1}{2} \times \frac{3}{8}$	$\frac{3}{8}$	3	$9 \times 1\frac{1}{2} \times \frac{3}{4}$	$1\frac{1}{8}$	13
$2\frac{1}{4} \times \frac{5}{8} \times \frac{3}{8}$	$\frac{1}{2}$	4	$9\frac{1}{2} \times 1\frac{5}{8} \times \frac{7}{8}$	$1\frac{1}{4}$	14
$3 \times \frac{3}{4} \times \frac{3}{8}$	$\frac{9}{16}$	5	$10 \times 1\frac{5}{8} \times \frac{7}{8}$	$1\frac{1}{4}$	15
$3\frac{1}{2} \times 1 \times \frac{1}{2}$	$\frac{5}{8}$ or $\frac{3}{4}$	6	$11 \times 1\frac{3}{4} \times \frac{7}{8}$	$1\frac{3}{8}$	16
$4\frac{1}{4} \times 1 \times \frac{1}{2}$	$\frac{3}{4}$	7	$12 \times 2\frac{5}{8} \times 1\frac{1}{8}$	$2\frac{1}{4}$	18
$4\frac{3}{4} \times 1\frac{1}{8} \times \frac{5}{8}$	$\frac{7}{8}$	8	$13\frac{1}{2} \times 2\frac{7}{8} \times 1\frac{1}{4}$	$2\frac{1}{2}$	20
$5\frac{1}{2} \times 1\frac{1}{8} \times \frac{5}{8}$	$\frac{7}{8}$	9	$14\frac{1}{2} \times 3\frac{3}{8} \times 1\frac{1}{2}$	3	22
$6\frac{1}{4} \times 1\frac{1}{4} \times \frac{5}{8}$	1	10	$15\frac{1}{2} \times 3\frac{7}{8} \times 1\frac{1}{2}$	$3\frac{1}{2}$	24
$7\frac{1}{4} \times 1\frac{1}{4} \times \frac{3}{4}$	1	11	$14 \times 4\frac{3}{4} \times 1\frac{3}{4}$	4	26
$8 \times 1\frac{3}{8} \times \frac{3}{4}$	$1\frac{1}{8}$	12			

Note: The sheave dimensions are diameter of sheave, width of sheave and diameter of pin.

Size of Rope. There should be a good allowance between the diameter of the rope and the thickness of the sheave. You will save trouble if you do not use larger rope than shown in table.

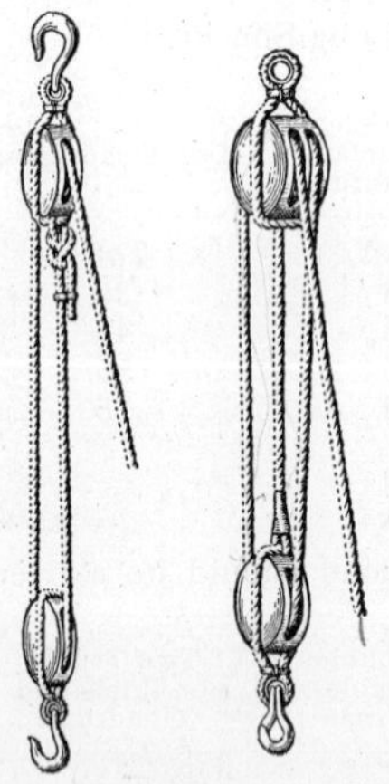

Gun tackle *Luff tackle*

Tackles

Various combinations of rope and blocks are shown and named in the following illustrations. The rope rove through a series of blocks is called a *fall.*

Single whip. Used for greater convenience. Block stationary, no power gained. The cargo block and whip used for ordinary lifts on board ship illustrates this combination.

Runner. Standing part made fast, and fall rove through a movable block. Power doubled (neglecting friction). The tye block on a yard is an illustration of this. The halyard purchase is shackled to the tye after it passes up over the masthead sheave.

Gun tackle. Two single blocks. Standing part of fall to becket in fixed block. Power doubled (neglecting friction).

Luff or watch tackle. This is one of the handiest and most useful purchases on board ship. Double block stationary, or movable, depending on how used. Standing part of fall to

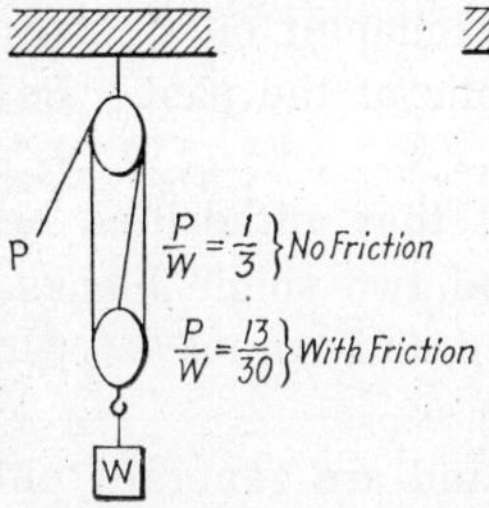

Luff

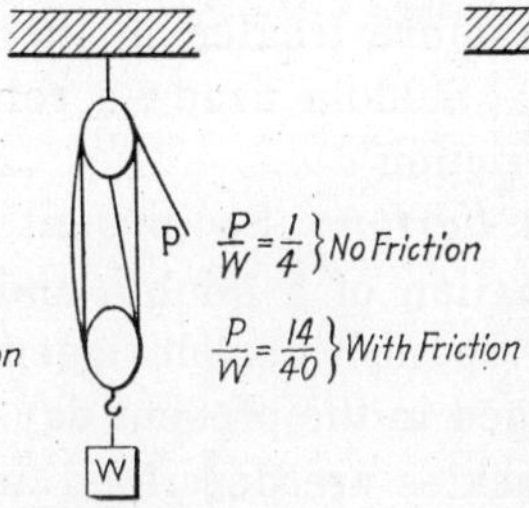

Twofold

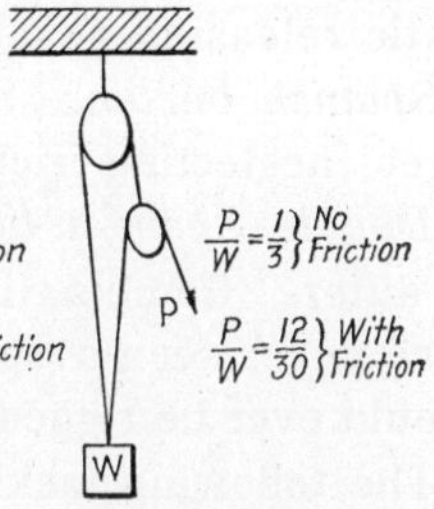

Spanish burton

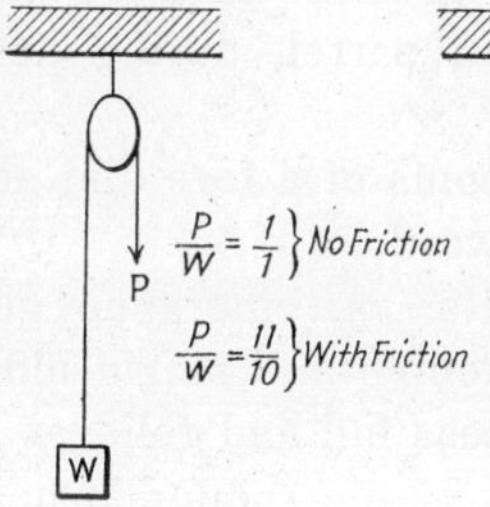

Single whip

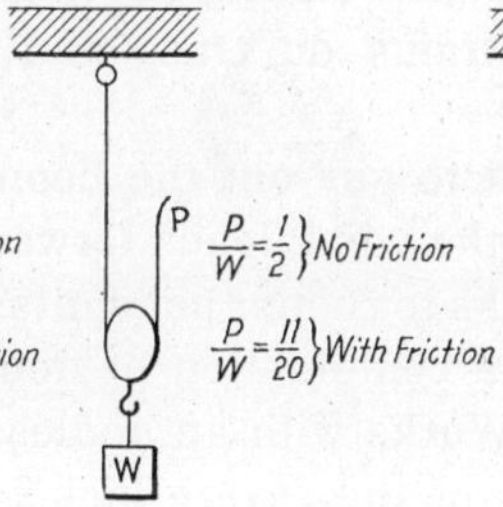

Runner

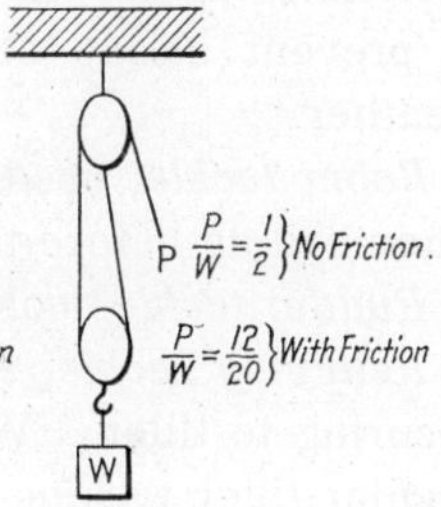

Gun tackle

becket in single block. Power three or four, depending on which block is moving. Here it might be well to say that the power, less friction, is found by *counting the parts of the fall at the movable block,* or *blocks.* Also power is always gained at the expense of time. The greater the purchase the more rope must be hauled through the blocks.

This purchase is used for many things on board ship, but finds its greatest use as a general utility tackle. The small watch tackle is called a *handy billy.*

Twofold tackle. Two double blocks. Power four or five, depending upon which is the movable block. Friction increases with the number of sheaves.

Combinations of double and triple blocks, and of two triple

blocks are used for heavy lifts. Fourfold purchases may be used.

When making these heavy purchases the falls are crossed, so that the hauling part reeves through a middle sheave. This is done so that the blocks, which are quite wide, will not cant over while hauling. Heavy boat falls should be rove this way.

Boat falls, with continuous falls, non-tipping blocks, and automatic releasing gear are treated in the chapter on Boats.

Spanish burton. Seldom used—a relic of the past. Power three (neglecting friction).

Double Spanish burton. So ancient that authorities begin to differ. Combination of a double and two single blocks. I have never seen a Spanish burton rigged and cannot see why it should ever be rigged in the present day.

The following tackles are described and are generally either gun tackle or luff tackle purchases.

Rolling tackles, hooked from quarter of lower yards to mast, to prevent undue strains on truss and parrel, during heavy weather.

Boom tackle, used to guy out the booms of a fore and after when sailing before the wind, leads forward.

Rudder tackle hooks to rudder pendants. An emergency gear.

Relieving tackle, a combination of double and single blocks securing to tiller. Works with an endless fall and relieves the regular tiller tackles of the severe kick of the rudder in heavy weather. Also may be rigged to steer with in the case of rudder tackles parting. A sailing ship rig.

Burton, a tackle hooked to a pendant near the mast head. Useful for heavy lifts, etc., on the deck or up and down the mast.

Yard tackle, used to hoist out over the side.

Stay tackle made fast to a stay, usually over a hatch, where no boom is handy.

The combination of *yard* and *stay* is found in the present *hatch* and *side* booms, for discharging or loading by deck winch.

Jiggers, used aloft as in lifting sails up on the yards.

Luff upon luff, a luff tackle clapped on to the hauling part of another luff. Theoretical power gained 12 times (neglecting friction), where the double block of the first luff is fixed. Where the double blocks of both luffs move, the power would be 16.

A tackle is "two blocks" when the blocks are jambed together and fall cannot be hauled through any more.

To make up a deck tackle. Haul through the fall until the blocks are about three feet apart. Place blocks down, points of hooks up (hooks should always point the same way) and coil the fall around the blocks. Then clove hitch the end of the fall around the whole tackle between the blocks. The tackle can then be stowed, carted about, and still it can be cast loose and *fleeted* or *overhauled*, without danger of jambing. All tackles should be made up so and hung in the boson's locker.

Remember the *cat'spaw* in hooking a tackle onto a rope—it is the most secure and handy method. (See page 92.)

When blocks capsize, be careful in taking out the turns in the fall. This applies to hanging tackles particularly, as the lower block is always liable to turn over when rounding up the fall.

When hoisting a heavy weight, have a stopper *beforehand*, that is near the pin or cleat and ready to clap on the hauling part so that when the order is given, " *Come up behind!* " and the men let go the fall, it can be belayed without loosing anything. Where there is not too much weight on the fall, a few hands hang on *beforehand* while the hauling part is taken around the pin. When possible the block from which the hauling part leads should always be hooked to the weight or object to be moved. In hauling the greatest tension comes on the hauling part. In slacking away it comes on the standing part of the fall.

Watch seamen at work—study their way of doing things, their way of *saying* things. Remember " tackle " is not pronounced like " fishing tackle." Sailors always refer to it as a " TAYKLE " the " A " as in *pay*. You see it " takes hold " of things. Only a lubber calls it anything else.

Hauling upon tackles, " singing " a rope, and the pleasant " click " of the " *PAYTENT* " sheaves, is something to be remembered for many a day. The chanties are almost gone, but here and there in the newer sailing craft old tunes remain, and sailors, even in steam, will *call* as a rope is swigged up. This is a song without words, a sort of plaintive cry. Scandinavian seamen are great at this.

" I hear them *hilly hollying* upon the weather brace " is the way Masefield expresses it.

Before leaving this little dissertation on tackles, let me say a word about " foreign seamen." The lad who goes to sea with foreign seamen is liable to be fortunate, if he keeps his eyes open and don't start off with narrow-minded prejudices. The more foreigners he meets at sea, the more he will know in the end. The writer shipped around Cape Horn in a three skysail yarder, as a lad, just to top off his schoolship training. There were eighteen hands before the mast (ship 2,500 D.W.) and these included twelve different nationalities. Much sailor lore was passed about during the dog and night watches.

III

Mechanics on Board Ship

Officers on board ship are constantly dealing with large forces. This is specially so in the seamanship division where the vessel itself, through its ground tackle, mooring lines, and propeller, is moved about and handled. It is necessary that the officer in charge have some definite idea of the forces he is handling. Many men, of course, are fully conversant with these forces and their practical action and reaction, but the fundamental facts may be unknown to them. The following short definitions may be of use in clearing up this part of a deep subject.

Mass is the scientific word for weight. It is the result of weighing by a balance scale. Weight by a spring scale may be quite different, depending upon the force acting on a body. Weight in that case will be different at the poles and at the equator.

Acceleration is the rate of change of the velocity of a body.

Force is the product of the *Mass* times the *Acceleration*. Force can be measured by a spring scale. Dynamometers are usually built on this principle.

The forces met with in the handling of cargo are largely *dynamic*, that is they are the forces of motion, of moving loads.

Force = *Mass* × *Acceleration*.

That is, if the velocity is uniform, and there is no acceleration, the force is simply equal to the weight so long as no attempt is made to *check* or *increase* the velocity.

In figuring force we use the following units:

Force (in pounds) = Mass (in pounds) × Acceleration (feet per sec.^{2})

Impulse or *momentum* is the product of *force* and *time* (foot/sec.)

Work is the product of *force* over *distance* (foot pound).

In order to do work, certain machines are used.

The lever. The principle of the lever is so simple and useful that it will merely be mentioned here in passing. This principle is employed on board ship in the lever and brake beam of the hand windlass. The point about which a lever moves is called the *fulcrum.*

When heavy freight cars are to be moved along a track, as often happens when alongside a railroad siding, this use of the lever is very handy. Get two pinch bars, place the ends under the rear wheels of the car and come down on the handles; the leverage here is one inch to four feet. Two men on a bar can easily lift under the wheel with a force of four tons (48 times 200 lbs.) and with this on two wheels the most stubborn car will move. The Japanese on the sugar wharves in Honolulu move the laden cars about in this manner with surprising ease. It is a good wrinkle to employ.

The wedge. This form of applied power, the wedge being one of the simple machines,* is very useful in setting up lashings, etc., and in battening hatches. The forces resolve themselves according to the angle of the point of the wedge, following the principles of the composition and resolution of forces.

Chain Hoists

Chain hoists have become an important part of all ship equipment. In the engine room these find constant use in lifting heavy machinery parts, in slinging oil barrels and in a number of different operations. On deck they are very useful in many ways and the ship's officer should make himself familiar with their application.

Many different designs are on the market.

Chain hoists are a combination of an endless chain, or chains, two or more blocks, and certain gears for the application of

* The simple machines are the *lever*, the *pulley* (block), the *wheel* and *axle*, the *wedge*, and the *screw*.

power, usually applied by a secondary hauling chain of endless construction transmitting the hand power to the upper block.

Differential hoist

Screw hoist

Planetary hoist

In the *differential* purchase the hauling part is part of the chain carrying the weight, an endless chain taken over two sheaves of different diameters or of the same diameter, and led around a lower sheave to which is attached the lifting hook.

The *planetary* is somewhat more complicated and depends upon a combination of gears within the upper block, these gears being worked by the hand chain. Very heavy weights can be lifted by such hoists. The heaviest special chain hoists are designed to lift as high as forty tons.

For a twenty ton lift 140 lbs. of pull are required on the hand chain and for each foot of lift the hand chain must be hauled 210 feet. Other lifts are in proportion, the twenty ton hoist being about the limit on board ship.

The *screw* chain hoist is of somewhat different construction, an endless screw working on a worm is its essential feature.

A useful application of chain hoists—unshipping a damaged rudder. Screw hoists

Before operating a chain hoist be sure it is in good condition, that the blocks are most favorably placed for the lift, that the full lift can be made, and be careful to avoid "*gagging*" of the chain.

As in all hoisting operations with heavy weights, take your time, *know* just what you intend to do, then go ahead slowly.

The Composition and Resolution of Forces

In *staying* masts, *plumbing* booms, and in *guying* booms, an understanding of the composition and resolution of forces is of the utmost value. Most men know these things instinctively. A straight pull is the best pull, etc. But the proper position of working cargo gear depends upon a clear understanding of the parallelogram of forces.

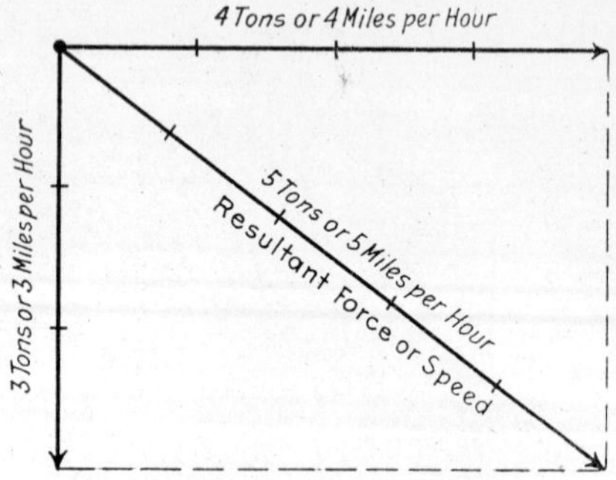

Resultant of two forces or velocities acting at right angles to each other

The composition and resolution of *forces* and *velocities* may be done by calculation, involving the elements of right and oblique plane triangles. The traverse tables may be used for this purpose. But the writer believes that it is simpler and quicker, and less open to error, if the position of masts and booms and lifts and guys be drawn *to scale* and the forces determined by graphic methods, setting off the force, or weight, to a given scale and measuring the resultant pulls and thrusts. There is less fiddling with figures, which sailors don't as a rule care for, and the *layout can be seen.*

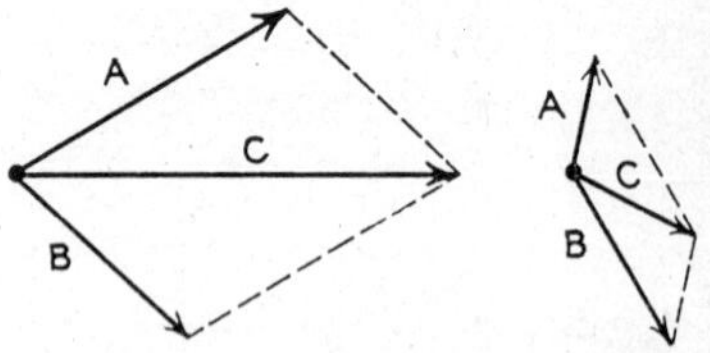

C = Resultants of A and B, showing how to plot a parallelogram of forces

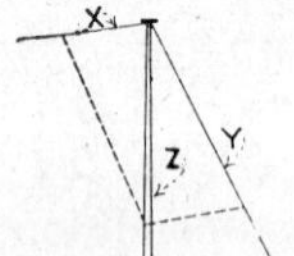

To find the stress on the stays or shrouds, we lay off the tension on the topping lift and resolve this along the line of the mast and shroud. Thus *X* is the tension on the topping lift, set off to any convenient scale, then *Y* is the tension on the shroud, while *Z* is the thrust transferred to the mast. The dotted lines being drawn parallel to the lead of the lift and the angle of the shroud.

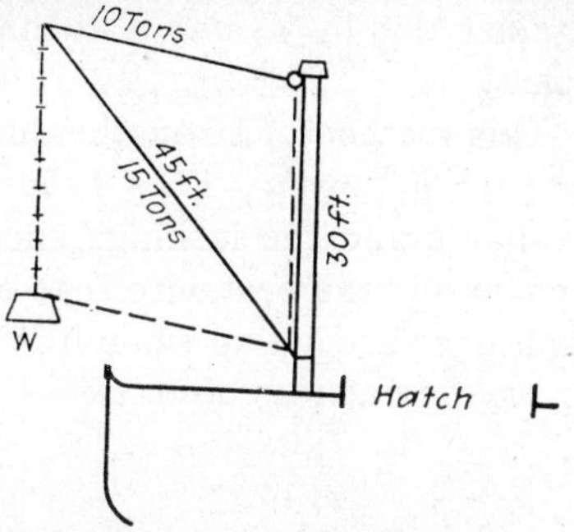

Diagram of stresses on a king post

The relation between booms, and gear, depends upon the materials at hand for making lifts, and where there is a choice in improvising booms and masts, or shears, the relative strength of the spars available and the rope on hand will determine how best to utilize your resources.

The stresses in masts and booms are *buckling* stresses. The longer the spar the more liable it is to buckle under a load. Where a long slight boom must be used it is well to guard

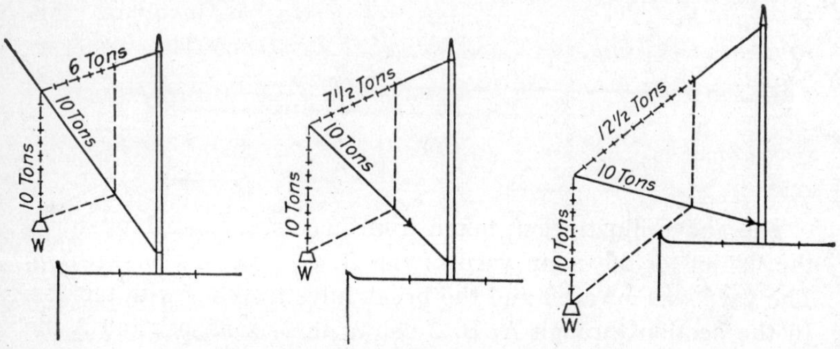

Mast and boom same length. Thrust or boom always the same for a given load. Note increase of pull on topping lift as boom is lowered.

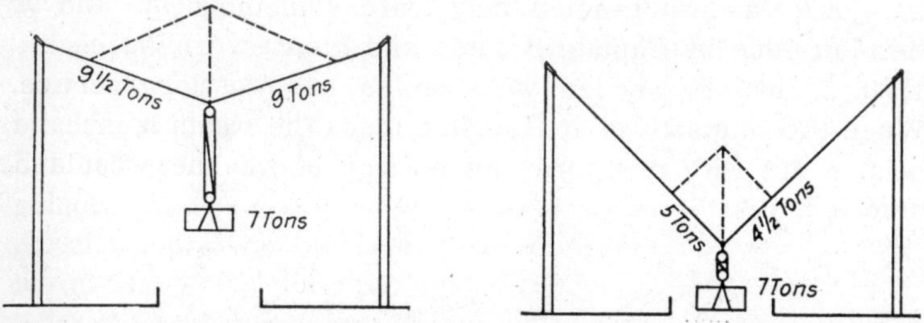

Showing effect of the same weight on a span at different angles with the masts. The pull is double on the flat span.

against this by *fishing* it at the middle with one or two shorter spars.

This method of strengthening is also employed when a boom or yard is sprung. The fishes should be of the best material available and the lashings should be hove down with a strong heaver and the best wire rope employed. Wedges are driven in and these are set up when it is necessary to tighten the lashings or *wolding* as it is often called.

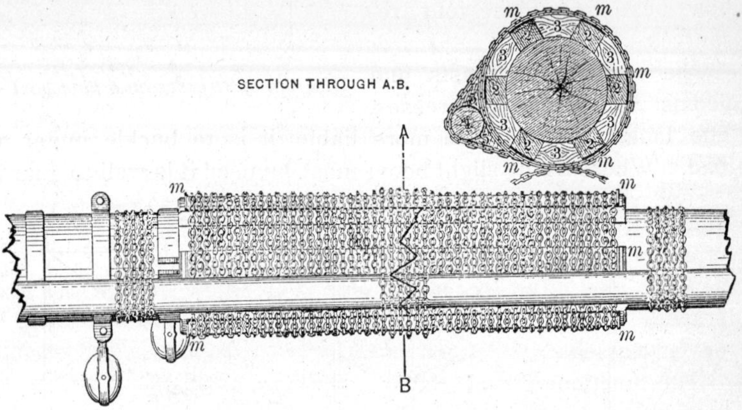

The above illustration, taken from Luce's Seamanship, shows the fishing of the main yard of the U. S. Frigate *Constitution*. The yard was lowered and the break hove together with tackles. In the section through A, B, 2 shows the six fishes, and 3 the chocking pieces in between. *m*, is the chain wolding. The chocks were spaced snugly between the fishes, nine inches apart. A spare gaff was used on the after side of the yard to reinforce the job. Modern seamen may learn something by studying this job done by Captain Stanton and his crew *at sea* back in 1880. (The old wooden walls had a habit of long service.) When the ship arrived at Hampton roads the steam launch was hoisted out with this yard and no sign of weakness could be detected.

CHAPTER V

STEAMER RIGGING—CARGO GEAR

I

Masts, Booms, Rigging—Heavy Hoists

In the steamer and motor vessel masts have lost their importance as the main stem of motive power—the support of sails, but on the other hand masts are more important than ever as supports for the booms necessary in the handling of cargo.

With this change in function masts have undergone a considerable change in position and size. Masts are lower, are often mere posts standing without stays, then called *King Posts*, and are now often stepped in pairs abreast of each other, this practice having first found favor abroad, particularly in Scandinavian vessels.

The functions of the modern mast in a steam or motor vessel may be summed up as follows:

Support of cargo booms and gear.
Support of radio antenna.
Support of signal stays, yards, and trucks.
Support of masthead and other lights.
Support of crow's nest lookout.

Masts, to a very limited extent, also serve as a support for storm staysails and storm trysails, this function becoming less important as the size of the vessel increases. Still, the judicious use of these sails on many vessels, serves to steady them, and in a strong wind sails are often of great use when engines are disabled.

Masts generally are *stepped* on the keelson, and pass up through the *mast holes* of the various decks between the *partners*, fore and aft members spanning the beams and closing in the mast at the deck openings. The masts are secured at the partners and mast holes by the *mast wedges*, and on the weather deck, the mast hole is made watertight by the *mast coat*, a circular canvas apron seized to the mast and fitted down close over the wedges. Its lower and often its upper parts are held in place by metal hoops set up with screws. The mast coats are of No. 1 canvas and are painted.

The part of the mast below decks is generally known as the *housing*.

In large steam and motor vessels masts seldom go all the way down to the keelson.

In many modern vessels masts are stepped on the main deck, and are held upright by a structure that runs up the mast and is called a *tabernacle*.

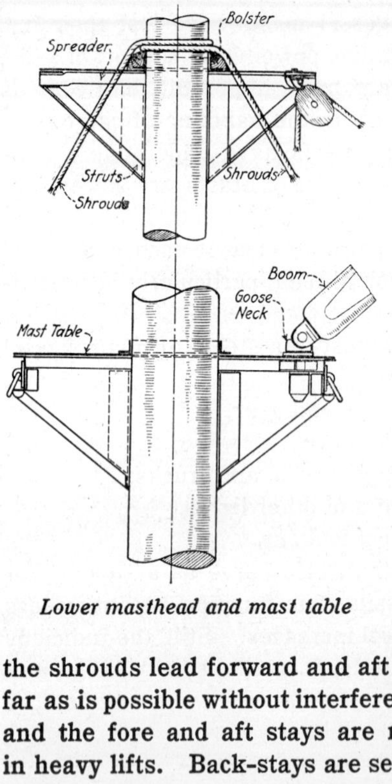

Lower masthead and mast table

Steamer masts are stayed against cargo loads, these being the greatest loads ever coming upon the masts.

The *stays* on a mast are the fore and aft stay leading from the masthead down forward and taking its name from the mast, as *fore stay, main stay, mizzen stay,* etc. The *shrouds* and the *backstays*, port and starboard, and named after the masts as above.

But in the ultra modern vessel, the topmast has degenerated into a mere stump, the shrouds lead forward and aft of the masts on either side as far as is possible without interference with the working of cargo, and the fore and aft stays are not counted upon for support in heavy lifts. Back-stays are seldom used.

Above decks masts have taken on many new departures. Lower masts are always built up of steel plating, generally circular. About eight or ten feet from the deck, *mast tables* are fitted. On many vessels these mast tables have grown of great size. On some vessels a combination of mast table and tabernacle is used. On other vessels the mast table has become a small raised deck about the mast, supported by stout columns and braces. These are the *winch platforms*, lifting the cargo winches clear above the deck. Mast tables are then fitted above these winch platforms.

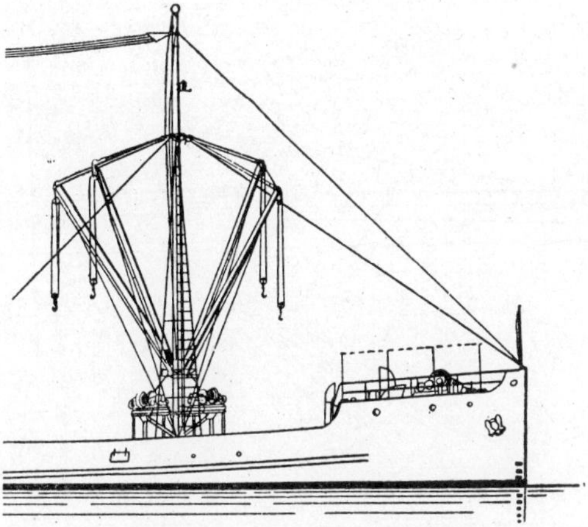

Pole foremast with winch platform

The mast table serves as a support for the cargo booms, the *goosenecks* upon which the heel of the boom pivots stepping in sockets let into the tables. The booms are so arranged that the outboard booms, step directly in back of the outboard winches. Directly under these booms are the eyebolts for the *lead blocks* carrying the *cargo fall* down the boom and to the drum of the winch.

At the mast heads we often find a smaller *cross tree* or spreaders of steel, carrying the supporting eye bolts for the upper blocks of the *boom topping lifts*. On some masts these are supported by a band about the lower mast head.

The topmast is generally of wood. A topmast carried forward of the lower mast, resting on *cheek plates* or *trestle trees* by means of a *fid* and supported by the *lower mast cap*, is called a *fidded topmast*. Where the lower and topmast pass each other is called the *doubling* of the mast. This is also the approved method of fitting one mast above another in sailing craft.

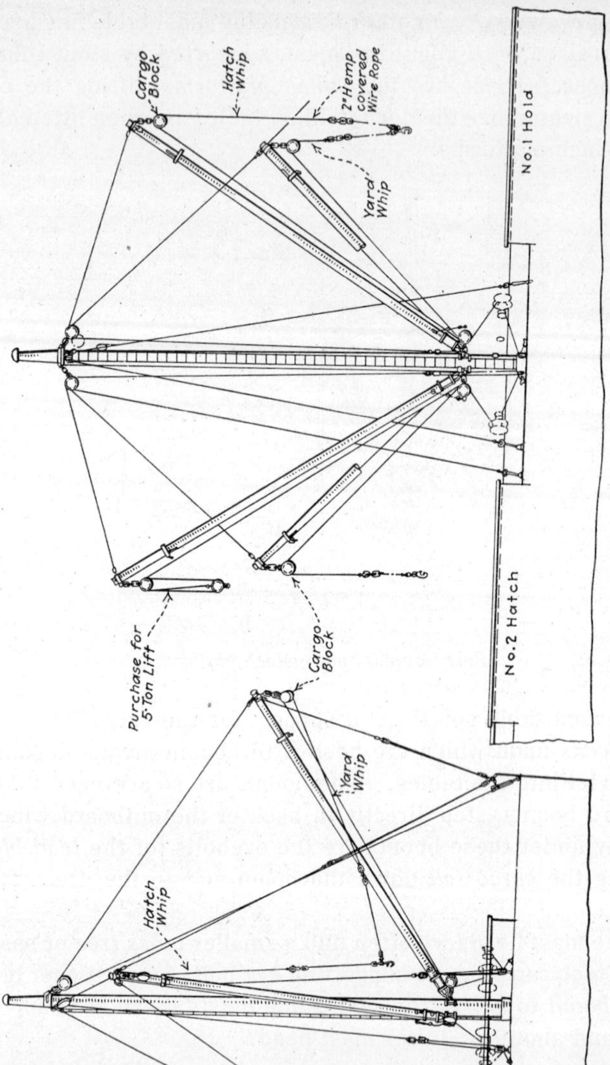

Regular cargo gear—5-ton cargo gear

Fidded masts are easily sent down on deck, where vessels are required to pass under bridges, such as the suspension spans across the East River, New York.

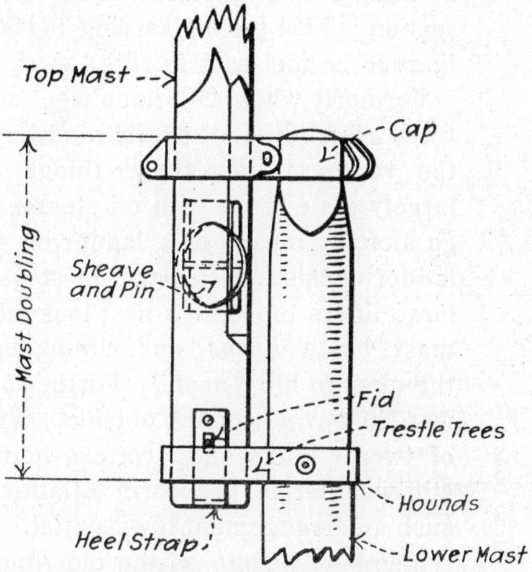

Fidded topmast doubling

Most topmasts nowadays, where topmasts are fitted, rise from the center of the lower mast. When the topmast lowered

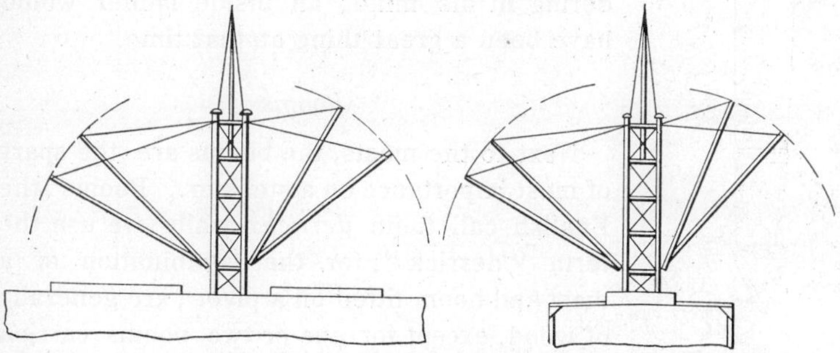

Tower mast. Four posts with steel braces. No stays or shrouds

into the lower mast it is called a *telescopic topmast.* The topmasts are generally of pine. The whole mast, where lower and topmast are one, is called a *pole* mast.

The writer when inspecting a "standardized ship" was astonished at *square* masts—an upright box column. And why not? Still, where time in building is not so essential, the circular cross section is best for the varying loads and vibrations to be met with in cargo work.

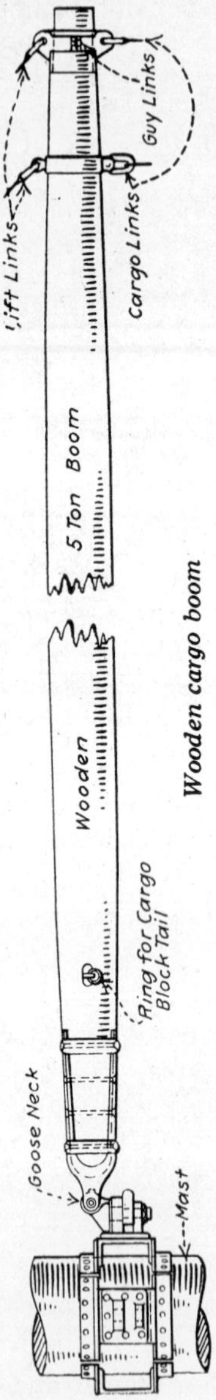

Wooden cargo boom

Formerly when sailormen went aloft they always clambered up the shrouds by means of the *ratlines;* now these things have been largely done away with on steamers and men go aloft by means of a ladder on the mast, a ladder consisting of bar iron steps. In some large liners the crow's nest lookout enters the mast below decks, and climbs up *inside* of the mast to his "nest." Further progress upward however is on the outside. Where speeds of twenty knots and over are being made, in stiff weather in the North Atlantic, in winter, such an arrangement is essential. The writer remembers a time on the old American Liner *St. Louis* when the weather was so bad the crow's nest lookout could not be relieved during the night. When the man was brought down at daybreak he was half frozen and wandering in his mind; an inside ladder would have been a great thing at that time.

Booms

Next to the masts, the booms are the spars of most importance on a steamer. Booms (the English call them *derricks* while we use the term "derrick" for the combination of a mast and boom fitted on a pivot), are generally of wood, except for one or two booms carried for special lifts. These heavy booms are made of steel and are sometimes of lattice construction though the most common practice is to form them of circular plates in the same fashion as the masts. Booms are usually shaped with a slight increase in diameter in the middle where the buckling stresses are greatest.

The boom fittings consist of the *gooseneck* at the *heel* and the *lift, guy* and *cargo bands* at the end. These bands are fitted with links for the *topping lift* block, the starboard and port *guy pendants*, and the *cargo block* through which is rove the *cargo fall*, generally of hemp clad wire rope.

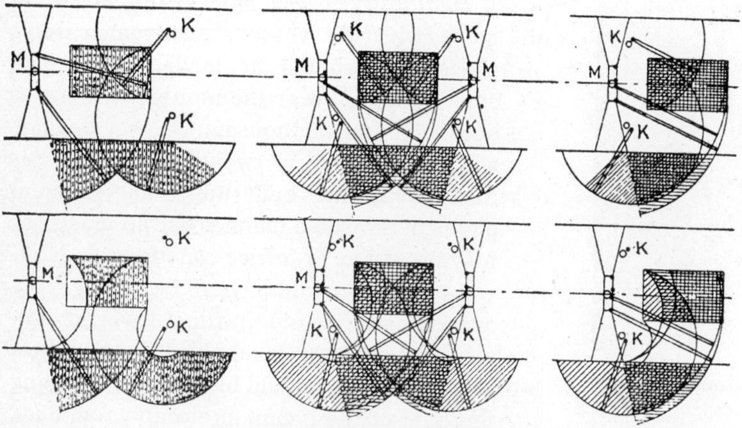

A study in cargo boom efficiency
M = Masts
K = King posts

Large booms are fitted with two or more lift bands when extra lift blocks are used.

Large steamers have three booms, at a hatch the starboard and port booms, for plumbing over the side, and the center boom for hoisting in and out of the hold. Where the hatches are wide enough four booms are sometimes fitted, two of them being center booms and cargo can then be worked over both sides from the same hatch at the same time.

The booms and their fittings, and the position of the cargo winches must all be carefully considered. Officers working cargo should make a careful study of these details as many hatch and winch men will work to a disadvantage through lack of proper staying of the booms.

The lead block at the heel of the boom should be triced up, beckets being fitted in the bottom of the block and small pendants led to the boom. It is usual to fit a small eyebolt in the under side of the boom some four or five feet up from the gooseneck. Tricing up this block prevents it dropping when the fall is slacked off. Some blocks are fitted with a tricing bale through which the fall runs without touching.

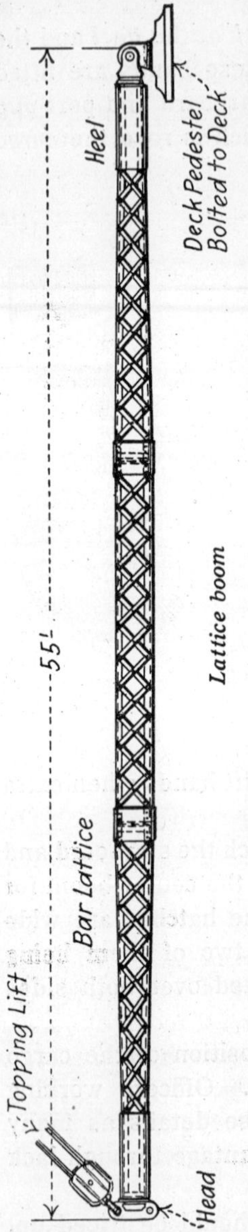

Heavy lifts. When heavy lifts are to be made with the vessel's own gear, careful preparation should be made. The large steel boom fitted at the number two hatch of an eight to ten thousand (D.W.) steamer will usually pick up twenty to fifty tons. Such booms are built up of curved steel plates in the same manner as the masts, or may be of *box* or *lattice* construction.

As the boom will have to be swung from amidships to the side, with the weight suspended above the level of the hatch coaming, great care should be taken in stepping the heel of the boom, preferably on deck in a special *step casting* securely bolted to the deck, and under deck beams shored up if the weight is extreme. This step should be as close to the mast as possible and directly under the suspension of the boom at the masthead to take the stress off the guy tackles.

The topping lift, in heavy lifting, is usually rove off in wire, with threefold steel blocks at masthead and boom. See that the hauling part, leading to the deck, will not interfere with the necessary movement of the boom.

The fall is usually a threefold wire purchase leading to a midship winch in double gear. Great care should be taken in the placing of the lead block *close to the step*, or from the movable block of the fall (next to the weight to be lifted) up through a strong lead block on the boom to the masthead just below the topping lift block and thence down the mast to the winch.

The lead of the hauling part of the fall is most important lest excessive stress be set up when the boom is swung over the side. The end of the fall should be securely stopped on the winch drum.

The guy tackles should be extra stout and led so that the pull on the boom end will not be too much *up* and *down*. See that the angle with the boom is as near a right angle as possible at all stages of the lift and swing of the boom.

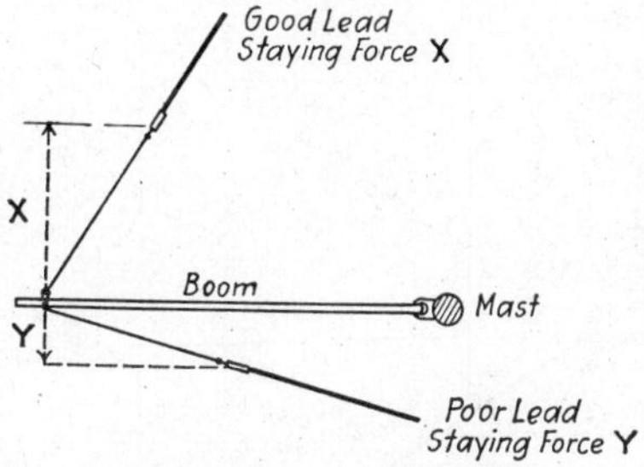

The lead of boom guys

With extra heavy weights, ***preventer guys*** should be rove, making four guys, two on a side. Lead the main guys on each side to winches, the others to bitts on deck.

A heavy steel boom—five-fold purchase blocks

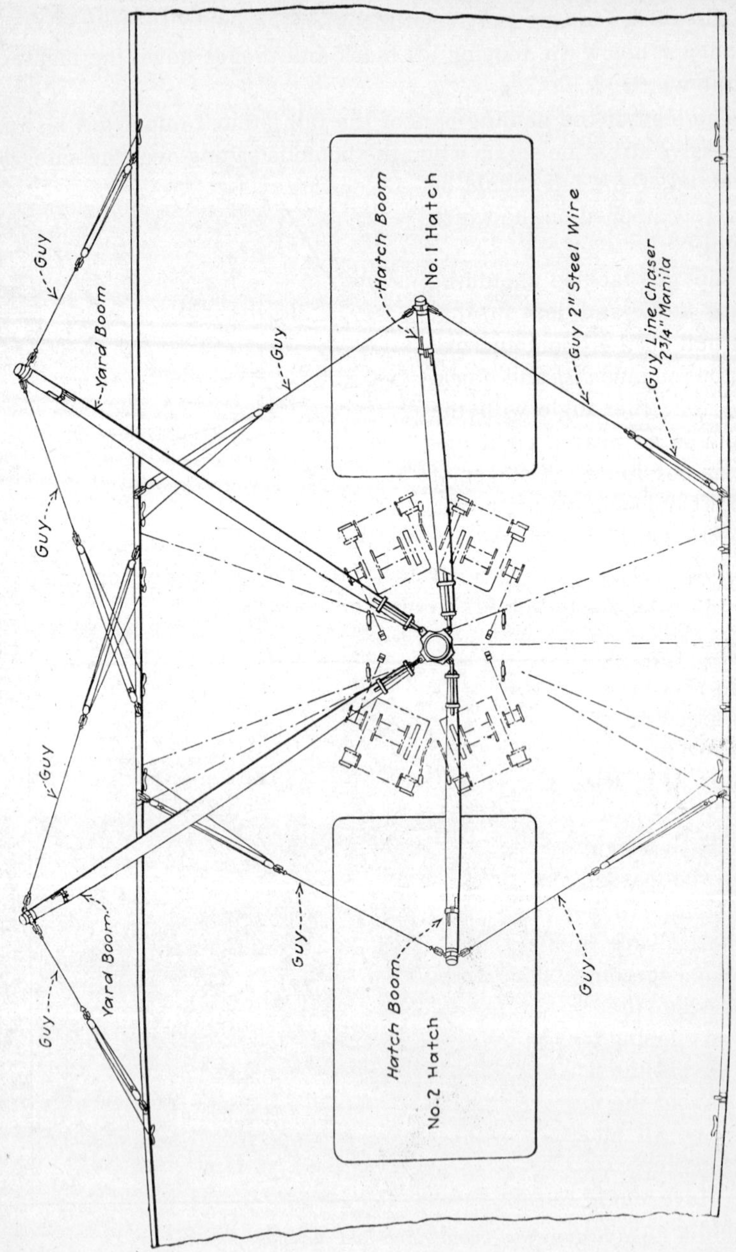

Guying of cargo booms

Preventer stays. Have preventer stays hooked to the extra bands at the mast head and led out to take the pull of the load from amidship to over side. Set up with strong turnbuckles and watch the standing rigging when setting these up. If the mast is well stayed do not take the pull off the shrouds by setting up *too* hard on the preventers.

If the ship is light, be certain that the cargo fall is long enough to drop the load in the lighter with plenty to spare on the winch drum. Be careful in winding the wire on the winch that it runs on evenly so as not to jamb, first round close together riding turns between ropes. This is most important with a heavy lift.

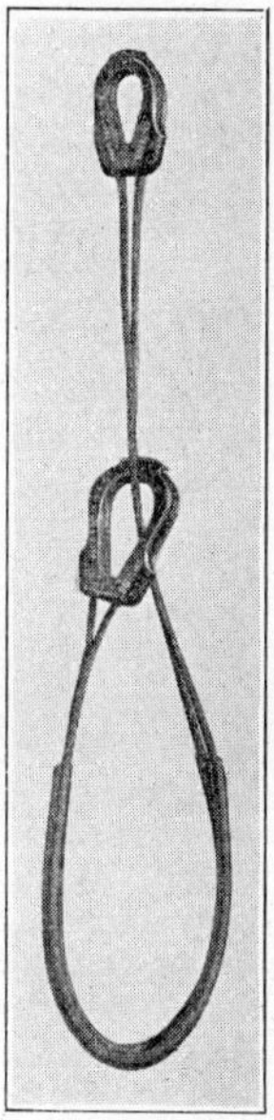

A steel wire sling protected by flexible armor

Test all shackles, bolts, links, and blocks. Examine all gear carefully. If the weight is to be picked up in a roadstead with some motion to the ship, still greater care should be taken.

In any event have a licensed engineer at the winch to see all well, steam pressure sufficient, etc.

The lashing on the weights should be of new wire rope passed through a large *lashing eye* on the lower block and turns about *sharp corners* protected by hard wood wedges and burlap, all turns hove taut with a handy billy. It is well to put stout wire *frapping turns* about the lashing near the block.

Each weight is different and requires judgment in the passing of the lashing. A locomotive is simple, a boiler fairly so. A great gun requires special care in balancing. If a gun has to be *up ended* to come out the utmost care is needed in passing the lashings to prevent it turning over and slipping free.

Avoid the use of chains as much as possible.

Avoid the use of hooks in lifting extra heavy weights.

See all blocks working free, bushing smeared with oil and graphite.

Have *sluing tackles* hooked or lashed to the weight at suitable points and led up through the hatch to eye bolts on deck, or in

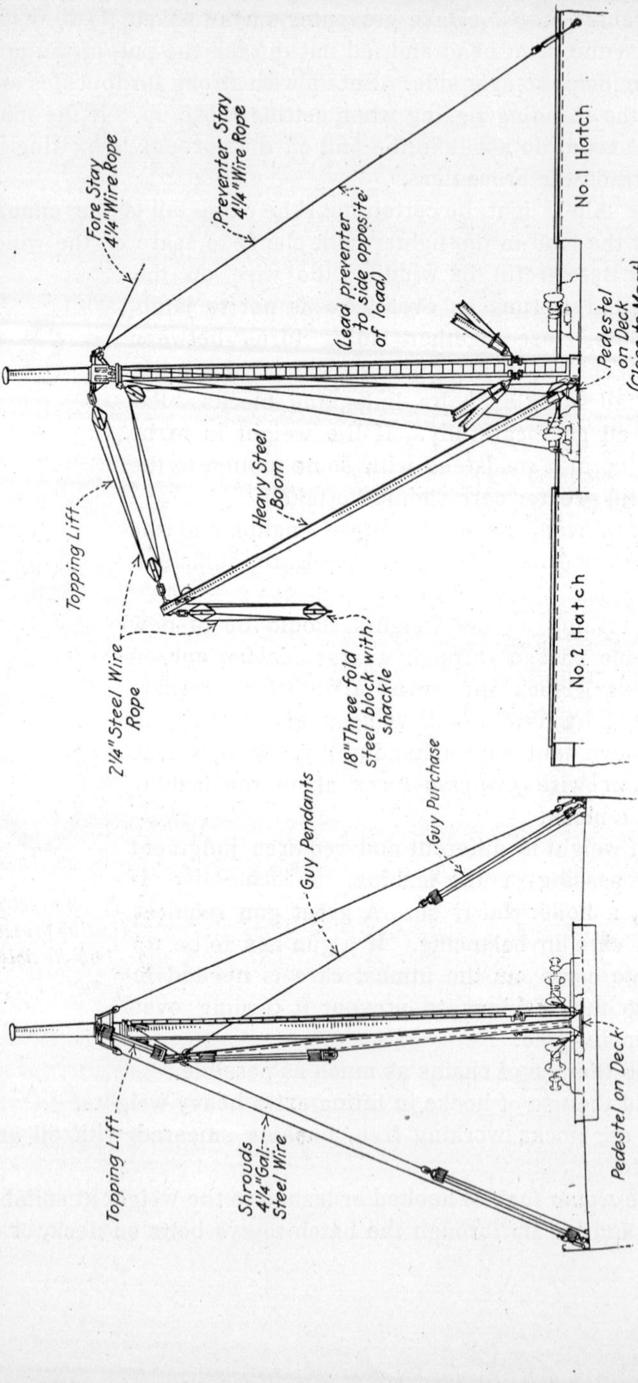

Rigging for a heavy lift

the 'tween deck if need be for swinging the weight clear of the hatch coamings. *A heavy lift may cause the fall to twist.*

Have three or four heavy manila tackles handy with wire straps, or chain slings. If needed they must be got at quickly.

Have reliable men at the guys, Second Mate and Third Mate. Have boatswain in the hold. Engineer at winch. Tend hatch yourself (Chief Mate).

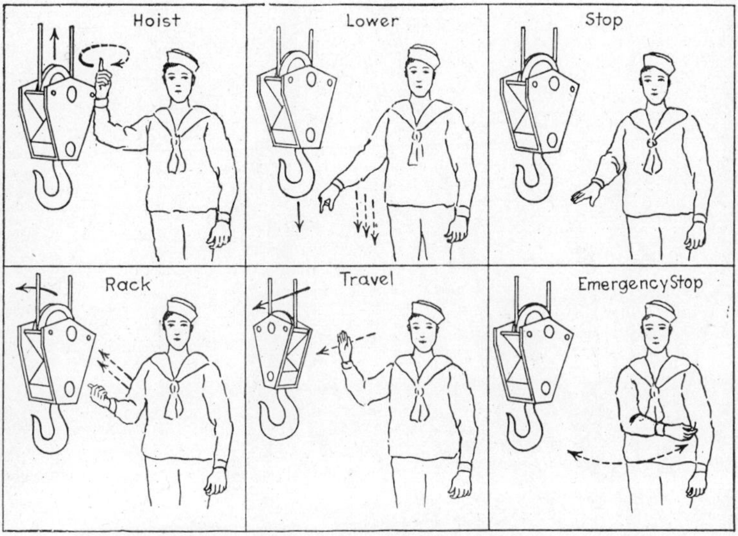

Conventional signals for working heavy derricks or booms

Leave nothing to chance; be sure the weight will clear hatch-coaming bulwarks, if up. Be sure the boom will swing out clear. Be sure lighter is ready with bed, or that dock will bear the weight with proper skids in place. If necessary have *out-haul tackles*, four fold new manila, on dock or lighter, for hauling weight out from ship's side. If weight is going on a lighter it may be very important to place it just in the center.

Take your time. It takes a long while to clear away a wreck, far longer than to prevent it.

All being ready—

"*Heave easy—stand by guys—round in sluing tackles.*"

If the boom has been placed properly it will not be necessary to lower it; it is advisable not to do so. Lowering a boom may cause step to move.

A pair of shore shears

Where several heavy weights are to be lifted, have a sufficiently heavy overhauling weight handy to hook on the extended fall so that it can be rounded in and lowered into hold without jambing. For heavy lifting gear this will have to be a considerable weight. Otherwise rig an overhauling whip.

Most vessels are now fitted with well-designed masts and booms, but often it will be necessary to lift weights in parts of the vessel other than the cargo hatches. Boilers have to be lifted, in the event of stranding and the buckling of plates, etc. Donkey boilers may have to be lifted in and out, etc. In such cases the use of shears may be called for.

Shears consist of two spars lashed near their heads and lifted by tackles. Shears are sustained in position by guys, their legs are spread and the heels placed in *saucers*, and secured by heel lashings to suitable deck fittings. Sometimes special shears are used, working from the shore. The illustration gives a general idea of the use and parts of a pair of shore shears.

Where other means are not available, the shear legs are *parbuckled* on board.

One of the favorite old time questions of seamanship was, " You are lying in the stream, with spars along side, get your shear legs on board, rig shears, and take in your masts and step them."

Parbuckles are ropes with ends secured at the rail, or upper part of lift, led down under a spar, or barrel, or object that can roll, and let up outside of it. The parbuckle then rolls up the spar, revolving as it comes in over the side.

(See next chapter for further details on shears aboard ship.)

Most heavy weights, however are lifted when alongside of wharves, or when the vessel is in dock, and nowadays heavy cranes are generally available for these lifts. Floating cranes are also provided to serve vessels lying at places not fitted with shore cranes. In the building and repair yards, heavy *gantry* cranes, *hammerhead* cranes, and *cantilever* cranes are always available.

Many short lifts, as in the engine room, holds, etc., are made by means of the chain hoists, blocking up under the weights as they come up from their beds.

Hydraulic and screw jacks are also used to lift weights for passing the lashings, and for wedging and securing them against rolling in the holds.

II

Cargo Gear

The development of modern cargo gear is shown in the accompanying sketches. It is well to learn the different kinds of gear in use and their special applications.*

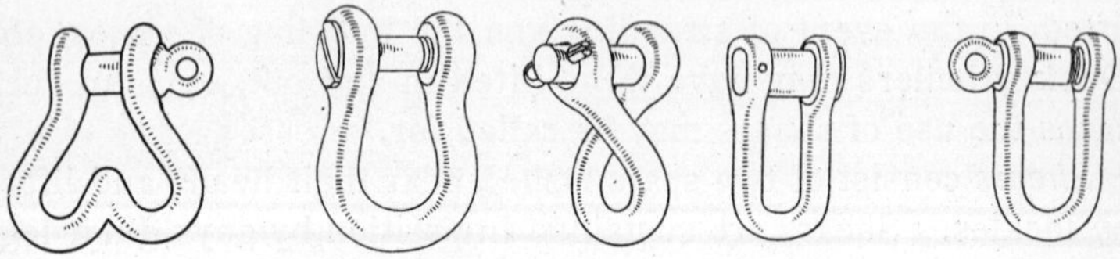

Heart *Flush head screw* *Reverse key* *Oval pin* *Eye screw*

Shackles

Blocks. Special cargo blocks with wide swallow and sheave and with curved lips and lignum vitae shell pieces are now generally fitted at the boom end and as lead blocks under the goose neck.

Guys generally consist of wire pendants and twofold manila purchases.

Topping lifts. Usually of four or five inch manila, rove two-fold, or rove through two blocks on the boom as follows:

Single block on outrigger at mast head, standing part hooked into becket of this block leading down to end block on boom, up through block on outrigger, down through second block on boom, up through single block under outrigger at mast band, and down to heavy cleat at table of mast. Stoppers are fitted at table and the topping lift fall is taken to the winch head, through a snatch block, boom hoisted, fall stoppered, and then belayed at the cleat. The spare end of the fall is then made up snugly and hung on the cleat with a half hitch. If the table is large enough it is sometimes coiled down on the table.

Boom rests. Booms when down rest in chocks on gallows frames, or on brackets. Long booms sometimes reach to chocks at the edge of deck houses. Chocks should be fitted with clamps, or lashings and eyes.

* Great improvements have been made in recent years in the handling of cargo both in and out of ships and on the docks. Special cargo trays, container loading, " jitney " trucks and trailers, mechanical lifting trucks, all aid in dispatch and help in safety to men and in reducing breakage. Advances are still to be made in this field.

The lifts, guys and falls for each boom and for each hatch should be marked on the upper block, or on the winch end of the falls, and this end should be on top, ready for running on the winch.

Where tabernacles are fitted the gear for each mast should stow in the tabernacle. Otherwise have a separate place in the

A mast tabernacle, showing lead of cargo falls to base of mast. Tandem friction drum winches

boson's locker for the gear. Some mates use heavy canvas bags for the gear, these being painted with the hatch and boom number.

As gear comes up and down frequently it is well to reduce this to a routine. Have a particular man in charge of the gear at each hatch, usually a quartermaster, or a seaman. In " home ships " where men " stay by " this works out very well.

Where runs are short it is often well to let the gear stand. If topping lifts are rove through a double block on the boom, unshackle, bring in to the mast table, set *moderately* taut and cover with a canvas coat if in the wake of the funnel. *Hang* the ends of the fall so it will not chafe.

Guys will usually slap on the boom and it is well to unhook them, even for short runs. Always unreeve the hemp-clad wire cargo fall, coil it neatly, winch end up, hook down and stow below where it will not get wet.

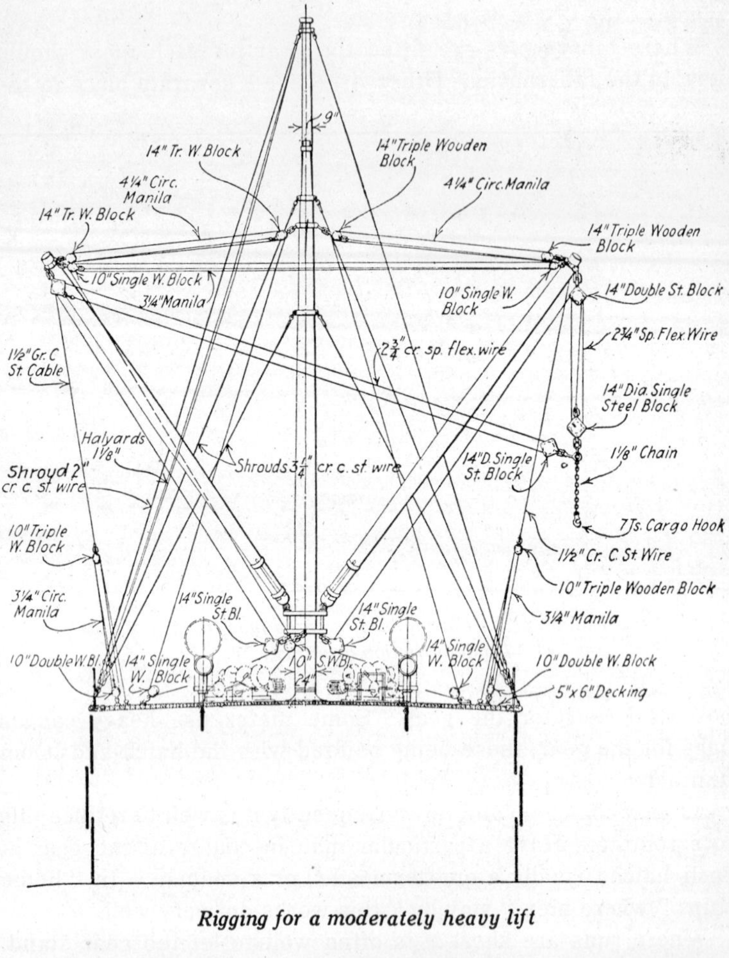

Rigging for a moderately heavy lift

Winches should be overhauled by the deck engineer between ports. Overhauling winches in port while cargo is to be moved is an expensive business.

King posts. The gear on king posts is smaller than on the masts. King posts usually serve smaller hatches, such as the hatch over the reserve bunker just forward of the bridge, or the trunk hatches on the bridge deck. One boom is usually fitted, both king posts working together. The post on the working side supports the " yard " boom and the post on the opposite side the " mast " boom. The words " yard " and " mast "

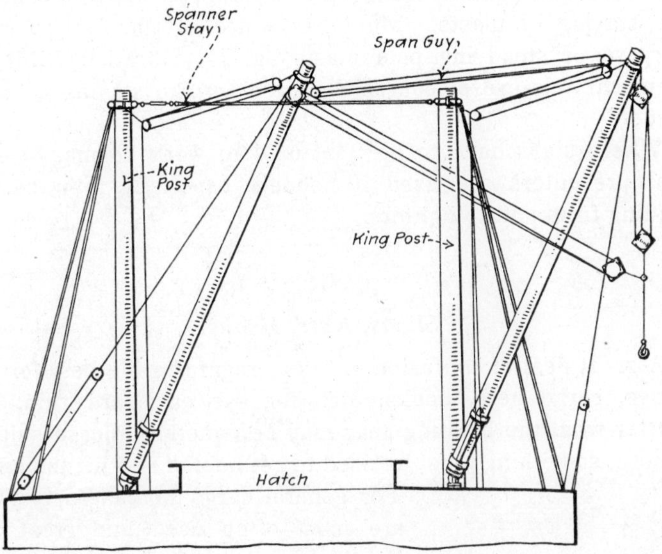

King posts or pair masts. Smaller rigs are usually referred to as king posts, larger rigs as pair masts, when stepped in thwartship line with the usual mast positions.

as explained under " tackles " come from sailing ships, where the lower yard is cocked up and used to sling cargo out clear of the side, while the midship hoist is from a pendant from the topmast head.

Where " pair masts " are stepped, the booms work in the same way but the gear is of full single mast size.

Stays. Before going on to the consideration of the lesser parts of cargo gear it is well to again say a word about stays. Cargo loads are not dead loads. That is the lift is not strictly a steady pull but is what engineers call a *live load*, that is the load is a *moving* load. In consequence we have to consider *force* acting on the cargo gear, and as force is the product of *mass* times *acceleration*, the *faster* a load moves the *greater* the *force*.

A moderate load of a few tons, may, if moved quickly, exert a *force* of four or five times its *weight*.

This is a facinating subject and merits careful study. (See previous chapter.)

In considering such loads and stresses, we have to consider the staying of masts. Many stays are set up for the main purpose of steadying pole masts against vibration. But the main shrouds are of course designed for the staying of cargo loads.

Where stays have to be "let up" to work booms, be sure that preventers are used if needed, especially in a seaway loading from and to lighters.

III

Slings, Nets, Hooks

A great deal of confusion exists in regard to the best form of slings, cargo nets, hooks, etc., for use on board ship. No matter what the hoisting gear may be, whether aboard ship, or ashore, something must be used to get hold of and lift the cargo.

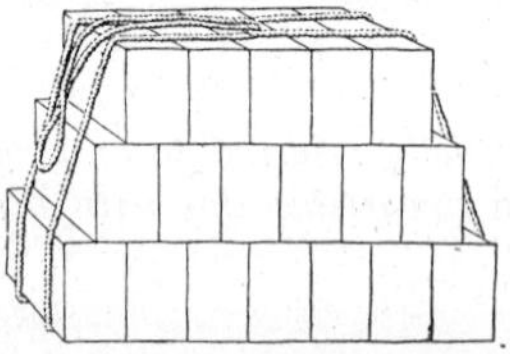

A draft of case goods
Note correct tiering of case and position of manila sling

For general cargo manila rope slings are most often used, and great care should be taken of them. Too many mates leave this important item go without much consideration and a large number of slings find their way into the junk boats at every port.

Manila slings for ordinary lifts of case goods and bales are the most commonly used.

Manila slings. Usually two and a half, three and four inch rope. Four to six fathoms to a sling. Short splice.

Many special sizes are made, depending upon the trade.

Wire slings. Wire slings are made for many uses. For the handling of heavy cases, for loading and unloading ballast. There is no set size or length. Slings are spliced as needed.

Wire ballast unloaders are usually made with an eye and thimble at each end, a small and large link and a small link and hook (to pass through large link) are fitted.

Chain slings. Chain slings are generally open with large link and hook. These are used for handling rails, pipe, pigs of ballast, etc.

Barrel slings. These are generally of chain with special cant hooks.

Chain slings should be of the best grade, and should not be used too long. Re-annealing is advisable after a year of use,

Bale sling

Butt sling

if the vessel is part of an outfit that does such things in a scientific way. Cargo gear is so expensive and so vital a factor that more attention should be given to seemingly small details. All metal gear should be stamped with the ship's name and date of issue.

Cheap chain slings, with faulty welds, or old chains, crystallized from years of racking, and painted over, have been the cause of many accidents, such gear giving way at some critical moment.

Chain cargo nets are made for general ship's use. The regular sizes and dimensions are: chain—1/4, 5/16 and 3/8 inch; mesh—7 inches square; complete net, 8 x 8, 9 x 9 or 10 x 10 feet square.

Hook with overhauling weight

Net slings. Cargo nets are of great use and are the most adaptable form of lifting device. Almost anything within reason can be taken out in nets. The nets are usually twelve feet square, with outer or bolt rope $3\frac{1}{2}''$ and the crossings of $2\frac{3}{4}''$ rope, ten inches apart. The mesh is made by tucking, and where four-stranded rope is used this works very well. In three-stranded rope tuck two and one, getting the one strand a different tuck each time. The ends of the mesh are tucked into the bolt rope, two full tucks one way, and one another way, whipping the strands with sail twine doubled and waxed.

The lifting bridles are spliced into the bolt rope between the corners, passing through the large thimbles at the corners. The hooking bridles are spliced into the lifting bridles.

Nets used for the handling of flour, grain, coffee, and other cargo packed in bags have been made as follows: Twelve by twelve bolt rope, mesh 21 thread hemp spaced on ten-inch centers. This net was covered on both sides with No. 4 coal-bag canvas, stitched to the bolt rope of the net, a four-inch tabling turning under. Give the canvas enough slack so the rope mesh will take the weight of the draft of cargo. This is a very satisfactory net for leaking grain bags.

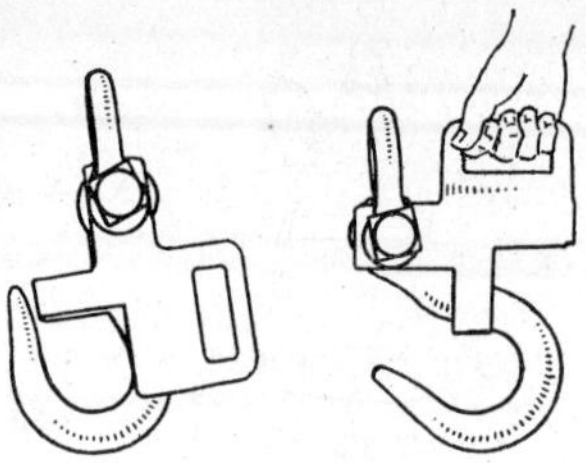

Safety hook

Many officers have their own ideas as to how nets should be made; those described here have been used by the writer and have proven satisfactory.

Cargo nets should be examined between ports. Inspect the bridles and renew when necessary. These will wear out about twice as fast as the nets.

Use for old nets. Old nets that have done a good turn of lifting should be repaired and set aside, two at a hatch, seized together, making a two fathom by four fathoms net, or larger if a big ship, cut off the bridles and splice in stout guy ropes at the corners and upper side (old boat falls are handy for this). We then have nets for use under the gangways between the wake of the hatches and the wharf or lighters. Where the vessel is light, and a long ladder is used in place of the gangway, it is well to stretch a length of this net under the ladder. The writer remembers a certain boatswain (one of the best steamboat bo'sons) who came aboard one night "lit up." He lost his footing, dropping off the ladder down between the ship and the wharf, striking a large spar fender. That bo'son never went to sea again. He lost his leg.

Coal bags. Where coal is handled in bags special roping and No. 4 canvas is used. Bags run to about five hundred pounds capacity.

In Coronel, Chili, coal is lifted onboard by means of square canvas slings, fitted with eyes and lifting bridles. A great deal of coal is lost overboard between the ship and the lighters —the more the merrier. It is hard bottom there and after a

A sling of coffee coming on board at Corinto, Nicaragua. Note use of nets

vessel leaves the local pirates come out with their dredges and pick up the coal spilled. At least five per cent. of the coal is dropped in hoisting; this is specially so in lively weather. Vessels anchor and then moor their sterns to a buoy. Old American-Hawaiian Line officers recall the place with no regret.

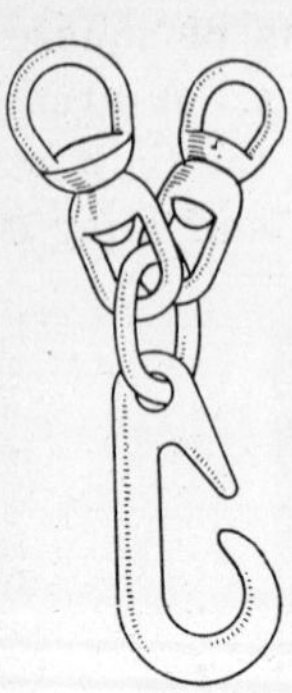

Western cargo hook

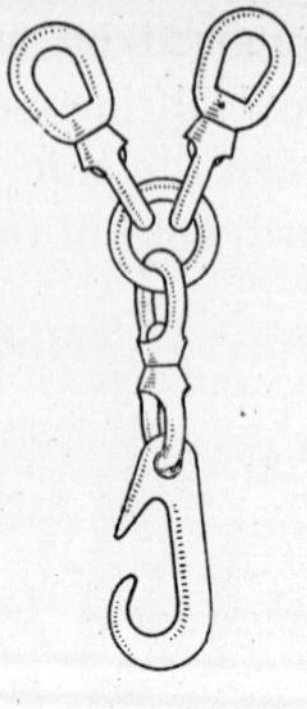

Seattle cargo hook

Nitrate slings. Eight by eight feet square roped around with 2″ manila, cross roped on under side with 3½″ manila fitted with hooking eyes, cross roping in two parts corner to corner and spaced a foot apart.

Canvas slings. Forty-two inch canvas No. 1, roped with 3″ manila. Short and long hooking bridles. A very good rig for hoisting flour, or other bagged stuff requiring careful handling.

Hooks. The various types of cargo hooks are shown in the illustrations.

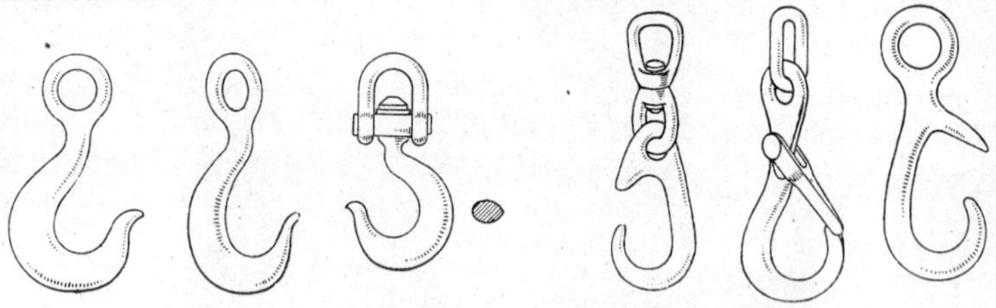

Plain hook — *Reverse eye hook* — *Double swivel hook* — *Swivel cargo hook (Liverpool) (hook)* — *Cargo hook with safety tongue* — *Hatch hook*

IV

Tables

In selecting the gear for a heavy lift it is well to have in mind the important fact that no chain is stronger than the weakest link. Examine everything, *take your time*, be sure before you go ahead. The Chief Mate going to a port where a heavy lift will have to be made with the vessel's own gear will usually have plenty of time to get together his layout.

The strength of fittings can be figured as follows, if the tables are not sufficiently comprehensive.

Let d equal the diameter of metal (steel) in inches. The figures should be taken in whole numbers and decimal parts of an inch.

Safe working load of hook	equals	$d^2/2$	tons
" ring bolt	"	$2d^2$	"
" eye bolt	"	$5d^2$	"
" straight shackle	"	$3d^2$	"
" bow shackle	"	$2\frac{1}{2}d^2$	"

Chain Table

Size of Chain	Dist. From Center of One Link to Center of Next	Weight per Foot in Lb. Approximately	Outside Width	Crane Chain		
				Proof Test Lb.	Average Breaking Strain Lb.	Ordinary Safe Load General Use Lb.
1/4	25/32	3/4	15/16	1,680	3,360	1,120
5/16	27/32	1	1 1/8	2,520	5,040	1,680
3/8	31/32	1 1/2	1 5/16	3,640	7,280	2,427
7/16	1 5/32	2	1 1/2	5,040	10,080	3,360
1/2	1 11/32	2 1/2	1 13/16	6,720	13,440	4,480
9/16	1 15/32	3 3/10	2	8,400	16,800	5,600
5/8	1 23/32	4 1/10	2 3/16	10,360	20,720	6,907
11/16	1 13/16	5	2 3/8	12,600	25,200	8,400
3/4	1 15/16	6 2/10	2 9/16	15,120	30,240	10,080
13/16	2 1/16	6 7/10	2 3/4	17,640	35,280	11,760
7/8	2 3/16	8 3/8	2 15/16	20,440	40,880	13,627
15/16	2 7/16	9	3 3/16	23,520	47,040	15,680
1	2 1/2	10 1/2	3 3/8	26,880	53,760	17,920
1 1/16	2 5/8	12	3 9/16	30,240	60,480	20,160
1 1/8	2 3/4	13 5/8	3 13/16	34,160	68,320	22,773
1 3/16	3 1/16	13 7/10	4	38,080	76,160	25,387
1 1/4	3 1/8	16	4 3/16	42,000	84,000	28,000
1 5/16	3 3/8	16 1/2	4 3/8	45,920	91,840	30,613
1 3/8	3 9/16	19 1/4	4 9/16	50,680	101,360	33,787
1 7/16	3 11/16	19 7/10	4 3/4	54,880	109,760	36,587
1 1/2	3 7/8	23	5 1/8	60,480	120,960	40,320
1 9/16	4	25	5 5/16	65,520	131,140	43,180

—Bradlee & Co., Philadelphia

Strength of Open Cargo Hooks

Drop Forged Steel

Diameter of Eye		Extreme Dimensions		Approximate Load Required to Straighten Out Net Tons 2,000 Lbs.	Estimated Weight Each Lbs.
Inside, Inches	Outside, Inches	Length, Inches	Width, Inches		
3/4	1 1/2	4 3/8	2 7/8	1.9	1/2
7/8	1 3/4	4 7/8	3 1/8	2.3	3/4
1	2	5 3/8	3 1/2	3	1
1 1/8	2 1/4	6 1/8	3 7/8	5.7	1 1/2
1 1/4	2 1/2	6 3/4	4 3/8	7	2
1 3/8	2 3/4	7 5/8	4 7/8	8.5	3 1/4
1 1/2	3	8 1/2	5 5/8	10	4 1/2
1 5/8	3 1/4	9 1/2	6 3/8	13	6
1 3/4	3 1/2	10 1/4	6 7/8	17	8 1/4
2	4	11 1/2	7 1/2	19	10 3/4
2 3/8	4 5/8	12 7/8	8 1/4	26	15
2 3/4	5 1/4	14 1/2	9 1/4	32	19 1/4
3 1/8	6 1/8	16 1/2	10 7/8	35	31 1/2
3 1/2	7	19	13	48	47
4	8 1/2	22	14 3/4	80	65

Size and Strength of Shackles

Size Diam. of Link	Length Inside	Width Between Eyes	Diameter of Pin	Gov't Test. Maximum Strength in Pounds
3/16 in.	7/8 in.	3/8 in.	1/4 in.	3,080
1/4 "	1 1/16 "	1/2 "	5/16 "	5,510
5/16 "	1 1/4 "	9/16 "	3/8 "	8,320
3/8 "	1 3/8 "	11/16 "	7/16 "	10,890
7/16 "	1 3/4 "	11/16 "	1/2 "	15,200
1/2 "	1 7/8 "	3/4 "	9/16 "	18,390
9/16 "	2 "	7/8 "	5/8 "	24,800
5/8 "	2 3/8 "	1 1/16 "	3/4 "	33,400
3/4 "	2 3/4 "	1 9/32 "	7/8 "	43,400
7/8 "	3 3/8 "	1 3/8 "	1 "	55,200
1 "	3 3/4 "	1 5/8 "	1 1/8 "	74,900
1 1/8 "	4 3/8 "	1 7/8 "	1 1/4 "	90,200
1 1/4 "	5 "	2 "	1 3/8 "	92,040
1 3/8 "	5 1/4 "	2 1/8 "	1 1/2 "	94,100
1 1/2 "	5 1/2 "	2 1/4 "	1 5/8 "	103,800
1 5/8 "	6 1/2 "	2 1/2 "	1 3/4 "	155,542
1 3/4 "	7 "	2 3/4 "	2 "	172,400
2 "	8 "	3 1/4 "	2 1/4 "	235,620

Recommended safe working load 1/3 of maximum strength

Table of Drop Forged Turnbuckles

Size Turnbuckle and Outside Diameter of Thread in Inches	Approximate Breaking Strength in Pounds	Recommended Working Load in Pounds	Amount of Take-up Length in the Clear Between Heads in Inches	Length of Buckle Outside in Inches	Length Pull to Pull when Extended in Inches	Approximate Weight Each in Pounds
$\frac{1}{4}$	1,350	270	4	$4\frac{3}{4}$	12	.40
$\frac{5}{16}$	2,250	450	$4\frac{1}{4}$	$5\frac{1}{4}$	$13\frac{1}{2}$	.60
$\frac{3}{8}$	3,350	670	$4\frac{1}{2}$	$5\frac{3}{4}$	14	.90
$\frac{7}{16}$	4,650	930	5	$6\frac{1}{4}$	$16\frac{1}{2}$	1.31
$\frac{1}{2}$	6,250	1,250	6	$7\frac{1}{2}$	$18\frac{1}{4}$	1.87
$\frac{9}{16}$	8,100	1,620	$7\frac{1}{4}$	9	$23\frac{1}{8}$	3.00
$\frac{5}{8}$	10,000	2,000	$8\frac{1}{2}$	$10\frac{1}{2}$	$24\frac{1}{4}$	3.69
$\frac{3}{4}$	15,000	3,000	$9\frac{1}{4}$	$11\frac{3}{4}$	$27\frac{1}{2}$	5.81
$\frac{7}{8}$	21,000	4,200	10	$12\frac{3}{4}$	$30\frac{1}{2}$	8.81
1	27,500	5,500	11	14	33	12.56
$1\frac{1}{8}$	34,500	6,900	12	$15\frac{1}{2}$	39	17.00
$1\frac{1}{4}$	44,500	8,900	13	$16\frac{3}{4}$	40	25.00
$1\frac{3}{8}$	52,500	10,500	14	18	50	36.00
$1\frac{1}{2}$	64,500	12,900	15	$19\frac{1}{2}$	51	40.00
$1\frac{5}{8}$	75,500	15,100	16	21	$51\frac{1}{2}$	48.00
$1\frac{3}{4}$	8,7000	17,400	18	23	$55\frac{1}{2}$	52.00
$1\frac{7}{8}$	102,500	20,500	18	23	66	89.00
2	115,000	23,000	24	31	74	98.00
$2\frac{1}{8}$	132,500	26,500	24	31	...	...
$2\frac{1}{4}$	151,000	30,200	24	32	...	...

V

Mechanical Loading and Discharging

Special rigs are now employed in the loading of coal and ore, clamshell buckets, self-trimming holds, chutes, pipes, etc. Grain is shot into the holds and sucked out.

Large side ports are used in certain trades, and on such craft the endless conveyor finds favor. Conveyor loading is growing in favor, taking sugar, flour, etc., to the deck and then sending it anywhere in the holds and 'tween decks by means of chutes. It would hardly be within the province of a work on seamanship to do more than mention these devices. They are of growing importance and are playing a larger and larger part in cutting down what the heartless statisticians tabulate as " turn around " and quick dispatch in and out of port means money.

A belt machine loading case goods at No. 2 hatch.
A net sling working at No. 1 hatch

Loading flour at Puget Sound by belt conveyor
(See Chap. IX—on Stowage)

CHAPTER VI

SAILING SHIP RIGGING—SAILS—CANVAS WORK

I

Masts and Spars

The masts usually consist of the following sections: *Lower mast, topmast, topgallant mast,* and *royal mast,* which includes at its upper end the *skysail mast.*

The masts of a square rigger are shown in the various illustrations, giving their locations and names.

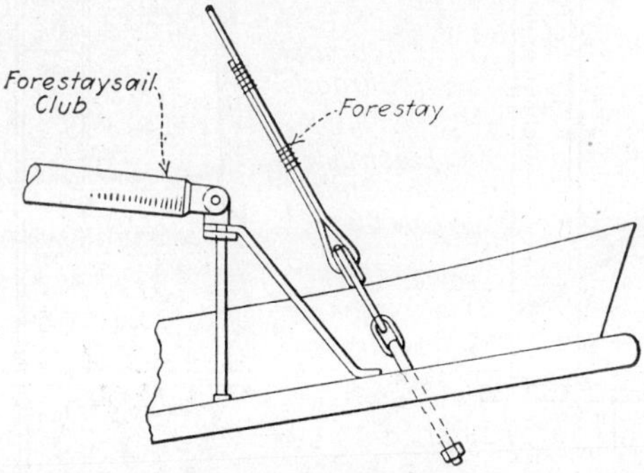

Fore stay of a schooner

The masts of a fore and after consist of a long *lower mast*, and a *topmast*, except in the case of a *baldheaded* schooner when no topmast is fitted.

When lower masts are made of steel (square rigged) the lower and topmast are often in one piece, making a change in the lower top fitting and getting rid of much top hamper. But the fidded topmast has much to commend it and still finds favor.

The other spars on a square rigger are the *yards*, names and locations given in illustrations, also the names and fittings of a yard.

Men go out on a yard by means of the *foot ropes*, held up by *stirrups.* The footrope extending from inside of the sheave hole to the yard arm is called the *flemish horse.* When hauling out on a weather or lee earing, a sailor must go out on the famous steed, straddle the yard and keep one arm around the *lift.*

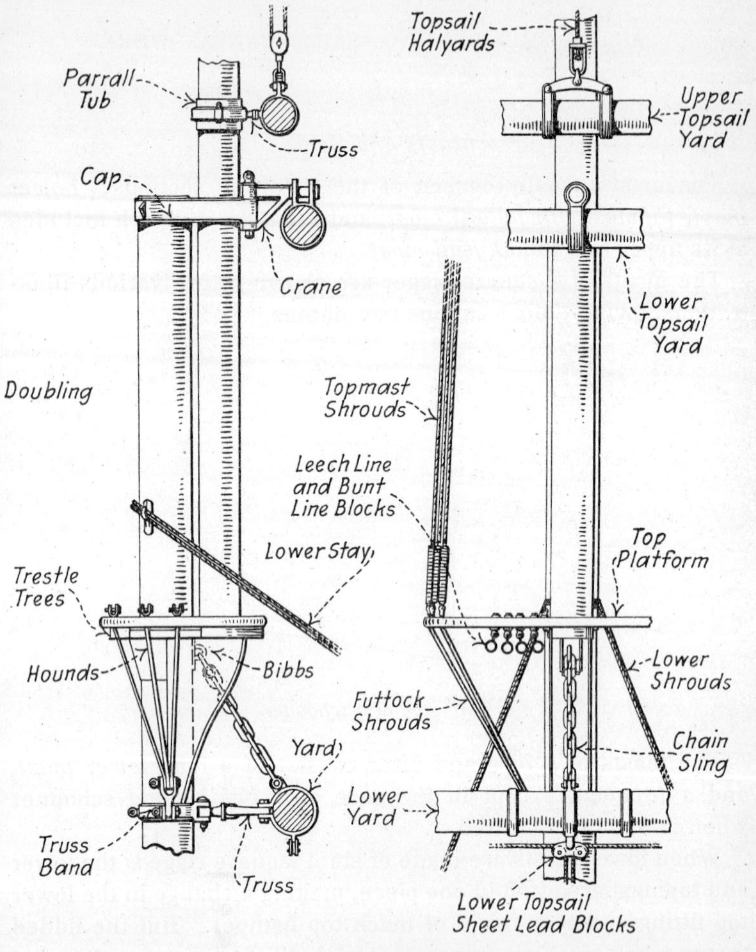

Lower mast head details—square rig

Gaffs and *booms* spread fore and aft sails, at head and foot, as shown.

A *club*, is fitted to the foot of inner fore staysails* in many

* The club on the foot of fore staysail is sometimes called the *jumbo* club.

schooners. The club swings freely from side to side, as the foot of the sail is short, and this rig makes for ease in tacking.

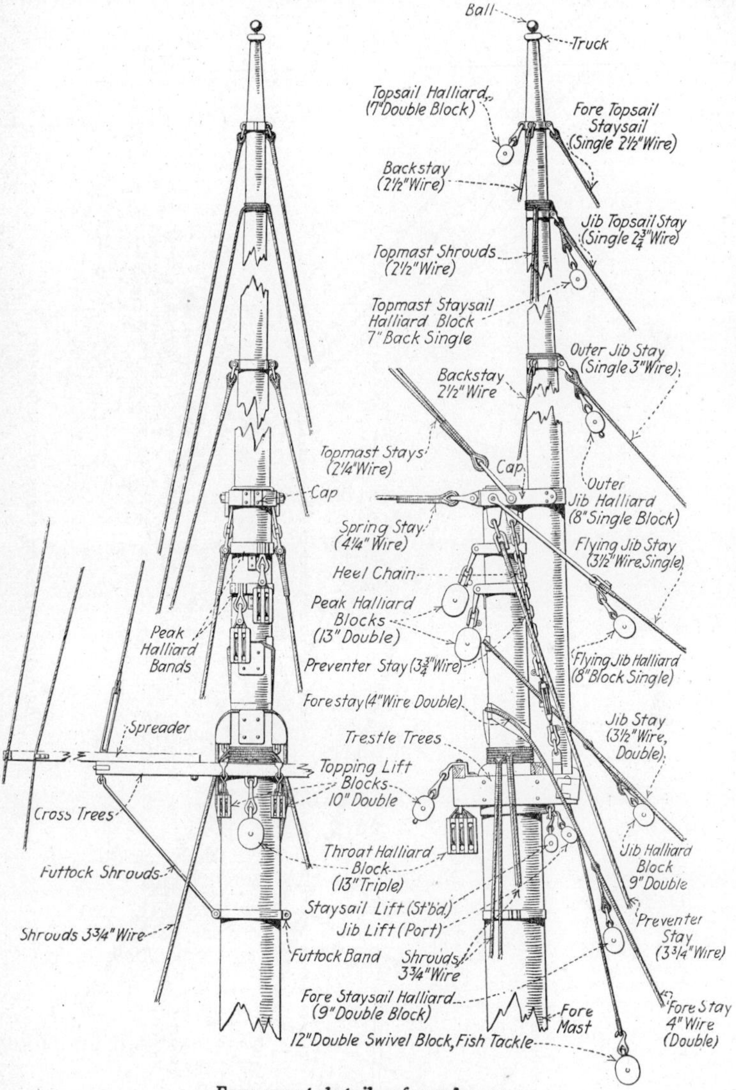

Fore mast details of a schooner

A club is also used in yachts to set the *club topsail*, the club extending beyond the reach of the gaff.

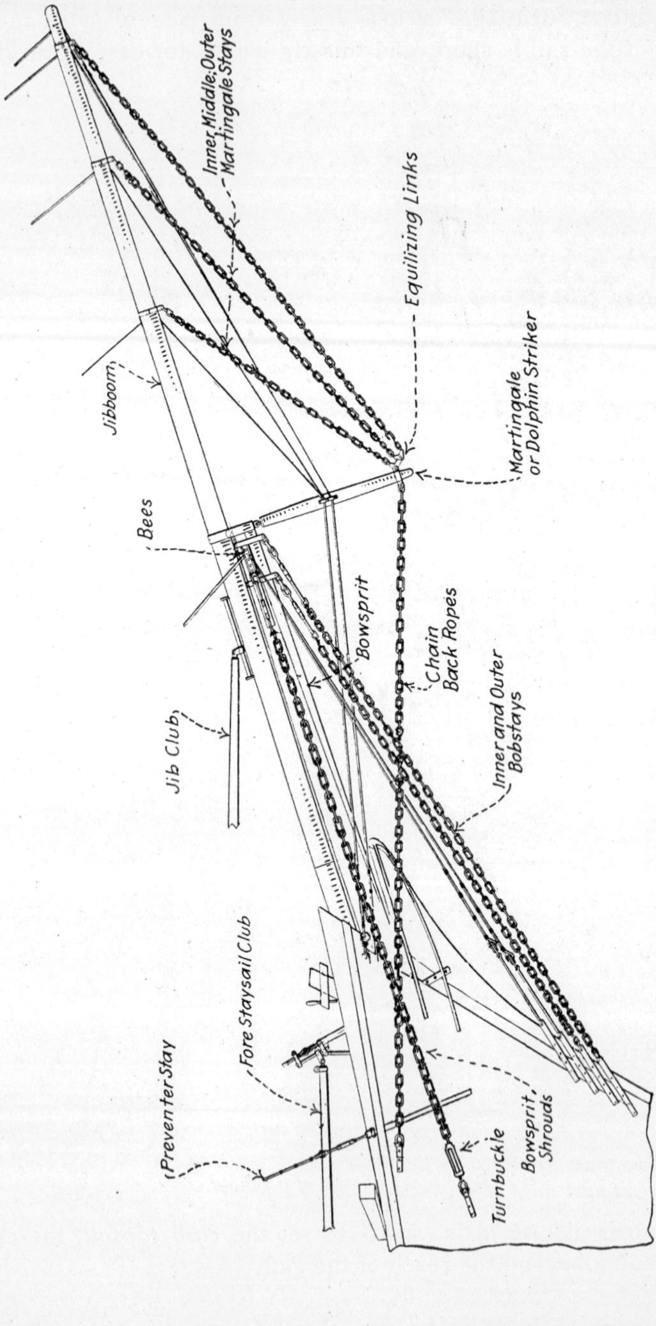

The head spars and stays of a schooner

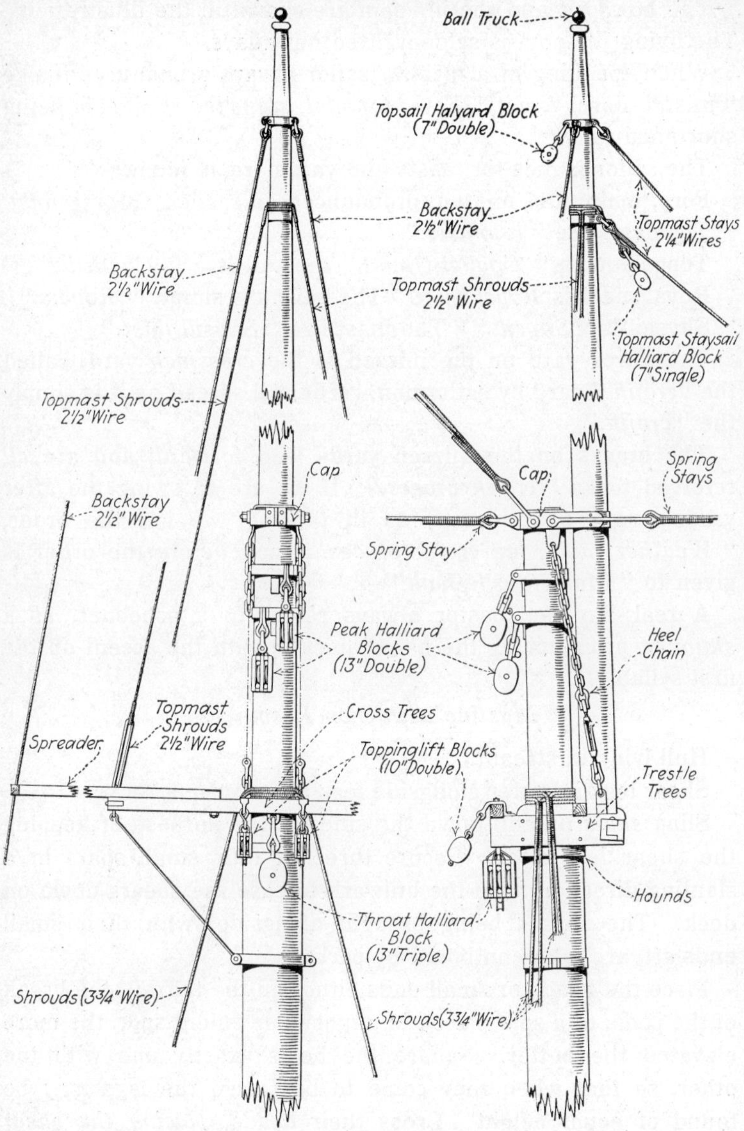

Main mast details of a schooner. Also other masts between the fore and aftermost mast. Aftermost mast has no spring stay leading aft.

The bowsprit and the jibboom are shown in the illustrations. The flying jibboom is seldom fitted nowadays.

When speaking of a mast, a sailor always pronounces it like "mist," Fore "*mist*," Fore *topmist stays'le.* Sail also being shortened to *sil!*

The sailor names for masts and yards are as follows:

Fore, main, and mizzen, pronounced as spelled, adding *mist.*

Topmasts are "*topmists.*"

Topgallant is "*T'gallant mist,*" the sail is a "*T'gansill.*"

Royal mast is *Royal mist.* The sails are simply "*Royals.*"

Skysail is "*Skysill.*" The mast is a "*Skysill mist.*"

The lower yard on the mizzen is the *crossjack* yard, called the "*crojik*" yard by sailormen. The sail spread on it is simply the "*crojik.*"

The braces on the mizzen yards lead *forward*, and are *all* referred to as "*crojik braces.*" If we are to swing the after yards (main and mizzen) as in tacking, we get the order, "*Weather main, lee crojik braces!*" just *before* the order is given to "*Main tops'le haul!*"

A real Yankee coaster always refers to a schooner, as a *skunner*, pronouncing the name quickly, with the accent on the first syllable.

Masting with Own Resources

Hull lying in stream.

Shear legs in water alongside legs aft, near quarter.

Sling *skids* up and down the side for the purpose of keeping the shear legs clear. Secure three or four small spars in a slanting direction from the bulwark to ease the shears down on deck. The shears being brought alongside, with their small ends aft, are taken on board by parbuckle.

Place the heads or small ends either on the taffrail, the break of the poop, or a spar placed in a most convenient spot, the more elevated the better. Square the heels exactly one with the other, so that when they come to be raised the legs may be found of equal height. Cross their heads, *placing the shear head of the side on which the mast is coming in uppermost,* and put on the head-lashing of *new well-stretched rope*, the lashing being at equal distances from the heels of both. After the lashing is on, the heels of the shears are *drawn asunder*, carrying one over to each gangway and placing it on a solid piece of oak or shoe. Lash them to the eye-bolts in the shoes; nail cleats on the heel of the shears to prevent the lashing slipping down. Clap stout tackles on the heels, two on each, one leading forward, the other aft; set taut the after ones and belay them. Lash a three or four-fold block, as the upper one of the main purchase, over the first lashing (so that it will hang plumb under the cross), with canvas underneath to prevent chafing, passing the lashing round each shear head alternately; also, sufficiently long to secure the free action of the block. Lash the small purchase block or truss block on the after horn of the shears, sufficiently high for the falls to play clear of each other, and a girt-line block above all. Middle a couple of hawsers and clove-

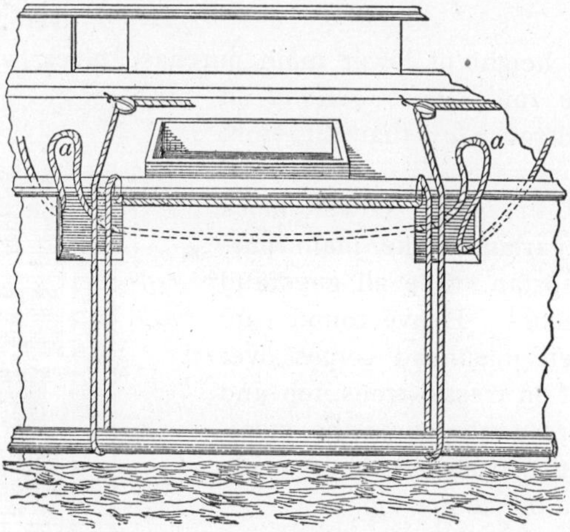

A parbuckle
a, a, counter parbuckle for easing spar inboard

hitch them over the shear heads—having two ends leading forward and two abaft, and *stout luffs clapped on them.* These should be sufficiently strong to secure the shears while lifting the masts. The lower purchase block is lashed forward to a toggle secured to lower deck beams in one of the foreward hatches, or in bowsprit hole. The fall is rove—the hauling parts leading through the middle sheave-hole—and led away to the capstan. The shears are raised by heaving upon it, and preventing the heels from slipping forward by means of the heel tackles previously mentioned. When the shears are up, the heels confined to their shoes, they can then be transported along the deck by means of the heel tackles and guys to the situation required, *taking care to make them rest upon a beam,* and to have the deck properly *shored up* below. Finally, give the shears the necessary rake by means of the guys, and set taut all the guys and heel tackles.

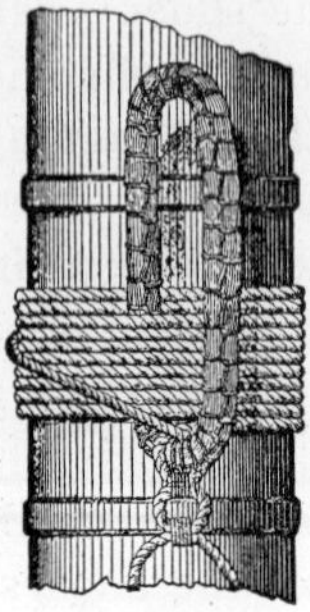

A garland

The mizzen mast is taken on board first, then main, fore, and bowsprit.

When getting in bowsprit shear heads are supported over the bow by a heavy purchase from the fore masthead.

Measure height of lower main purchase block when "two blocks" to rail. Place *garland* on mast at a distance *less* than this from the heel.

To take in mast. Lower block lashed to garland, take main purchase to capstan. See all guys and lashings secure. Heave round capstan. When masthead comes over the rail put on trestle trees, top and cap. Secure gantlines to the masthead and the truss tackle is made fast to band below the top.

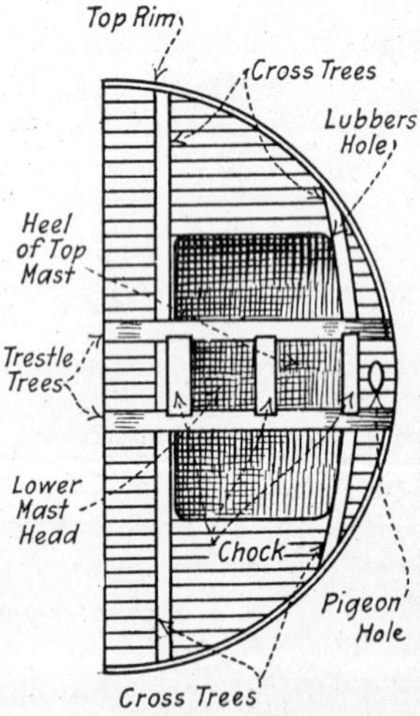

Top platform details

Heave away till mast rises near top of rail. Secure a tackle for easing it inboard.

Heave over rail, ease inboard and by means of truss tackle and gantlines point mast fair for stepping. Wipe tenon dry. White- lead it, also step (tar will do as well). Lower main purchase and step mizzen mast. The mast is then *wedged.* Shrouds and stay are got up and shears are worked forward to take in main mast.

To get shears forward proceed as follows:

Haul the shears upright by the tackle on the guys, and bowse the heels forward, taking care to have a tackle on the after part

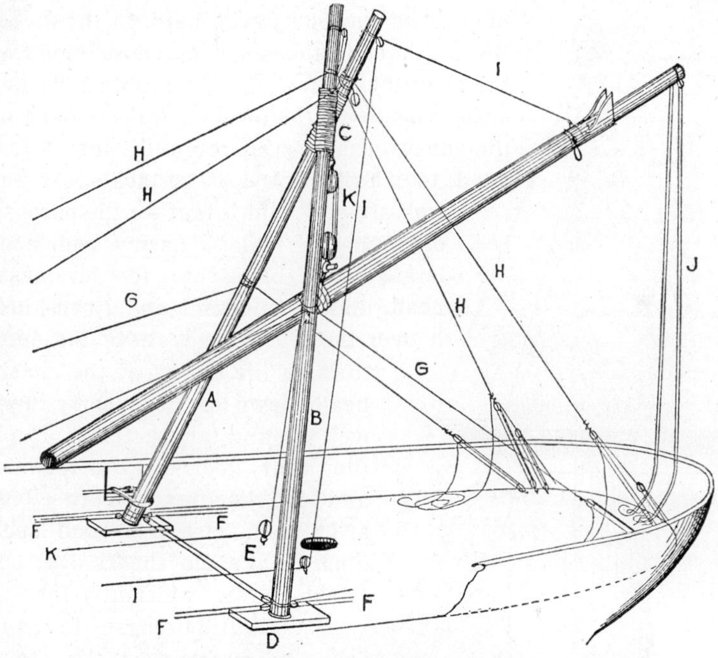

Stepping a mizzen mast by shear legs

This serves to illustrate the method of using shears and of staying them. The same rig may be employed, with necessary changes, wherever weights have to be lifted without regular masts and booms.

A and B—shear legs, rigged for taking in mast on port side. C—shear head lashing. D—shoes for heel of shear legs. Starboard shear leg is shown lashed to spar outside of port in bulwark. E—Lead block for main purchase. F—Heel tackles, leading fore and aft, for shifting the shear legs along the deck. G—Belly guys for steadying the shear legs against heavy stresses. H—Head guys for staying the shear legs. These are the principal guys—the others may be dispensed with except for the heaviest lifts. I—Topping Lift or truss tackle. J—Mast guys. K—Main purchase.

When shifting shear legs wet the deck under the shoes.

of the heels to ease away with. Next slack away the after guys and haul on the fore ones at the same time.

In taking out a mast, the shears are hoisted up singly and lashed aloft, and generally remain up till the new mast is taken in.

To take in the bowsprit proceed as follows:

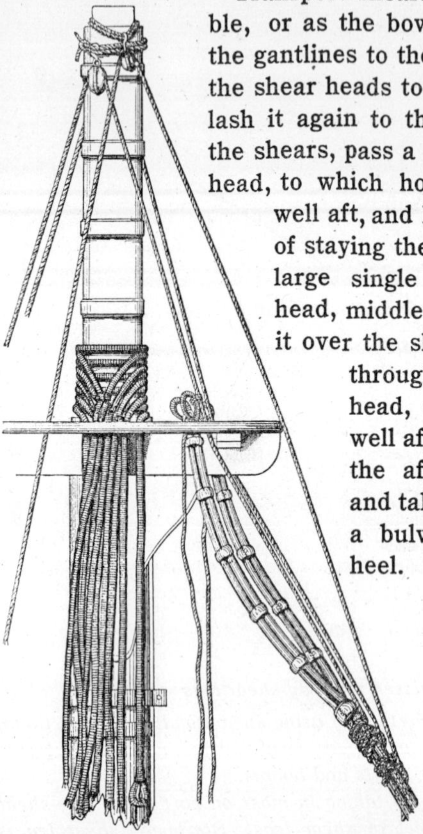

Sending up fore stay (fitted with lashing eyes)

Transport shears as far forward as possible, or as the bows will permit. Bend on the gantlines to the small purchase block at the shear heads to light it up, unlash it and lash it again to the forward fork or horn of the shears, pass a strap round the fore-mast-head, to which hook a large tackle, carry it well aft, and haul it taut for the purpose of staying the mast. Lash a couple of large single blocks to the foremast-head, middle a hawser and clove-hitch it over the shear-head, reeve the ends through the blocks at the mast-head, down on deck, carry them well aft, and take a turn. Hook the after heel tackles forward and take the after guys aft. Pass a bulwark lashing round each heel. Rake the shears over the bows sufficiently for the main purchase to hang directly over the stem, and make all fast.

The shears being dropped over the stem and secured, the large tackle is made fast to the bowsprit *outside the distance from the heel to the knight-heads.* The truss tackle (or topping lift) is fastened to a strop through the cap, and two guys are hitched to bolts in the cap, the former to cant the heel, and the two guys to assist in steadying the bowsprit when pointing the heel through the knight-heads. Now bring the fall to the capstan and heave round, taking in the slack and topping on the cap purchase when necessary. When high enough point the heel, having the partners well greased, when by easing away the main and topping on the cap purchase, working the guys at the same time, the bowsprit will come down in its place.

If the ship has a top-gallant forecastle the bowsprit cannot be taken in with the shears without the assistance of a small derrick further forward, on account of the break of the forecastle, it not being prudent to step shears on the top of it.

Having topped the bowsprit well up by means of the truss tackle, and finding that you cannot get the shears sufficiently sloped to point the heel, rig a jibboom or any other spar over the forecastle, lash the heel, and have a tackle on the outer end to haul the heel of the bowsprit out and point it fair for stepping.

When masts are stepped without shipping the tops and caps, these must be got up by special rigs. Gantline blocks are lashed at the square of the masthead and the trestle trees, tops and cap are hoisted up and eased over.

Topmasts are sent up through the trestle trees and cap by the *mast rope* rove through the heel sheave. After lower masts are stayed the remainder of the rigging is simple. Masts and yards go up by virtue of the lower mast purchases.

Many modern ships have lower and topmasts in one piece of steel. Such masts can only be secured at fitting out yards. They are *not* floated alongside and stepped by your own resources. Wooden lower masts are generally built up, made of four sections, held together by steel hoops.

Lower yards and lower topsail yards are often of steel.

Spare spars and sails. All sailing vessels are to have, at least, one complete suit of sails, and a second suit for the foremast, consisting of course, topsails, topgallant sails, and two spare jibs or foresails; they are also to carry a spare topmast and a spare topsail yard. (A.B.S. Rules.)

II

Rigging

Rigging is conveniently divided into *standing* rigging and *running* rigging.

Standing Rigging

Lower rigging or shrouds, support the lower mast at each side and extending aft. The forward legs of the shrouds are also

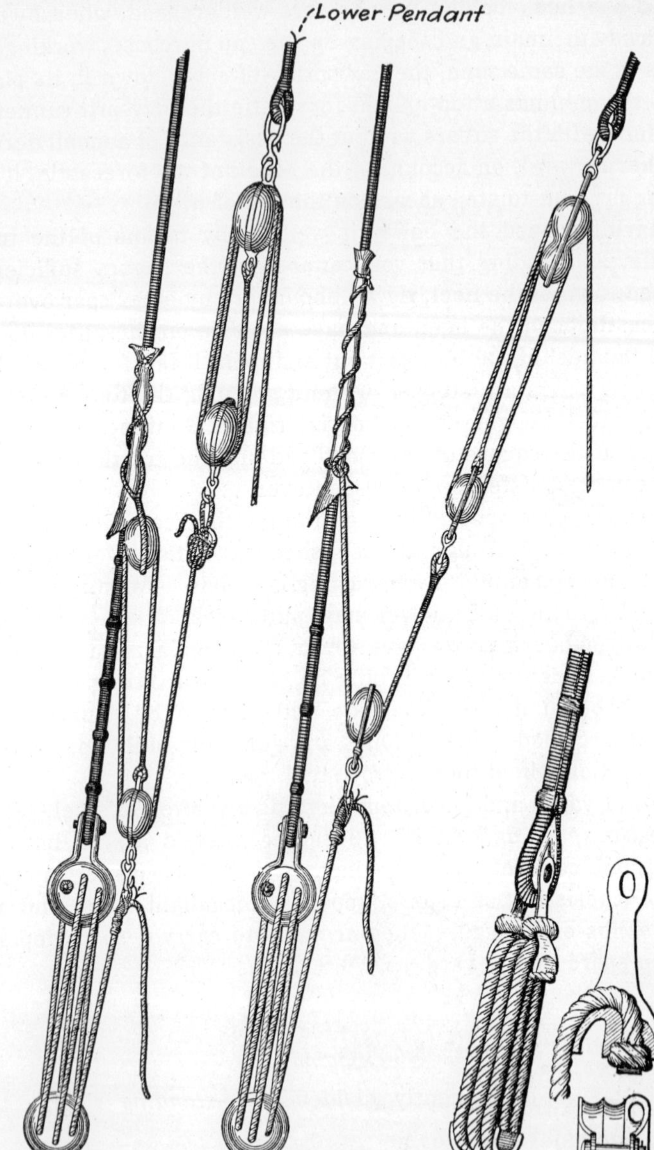

Setting up rigging, old style

called *swifters.* When lower yards are braced *sharp up,* they lie close against the swifters.

Ratlines, are cloved hitched across the shrouds and form the ladder for climbing aloft. Every fifth ratline extends to the swifter and after shrouds and is called a *catch ratline.*

Topmast shrouds, extend from topmast head to the rim of the *top.* The top is the platform about the lower masthead.

Topgallant shrouds, royal shrouds, are similar but much lighter.

Topmasts, and masts above, are supported aft by *backstays,* leading down to the channels on either side.

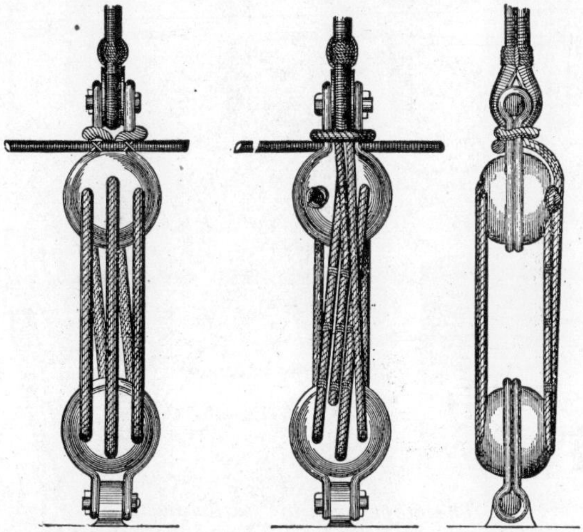

The proper way to secure lanyards. Knots are inside. Forward hole to starboard, after hole to port. The holes for the knots are finished square. Dead eyes are of lignum vitae. Lanyard ends are hitched, as shown, and seized in place.

All masts are supported forward by *stays,* the stay taking its name from the mast it supports.

Bowsprit shrouds lead aft from the bowsprit on either side, supporting it from side thrusts.

Bobstays lead down from the bowsprit end to the cutwater, and support it from lifting. They are usually made of chain and set up with hearts and lanyards to add some *give* to the rigging.

Jib guys lead out on either side from the jibboom.

Jib martingale and back ropes lead down to the *martingale,* or *dolphin striker*, and support the jibboom from lifting.

The *gammoning* is the ring that secures the bowsprit to its bed on the top of the stem.

In old ships this was a lashing passing over the bowsprit and through the gammoning hole in the head of the stem. When rope or chain is used for a gammoning it is crossed, that is, the forward turn over the bowsprit is the after turn through the gammoning hole. Old seamen sometimes refer to a crossed lashing as a " gammon lashing."

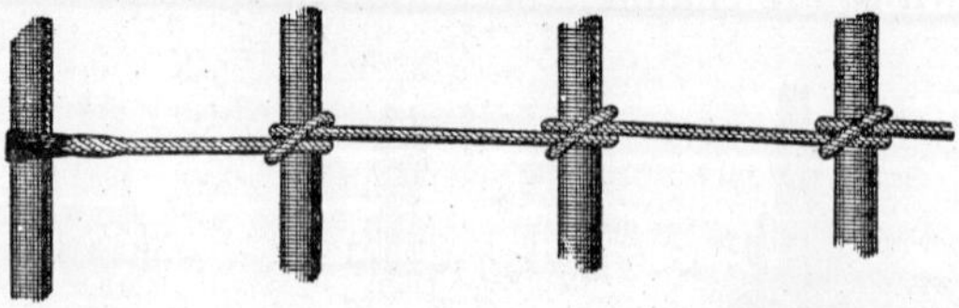

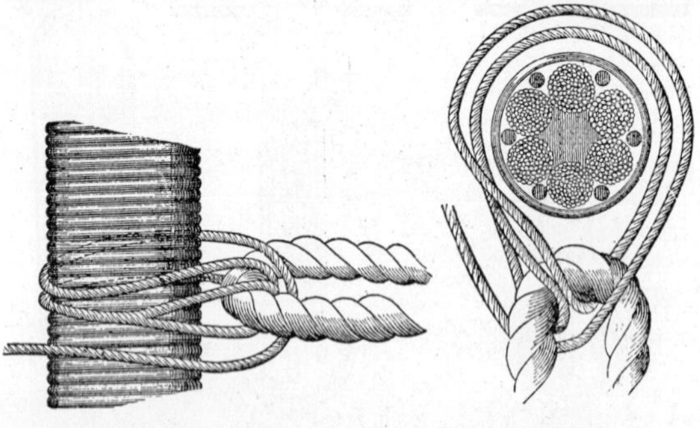

The proper way to " rattle down "

Standing rigging is *set up*, that is, it is hauled tight, or *taut*, as seamen call it. In setting up modern rigging use is made of *screws* and *turnbuckles*. In older rigs *dead eyes* and *lanyards* were used, or *hearts* and *lanyards*. The latter are still used to a great extent on the bowsprit shrouds. In wooden vessels, the dead eye and lanyard is preferred because of its *give*. In steel vessels screws and turnbuckles are most often found. Many ships have been dismasted because the standing rigging was not set up properly. Too much tension is almost as bad as too little. When rigging works loose in a heavy gale and it cannot be set up, luff tackles are hooked to the shrouds on opposite sides and they are *swiftered* in. This puts a temporary tension on them and steadies the masts. This principle can be used in many ways where masts work loose in heavy weather.

The setting up of rigging cannot be learned from a book. Watch this work when it is being done, and when you have to do it yourself you will know something about it. Masts are generally *stayed* by the fore and aft stay and the first pair of shrouds. The shrouds usually go over the masthead in pairs, the legs of each pair setting up on the same side. But a great deal of irregularity has crept into this matter with steel construction and where masts are longer, lower and topmast in one piece and of steel, shrouds for lower rigging may set up from eyebolts on the mast to the channel plates, being fitted singly. Each ship is a study in itself. Steamship rigging is mainly set in this fashion.

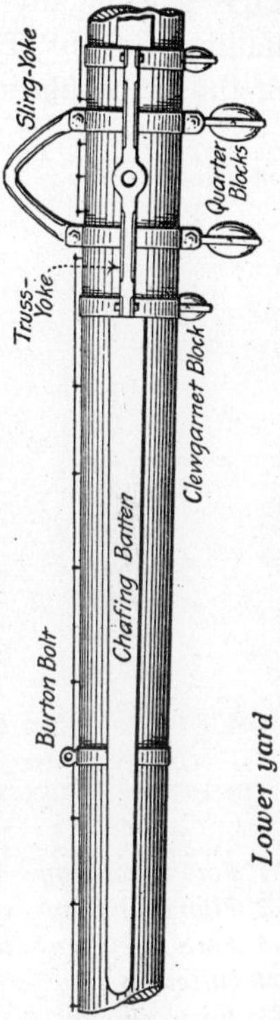

The Standing Rigging of Yards

Stationary yards, like the lower yards, lower topsail yards, and lower topgallant yards are supported in the *slings* or center of the yard, by a *sling* and *truss*. Or by a *crane* in the case of lower topsail yards. Some lower topsail yards are supported by a standard coming up from the trestle trees, or the cap.

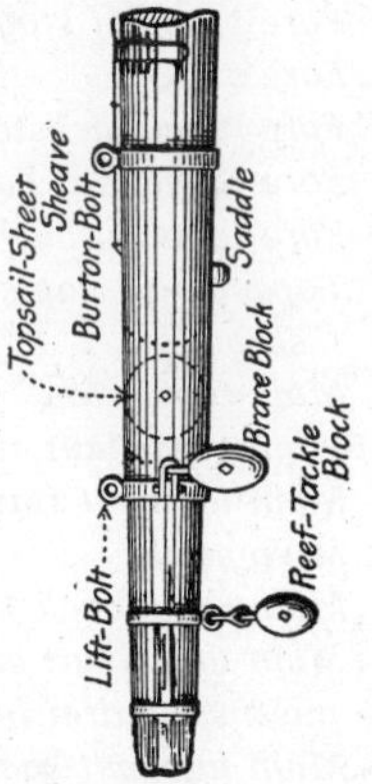

Yards that ride up and down the mast are held in contact by a *parrel*. This may simply be a set of wooden jaws, or saddle, held in by a metal hoop covered with leather. Or, in the case of a topsail yard, it may be an elaborate *tub* of steel, lined with leather.

The yard arms are supported, when the yard is down, in the case of a hoisting yard, and at all times in the case of a lower yard, by standing ropes called *lifts.* Lifts are usually wire pendants fitted with purchases on their hauling parts. The handling of the lifts is an important part of the manipulation of the courses.

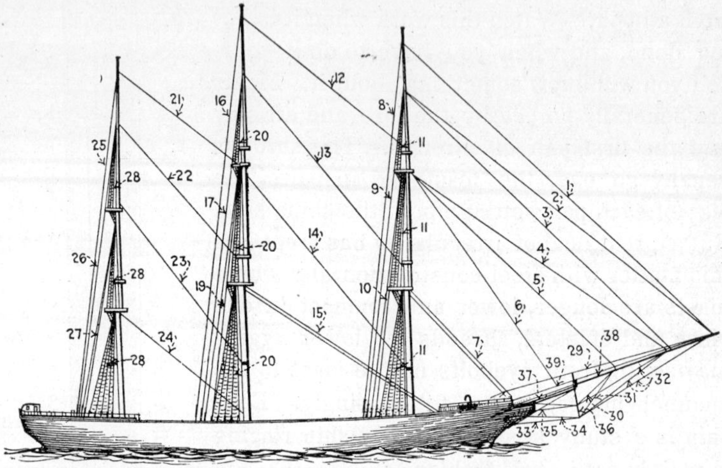

Standing rigging of a ship

1 Fore royal stay
2 Flying jib stay
3 Fore topgallant stay
4 Outer jib stay
5 Inner jib stay
6 Fore topmast stay
7 Fore stay
8 Fore royal backstay
9 Fore topgallant backstay
10 Fore topmast backstays
11 Topgallant, topmast and fore shrouds
12 Main royal stay
13 Main topgallant stay
14 Main topmast stay
15 Main stays
16 Main royal backstay
17 Main topgallant backstay
(18 missing on drawing)
19 Main topmast backstays
20 Topgallant, topmast and main shrouds
21 Mizzen royal stay
22 Mizzen topgallant stay
23 Mizzen topmast stay
24 Mizzen stay
25 Mizzen royal backstay
26 Mizzen topgallant backstay
27 Mizzen topmast backstays
28 Topgallant, topmast and mizzen shrouds
29 Jibboom guys
30 Martingale stays
31 Martingale stays
32 Martingale stays
33 Back ropes
34 Back ropes
35 Bobstay
36 Martingale, or dolphin striker

Footropes are fitted along all yards, hanging from stirrups from the after side. The footrope from the yard arm to inside of the sheave hole is called the *flemish horse* and is only found on lower yards and on upper topsail yards.

Fore yard and fore topsail yard. Schoolship Newport. This vessel carries a single topsail. Note the harbor furl.

Booms are fitted with *topping lifts*, similar in purpose to the lifts on a crossed yard. The lee lift is always allowed to hang slack and the weather lift is hauled taut.

The bowsprit is also fitted with footropes.

Running Rigging

Running rigging may best be considered as follows:

The rigging of spars—halyards. Yards, except the lower, lower topsail and lower topgallant, are hoisted up and lowered by means of *halyards*. Halyards always lead to the deck and are found as follows:

Yards and principal running rigging of a ship

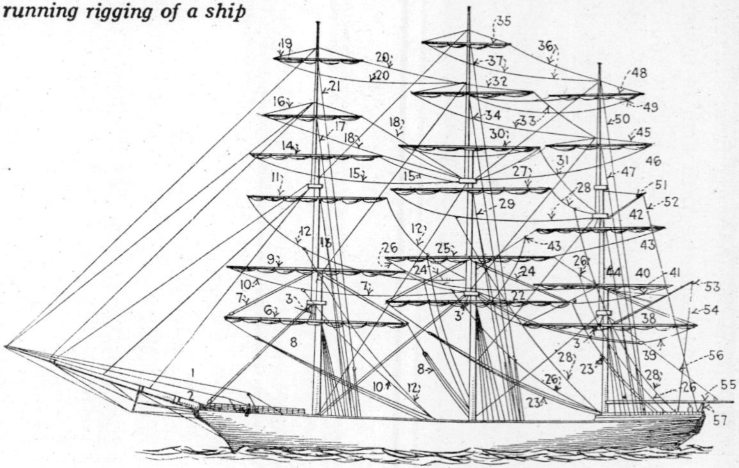

1 *Jibboom guys (not running rigging)*
2 *Whisker guys (not running rigging)*
3 *Slings of fore, main and crossjack yards*
4 } *(The artist lost these numbers, we don't*
5 } *blame him.)*
6 *Fore yard*
7 *Fore lifts*
8 *Fore braces*
9 *Fore lower topsail yard*
10 *Fore lower topsail braces*
11 *Fore upper topsail yard*
12 *Fore upper topsail braces*
13 *Fore upper topsail halyard*
14 *Fore lower topgallant yards*
15 *Fore lower topgallant braces*
16 *Fore upper topgallant yard (arrow points to lift)*
17 *Fore upper topgallant halyards*
18 *Fore upper topgallant braces*
19 *Fore royal yards*
20 *Fore royal braces*
21 *Fore royal halyards*
22 *Main yard*
23 *Main braces*
24 *Main lifts*
25 *Main lower topsail yard*
26 *Main lower topsail braces*
27 *Main upper topsail yard*
28 *Main upper topsail braces*
29 *Main upper topsail halyards*
30 *Main lower topgallant yard*
31 *Main lower topgallant braces*
32 *Main upper topgallant yard*
33 *Main upper topgallant braces*
34 *Main upper topgallant halyards*
35 *Main royal yard*
36 *Main royal braces*
37 *Main royal halyards*
38 *Crossjack yard*
39 *Crossjack braces*
40 *Mizzen lower topsail yard*
41 *Mizzen lower topsail braces*
42 *Mizzen upper topsail yard*
43 *Mizzen upper topsail braces*
44 *Mizzen upper topsail halyards*
45 *Mizzen topgallant yard*
46 *Mizzen topgallant braces*
47 *Mizzen topgallant halyards*
48 *Mizzen royal yard*
49 *Mizzen royal braces*
50 *Mizzen royal halyards*
51 *Monkey gaff (for signals and ensign)*
52 *Signal halyards*
53 *Spanker gaff*
54 *Spanker vangs*
55 *Spanker boom*
56 *Spanker boom topping lift*
57 *Spanker sheet*

Fore	upper topsail	halyard	port	side.
Main	"	"	st'b'd	"
Mizzen	"	"	port	"
Fore	topgallant	halyards	st'b'd	side.
Main	"	"	port	"
Mizzen	"	"	st'b'd	"
Fore	royal	"	port	side.
Main	"	"	st'b'd	"
Mizzen	"	"	port	"
Fore	skysail	"	st'b'd	side.
Main	"	"	port	"
Mizzen	"	"	st'b'd	"

This system of alternating the side to which similar halyards lead is followed through when the masts are increased.

A, A, Starboard mizzen topmast backstays
B, Starboard spreader
C, Shoe of spanker gaff
D, Tack of spanker topsail
E, Spanker peak halyard blocks
F, Spanker throat halyard blocks

The jib halyards, foretopmast staysail, and flying jib also alternate. The same holds good of the staysails on other masts.

A fore and aft sail hoisting to a gaff is carried up the mast by means of two sets of halyards.

The *throat halyards*, lift the spar next to the mast.

The *peak halyards*, usually rove with two or more blocks on the gaff, hoist up the outer end, or peak, of the gaff.

Throat halyards usually belay on the port side of the mast and peak halyards on the starboard side.

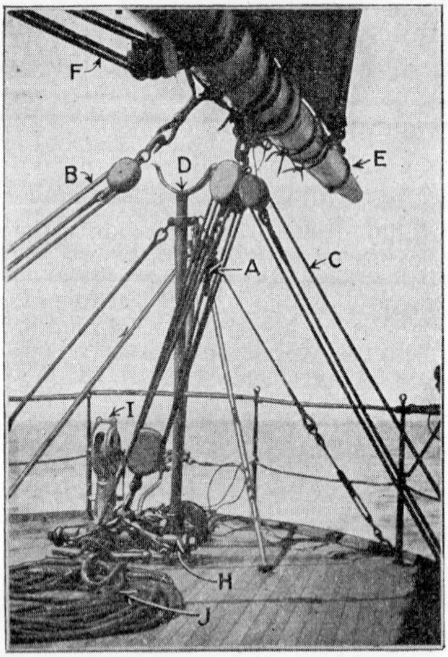

A, Spanker sheet
B, Boom guy
C, Boom guy
D, Boom crotch
E, Wythe, the aftermost band on the boom
F, Boom tackle, hooked to becket at forward end of boom. This is only hauled out when the boom is trimmed for a wind nearly aft.
H, Rubber buffers at deck connection for spanker sheet traveller. Deck cleat just forward of this.
I, Sounding machine
J, End of spanker sheet, faked down clear for running

Braces, as the term implies, are to steady the yards, brace them in and *trim* or square them, as the case may be. The

braces all lead aft, except upon the mizzen where they necessarily lead forward. This arrangement is not very good and in four-masted vessels gives added reason for fitting the jigger mast fore and aft.

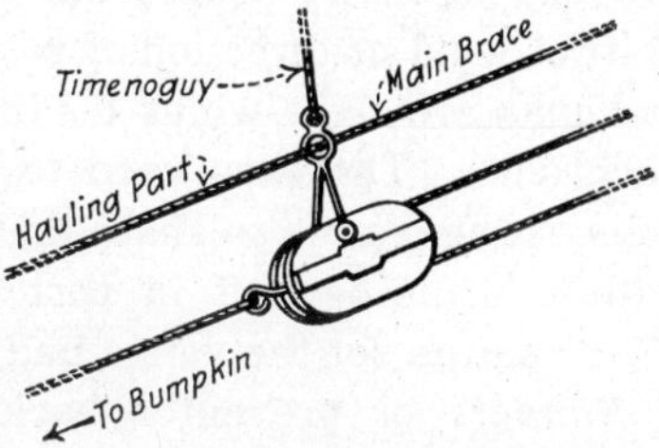

Method of fitting deck end of main brace

Braces on the lower yards consist of wire pendants with purchases, or whips. Braces in large ships are now entirely of wire and small hand winches are fitted on the bulwarks for heaving them taut in heavy weather. Strong new manila, however, is preferred by most seamen because of its greater ease in handling and slacking.

Sheets **are fitted to booms, and in the case of large vessels these ropes are rove off with double blocks. On some large booms spans of wire are fitted to carry the pull of the heavy sail along the boom.**

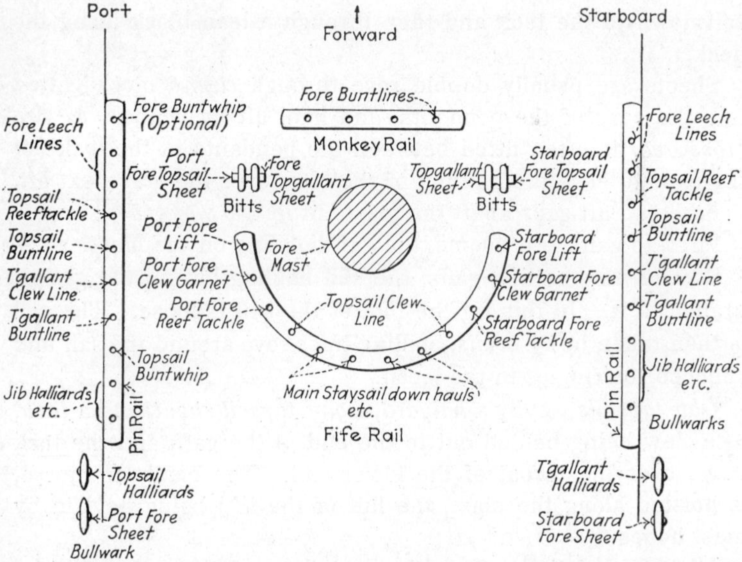

Diagram of the deck. Lead of running gear at foremast. Schoolship Newport. This gives a general idea of the lead of gear to the deck on a square rigger. There are no down hauls as the schoolship has a single topsail.

Boom tackles, are heavy tackles used for hauling the booms forward when running and for hooking against the sheet to prevent the heavy boom from slamming over if taken aback by a shift of wind or direction of vessel.

Vangs are light whips leading from the gaff to the deck on each side. They are used to steady the gaff when the vessel rolls. The lead is so sharp that vangs are not much good except with a standing gaff in port, when they steady it amidship. When sail is set the vangs had better be left loose.

Runners or preventer backstays are fitted on most large yachts—sloop and schooners. In going about, set taut weather runner; let go lee runner.

The Rigging of Sails

The gear of a square sail is explained further along in this chapter.

Stay sails hoist by a single halyard, usually rove as a whip, standing part in the fork of the stay, and a single block at the head of the sail. The *down haul* reeves from the head of the sail down to the tack and then through a lead block along the deck.

Sheets are usually double rove through *clump* blocks fitted into the eyes of the pendants, and haul aft by whips. A wire *cross over* is often fitted between the pendants in the wake of the clew to ease the hauling of the clew over the stay next aft.

Fore and aft sails abaft the masts fit in two ways:

First, to gaffs and booms, the gaff hoisting on the mast.

Second, to standing gaffs, the sail hauling out on the gaff or brailed to it. In this rig the foot of the sail is loose. The sail is then taken in by *brails*, spilling lines rove around the sail and clinched to cringles in the leech.

Gaff topsails, set by a *halyard,* a *gaff topsail sheet*, and a *tack.* The clew being hauled out to the end of the gaff, and the tack down over the throat of the lower sail. The head, of course, is hoisted along the mast, the luff of the sail being held in by mast hoops.

All large *hoisting* gaff and boom sails are held to the mast by *hoops.* Hoops are a most important part of the rigging of a fore and aft vessel and should only be made of *straight grain oak.* If the mast hoops fail, the vessel may meet with disaster.

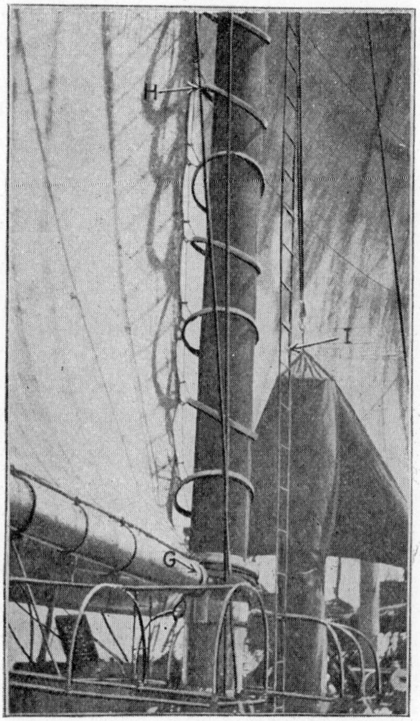

G, Goose neck
H, Mast hoop, beginning of lacing under reef band. Hoops above this are stopped to the leech of sail
I, Mast ladder, one on each side
A windsail is shown forward of the mizzen mast, used for ventilation in fine weather

Hanks are another important fitting of all sails that hoist along a stay. Where double stays are fitted be sure the hanks used are *double hanks*, with wide flat bows.

The whole subject of gear and sails, of canvas and rope, is so closely allied that much of the running gear will be described under the heading, *sails*.

III

Sails

Canvas used for sails on American craft is almost entirely of cotton. The standard width for sailmaking is 22″, although special wider sizes are used for racing craft, and 24″ duck is sometimes employed. Narrow duck runs 14″, 16″, 18″ and 20″.

Canvas is designated by numbers beginning with 00 as the heaviest. It runs as follows:

00, 0, 1, 2, 3, 4, 5, 6, 7, 8, 9, 10, 11, 12.

Sails of a ship

1 Flying jib
2 Outer jib
3 Inner jib
4 Fore topmast staysail
5 Fore royal
6 Fore upper topgallant sail
7 Fore lower topgallant sail
8 Fore upper topsail
9 Fore lower topsail
10 Fore sail, or fore course
11 Main royal staysail
12 Main topgallant staysail
13 Main topmast staysail
14 Main skysail
15 Main royal
16 Main upper topgallant sail
17 Main lower topgallant sail
18 Main upper topsail
19 Main lower topsail
20 Main sail, or main course
21 Mizzen topgallant staysail
22 Mizzen topmast staysail
23 Mizzen royal
24 Mizzen topgallant sail
25 Mizzen upper topsail
26 Mizzen lower topsail
27 Crossjack (hanging in gear—not set)
28 Spanker

Flax duck (Scotch) is soft and handles easily when wet. It is extra strong and makes good storm trysails. This duck runs 24″ wide.

But, as stated before, the standard width and kind of canvas used on merchant craft is 22″ cotton. Canvas comes in *bolts* of ninety yards. Sails are said to be made up of a certain number of *cloths*, referring to the widths of canvas used. Canvas is tested by boring through with a fid. If the threads break easily use it with suspicion.

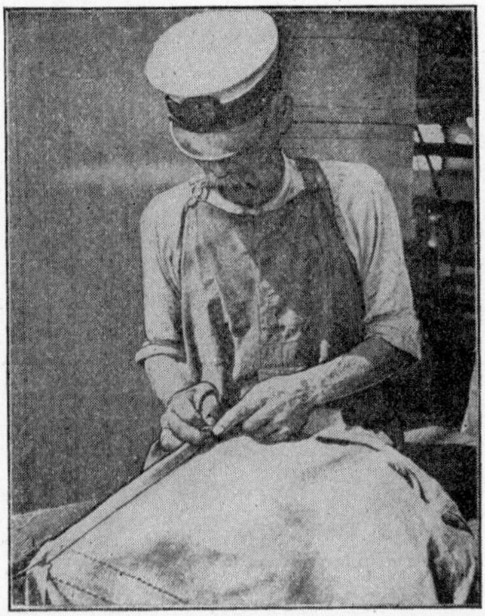

Beginning stitch, round seam

Twine. Cotton sail twine usually comes in half pound balls and is known by the *ply*, that is the number of threads.

Sewing twine runs as follows: 4, 5, 6, 7, 8 ply.

Roping twine, 9, 10, 11 ply.

Canvas and twine. The following is considered good practice in sewing canvas, although sailmakers may differ some on this point.

Canvas	00 and 0	Twine	8 and 7 ply.
"	1	"	7 and 6 "
"	2	"	(6 ply used two parts same as for No. 1.)
"	3, 4 and 5	"	6 ply single.

4 and 5 ply twine is used for very light work.

Twine must always be well waxed.

Seams. Seams are of two kinds, *round* and *flat*.

The *round seam* is used to join the edges of two pieces of canvas, and the needle is taken through the canvas almost at right angles, the edge being up. To make this lie flat, the round seam is then *rubbed*.

The *flat seam.* Here the canvas lies flat, and the needle is taken through the lower piece and up through the edge of the cloth to be joined. This is the most general way of sewing canvas aboard ship.

In stitching flat seam make four stitches to the inch.

Sewing canvas, flat seam. A pleasant summer job on deck

A good sailmaker can sew forty yards of canvas in an eight-hour day. It is sometimes useful to know how much a man can *do* in a day, in these times when most folk only think of what they can *get* in a day. Seams are 1½″ wide for heavy sails and generally run to the blue edge line on the cloth.

Roping. In roping sails, awnings, dodgers, etc., the following proportions are considered good practice:

Use roping twine, well waxed.

Leech rope on fore and aft sails, 5½″ manila bolt rope, use 9 ply, six parts through needle, making twelve parts in all.

4″ rope, use four parts of 8 ply.

3″ " " three parts of 8 ply.

2″ " " three parts of 6 " .

1½″ rope, use two parts of 8 ply.

Wire bolt rope. Heavy square sails are roped with wire on the leech and foot and with hemp on the head.

Wire bolt rope is sewn on, the stitches being taken *around* the rope. After sewing a canvas chafing strip is sewn over all and then leathered in the wake of bull's-eyes, blocks, and at any point where chafe will take place.

Pulling through, round seam. Canvas is held by a sail hook

Bolt ropes are also *marled* to the sail. First splice in clew irons, get rope on a stretch along the edge of the tabling. Use a "Lolley" needle, with 10 or 11 ply roping twine, and make the marling hitches on the *fore* side against the canvas, and *opposite* to the roping.

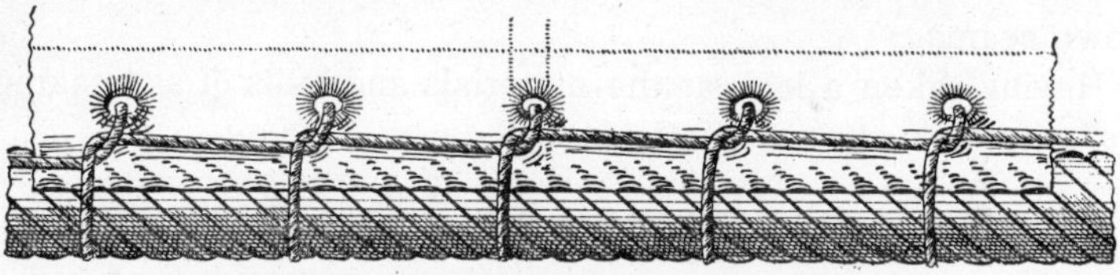

Wire bolt rope. Marled to foot of square sail

Marling hitches are placed about one inch apart.

Long spur sail needle

Short spur or Lolley needle

Needles. Sail needles are triangular in section for half their length from the point, then round.

Long spur needles are used for sewing canvas, and are designated by numbers as follows 6, 7, 8, 9, 10, 11, 12, 13, 14, 14½, 15, 15½, 16, 16½, 17, 17½.

The needle most generally used is the 15 two and a half inches long, for general repair work on medium canvas.

The higher the number the smaller the needle.

Roping needles are of the *short spur* or *Lolley's* pattern, and are designated according to use, as follows: *flatseam, tabling, old work, store, headrope, small boltrope, middle bolt rope, large bolt rope, small marline,* and *large marline.*

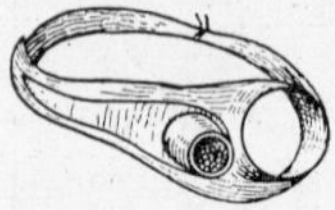

Palm

Palms are classified as *seaming* and *roping* palms the former being light with small seat for the end of needle. Roping palms are broad and heavy, giving the hand a good purchase in forcing through heavy needles. Some are buckled, being adjustable with brass cup and pitted iron seat.

Sail hook is attached to the end of the bench by a lanyard and is used to hook into the canvas to keep it on a proper stretch while sewing.

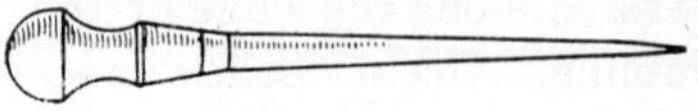

Pricker

Creasing stick is a wooden or metal tool, split at the end and used for creasing seams.

Pricker is a small marling spike fitted with a wooden handle. Used for opening holes in stiff canvas.

Rubber is a piece of steel set in a handle, used for rubbing down seams.

Having taken a look at the materials and tools of sailmaking we will now name the parts of a sail.

Square Sails

A square sail is rarely " square "; in fact the writer has never seen a perfectly square sail. The top of the sail is the *head*, on either side are the *leeches*, and the bottom edge is the *foot*. The corners of the sail are known as *head cringles* where head and leeches join and *clews* where foot and leeches join.

The sail is bounded by *roping;* the *head cringles* are rope or metal loops into which the *head earings* are spliced. These earings are long tails of rope, usually ratline stuff, and are used in hauling out the head of the sail along the yard, stretching it on the *jackstay*, a rod fitted to the yard, to which the sail is fastened by means of *robands*, long rope yarn stops, hitched in the *head holes* of the sail, these being small *stitched* holes at each seam, worked where the clothes of canvas overlap. Robands are passed up *forward* over the top of the jackstay, and down through the head hole from aft forward, until end is nearly expended; the two ends are then brought up *between* the head of the sail and the jackstay, one on each side, and knotted on top of the roband with a square knot.

The middle roband, which may be of houseline, is called the *midship stop*. In *bending* sail this is *passed* and then the weather and lee earings are hauled out (see bending sail).

Roping is always on the after side of a square sail with one exception. In large American ships, *cross leeches* are fitted on the main course, running from the head cringles to the middle of the foot where they splice into a ring to which is shackled the *midship tack*. The cross leeches consist of a line of tabling, with a rope sewn down the center on the forward side of sail. The use of the cross leeches is as follows: When sailing with wind on the quarter the weather clew of the mains'le is hauled up, leaving the cross leech, from head to middle of foot, to take the pull. The midship tack is hauled aft and belayed to a cavil (a heavy square belaying pin) on the main fife rail. This rig makes the mains'le set perfectly under these conditions.

Some sailmakers rope "down leech" portside and "up leech" starboard side—a mere technical point.

Tabling, except at head, is always sewn on the forward side of the sail, and the belly bands, reef bands, and lining cloths are also sewn on forward, leaving the after side smooth for the action of the wind when close hauled or sailing with the wind abeam.

The canvas and roping of the sails of a ship, three masted, square rigged, of two thousand tons, or over, are as follows:

Courses

Fore	No. 0 canvas	Bolt rope, $\frac{5}{8}''$ flexible steel wire. $2''$ tarred Russian hemp on head.
Main	No. 1 "	
Crossjack	No. 1 "	

Lower topsails*

Fore	No. 0 canvas	Roping same as courses.
Main	No. 0 "	
Mizzen	No. 0 "	

* The division of the great single topsails of a ship into lower and upper topsails, by means of the stationary lower topsail yard, was the invention of

Upper topsails

Fore	No. 1	canvas	Roping next size smaller than lower topsails.
Main	No. 1	"	
Mizzen	No. 1	"	

Topgallant sails

Fore	No. 3	canvas	Bolt rope flexible wire ½″ and 1¾″ Russian hemp head.
Main	No. 3	"	
Mizzen	No. 3	"	

Royals

Fore	No. 4	canvas	Bolt rope, wire next smaller. 1½″ Russian hemp at head.
Main	No. 4	"	
Mizzen	No. 4	"	

Skysails

Fore	No. 5	canvas	Roping of 2″ manila on foot and leech. 1½″ Russian hemp on foot.
Main	No. 5	"	
Mizzen	No. 5	"	

Tabling on these sails is as follows:

At head, ¾ of a cloth to take chafe of yards, sewn on *after* side of sail.

Courses and both topsails, tabling of ½ cloth at leeches and foot, on forward side.

Topgallant and royals, tabling of ⅓ cloth at leeches and foot, on forward side.

Skysails, five or six inches, on leech and foot.

Spanker, No. 2 canvas. 4 to 5 inch manila bolt rope.

an American, Captain Frederick Howes, of Brewster, Massachusetts. He first put the rig on the ship *Climax*, of Boston, which he commanded, in 1853.

This was the greatest advance in the rigging of ships since the beginning of the age of sail. It made possible the huge sailing craft of the present day where Captain Howes' improvement extends upward to the topgallant sails.

It is interesting to note here that two American shipmasters stand in the forefront of achievement in the history of their profession. Howes with his double topsails, in seamanship, and Sumner with his discovery of the use of the line of position, in navigation. It is clearly before the present generation of American seamen that they will be expected to contribute as well to the advancement of theory and practice on the sea.

Staysails.

Fore topmast staysail	No. 2 canvas
Jib	No. 1 "
Flying jib	No. 2 "
Outer jib	No. 3 "
Main staysail	No. 1 "
" topmast staysail	No. 2 "
" topgallant staysail	No. 3 "
" royal staysail	No. 4 "
Mizzen staysail	No. 1 "
" topmast staysail	No. 3 "
" royal staysail	No. 5 "

All of these staysails are roped with manila bolt rope, average size 3¾″ to 2½″.

I am indebted to Mr. James Stafford, sailmaker, of 26 South Street, New York, for this valuable table, and to Mr. Henderson, expert sailmaker, with John Curtin of South Street, for much valuable assistance and data on sail making.

Machine sewing. Power-driven sewing machines are now used in all large sail lofts. The machine-sewn seam is more uniform, the tension is regulated and the result is superior to hand-sewn work. Machines use a 12 to 15 ply twine.

All roping is done by hand, as no satisfactory machine has as yet been developed for this purpose.

Eyelets. The brass-bound eyelets used for screens should not be used on sails. Eyelets for sails are formed by punching a hole in the canvas, about a quarter inch *smaller* than the finished eyelet. This leaves the edges of the canvas under natural tension. Never stab, or pry a hole for an eyelet. The eyelets are then worked around a small rope or galvanized iron grommet. In large hauling out holes, as for heavy awnings, the stitching about the hole (well-waxed roping twine) is further protected by crimping in a brass rim to prevent cutting the twine. Eyelets are generally placed where seams over lap. Head eyelets are always so placed.

The fittings of a square sail.

Head cringles are now made of iron, as shown in drawing.

Clew, or spectacle irons at the clews of a course are shown in drawing. Lighter fittings are used on the smaller sails. Where sails do not *clew up*, such as some modern upper topsails and upper topgallant sails, no fitting for clewline blocks is needed.

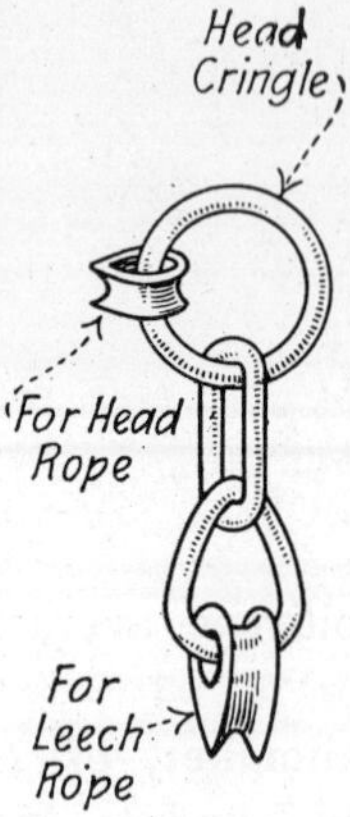

Reef cringles are of hemp worked into the leech rope of the sail and a heavy galvanized iron thimble is forced into them. Where leech ropes are of wire the cringle is also of wire rope.

The bands, *reef*, and *belly* are sewn across the forward side of the heavier sails.

Lining and *chafing cloths* are sewn on in the wake of gear, such as *leech lines, buntlines*, etc.

Reef points are used on modern sails, they are seized to the grommet holes stitched in the seams as described above. These reef holes are in line along the middle of the reef bands. Reef points differ in square and fore and aft sails. In *square* sails the reef point is seized on the *upper side* of the grommet hole. In *fore and aft* sails it is seized on the *under* side of the grommet. The reason for this is readily apparent (sketches).

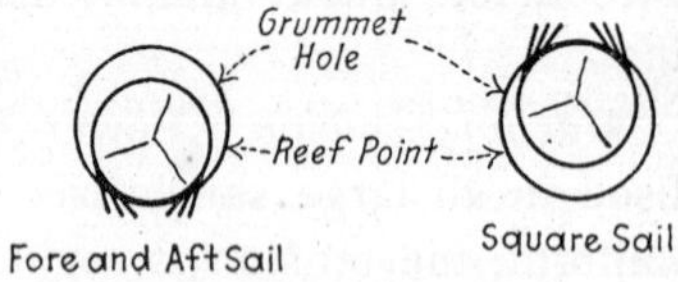

How reef points are seized into grommet holes

Double reefs are no longer used in modern sails. Sails are *squarer*, have less *drop* or *hoist*, and a single reef is sufficient.

Length of reef points is as follows:

Fore course,	7 feet, 6 inches.
Main course,	"
Crossjack course,	no reef.
Upper topsails, all masts,	7 feet.
Topgallant sails, all masts,	6 feet, 6 inches.

The length of reef points is of course dependent upon the diameter of the yards. Some seamen fit shorter reef points at the yard arms. Reef points are brought up, around the reefed portion of the sail and *reef* or *square* knotted on top of yard. Reef points are 1½ feet shorter on forward side of sail.

Reefing fore sail. Hauling out the weather reef earing. The man at the earing is bracing his left foot against the flemish horse

Reef earings, are hauled out to a ring bolt on the yard arm and passed three or four times, to get a purchase, the end is then taken from *forward* aft and *up* through the cringle around the yard and in that way expended, hitching it to its own hauling out part.

The Gear of a Square Sail

Halyards (haul yards) haul the yards to their respective mastheads, except the stationary yards.

Stationary yards are:

Fore yard
Main yard
Crossjack yard
All lower topsail yards
All lower topgallant yards

The others are hoisting yards.

Upper topsail
Upper topgallant sail
Topgallant sail (single)
Royals
Skysails

The *sheets* haul the clews of the sail down to the yard below, or, in the case of a course, they haul the clew aft.

The *tacks*, in the case of a course, haul the sail forward. When on a wind, a course is hauled forward by the tack on the weather side, and aft by the sheet on the lee side. Therefore a vessel is said to be on the starboard or port *tack*.

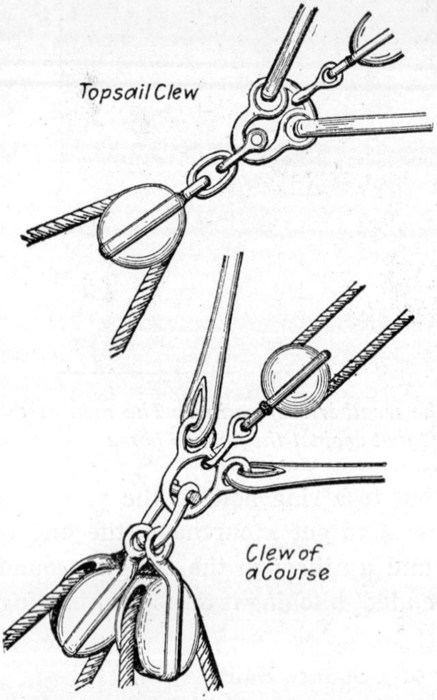

Spectacle irons. The ropes shown on the sails are topsail clewline, topsail sheet. Clew garnet, tack, sheet, on the course

Clewlines attach to the clews, and haul them *up*, when furling sail. Modern clewlines generally haul up to the yard arms. Sails are now very wide compared with their depth and this is simpler and makes the sail easier to stow. Old fashioned practice was to clew into the quarters of the yard forming the sail into a large *bunt*. This was very difficult to stow in heavy weather.

Clew garnets are the clewlines of a course. These still clew up to the quarters on most ships.

Upper topsails, and upper topgallant sails do not have clewlines, as the yards come down close to the lower topsail and topgallant yards and the clews need not be started, accept for a close stow when they may be slacked up.

Clewlines perform a double service.

In taking in a square sail there are two operations.

Halyards are eased down, sheets remain fast, clewlines are manned and we have the order "*clew down.*" The clewlines help haul the yard down to the cap. When the yard is down, the sheets are eased off, and we have the order "*clew up,*" as further hauling on the clewlines then brings the clews up to the yard.

The *downhauls*, on upper topsails and topgallant sails haul the yards *down* in furling. It will be noted that no clewlines are fitted on these sails.

A—Port fore reef tackle—hauled out for reefing
B—Port fore topsail reef tackle
Port head earing has just been hauled out and men on the yard are passing the reef points

Buntlines run from the foot of a sail to the yard, leading through *bull's eyes*, fitted to *lizards* on the yards then into the mast. They lift up the foot of the sail to help in furling. On most sails buntlines are now carried from the after part of the yard, down under the foot of the sail, through bulls eyes worked into the foot, and *up* on the forward side of the sail to the other bull's-eyes on the top of the yard. These lines are sometimes called *spilling lines.* They practically furl the sail from the deck. Such lines are only used where the clews come up to the yard arms. This is a great advantage in working a large ship with a small crew, merchant service fashion.

Leechlines, are the same as buntlines, and are fitted to the leeches of courses, hauling them in along the yard.

Reef tackles. These are usually fitted to courses, and the lower block hooks into the *reef tackle cringle, below* the reef cringle. The upper block hooks to an eye bolt on the bottom of the yard arm, well out. In reefing the tackles lift the heavy canvas up to the yard and stretch it for the passing of the earing.

The purchase is generally two single blocks, standing part in becket of yard arm block.

Leathering. The corners of all square sails should be leathered. Canvas is sometimes used, but is not as satisfactory. Leather is soaked in *fresh* water, and sewn on while wet. When dry it shrinks tight on the bolt ropes.

Fore and Aft Sails

The canvas for a large schooner will run about as follows:

Fore	No. 00
Main	" 00
Mizzen	" 00
Jigger	" 0
Spanker	" 0
Driver	" 0
Fore staysail	" 0
Jib	" 1
Flying jib	" 2
Outer jib	" 3
Jib topsail	" 4

Bolt roping will run about as in the staysails of a square rigger.

In roping a large gaff and boom sail the bolt rope will run about $5\frac{1}{2}''$ on the leech and $4''$ on the luff (or " mast " as sailmakers term it).

Fore and aft sails are usually fitted with complete sail covers, of No. 3 canvas, or even lighter. Sometimes these are waterproofed.

Roping on fore and aft sails is generally sewn on the port side, tabling to starboard.

Marking. The names of all sails should be plainly marked with a stencil on the canvas just above the clew. This should be left near the edge of the roll in making up for easy inspection. Stow in lockers so that the clews are near the front.

Stowage. Sail locker should be dry, and clean. The Chief Mate should see that all officers know the stowage of the locker, himself included, so that a required sail may be taken out at night without much trouble.

If the ship is troubled with rats, place a good deal of dry newspaper in the locker for the rats to chew on.

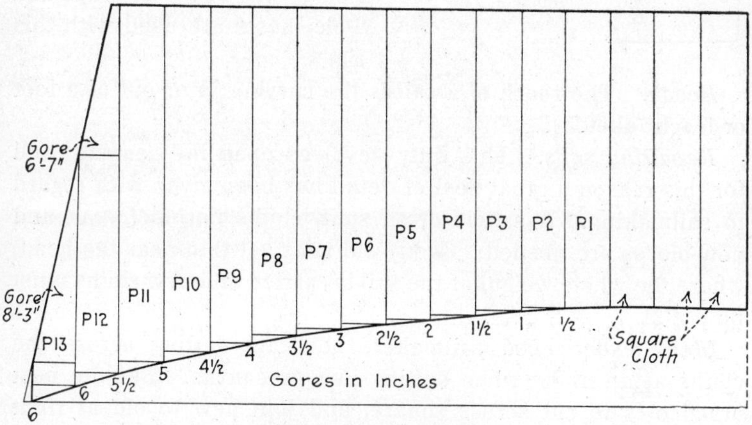

Draft of a lower topsail

Making sails. Sails are seldom made on board ship. The writer has seen light sails made on long voyages, but this is seldom done nowadays. Should it be necessary to make a sail, or to cut down an old sail for use as a jury rig, make an accurate draft of the sail to scale. Lay off the cloths on the paper, number them, allow for tabling, and then start a square sail at the midship cloth, and a fore and aft sail at the leech. In roping, pay special attention to the work so that when the roping is got on a stretch the sail will set flat.

Fore and aft sails. The parts of a fore and aft sail are illustrated under boat sails. The principal fittings are the same in large schooners. The "leg of mutton" sail sometimes set on the spanker or jigger mast is called a *ring tail* when hauled aft and not set to a boom.

Barkentines. The sails and rigging of barkentines, now coming into favor, is simply a combination of square rigger and schooner.

Gaff topsails. These sails run about three numbers lighter than the sails they set over, and are roped accordingly.

Marconi rig. Very lofty leg of mutton mansail. No gaff topsail, the main sail and topsail being in one piece. Head hoists to head of topmast. Pole masts are used with this rig.

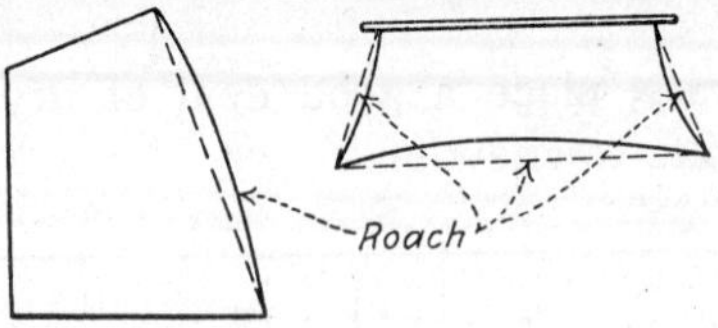

Roach. The roach of a sail is the curving in or out of a foot or leech (sketch).

Repairing sails. This duty devolves upon the seaman, and for this reason a great deal of detail has been given with regard to sailmaking. A sail is often split, cloths become weak and new pieces are needed. Many old sails get thin near the head, where the whole weight of the sail is carried and new cloths must be put in.

Many experienced sailmakers advocate cutting across the cloths at an angle when setting in new canvas. But the best practice is to cut across square, and join new to old at right angles to the seams. Where a number of new cloths are to lie side by side, stagger the joints.

In repairing old sails with new canvas use a lighter canvas for the new work. One number lighter at least. On a very old sail use two numbers lighter.

Middle stitching. It is often advisable to middle stitch old seams. This is sometimes called "snake stitching." This is fine practice for the boys and ordinary seamen in trade wind weather.

Bending Sail

The lower sails on a schooner are bent on deck, that is, the gaff is lowered, the head is bent, throat and peak lashings are passed, and the foot is bent to the boom, usually to a *bending jackstay.**

Topsails are sent aloft and are bent to the hoops, and tack and sheet hooked on. The halyard is sent down to the deck and is used as a *gantline.*

Staysails are bent to the *hanks* as the head of the sail is hoisted along the stay by the halyards. Tack lashing passed, and the sail is ready for business.

In bending square sails the sail is made up for bending, *head out,* robands inserted in head holes, head earings clear, and clews out. The sail is loosely stopped with spunyarn, and the middle is taken up by a *gantline,* this being a single rope, or a single block, hooked to a strap about the sail.

Sending aloft a square sail

* A great deal depends on the way a new sail is bent and on its care during the first few times it is in use. The first operation of bending a mainsail is to make the throat fast, being sure that there is enough slack canvas left there so that when the gaff is peaked up there will not be an undue strain. The head is then pulled out "hand taut," the peak lashed in place and the head then laced to the gaff—not with one long lacing round and round the gaff, but preferably by a lashing at each grommet. If a single lacing is used it should be hitched at each grommet, as otherwise the sail will hang from the peak. Then hoist the sail and seize on each hoop. If blowing too fresh the gaff may be hoisted only a few feet and each hoop triced up as it is made fast. Then secure the tack, either by a shackle or a lashing, make the clew fast and lace the foot to the boom. A tag will be found on the sail giving the measurements of head and foot. Do not guess at these, but measure them on gaff and boom, and do not haul the sail out beyond the proper points. . . .

It is probable that the art of sailmaking has never reached as high a degree of perfection (especially as regards yacht sails) as at the present time, and the advent of steam and the gasolene motor hasn't driven the sailmaker out of business, as many predicted. Indeed, the sailmakers have specialized not only on yacht and schooner sails, with sails for the occasional square rigger that still ploughs the sea, but on vessel awnings, boat covers, spray hoods and wind cloths and the many kinds of canvas work required on the modern steamship. Indeed, good sailmakers are in great demand, and the larger sail lofts sometimes have difficulty in getting enough men that have had experience in all the intricacies of broadseaming, roping, turning in cringles and thimbles, and the like.—Henry C. Ames in *Yachting.*

Hoist up middle of sail well above the yard to which it is to be bent, send it up *forward* of the yard. Have men on the yard lead out the head earings. If a very large sail, hook handy billy to each head cringle. Haul away on these and lower gantline. Pass midship stop, haul out head earings, pass robands, hook and *mouse* all gear.

To unbend, haul up sail in gear, cast off midship stop, pass strop around middle of sail, hook gantline, haul taut, cut robands and ease away on head earings, having detached all gear.

To shift sail. Sail is usually shifted at sea when making a passage, from fine to bad weather or *vice versa.* This is done, one or two sails at a time and a smart crew can shift the canvas in a day or two. All gear is kept aloft and unhooked and hooked as the case may be as the sails come up. Watch the weather carefully before starting this work.

To bend a course in blowing weather. Stretch the head of the sail across the deck as near as possible; bend the gear, then bring the leeches of the sail as near where it should haul up on the yard as possible, then stop sails well about every two or three feet; besides the yard buntlines, have one in 'midship of the sail. When ready, man altogether, and run up to the yard; then the sail may be bent and furled with very little difficulty.

Care of sails. At sea sails naturally dry out, as sail is set whenever it will draw. Do not stow wet sails in the locker with other dry canvas.

In port always loose sail after each rain. Be certain to do this in warm weather as canvas will sweat. Even if no rain has fallen loose sail when conditions are favorable.

When alongside unbend sail and stow away. Stow all running gear, reeving off temporary braces and gear with old stuff.

When in an open harbor do not strip the vessel of all sail. Leave enough sail on the yards to work ship with in case of a sudden blow.

The writer recalls an incident on the auxiliary bark *Frithjof* in the arctic. Her sails were never loosed and he thought it a good idea to try them on the voyage home. As soon as sheeted home they began to melt away, the canvas being thoroughly rotten. A few months later, in 1907, this vessel was lost with all hands on the coast of Iceland. Her canvas had not been replaced, the spare sails being as poor as the ones we lost. She went ashore before a heavy gale, being unable to ratch off.

IV

Canvas Work

On board ship, whether sail or steam, there is a great deal of canvas fitting. The following notes may be of service and are given as a guide.

Tarpaulins. For schooners, where the hatches are liable to be under water, No. 1 canvas is used, at least for the top cover.

Steamers use No. 4 canvas, waterproofed.

Tarpaulins are made large enough to cover the hatch and fold down six inches below the battens. The custom is to use three tarpaulins one over another.

Tarpaulin canvas comes waterproofed in the bolt, and the seams are treated after making.

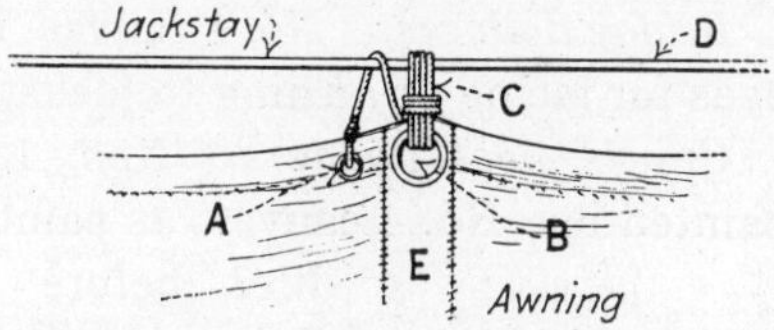

A, Hole into which awning stop C is spliced
B, Hauling-out hole
E, Seam
D, Jackstay

Awnings. Large steamer awnings are made of No. 2 canvas. Ridge rope 2″ manila. Bolt rope 2″ manila or 1½ inch hemp. Stops on a heavy awning should be fitted to two grommet holes as shown in sketch.

Smaller awnings run down to No. 5 canvas.

Awnings are held up by a *euphroe* and crow's foot, the latter with ends spliced into the ridge rope.

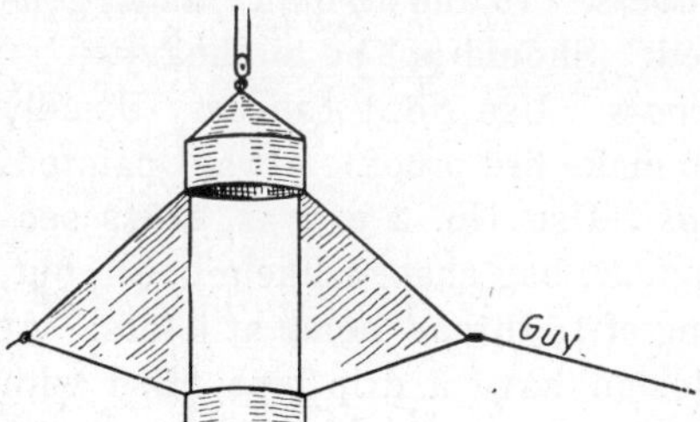

Wind sail

In tropical trades it is sometimes the custom to fit double awnings, the upper one of white canvas, the lower one, about a foot below it, of dark blue canvas of lighter grade. The lower awning should be furled at night. The reason for this rig is obvious. Side screens are fitted *below* the edge of the lower awning.

To house an awning. On the approach of a squall, cast off stops and bring them down below the rail, or if no rail, close to the deck, securing where handy. This keeps out the wind and rain. Many ships, where sudden squalls come up at night, always house or furl awnings after sunset.

Windsails. Windsails find much use in hot climates where extra ventilation is needed.

Make of No. 5 or 6 canvas. Roped with 21 thread manila or hemp (sketch).

Bridge dodgers. No. 1 canvas, roped and fitted with grommet eyes for lacing or lashing to jackstay.

Crow's nest dodgers. Nos. 1 or 2 and 3 canvas. When painted use No. 4 canvas, as paint makes dodger much heavier. *Wet* before painting with soapy water. Takes less paint and keeps canvas half way pliable.

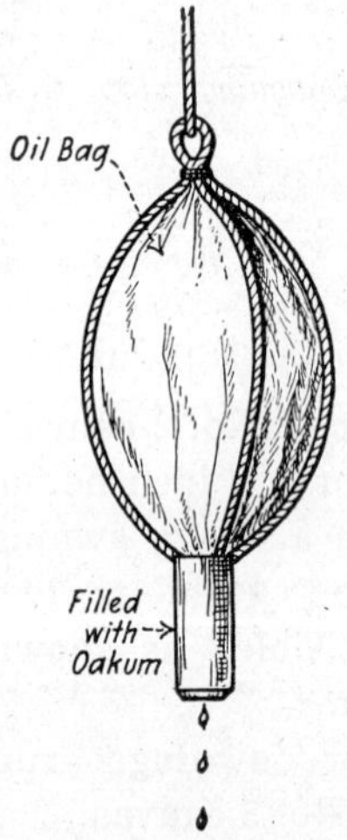

Canvas oil bag

Rail screens. No. 5 or 6 canvas. Brass eyelets along tabling, lace top and bottom. Do not paint, keep scrubbed.

Ventilator covers. No. 3 to 6 canvas. Fit with draw strings long enough to run down to handle of ventilator. Covers often blow off and this keeps them on board.

Boat covers. 10 and 12 ounce duck, generally used. Should not be too heavy.

Mast coats. Use No. 1 canvas. Usually treated to make fire proof. Always painted.

Oil bags. Use No. 2 canvas, cross section triangular, bag shaped like a beech nut, with roping of 15 thread hemp at joints. At bottom the bags of good design have a drip pipe filled with oakum (sketch).

A vessel kept in good order will have neat canvas covers for hose and wire, reels, for sounding machines, binnacles, pelorus, telegraphs, cargo winches and other fittings.

CHAPTER VII

DECK MACHINERY

The various mechanical devices, engines, winches, capstans, windlasses, steering and towing machinery, and deck pumps, are usually taken care of by the engineering force of the vessel, but their use, and very often their management, is part of the duty of the deck department and a book on seamanship may well include a brief description of the most usual types of these machines.

The windlass, steering engine and towing engine will be treated under later divisions of *Standard Seamanship.* In this chapter we will confine our attention to winches, capstans, and deck pumps.

I

Cargo winches.

There are in general six types of steam winches in common use on board ship.*

1. Friction drum winch. Drum held to gears by cone friction band.
2. Winch having keyed drum and reverse link or valve motion.
3. Steam reverse valve winch operated by a single lever. Raising lever hoists the load, lowering lever pays out the rope and lowers load.
4. Friction gear winches.
5. Two speed winch. The favorite English type and used on American vessels frequently to handle extra heavy booms.
6. Winches having winch heads but no drum; used for light loads and quick handling with manila rope hoist.

In addition to these types there are of course many combinations of the same; for instance, friction drum with link motion,

* Mr. J. S. Carswell, of the Lidgerwood Manufacturing Company's Marine Department, very kindly supplied me with valuable data on ship winches.

varying numbers and arrangements of winch heads, and also multiple drum winches.

Double drum winches of the friction type are quite common on the smaller ships where they do not have room for two winches at a hatch.

When operating under high steam pressure, say over 125 lbs., the ordinary slide valve commonly used on winches is not successful, and piston valves are required.

Steam reverse valve winch. Drum keyed to gear. To hoist load, raise lever. To lower load, lower lever. Brake shown at right edge of cut is for emergency only.

Winches may be made with straight or *herringbone* gears.

The following rules for the operation and care of ship's auxiliaries have been drawn up by the Lidgerwood Company:

1. Auxiliaries of any type will give better service if they are oiled up thoroughly and turned over at least every day, whether the ship be in port or at sea.

2. On steam auxiliaries drip cocks should be opened before each operation and the throttle opened very slowly and steam chests and cylinders given a chance to warm up before the engine is operated.

The *Dew Valve* is an automatic relief valve for draining steam cylinders, and has proven efficient on auxiliary ship machinery such as winches, windlasses and pumps.

3. Care should be taken that *every* bearing and outside rubbing surface is lubricated. This is usually done twice a day when in operation.

4. On shipboard no lubricant is used in the steam chest or cylinders on account of the steam being condensed and returned to boiler. The Lidgerwood Mfg. Co. makes it a practice on ship's auxiliaries to coat all cylinders and rubbing parts of the

A compound geared winch (two speed). Gear shift shown at back of winch.

reciprocating parts with a special compound of graphite and vaseline. The engines are given a run before leaving the shops and this compound is thoroughly worked into the rubbing surfaces.

5. Care should be taken in winding the rope on the drum to see that it lays evenly across the face and in succeeding layers. This should be given exceptional care at the start and should be watched as closely as possible during the operation of the winches. Due to the frequent short leads on shipboard it is hard to have a perfect rope lay. The life of the rope and of the face of the drum will be very materially lengthened by care being taken in this respect. The rope leads from drum to first sheave should be as great as possible at all times, care being taken in this respect especially when making new installations. This materially aids the lay of the rope.

6. Winch heads should be carefully polished before shipment and should be kept so. It will materially increase the life of the manila rope used on them. When not in operation they should be coated with lubricant to prevent rust. As soon as grooving appears on the face of any winch head due to cutting from slipping the rope too long in one position, this face should immediately be turned off to eliminate such grooving.

7. Care should be taken to watch for any knocks that may occur in the engine elements. This usually means a loose bearing. If the bearings are tightened down promptly on discovery of knocks, they will last longer, wear more evenly, and save wear on the engine elements. The heating of bearings or rubbing parts is due either to insufficient lubrication, improper adjustment (too tight), or grit in bearing.

8. Gearing should be kept lubricated. Experience has indicated that in normal weather a good lubricant is " Crater Compound " manufactured by the Texas Co. In very severe weather this becomes too stiff and a lighter compound " Thuban Compound " is more desirable. Many other good lubricants are of course available.

A friction gear winch. Note absence of cogs. For fast light loads.

9. Worm gearing, which is more commonly used on steering engines than other types of auxiliaries, should be furnished so that the worm will run in an oil bath, and this bath should be kept full. The worm is usually provided with some sort of adjustable thrust washers, and care should be taken that these are kept in adjustment and the worm kept in a central position as regards the worm wheel.

10. Bearings should be occasionally examined to see that they are wearing evenly, and the gearing should be examined to see that it is in proper mesh. Should the drum shaft bearings chance to wear more quickly than the crank shaft bearings, the gear may tend to drop toward the pinion and bottom, possibly breaking the teeth of one or the other.

11. On friction drum winches the load should be lowered on the brake and not by slipping the frictions. The brake is designed for the purpose of slipping to lower the load, while if the frictions are continually slipped they will wear quickly, perhaps burn, and present an uncertain holding power which may result in disaster, possibly dropping a load and badly damaging the ship or injuring stevedores in the hold.

12. Electrically driven auxiliaries must have the electrical equipment protected from the weather. When auxiliaries cannot be under cover they may be protected in several other ways.

1. Watertight electrical equipment supplied.
2. Waterproof motor—controller and resistance mounted below deck.

   Note: This cannot usually be done on freighters because there is danger of the hot resistance igniting or exploding cargo in the hold.
3. Removable watertight casings mounted over equipment.

13. On electrical auxiliaries care must be taken to keep the commutator and brushes free from oil and dirt.

Repairs

14. It is the present custom of almost all large manufacturers to give their finished products serial numbers. Any officer in charge of auxiliaries should be instructed to learn (from inquiring of the manufacturer direct if information is not otherwise available) where these serial numbers are placed on the auxiliary, and in ordering repair parts the serial number of the auxiliary for which the parts are used should always be stated. On Lidgerwood steam winches and steering engines the serial numbers are stamped on the tops of the rear cylinder heads and on the rear ends of the top surface of the slide bars. On electric auxiliaries they are stamped or cast on plates mounted on the resistance and are stamped on the side of the bedplate under the right hand main bearing.

15. On most auxiliaries, particularly single drum winches, the hand should also be stated. The hand is determined by the side on which the operating levers are placed viewing the auxiliary from the cylinder end.

16. Repair parts should be ordered by name of part, and the number wanted should be given rather than ordering by sets.

On American craft the *reverse valve* type of winch is gaining in favor, while foreign practice favors the link motion. The link motion, by the way, is the famous Stephenson's Link. With a working pressure of 100 lbs. per inch, a good steam winch should attain a hoisting speed of 250 feet per minute slinging a one ton load. The loads of course depend upon the type of cargo, and the gear used. With heavy loads winch speeds must decrease.

Electric winches are gaining in favor and will undoubtedly be largely used when motor ships become more common. The electric winch is more flexible than the steam winch, the decks are kept clear of steam pipes, heat losses are avoided, and power is available at shorter notice, with chance of freezing up eliminated.

An electric cargo winch. Control at right.

The first cost of electric equipment is considerably higher than for steam winches; but offsetting this are a number of important advantages. The electric winch is more economical to operate; it is claimed that it cuts loading or unloading time in half, affords much better control of the load, eliminates standby charges that increase steam operation costs when delays occur, makes the winches available any time on short notice and eliminates trouble.

The greater speed with electric winches is credited to the degree of control which the operators have over the load. It can be dropped rapidly to within a few feet of the bottom of the hold and then slowed down to enable it to be swung into place. The return of the empty hook is also made much faster than with steam winches.

The positive unwinding drive of the electric winch brings down the empty hook as rapidly as desired. Should the current fail during operation, the automatic brake will hold the load suspended until the current comes on again. The motors are protected against overload on low voltage by a double point circuit breaker and contactor panel. If an overload comes on the circuit breaker goes out and is cut in again automatically when the control lever is returned to neutral position. A single lever controls each winch, and no foot brakes are required. *It is notable that levers and directions of movement are the same as in the old steam winches, so that new operators have no difficulty in " breaking in."*

Trouble heretofore experienced with electric machinery above deck is believed to be due very largely to inadequate protection from salt air and water. As now installed, the motors are not merely weatherproof, but are made absolutely watertight. The controlling apparatus is enclosed in a watertight steel case with two watertight doors, which can be opened for ventilation during use. The lever shaft which operates the controller is carried through the side of the control case in a stuffing box, packed like a piston rod. Wires are led through watertight conduit. The motors are direct geared to the winding drum, and friction drums and hand brakes are entirely eliminated.

II

The Placement and Use of Cargo Winches

The following series of valuable photographs have been given to *Standard Seamanship* by Mr. Ernest Pulsford, manager of the Marine Department of the Lidgerwood Manufacturing Company. Careful study of the location and method of rigging and operating ship's winches has been made by this company. The author wishes to express his appreciation of the generous way in which these photographs are made available for the benefit of seamen and all others concerned in the efficient design and operation of vessels.

Illustration *A* shows a pair of single friction drum winches with reverse gear, installed at the hatch.

Stevedores lay particular stress upon the advantage gained with these winches in overhauling the empty line by the reverse gear.

A Second Mate in referring to these winches said: " They will handle any kind of load, and you don't have to wear a man

A. *Single friction drum winches.*

out overhauling a light line all day—just kick it over with the reverse."

Illustration *B* shows an interesting group of single friction drum winches. At the hatch in the foreground the stevedores are operating a pair of two speed (compound gear) winches with single friction drum. These two speed winches are designed for handling cargo of greatly varying weights. Forward of the mast are two single friction drum winches.

Illustration *C* shows the rigging provided for fixing one boom over the hatch and the other over the side of the vessel, both whips being permanently attached to a single hook forming what is called " yard and stay method " or " burton method." These winches are installed so that one operator, standing where he can see down into the hatch while hoisting, operates both

B. Two-speed single friction drum winches.

Note: The figures on the hatch coaming are: The register number. The net tonnage. The vessel's signal letters of the International Code.

C. Reverse lever winches at hatch. Wooden steamer.

winches, the one to hoist and the other to swing the load out to the dock or barge alongside.

Illustration *D* shows "two speed" ship winches (compound gear). They are particularly well-adapted for use with heavy derrick booms, the base of such a boom showing in the illustration.

These drums are so constructed that they may be bolted fast to the friction gear, and the winch used as a fixed drum reverse

D. Heavy duty winches.

motion winch. This is generally done when hoisting very heavy loads, the drum being driven through the compound intermediate gear giving high hoisting duty at low speed. The drum is of ample size to hold the large amount of rope required with the multi-part blocks generally used on the heavy booms.

The same winch rapidly handles light loads on the single gear reduction, the drum being operated through the friction.

A foot operated band brake is provided on the drum to control the lowering of the load when hoisting with the friction, or to hold the drum while hoisting on the winch head.

Illustration *E* shows a "side by side" double friction drum winch.

When this photograph was taken only one of the drums was being operated. Each drum operates independently of the other, and hoisting and lowering can be done on both drums simultaneously, or independently, by two operators. The operators stand one on each side of the engine, each operating the drum on his side. Each side of the engine is the same, with separate throttle valves, and each man handles his own friction lever,

E. "Side by side" winch.

foot brake and throttle valve, entirely independent of the other. The loads are hoisted by the friction drums, then taken upon the brakes, and either held or lowered.

The advantage of this type of winch is that a hoisting line is always attached to each drum and they are always ready for immediate use, saving delay in changing ropes which is necessary when using a single drum engine working two booms.

Illustration *F* shows two of our double side by side friction drum winches, each arranged for the operation of two booms, using one winch with two booms at each hatch.

This is a very good illustration of an equipment suitable for

F. Light duty " side by side " winches.

G. Operator's platform and raised winch bed.

the smaller size cargo steamers, showing how the compact double drum winch can be more conveniently installed on such ships than two single drum winches.

Illustration *G* shows how an experienced marine superintendent set the winches. It is a good form of structural foundation.

This foundation serves the three-fold purpose of securing the winch, leveling it, and raising it above the wash of the sea.

H. The yard and stay method of hoisting cargo.

The illustration also shows an operator's platform adjusted to correct height for easy handling of the levers, and which also gives the operator a full view of the hold.

Illustration *H* shows the "yard and stay" or "burtoning" method of hoisting cargo.

Two booms, with two winches, are generally used at each hatch. One boom is swung over the center of the hatch, carrying the main hoisting whip leading from the drum of one of the winches, and this whip hoists the cargo from the hold. The other boom is swung out-board, and the second winch operating the whip on this boom swings the load after it is hoisted clear of the hatch, and then lowers it alongside. In loading, the operation is reversed.

There is one operator at each winch. The far winch has just hoisted the load from the wharf, and the near winch is pulling the load over the hatchway, preparatory to lowering it into the hold; the far operator releasing the friction, controlling the height and swing of the load by the brake. When the load arrives over the hatch it is lowered into the hold, controlled by the brake on the near winch.

I. Loading with a single winch.

Illustration *I* shows a method of cargo handling by the use of single friction drum winch particularly well adapted to the handling of light loads. With this method one winch and one boom are employed, the boom being held over the center of the hatch. The winch hoists the load from wharf or lighter sliding it on a broad skid, and when the load clears the bulwark it swings over the hatch by gravity. The hatch tender by means of a guide line prevents the load from taking an excessive swing and bringing up against the hatch coaming. The load is then lowered into the hold by the brake and friction. As soon as the load is unhooked the hatch tender snaps the hoisting line, twirling it over the side of the ship, and it is in position to hook on the next load. With an experienced man on the guide line remarkably rapid work is done in this way.

II

Capstans and Warping Winches

Steam capstans. These should be readily unkeyed for use by hand with pigeonholes and bars ready. Capstans driven by power, either steam or electricity are generally placed on the forecastle head, amidship, and on the bows, depending upon the size of the vessel. Additional capstans just forward of the bridge, amidship, and on the quarters as well as in the stern are to be found on large vessels for use in handling lines when going alongside. The large mooring lines are so heavy, and the side out of water so great, that such power must be used both in docking and in handling lines with the change in tide. The use and location, with leads, bollards, and reels for wire should be understood by the officers charged with

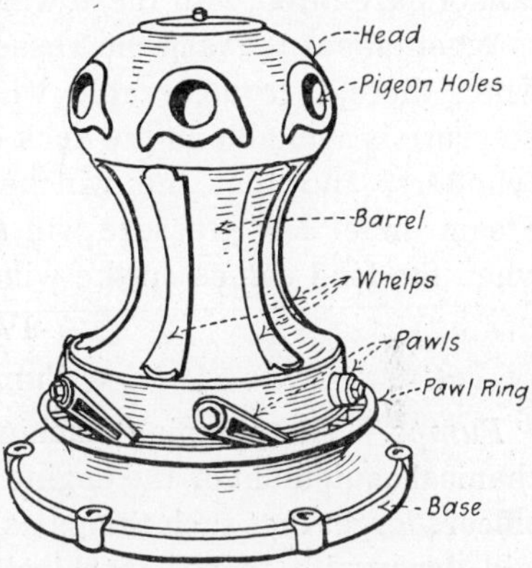

A deck capstan (*see illustration of forecastle head capstan, page 641*).

Docking winch.

their use, and petty officers should also be familiar with their working.

Docking and warping winches. These take the place of capstans in some vessels and are often preferred. They are geared at least 10 to 1 and have large winch heads. Many tankers are fitted with these winches on the after deck.

When about to warp the vessel, particularly in a tide way, or when there is considerable wind, be certain that full steam pressure is available in the deck lines, that all water is out of the cylinders, and that the winches and capstans are in order. Steam under low pressure will sputter around quite lively, but when the load comes on the winches there is nothing doing.*

IV

Pumps

Pumps. The pumping machinery is so much a part of the mechanical equipment of the engine room, that nowadays most deck officers forget that such things as pumps exist. No rules can be laid down with regard to ships' pumps, but deck officers, and masters especially, should know what the ship's pumps can do. How fast ballast can be shifted from forward trimming tanks aft, and the reverse, and how long it will take to pump out any tank, and the *amount* of water (weight) that will be discharged. A study of this and the *tons per inch scale* will give an officer a fair idea as to how much he can lighten, or list, his ship at any given time, knowing the condition of the ballast tanks.

Pumps for fire use are as important as the bilge and emergency pumps. In any emergency—grounding, collision or fire—the efficient use of pumps is an important part of seamanship.

Roughly the pumps in a ship are as follows: *Condenser circulating pump.* (This is the pump that discharges the great stream of water we see coming from the side of ships a few feet above the load line. The water has been taken in low down, passed through the condenser to cool off the exhaust steam, and is discharged as above. The exhaust steam, in a coil of pipes, returns to the hot well as hot water and is ready to go back into the boilers and work again as steam. This circulating pump should always be in mind when a vessel goes aground on a sandy bottom.

* In freezing weather keep steam on all deck lines and turn winches over as often as necessary to avoid freezing. When laid up be certain all water is drained from pipe lines and cylinders.

The pump should be stopped at once to prevent the condenser filling with sand.)* *Main boiler feed pumps; Auxiliary boiler feed pumps; Fire pumps; Bilge pumps; General service pumps,* fresh water, sanitary, etc.; and on a tanker, *Cargo pumps.* There are also *oil pumps,* and *air pumps.*

The American Bureau of Shipping has set certain requirements for steam pumping arrangements with which the master and chief mate should be familiar. Tank suctions are regulated by the size of the tank, running from 2½ inches in diameter for a tank under 20 tons, to 7½ inches in diameter for a tank over 1,000 tons and under 1,300 tons. Also the *main suction line* must not be of less diameter than that required for the largest tank in the vessel.

Extracts from the A.B.S. rules follow:

All steamers are to be provided with efficient steam pumping plant, having the suctions and means for drainage so arranged that any water which may enter any compartment of the Ship and any watertight section of a compartment can be pumped through at least one suction when the Vessel is on even keel and upright, *or has a list of five degrees.* Satisfactory means are to be provided for draining the tops of tanks in order to comply with this requirement.

All pipes from the pumps which are required for draining cargo or machinery spaces should be entirely distinct from pipes which may be used for filling or emptying spaces where water is carried; the arrangement of the valves, etc., should be such to prevent water passing from the sea and from such water spaces into the machinery and cargo spaces, or from one compartment to another. If a suction pipe from the engine room is led to the fore peak, a screw-down stop-valve capable of being operated from above the bulkhead deck, is to be fitted on the suction inside the fore peak.

(*Note:* This is to prevent pumping the ocean through the ship if she is stove in *forward* of the collision bulkhead.—*Author.*)

The Main and Donkey Pumps are to draw from all compartments, and in addition, the donkey is to have a separate bilge suction in the engine room. The pumps are to be of sufficient capacity to give a speed of water through the pipes of not less than 400 feet per minute, under ordinary working.

Main circulating pumps should have direct suction connections to the lowest drainage level in the machinery space. The diameter of these connections should be at least twice the diameter of the engine room main suction line.

* (See page 739.)

Distribution Boxes, cocks, and valves are to be in positions which are accessible at all times under ordinary circumstances.

Bilge and Ballast Suction Pipes are to be efficiently secured, and straps are to be fitted at the middle of the length of each range of pipes to prevent fore and aft movement. Efficient expansion joints are to be fitted, and where the connections at the ends of each range of pipes are made with lead bends, the radii of the bends and the distance between the centers of the radii should each be equal to 3 diameters, and the length of the bend to 8 diameters of the pipe.

Roses and Boxes are to be easily accessible for examination and cleaning. The bilge suctions in machinery spaces and tunnel wells should be led from easily accessible mud boxes placed wherever practicable above the level of the working floor, and should have straight tail pipes to the bilges. The suction ends in other spaces should be enclosed in strum boxes having perforations whose combined area is not less than three times that of the suction pipe, and so constructed that they can be cleared without breaking the joints of the suction pipe.

Sounding Pipes are to be fitted to each compartment and ballast tank, with a thick doubling plate securely fixed under each pipe, for the rod to strike upon. These pipes are to be fitted, without bends, directly into the compartment intended to be sounded, and are to extend to the bulkhead deck or to a position which is always accessible; if in accessible positions below the bulkhead deck they are to be fitted with non-detachable screw caps.

Air Pipes, not less than 2 inches in diameter, are to be fitted at each corner of each ballast tank; this requirement may be modified in the case of small tanks and increased for large tanks; the total area of the pipes should always be greater than that of the supply pipes and in the case of deep tanks should be at east twice that of the supply pipes. Efficient arrangements must be made to permit of the air getting freely to the pipes while the tanks are being filled. Where the tank top is peaked, cambered, or has sheer, air pipes are to be fitted at the highest position.

Air, *sounding* and *suction pipes* are to be effectively protected against the risk of damage from cargo, coal, etc.

In the old days the mates and "chips" knew all about the ship's pumps. It might be a good idea to find out all about the pumps of a modern vessel.

Installation and Care of Pumps*

Alignment. Pumps should be set positively in line on a stiff foundation. Particular care should be taken with long stroke

* From *Marine Engineer's Handbook,* Sterling.

vertical pumps which have tie bar connections. When set, to test alignment, remove glands from both piston rod stuffing boxes, move piston rod to one end of stroke, try glands in both boxes. Remove glands, move piston rod to opposite end of stroke and try the glands again. If any sign of binding exists make proper adjustment in setting of pump.

Location. The pump should be located in the ship as close to its work as conditions will conveniently allow, with as short and direct suction and discharge pipe connections as circumstances will permit. An *air pump should be located* lower than the condenser so that condensate will drain directly into pump cylinders. Provide a proper space around pump so that all parts requiring inspection or adjustment are conveniently accessible.

Pump connections. Always connect pump so as to secure a full and uniform supply of liquid to be handled. The extreme theoretical height to which water can be lifted by atmospheric pressure alone is 33.9 feet. In practice this seldom exceeds 25 feet; the smaller the suction lift can be made, the better. Suction pipe should be as short as possible and never smaller than opening on pump. As there is a considerable loss of head due to friction, the diameter of long lines of pipe should be increased to allow for this, and for the same reason bends of large radius and as few in number as possible should be used.

The same remarks apply to discharge pipe, although not with the same force, since in the discharge pipe the full power of the pump is always available to force the liquid through the piping, while in the case of the suction pipe, only the atmospheric pressure is available to force the liquid into the pump. Avoid all air leaks in air pump connections; otherwise vacuum will be impaired.

All valves in the suction and discharge piping should be gate valves, and at least as great in opening as the area of the pipe. Globe valves offer too much resistance to the flow of the liquid.

Steam connections. Steam and exhaust pipe connections should always be made with due allowance for expansion of steam pipe, and of ample size—never less than the opening on the pump.

A throttle valve should be placed in the steam pipe as close to the pump as possible, and a drip cock or bleeder valve should be provided for draining the main steam pipe before starting the pump.

Blow out the steam pipe thoroughly before connecting the pump. Any dirt or chips carried into the steam cylinder will cut and injure it seriously.

Air chambers. A suction air chamber placed on the suction pipe close by the pump is distinctly recommended for fire pumps with high suction lift, short stroke pumps and pumps running at high speed. Care should be taken to locate this suction chamber in a continuation of the line of flow in the suction pipe so as to receive the impact of the water column and thus cushion the pulsations in the most efficient manner.

A discharge air chamber should also be provided on the discharge of a heavy pressure pump in a continuation of the line of discharge pipe; in exceptional cases where the pump is subject to very heavy duty, it is an advantage to provide an air pet cock on the suction pipe close to the pump. By opening this pet cock slightly, a small amount of air may be admitted to the pump with the water, and the discharge air chamber kept supplied with the proper quantity to cushion the outflowing water.

Lubrication. All bearings, joints of moving parts and piston rods should be lubricated before starting pumps, and also at short intervals when in operation. All grease cups should be packed with Albany grease. Where bearings are divided, keep same adjusted with shims.

Packing. Keep stuffing boxes well filled with a good quality of packing, but do not screw up glands too tight, and do not allow same packing to remain in stuffing boxes long enough to become so hard that it will score the piston rods.

Both main and auxiliary *steam pistons are packed* by means of carefully fitted cast iron spring packing rings, which are self-adjusting and need no attention whatever; replacement on account of wear is necessary only after many years of service.

When *water pistons are packed* with fibrous packing, trouble sometimes arises from swelling of the packing, causing the pump to operate stiffly and make uneven strokes, etc. This is especially so when pumping hot liquids, and sometimes it is necessary to take out the packing and thin it down. This is done by stripping a layer from one side of the strand or ring, or hammering it if packing is of the braided type, as the swelling is usually lateral. In fitting a piston with new packing, it is well to soak the packing in warm water over night before fitting it. New packing should not be crowded into the piston, but should fit the packing space loosely. When it becomes wet the swelling will cause it to fit in the space.

Pump air bound. Hot water cannot be raised by suction, as it vaporizes when atmospheric pressure is removed, and the vapor is alternately expanded and compressed in pump cylinders without being expelled.

Laying up. When pump is to be kept out of commission for any considerable time, slush interior of steam chest with cylinder oil to prevent corrosion. If steam end is fitted with lubricator, fill this with oil and open cock so oil can flow to steam chest. A few quick pump strokes will distribute oil over steam end of pump.

CHAPTER VIII

HOLDS, PEAKS, TANKS

I

Holds

In many respects the most important compartments in the hull of a vessel are the holds. In a vessel devoted to the carriage of cargo this is strictly so, for the holds represent earning capacity. The holds are usually numbered commencing from forward, for convenience of reference, and for the purpose of allocating cargo or locating it by its markings in the cargo book.

Number 1 hold comes immediately abaft of the collision bulkhead.

In a typical cargo vessel, as shown in the illustrations*, number 2 hold extends forward of the cross bunker, the division bulkhead between holds 1 and 2 being in the vicinity of the fore mast. Hold number 3 comes abaft of the engine room space, and hold number 4 is immediately forward of the after peak bulkhead, the division bulkhead between these holds being near the main mast.

Other hold arrangements are employed and in larger vessels the holds are more numerous, but vessels devoted to the carriage of freight have very large holds and the four-hold system is followed up to about fifteen thousand tons D.W.

The parts of a hold are briefly enumerated:

The *wake of the hatch* is that part immediately under the hatch opening.

The *wings of the hold* are the spaces on either side of the hold, usually considered to lie above the upper side stringers.

The *limbers*, are the gutters on either side of the keel, or where a double bottom is fitted at the sides of the tanks, next the margin plates. It is here that the water collects which comes into the bilge of the vessel.

* See pages 244–254.

Limber boards are removable boards, or steel shutters, covering the limbers. They are a part of the flooring, or ceiling of the hold.

Hold stringers are simply the stringers where they pass through the holds. The loose dunnage and chocking pieces are usually stowed on these where they can be got at when loading. *Stanchions* and *pillars* are the upright columns, often bolted in place so that they can be removed when stowing or discharging very large pieces of cargo.

A typical No. 1 hold. Note lower 'tween deck seen looking up through the hatch. Note flat floors over tank tops. Limber boards lifted at far end of hold. Ancient dunnage rules are useless in such holds.

Cargo battens, substantial wooden planking, are fitted at the sides of the hold to keep cargo from contact with the steel frames and shell plating of the vessel.

Hold ladders are usually permanent and on the center line on either the fore or aft side of the hatch opening, these should be examined whenever the holds are empty as the rungs are often knocked or pulled loose while loading and discharging.

The pipe lines running through, or into the holds are generally as follows:

The *sounding pipes*, leading from the upper deck to the tanks and bilges. Great care should be taken that these pipes are not injured by cargo; they should be examined after each cleaning of the hold.

The *smothering lines*, steam lines leading into the holds, or piping for conveying CO_2 gas for the extinguishing of fire.

The *water lines*, hose connections for fire and washing purposes.

The *pumping lines*, from tanks and bilges. The *rose boxes*, or *strums*, or *strainers*, located at the suction ends of these pump lines should be examined whenever the holds are empty and just before starting to fill tanks or load cargo.

A No. 2 hold. Limbers opened for inspection. Ready for cargo.

Light conduits, the piped wiring for light connections should be in good order and guarded against damage or chafing by cargo. Too much attention cannot be given the wiring in the holds.

'Tween decks. The between deck cargo spaces, or passenger spaces, are fitted in many ways. Where cargo is carried the battens, etc., are similar to those in the holds. The fittings for fire fighting, washing, lighting are similar and a part of the hold system. Sounding and air pipes pass through the 'tween decks into the hold below, and the same care of inspection should be followed in the 'tween decks.

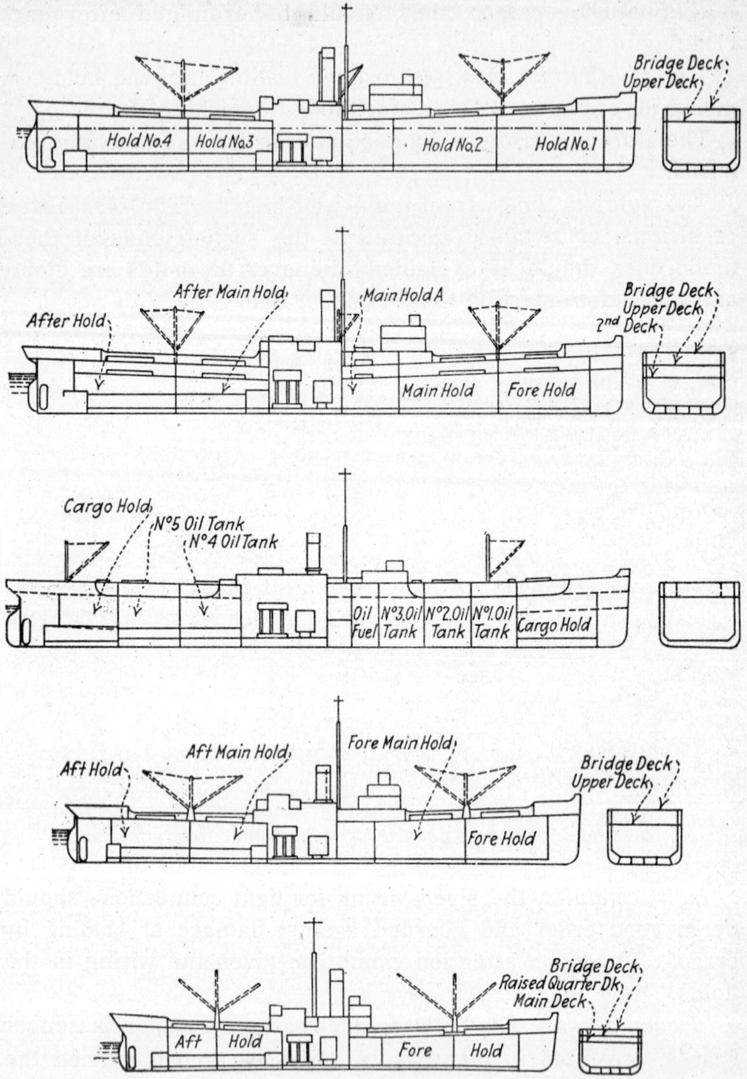

Hold divisions found in various types of cargo vessels

Shifting boards and special stanchions are used in holds and 'tween decks. These are temporary bulkheads, usually fore and aft, to prevent the shifting of bulk or bag cargoes.

"Soundings are taken at sea periodically, by passing a rod 3 or 4 feet long, with cord attached, down the pipe, and on its withdrawal noting how much of it has become wet. (The sounding rod is usually chalked.—Author.) The pipe usually extends to the upper deck, where it terminates with a screwed plug; if the upper deck is not sheltered from the weather, it is preferable, where cargo is not carried in the 'tween decks, to stop it at the second deck, for when deck water is washing about it is a difficult matter to keep the rod dry when sounding. When on the exposed upper deck, it is well to raise the end of the pipe a few inches above the deck, so that deck drainage water may not pass down the pipe and wet the rod. When a tank air pipe is at the center line it may also serve as a tank-sounding pipe, and sometimes sluice valve rods are arranged for this purpose (when the valve spindle is a tube). Of course when a tank-sounding pipe is extended below the tank top, as is not uncommon, it cannot also serve as an air pipe. Every time soundings are taken the rod strikes the same patch of cement on the vessel's bottom, so that in the course of time it may break it away. Cases are not common where the continued bumping of the sounding rod (aided by corrosion) has worn a hole right through the shell plating. To prevent this a small iron plate should be embedded in the cement just below the pipe, otherwise a plug may be screwed into the end of the sounding pipe and slots cut immediately above it to admit the water."—*Practical Shipbuilding*, Holms.

Trunks are built up boxes, usually of timber, in the holds and sometimes in the 'tween decks, to raise the center of gravity of a bulk cargo. Trunk hatches are hatch openings leading from an upper deck to a hold or lower deck through a trunk, closing off passenger or other spaces.

Cargo ports are large side ports into the 'tween decks or holds for the loading of cargo.

Bow and *stern ports* are sometimes fitted for loading long spars. These are most often seen in wooden single hold sailing craft.

II

Peaks

The peaks are the narrow compartments at the ends of the vessel. The *fore peak* lies between the stem and the collision bulkhead. It is usually divided into two parts horizontally. The lower part forms the fore peak tank, and the upper part, between the stem and the chain lockers, or if the chain lockers are abaft of the collision bulkhead, then between the stem and this bulkhead, is used for the stowage of the forward cargo gear, for awnings, and for boatswain's gear in general. Many vessels have this space fitted up as a general deck storeroom for wash-deck gear, spare parts, rope, canvas, etc.

The *after peak* is between the stern frame and the after peak bulkhead. It is generally completely filled by the after peak tank, occupying all space above the stern tube to the level of the lower deck.

The *peak tanks*, fore and aft, are *deep tanks* and are also the principal *trimming tanks* of the ship.

III

Tanks

The tanks, in general, may be divided as follows:

Double bottom, or cellular double bottom water ballast tanks, fitted with manholes, and the necessary pumping arrangements.

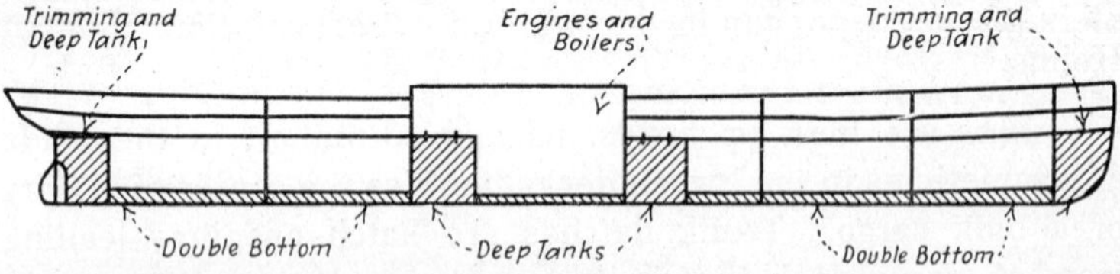

The double bottom water tanks do not, as a rule, extend beneath the engine space but generally cover the floor of the holds.*

Double Bottoms

* Vessels are now built with double bottoms for the carriage of water ballast, which has become more and more of a necessity to facilitate the handling of the ships when light or in motion without cargo. Double bottoms also offer great facility for the storage and use of any of the varieties of liquid fuel, which frequently are found to be more advantageous, if not more profitable, than coal, particularly when the cost of stowing it in the ship's bunkers and the cost of firing it with man power are considered.

Great Advantages of Double Bottoms

All liquid fuels are piped direct to the furnaces, fed and sprayed into them under pressure which makes the fuel supply and combustion constant and

The *wing tanks*, fitted in the wings, often on the 'tween decks amidships, offer an easy means for trimming ship to port or starboard.

Deep tanks, placed fore or aft of the engine spaces carry fresh water supplies and give stability when needed.

It is highly important that the officers of a vessel understand the capacity and effect of the various tanks, empty and filled upon the trim and stability of their vessel, when loaded, partly loaded or light, and with bunkers filled or empty.

In cases of grounding, this knowledge may be of the most practical value, if instantly applied.

The tank vessel is treated in a separate chapter, as it presents many special conditions.

Fresh water tanks. Fresh water should not be carried in deep tanks unless the tanks are specially strong so that *free water* may be carried in them. Strong *swash plates* should be fitted in such tanks, as of course fresh water tanks are liable to be partly filled at times. Such tanks, when partly filled are referred to as *ullage tanks.*

Air pipes are fitted to all tanks and should be open when filling

uniform, thus doing away with all inequalities of steam pressures incident to replenishing, slicing, and cleaning of fires when coal is the fuel being utilized. It should be here noted that much of the space contained within double bottoms exists between the floors of the ship which internally support the bottom plates of the vessel, and while this space exists between the ceiling of the ship's hold and the outer plating of the vessel's bottom absolutely no use was ever heretofore made of it except as a receptacle for the accumulation of bilge water. In the double bottom, therefore, it will be seen that liquid fuel utilizes a space for its storage that was not and could not be utilized for any other purpose, since many parts of the internal portion of the double bottom are quite inaccessible to the hand or the eye after such portion of the ship has been constructed. Previous to the use of the space herein referred to for water ballast or the storage of liquid fuel it was customary and necessary to coat all surfaces of such spaces with cement to protect them against oxidization incident to their being bathed more or less continually with bilge water, invariably impregnated with the impurities common to the drip from every known variety of cargoes. It can therefore readily be seen that double bottoms not only utilize to a great extent much cubic space of a ship heretofore unusable, but in doing so have a tendency to preserve tnose portions of the vessel heretofore most subject to deterioration from oxidization.—*Standardization in the Construction of Freight Ships,* E. Platt Stratton, Department of Commerce, Washington, D. C.

to prevent *air lock* in the tanks. Locate such pipes and see them in good order and *closed after filling.*

IV

Bunkers

The loading of bunker coal is an operation that falls to the deck department of a steam vessel, while the trimming is generally attended to under direction of the engineers.

The usual bunkers are as follows:

Cross bunkers, extending athwartship, either fore or aft of the boilers, but generally forward. On short passages these are sometimes used for the stowage of cargo.

Side bunkers, adjacent to the machinery space and upwards in the wings of the vessel. These bunkers feed down by gravity through *pocket bunkers*, leading from the side bunkers in the 'tween decks to the fire rooms.

The *reserve bunker* is a name given to the cross bunker, when it is entirely shut off from the boiler space by a watertight bulkhead.

The filling of bunker spaces is accomplished through small *coaling hatchways*, usually round scuttles, screwing tight to the deck and made watertight by means of a gasket.

On the weather decks the coaling hatchways are larger and are usually fitted with a small coaming and the usual means for battening down with tarpaulins, battens and wedges.

Coaling ports are fitted in the sides and this is specially so in the case of large liners where the coal is carried in side bunkers and huge cross bunkers running the width of the vessel between the boiler rooms and under the passenger decks. Great care must be exercised in the closing of the coaling ports at all times when not actually in use. The sinking of the S.S. *St. Paul*, due to this neglect, is still fresh in mind.

The small holes in the wings of the bunkers for the admission of trimmers, and for their exit, are generally known as *escape holes.* These holes are sometimes used for loading when the last coal is taken into the ship.

Oil fuel bunkers. The following excellent description of oil fuel bunkers is taken from Holms' *Practical Shipbuilding.*

"The use of crude petroleum as fuel, *i.e.*, as a substitute for coal in the furnaces of seagoing steamers, although far from general, is now common in the case of vessels carrying bulk oil, and in those trading to ports where oil is produced. In raising steam, two tons of oil may be taken, roughly, as equivalent to three tons of coal. It follows, therefore, that in vessels which burn oil fuel there is a considerable saving in weight; and there is also a saving in space, for the oil, if high-flash may be carried in the double bottom and peak tanks, spaces that are valueless for cargo. (The *flash point* of an oil is the temperature at which its vapor will ignite and explode. The flash point of a *high-flash* oil is above 150 degrees Fahrenheit. On the other hand, the flash point of gasolene is below the freezing point, that is, it will explode—when air is present, and a spark comes across it—at any ordinary temperature.) Ordinary coal bunkers are unnecessary, but many vessels are arranged to use coal as well as oil (in case the latter might be temporarily unobtainable), it is common to retain the coal bunkers, but to design and build them in the manner required for an oil tank (*i.e.*, with oil-tight hatches, doors, wash bulkheads, pump suctions, heating coils, and air pipes), so that either coal or oil may be carried as required. Some vessels which trade regularly to Eastern oil ports, where the oil is cheap, fill their fuel-oil tanks with sufficient oil to take them home to Europe and out again. Compared with coaling operations, the filling of the oil-fuel bunkers is a very quick and simple operation, requiring no manual labor and creating no disturbance on board.

"Any kind of oil may be used as fuel, but the great majority of vessels employ only high flash-point oil, on account of the absence of danger in using it and the simplicity of its stowage. . . .

"When the double bottom tanks are used for carrying oil the vertical keel must be oil-tight, to lessen the heeling effect of the oil when the tanks are only half full. The tanks must also be of moderate length, and be specially constructed to insure absolute oil-tightness."

Note: Tanks and bulkheads that are *watertight* are not necessarily *oil-tight*. Special care in riveting and caulking is necessary to insure oil-tight seams and joints.

"When the sides of the oil tanks are at any point close to the boilers they must be insulated to avoid any chance of the oil becoming dangerously heated. Each oil tank must be provided with one or more air pipes having permanently open ends debouching above the upper deck, so as to prevent the possibility of the tank bursting or collapsing by expansion of the oil through heat, or by careless pumping. (In tanks which may be pumped up the air pipes should be as large as the filling pipes to prevent the accumulation of excessive pressure by continued pumping after the tank has been filled.)

" The pipes and valves used for pumping the oil tanks must be distinct from those used for pumping the bilges, or pumping and flooding the water ballast tanks, otherwise oily water might gain access to the latter places, with danger of explosion through unsuspected accumulation of oil vapor.

" When fuel oil is taken on board it usually contains some water, which must be removed before the oil is sprayed into the furnaces. For this purpose *settling tanks* are provided, usually to port and starboard, in the 'tween decks. All fuel oil taken from the supply tanks is first pumped into a settling tank, at the bottom of which the contained water accumulates by gravity and may be drained off."

To sum up, the use of oil fuel has the following advantages where it can be readily employed:

Oil requires less bunker space than coal for a given steaming radius.

It can be carried between double bottoms and in other places where neither coal nor cargo can be stored.

The space usually given to coal can be occupied by freight paying cargo.

Bunkering can be effected with greater dispatch, and is not interfered with by darkness or the state of the weather.

It is not attendant with dirt and other discomforts incident to coal bunkering.

Labor and machinery are not required for handling ashes.

Oil fuel eliminates stoking, thus reducing the size of the crew and labor costs.

It possesses greater thermal efficiency than coal and reduces fuel costs.

The modern seaman will be more and more concerned with

the stowage of oil, in the oil burners under steam boilers, and in the bunkers of motor ships. Many things are yet to be learned about oil carriage as fuel and cargo. See Chapt. XI on Tankers.

Bulkheads. A few words may be said about bulkheads. Many vessels have met with disaster through faulty bulkheads. Sluice gates have been left open, watertight doors have not functioned when needed, or have been left open in time of collision. No sluice valve or cock is to be fitted in a collision bulkhead. All such valves and cocks are to be worked by control rods leading up to the bulkhead deck and should indicate whether the valves are open or closed. Every officer in the ship should be familiar with their location and working.

In closing this chapter, the writer wishes to remind the reader that apparent repetitions here and there are made with the purpose of driving home essential facts regarding the working of the vessel. No one is expected to read the seamanship at one sitting, and no one will fail to see the need for warnings and advice given under different headings. Holds, peaks and tanks are so important that this special chapter was considered necessary.

Sluice valves are no longer looked upon with favor as they reduce the reliability of the bulkheads as watertight partitions.

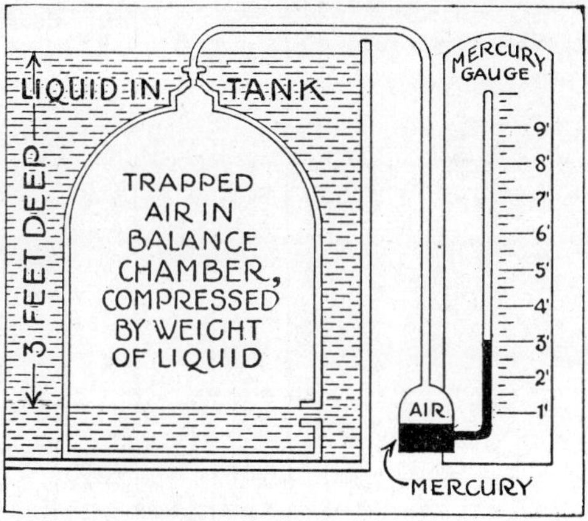

The Pneumercator Gauge

This is a very ingenious application of the pressure in a tank, or under the ship to measure the liquid in the tank or the draft of the vessel. The pressure of liquid is measured by means of an air chamber as shown in the diagram. The higher the liquid above the balance chamber (air chamber) the greater the air pressure. That

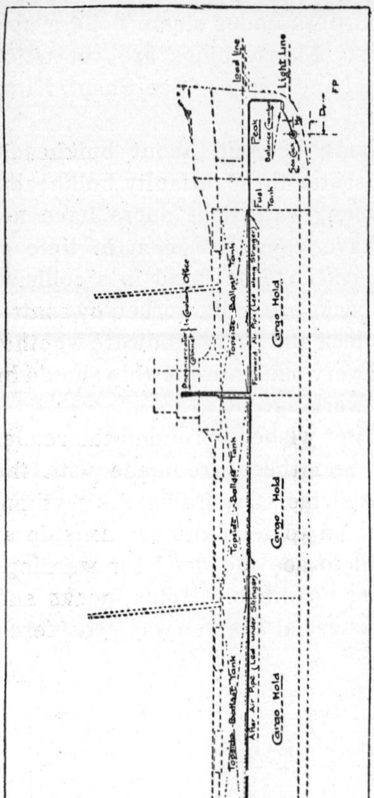

Location of draft gauges.

is, the air pressure and the liquid pressure must be the same. This air pressure is communicated to a column of mercury and as the pressure increases, or decreases, the mercury is forced up, or is allowed to fall lower in the gauge. The gauge is calibrated so that the height of mercury will show the height of liquid in the tank. The gauge is calibrated for water, or oil, or whatever may be the density of the liquid to be measured.

Although made in many types to meet varied requirements, all Pneumercator gauges have the same essential elements, which are (1) balance chamber, (2) a mercury or other gauge, calibrated in feet and inches and in the corresponding weight or volume, (3) a pump or other means of furnishing compressed air, (4) a control valve or valves connected to the gauge and also connected through small piping to the balance chamber and the air pump.

When installed in a tank the orifice in the balance chamber is located at a predetermined point below the surface of the liquid to be measured. This type of gauge works equally well on tanks at atmosphere or under pressure or vacuum.

In the type of instrument used to indicate the draft and trim of a vessel, the balance chambers, connected by one-inch sea valves, are located at predetermined points forward and aft below the light draft line of the ship, and also connected by one-quarter-inch copper tubing to the instrument located in the pilot house or captain's office. Thus installed, the Pneumercator draft gauge indicates the fore and aft draft, registers the mean draft and corresponding tons displaced, shows trim, checks invoices and deliveries, weighs cargoes and bunkers.

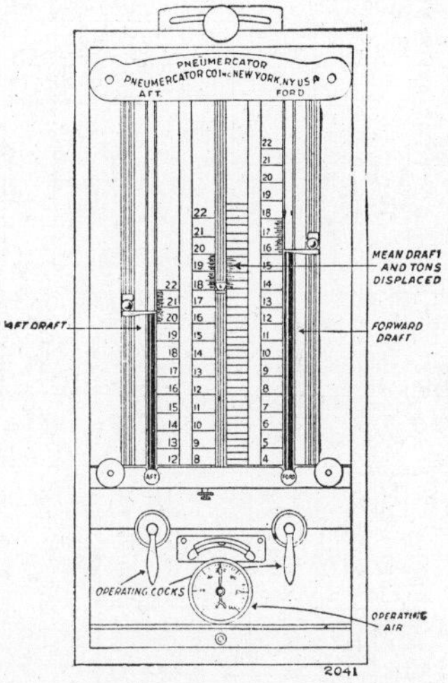

Pneumercator draft and displacement scale.

The scales are calibrated in accordance with the requirements of the service, the reading is direct and instantaneous in every case, requiring no special skill.

(*Note:* The air in the *balance chamber* must be constant in volume in order to obtain correct readings on the mercury gauge. A few strokes of a small hand pump will restore the correct balance, or, where compressed air is used, a turn of the air cock will do the same thing. If too much air is forced into the chamber it bubbles out through the bottom, no harm is done.) Read gauge, pump or turn on air (it only takes a fraction of a minute) and read gauge again. The second reading is the correct one. The draft gauge is useful, when loading or discharging. At sea the draft can be read to a fraction of an inch when it is impossible to get the draft by reading the numerals on bow and stern. In case of collision the scale will show whether the vessel is settling, or not. If she starts down, even a small fraction of an inch, the warning is most important. On the other hand the draft gauge will show when the pumps start to gain on a leak, or if they fail to do so.

CAPACITIES OF CARGO SPACES

Hold No.	Section	Dimensions for Bales: Depth	Max Length	Max. Breadth	Capacity (Bales) Cubic Feet	Capacity (Bulk Grain) Cubic Feet
1	Upper	9'-2"	57'-10"	43'-4"	19700	22400
	Lower	14'-6"	57'-10"	43'-4"	29300	34340
	Total				49000	56740
2	Over Tank	8'-9"	20'-0"	43'-8"	7600	10000
	Main Body	23'-8"	55'-8"	43'-8"	56900	65500
	Total				64500	75500
3	Total	23'-8"	55'-8"	43'-8"	53950	64200
4	Upper	8'-9"	49'-1"	43'-2"	13500	18900
	Lower	13'-6"	49'-1"	42'-0"	8800	11820
	Total				22300	30720
Under Bridge Deck	Total	(Irregular) 7'-6"	89'-0"	43'-8	22800	25840
Under Poop Deck	Total	10'-11"	29'-0"	8'-10"	2300	2800
Deep Tank	Total	14'-1"	18'-3"	43'-9"	11300	13800
Total Capacity					276150	269600

HATCHES AND BOOMS

Hatch No.	Size of Hatch	No. Booms Serving Hatch	Capacity of Booms
1	24'-9" × 18'-0"	2	5 Tons Each
2	29'-3" × 18'-0"	2	5 Tons Each
Tank	9'-0" × 16'-0"	2	1½ Tons Each
3	29'-3" × 18'-0"	2	5 Tons Each
4	24'-9" × 18'-0"	2	5 Tons Each

DOUBLE BOTTOM & AFTER PEAK TANKS

Tanks: Description	No.	Location	Capacity: Cu. Ft.	Gallons	Pounds
Fuel Oil	1P	Fr. #9 to 33	2532	18930	139260
	1S	do.	2532	18930	139260
	2P	Fr. 34 to 58	3904	29200	214720
	2S	do.	3904	29200	214720
	3P	Fr. 59 to 70	1784	13340	98120
	3S	do.	1784	13340	98120
	5P	Fr. 89 to 113	3301	24680	181555
	5S	do.	3301	24680	181555
	6	Fr. 114 to 126	1068	7980	58740
	After Peak		2480	18520	136400
	Total		26590	198800	1462450
Feed Water	4P	Fr. 71 to 88	2772	20730	173250
	4S	do.	2772	20730	173250
	Total		5544	41460	346500
Total Capacity Fuel Oil and Feed Water			32134	240260	1808950
Fresh Water Tanks			936	7000	58300
Fuel Oil Settling Tank A			526	3930	28900
Fuel Oil Settling Tank B			581	4340	31950

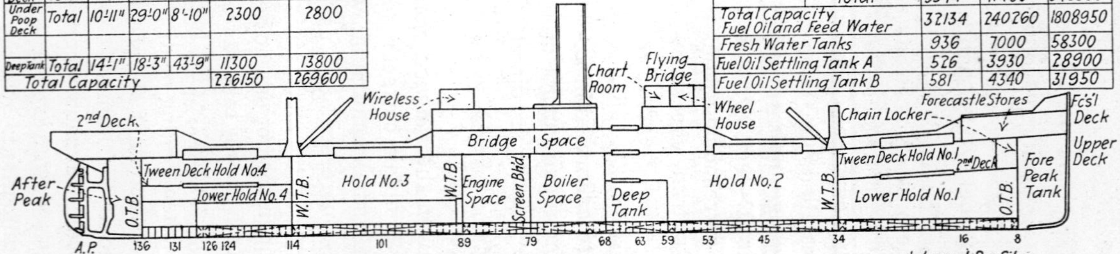

Inboard Profile

Length Over All 335'-6"
Length between Perp's. 324'-0"
Breadth Moulded 46'-0"
Depth Moulded at Sides 28'-6"

Underdeck Tonnage Assigned by U.S. Customs Officials = 3004.70
To Tank Top only = 2922.80
Gross Tonnage = 3545
Net Tonnage = 2174

Note:-All Dimensions used in Figuring Cargo Holds are taken Inside of Timber Ceilings and 2 Inches under Bottom of Deck Beams.-For Bales Deduction made for Shaft Alley & Alley Flat

Capacities for Bulk Grain are Figured to Moulded Lines at Top and Sides and to Tank Top Ceiling Minus All Obstructions.

COAL BUNKERS		CU.FT.
Permanent Bunkers		None
Convertable Bunker Space	Deep Tank	13800
	Cargo Space Under Bridge Dk.	25840
	Total	39640

TRIMMING TANKS

Location	Cu. Ft.	Gals.	Tons
Deep Tank	13800	103170	394
Fore Peak	3882	29037	111

CHAPTER IX

STOWAGE

I

Foreword

Stowage in the modern cargo vessel is becoming of greater importance as the size of holds increases and the variety of cargo continues to become more and more diversified. Where in the old days a vessel stowed a few thousand tons, now more than that is carried in a single hold. Many writers set down nice little rules for the stowage of cargo, but the practical sea officer knows that such rules are hard to follow. Stowage is a continual compromise between the filling in of *deadweight* and *measurement* cargo. The following item from a shipping paper illustrates the point:

> " After being detained at Boston two weeks waiting for fuel oil, the steamer *West Togua* has left for the Pacific Coast with a very large cargo. She will call at Philadelphia for more fuel oil and, if the dock laborer's strike is settled, will take on 1,500 tons of steel. From Boston she carries paper, shoes, dry goods, soap, drugs, machinery and confectionery."

Here was a problem in stowage for the Chief Mate, to get in the 1,500 tons of steel, somewhere in the 'tween decks *under* the measurement cargo.

Such problems are always happening. Sometimes the complications pile on each other to the point of distraction, especially where a vessel is to discharge at a number of different ports and the question of trim and stability after each unloading comes into play.*

Every modern vessel should carry a capacity sheet containing the following information: (See opposite page).

Capacities of cargo spaces	Dimensions of cargo spaces
Capacities of bunker spaces	Dimensions of bunker spaces

* (See page 717.)

Capacities of trimming tanks Size of hatches
Capacities of booms
Plan showing location of holds, tanks and hatches

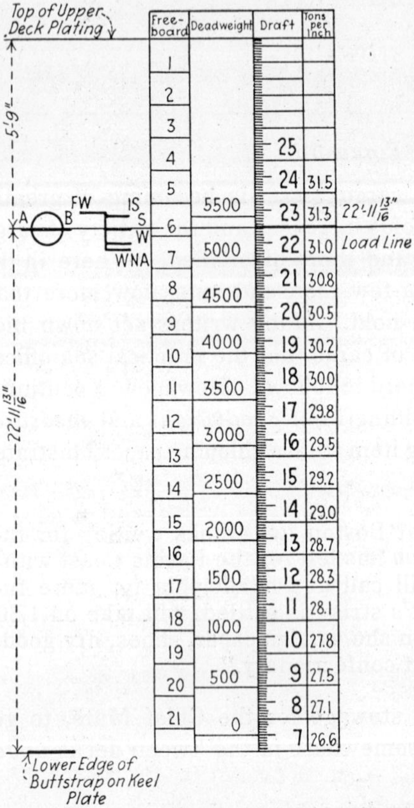

Tons per inch scale. Note A.B.S. load line marking.

Tons per inch scale, showing the freeboard, displacement, deadweight and draft in their true relation and the number of tons of displacement per inch of draft.

A displacement curve is also given in the set of blue prints supplied the ship. (See page 22.)

In old vessels not supplied with this information the Chief Mate should collect as much of the data as possible, measuring holds and hatches to satisfy himself.

When cargo is taken for a vessel the freight and traffic department ashore, in a well-organized concern, see to it that cargo assigned to the ship is suitable, dead weight and measurement so proportioned, if possible, that the best stowage can be made.

Where cargo diagrams are prepared, and this should be done where mixed cargoes are carried, these diagrams should be kept for reference from voyage to voyage in a cargo book. Carefully prepared diagrams are of the utmost importance in settling claims for damage due to faulty stowage, pilfering, and the like.

Duty to cargo. This old sea term stands for the integrity of merchant seamen. It sums up their faithful care and handling of the goods entrusted to them.

Hatch tents. Useful in the case of sudden showers. Save work, and damage to cargo. Never use at night, in lieu of covering hatches properly and safely.

II

Preparing for Stowage

This duty falls to the ship and is one of the most important to be attended to after discharging. Holds and 'tween decks should be swept clean. If it is necessary to wash down the 'tween decks and hold use fresh water if this is available.

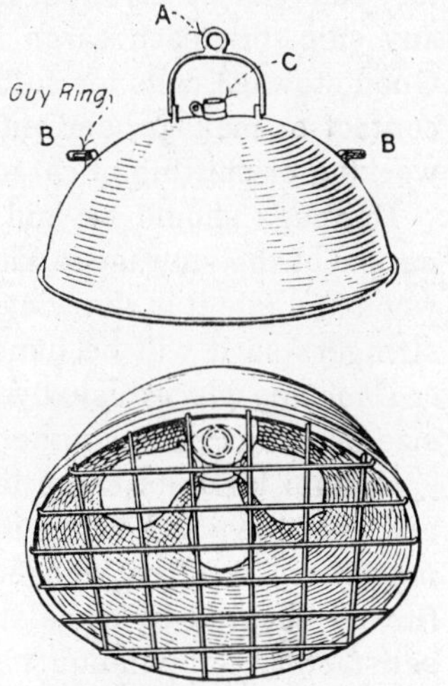

Always have your cargo lights and cables, in good order. A, Ring for the lanyard to carry weight of the reflector. B, Guy rings to point reflector. C, Connection for cable. Do not hang the light by the cable.

Lift limber boards and clean out the limbers, see that the rose boxes (the strums or strainers over the bilge suction pipes) are clean and clear.

See that all battens and tank top covers are in good order.

See that all piping, sounding pipes, smothering lines, fire and water lines through the hold are in good order.

See that all wiring is in good order, pipe or armored conduits are not chafed or bent.

See that all ports are tight, deadlights screwed down and that all side ports are secure.

Make careful examination of the under side of the weather deck, under winch beds, around mast and king post wedges. Examine well for leaks. Look after ventilators for leakage.

See that all hold ladders are in good order. Look after all strong backs, fore and afters, and hatch covers to be certain that these fittings are in shape for closing hatches.

Look after the hatch tarpaulins, two or three at each hatch as required. See that the tarpaulins fit, or are properly marked, and are not torn or cracked.

See that the battens and wedges are handy.

Note: After working cargo at night always see all cargo lights disconnected before covering hatches.

*Dunnage.** The modern steamer is so designed that dunnage, except for chocking and filling between battens (when necessary) is largely dispensed with. The old rule " ten inches of dunnage on the floor and fifteen in the bilge " is a dead letter.

Rough spruce planking is usually employed, and this is used where needed; baled goods, liable to damage through sweat are protected with a layer of planking over the steel decks and against the steel framing of the ship.

Dunnage is also used in flooring off between different kinds of cargo where contact would result in damage. No hard and fast rule can be given as to the amount of dunnage needed for any ship, but each cargo is a rule unto itself in this respect. Good stowage calls for sufficient dunnage to prevent damage by contact or leakage, and enough chocking pieces to prevent the working or shifting of cargo when in a seaway.

Dunnage should be laid as directed by the Mate, when the nature of the stowage is known. It is well to sweep off dunnage wood and pile it in the wings of the 'tween decks and on the hold stringers so it will be handy when the time comes for its use.

Chocking pieces usually consist of rough cord wood of handy size useful as *quoins* under the quarters of casks, etc.

Certain kinds of cargo lend themselves to chocking purposes and may be used when it will not result in damage. Heavy machinery is often wedged and lashed in the holds and then further secured by close stowage of baled hay. This is a very satisfactory combination. Of course, cotton, or other baled stuff may also be used, care being taken to protect it from damage by oil or grease.

* Whether the ship owner, in a lump sum charter, should deduct the dunnage from the carrying capacity of the ship, or include it in the tonnage carried, was again under discussion in the King's Court in London. The case at point was that of the steamship " Ben Lodi," which was fixed at a lump sum, " owner's Guarantee to place 5,600 tons deadweight carrying capacity and 300,000 bale space, as per builders' plan, at disposal of charterers, and it was provided that, " if the deadweight, or bale space placed at charterers' disposal be less than the above, then the lump sum is to be reduced pro rata." The charterers loaded a general cargo, which required thirty-two tons of dunnage, and the point in dispute was whether the charterers were entitled to the deduction of those thirty-two tons.

Justice Atkin held that when the owner placed a ship at the disposal of the charterer, having a carrying capacity of 5,600 tons, he had satisfied his contract, and gave judgment for the shipowner.

Cargo should always be stowed so it will not move or chafe with the rolling of the vessel.

Before starting stowage. Know the condition of tanks, usually filled, as ballast.

Locomotives stowed in a lower hold, blocked off with compressed hay in bales. In addition to this they are also lashed and wedged securely on their beds.

Know the state of the bunkers. Where a vessel must bunker, *after loading*, this extra weight of fuel must be considered when bringing her down to her load marks.

The trimming tanks may be emptied as the vessel takes on her cargo. Special care must be taken to see these tanks completely free of water, also of mud. A few inches of water will make a difference of 100 tons in a large ship's cargo capacity.

Depth of water. Make certain of the depth of water in the loading berth, forward and aft. This is most important. Be sure to get the depth at *low tide.* Make certain whether you are in a *clear* or a *foul berth.* A clear berth is one where there is no obstruction, rocks, etc. on the bottom. When you come into a new berth with a larger vessel than has used it before be most careful. If the ends are free, there may be too little water amidship, careful soundings should be made with a ship's boat at low tide before going into the berth.

It is very dangerous to continue loading a vessel that is aground.

The writer remembers a certain ship taking bunker coal at St. Lucia. When her bunkers were filled she would not budge, she was fast in the mud. The lack of care on the part of some one cost that vessel several thousand dollars, at a time when a chief mate had to work two years to *earn*, what his lack of foresight *cost* the ship within an hour. And, by the way, a master or chief mate who is constantly on the job will save his salary many times over on almost every voyage. At present the master is so *underpaid* with respect to his responsibilities that this point may well be considered by wide-awake ship operators.

Hatches. The hatches of vessels differ, and in every ship, unless perfectly designed, certain hatches will be *slow hatches*, that is, all things being equal, these hatches will be the last to load or discharge. These factors should be taken into account when loading.

The reserve bunker or tank hatches are usually slow. In these spaces, when cargo is to be carried, stow things liable to do damage, but do not stow cargo liable to damage from the heat of bunkers or fire room.

III

Order of Stowage

In deep holds, only heavy and securely boxed or crated cargo should be placed below for the weight of stowage on top will cause considerable damage unless this is attended to.

Stowage generally takes the following course:

Lower holds—

Heavy weights, stout packages, deadweight cargo. Followed by measurement to lower 'tween deck beams, using small cases for beam filler if possible.

Lower 'tween decks—

Heavy stuff, steel rails, billets, etc., casks, cases, and measurement.

Upper 'tween decks—

Some heavy stuff to carry up the weights, and mostly measurement cargo.

The order of stowage depends, largely upon the order of discharging. Consignments for any single port should be kept as close together as possible.

So many factors enter into the practical work of stowage that only general principles can be given. Never allow drafts of cargo to bang against the side when loading. Heavy slings of cargo will batter in the shell plating abreast of the hatch ways.

Scales of Permissible Loading and Ballasting

Holds and 'tween decks should be marked with their safe stowage weights for full cargo loading. A scale of such safe loading weights should be given the vessel by her designers with the approval of the classification society. The correct proportion of cargo weights for ore, coal, sugar, and general cargo could easily be determined, using certain " type " cargoes.

With such a scale should be given the minimum ballast requirements of the vessel when flying light.

Most sailing craft carry a certain weight of *kentledge* permanent pig iron ballast. This is not taken out when stowing cargo.

IV

Railway Iron

" Stow fore and aft until level with the keelson, then ' grating fashion,' keeping the rails well apart so that the weight will be raised to make the ship easy in a seaway."

The above ancient instruction keeps finding its way into the newer books, one man copies from another and it is even now the standard answer to the ancient question. "*How would you stow a cargo of railroad iron?*"

" Both sides of the keelson " are now filled with tanks, and the floor is flat.

Stow railroad iron (rails) and other steel, as close as possible. Chock it against shifting and place dunnage between tiers for greater ease in passing the chain slings in hoisting out. In loading a deadweight cargo of steel put one third in the 'tween decks, of number 2 and number 4 holds.

This cargo is generally best stowed fore and aft.

V

Steel Billets

Steel billets are often stowed in the 'tween decks to bring up the weight. Such billets weighing from 450 lbs. to 600 lbs. *are often thoroughly magnetized due to handling with an electric magnet,* and may be a very disturbing factor in the performance of the compass when stowed in the hatch just forward of the bridge. It is worth while looking after this point. In discharging billets sling with a sound chain sling, *three in a draft.*

Steel plates are handled by means of screw clamps and slings. Use great care in slinging.

Weight of Steel Plates per Square Foot

—	In.	In.	In.	In.	In.	In.	In.	In.	In.
Thick	$\frac{1}{16}$	$\frac{1}{8}$	$\frac{3}{16}$	$\frac{1}{4}$	$\frac{5}{16}$	$\frac{3}{8}$	$\frac{7}{16}$	$\frac{1}{2}$	1
Pounds	2.55	5.10	7.65	10.2	12.8	15.3	17.9	20.04	40.08

To calculate the weight of angle-bars take the sum of the flanges, and treat as a plate.

VI

Sugar

Sugar cargoes, as taken in the Hawaiian Islands, are carried in gunny bags, weighing in the neighborhood of 150 lbs. It is a clean cargo, readily stowed, and weights should be carried up into the 'tween decks, as the vessel will be down to her marks before she is filled. Cuban and Porto Rican sugar is handled the same way.

In dunnaging be careful to keep clear of all steel work, and arrange for ventilation in the holds as the cargo is usually warm and in coming into cool weather the deck beams will sweat and drip onto the bags; though no real damage results from this, it is as well to avoid it.

In loading from lighters be careful not to receive cargo that has been wet with salt water. This can usually be ascertained by opening a suspicious bag and tasting the sugar.

Loading bag grain. Hides on wharf to go into tank hatch.

The sugar is only partly refined and is taken to Atlantic Coast ports to the refineries.

Much of the loading and unloading is now done by conveyor. When loading, long hard wood chutes are employed and the bags are slid to every part of the hold and 'tween decks.

VII

Hides

Confine hides to a single hold if possible. Dunnage well against contact with steel or other cargo. Best to carry these in the tankhatch, if other perishable cargo is carried.

VIII

Jute

Jute cargoes are carried from East Indian ports and require special care in handling. Cases of spontaneous combustion have been noted and the sweating of hold beams and exposed metal parts is very pronounced. The following recommendations have been made with regard to the stowage of this cargo.

1. That there shall be at least six ventilators of not less than 18 inches diameter, elevated 7 to 8 feet above the main deck, continued by Venetian shafts through the 'tween decks into the hold, with an air space under both decks of not less than 3 inches—fore and aft the vessel—these ventilators being placed at equal distances between the fore and aft hatches.

2. That two strong ventilators, about 3 feet high and 15 inches diameter, be fitted with screw covers in the main hatch.

3. That one of each of the hatches is to be kept open during the voyage, when the weather permits.*

4. That the hatches are not to be filled close up with jute, but an air space left all round the coamings.

5. That the spaces between the vessel's frames adjoining the lower deck are to be kept open, to allow the steam to ascend from the lower hold.

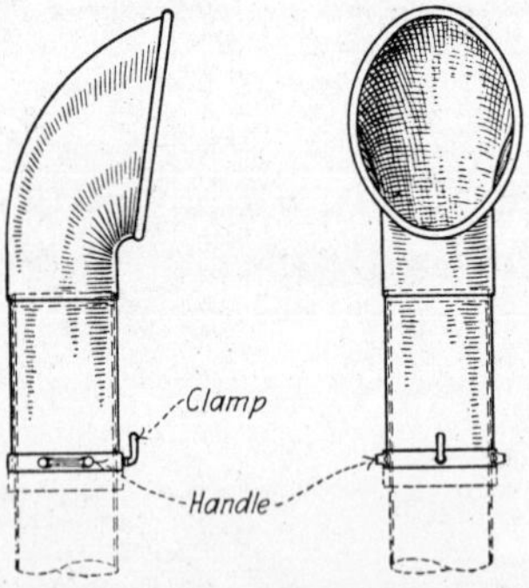

Ventilator cowls. Should have wire mesh fire screens fitted in the necks. Screens must be kept clean.

6. That the ventilators are to be carefully attended to at sea. Also,

1. That the old plan of sweat boards, formerly fitted under the stringer plates of the upper deck, would be very beneficial to a jute cargo, by carrying off much of the condensed sweat, also forming an air space where most required.

2. That matting round the sides be discontinued, as mats get saturated and retain the sweat; dry sticks or permanent dunnage being preferable, allowing it to escape.

* A precaution to be taken when carrying copra.

3. That no bone meal or broken stowage be carried with jute cargoes.

Bales average 300 lbs., and 400 lbs. should be the limit. Damp bales should be rejected.

Jute bags and waste are pressed in bales 15 lbs. to the cubic foot, and 149 cubic feet to the long ton.

Bales are generally stowed flat, amidship, marks and numbers up and on the edge in the wings, marks and numbers inboard.

IX

Silk

Silk will be in bales or packed in cases. Silk should be stowed with great care as to dryness, and away from all drip or offensive odors.

Tea

Japanese waste silk (the combings after the silk is drawn) emit an odor very injurious to tea.

Tea must be carefully stowed, holds specially cleaned, bilges free and clean, sweetening them with lime water. It is often desirable to coat the iron work in the holds with a cement wash and then whitewash the holds, where tea is being carried.

Tea shipped from Canton or Macao is packed in cases measuring two to three cubic feet and weighing between fifteen and twenty pounds net.

Tobacco

Manufactured tobacco and cigars should be kept free from odors and moisture. Bales of leaf tobacco will heat and may cause spontaneous combustion. Tobacco is shipped in hogsheads, tierces, or bales. Use ample dunnage.

X

Cotton

Cotton is pressed in bales running from 480 to 500 lbs., the latter figure in the case of cotton waste. Oil, turpentine, and grease should be kept away from cotton. All bales should be watched when stowing; this is best done on the dock and no bales showing signs of wet should be accepted, or if acceptance is insisted upon a remark as to their condition should be made on the bill of lading and signed by the shipper or his agent and the master. This should be done with all damaged cargo.

All naked lights should be kept out of the hold—" no smoking " enforced, and all ventilator cowls should be watched where same are liable to be in the wake of sparks from the vessel's funnel, or from the funnel of tugboats, etc. Use fire screens in all ventilators.

The fire risk is great and every precaution should be taken when carrying a cargo of cotton.

Cotton bales swell or " spring " some in handling and this should be taken into consideration when estimating stowage. Extra dense bales stow 80 cubic feet to the ton, while the ordinary bale will stow 130 cubic feet to the ton *before* springing. This enlargement of the bales may amount to ten per cent. Cotton is no longer screwed into holds.

XI

Wool

Wool is shipped in bales of various sizes depending upon the part of the world in which the cargo is shipped. Before beginning stowage get full particulars from the local people. Roughly, if engaging a cargo of wool by cable, figure 200 cubic feet to the ton. The " screwing " of wool and cotton cargoes is no longer practiced as the bales are sufficiently compressed to make this practice unnecessary.

XII

*Casks**

The time-honored formula, " bung up and bilge free " sums up the whole of cask stowage. When casks are supported by beds under their quarters, and the second tier stowed in the cuntlines of the lower tier, ends wedged off in the wings, little damage will follow with sound casks.

* To calculate the capacity of a cask, multiply half the sum of the areas of the two interior circles, viz.: at the bung and head by the interior length, for the contents in cubic inches, which sum, divided by 277.27 (the number of cubic inches in a gallon), reduces the result to that measure.

A dirty cask covered with grease or tar is often found. The bung will be hidden but this is always in a line with the rivets on the hoops, and the heads of the casks run up and down when the bung is on top.

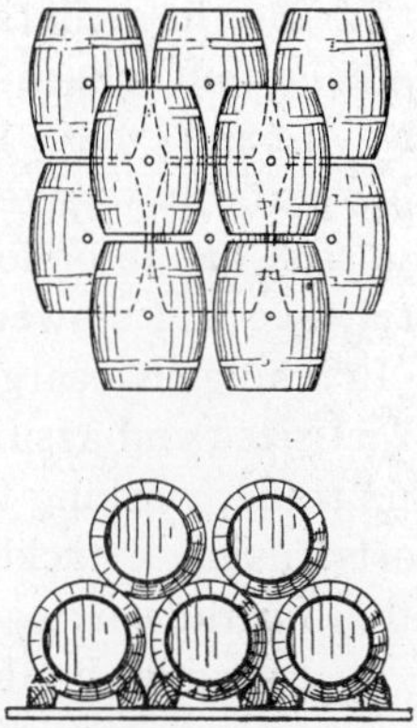
Cask stowage

The staves of a cask projecting beyond the heads form a ridge called the *chimes*. When the chimes are broken the cask should be sent to the cooper for repairs *before* stowing. A cooper should always be at hand when taking on a cargo of casks. *Be careful not to get the bung down.*

Casks are usually stowed fore and aft, working out to the wings from the keelson and foreward and aft from amidships. Care should be taken that the casks are also " bilge free " at the side. Nothing should be touching but the quarters. Stow "bilge and cuntline."

Hogsheads	contain	63	gallons
Puncheons	"	84	"
Pipes	"	126	"

Hogsheads may be stowed to six tiers, puncheons to four tiers, and pipes, or buts to three tiers.

When casks are stowed with heads pointing to the wings they are said to be " a burton."

A great deal of loss will be avoided by careful attention to the stowage *and slinging* of casks. The writer has a vivid recollection of a huge puncheon of stuffed Spanish olives slipping from a sling when well up above the hatch on a vessel discharging in San Francisco. Hundreds of stevedores filled their pockets with olives and the thirst raised in consequence was simply consuming.

Asphalt

Holds are smeared with mud before loading, on the same principle that pans are greased before baking. The cargo consolidates on the voyage north, and is then dug out. Of course all holds are lined, the mud prevents the cargo from adhering to the lining.

XIII

Lumber

Lumber in moderate lengths and sizes will stow through deck hatches, but where heavy baulks of timber, running forty feet or more and twelve to fourteen inches square, are to be shipped, bow ports may have to be employed, or, if the hatches permit, the stuff has to be lowered and dragged into the holds one piece at a time and stowed by hand, with pinch bars and jiggers.

In taking on a cargo of lumber the Master will do well to see the exact sizes and assure himself of proper stowage. Schooners in this trade, working their long sticks in and out through the bow ports, using a tackle from the end of the bowsprit, are best fitted for the carriage of large sizes.

As a straight lumber cargo will not send a vessel down to her marks, from fifteen to twenty-five per cent. of this cargo is often carried on deck. Usually the deck load is not covered by insurance.

The greatest care should be exercised in properly securing the deck load when carried, due regard being given to the season of the year and the trade. A clear space should be preserved between the bulwarks and the bulwark stanchions for the passage of water. Also see that all freeing ports are working clear. Great care should be taken that the uprights are secure and that none of the pipe lines or wheel chains are in danger of being rendered useless by shifting of the deck load. The precautions are strictly up to the officers of the vessel.

All chains should be shackled to the deck eye bolts before the lower tier of timbers is placed. The deck lashings should be so passed that extra frapping turns can be taken, swiftering in the lashing if need be to hold down the load if it works loose.

No specific rules can be given as vessels differ so, but in securing the deck load make no mistake in regard to safety. When it starts to go it will be too late.

The use of wedges is doubtful on a deck cargo.

Long timbers are the safest for deck stowage.

Keep steam winches clear.

Keep hatch covers clear so you can get at wedges.

Don't trust the stevedores with the lashings; they will not be out to sea with you when the ball begins.

Mahogany logs are irregular and generally of large size. Being a very dense wood, it is well to rig special gear. Most of the trade in mahogany logs is from Central America, Mexico, the West Coast of Africa. Some come from Cuba. A few winters ago the writer watched two French barks discharging cargoes of African mahogany in Pensacola. Some of the logs running as high as ten tons. The loading of this cargo is difficult, usually by ship's gear alone and in open roadsteads. This sort of cargo calls for seamanship of a high order.

XIV

General Cargo

This may include anything, and as the term implies is a general assortment of cargo, weight and measurement. When such cargo is well assorted the vessel will be able to earn her maximum freight money, filling every space and going down to her load marks with ballast tanks empty and bunkers full.

Cases make good beam and hatch filler

Rules for loading are based upon common sense. Each cargo will require different handling, each port will bring its own problems. As shown at the beginning of the chapter, the method of stowage will often be subject to conditions upsetting all fixed rules.

The following general idea should be kept in mind.

Keep accurate diagrams of mixed stowage to be discharged at several ports.

Keep a balance between weight and measurement stuff.

Weights down in holds, light stowage up. Heavy stowage in 'tween decks, for a tier or two. Cargo giving off odors to be kept separate. Cargo to be protected from wet. Cargo to be ventilated. Keep a sharp lookout for pilfering. Look out for loose stowage. Stevedores say a vessel is "blown up" when they manage to "get away" with this sort of stowage.

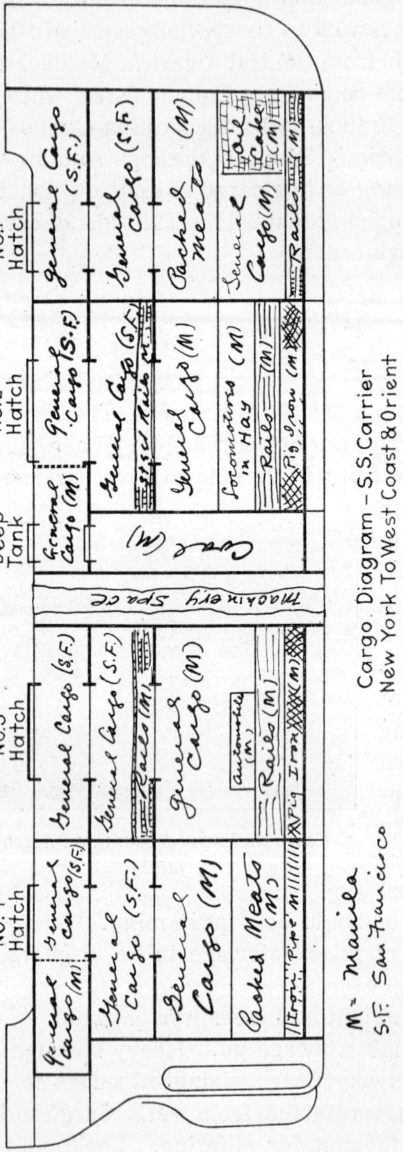

Cargo Diagrams

Cargo diagrams are often of great use when a vessel is to discharge at two or more ports, or where she carries a general cargo and it may become necessary to jettison, or break out cargo for any other reason. And, by the way, it is a good plan to always throw overboard the least valuable cargo, taking it by weight, if there is any choice, when the necessity for jettisoning cargo arises. Here the cargo diagram may be very useful.

The diagram shown here is the usual fore and aft section, somewhat exaggerated as to depth. Of course any cargo diagram is worthless unless prepared carefully and *from actual knowledge of the stowage*. The officer in charge of the hold should prepare this diagram himself. Where goods liable to pilferage are "blocked off" by less tempting cargo, the diagram shows *when* and where to be extra careful while discharging. The writer recalls a cargo of Canadian Club whisky (*!*) blocked off in the number two lower 'tween decks. The "stevies" in Frisco wondered at the extra precautions when they began to " break out " the cases of wooden ware in front of the whisky.*

An elaborate cargo diagram is used by some in which the hold and 'tween deck is shown in sections all lettered, and the plan is shown in squares, each one given a number. Cargo is accurately placed by hold number and by letter and number on the stowage diagram. This seems to be a bit too " scientific " for the average seagoing mate.

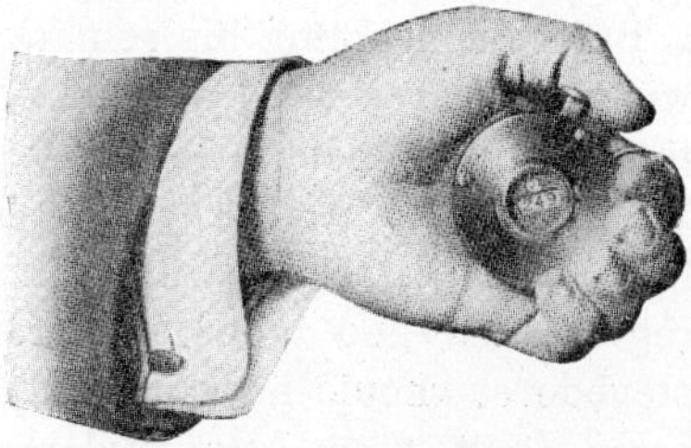

A hand counter.

Talleying is often necessary. A small hand counter is very useful on board ship both for cargo talleying as well as for checking on board stores, etc.

In China the *talley stick* is still in use. When discharging flour, as shown in the photograph, the Chinaman touched each

Passing talley sticks.

* The agent sent down a few bottles with his compliments after talleying the whole lot ashore without loss.

bag with a stick as he handed it to the young man with the golf cap (the supercargo). The chinaman is very honest but he thinks it a good joke if he can avoid passing over his stick as a bag slides past him. When loading he very often is absent-minded and hands over two thin bamboo sticks at once.

Before concluding his remarks on General Cargo, the writer wishes to say a word about Department of Commerce publication. Miscellaneous Series, 92, "Stowage of Ship Cargoes," by Thomas Rothwell Taylor.* This book of three hundred and fifty pages is filled with valuable data. Stowage factors—regulations—and general information. Ship's officers and stevedores should have it handy at all times. Sailors may find some fault with Mr. Taylor's rather musty-looking splices (hooks without thimbles, etc.) but we can easily forgive him this as long as we have *Standard Seamanship* at hand to show us the *shipshape way* to do these things. The Department of Commerce is to be distinctly congratulated on the production of this work. Let us hope the Department will be *more* than thankful to Mr. Taylor.

XV

Dangerous Cargo

Dangerous cargo includes explosives, shipped under strict government supervision in magazines. When shipping explosives ascertain their exact nature before taking on board and get full directions for stowage.

In a general way, if taking on explosives abroad without direct supervision, the following points should be observed:

Nature of cargo.

Keep away from fire; there must be a compartment with steel bulkheads between stowage and the engine room or fire room.

Bank furnace fire before starting to ship. See that no sparks are coming from the vessel's *or any other funnel.*

See that hoisting gear is new—use new manila nets, place wooden skids on deck for landing. Have reliable men at hatch and winches and in the magazine.

Lower drafts easily. Do not allow boxes to be dropped. Avoid all hurry.

* Price 35 cents, from Supt. of Documents, Government Printing Office, Washington, D. C.

No smoking.

Take special care against all fire risks. Do not permit skylarking of any kind. Be careful of tally.

Acids. Acids, through danger of leakage because of broken carboys, are the most uncertain of cargo. *Sulphuric acid* forms the bulk of this sort of cargo, which also includes *hydrochloric, hydrocyanic, nitric,* etc. The milder acids, *citric, acetic,* etc., are not so dangerous.

Where carboys are cased, the bottles are usually packed in whiting or chalk upon which the acid expends itself in the event of leakage. When shipped in carboys without chalk, this material should be used liberally in stowage. A hundred tons of sulphuric acid blocked off in the 'tween decks, should be bedded in at least ten tons of chalk. Of course all other cargo liable to damage would have to be protected, a very difficult thing to do. This cargo should be well ventilated to carry off all fumes.

Do not allow men to pick up leaking acid cases with their bare hands.

Acids are usually carried on deck where they are securely lashed and can be thrown overboard when damaged. Such cargo is taken on deck " at shipper's risk and expense."

Where sulphuric acid is shipped in steel drums, they may be carried under hatches if bedded in coal of sufficient amount to take up any acid that may leak out. A foot of coal at least must be bedded for each hundred pounds carried in the largest drum. This is a very safe way of carrying acid.

Nitrate of Soda. This is not combustible unless in contact with carbon or wood. The bags in which it is shipped offer a certain amount of carbon for the support of combustion.

To extinguish nitrate fires a mixture of nitrate and water is employed. This is the *aqua viega* of the West Coast.

At Iquiqui nitrate bags run 200 lbs. each and are taken on board six bags to a sling.

The following memoranda are taken from the instructions relating to dangerous cargo issued by the British Board of Trade.

Sulfuric acid. When sulfuric acid escapes into the bed of coal beneath the drums in which it may be stowed spontaneous combustion will not take place within the region of the leakage.

Sulphurous acid vapor will extinguish a coal fire.

Coal that has been wetted with sulphuric acid should not be used for firing.

Carbolic acid. There is great danger of death from absorption of this acid through the skin. Casks containing it should be specially sound and carefully handled.

Phosphoric acid. This can be carried under deck if contained in strong stoppered bottles packed with wool or sawdust and not more than six to a case.

Picric acid. The Board of Trade have advised their surveyors that this acid may be carried under deck without a magazine in ships other than emigrant ships, if the following conditions are complied with—

1. The packages must be of sufficient strength not to allow any of their contents to escape when subjected to rough usage.

2. It must be stowed away from boilers and strong mineral acids, paints, etc., and not in contact with lead.

3. Each package must be marked as follows:

Explosives Class III, Division 2

Picric acid. (If not crystals state percentage of water.) To be stowed away from boilers, also strong mineral acids, paints, etc., and not in contact with lead.

4. Subject to these provisions the total quantity of picric acid to be stowed on board any one ship is limited to not more than ten tons in each separate hold or compartment.

Nitre cake. Nitre cake is a byproduct of the manufacture of nitric acid and contains free sulphuric acid and sulphate of soda, with a small percentage of free nitric acid. When dry it is harmless, but it absorbs moisture very readily from the air and when wet will corrode wood and iron. It will also, when in contact with iron, cause hydrogen gas to be given off. Masters should always be informed of these qualities of the substance.

It should be packed perfectly dry in airtight vessels.

Coastwise it may be shipped in bulk, if perfectly dry. After this cargo the hold should be thoroughly cleansed.

Chlorate of potash. Although incombustible itself chlorate of potash is an ardent supporter of combustion and some of the mixtures with this substance are subject to spontaneous combustion. All such mixtures are sensitive to percussion.

Many mixtures of chlorate of potash will be set on fire if acted upon by strong sulphuric acid.

The following rules are given for its handling.

1. Pack in iron drums or in strong paper-lined casks capable of rough handling.

2. Do not stow in the same hold with other combustible material.

3. Keep away from strong mineral acids.
4. Not more than ten tons should be carried in one hold.

Amorphous phosphorus. This form of phosphorus also known as "red" or "Schrotter's" phosphorus is not liable to spontaneous combustion and does not take fire in the air until heated to 500 degrees Fahrenheit.

There is no objection to its stowage below deck if packed in tin. Shipments are usually made in ten pound tins, ten tins to a case. Unlike yellow phosphorus, it need not be kept under water.

Sulphide of sodium and *sulphide of potassium.* Liable to spontaneous combustion. Should be packed *dry* in strong air-tight drums of steel.

In the *hydrated* condition these chemicals are not subject to spontaneous combustion and there is no objection to their shipment on this account.

Peroxide of sodium. Not explosive by itself but dangerous when in contact with any combustible substance. Pack in steel drums, not too large and stow away from combustibles.

Caustic potash. Packed in steel drums and stowed where possible leakage will not come in contact with passengers or crew.

Bi-sulphide of carbon. This is considered "Dangerous Goods" under the meaning of the Merchant Shipping Act, and should be so marked.

It is a colorless heavy mobile liquid, which evaporates quickly and produces a pressure in any vessel containing it. It easily passes through the smallest opening.

It has a bad odor, as of decaying vegetables.

The vapor will ignite on a warm surface and flash back, igniting the liquid. This has been known to happen across a distance of 20 feet.

It should be carried in strong drums, packed two to a case and cases perforated.

It should only be carried as deck cargo. Take the greatest care to keep it out of the sun's rays. Do not cover with *black* tarpaulin. Keep away from all steam pipes.

Inspect every day for the odor of leakage. If any odor throw drums overboard.

Sulphur dioxide. Carry on deck, not dangerous however.

Liquid ammonia. Ammoniacal gas compressed into liquid form should be classed with dangerous goods. It is liable to explosion, and the vapors, when released, are dangerous.

Should be carried in steel "bottles" tested to a pressure of at least 675 lbs. per square inch.

The *aqueous solution* of ammonia should be carried in drums not exceeding 12 gallons capacity, with an empty space equal to 33 per cent. left in each drum.

Stow away from fires or engine room and apart from living quarters.

Dinitrobenzol. Although a constituent of certain powerful explosives, it is not dangerous in itself and no special rules are necessary with regard to its carriage.

Napthalene. Not an explosive; no special risks attach to its conveyance.

Liquified carbonic acid. Must be carried in steel cylinders of approved strength.

Matches. May not be carried on emigrant ships. No objection to shipment in cargo vessels. Should be packed in tin-lined airtight cases.

Safety matches may be carried on emigrant ships if packed in zinc- or tin-lined hermetically sealed cases and stowed in the square of the hatchway.

Oiled materials. Should be soldered in metal-lined cases after the goods have been " seasoned " for at least a month.

Stow in a cool place.

Inodorous felt. Liable to spontaneous combustion.

Should always be marked in red letters 1¾″:

INODOROUS FELT

Roofing and *sheathing felt.* Black felt made from coal tar and pitch is safe. Brown felt, made from jute waste is liable to spontaneous combustion if the rolls are stowed in the hold of a ship before they have cooled to the temperature of the surrounding air.

Lampblack. Spontaneous combustion extremely rare, but stow near hatchways. *Printed* paper should not be used for packing this material. Packed in cases or casks lined with clean dry paper it is safely carried.

Carbon papers. Containing fatty substances and finely divided carbon, these are liable to spontaneous combustion under certain conditions.

In limited quantity packed in airtight tins there is no objection to them as " general cargo."

If not packed in tins they should be carried on deck.

Glue pieces. Liable to spontaneous combustion. Be careful in stowage away from combustible cargo and near square of hatch.

Calcium carbide. Calcium carbide or carbide of calcium may be transported on passenger vessels when the same is contained in steel drums or steel receptacles, the seams of which are lapped and properly riveted or fastened in such manner as will insure the maximum strength of the joints and when the said drum or receptacles are fitted with double covers, so that such drums or receptacles shall be watertight and airtight, during such transportation. For packages of 110 pounds or less, such drums or receptacles shall be made of open-hearth steel of not less than No. 26 gauge. For packages of more than 110 pounds, such drums or receptacles shall be made of open-hearth steel of not less than No. 24 gauge. Calcium carbide or carbide of calcium may also be transported on passenger vessels in cans containing not more than ten pounds each.

Regulations of the Board of Underwriters of New York for the Loading of "Calcium Carbide"

"Calcium Carbide," may be stowed under deck of General Cargo Vessels in quantities not exceeding ten (10) per cent. of a vessels net registered tonnage.

The packages to be of one (1) cwt. Drums crated and two (2) cwt. Drums incased in wood. Same to be stowed in between decks close to the Hatches (but not under them), with no other cargo on top, and as far from the Ventilators as possible.

In Single Deck Vessels, to be stowed close to the Hatches (but not under them) with no other cargo on top, and not within eight (8) feet of the bottom of the hold.

Not to be stowed in fore or after peaks, and not to be used for broken stowage, not to be distributed in various parts of the vessel, but to be stowed in one compartment if possible.

The compartment must always be well ventilated, the packages to be stowed on their ends, clear of all steam, fire, scupper pipes and deadlights, and in the forward ends of compartments where bunkers adjoin, and not in the empty bunker space below.

"Calcium Carbide" should be stowed in Poop and Bridge spaces when practicable.

This commodity must always be stowed under the personal supervision of a Surveyor of this Board.

Construction of Magazines for the Stowage of High and Low Explosives

Regulations of Board of Underwriters of New York

All iron work inside carefully covered by wood, planed on one side, and all nails to be of Copper.

Iron decks are to be covered with feather-edged boarding which is to be an inch on one edge and one-quarter of an inch on the other, and to lap over two inches.

Uprights are to be fitted to cargo battens and bulkheads before sheathing.

Magazines are always to be built in between decks if possible, and must be so placed that the doors are easily accessible from a hatchway.

All electric lights running through compartments where magazines are fitted must be disconnected at the bulkhead.

Iron decks may be covered with tongued and grooved boards instead of feather-edged boarding in constructing magazines as noted above.

The following amendments to the rules of the Board regulating the construction of magazines for the stowage of high and low explosives, have been adopted:

1. Cover all iron with fair quality 1″ unplaned lumber, properly secured with wire nails, heads counter-sunk, and fully protected by putty and paint, or thoroughly covered with saw-dust. Deck to be sheathed with same quality of lumber laid on 1″ thwartship strips about 2′ apart. Use sufficient saw-dust on deck to prevent possibility of friction.

2. Black powder in steel drums to be stowed on heads with strips of lath between each tier. All to be thoroughly secured with dunnage in every possible way to prevent possibility of moving. An 8″ air space must be constructed against fire-room bulkhead, when explosives are carried in a compartment adjacent to such bulkhead.

The old rules of the Board relative to the construction of magazines were to be modified, until further notice, only with respect to the above two amendments, otherwise the rules were to apply as heretofore.

Hazardous cargo. The following rule has been adopted by the Commissioner of Docks, New York.

"The loading or discharging, or keeping on any wharf, pier or bulkhead, or any lighter, barge or other craft moored to any wharf, pier or bulkhead in the city, of benzol, toluol, or explosives or explosive material in excess of the amount required for the vessel's own use for signaling or life-saving purposes shall not be permitted, without a written permit therefor being first had and obtained from the Commissioner of Docks."

The limit of weight of explosives which may be loaded at the docks is one ton. All explosives above this weight must be transferred to ship from lighter only in anchorages in Gravesend Bay or Sandy Hook bight. No transfer of explosives can be made except under the supervision of the captain of the port. The latter has directed that where small quantities of explosives are transferred to ship at her loading pier, it must be from lighter on the offshore side.

Every package containing explosives or other dangerous articles, when presented to a common carrier for shipment, *must have plainly marked on the outside thereof the contents thereof;* and it is unlawful for any person to deliver or cause to be delivered to any common carrier engaged in interstate or foreign commerce by land or water, for interstate of foreign transportation, or to carry upon any vessel or vehicle engaged in interstate or foreign transportation any explosive or other dangerous article under any false or deceptive marking, description, invoice, shipping order or other declaration, or without informing the agent of such carrier of the true character thereof, at or before the time such delivery for carriage is made. Anyone who knowingly violates or causes to be violated any provision of this section may be fined not more than $2,000 or imprisoned not more than eighteen months, or both.

The Department of Commerce and Labor has decided that "Commercial alcohol, including grain, wood and denatured, is not a like explosive burning fluid or a like dangerous article to the several articles enumerated in the statute, covering the carriage of such articles by passenger steamers, and hence its carriage as freight or use as stores on passenger steamers is not prohibited by Section 4472, of the Revised Statutes."

Shipments of varnish may be accepted by steamers carrying passengers, subject to the following requirements: Varnish with a flash point not lower than 50 degrees F. may be shipped when contained in securely closed metal cans containing no more than 5 gallons in each can; or with a flash point of not less than 20 degrees F. in securely closed bottles or cans containing not more than 1 gallon in each vessel. The cans or bottles to be packed in strong boxes or barrels, and described as "Varnish in metal cans" or "Varnish in glass." Shipping receipts must state as part of the description of the articles therein "No label required." They must also bear the following certificate signed by the shipper or his authorized agent. "This is to certify that the above articles are properly described by name, and are packed and marked and in proper condition for transportation according to the regulations prescribed by the Interstate Commerce Commission."

XVI

Case Oil

The five-gallon oil tin came into being originally to cut down cost in transportation. Case oil is stowed in wooden boxes, two five-gallon rectangular tins to a case. The cases cut transportation charges, for the vessel taking out case oil is able to get a return cargo from a foreign port (not always possible in tankers) and the cases are very handy for primitive transport after landing, as on the rivers of China, and on mule back inland.

Case oil stows quickly, can be used as a " flatter " stowed on its side as " beam filling."

Recently a stevedore was reported (in *The Oracle*, the Oriental Navigation Company's house paper) to have taken in 10,000 cases of oil in seven hours through one hatch on the S.S. *West Avenal.*

Case oil is taken on board in " drafts " of eight cases and is run to the wings of the hold and 'tween deck on light trucks, a draft to a truck load. The work is very rapid. The cases are stowed singly with little waste room or chocking.

Ruling as to the Loading of Gasolene, Naphtha and/or Benzine

By New York Board of Underwriters

When one or more holds and 'tween decks are completely filled with Oil and Gasolene, Naphtha and/or Benzine, 8,000 cases of Gasolene, Naphtha and/or Benzine will be allowed as the maximum amount to be carried under deck of any one General Cargo steamer, it being understood that when 8,000 cases have been loaded in a hold, no Gasolene, Naphtha and/or Benzine can be carried in any other enclosed space, whether that space be a poop, bridge, fore peak, or otherwise.

Any amount consistent with proper stowage and the stability of the steamer can be carried on the open deck.

Owners and Agents of steamers desiring to load Gasolene, Naphtha and/or Benzine in any other manner than allowed as above, should lay all the facts of each such case before the Surveyor who is to inspect the said steamer, describing the kind of steamer and the compartment in which it is desired to take the Gasolene, Naphtha and/or Benzine, the manner of ventilation, etc., when, after investigating each such case, same will be passed upon and a decision rendered by the Surveyor.

XVII

Grain Cargoes

The carriage of grain is one of the most important functions of a merchant marine. Grain is the very life blood of the people of all lands and involves the most basic transaction of our civilized world. Explicit rules have been set for the stowage and carriage of grain, for the cargo flows like water and many vessels have been lost in consequence of careless stowage. Grain is carried in bulk and in bags. It finds its way into every corner of the hold and great precaution must be taken in preparing for its reception.

Grain is taken on board from elevators and as much as twenty-five thousand tons will be shot on board ships in the course of twenty four hours. It is often discharged by suction apparatus.

A vessel carrying more than one third of her net tonnage in grain is considered to be "laden with a grain cargo."

The regulations of the various boards of underwriters and of the New York Produce Exchange are given. These regulations should be thoroughly understood by the master and officers of a vessel about to load grain. A great deal of trouble will be saved if the rules are studied beforehand.

Grain shipped from different ports should confirm to the local requirements for stowage and the master should inform himself of these regulations before taking on cargo. The Port Warden will usually be able to supply the required information.

The Rules of the National Board of Marine Underwriters at New York are very comprehensive. They are given in full. These rules are the same as those of the Board of Underwriters of New York, and the New York Produce Exchange.

The Rules of the Board of Underwriters of New Orleans, of the Mobile Board of Underwriters, of the Wheat Tariff Association, San Francisco and of the Port Warden's Office of Montreal, Canada, may be cited. When loading grain at these ports these rules will hold. Essentially they are similar to the rules quoted.

Shifting Boards. The regulations regarding the placing of shifting boards are very precise and the actual fitting of these should receive the greatest attention. Barden's method of fitting shifting boards is shown in the illustrations. In Europe this method has been widely adopted and has received the approval of the New York Board of Underwriters and the British Board of Trade.

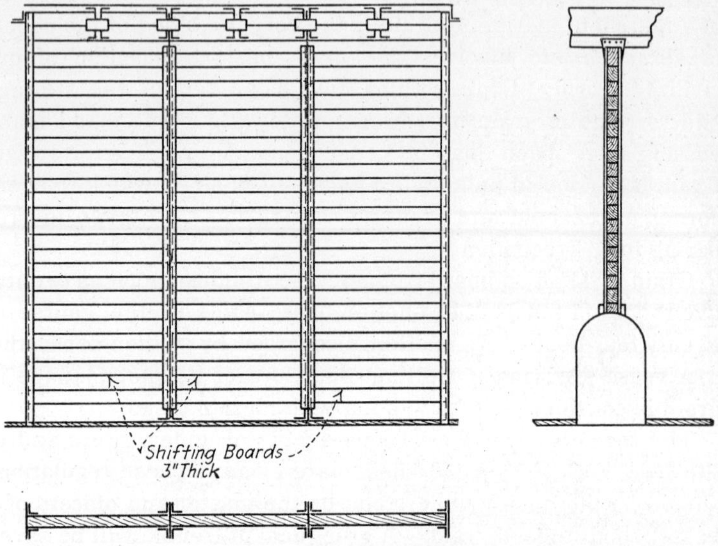

Method of fitting shifting boards in a forward hold and over the shaft alley in an after hold.

The stanchions consist of a combination of four angle irons and a web plate forming a slot on each side of the web into which the shifting boards are shipped. The manner of operation is shown by the cuts.

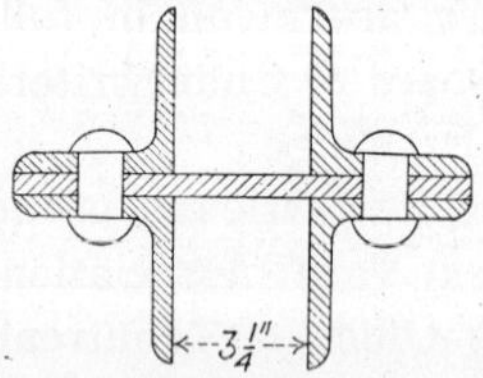

A shifting board stanchion.

There is a considerable saving in time and trouble when this system is employed. The illustrations are taken from the McNab Encyclopedia of Marine Appliances.

Bags. Grain bags should be of the best quality and well sewn. The stowage where bag grain is used on top of bulk cargo should be carefully made and where this cargo is used as end stowage the bags must be "boulked." However, this is also a dangerous practice and solid bulkheads should be fitted instead.

Grain cannot be adequately secured on a slope or level by use of tarpaulins, with weights on top of them.

Loading and Discharging. Grain cargoes are rapid and the vessel's draft should be watched and lines attended carefully during the period of loading and discharging.

Rules for Loading Grain

By the National Board of Marine Underwriters

1. The Free-Board shall be measured from top of deck at side of the vessel to the water's edge at the center of the load Water-Line; Vessels having Free-Boards assigned by the Rules of the Board of Trade (Marine Department), London, shall not be loaded deeper than permitted by those rules. No grain shall be carried in the fore and after peaks except in bags.

2. Shifting Boards (except as provided for in Rule 11) must extend from the upper deck to the floor when grain is carried in bulk, and must be grain-tight, with grain-tight fillings between the beams, and are to extend to the top of all amidship feeders. When grain is carried in bags the shifting boards must extend from deck to deck in the between decks, and not less than four feet downward from the beams in the lower hold.

3. Shifting Boards referred to in all rules shall be of two (2) inch yellow pine, or of three (3) inch spruce (or equivalent).

4. All hatch feeders and end bulkheads must be boarded on the inside.

5. The grain must be well trimmed up between the beams and in the wings, and the space between them completely filled.

6. No coal shall be carried on deck of steamers sailing between the 1st of October and the 1st of April beyond such a supply as will be consumed prior to vessels reaching the ocean.

7. Care must be taken that when grain in bags or other cargo is stowed over bulk grain, the bulk grain must be covered with two thicknesses of boards placed fore and aft and athwartships, with spaces between the lower boards of not more than four (4) feet, and between the upper boards of not more than nine (9) inches. Care must be taken that all the bags are properly stowed, in good order, and well filled and that the tiers are laid close together.

8. Grain in poop, peaks and/or bridge deck must have such grain in bags and have proper dunnage and shifting boards.

9. Steamers having water ballast tanks must have them covered with a grain-tight platform made of 2½ or 3 inch sound and dry planks, but this platform may be dispensed with where the top of the tanks are of heavy plates and precautions are taken against overflow from the bilges.

10. Steamships without ballast tanks, having a cargo platform in good order, will not be required to fit a grain floor over it, otherwise such grain floor will be required.

11. Vessels carrying small quantities of grain in bulk must have shifting boards to the top of the grain, and the bulk must be properly covered with boards before any other cargo is stowed over it.

12. Single deck Steamers with a continuous hold forward will be required to have a closed bulkhead to divide the same. This rule will also apply to the after hold.

13. Shifting boards must be properly secured to stanchions, or shored every eight feet of length and every five feet of depth of hold, including hatchways. Shores may be 3 x 8, 4 x 6, 5 x 7½, 5½ x 8, or 6 x 8½ inches according to their lengths, which are not to exceed 13.6, 18, 25, 27.6, or 30 feet respectively.

14. The use of Grain-tight Divisions, Shifting Boards, Shores and Wire Rope Stays when already fitted and in good condition will be permitted if as set out in paragraphs 21 and 24 to 28 inclusive, pages 41 to 45 inclusive of the Memorandum relating to Grain Cargoes 1914 issued by the Board of Trade, London.

15. No bulk grain or seeds in bulk (except Oats and/or Cotton Seed, as hereinafter provided in Rules 22, 23 and 24) to be carried in between decks, nor where a ship has more than two decks, between the two upper decks, unless in feeders, properly constructed, to fill the orlop and lower hold. Bulk grain may be carried on orlop or third deck below, provided said orlop has wing openings and amidship feeders to feed same.

16. Steamers with two or more decks not having sufficient and properly constructed wing and 'midship feeders, will be required to leave sufficient space above the bulk in lower hold not less than 5 feet under deck beams to properly secure it with bags or other cargo; the bulk to be covered with boards as in Rule 7. If an orlop deck has sufficient openings to the lower hold the orlop and lower hold may be considered as one hold and loaded accordingly.

17. Steamers having one deck and beams may carry bulk to such a height as will permit the stowage over it of not less than four (4) tiers of bags or other suitable cargo. All bags or other cargo to be stowed on two tiers of boards as provided for in Rule 7.

18. Steamers with laid between decks must have hatchway feeders, and if the distance in the lower holds, between the forward bulkhead in said holds and the nearest end of the hatchway feeders exceeds sixteen (16) feet (unless in the opinion of the Surveyor the distance should be less) then vessel must have a wing feeder on each side provided in the between decks to feed this space. If there are no openings in the between

decks for wing feeders, four (4) heights of bags must be put on top of the bulk grain from the bulkhead to within sixteen (16) feet of the feeders.

The same rule applies when the distance between the after end of the hatchway feeders and the after bulkhead in lower holds exceeds sixteen (16) feet.

19. All bags stowed in between decks must be dunnaged.

20. Steamers of the type known as "Turret" with single deck or single deck and beams, may load full cargoes of grain in bulk, but must have shifting boards as required in Rules 2, 3 and 13, and if required by Surveyor, trimming bulkheads forward and aft extending from deck to floor, or if coming under hatches to top of coaming as directed by the Surveyor, and substantially fitted under their supervision. The loose grain in the end compartments to be secured by not less than four tiers of bags on boards properly laid, as provided for in Rule 7.

21. Steamers that are partly single deck and partly double deck known as Switchback and as part Awning Deck steamers may load all bulk grain in the lower holds of their double deck compartments, providing proper midship feeders and wing feeders are fitted, but the space in the between decks around the feeders must be filled with bagged grain or general cargo, but if the vessel is too deep to carry any grain or other cargo in the between decks the feeders are to be shored or properly secured to the satisfaction of the Surveyor.

If there are no openings in between decks for wing feeders and the bulkheads are more than sixteen (16) feet away from the nearest end of the midship feeders four (4) heights of bags must be put on top of the bulk grain from the bulkheads to within sixteen (16) feet of the feeders, unless in the opinion of the Surveyor the distance should be less.

Bunker hatches may be used as feeders when feasible. The quantity of bulk grain in the feeders must be at least two and one-half per cent. ($2\frac{1}{2}\%$) of the carrying capacity of the hold.

22. *Full cargo of oats and/or cotton seed.* Steamers with double bottoms for water ballast may carry a full cargo of Oats and/or Cotton Seed (except as provided for in Rule 8), but if with two or more decks must have tight wing and hatch feeders to feed the lower hold or orlop as provided for in Rule 18.

23. *Part cargo of oats and/or cotton seed.* When the quantity of Oats and/or Cotton Seed carried in bulk between the two upper decks exceeds 60% of the capacity of said deck, the excess over 50% may be stowed in bulk in compartments fitted with wing shifting boards extending from bulkheads at each end of hold to within four (4) feet of the hatches, one of such compartments shall be the largest between deck compartments; *or* where a steamer has four or more compartments in between

decks Oats and/or Cotton Seed may be loaded in bulk in all of these compartments if they are provided with wing feeders of increased size to reach from the forward and after bulkhead to within four feet of hatches. The hatch feeders or feeders for lower hold must be capped boxed feeders, five or six feet in depth. All holds are to be so fitted.

24. In Single Deck Steamers Oats and/or Cotton Seed may be loaded over heavy grain with proper separations in two holds, but the grain in all other holds must be properly secured with bagged grain or other cargo easily handled. This Rule applies also to Steamers where some holds are double and some single deck.

25. Modern two (2) deck steamers with large trimming hatches may have properly constructed feeders, not to exceed twelve by sixteen (12 x 16) feet.

26. Stoke Hold Bulkheads and Donkey Boiler recesses are required to be sheathed with wood and made grain-tight, with an air space between the iron and the wood, when exposed to heat from fire-room or donkey boiler. When already properly sheathed Surveyor may pass the vessel, but not less than nine (9) inches of space will be required where the sheathing is to be erected or renewed. This rule applies where the fires are liable to cause damage by excessive heat from the stoke hold or donkey boiler.

27. *Single Deck Steamers with high hatch Coamings loading full or part cargoes of Grain in bulk.*

1. The Hatch Coamings may be used as feeders and must be of sufficient size to admit of not less than two and one-half per cent. ($2\frac{1}{2}\%$) of the total grain in the hold being stowed within the coamings; otherwise the bulk grain must be secured by four (4) heights of bags.

2. When Hatch Coamings are utilized for feeders and such coamings extend into the hold a foot or more below the main deck, such coamings, in the part below the deck, are required to have two (2) two-inch openings in the coamings, between the beams, to allow the grain to feed into the wings and ends of the hold.

3. The Hatch Coamings must be properly supported by heavy Iron cross beams and fitted with fore and aft shifting boards.

4. The Hatch Coamings must be so placed that they are capable of feeding the center and both ends of the holds.

Sailing Vessels

28. Vessels being loaded with grain in Bags shall be dunnaged from six to twelve inches on the floor and from six to fifteen inches on the bilges, according to the form of the ship's bottom; and two (2) inches at the sides.

The between decks shall be dunnaged two (2) inches from the sides and decks.

The dunnage in the hold must be laid over with boards and entirely covered with sails, or approved mats, so as to prevent any of the loose grain from running down on to the floor of the vessel and thence to the pump-well. If sails are used they must be of good quality and free from holes. The sails and mats must cover the keelsons.

29. Bulk or loose grain must be taken in Bins prepared for that purpose. Materials for Bins must be of well seasoned stock; unseasoned lumber must not be used where it will come in contact with the grain.

30. The floor of the Bin must be laid on sleepers of scantling 2½ by 4 inches in size, sixteen inches apart from center to center, supported by studs of corresponding size, also sixteen inches from center to center.

It must be raised from six to twelve inches over the floor of the vessel—in the bilge from six to fifteen inches, and in vessels that are very flat or sharp, may be increased or diminished at the discretion of the Surveyor.

In no case shall the floor of the bin be laid on loose dunnage.

The floor is considered as extending from the keelson to the turn of the bilge. It must be laid with two thicknesses of one inch boards, so that they will break joints at the edges and ends, and care must be taken that it be grain-tight. Vessels under three hundred (300) tons register may be permitted to have a single floor laid with one inch boards placed edge and edge and seams covered with battens two by one (2 x 1) inch, or edges lapped one inch.

31. The studs for the forward and after Bulkheads for vessels not exceeding fourteen (14) feet depth of hold must be equal to four by six (4 x 6) inches in size; for vessels of a greater depth than fourteen (14) feet, they must be equal to four by eight (4 x 8) inches. They must be set twenty (20) inches apart from center to center, firmly secured at the top and bottom, and properly braced, in the center, also cleated on the ceiling to resist the pressure of the grain, and made grain-tight.

32. All air strakes and open seams must be closed and the sides of the vessel above the turn of the bilge must be sealed after the manner of clapboarding reversed, and not furred where it can be avoided. When furring is used the ceiling must be made grain-tight at the bilges and sides. All lodging and bosom knees not fitted tight to the deck must be cleated grain-tight around the face of the knees.

33. Vessels with single deck or with one deck and beams carrying a full cargo of grain are required to have, in addition to the forward and after end bulkheads, two trimming bulkheads

(thus making a division of three compartments), to extend from the upper deck to within two feet from the bottom of the vessel, except where the between decks are laid aft, the after one may extend only to the lower deck, and be so placed that in loading the middle compartment will be entirely filled and the end ones left to trim the vessel. If the end compartments are not entirely filled care must be taken that the cargo be properly covered and secured on top to prevent shifting. The studs of the trimming bulkheads to be not less than three by six (3 x 6) inches and set twenty-two (22) inches from the centers, and all studs to be firmly secured at top and bottom and properly braced and cleated.

34. Vessels carrying bulk and bags, must not carry bulk higher than to admit of the stowage of one-quarter of the cargo in bags or not less than five heights of bags over it (except the vessel be under five hundred (500) tons register when the height may be regulated by the Surveyor).

35. Vessels with two decks having bulk grain in hold as high as the between deck, shall have strakes of between deck-plane opened on each side over the bulk in the wings and amidships, and have three or four feet of bulk grain in wing and amidship feeders, upon which sufficient grain in bags or other cargo may be stowed over board coverings, as provided for in Rule 7. When the hold is not filled with bulk grain to the between deck, enough space must be left and sufficient cargo stowed over it to properly secure it, as provided for in Rule 7.

36. The Pump-Well must be sufficiently large to admit of the passage of a man to the bottom of the hold, and with room to work conveniently when there, say not less than four (4) feet fore and aft, and five (5) feet athwartships (reference, however, must be had to the size of the keelson and assistant keelsons), and must be grain-tight and ceiled.

37. Access to the pump-well must be had either by a manhole through the upper deck or by a clear passage-way between decks from the after hatch. In no case must it be from the main hatch.

38. Masts, Water-Tanks and Pumps, either of wood or iron, must be properly cased, to prevent damage from leakage, and mast coats must be strong and tight.

39. The between deck hatches must be kept off, and the scuppers safely plugged to prevent loose grain from running down the ship's timbers.

Iron or Steel Sailing Vessels

40. The foregoing rules are also to apply to Iron or Steel Sailing Vessels, excepting that in cases where the floor and

ceiling are in such good condition as to warrant it, the extra floor and ceiling may be dispensed with, and if the stanchions are not over four (4) feet apart and are double, two or three inch plank can be fitted between them for shifting plank.

Vessels having iron or steel between decks without openings for wing feeders, the bulk grain in the lower hold must be secured by at least five heights of bags or its equivalent in other cargo laid over board coverings as provided in Rule 7.

41. In the event of unusual construction of vessels which may necessitate deviation from the foregoing Rules, the Surveyor must obtain the approval of the Inspection Committee of the Board.

Rice. The stowage of rice follows that of other grains with regard to shifting precautions. In addition rice should be specially protected against damp air; and ventilation provided for as in the carriage of jute. Rice readily absorbs odors and should be kept clear of hides, saltpeter, etc.

Dunnage carefully keeping all bags free from contact with ironwork.

Rice is of two general kinds, *clean rice*, and *paddy rice,* the latter being lighter as the husk is still on the kernel.

Rice bags run from 100 to 250 lbs. depending upon the kind of grain.

Dampness and wet of all kinds are fatal to rice. When coming to a cold weather port be careful in taking off hatches. A rush of warm air from the hold, if up from the tropics, is followed by cold air going down from the decks. Condensation takes place and dripping sweat from the beams rains down on the cargo.

XVIII

Special Cargo

While the freight rate on ordinary cargo is based on either weight or measurement, what is called "special cargo," such as revolvers, jewelry, boots and shoes, and goods of an unusual value according to bulk, have always to pay an *extra rate*, based on a small percentage of the value, in addition to the regular freight rate. This extra charge is made because of the necessity of special stowage for its protection. In some cases cargo of this character is delivered specially to the captain personally, and is placed under the care of the purser or some other responsible officer of the ship. The extra rate may vary anywhere from one per cent. to three and one-half per cent. of the value of the

Loading a locomotive.

shipment. Sometimes, the extra charge is made on the basis of so much extra per 40 cubic feet, and sometimes on the basis of so much ad valorem, whichever produces the most revenue for the steamship company.

Ship's option (weight or measurement). When a steamship company makes a freight quotation " per ton, weight or measurement, ship's option," it is understood that the charge will be made on a weight basis if the weight of the shipment exceeds the cubic measurement of same or on a measurement basis should the cubic measurement exceed the weight. While practically all the foreign steamship lines quote freight rates on the basis of 2,240 pounds or 40 cubic feet measurement to the

Special cargo—loading a forty-ton sampan at Yokohama.

ton, such companies as the Panama Railroad Co. and the American-Hawaiian Steamship Co. (which also do a domestic business) figure the ton as 2,000 pounds. Transpacific business handled by the Southern Pacific Company and other transcontinental lines, is also done on the basis of 2,000 pounds to the ton. These companies usually quote rates, however, at so much per 100 pounds, or so much per cubic foot, so that it is practically immaterial whether they figure the ton as 2,240 pounds or 2,000 pounds.

Cargo marked "fragile," "handle with care," etc. Shippers should appreciate the fact that it is quite useless to mark in English *only*, such expressions as "handle with care," "this side up," etc., on packages intended for foreign countries, where English is not spoken or understood by those who will handle the freight. If such instructions are necessary, they should be made in the language of the country for which they are destined, as well as in English.

Heavy packages. Unless otherwise stated it is understood that the freight rates quoted by the steamship companies apply to packages not exceeding two tons weight. When packages exceed this weight provision must be made by the shipper either to put the pieces aboard the steamer through direct arrangement with a hoisting company or to arrange with the steamship company for freight rates to include the hoisting charges. Similar extra charges are liable to be made at the port of destination or at transshipping points, so that shippers should be careful to find out when shipping heavy pieces just what the freight rate covers.

XIX

Pilfering

The constantly increasing amount of theft and pilferage from cargoes of merchandise has compelled insurance experts all over the world to consider ways and means for correcting it, as *losses from this source are declared to equal if they do not exceed marine losses from all other sources combined.*

"No port in the world," says *World's Markets*, "is free from this evil and the records of many are very discouraging. Organized pilferage is carried on in New York with the utmost effrontery; in fact, it has become so extensive in certain instances as to render questionable the wisdom of keeping certain lines of transportation open. Shoes and leather are the articles most frequently stolen, but other commodities are by no means immune. Longshoremen fill their blouses with crude rubber and dispose of it over the nearest 'speak-easy' bar at the rate of about 50 per cent. of its market value.

"Frequently cases of silk destined for foreign markets are emptied of their contents and filled with worthless junk of equal weight before they are delivered to the ship. The truckman receives a clean bill of lading and the loss is not discovered until the merchandise is delivered at the foreign port. The only way to beat the game is to watch the goods until they are stowed away in the steamer's hold—*and sometimes even after that.*

"A foreign agent in Guayaquil writes: 'I regret to have to report a most serious system of robbery on the wharf and in the Guayaquil Custom House, which the government does nothing to repress. The officials of the Custom House even pretend to refuse to grant a certificate of such robberies on grounds that this would enable the consignees to make claims against the officials on the wharf of the Custom House.'

"Havana importers state: 'Theft and pilferage of goods consigned to this port are of daily occurrence, and no efficient measures have been taken to prevent it. Sometimes whole packages are missing, which the agents of the steamer certify they have delivered, while the warehouse authorities certify that delivery has not been made. It is argued that the insurance interests doing business in Havana should appoint a lawyer to take care of their difficulties of this nature.'"

Supervision of loading and discharging is up to the ship's officers. Every hold working cargo liable to damage or pilfering *should be watched at all times.* Holds should be under the responsible care of a deck officer. Under him certain reliable quartermasters and seaman should always be on the job studying the stowage, watching the slings and gear, looking out for the interests of the ship. These men, keeping notes of stowage and discharging, calling the mate at every breakage, getting marks and numbers, and protecting the ship against loss, also protect the shipper and, indeed, perform a still larger service. Such vigilant work on the part of officers and crew results in a real national gain to commerce. The money loss from pilfering and careless breakage is exceeded and added to by the business loss that follows non delivery of the goods. On an *efficient honest ship* the whole crew are worth, *and earn* every dollar they get—every sensible owner knows this.

Duty to Cargo should always be foremost in the minds of the ship's complement. The ship is liable for loss from the time her tackles take hold of the cargo for loading to the time they release it, without damage, for discharge. Telephone connections should be fitted in all holds.

Analysis of Hoisting Cargo

The cycle of a full unloading operation is analysed as follows:

Slinging (in hold or 'tween decks)	——	seconds
Drag to hatch	——	"
Hoist	——	"
Swing over side	——	"
Lowering	——	"
Landing	——	"
Return of hook to hold or 'tween deck	——	"
Total	——	"

In loading the cycle is as follows:

Hooking	——	seconds
Hoisting and swinging inboard	——	"
Lowering into hatch	——	"
Landing	——	"
Return of hook to dock or lighter	——	"
Total	——	"

Note.—Number of men in hatch, on deck, on dock; kind of cargo, weight per draft, etc.

A stop watch in the palm of the hand and a note book will give an officer a great deal of important information with regard to his hatches, the kind of work going on, and the comparative speed of hatches and gangs.

To get a correct average. Take each operation ten times on stop watch then divide by 10.

Of course most men know whether a hatch is going to capacity, but a great deal can be found out by a study of the longer time taken to adjust poorly made slings and nets. An hour lost each day through poor gear is an expensive proposition. The writer has seen stevedores fussing around with worn out nets (good enough for light cargo) and wasting valuable time. Such work makes hold duty interesting and also adds a lot of valuable data to an officer's note book.

XX

Rats and Cargo

The old adage about the rats leaving a sinking ship, brings a sort of friendly feeling to the minds of many with regard to these ancient rodent voyagers. If there are plenty of rats on board, all is well, etc. The author is indebted to Mr. S. S. Rosen, General Manager of the Guarantee Exterminator Company, of New York, for the data given in this section of the chapter on Stowage.

A rat consumes its weight in food every week.

Rats spoil more cargo than they consume.

Rats increase at an alarming rate—the figures are almost unbelievable. Dr. Rucker, Assistant Surgeon General of the U. S. Public Health Service has computed the actual increase of a pair of rats for five years at 940,369,969,152, assuming, of course, that we organized a special truck and carting service to bring in their food, and passed and obeyed a few hundred laws against killing rats. But, with this in mind, it is no wonder that they appear numerous and grow rapidly in places such as ships' holds when they are often left alone.

The Bureau of Biological Survey tells a lot about the rat that has nothing to do with cargo directly, but we understand from their learned report that the rat is a first-class pest and carries practically all diseases, many of them fatal to man.

Out of 46,000 bags of grain a steamer recently lost 40,000 bags on a twenty-nine-day voyage due to the depredations of rats. Flour is a favorite food with rats. Rats wallow in the flour and from time to time shake themselves free from it, filling the cargo with germs. Cargo partly touched by rats should be condemned. It is a total loss.

Fire risk. Rats add greatly to the fire risk on board ship. They collect oily rags, and form nests where spontaneous combustion may take place. *Use rat guards—Fumigate.*

XXI

Refrigerating Ships

Vessels with one or more holds or compartments lined, and insulated and fitted with refrigerating machinery* are now very

* "*Operations of a refrigerating machine.* Apparatus designed for refrigerating is based upon the following series of operations:

Compress a gas or vapor by means of some external force (the compressor), then relieve it of its heat so as to diminish its volume further (cooling coils circulating sea water through hot compressed gas), next, cause this com-

common. Such vessels are used mainly for the carriage of frozen and chilled meat.

Insulated compartments are constructed by bolting wooden furring pieces to the framing. One-inch tongued and grooved planking is placed inside the shell plating on two by two studs, leaving a two-inch air space; eight to ten inches inside of this,

Freezing pipes in a refrigerating hold.

a wall is built up of two layers of tongued and grooved plank, the one next the furring pieces 3/4″ thick and the covering 1″ thick. The space between is filled with the insulating material. Sheet zinc is used for a lining inside of plank next shell plates.

Underdeck insulation is placed against the deck without the air space.

pressed gas or vapor to expand so as to produce mechanical work and thus lower the temperature of surrounding brine (brine coils). The absorption of heat from the brine when the gas or vapor resumes its original volume constitutes the refrigerating effect of the apparatus.—Adapted from Kent's *Mechanical Engineer's Pocket Book.*

Air, ammonia, sulphur-dioxide, carbonic acid gas (CO_2), are among the agents used for mechanical refrigeration.

Flooring over tank tops is placed between two casings of two and a half inch tongued and grooved plank. The strength being required to support the cargo to be carried. In *chill* rooms, where beef is *hung*, means must be provided for the hanging of hooks and chains from the beams above.

Insulating materials generally used are as follows:

Charcoal, silicate of cotton, or slagwool, granulated cork, pumice, sawdust and balsa wood. For small refrigerating spaces felt and cow hair are sometimes used. This material was used in some of the storage spaces on the older interned German liners and was evil-smelling stuff when ripped out.

Charcoal is highly combustible, and absorbs odors.

Balsa wood is coming into use as an insulating material. The following data is supplied by the American Balsa Company:

Balsa possesses a high insulating efficiency, comparing about equally with cork, and it has the advantage that the encysting and water-proofing treatment causes it, by the exclusion of dampness, to retain its insulating qualities indefinitely and preserves it against rot and the attacks of insects and bacteria.

Though only recently in use for this purpose, balsa has already been employed as the insulating material for the refrigerated spaces on about fifty ships, including fourteen of the new 535 ft. passenger-and-cargo vessels now being completed for the U. S. Shipping Board (1920).

Added advantages over other high-grade manufacturing materials are its combined strength and light weight, and the saving of labor and of the greater part of the usual supplementary material required for installation, such as sheathing and water-proof paper.

Balsa for insulation is supplied in sections up to 24 in. x 8 ft. x 3 in., cut to the required sizes, each section separately water-proofed. The sections are made up of individual pieces of balsa dovetailed by special machinery to form solid, airtight planks. These large sections are erected in one or a very few thicknesses. The relatively small number of shiplap joints are practically air-tight, thereby reducing the required number of layers of water-proof paper from the now usual twelve, to one or two.

Where lower holds are insulated trunk hatches are usually fitted and these are insulated also and provided with removable brine coils under hatches.

Brine coils under hatches.

Frozen cargo. This requires a temperature of 15 degrees F. and usually includes the following, *sheep, poultry, fish, butter, milk.* The contents of the hold is frozen solid. Stowage is close. Sheep carcases admit of air circulation through their centers.

Chilled cargo. This requires a temperature ranging from 29 degrees F. to 42 degrees F.

Beef and other large meats are carried at 29 degrees F. and must be hung from the deck above so as to allow a free circulation of cold air.

Eggs require a temperature of 33 degrees F.

Tinned meats and *fruits* require a temperature of 38 degrees F.

Beer and *wine* are carried in a temperature of 42 degrees F.

General remarks. Officers in charge of refrigerator ships should take the time to learn the details of their operation. The master should at all times know the condition of the refrigerating plant, and should require full information.* Cases have recently

* Two hundred and fifty quarters of frozen beef are reported to have been damaged on the steamer *Muscatine* because of the brine pipes being out of order, which occurred while the vessel was bound from Buenos Aires.

Oct. 25, 1920.

This is a moderate case. When a refrigerator ship breaks down in a tropical port with a full cargo the story is different. The *Polar Sea* disaster is still remembered.

occurred where heavy losses have been suffered through the breaking down of the cold storage system with cargoes of valuable meats thrown on an inadequate market in tropical ports.

Proper care and use of the refrigerating plant will result in saving and comfort for those on board. The chambers should be kept sealed, and cold storage rooms for ship's use should only be unlocked once a day under proper supervision.

The American Bureau of Shipping requires that the machine room is to be efficiently ventilated and drained; it is to be effectively separated from the insulated spaces by watertight plating.

The insulation of the containing walls and floors and all metal which might otherwise come in contact with the cargo is to be complete and the insulating material in thoroughly efficient condition. Full particulars of the nature and construction of the insulation are to be reported to the Bureau's Committee and approved.

All pipes, trunks, etc., in insulated spaces are to be well placed, secured and protected from risk of damage from cargo. All bilge suction, sounding and air pipes which pass through insulated spaces are to be properly insulated, and bilge suctions from the engine room are to be fitted with non-return valves.

All thermometer tube flanges and covers are to be of brass and arranged so that water cannot enter and freeze in the tubes.

Sluice valves should not be fitted in bulkheads of insulated spaces, and if fitted are to have brass non-return valves and are to be accessible at all times.

Provision is to be made for the ready examination of the bilges, rose boxes, etc., and it is recommended that the bottoms, sides and coamings of all hatches and limbers be varnished.

Cargo battens are to be fastened to the sides and bottom of all insulated cargo spaces before shipping the cargo to be refrigerated. The battens on the bottom are to be at least 2″ by 2″ and those on the sides by 2″ by 1½″, while their spacing is to be about 12″.

The refrigerating machinery is to be of approved construction and of sufficient power to maintain the required temperature in the cargo spaces when in tropical climates and with the machines running 18 hours per day. Duplex or duplicate machines are to be fitted where the refrigerated spaces have a greater capacity than 70,000 cubic feet. Upon completion the machinery is to be tested under working conditions, the time and fall of temperature being noted. After the spaces are considered to be properly refrigerated the machinery should be stopped for at least two hours, or two and a half hours with a brine installation, and a note taken of the rise in temperature at the end of the period of stoppage.

Spare gear is to be supplied as required and is to be stowed where readily accessible. Where two sections or compartments are each cooled by machines of the same pattern only one set of spare gear will be required. Where two machines are fitted, each being capable of keeping the whole of the refrigerated spaces at the required temperature in tropical climates, when running 18 hours per day, no spare parts will be required, provided all similar parts are interchangeable.

Brine and water circulating pumps should be in duplicate, or there should be independent connections to auxiliary pumps. Spare piston rings, pump valves and rods, for independent pumps, should be carried.

When the air, circulating, and feed pumps are all worked by one independent engine and there are no independent connections to the main engine pumps, the following additional spare gear is to be carried.

1 piston rod, complete, of each pattern.

1 set piston rings of each pattern for steam cylinders.

1 eccentric strap and rod of each pattern.

1 slide valve spindle, complete, of each pattern.

1 set connecting rod and crosshead bolts and nuts.

A sufficient supply of spare liquid and calcium chloride is to be carried to ensure an ample margin for any leakage in the refrigerating plant during the voyage.

All brine regulating valves are to be fitted outside the insulated spaces so as to be accessible without entering these spaces.

Before the Certificate of Survey is issued all the insulation is to be carefully examined and tested for dryness and fullness and all test holes subsequently closed. All limbers and hatches are to be removed, the limbers cleared, and the suctions, sluices and sounding pipes examined. All hatches, trunks, thermometer tubes, ventilator coamings, and deck connections are to be examined, and water-tight doors to be worked. Where brine may escape to the bilges, the cement is to be examined at each survey.

It is recommended that the machinery be examined and tested at a home port, before the cargo is fully discharged, but in all cases all parts of the refrigerating machinery, pumps, steam and water pipes, condensers, coolers, coils and connections, brine pipes and tanks are to be opened out and examined, and the condensers, coolers, coils and brine pipes tested if considered necessary; in the case of condensers containing iron or steel coils, the coils are to be withdrawn from the casing and tested at intervals of not more than four years; corroded parts should be tinned or otherwise made good; the coils are to be scraped, cleaned and painted with good anti-corrosive paint. The machinery is to be afterwards tested under working conditions.

A further survey is to be made at the port of shipment of the cargo to be refrigerated, in order to ascertain that the dunnage battens are in good order, that the insulation has not sustained damage since the home port survey, and also to test the refrigerating machinery under working conditions, the temperature in the holds being noted.

At ports where the services of a Surveyor to the Society are not available, a report of survey by a reliable, practical Surveyor will be accepted by the Committee, or if such a Surveyor is not available, they will accept a report of survey made by two competent Engineers of the Vessel.

Ventilation; Fruit—Oranges, Lemons. The ventilation of cargo spaces is becoming more thoroughly understood. Forced draft ventilation is perhaps the best for certain kinds of cargo. Fruit cargoes, shipped green will heat rapidly and decay unless well ventilated. Bananas are carried in racks on their sides the bunches and foliage together. Great care and experience is needed in the handling of this fruit, and vessels in the trade are specially fitted for it. Oranges and lemons are packed in boxes. Where stowed together place lemons on bottom, being heavier.

Bananas. The carriage of bananas has become a highly specialized business. Vessels are loaded and unloaded by conveyors, generally through large side ports or over the deck through hatches. The fruit steamers are usually painted white.

William Fawcett, in the "The Banana, Its Cultivation, Distribution and Commercial Uses," gives this description of the general arrangement of the SS. *Barranca*, one of the ships which carry United Fruit Company's bananas to Europe:

Loading bananas by conveyor

"The refrigerating machinery and cooling appliances are in deck-houses on the upper deck, thus leaving the spaces below as clear as possible for the cargo. There are three decks for fruit forward and aft respectively, and each deck has a run of about 130 feet between bulkheads, making six fine chambers, each taking about 10,000 large bunches, the total of 60,000 being about three times the number carried by the *Port Morant*, which initiated the service in 1901.

"The fruit comes on board within a few hours of cutting, and is stored without covering of any kind, the lowest bunches being arranged with the stems vertical, with a final layer placed horizontally, this giving the best results both in utilizing space and freedom from damage. Every cargo space is divided into bins by portable horizontal sparring fitted into vertical posts, thus checking the movement of the fruit in rough weather. Sparred gratings are laid on the steel decks to carry the fruit clear of the plating, and to allow the air to circulate below and up through the fruit. The ship's sides and bulkheads and the highest and lowest decks are insulated with granulated cork and wood boardings, forming a complete envelope about seven inches thick. Along each side trunks conveying the cool air are formed by boarding, in which are a number of openings fitted with adjustable slides, and spaced at suitable intervals and levels.

"Powerful fans of the centrifugal type, arranged in pairs and coupled with electric motors, draw the air from the fruit chambers through the suction chambers on one side, pass it over closely nested brine piping, thereby cooling and drying it, and returning it through the delivery trunks on the opposite side. The cooler pipes are electrically welded into grid form, there being no screwed joints except those on the headers, the brine flow being regulated by valves controlling a number of separate groups of grids. The cooling surface is properly proportioned to the work to be done, and the cooler with its fans is completely insulated. Ventilators are provided, enabling the air in the fruit spaces to be changed in as few minutes as may be found desirable from time to time, the fresh air passing through the cooler before reaching the fruit, and the vitiated air being discharged to the atmosphere. The brine pumps are of the vertical duplex type, two in number, either one capable of performing the full duty in emergency.

"The machines and fans are run during the last day or so of the outward voyage to cool down the spaces in readiness to receive the fruit. Stowage is rapid, owing to the use of power-driven conveyors, and discharges even more rapid, some of the fruit in the square of the hatches being stowed in special cribs, which are lifted out by the ship's derricks immediately the hatches are off, leaving space for the discharging elevators, which are promptly lowered into position. During the first two days of the homeward voyage the plant is run continuously to extract the sun heat from the fruit and to retard ripening. The condition of the fruit is kept under close observation, temperatures being taken at regular intervals day and night, the captain, assisted by the ship's officers—all carefully trained men—personally attending to these duties. After a few days at sea the temperatures are generally well in hand, and care then has to be taken to avoid the risk of chilling, the machine being slowed down, and probably one of the compressors disconnected, just sufficient power being developed to maintain the temperature at about 55° F."

Pumps—Bilges—Rose Boxes

A vessel having frozen holds is liable to have her bilge suctions freeze up and in the event of a leak, or a collision, be unable to pump out the refrigerator compartments. This might even happen in very warm weather, so far as the outside temperature is concerned. The following requirements from the A.B.S. Rules cover this possible condition.

All pipes, trunks, etc., in insulated refrigerator spaces are to be well placed, secured and protected from risk of damage from cargo. All bilge suction, sounding, and air pipes which pass through insulated refrigerator spaces are to be properly insulated, and bilge suctions from the engine room are to be fitted with non-return valves.

All thermometer tube flanges and covers are to be of brass and arranged so that water cannot enter and freeze in the tubes.

Sluice valves should not be fitted in bulkheads of insulated spaces, and if fitted are to have brass non-return valves and are to be accessible at all times.

Provision is to be made for the ready examination of the bilges, rose boxes, etc., and it is recommended that the bottoms, sides and coamings of all hatches and limbers be varnished.

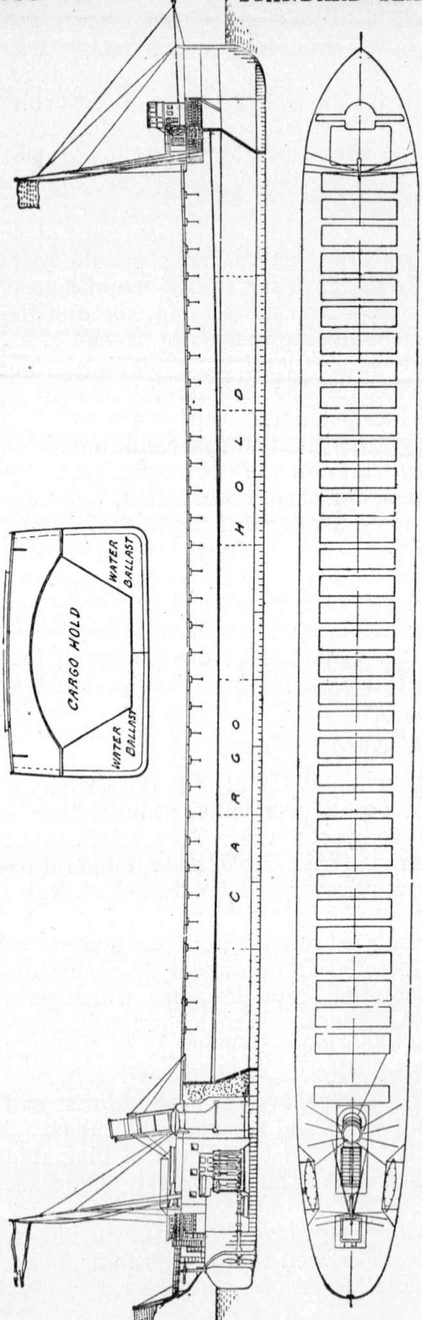

A Great Lakes ore carrier. Note the thirty-three cargo hatches!

XXII

Ore Carriers

Ore Cargoes. Vessels designed for the carriage of ore, as in the Great Lakes trade, have specially designed holds and hatchways admitting of exceptionally rapid loading and discharging. In fact the mechanical handling of this sort of cargo has reached a high state of perfection in the lake ore ports, and is now being adopted on the Atlantic seaboard with increasing satisfaction.

The ore unloaders are now designed to handle as much as eight hundred tons per hour. Rising labor costs and the striving for more rapid *turn around* is working wonders toward the use of heavy machinery for this kind of cargo handling.

The many hatches shown in the photograph, and further illustrated on the succeeding pages, enable these machines to work with maximum efficiency. 50 seconds is required for the bucket to dip into the hold pick up 17 tons of ore or 8 tons of coal, lift it clear of the hold, slide back and drop it into cars, or hoppers, and again return for another " bite " of the cargo.

A battery of fifteen ton Hulett Automatic Ore Unloaders at work in the hatches of a Great Lakes ore carrier.

Mr. H. T. Simmons, Chief Engineer of the Wellman-Seaver-Morgan Co. of Cleveland, manufacturers of the Hulett unloading machines has kindly supplied me with operation data and this and the succeeding photograph.

Only two men are required for the entire operation of one of these machines. One of the operators, whose station is in the bucket leg directly over the bucket shells, controls all of the motions of raising and lowering the bucket, of traveling the trolley back and forth, and moving the machine along the dock from one hatch to another. The second operator is stationed in a cab on the larry* and from this station he controls the movement of the larry, the operation of the larry gates, and the weighing of the ore.

Some idea of the capacities of unloading by this method may be derived from a record which was made in Ashtabula by eight machines of this type, having a capacity of fifteen tons each, unloading seven boats having a total capacity of 70,000 tons in

* The weighing car into which the ore is dumped by the bucket. The larry weighs the ore as it transports it.

twenty-two hours' actual time. At other points, four machines working in boats having capacities up to 13,000 tons have unloaded these cargoes in about three hours and twenty-five minutes.

In addition to the vertical movement, which is given to the bucket leg by means of the walking beam, it also has a motion of rotation around its vertical axis. This motion is introduced

Buckets cleaning up in hold of a lake vessel. Note man in bucket leg.

to enable the machine to reach along the keel of the boat and clean up ore between hatches. The distance from point to point of bucket shells when open is approximately twenty-one feet. About 97 per cent of the ore is removed from the hold without hand labor.

The machines are all operated by electric power. Machines are also being used on the Atlantic Coast.

Records of fifty machines in operation indicate that this type of machine will handle ore at 2½ to 4½ cents per ton, including all fixed charges, and records of as high as 783 tons of ore per hour per machine from tie-up to cast-off of boat have been made.

Ore and coal is loaded by lifting the car and turning it over sliding the ore into the hold. Dumping direct from car to ship saves breakage.

Where vessels are not specially designed for the carriage of ore a cargo in a four-hold vessel can usually be stowed in a very satisfactory manner by the following method:

Run ore into the middle holds, No. 2 and No. 3, then trim the vessel for sea with No. 1 and No. 4.

If a vessel is well constructed she will suffer no straining from this method of loading. Where no cargo is carried, other than the ore, a trunk should be built up in the lower No. 2 and No. 3, or a certain amount of the cargo should be carried in the 'tween decks of these hatches.

The weights should be kept fairly well up and back from the ends, making the vessel less crank in bad weather with a beam sea. By trimming back from the ends, fore and aft, the vessel will be more *sea kindly* when meeting a head sea or running before a sea aft, or on the quarter.

Ore cargoes present certain difficulties and before taking ore on board, especially in a foreign port, the master will do well to find out its characteristics.

Certain sulphur ores are subject to a process of kiln drying and are liable to fire and as the ore contains a large proportion of sulphuric acid, water played on the cargo will not always quench the fire and may cause the loss of the vessel. (See page 755).

The greatest care must be taken in arranging for cargoes of this kind in foreign ports. In the very excellent work on *Seamanship* by the late Captains Todd and Whall the following incident is cited:

"The writer once, many years ago, was coming from Huelva, bound to the river Tyne with a cargo of mineral. In the No. 1 hold was placed 160 tons of such mineral described as above. When nearing our destination off Flamborough Head this 160 tons was discovered to be a mass of fire. Water was freely poured down on it, with the effect that it kept the ship's deck and upper works from breaking into a blaze, and placed a dark crust over the mineral on fire. But that was all, it did not quench the fire.

"The mineral was afterwards discharged on fire into iron lighters, and burnt itself out on shore. Unfortunately for the vessel, the water poured down on the mineral had circulated through her ballast tanks to the engine-room, where it was pumped out by the donkey ballast pump. This water, being highly charged with sulphuric acid, attacked all iron with which it came in contact, the result being that chemical action took place in all iron in the ship's bottom unprotected by cement, and caused serious deterioration to many of her plates, floors, and tank divisions, which cost a round sum of money to replace. Therefore, before any vessel ships kiln-dried mineral of the above description, fire should be warily guarded against. Whole cargoes of such mineral are seldom shipped, and when packages of it are carried it should be bedded on other mineral, and isolated from the sides of the vessel. This mineral is shipped in small bags containing about 100 lbs. each."

Cargo liable to absorb gases should not be placed near holds containing ore. The temperature of hold loaded with ore should be taken regularly and surface ventilation should be resorted to. In general, the rules for the care of coal cargo will apply to cargoes of ore.

The danger of ore shifting is very great. Where trunks are built up of empty barrels (a poor practice) the collapse of the trunk may mean the loss of the vessel. A shifting ore cargo is about the worst proposition to be met with at sea.

Trunks. The construction of trunks, in single-hold vessels, and in the large holds of steamers or motor vessels should be most carefully provided for, with extra heavy bracing and ceiling.*

The Cyclops. The following extract from a paper by Lieutenant Commander Mahlon S. Tisdale, U. S. Navy, printed in the *Proceedings, U. S. Naval Institute,* sheds some interesting side lights on the possible fate of the U. S. Collier *Cyclops* one of the unsolved mysteries of the World War. *The Cyclops was carrying a cargo of manganese ore.*

After describing the custom of keeping the topside tank man-

* A recent development in the field of ocean-going ore carriers is the combination of ore and coal carriers, fitted for either kind of cargo, and the combination of ore and oil, that is, a tanker with expansion trunks in the wings, and ore trunk amidship.

Such vessels have been designed by Mr. Hugo P. Frear, naval architect, Bethlehem Shipbuilding Corporation.

Of course they *do not* carry both cargoes at the same time. Two of each of this type are under construction, D.W. tonnage about 20,000.

hole openings uncovered, Commander Tisdale draws the folfowing conclusions:

" Now let us take the case of the *Cyclops* on her ill-fated voyage of last year when she was lost. She was carrying manganese ore (according to newspaper reports we received abroad at the time). Due to the great weight per cubic foot of this ore as compared to coal it is probable that her cargo holds were loaded by weight and not by volume and were therefore far from full. Perhaps the cargo was braced to prevent shifting—but this would have required very strong braces, far beyond the capacity of the ship's carpenter. Unless these braces were installed at the loading port they were probably not installed at all. Now the matter sizes up as follows:

" The ship was heavily loaded—hence deep in the water with a correspondingly small freeboard—but her holds were not full by *volume.*

" It was customary to leave the manhole plates off the topside tanks according to the statement of the captain (she had the same captain when I made my cruise on her as she had when she was lost) in order to ' preserve the bitumastic.'

" Due to her load her sea connections from the topside tanks were probably submerged. These were in the skin of the ship and led from the bottom of the tank.

" In any sort of a storm it was always customary in the colliers, due to their liveliness and to their great amount of top hamper, to secure *everything* for sea. I have seen even the huge iron sister-blocks which are shackled to the fore and aft girder, lashed together to prevent pounding.

" Is it not plausible to assume that the cargo may have shifted, perhaps only a little, but enough to increase the average list sufficiently to cause the free water in the double bottoms to rush toward the down side thus further increasing the list? Suppose the heavily laden *Cyclops* now shipped a sea. Would not this sea run into the open manholes of the topside tanks and immediately give the ship a tendency to capsize?

" This could all occur in a few seconds and the ship would be bottom up before any one could abandon ship. Some few men from the bridge and poop might have been thrown clear of the ship. But with everything secured for sea there would be little wreckage. Remember that there would be nothing adrift except such gear as would be free to float off during the few seconds during the turn. There would be no debris such as always follows a sinking due to other marine casualty, as in the case of striking a mine or torpedo. There would have been no time for an ' S. O. S.' There would have been no time for anything. The few men in the water could not have lived long of their own accord. Such small gear as did float off would have been lost in the vastness of the ocean long before the rescue vessels started their search.

"This seems to me a plausible solution of the loss of the *Cyclops*. Of course it is only a theory based upon several assumptions, some of which may be faulty. As several officers have said, 'Yours seems to be the only plausible theory,' it occurred to me that the service as a whole might be interested."

Caution. When an exceptionally high rate of freight is being offered for an ore cargo, or any other unknown cargo, be very careful and obtain all particulars with regard to its characteristics.

The precaution as to lines, berth, etc., should be observed when ore is being rapidly loaded or unloaded by machinery.

XXIII

Carriage of Coal

Coal. The stowage and ventilation of coal cargoes is of the utmost importance. No cargo of coal can be thoroughly ventilated throughout its bulk and at present the practice is to make use of *surface* ventilation alone, having two ventilators in each hold, an intake and an uptake, one cowl into the wind and one cowl away from the wind, keeping them trimmed properly at all times.

The following questions and answers from a pamphlet by Mr. H. H. Stoek "*The Safe Storage of Coal*" published by The Department of The Interior, Washington, D. C., are of interest in connection with the stowage of coal cargoes:

Prevention of Heating of Stored Coal

"*What is the cause of spontaneous combustion?* It seems due to an oxidation of the coal surface. This generates heat. If the heat is not dissipated, the temperature will continue to rise. The oxidation is more rapid at increased temperatures, so that the process is self-aggravating. A temperature may finally be reached where the coal is afire.

"*How may heating be detected?* By the odor given off from the pile or by thrusting iron rods into the pile and feeling them with the hand, or by a thermometer. Steam should not be confused with smoke, for water vapor coming out of the pile in winter time may produce visible steam when there is no appreciable heating within the pile. Temperature tests with an iron rod should be made if possible; actual temperature determinations should be made with any suitable type of thermometer.

" *What temperature is dangerous?* When the temperature rises above 140° F., the pile should be carefully watched. If it rises rapidly to 150° or 160° steps should be taken to move the coal and cool off the heated part.

" *What is the best way to stop heating which has started?* The best way is to move the coal as quickly as possible to a place where it can cool off. It should be allowed to become thoroughly cooled before replacing it in storage, or, better still, used at once and not returned to storage.

" *Can heating be stopped by putting water upon the pile?* Only if the water is applied in quantities sufficient to extinguish the fire and cool the mass. The water must reach the point at which heating occurs, for it can do little good if the stream is played only on the surface of the pile. Most bituminous coal cokes on heating, and a shell of tarry material forms about the hot spot, which prevents the water reaching it. To be sure that the water reaches the burning coal, it usually is necessary to dig into the pile and turn it over. Generally it is better to move the coal and not depend on water.

"*Does time have any effect on the heating of coal?* Three fourths of the coal fires studied have occurred within 90 days after the coal was placed in storage. Oxidation is most rapid on a freshly broken surface.

" *What effect has sulphur on the heating of coal?* Oxidation of the pyrite in the coal also produces heat and assists in breaking up the lumps and thus increases the amount of fine coal in the pile. Rise in temperature, either from external or internal causes promotes the oxidation of pyrite and thus increases the liability of the coal to spontaneous combustion. It is wise to select low-sulphur coals for storage if these are procurable; but it must not be taken for granted that a low-sulphur coal will necessarily store well, or that a high-sulphur coal will fire in storage.

" *Is it bad practice to mix different kinds of coal in storage?* Such mixing is generally believed to be bad practice, but there seems to be no logical basis for the belief except in so far as mixing may produce conditions within the pile that tend to retain heat.

" *What precautions prevent spontaneous combustion?* Avoid storing fine coal. Store screened nut and lump. Avoid external sources of heat, such as steam pipes, warm flues, and boiler settings. Avoid making fresh broken surfaces in handling the coal into storage.

" Avoid foreign combustible matter which may itself spontaneously heat, such as oily rags, paper, waste, etc.

" Avoid sticks and timbers in the pile, as these, surrounded by coarser coal, form ducts or flues that concentrate the warm currents from the coal below."

In connection with the carriage of coal, it is well to remember that the master is held responsible for the proper ventilation of the cargo, and any fault through this neglect will react upon him.

As cargoes loaded in wet weather will loose from 2½ to 3% of their weight, the necessary *excess* weight on the bill of lading weight should be insisted upon under these conditions, otherwise the cargo will be delivered short of the called for amount.

Where coal is loaded in a lower hold, partly filled, stout shifting boards should be fitted at the midship stanchions. Great care must also be taken with the limbers and the pump wells, all chance of clogging must be guarded against.

Temperature. A pipe with perforated end, preferably two of them, should be let down into the body of the coal and thermometers lowered each watch and temperature recorded. Coal is supposed to absorb twice its own volume of oxygen in ten days, and this is most rapid on a freshly broken surface.

Coal dust. Special care should be taken to prevent the damage of other cargo by coal dust. After a hold has been used for coal, special care should be taken in cleaning it for the next cargo. The bilges should be completely free from the dust.

Never close up ventilators leading to a coal hold to keep down the dust.

Never enter a coal hatch with an open light.

Uptakes. The heels of steel masts and king posts, sometimes fitted with a ventilating uptake, should be closed before stowing coal. Every possible point of *uptake*, should be stopped off. Where H section hold pillars are fitted see that no dunnage boards are in place about them forming possible flues from the bottom of the coal cargo.

Bunkering. This may be either coal or oil, both, or a combination product of coal dust and oil called *colloidal* fuel.

Coal bunkering is the most common and is carried on in a number of different ways.*

Mechanical bunkering arrangements are provided in most ports and the coal is shot into the bunker hatches and trimmed by the black squad.

* 43 cu. ft. = 1 ton of bunker coal (bituminous).

Coal may be taken from lighters, as at Coronel, Chili, using the ships winches, special cargo booms, or pendants and spans.

Coal may be carried on board by coolies, as in the East Indies, or by negroes as in the West Indies. Or it may be passed up on stages in small baskets lifted from hand to hand as in Japan and China. This is a very rapid way of coaling and involves no

Coaling S.S. Texan at Yokohama.
The women carry their babies on their backs while coaling.

special effort on the part of the ship except to see the lighters shifted, if in the stream, and to keep them clear of gangway and propellors.

Oil fuel and colloidal fuel is pumped on board through a hose.

Carrying of Coals on Deck for Use as Bunker Coal, from Ports North of Hatteras to Ports South of that Latitude

Board of Underwriters, N. Y.

Steamers of the three (3) deck rule and spar deck vessels are permitted where the stability and spare buoyancy are guaranteed, to carry during the winter months, October 1st to April 1st, eight (8) or ten (10) per cent. of their net register tonnage of coal on deck for consumption during the voyage.

Well deck steamers. If the coal is carried on the raised quarter deck the amount is not to exceed seven (7) per cent. of the net register tonnage, but if stowed over the bunkers, on the bridge deck, the amount not to exceed five (5) per cent. of the net registered tonnage.

Bulwarks to be ceiled up leaving a clear water course to the scuppers and other openings. Steering gear to be free of any obstructions.

Sufficient coal to be put in bags to secure the ends and cover the loose coal; the same not to be higher than the rail.

Where suitable bins are provided of a moderate size the coal in bags may be omitted.

Grain laden vessels are not permitted to carry coal on deck beyond sufficiency to carry them to the open sea.

Vessels other than those described to be submitted to the Loading Committee.

Hoisting coal on board at Coronel, Chili, using canvas slings.

XXV

The Michener Coaling and Trimming Gear

This apparatus is designed to reduce to a minimum the disagreeable features of supplying ships with bunker coal and to eliminate, to a large degree, the employment of men in the actual handling of the coal.

The mechanism falls into two divisions, the first the transfer of the coal from the coaling lighter alongside to the coal-port of the ship. The second the stowage of the coal in the bunkers after it has been delivered through the coal-port.

The mechanism for the first division comprises:

The Michener Portable Elevator

This machine is a self-contained portable, flexible-leg, two-way discharge, electrically driven and controlled device for raising coal from a lighter alongside delivering it to the side-ports or deck-hatches of a ship. In Photo *A* is shown four of these elevators at work on the side of a large liner. Each of the elevators is rigged to discharge into two hoppers at two coal-ports. The leg of the right hand elevator in the illustration is raised to permit the removal of an empty lighter and the replacement by a loaded one.

Fig. A. Coaling the S.S. George Washington.

Referring to illustration *B*, the machine comprises a triangular head 2 which is hung to the ship's side from ears 3, 3, and fended off by rolls 4. In this head is the driving mechanism including an electric motor, not shown, driving, through suitable reducing gearing, bucket chain main-shaft 6. The motor is

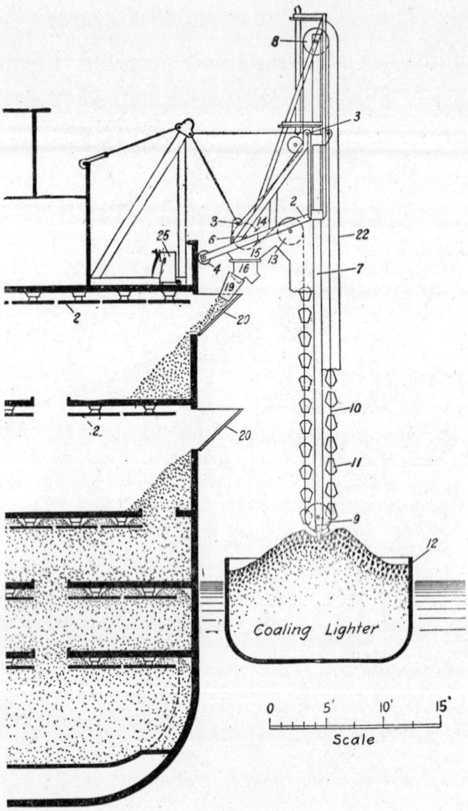

B.

connected by an insulated wire cable with a portable controller 25 preferably located on the ship's deck, and the controller is similarly connected with the source of power.

Mounted for vertical movement through head 2 is leg 7, having at its upper and lower ends suitable sprockets 8 and 9, respectively, for the endless bucket chain 10. This chain carries a series of buckets 11, 11, which, as the chain is driven downwardly on the off side and upwardly on the near side, dig into the coal in the lighter, filling the buckets which travel upward over sprocket 13 and dump before reaching sprocket 14, into hopper 15. The hopper is provided with a two-way discharge nose 16, having a gate whereby the stream of coal may be divided and directed to both discharge openings of nose 16, or to either to the exclusion of the other. From these the coal descends by gravity down chute 19 into hopper 20 and so

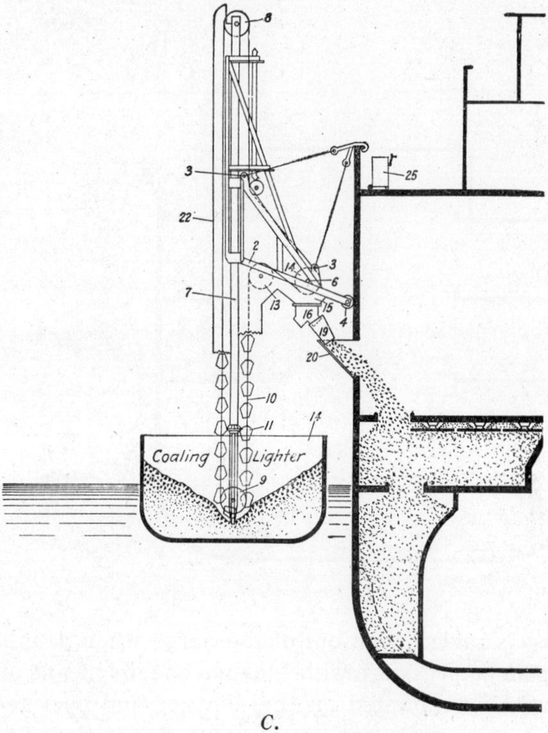

C.

on through the coal-port into the ship's bunker. As the buckets pass around the lower end of the leg, scooping up the coal, the pile of coal is correspondingly reduced and the elevator leg automatically descends so as to keep the buckets constantly in digging relation to the pile—compare the elevator of illustration *B* with the elevator of illustration *C*.

The lower end of the leg, below the head, is provided with a telescopic cover which shows plainly in Photograph *A*, and which opens out as the leg descends. The members of this telescopic cover are connected by chains, not shown, so they can never slide out of coacting relation. This cover and fixed cover 22 at the back of the leg prevent coal from falling out onto the men at work in the barge.

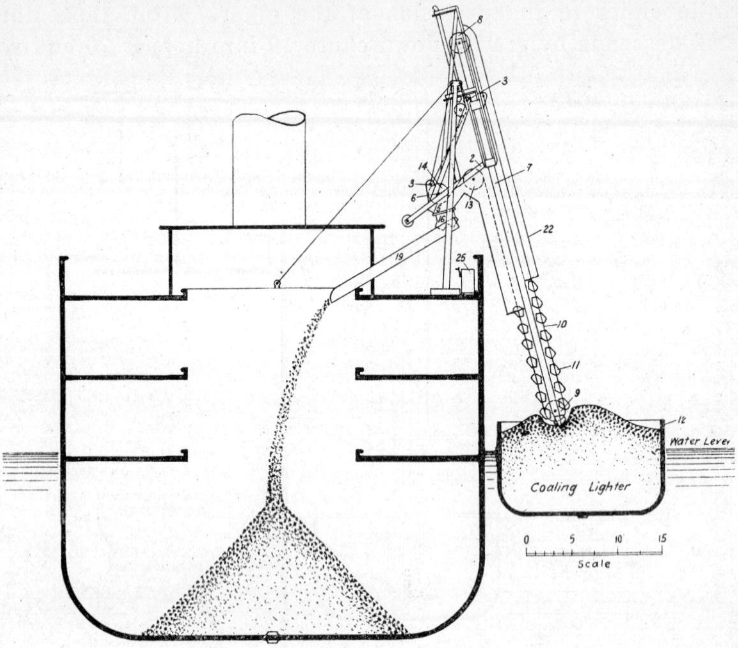

D.

The leg is raised from out of the barge when desired, as for replacing an empty barge with a loaded one, by means of gearing, not shown, but mounted on the elevator and operated by the elevator motor when the direction of drive of said motor is reversed by the operator through the controller on the ship's deck. Illustration *C* shows the elevator hung from a rigging on the ship's deck so as to discharge into a high port. Illustration *D* shows the Michener Elevator erected for over-deck coaling. This machine is delivering coal through chute 19 to a midship-hatch and thence into the lower hold. It will be understood that the coal can be diverted to any of the between-deck side spaces as required.

When a ship at sea is approaching a port where coal is expected to be received by means of this apparatus the crew will have only to free the coal ports for opening, or in case of overdeck coaling, illustration *D*, to erect shears for the suspension of the

E. The bunker trimmer discs.

elevator. Usually the elevators will be erected on the ship's side from a barge having the necessary mast and boom for handling and erecting the elevators and for setting the hoppers at the coal ports.

Directing attention now to the second division of the apparatus Photograph *E* shows a portion of an installation of

The Michener Bunker Trimmer

This apparatus is complementary to the Michener Elevator, which raises the coal from the barge alongside and delivers it to the coal-port and thence into the bunker. The bunker trimmer is permanently installed in the ship's bunker, is electrically driven and controlled and is efficient for distributing the coal, received through the coal-port, to the most remote portions of the bunker and for piling that coal up to substantially fill the bunker.

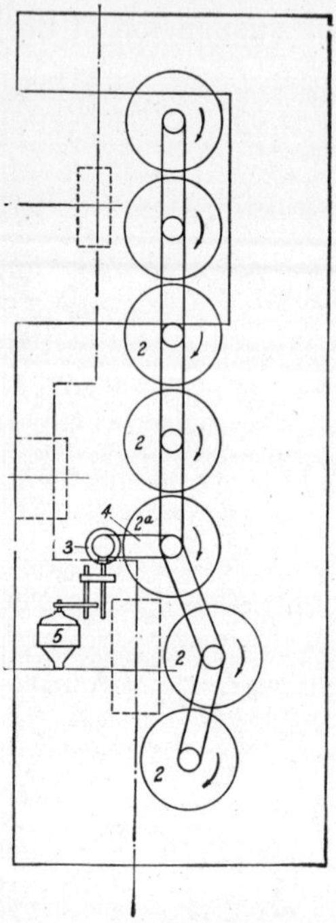

F.

The apparatus comprises a series of rotating discs 2, illustrations *B* and *F*, suspended from the deck beams of the bunker ceiling, and connected together and with the driving head 3 of the motor gearing by driving chain 4. The motor is preferably located near the principal hatch or port so as to be easy of access at all times and the controller, not shown, may be located at any convenient place in the bunker or just outside. The motor 5 drives through its reducing gearing to disc 2a, and fiom that disc power is transmitted to the other discs in either direction.

In illustration *F* is shown a plan view of one of the bunkers of a cargo ship of medium capacity. The dotted rectangles indicate the overhead hatches of the bunkers through which the coal is received. It will be noticed that some of the discs are arranged so that their peripheries come close to the hatch openings, in one instance there being three discs adjacent the hatch edge. It will also be noticed that the motor 5 is located near the principal hatch, so as to be easy of access at all times.

As the coal falls through the hatches which have discs adjacent them, that coal piles up on the bunker floor, presently rising to the level of the discs and then crowds over onto the top faces of these discs. The motor is then started and these discs immediately pass the coal on to the next succeeding disc, and from which disc it is scraped off by fixed *plows*, not shown, until the pile rises at that point sufficiently to be delivered to the next disc and so on throughout the line. The small angular spaces in the upper corners of the bunkers illustration *C* may be left as they are, or, if it is desired to use every available cubic foot of bunker space, one or two men with shovels can quickly flatten out the angles of the pile and fill even the remotest corner with coal.

It will be understood that the discs do not operate by centrifugal force, throwing the coal off by their speed, but that they rotate slowly and the coal is scraped from their faces by the plows, to which reference has been made. These plows are of heavy sheet steel and about six inches high and each plow may be set at any desired location about the axis of the disc so as to spill the coal from the disc at any desired point. Where discs are arranged in sequence as shown, the plows are set so as to deliver the coal from disc to disc. Assuming that the coal is delivered first to that disc 2*a* which gets its drive directly from the motor, the coal being received through the main hatch and all the discs being rotated in clockwise direction, such coal as lies near the periphery of that disc will encounter a plow, which will scrape a portion of the coal off onto the next adjoining disc above in the illustration. That disc will pass its load on, spilling most of it, until such time as the pile from the floor mounts sufficiently to form a wall, when that second disc will deliver to the third and so on to all the discs to the end of the series. One motor is shown in illustration driving seven discs. This is quite sufficient as it takes only about one half horse power per disc to operate the device.

The efficient operation of the elevator in delivering coal from the barge to the coal port is governed by the rapidity with which the coal is removed from the vicinity of that port, inside the bunker. The trimming mechanism will handle up to 150 tons per hour delivered at any one coal port. Speed of coaling is governed by the number of ports, or hatches, that can be worked at one time.

CHAPTER X

CARRIAGE OF LIVE STOCK

I

Loading

Where cattle is walked on board over *gangways* or *brows** the matter of loading is simple and care is taken to portion them properly to stalls or pens. When animals are to be lifted on board from lighters great care must be taken in slinging. Horses and other heavy cattle can be lifted on board by a single whip and one boom, swinging the boom inboard by the guys as the animal comes over the side. It is often best to blindfold the animals if the ship's side is high and they are lively.

Slinging cattle

Slings are generally made of number 1 canvas, roped, and fitted with breast and rump bridles in addition to the sling band terminating in stout loops of the *sling strop* sewn to the bands.

Very valuable horses or cattle are often sent on board in a padded box, the horse being secured in the box and this carefully slung with a good guy rope attached to each end.

Horned cattle are often lifted with a stout strap around the base of the horns.

Horses are more liable to kick in lifting and should be slung with great care.

Very valuable horses are carried in thwartship padded stalls. They are protected from injury by slings made to hang six inches below their bellies when standing. These slings are a

* Heavy gangways stretching from the ship to a dock.

great help when the vessel is in a seaway and the animals rest their weight in the slings.

Most countries have stringent laws governing the carriage of live stock. These rules should be obtained by a master before loading and strictly complied with. The regulations of the United States Department of Agriculture, prepared by the Bureau of Animal Industry, are very comprehensive and should be carefully studied by the master and mates of all vessels engaged in the carriage of horses and cattle. These regulations follow:

II

Regulations Governing the Inspection, Humane Handling, and Safe Transport of Export Animals

General Provisions

Regulation 1. Except as otherwise herein provided, no cattle, sheep, swine, or goats shall be exported from the United States to any foreign country, unless and until the same have been inspected and found free from disease or exposure thereto, by an inspector of the Bureau of Animal Industry of this department. Unless the Secretary of Agriculture shall have waived the requirement of a certificate of inspection for the particular country to which such animals are to be exported no clearance shall be issued to any vessel carrying such animals, unless and until a certificate of inspection showing freedom from disease or exposure thereto shall have been issued by the Department of Agriculture. The requirement of a certificate for shipments of such animals to Cuba, the West Indies, Mexico, Central America, and the countries of South America, except Argentina, Uruguay, and Brazil, is hereby waived.

Definition of Terms

Regulation 2. Whenever in these regulations the following words, names, or terms are used, they shall be construed as follows:

Inspector of port, inspector, assistant, employee. These terms shall mean, respectively, the inspector in charge of the Bureau of Animal Industry station at the port from which the animals are to be exported, and inspectors, assistants, and employees of the Bureau of Animal Industry.

Lumber. This word, unless otherwise stated, shall mean hard pine, spruce, oak, or other hardwood.

Animals. This word refers to cattle, sheep, swine, and goats; also horses, unless it is inapplicable to them under Regulation 3.

Horses. This word shall include generally mules and asses.

Horses

Regulation 3. Horses shall be entitled to the inspection provided for in these regulations, and certificates shall be issued whenever required by the country to which the horses are to be exported, but horses may be shipped without inspection and certification, at shippers' risk, to countries which do not demand such inspection and certification as a prerequisite to admission.

Inspection and Shipment (Canadian Shipments)

Regulation 4. Only animals found to be healthy and free from disease and shown not to have been exposed to the contagion of any disease shall be allowed shipment, and all animals inspected and passed shall be loaded into clean and disinfected cars.

All dairy and breeding cattle must pass a satisfactory tuberculin test either by an inspector of the Bureau of Animal Industry or by a duly authorized representative of the country to which the animals are to be exported. Animals for export to Canada will be inspected at any point the bureau may direct. All animals shipped on ocean steamers shall be inspected or reinspected at the port of export. Railroad companies will be required to furnish clean and disinfected cars for the transportation of animals for export, and the proprietors of the various stockyards and stables located at the ports of export shall keep separate, clean, and disinfected stockyards, and pens or stables for the use of export animals.

Shipment of Animals on Ocean Steamers

Places of Inspection

Regulation 5. The inspection provided for animals shipped on ocean steamers will be made at any of the following-named stockyards: Chicago, Ill.; Kansas City, Mo.; Omaha, Nebr.; South St. Joseph, Mo.; National Stock Yards, Ill.; Indianapolis, Ind.; Buffalo, N. Y.; and Pittsburgh, Pa., and at the following ports of export: Portland, Me.; Boston, Mass.; New York, N. Y.; Philadelphia, Pa.; Baltimore, Md.; Norfolk and Newport News, Va.; New Orleans, La.; and Galveston, Tex. Other ports may be designated in special cases by the Chief of the Bureau of Animal Industry. All animals will be inspected at ports of export, regardless of the fact that they may or may not have been inspected at the above-named stockyards.

Identification of Animals and Notification of Shipment

Regulation 6. Shippers shall notify the inspector in charge of the yards of intended shipments of animals and the number and designation of cars in which they are to be shipped, and shall inform said inspector of the locality from which said animals have been brought, and the name of the feeder of said animals, and shall furnish such other information as may be practicable for the proper identification of the place from which said animals have come.

Regulation 7. The inspector after passing said animals shall notify the inspector in charge of the port of export, and inspectors located at intermediate cities where the animals may be unloaded for feeding and watering, of the inspection and shipment of such animals, the number and kind of animals shipped, and the numbers and designations of the cars containing them.

Transportation from Yards to Steamers

Regulation 8. Export animals shall not be unnecessarily passed over any highway or removed to cars or boats which are used for conveying other animals. Boats transporting said animals to the ocean steamer must first be cleansed and disinfected under the supervision of the inspector of the port, and, before receiving said animals, the ocean steamer shall be thoroughly cleansed and disinfected in accordance with the directions of said inspector. When passage upon or across the public highway is unavoidable in the transportation of animals from the cars to the boat it shall be under such careful supervision and restrictions as the inspector may direct.

Animals not Allowed Shipment

Regulation 9. Any animals that are offered for shipment to a foreign country which have not been inspected and transported in accordance with these regulations, or which, having been inspected, are adjudged to be infected or to have been exposed to infection so as to be dangerous to other animals or to be otherwise unfit for shipment, shall not be allowed upon any vessel for exportation.

Supervision to Steamers—Clearance Papers

Regulation 10. The supervision of the movement of animals from cars, yards, and stables to the ocean steamer at the port of export will be in charge of the inspector of the port.

The inspector at the port of export shall notify the collector of the port, or his deputy, of the various shipments of animals that are entitled to clearance papers.

Notification to Inspectors of Intended Shipments on Steamers

Regulation 11. The exporters of animals, the owner or agent, desiring to transport animals from any port of the United States to a foreign country shall notify the inspector in charge of the port from which said vessel is to clear, of such intended shipment at least two days in advance thereof, and if the regulations prescribed have been complied with, a clearance shall be authorized by such inspector.

Space on Vessels

Regulation 12. Export animals must not be carried on any part of the vessel where they will interfere with the proper management of the vessel, or with the efficient working of the necessary lifeboats, or with the requisite ventilation of the vessel, and may be carried only as hereinafter specified.

Cattle

Regulation 13. Cattle must have 6 feet vertical space by not less than 8 feet in depth on all decks free of all obstructions. Cattle may, however, be placed on raised floors over pipes and other similar obstructions where the vertical space is not less than 5 feet 6 inches from under edge of beam overhead to flooring underfoot. Cattle over 850 pounds in weight must be allowed a space of 2 feet 6 inches in width by 8 feet in depth and no more than 4 head of such cattle will be allowed in each pen, except at the end of rows where five may be allowed together. Cattle of 850 pounds' weight or less must be allowed a space of at least 2 feet in width by 8 feet in depth and 5 may be allowed in each pen. Calves and young stock or yearlings may be stowed at the discretion of the inspector. Cattle standing between stanchions, sounding tubes, ventilators, and other obstructions, though in continuous pens, must be allowed 3 feet in width. Cattle carried in crates or single stalls must be allowed not less than 3 feet in width by 8 feet in depth. Additional space and separate stalls may be required by the inspector for large dairy and breeding cattle and for cows in advanced pregnancy. Large cows, in the discretion of the inspector, may be placed 3 in a pen of 10 feet in width by 8 feet in depth. Special permission for carrying cattle on the steerage deck must be obtained from the inspector and will be granted in cases where said deck is provided with sufficient ventilation as hereinafter prescribed.

Sheep and Goats

Regulation 14. The space for each sheep or goat shall be 4 feet long by 14 inches wide, and for lambs or goats under 100 pounds in weight 4 feet by 12 to 13 inches.

Sheep pens shall not exceed 20 feet by 8 feet, where two tiers are carried, and each tier shall have a clear vertical space of not less than 3 feet. During the summer season sheep shall not be loaded in tiers under decks, but during the winter season two tiers may be placed in each wing and only one tier amidships. One single deck of sheep may be carried upon the roof over cattle when said roofs are permanently built and are composed of 2-inch tongue-and-groove boards, provided such sheep fittings do not conflict with Regulation 13. Sheep pens on roof of cattle fittings shall not exceed 12 feet in width and must be supplied with athwartship partitions every 14 feet. Such fittings shall be secured to roof of cattle fittings by placing outboard stanchions and bolting through both outboard stanchions with not less than three ⅝-inch bolts.

Stanchions for sheep pens must run up through cattle-fittings roof to the required height for the sheep pens. These stanchions shall not be less than 4 by 4 inches. Space for sheep and goats for breeding purpose shall be not less than 5 feet in length by 20 inches in width.

Swine

Regulation 15. The space for swine not exceeding 150 pounds in weight shall be the same as that specified for breeding sheep and goats, and for those under 100 pounds in weight the same as for lambs and for goats of less than 100 pounds in weight. Additional space and suitable pens shall be required by the inspector for unusually large hogs or for swine for breeding purposes.

Horses

Regulation 16. All horses must have not less than 6 feet 3 inches clear vertical space from beams of deck overhead to deck underfoot, and, so far as possible, shall be placed between the overhead athwartship beams. Each horse must be allowed a space 2 feet 6 inches in width by not less than 8 feet in depth. Division boards shall not be less than 2 by 9 inches and shall be of sound lumber, planed, upper corners rounded and placed horizontally between 2 horses, except that horses may be placed in pens of 4 each on application of owner or shipper. Additional space shall be required by the inspector for very large horses. The 8-foot depth of stalls for horses may be reduced to 7 feet for medium-sized horses in order to avoid losing a row of stalls in the forward and after ends of the ship, abreast of hatches, alongside of engine and boiler casings, etc. Additional stalls, distributed in the different compartments or decks in which horses are carried, must be provided for use as hospital stalls for sick animals, as follows: One additional stall 2 feet 6 inches in width by 8 feet in depth for the first 4 to 10 horses shipped.

Two additional stalls, of 5 feet in width by 8 feet in depth, for the first 25 horses shipped and 2 feet 6 inches in width by 8 feet in depth for each additional 25 horses, allowing four extra stalls for each 100 horses shipped.

Separate stalls will not be required for unbroken fillies and mules. When horses are placed directly under athwartship beams, the beams must be guarded by 4-inch strips of wood. When placed in the same compartment with cattle, horses must be separated by fore-and-aft alleyways and temporary athwartship bulkheads, the length of which shall not be less than the depth of the stalls. Small numbers of horses may be shipped in boxes or portable stalls of sufficient size and strength to carry same safely.

Upper-deck Fittings

Regulation 17. No animals shall be allowed within 20 feet of the breakwater on the spar deck, between the 1st of October and the 1st of April, except on ships provided with houses constructed of iron in each wing and of sufficient width and height to protect the fittings, when the fittings may be constructed to abut such houses. Horses may be carried upon the bridge deck of steamers having a strong rail outboard to secure the fittings. No cattle or horses shall be carried upon the upper decks where the outside rails are not of sufficient strength to hold fittings securely and measure less than 3 feet in height from the deck. When animals are carried upon the upper decks, strong breakwaters shall be erected at each end and on both sides. Permanent fittings may be constructed of either iron or wood, as hereinafter specified.

Alleyways

Regulation 18. All steamers engaged in carrying animals for export will be required to provide alleyways as provided by this regulation. Alleyways in front of and between pens used for feeding and watering cattle must have a width of 3 feet; however, for a distance not to exceed 12 feet at end of alleyways in bow and stern of ship, and where obstructions less than 3 feet in length occur, the width may be reduced to a minimum of 18 inches. Alleyways in front of and between pens used for feeding and watering horses must have a minimum width of 4 feet except in bow and stern of ship, where the alleyways may be reduced to a width of not less than 3 feet. Two or more athwartship alleyways at least 18 inches wide in the clear must be left on each side of upper deck, so that the scuppers can be readily reached and kept clear of obstructions. Three or more alleyways at least 18 inches wide must be left open on each side in 'tween or other under decks, where deck is not divided into compartments. Where 'tween or other under decks are divided into compartments, one or more athwartship alleyways, 18 inches wide on both sides of ship and in every compartment, must be left clear and open so that the scuppers can be readily reached and cleared of all obstructions. In forward compartments the alleyways to scuppers must be placed at after end of compartments. In after compartments the alleyways to scuppers must be in forward ends of compartments. Athwartship alleyways not less than 2 feet in width must be provided, so that the attendants may cross ship's deck with feed and water for animals, and for other purposes. When animals are not carried in the decks beneath, passage from side to side of ship can be made by crossing over hatches where the coamings do not exceed 18 inches in height. Sufficient space must be left at the sides of hatches to permit of the feed in decks beneath being readily removed and handled. Where animals are carried in under decks, proper brows, or runs, must be placed in hatches, on which animals may be walked in loading or discharging. Where horses are carried on upper deck and in under deck, said brows must remain shipped, in hatches, so that horses may be led from deck to deck during voyage.

Wooden Stanchions and Rump Boards

Regulation 19. Stanchions at least 3 inches higher than the required vertical space for cattle must be of 4 by 6 inch clear, hard pine or 4 by 6 inch good, sound spruce, set at 5 feet from centers against the ship's rail, or at points midway between two animals, and inside stanchions in their proper place must be in line with outboard stanchions, and set up so that the 6-inch way of the stanchions shall set fore-and-aft. A 3-inch shoulder may be cut on head of stanchion to receive beam and must be bolted through and through with 5/8-inch bolts for all stanchions, or stanchions may be of same height as required vertical space for cattle to butt up square to beams with 2 by 8 inch cleat butted against both sides of stanchions and well nailed to beams, and 1 by 6 by 24 inch angle braces properly placed and nailed to secure each stanchion to its beam. Inboard stanchions supporting roof fittings shall be 2 inches higher than outboard or rail stanchions. In amidship fittings and where fittings are brought forward to clear rigging bitts, etc., the rump-board stanchions may be 3 by 4 inch braced or cleated to beam or roof or deck as required. A piece 2 by 3 inch, or 2-inch plank, shall be fastened to the outside of the stanchion and run up to underneath the rail to chock down the stanchion and prevent lifting when the beam is sprung to the crown of the deck. Open-rail ships shall be blocked out on backs of stanchions fair with the outside of rails to receive the outside planking. Where upper-deck fittings are not permanent, the heels of outside stanchions shall be secured by a bracing of 2 by 3 inch lumber from the back of each stanchion to sheer streak of waterway, the heels of inside stanchions being properly braced from and to each other.

Rump boards must be provided on all decks, and when covering bitts, rigging, braces, or other obstructions located at a distance from ship's sides, rump boards must be brought forward to cover same, with a solid partition behind the animals; and when necessary to extend fittings opposite bitts, rigging, braces, etc., fittings for two or more animals must be brought forward. Rump boards in such cases shall be not less than 1⅛ inches in thickness, tongued and grooved, and built to a height of 4 feet 6 inches from the deck. Where deck is clear and without obstructions, such as braces, etc., rump boards may be set on the inside of rail stanchions. In such case and where beef cattle stand rump to rump in amidship stalls 18 inches (or two boards of 1⅛ by 9 inches) of tongue and groove, good, sound spruce or hard pine will be used. In 'tween-decks when ship's ribs are of the bulb-edge type, or of channel-iron type, the above-mentioned rump board may be used. When ribs are of the thin-edge type close backing shall be run down, same as in offsets on upper deck, or ribs may be covered with wood. Where ship's cargo battens are in good order same may be used as backing or rump boards by filling in spaces between, when necessary. Stanchions for horses will be placed as hereinafter specified.

Iron Stanchions

Regulation 20. Iron stanchions may be used in place of wooden stanchions and shall not be less than 2 inches in diameter, set in iron sockets above and below, and fastened with ⅝-inch bolts. For horses the same number of iron stanchions are required as when wooden stanchions are used.

Hook Bolts or Clamps

Regulation 21. Hook bolts or clamps must be made of ⅝-inch wrought iron, with hook on outboard end and thread and nut on inboard end to pass over and under rail and through outboard stanchion and set up on the inside of same with a nut. These bolts may be double or single. If double, no thread or nut is necessary, but the stanchion will lie shipped through it, thus double-hooking the rails. This will be found very useful where funnels or other deck fittings come in the way of beams passing from side to side of ship.

Beams

Regulation 22. Beams must be of good, sound spruce or hard-pine lumber, 3 by 6 inches, to run clear across the ship's beam where practicable. Should any house or deck fittings be in the way, the beams should butt up closely to the same. When there are no stalls amidship a stanchion must be set under beam at center of ship's deck and be properly secured.

Braces

Regulation 23. Diagonal braces shall be fastened on each stanchion on both sides of same, running up to top side of beam and properly secured by nailing well to both stanchions and beam. Where stanchion is gained out to receive beam, a piece of 2 by 3 will be nailed on side of stanchion to flush with beam, and diagonal brace will be nailed on beam and on the 2 by 3.

Breast Boards

Regulation 24. Breast boards shall be not less than 1¾ by 9¾ inches dressed lumber, or 2 by 10 inches rough, of good, clear spruce or hard pine and secured at every stanchion by ⅝-inch screw bolts passing through same and set up with nuts. All breast boards must butt on the stanchions. An iron plate one-quarter of an inch thick and 3 inches square shall be placed over the boards like a butt strap, bolt passing through same. All breast boards shall have 1-inch holes bored through them at proper distances for tying the animals.

Footboards

Regulation 25. Footboards shall be of wood and of not less than 2 by 9 inches in the rough, and shall be properly nailed or bolted to stanchions.

Division Boards for Cattle

Regulation 26. Division boards for cattle shall be 2 by 8 inch boards, sound spruce or hard pine, and so arranged as to divide the animals into lots of four, except at the ends of rows, thus making compartments for that number all over the vessel. Division boards shall be four in number at ends of hatches, passageways across ship, at alleyways to scuppers, and for dairy and breeding cattle, whether divided into lots of four or placed in single stalls. Division boards shall be placed horizontally with 3-inch openings between and fitted perpendicularly. All division boards must be portable.

Division Boards for Horses

Regulation 27. Division boards for horses shall not be less than 2 by 9 inches of good, sound spruce or hard pine, dressed on both sides, with top edges rounded, and placed horizontally between the horses. All division boards must be portable. Fittings at ends of hatches, alleyways, etc., must conform to Regulation 26.

Flooring for Horses and Breeding Cattle

Regulation 28. Ships with iron decks shall be sheathed with 1 or 2 inch spruce or hard pine, but if 1-inch lumber is used the footlocks shall be 3 by 4 inches and laid so that they will properly secure the 1-inch boards, thus preventing them from slipping and at the same time acting as footlocks by showing a surface of 2 by 4 inches. It is optional with the owners whether they permit sheathing to be used on their ships with wooden decks, or whether they allow footlocks to be secured to the deck, but it is absolutely necessary to sheath iron decks before putting down footlocks in order to fasten same. Cement diagonally scored one-half inch deep may be used on iron decks instead of wooden sheathing if the footlocks be molded in the same and bolted to the deck. If the flooring is raised on any of the decks, it shall not be less than 2 inches thick, with scantling 2 by 3 inches laid athwartships on the deck not more than 2 feet 6 inches apart with 2-inch plank for flooring nailed to them. Flooring may be in two or three sections in the depth of the stalls so as to provide for its removal and relaying after cleaning and disinfecting of decks and fittings, or, if owners prefer, flooring for horses or mules may be made with 2-inch plank laid athwartships in stalls with one-half or three-fourths inch openings between, with 1-inch cleat at each end and nailed to same, which will allow flooring to clear lap in deck plates and prevent rocking. Footlocks must be bolted to such flooring. This flooring may be made in separate sections, one for each animal. On upper or exposed decks such flooring must be cleated down by placing a piece of 2 by 3 inches on inside of footboard and on stanchions in rear end of stalls and nailing to same. For breeding and dairy cattle on all decks where these animals are carried the flooring must be raised; 1¼ by 9 inch lumber may be used as flooring for these animals with 2 by 3 inch scantling underneath, placed not more than 2 feet apart and the flooring nailed to each piece of scantling. This flooring may be laid in portable fore-and-aft sections.

Footlocks

Regulation 29. Footlocks shall be of good, sound spruce, hard pine, oak, or other hardwood, size 2 by 4 inches (where 2-inch flooring is used), laid flat side down and fore-and-aft, placed 12 inches, 14 inches, 2 feet 2 inches, and 14 inches apart, the first one distant 12 inches from the inside of footboard. Where temporary fore-and-aft footlocks are used, they shall be filled in athwartships opposite each stanchion, properly secured to sheathing or deck, and secured by a batten of spruce or hard pine, size 2 by 3 inches, to go over all from stanchion to stanchion. This batten must be in one piece. Pieces 2 by 3 inches must be nailed on stanchions or backing over batten to prevent floor raising. These pieces over battens over all will not be required in under decks. When permanent footlocks, securely bolted to decks, are used, the athwartship braces between footlocks from stanchion to stanchion and batten may be omitted when the stanchion is securely fitted in iron socket bolted to the deck. A space of 2 inches will be left between the ends of athwartship footlocks and fore-and-aft footlocks when the former are securely bolted to the deck. When the fore-and-aft footlocks are permanent, a 3-inch space shall be left between the ends at end of each section. In under decks, the footlocks will be 1 by 4 inches above the flooring where cattle for dairy and breeding purposes are carried.

Outside Planking

Regulation 30. All outside planking on open and closed rail ships must be properly laid fore-and-aft of ship and nailed to backs of stanchions as close as possible for the cold season, and for the warmer months the top-course planking shall be left off fore-and-aft of ship in order to allow a free circulation of air. Nothing less than 1⅛-inch tongue-and-groove spruce or hard pine will be allowed for this purpose. Outside planking may be laid in mill-run lengths, butts to be broken, and reinforced with 1⅛-inch lumber, forming butt straps, these to be well nailed and nails clinched.

Roof Planking

Regulation 31. The planks to form the roof, which must be erected on all exposed decks, must be laid fore-and-aft; 1⅛-inch sound spruce or hard pine lumber, tongued and grooved, may be used sufficient to cover, from outside planking to 2 feet beyond the line of breast boards. These planks must be driven tightly together and shall be well nailed to the athwartship beams. It will be optional with owners whether tar paper or other covering will be laid over roofing. Where permanent boat platforms are not provided, a roof of 2-inch lumber must be laid, from which boats may be worked. When 1⅛-inch tongue-and-groove lumber is used as outside planking, or for roofing, the butts may be broken. Where butts are broken, same must be reinforced by 1⅛-inch boards well nailed to underside of roof. The nails used for this purpose must in all cases be clinched.

Cattle Fittings over Spar Deck

Regulation 32. No cattle fittings shall be erected over permanent spar-deck fittings forward and aft of the amidship sections until permission has been obtained from the Chief of the Bureau of Animal Industry.

Under-deck Fittings

Alleyways

Regulation 33. Alleyways on under decks shall be of the same dimensions as the alleyways on the upper decks.

Stanchions

Regulation 34. Stanchions on under decks shall be of 4 by 6 inch clear, hard pine or good, sound spruce, set 6-inch way fore-and-aft, and may be set 7 feet 6 inches from centers, for three animals, provided the space for animals is 2 feet 6 inches per head. If space for animals is more than 2 feet 6 inches per head, the distance between stanchions may be changed accordingly. Thus, if two cattle or horses are given 4 feet each, stanchions may be set at 8-foot centers and driven tight between the decks, securely braced with 2 by 3 inch raking shores from stanchion to stanchion and sides of ship. If one or both decks are of wood, then the stanchions may be secured by cleating well to one or both decks, at heads and heels of same. When 3 by 10 inch breast boards are used, 4 by 6 inch stanchions may be set at 10-foot centers.

Breast Boards, Etc.

Regulation 35. Breast boards may be of 1¾ by 9¾ inch lumber dressed, or of 2 by 10 inch in the rough, of sound spruce or hard pine, when stanchions are set at 7 feet 6 inches for 3 animals. In no case will 1¾ inch dressed, or 2 by 10 inch rough breast boards be allowed when the distance between centers of breast-board stanchions is more than 8 feet. Breast boards of 2¾ inches by 9¾ inches, dressed, or 3 by 10 inches in the rough, may be used when stanchions are set at 10-foot centers for 4 animals, and the distance between stanchions to centers will in no case exceed 10 feet. Proper gates or openings in breast boards must be provided at convenient distances, so as to allow animals to be loaded and moved from pens when necessary. These must be formed of breast board and must be properly cleated with wood or iron cleats, with stop, or chock, over top of breast board to prevent raising. These gates must be on all decks where animals are carried.

Troughs

Regulation 36. Suitable troughs may be built when required for cattle on either deck, by placing footboard on outside of front stanchions. When flooring is raised, the floor forms the bottom of trough, the footboard the outside, and 2 by 3 inch run on 2-inch edge on first footlock, and well nailed, forms inner side. In 'tween deck when footlocks are of 1 by 4 inch for cows, etc., the first footlock inside of breast board will be 2 by 4 inches showing a 5-inch depth of trough.

When flooring is not raised in stalls, the first section of flooring, or the section between footboard and first footlock shall be raised 2 inches, thus forming the bottom of troughs, then built up on first footlock to form inner side of trough. Shippers of cattle may use metal troughs, when same are desired. Removable and separate troughs must be used for horses. They may be of wood or metal, and must have hooks for hanging same on breast board. Suitable troughs for grain and water must be provided on three sides of each sheep, goat, or hog pen.

Pens at Ends of Hatches

Regulation 37. When pens or stalls for horses or cattle run up to the ends of hatches, 4 athwartship boards, 2 inches thick, must be placed to prevent animals from getting out of such pens. These boards must be portable. When stalls or pens for horses or cattle are built alongside of hatches, rump boards will be carried down to line of coaming.

Protection from Heat of Boilers and Engines

Regulation 38. No animals shall be stowed along the alleyways by engine and boiler rooms, unless the sides of said engine and boiler rooms are covered by a tongue-and-groove tight sheathing, making a 3-inch air space.

Covering for Steering Gear

Regulation 39. Raised flooring of 2-inch plank must be placed over steering gear when found necessary. This may be made up of portable sections so as to be easily removed in case of accident. It must, however, be properly cleated to prevent shifting.

Sheep, Pigs, and Goats

Shelter Deck

Regulation 40. A single tier of sheep, pigs, and goats may be carried on the shelter deck. Stanchions shall be not less than 3 by 4 inch spruce or hard pine, set 5-foot centers, the 4-inch way of stanchions to be set fore-and-aft, with 1½-inch shoulder to be gained on stanchions to receive rafters. Rafters shall be 3 by 4 inch spruce or hard pine set on 3-inch side, and bolted to stanchions with ⅝-inch bolts. On open-rail ships, the backs of rail stanchions will be filled out to flush with outside of rail, on which outside planking will be nailed. Troughs must be constructed of 3 pieces of 1 by 6 inch lumber nailed together, and fastened between stanchions. Hayracks shall be made of 1 by 2 inch strips, placed fore-and-aft, and on athwartship partitions. One by 2 inch strips will be used for footlocks. Fronts and ends of pens shall be of 1 by 6 inch spruce or hard pine and sufficient in number properly to secure the animals in the pens. Roofing and outside planking shall be not less than 1⅛ inches thick and must be tongued and grooved. Double tiers of sheep, pigs, or goats may also be carried on the shelter decks when rail is of sufficient height and strength, as for cattle. Fittings shall be of same dimensions as for cattle. Space must be regulated to suit size of animals to be shipped.

Well Decks

Regulation 41. Single tiers of sheep, pigs, or goats may be carried on well decks, the same as on shelter deck, except on ships with closed bulwarks. Outboard stanchions must be cut at least 4 inches higher than bulwark, and must be hook-bolted to rail. Five-eighths-inch hook bolts must be used for this purpose. All stanchions must be not less than 3 by 4 inches. When bulwark is of sufficient height to permit of rafters running underneath the head of rail, this will be done by cutting out 1½ by 4 inches of side of stanchion at that point, allowing same to run through to underneath the head, thus forming check to prevent fittings lifting. This will bring roof of pens flush with top of bulwark. An inner backing in pens on these decks will be required. Not less than 1-inch flooring, raised 2 inches, will be allowed on these decks.

Two tiers of sheep, pigs, or goats may be carried on well deck, in fittings as for cattle, as per Regulation 40.

Under Deck

Regulation 42. When the pens for sheep, pigs, or goats in under decks are built for two tiers, stanchions may be of not less than 3 by 4 inch good spruce or hard pine lumber. Joists not less than 3 by 4 inch spruce or hard pine must be used, supported in centers by 2 by 3 inch pieces run from deck to underside of joists, securely nailed to same. The flooring shall be not less than ⅞-inch tongue-and-groove spruce or hard pine and 1 by 2 inch battens shall be laid fore-and-aft on flooring 18 inches apart to act as footlocks. Troughs, hayracks, fronts and ends of pens, etc., will be as provided in Regulation 40.

Ventilation

Regulation 43. Each under-deck compartment not exceeding 50 feet in length must have at least four bell-mouthed ventilators of not less than 18 inches in diameter and with tops exceeding 7 feet in height above shelter deck, two situated at each end of the compartment. Compartments over 50 feet long must have additional ventilators of the same dimensions or efficient fans. Animals must not be placed at greater distance than 10 feet beyond ventilators.

Spar Deck

Regulation 44. When the fittings on the spar deck are permanent and hatches overhead are provided, the same regulations for ventilation shall apply as provided for under decks.

Third Deck

Regulation 45. When it is desired to carry animals upon the third deck, written permission must be obtained from the inspector of the port. The vessel must be fitted as hereinbefore specified, lighted with electric lights, and properly ventilated. One set of ventilators should be trimmed to the wind and another set in the opposite direction. The ventilators must be tested and kept in easy working order.

Hatches

Regulation 46. No cattle, horses, sheep, goats, or swine shall be loaded upon hatches on decks above animals, nor shall any merchandise, freight, or feed for animals be loaded upon said hatches, but said hatches shall at all times be kept clear.

In loading animals upon exposed decks, such as bridge, spar, well decks, etc., where hatch coamings do not exceed 2 feet in height at center of hatch, animals may be placed on hatches, provided that on all hatches on upper decks sufficient space be left clear so that entrance to deck beneath may be possible at all times. There must also be left clear on all hatches, under which hay and feed are stowed, space for the proper removal and handling of same.

When animals are carried in the 'tween-decks, animals may be placed on hatches. In no case will horses be allowed on hatches when the vertical space between beams or coamings overhead and flooring underfoot is less than 7 feet.

In no case shall cattle be placed on hatches when the vertical space between beams or coamings overhead and flooring under foot is less than 5 feet 6 inches.

When animals are carried on third or steerage deck, they may be carried on third-deck hatches.

In carrying animals on under-deck hatches, sufficient space must be left clear on hatches for passageway across ship, for proper removal and handling of hay and feed, and also for brow.

Lighting

Regulation 47. All vessels designated as cattle ships must provide at all times electric lights for the proper attending of all animals.

Feed and Water

Regulation 48. All vessels not provided with pipes for watering animals shall carry casks or hogsheads of not less than 400 gallons' total capacity for each 100 head of cattle and horses, and an additional amount in equal proportion shall also be carried for sheep, and these containers shall be filled with fresh water before sailing and refilled as emptied. All water tanks for use of animals must be filled with good, fresh water before sailing.

Each vessel shall carry water condensers which are in good working order and of sufficient capacity to provide 8 gallons of fresh, cold water each 24 hours for each head of cattle, in addition to the amount required by other animals on board and for other purposes.

Regulation 49. Not more than two days' feed for the animals shall be allowed to be carried on the shelter deck, and no feed shall be carried on the shelter deck when same interferes with the proper care of sheep; neither shall any feed be stored on top or inside of sheep pens. When feed, as provided above, is placed on the shelter deck, it must be properly covered and shall be the first feed used. All other feed shall be under hatches, and, so far as possible, shall be placed in the holds contiguous to the animals on board.

Attendants

Employment and Character

Regulation 50. The employment of all attendants shall be subject to the approval of the inspector of the port, and men so employed shall be reliable and signed as a part of the ship's crew and under the control of the captain of the vessel. They shall be furnished with heated, well-lighted, and well-ventilated quarters and with bedding and table utensils. Experienced foremen shall be in charge of the animals, and not less than one-half of the attendants must be experienced men who have made previous trips with stock.

The shippers of export animals, or their agents, shall make

affidavit concerning the character of the attendants. The attendants shall be assembled a sufficient time before the sailing of the steamer for an employee of this department to examine them. The examination shall be made before the signing of the ship's articles by the attendants, and any man who fails to conform to the following conditions shall be rejected: (1) The men employed must be able to speak English sufficiently to make themselves understood, or to understand orders given them; (2) they must know for what purpose they are employed and the duties that will be required of them; (3) they must be able-bodied and physically competent to perform the duties required; (4) each man entitled to return passage shall be supplied with return transportation before acceptance, unless he informs the inspector that he does not wish to return. The department has no control over the return of attendants. Inspectors in charge of the ports are directed to enforce carefully the above-enumerated regulations.

When any attendant is found to be incompetent, intemperate or otherwise unfit to care for the animals properly, the captain of the vessel is requested to report the facts to the inspector of the port.

Cattle Attendants

Regulation 51. There shall be one attendant for each 35 head of cattle, not including foremen, upon steamers having water pipes extending the entire length of both sides of compartments; and upon steamers not so fitted there shall be one attendant for each 25 head of cattle shipped. *Provided, however,* That when all the attendants are experienced and capable men, there shall be one attendant for each 50 head of cattle upon steamers having water pipes extending the entire length of both sides of compartments, and not less than 3 feet in width of alleyways, if a competent watchman for night duty for each shipper is furnished in addition; and upon steamers not so fitted there shall be one experienced attendant to each 35 head of cattle shipped, together with watchmen as provided above; except that for fresh cows and forward springers the number of attendants must be increased in proportion to the number of animals of these classes and there must be not less than one additional experienced attendant to each 15 head of such cows.

Sheep and Goat Attendants

There shall be one man in charge of each 150 head of sheep and goats during the winter season (October 1 to April 1), and one to each 200 sheep and goats during the summer season.

Horse Attendants

For horses there shall be one attendant to each 22 head.

Additional Help

There shall also be additional help furnished by the captain of the vessel when water has to be pumped by hand.

Rest, Loading, Inspection, Certificates, Etc.

Rest before Embarkation

Regulation 52. No vessel shall be permitted to take on board any cattle, sheep, swine, or goats unless the same have been allowed at least five hours' actual rest in the yards at the port of embarkation before the vessel sails, *nor until the loading of the other cargo has been completed.*

The phrase "actual rest" as applied to live stock in transit for export must not be interpreted to include any of the time occupied in unloading animals from the cars, or in their inspection, handling and roping, or in loading them on the cars again for transportation to steamer.

All animals must remain a sufficient length of time in stables or yards during daylight at the port of embarkation before the vessel sails, for the purpose of inspection.

No vessel shall be permitted to take on board any horses which have been shipped more than 500 miles unless the same have been allowed at least 18 hours' actual rest in the stable or stables designated by the inspector for export horses at the port of embarkation before the vessel sails. Horses shipped less than 500 miles shall remain in such stables or yards as the inspector may designate not less than 6 hours for the purpose of inspection and rest. Horses shall not be placed upon steamers until the loading of the other cargo has been completed.

Loading, Etc.

Regulation 53. The inspector, or one of his assistants, shall supervise the loading of the animals and see that they are properly stowed, and, so far as practicable, tied; that a sufficient amount of good, wholesome feed is properly stowed; and that all the requirements of these regulations have been complied with. In case the regulations have not been complied with, he shall immediately notify the Chief of the Bureau of Animal Industry. In hot weather the tying of the cattle may, in the discretion of the inspector, be in part omitted until after the steamer has cleared and is in motion.

Certificates of Inspection

Regulation 54. The inspector at the port of shipment shall issue certificate of inspection for cattle, sheep, swine, and goats, which are to be exported to any foreign country, unless the

Secretary of Agriculture shall have waived the requirement for such certificate of inspection for export to the particular country to which such animals are to be shipped. Each certificate shall cite the name of the shipper, the name of the consignee, and the destination. The certificates shall be issued in serial numbers; only one certificate shall be issued for each consignment, unless otherwise directed by the Chief of the Bureau of Animal Industry. The certificates shall be delivered to the chief officer of the vessel upon which said consignment of live stock is to be transported after the loading and stowing is completed, and continue with the shipment to destination, where it may be delivered to the consignee.

Defective Fittings

Regulation 55. The inspector may, in case he finds that any of the fittings are worn, decayed, defective in construction, or appear to be unsound, require the same to be replaced before he authorizes the clearance of the vessel.

Cleansing of False Decks and Temporary Troughs

Regulation 56. False decks upon which live stock are loaded and temporary feed troughs must be removed and the manure and dirt cleaned from underneath and disinfected before receiving another load of live stock.

Headropes, Etc.

Regulation 57. Cattle shall be tied with ¾-inch rope, which shall not be used more than once, and must be either manila or sisal.

All headropes, halters, blankets, stable utensils, feed bags and feed troughs, if returned to this country, must be disinfected under the supervision of the inspector of the port unless an affidavit is furnished by the captain of the vessel that the same have been disinfected, describing the manner of disinfection, or unless such affidavit is furnished by the proper official at the port where the animals are unloaded.

Injured Animals

Regulation 58. Animals suffering from broken legs or other serious injuries during the voyage shall be slaughtered by direction of the Captain of the vessel.

Markings of Valves Generally Adopted on American Tankers

	Live Steam Valves	*Bright Red.*
	Exhaust Steam Valves	*Blue.*
	Master Cargo Valves	*Yellow.*
	Starboard Cargo Line Valves	*Green Center* and *Yellow Border.*
	Port Cargo Line Valves	*Red Center* and *Yellow Border.*
	Bunker Fuel Oil Valves	*Black.*
	Sea Water Valves	*Green.*
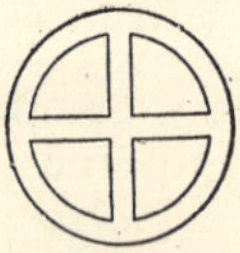	Fresh Water Valves	*White.*
	Emergency Valves	*Half Bright Red* and *Half Black.*

Note.—All valve wheels to follow this system, in *Pump Room*, *Engine Room*, and on *Deck*.

CHAPTER XI

THE TANKER

I

The Action of Tank Vessels

The carriage of bulk oil in tank vessels has now become of immense importance and this type of craft is increasing in size (20,300 D.W. tankers are building) and many important rules for the handling of this special cargo have been evolved.

In the first place, masters taking charge of an oil tank vessel for the first time should be watchful of certain peculiarities due to the fluid nature of the cargo. At the present time much study is being given to the apparent differences in the behavior of vessels of similar size and tonnage when loaded with fluid cargo and with solid cargo. It is claimed that the tank vessel, full loaded, is more sluggish in a seaway than other ships. It has been said that vessels loaded with oil are more liable to drag their anchors, and that, due to the peculiar inertia caused by the fluid nature of the cargo (with tanks full) where the molecules of oil have a circulation and movement within their own confined mass, greater stress is put on rudder stocks, etc., resulting in a higher percentage of breakage on tank vessels.

The *Nautical Gazette* in a recent issue discusses the matter as follows:

"Among the things which Solomon confessed he could not understand was the way of a ship in the sea. While a good deal of maritime knowledge has been gained since Solomon's time, shipbuilders and ship operators have still something to learn as to the ways of vessels when they breast the waves.

"At the present time research work is going on in various parts of the world as to the behavior of tankers in a seaway. Certain puzzling phenomena have been observed in connection with them, which, so far, have not been explained on a scientific basis. Frequently tankers are said by shipping men to be 'sluggish.' In other words, they fail to rise and fall with the same readiness as do other vessels.

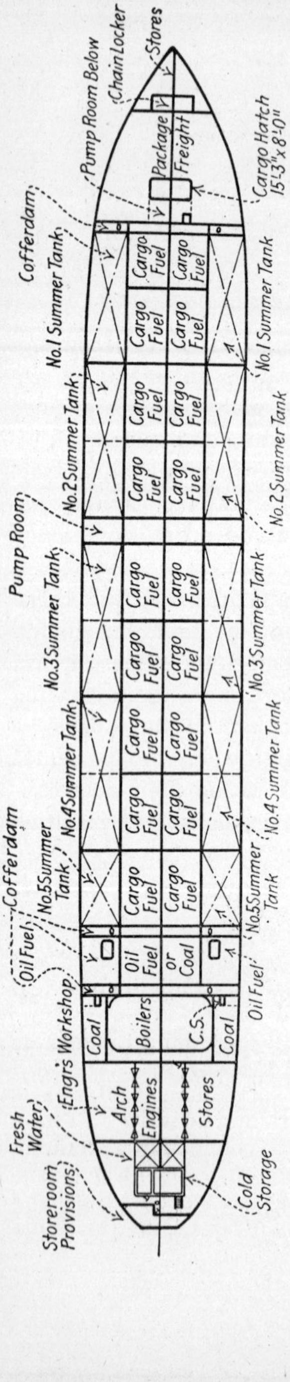

Subdivision of a tanker.

"Again there appears to be no doubt that a tanker gathers more momentum than a ship in which the cargo is a general one. When a tanker rams another vessel, the smash is usually more serious than if an ordinary freighter had done the damage. These various phenomena are understood to result from the fact that a tanker's cargo is in a fluid state and in a constant condition of circulation."

II

Subdivision of Hull

In the modern American tanker there are usually from eight to ten tanks divided into port and starboard compartments by a continuous longitudinal oil tight bulkhead. Some of the largest British tankers are divided into twelve tank compartments. The *San Fernando*, one of the latest built by Messers Armstrong, Whitworth and Company being of 18,550 tons D.W.*

* The steamship *San Florentino*, the latest addition to the fleet of the Eagle Oil Transport Co., successfully underwent her speed and other tests off the mouth of the Tyne (1920), an average speed of 11.4 knots per hour being accomplished. The San Florentino carries a deadweight of 18,000 tons. She is 530 feet in length and 68 feet 5 inches in width.

Four-and-a-half miles of oil pipes are fitted in the vessel, and these are so arranged that four different grades of oil can be either loaded or discharged simultaneously without becoming mixed. The after and forward pump rooms are each fitted with two powerful duplex pumps ca-

Further subdivision athwartship is made by the pump room, located near the middle of the tanks in American practice.* In the largest British tankers two pump rooms divide the tanks into three sections.

The cofferdams, parallel cross bulkheads, are placed aft between the fuel bunker and the aftermost oil cargo compartment, and forward between the dry cargo hold and the forward tank.

Sometimes a cofferdam is placed between the tanks amidships, and in this design it is necessary to have two pump rooms located in the middle of the two sections of tanks.

The fore hold is designed for the carriage of dry freight usually over a deep tank for reserve fuel oil, additional cargo oil, or water ballast. This is in fact a huge forward trimming tank and is useful in maintaining a balance between the engines and bunkers placed far aft.

Cofferdams. These are peculiar to oil tank vessels, and are of *oil tight* construction. It must be understood that a watertight bulkhead is not necessarily oil-tight. An oil tight bulkhead calls for the most careful close-spaced riveting, all rivet holes being absolutely fair and completely filled.

The forward cofferdam is usually left empty, as tankers when loaded generally trim by the head, though at times it may be used for the carriage of additional fuel oil when on a long voyage, and some advocate that it be filled with water.

The space between cofferdam bulkheads in ships of transverse framing is two frames, and when the vessel is built on the

pable of discharging 300 tons of oil an hour. The main suction pipes are 10 inches and the discharge pipes 8 inches in diameter. Suctions are fitted closely to the center line of the ship to enable the tanks to be thoroughly drained.

For discharging the oil there are nine outlets on each side of the ship. The propelling engines consist of a set of compound-geared turbines of the Brown-Curtiss type, working a single propeller. The turbines work in series, but their connections are so arranged that they can each run independently and be coupled to gearing to operate the propeller. In the casings of the main turbines there are incorporated astern turbines capable of giving not less than 60 per cent. of the total power for driving the ship ahead. Oil fuel burning apparatus is fitted to the boilers, which are cylindrical and five in number. The working pressure is 220 pounds per square inch.

* The pump room is often located forward of the tanks and in some vessels is placed aft, just forward of the fuel tank.

Isherwood system of longitudinal framing these bulkheads are spaced from 3½ to 5 feet apart.

Just forward of this cofferdam is located a small pump room for serving the deep tank under the cargo hold. This pump room usually carries a fuel-oil transfer pump for sending fuel oil aft when same is being used from the forward tank.

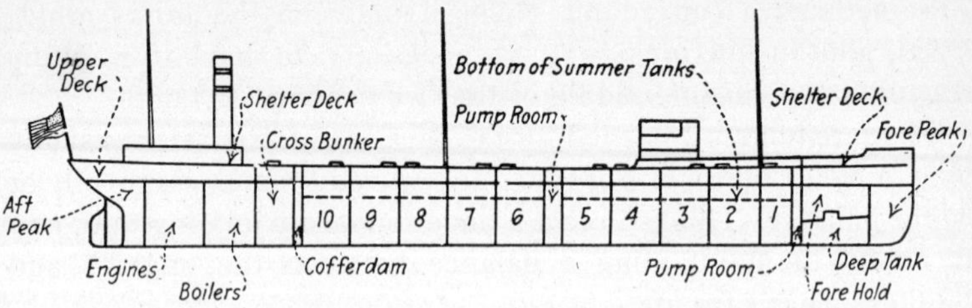

In American practice the tanks are numbered from forward aft, as in the case of cargo holds. The British practice is to number them from aft forward. Thus we have No. 1 starboard, and No. 1 port, beginning abaft the forward cofferdam.

In a ten tank vessel the pump room will generally be located between No. 5 and No. 6 tanks. In some vessels it is aft, just forward of the bunker space.

Abaft of No. 10 tank (in a ten-tank vessel) is the after cofferdam, built and spaced as forward. Where napthalene or other dangerous oils are being carried this cofferdam will usually be filled with water.

Bunker. The bunker extends across the vessel abaft the after cofferdam, following the general arrangement of the tanks with wing bunkers abaft of the cross bunker, and the usual expansion trunk and summer tanks above.

The bunker may also be used for the carriage of coal, when coal fuel must be used. Also, when going light, a tank vessel may bunker from her forward tank and may fill the fore hold with light dry cargo.

III

Pump Room

The Standard Oil Company, and many of the other large tanker operators, place the Chief Mate in full charge of the entire cargo pipe lines, valves, pump rooms, etc. The pumpmen work under his direction. Repairs are attended to by the Chief Engineer.

This places the operation of loading and discharging under control of the Master, through the Chief Mate.

When loading or discharging, the officer in charge of the deck must watch his trim and his lines, having careful consideration of the state of the tide, and he must be ready to pass his orders to the man in charge of the pumps.

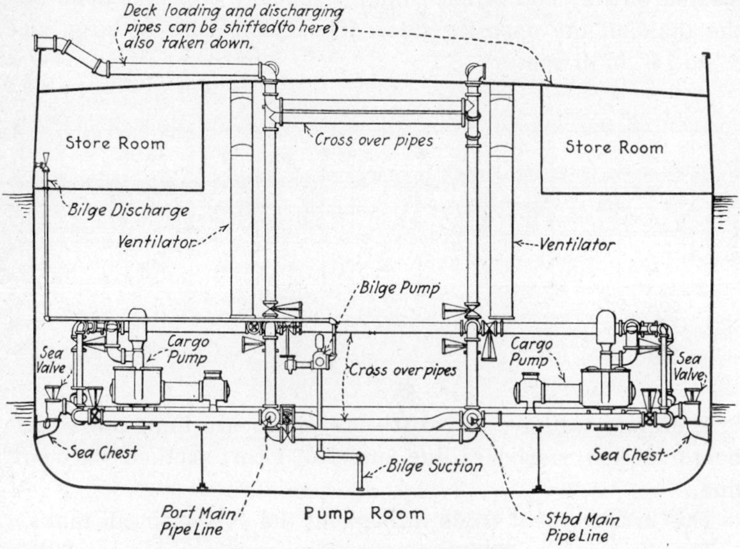

Section through pump room.

The pump room generally contains two large cargo pumps, one to port and the other to starboard.

Crossover pipes are fitted between the two main pipe lines and these are controlled by master valves usually operated from the shelter deck.

In the latest practice the suction valves are actuated only

from the deck, but the transfering valves are operated only from the pump room and are under the sole control of the pump-room engineers.

IV

Pipe Lines.

While the arrangement on different tank vessels will vary the general principle governing the piping on all of them may be laid down and an officer joining one of these vessels will study her piping plan and will trace out the lines and the location of valves as a matter of course.

The two main pipe lines are the starboard and port pipe lines running fore and aft from the pump rooms and serving the various tanks, first by direct suction or delivery to the tanks located on the side of each line, second by cross suctions into the tank on the opposite side. These lines are of large pipe 8″ to 14″ in diameter.

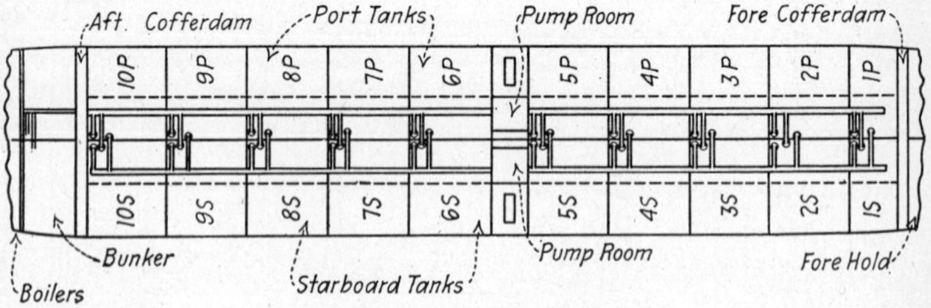

Diagram of main pipe lines.

Therefore we have in No. 1 tank, Starboard line, No. 1 starboard suction, starboard line, and No. 1 port suction, starboard line.

This arrangement holds throughout the system in all tanks.

Therefore remember that four prime suctions are located in each tank, viz: Starboard line; Starboard suction, Port suction, Port line; Port suction, Starboard suction.

In special tankers designed to carry different grades of oil, cofferdams are placed between groups of main tanks and each group may have an independent system of piping.

Some designs carry large crossover pipes at the ends of the main lines in the extreme forward and after tanks, but many authorities do not consider this necessary where double suctions are fitted in each tank.

Stripping Lines are 2″ to 6″ pipe lines for clearing tanks, these do not generally have bell mouthed suctions. They discharge into main pipe lines or overboard on either side. Separate pumps are provided.

V

Valves

Gate valves are fitted at the ends of the suction pipes leading into the tanks, these gates are worked from the shelter deck, in vessels of that type, and are opened and closed by means of long rods running up to the deck through proper stuffing boxes.

Sometimes *cross* or *angle valves* are used to obtain better drainage.

The construction of a gate valve should be familiar to the modern officer so we will not go into this further than to describe it as a metal door lifting into a recess when open and shutting down across the orifice of the pipe when closed.

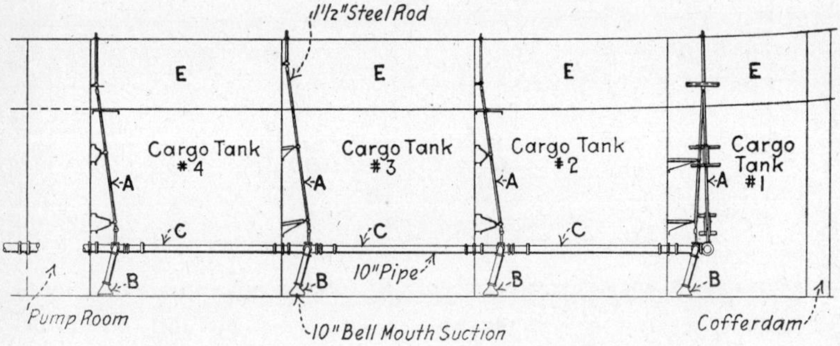

Diagram of valve connections. Longitudinal section.

It is important to know that the suctions in all tanks are located at the after ends of the compartments and when discharging it is well to have the vessel trimmed by the stern.* To this end watch the trim and empty the forward tanks first if possible.

Also, to completely drain tanks the vessel must be given a list to port when cleaning out the starboard tanks, and *vice versa*, as the suctions are close to the midship bulkhead.

* Tank barges generally have suctions forward.

Suctions are generally bell mouthed and are sometimes fitted with strainers, and it is important that these be clean before taking oil on board. The bell mouths are about 3/4" above tank bottoms.

Master valves. These are gate or sluice valves (same thing) situated on the main pipe line itself in order that different compartments may be worked as required.

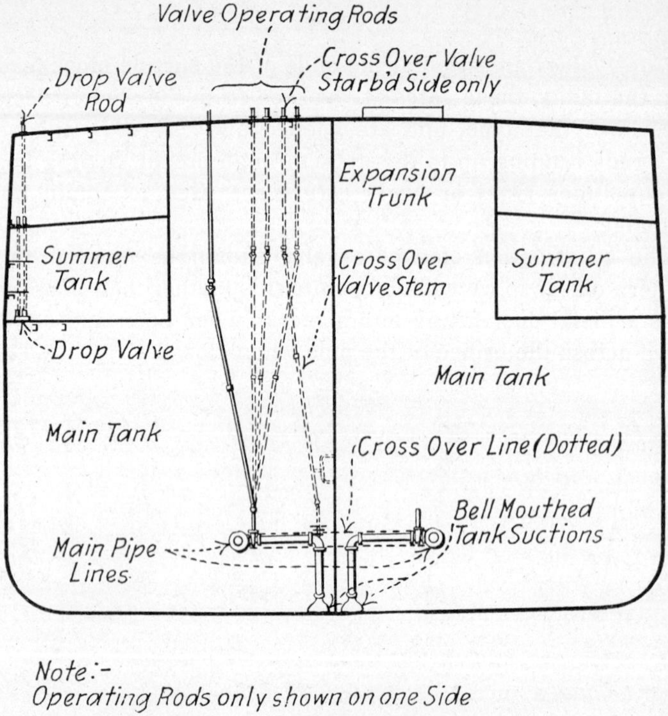

Diagram of valve connections thwart ship section.

Caution. Great care should be exercised in the use of valves. Study the system, be certain you know what you are about. The general practice is to paint valves according to the color chart. This system is in use by the vessels of the Standard Oil Co. and on many other tank vessels. See page 342.

In addition to the colors, each valve should have a brass plate screwed down on deck alongside of the spindle stating clearly its function. Know at once whether a valve is open or closed. Be certain about this and do not be afraid to ask questions if need be. Valves should be fitted with an indicator showing whether opened or closed.

Air valves. Each tank carries an air valve for each side.

Air lines, served by blowers, are fitted to clear tanks of gas when emptied.

Steam valves. Each tank carries steam valves for the *heating coils* and *steam smothering lines.*

Steam lines, serve coils placed in the bottom of the tank, much after the fashion of a radiator, and in fact on the same principle. These coils are used for the purpose of keeping the cargo fluid. Where Mexican crude oil is carried it should not be allowed to cool down, as it will if the vessel proceeds northward into winter weather. The transference of temperature through the sides of a steel tank vessel is rapid and must be taken into consideration. For this reason the sea temperature must be carefully observed. The lighter oils are more quickly cooled than the heavy ones.

Caution. When oil is heated the most careful handling of steam and exhaust valves is necessary to prevent blowing steam through too fast or of breaking coils by water hammer (the pounding of condensed water) in the coils.

Note: Heater coils should have test cocks in return lines to show whether coils are leaking and oil going back to boilers. Coils return to inspection tank in engine room.

American valves are all *right-handed.* British practice is to fit *left-handed* valves.

In any ship the valves should *all* be the same. This is most important.

Valve rods in tanks have a sliding fork connected to valve stem so that rod does not rise and fall with stem of valve. Collars are fitted to take the weight of the rod, and lignum vitae guides are fitted in the tanks.

VI

Hatches

Hatches on a tanker are comparatively small and are placed in groups of four close to the crossing of thwartship and fore and aft bulkheads. These hatches are usually edged by a coaming extending 6 inches to 30 inches above the deck and are closed by a

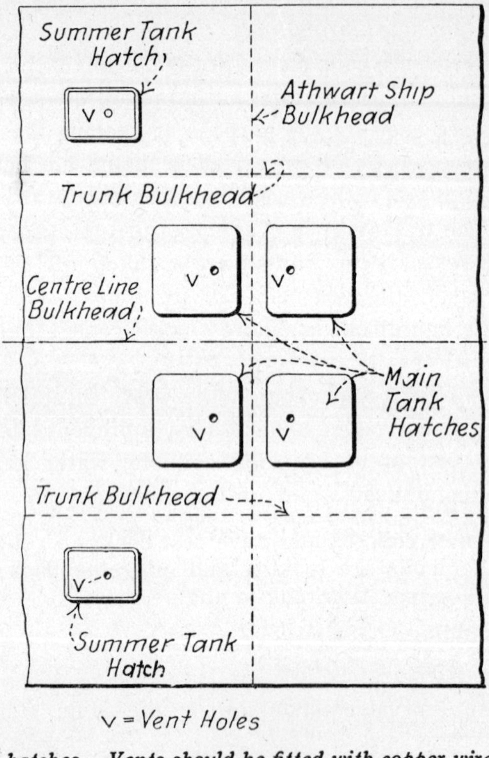

Tanker hatches. Vents should be fitted with copper wire gauze.

steel plate resting on a gasket of plaited hemp or asbestos (rubber rots) and screwed down by dogs, much as a watertight door is held in position.

Hatches are also held shut by brass nuts and steel bolts.

Tanker hatches should be fitted with mechanical lifting means, falls or gears; they should never be lifted by hand. Hatches are hinged and are fitted with rest rods. Hatches are small, about 6′ x 4′ on main tanks, 4′ x $2\frac{1}{2}$′ on summer tanks.

Hatches should also be fitted with a smaller oil-tight cover, hinged so that *ullages** may be taken without lifting the entire hatch.

Vents. Each hatch is also fitted with an air hole, or sight hole, that must be unplugged when loading or discharging so that the air may escape or enter the tank as the oil level is changing. Vents and ullage holes are generally the same being used for both purposes.

Other vents running through four inch pipes should be fitted to tanks with a gooseneck or automatic relief valve at the top and the ends should be covered with copper wire gauze.

The automatic relief valves are also known as *pressure and vacuum valves* — and work both ways. They will not admit sea water.

VII

The Mooring Lines and Hose

Oil being a *quick* cargo, the usual precautions with respect to mooring lines, gangways, *hose connection*, etc., should be observed.

Hose is usually carried over a curved saddle. At exposed anchorages hose is fastened with *clamps*. Keep a maul ready to knock off clamps if necessary.

Prevent hose from chafing.

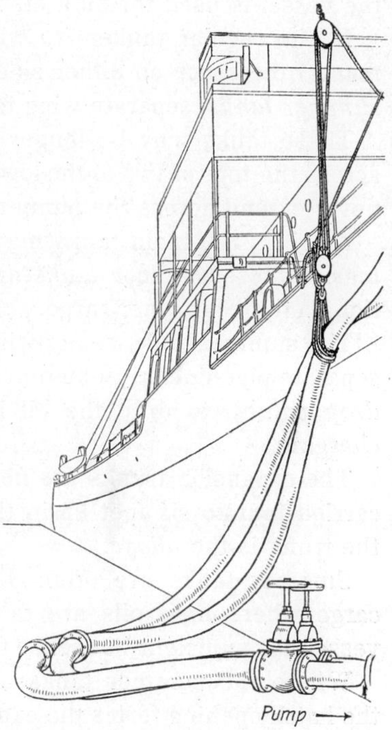

Method of slinging hose.

VIII

Expansion Trunks

As in the case of grain cargoes, the carriage of oil in tanks is made more safe by the construction of a trunkway above the

* An *ullage tank* is a tank partly filled, also called a *slack tank*.

main cargo tanks. This expansion trunk, as it is called narrows down the upper level of the oil and as the oil expands and contracts (1/20 of one per cent. for each degree F. change in temperature) the lower tank remains filled, and the live surface of the oil is confined in its motion.

Oil being a *live load*, it would be extremely dangerous to have tanks rising their full width with the resultant disruptive force of the free fluid acting against the bulkheads as the vessel moved in a seaway.

Another method of avoiding this is to make use of upright *cylindrical* tanks. This method is most often used where regular cargo carriers are transformed into tankers, or where a part of the vessel is used for bulk oil and the remainder for dry cargo.

In the regular tanker (to which we must confine our statements) the space on either side of the trunk is occupied by the *summer tanks*, separate wing tanks.

These tanks may be longer than the main tanks, extending across the tops of two of the lower tanks. Summer tanks should never extend across the pump rooms.

As oil in the main tanks may not bring a vessel down to her marks, these summer tanks are then utilized, either for additional oil, or for other cargo.

The summer tanks have their own hatches, and are fitted with separate pipe lines. Sometimes these tanks are only fitted with *drop valves*, to drop the oil into the lower tanks when discharging.

The expansion trunks are never filled but the oil is generally carried four to six feet up in the trunk. The empty portion of the trunk is the *ullage*.

Summer tanks are often designed for the carriage of dry cargo where light oils are taken in the main tanks and the vessel has sufficient buoyancy for extra freight.

Where the summer tanks are used for the carriage of oil, the hatch opening forms the expansion trunk for the tank, as it is important that all tanks be *full* to avoid the *swash* of the oil.

The summer tanks are usually served by a 6″ line and by adhering to this line of pipe for filling different grades of oil may be safely loaded and discharged.

When extra fuel oil is carried in the summer tanks, the tanks so utilized must be disconnected from the cargo pumps.

Where summer tanks have no separate system of pipes, they can only be filled to the level of the trunk oil, by opening the drop valves when filling lower tanks, allowing the oil to rise into the summer tanks. The summer tanks should then be so constructed that they will be *filled* when this occurs.

Summer tanks are sometimes fitted with heating coils, and should also be fitted with air pipes to drive out the gas. *As many are without air pipes*, officers should take this into account when sending men into the tanks.

IX

Important Points

1. When loading or discharging two different grades of oil at once utmost care must be used to prevent mixing. Valves should be set and then *checked* by a second person before starting to move the oil. Remember this—*Avoid mixing.*

2. When a tank is finished (empty) the pumps should be stopped, valves set and *checked* before starting another tank.

3. When loading, as a tank becomes nearly full, the shore pump must be slowed down to "top off" to required level.

4. When full, the shore pump must be stopped while valves are set and *checked* for next tank.

5. Never start the pumps, ashore or aboard, without making doubly sure there is no valve closed or other obstruction in the line which might burst it. Always watch the discharge pressure gauge. If it goes up, shut off pump *at once* until cause is determined.

6. When handling oil cargo display a *red flag* (B) or *red light* between the fore and main masts.

Deck delivery line. This is the line rising from the main cargo pumps connecting to the pipe line on deck.

When loading through the deck lines, using the shore pressure, the oil is sent through a *by-pass* around the pump on board ship and into the main pump line direct.

The sea delivery line. This line runs from the main pump to the ships side. Two valves control this line, the *outer sea valve* next to the ship's side, and the *inner sea valve* next to the pump.

Caution. Sometimes it is necessary to discharge ballast through the sea delivery line while cargo is being loaded in another part of the vessel. This is seldom done, but when necessary great care should be taken that the correct valves are opened and closed.

Bilge suctions. The pump room has two bilge suction pipes, these being the only bilges in the vessel, except forward and aft of the oil tanks. Either an independent bilge pump is fitted, or extra suctions are connected to the cargo pumps. In either case the bilge pumping should be controlled by rods from the deck, in case a pipe breaks and floods the pump room. This may happen very quickly as the space is comparatively small. Pump-room ladders should at all times be kept clear.

Barge delivery pipe. This is a branch pipe running through the ships side just above the load water line. Oil can be discharged into barges without lifting it up over the deck.

Control of steam valves. The steam valves of all cargo pumps should be controlled from the deck.

Signals. A bell-pull should be fitted from the deck to the pump room to signal orders when loading and discharging.

Captain G. M. Brodthage, commanding the oil tanker *Halsey*, has kindly given me the following practical notes on the pumping out of tanks.

"We carry crude oil from Mexican ports to Bayonne, N. J., taking our cargo on board at a temperature of about 82° F. Twenty-four hours before making our discharging port we start the heater coils and bring the temperature to about 75° F.

"In pumping out tanks carrying crude oil difficulty is often experienced in completely emptying them. The heating coils, lying above the frames, may be three feet from the bottom of the tanks. In cold weather when the oil drops below the coils it may cool off to a point where the pumps are no longer able to take it out. This is specially so in the case of oil with grit, or other heavy impurities, which have settled to the bottom.

"I have found it a good practice to stop pumping in these tanks when the oil is a few inches above the coils and to go on with the pumping out of other tanks leaving the almost empty tank heat up to about a hundred degrees. When the residual oil is warm it is possible to get it all out without trouble as it holds its heat until the stripping lines suck.

"Unless this is done a vessel may carry out with her from two hundred to three hundred barrels of oil lying cold below the coils depending, of course, on the size of the tanks, height of coils, etc."

A small steam jet is sometimes used when oil is being heated to expel gases rising from above the surface of the oil.

Keep test hatches covered. Keep all screens in vents clear. Allow no visitors on board unless under proper supervision.

The heating of oil is being investigated. A method of heating oil outside of the tanks, passing the warm oil back into the tanks is being developed. This does away with the troublesome heating coils. This is the Row & Davis system.

When changing grade of oil discharge, blow out hose.

X

Ballasting a Tanker

As tankers, strictly speaking, are one way carriers, the question of ballast and trim is of much importance.

Some authorities recommend the use of one main pipe line for cargo, and the other for ballast (Herbert John White, in *Oil Tank Steamers*) but the best American practice calls for the use of both pump lines in discharging in order to cut down the "turn around."

The number of tanks to be loaded with "ballast" depends upon the trade and the season of the year. Weather conditions along the route should be known and the vessel managed accordingly. The carriage of excess water cost time and money, while too little will cause delays and may even endanger the vessel. One advantage, however, is the fact that extra ballast can be taken on, and excess ballast discharged almost at will as there is an ample supply at hand just over the side.

Always ballast in *alternate* tanks while on a "ballast passage."

When running with ballast have the empty holds carefully inspected by the officers for leaks. The vessel in a seaway will show up leaks in the bulkheads. These should be caulked, if possible, and if not the leaks should be marked and reported for attention when in port on overhaul. Also examine all pipes and valves.

Once during the passage, if time permits, transfer the ballast and examine the holds previously filled with water. Empty tanks should be "steamed" during a "ballast passage."

If not possible, fill the next series of holds on the succeeding "ballast passage."

In ballasting avoid " slack tanks," that is tanks only partly full, for free water is even more vicious than free oil.

The taking on of ballast through the sea valves is simple, and if in no particular hurry much of the ballast can be allowed to run in without pumping, until on a level with the load line.

The reverse condition prevails in discharging, for the water in the trunks and above the load line will run out without using the pumps.

Life on a tanker is one continuous problem in the hydraulics of seamanship. Many officers, having learned their *pipes*, as it were, prefer this service to all others. Where decent shore periods are allowed the crew, this service has much to recommend it.

Clean water. Do not ballast in a muddy river, or in a place filled with sewage. Some care in this respect will save a great deal of trouble and will add to the efficiency of pumps.

Also, do not go out for clean water in a dangerous condition of stability.

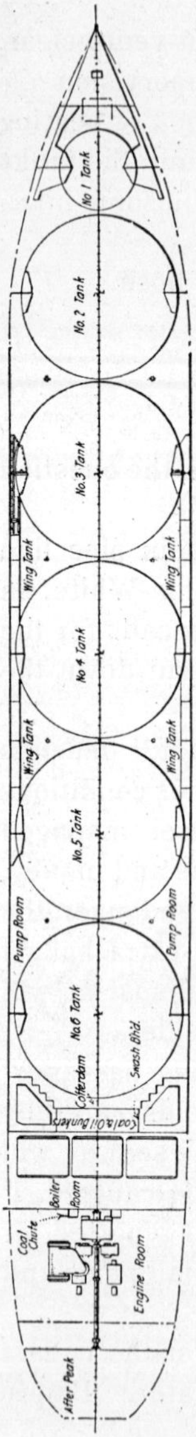

Circular tanks are built in many tankers. This system is shown in the drawing.

XI

The Care of Tanks

Before receiving oil the tanks must be ready for inspection by the persons shipping oil. It is well to have the tanks " pass inspection " and note same in the log in the event of future disputes with regard to the cleanliness and condition of the cargo.

The tanks will have to be dry, before passing inspection.

First steaming. To clean a foul tank shut down the hatches, and fill with live steam from the smothering pipe (same as smothering pipes fitted in ordinary cargo holds). It is good practice to carry the smothering pipes to the bottom of the tank, as the hot vapor rises. A hole in the top would be useful for smothering in the event of fire, and with a full tank would function with the lower end plugged by oil.

Where no smothering lines are fitted a steam hose is led into the tank through the plug hole, which is stopped with an oakum and canvas gasket.

The heat generated in the tank will melt down the thick oil which can then be pumped out.

Steam for six hours, lift the hatches, and continue the steam for an hour or two more.

Next shut off steam and turn on air. Sometimes a windsail in each hatch will help in the drying out.

Then wash down top and sides of tank with water, using a hose with a good pressure.

Before sending men into the tank for the washing, be certain that gas is out. Send first man down in a bowline (see French bowline, page 86).*

The bottom of tank is scrubbed with brooms, refuse and other solid matter lifted out in buckets, rose boxes are cleaned.

Second steaming. Having gone so far, close down hatches and turn steam on for two hours more. Wash down again with hose. Pump out and turn on air.

Oil wash. The tank is now ready for the wash with light oil. *Gas oil* is best. This is usually supplied by the shippers of the cargo. Fill each tank in turn with this oil and transfer it to the next. And send it through all pumps and lines.

Having completed this process advise the shippers that you are ready to pump it ashore where it is again refined.

The vessel being empty will trim aft, and the men are sent into each hold as it sucks dry to swab up air having been driven into the hold in sufficient quantity to clear the tank. Always use the bowline to make sure.

The method given is used when a creosote oil has been carried. To clean up after a cargo of refined oil the second steaming and second washing are not usually required before washing out with gas oil.

*In most modern tankers the cleaning of tanks is accomplished mechanically by means of the Butterworth System of high-pressure water and steam, a pipe with a revolving spray-head being lowered into the empty tanks. This has been a boon to seamen serving on tank ships.

It is bad management to put dirty oil into a clean vessel as the clean tanks are a great asset.

XII

Repairs in Dry Dock—Precautions

When tankers are put into dry dock and rivetings is to be done about the tanks or hatches, it is necessary to have the vessel " gas free."

The three methods of doing this are as follows:

1. Steam out and put down windsails.
2. Force air into the holds by the blower.
3. Fill tanks to overflowing with sea water so that any oil in the tank will float up and flow over the top.

Very often these methods are combined, beginning with the last and following with the other two.

Where red hot rivets are to be used, or electric torches, etc., it is most important that the tanks be absolutely " gas free."

When a tank has been passed by a chemist as " gas free " no piping should be opened up without another test as gas lodged in the pipes may be liberated.

Water tests. Where hydraulic tests are made each tank in turn must be filled and examined carefully from the dry sides. These should be perfectly dry *before* beginning the test.

Every bulkhead must be examined under pressure from both sides in turn, except, of course, the pump-room bulkheads.

Leaks are marked with chalk or paint.

Before going into dock it is the custom to bring in two tanks filled with clean sea water for this test.

In conclusion. After testing and repairs, sweep clean, make careful examination of the heating coils, as staging may have been dropped on them. Set up glands on expansion joints in piping.

Caution. Never remove " bleeders " (bottom plugs) of oil tanks while in dry dock without obtaining permission from the dock master. There may be regulations with regard to running oil into the dock. Barrels may be used to catch the oil from the bleeders, if necessary.

Do not *caulk* in a hold unless " gas free." A spark from the chisel may set off an explosive mixture.

Tankers must be very strict about the regulation of smoking and carrying naked lights. American custom is to only permit smoking abaft of the fire line, a red line painted at about the middle point of the poop deck house. Smoking is permitted in quarters.

Caution!

"The body of S. H., 43 years old, who was drowned Saturday night in crude oil in the tanks-ship *De Soto* at Bayonne, N. J., was recovered early to-day, after 200,000 gallons of oil had been emptied from the vessel.

"The tanker reached Bayonne Saturday afternoon with a cargo of Mexican crude oil and docked at Pier 5, Constable Hook. That night H—, employed as a pumpman, went to repair a feed line that was leaking. When he failed to reappear on deck, members of the crew went in search of him. It is believed H— became overcome by the fumes and fell into the oil. The pumps worked continuously from the time of the accident until the body was recovered."—*From a news report.*

Suggestions for the Prevention of Explosions Aboard Oil Carriers Under Repairs

Immediately following the fatal explosion aboard the Jack Tank steamer "G. R. Crowe," at the plant of James Shewan & Sons, Brooklyn, New York, October 6th, 1920: Continuous investigation and inquiry has revealed the absence of proper Rules and Regulations for the handling or repairing of oil burning or bulk oil carriers and a total lack of due regard of the explosive character of the gases and absolute necessity of freeing all oil carrying spaces of same before any work is started within such compartment, or adjacent thereto.

It is an established fact, learned in many cases only by painful experience, that all tanks or compartments of vessels containing, or having contained fuel oil of any gravity whatsoever are extremely dangerous, and special precautions are absolutely necessary to avoid accidents from explosions and fires.

All existing methods have been tried, and all failed to render tanks non-explosive when the inevitable explosions occur.

Gas is always generated wherever oil lies, whether the oil is in great quantity, the light coating left on sides of tanks or the heavy bottom scum or sediment, and this gas is explosive when mixed with air, being readily touched off by a spark or naked flame.

To say that this gas is explosive when mixed with air is not theoretically true—the percentage of gas and air must be within certain limits—the mixture, however, has so often been by test

" non-explosive " when explosions have occurred that this theoretical condition should be forgotten and *all gas* treated as the *ideal* explosive mixture.

Were it possible to discover the cause of all explosions, specific methods could be applied. It is our opinion that but one cause will cover, and that cause is " *Carelessness*."

Admitting that all tanks with or having contained oil are explosive, the following precautions are essential before work is started:

1. Compartments steamed for 12 hours, after which they should be hosed down with hot salt or fresh water, pumped out dry and steamed again for 24 hours more. Compartments then ventilated with assistance of mechanical blowers or windsails led to lowest possible point for 24 hours. Ventilation continued during work.

During the first 12 hours of ventilation, the oil and scum to be mopped and scraped entirely out of every corner. Workmen to wear rubbers, or rubber boots, to avoid spark from contact with shoe nails and steel plating. No iron or tin scoops, or wire brushes to be used—Brass scoops or shovels only. Should ladders be necessary, only wooden ladders with no metal rungs, sides or ends to be used.

2. Chemists' samples of gas to be taken from all isolated parts upon completion of steaming and ventilating, and Certificate for gas (free) issued in writing to foreman in charge and posted at entrance to ship. This should be repeated every morning, before work is started and a new Certificate issued and posted.

In order that the above may be more effective, signs 18 inches by 12 inches, on cardboard, should be posted on the *Gangplank* and about the ship in *conspicuous places*, to read as follows:

Be Careful!

1—This vessel carries oil. *All* compartments *are dangerous* unless cleaned and these precautions followed:
2—No *naked* lights allowed.
3—*Smoking* positively prohibited.
4—Satisfy *yourself* that *Chemist's Certificate* bears the *date* that *you* board the vessel.
5—Wear *rubbers* or *rubber boots*.
6—Do not *drop* or *throw* tools.
7—Avoid injury to all electric lines or cables. Report defective lights or wiring to foreman.
8—Report your fellow workmen should they *neglect* any precaution. *One (1) match* or *spark* is sufficient to cause an explosion.

Be Careful!

Eads Johnson, M.E.

XIII

General Remarks on the Tanker

The following notes of interest to the tank vessel officer are taken from an excellent paper by Mr. Robert W. Morrell,* M.E., read before the twenty-fifth general meeting of the Society of Naval Architects and Marine Engineers November 15, 1917, on "Recent Developments in Tank Steamer Construction." (The subheads are inserted by the author of this book.)

Shelter-decked Vessel

"Along with the increased size (in tankers) came the development of the shelter-deck type of vessel. The term 'shelter-decked type,' as commonly used in this country in referring to tankers, applies to a vessel having three continuous steel decks, the uppermost of which is the strength deck. A shelter-decked vessel according to the A.B.S. is one in which the uppermost or shelter deck is a light, continuous superstructure, with one or more tonnage openings. If without tonnage openings, it is an awning-decked vessel, while if the upper scantlings are heavier it becomes a spar-decked vessel. The commonly accepted use of the term 'shelter-decked vessel,' however, is in reference to any vessel having a continuous weather deck, as opposed to the type having raised forecastle, bridge and poop."

Oil Hatches and Gas Trunks

"The first shelter-decked tankers built in this country were the sister ships *John D. Archbold* and *John D. Rockefeller*, of 11,500 tons deadweight each. These vessels had the oil tanks carried up to the upper deck, which is the next deck below the shelter deck. The oil hatches were located on the upper deck, and gas trunks were built around the hatches and extending from upper to shelter deck, to keep the gases from permeating the 'tween-deck space.

"Experience has proven these trunks a source of danger to the ships, as the heavy gases accumulate at the hatches and great caution is necessary to prevent men from being overcome when entering the tanks. Apparatus for clearing these spaces of gas has since been installed."

* The writer is indebted to Mr. Morrell for a great amount of valuable information pertaining to present-day American tank steamer practice. As a naval architect specializing in tanker design, Mr. Morrell is taking a leading part in this rapidly growing field of marine activity.

The Expansion Trunk

"The next step in the development of the shelter-decked type was the carrying of the expansion trunks right up to the shelter deck. This was embodied in the *Charles Pratt* and subsequent vessels of that type with great success.

"With this arrangement, the expansion trunk bulkheads extend from the second deck (or main deck or tank deck, as it is variously called) up to the shelter deck, thus making the expansion trunk two decks in height. The summer tanks are arranged outboard of the expansion trunk between the second and upper decks. The oil hatches for both main and summer tanks are located on the shelter deck, and small trunks, extending between the upper and shelter decks, are built for the summer tanks. Outboard of the expansion trunk, between the upper and shelter decks, are open 'tween-deck spaces above the summer tanks. . . ."

"There have recently been built several shelter-deck vessels in which the oil hatches are located on the upper deck, and the 'tween-deck space is entirely open, without gas trunks, but the majority of the shelter decked ships are now of the type described, namely, with the trunk to the shelter deck. This type is highly satisfactory for an all-round tanker."

Mr. Morrell, in the course of this valuable paper, points out the following advantages of this construction that are of special interest to the seaman—we cannot quote him at length due to lack of space.

"The center of gravity of the cargo is higher, making an easier ship.

"On account of the oil hatches being on the shelter deck, the danger of getting gas in the 'tween deck is avoided.

"The vessel can be trimmed when loaded with much better results, as the expansion trunk extending through two deck heights gives great scope for the desired ullages. If the vessel has a tendency to trim by the head when leaving port on account of full fuel tanks forward, this can be overcome with the design in question by leaving large ullages forward and smaller ullages in the after cargo tanks. It is possible also, as the fuel is used, to maintain any desired trim by transferring the cargo. The deep trunks allow great leeway in this respect."

A Special Design

"A recent special design which is worthy of note is embodied in the tanker *D. G. Scofield*, in which the entire 'tween-deck space, between upper and shelter decks, is made suitable for carrying case or barrel oil, in addition to the bulk cargo in the tanks. The oil hatches are on the upper deck and large cargo hatches are provided in the shelter deck each side of the center strake, which is continuous. Three masts are fitted with complete cargo handling gear consisting of booms and winches.

" This is another instance, however, of adaptation of a tanker to special trade. Such package cargo handling equipment on the majority of tankers would be useless.

" In considering the subject of shelter-decked tankers, the question naturally arises as to what determines whether a vessel shall be built with a shelter deck or a forecastle, bridge and poop deck. The answer is somewhat obscure, but the determining factors seem to be mainly matters of size and of personal preference. The dividing line seems to be in the neighborhood of 10,000 or 11,000 tons deadweight, the vessels above that size being, almost without exception, shelter-decked vessels."

Subdivision of Tanks—Cofferdams—Fire Precautions

" A prominent feature of recent construction has been the subdivision of the cargo tanks into groups for the carrying of different grades of oil. If two different grades are separated by a single bulkhead there is danger that a leak in the bulkhead, permitting a mixing of the grades, will spoil the cargo. The first step was to place the pump room amidships, which, aside from being a most convenient location for pumping, divides the tanks into two groups in which different grades of oil can be loaded without danger of mixing.

" This was carried further and cofferdams inserted between the tanks. Some 15,000-ton deadweight tankers have ten main cargo tanks divided into three groups with a separate pumping system for each. Several smaller tankers have similar divisions.

" This is another example of the incorporation of special requirements for a special trade. As an extreme case, there is one vessel which has five cofferdams and a pump-room dividing the cargo tanks into four separate blocks. One of the cofferdams, however, is located between the after fuel oil tank and the fire-room. Many of the modern tankers have this arrangement, which is a wise safety precaution originated on account of fires started by oil in the fire-room due to leaky bunker bulkheads.

" Where such cofferdams are built, they are provided with tunnels for use in the event of the vessels burning coal. The tunnels are blanked by oil-tight bolted doors on each end, but if used for coal the oil-tight doors will be removed and vertical sliding bunker doors fitted. The fuel-oil piping passing through the cofferdam is fitted with a valve on each bulkhead, the valve on the bunker side being controlled from the deck. The cofferdam is also provided with a sea valve controlled from the deck, for flooding in case of fire. Thus, if a fire originates in the boiler-room, it can be isolated from the fuel supply, while if the fire starts in the tanks the propelling machinery can be kept intact."

A Short Essay on Tanker Design

"Practically every oil company and every shipyard has its own standard type of tanker, or in many cases three or four standard types, all varying in accordance with the different needs of the business and with the different ideas as to how these needs are best met.

"It has already been pointed out that special vessels are required for special trades in order to obtain the best results. A vessel designed to carry heavy oil is not suitable for transporting refined oil, and vice versa. A vessel designed for straight cargo is not suitable for a mixed cargo, but a vessel designed for mixed cargo is needlessly complicated and expensive for shipping straight cargo. Owners trading on the west coast only naturally desire to take advantage of the deep water to adopt wholesome proportions of length to depth, whereas other owners, trading in ports where draught is restricted, must adopt different proportions. Some trades require vessels with fuel capacity for ten days, others for forty days. In many cases large vessels are the most economical, but large vessels cannot be built in all yards and cannot enter all ports.

"It is obviously impossible to find a single vessel to meet all requirements, and if an attempt at a compromise is made it will place practically every oil company at a disadvantage in having to operate vessels which are not quite suitable.

"The nearest approach to efficient standardization would be in the adoption of at least four standard designs, consisting of two vessels, a large one and a small one, for the sole purpose of carrying cargoes of heavy oil, and two vessels, a large one and a small one, especially for carrying mixed cargoes of light oil.

"In carrying heavy oil, such as fuel oil or crude oil, it is possible to load different kinds in the same vessel without danger of mixing, due to leakage or due to pumping one kind through the same pipe line as another. Therefore there is no need of subdividing the tanks for different grades.

"The smaller vessel for this purpose would naturally be of the forecastle, bridge and poop type, and the larger one of the shelter-decked type. In both cases small fuel tanks for bunker use are sufficient, as it is possible for a long voyage to carry half a main cargo tank of fuel, or to carry it in summer tanks. The permanent fuel-oil tanks should consist of a short tank at the forward end of the cargo tanks, and another at the after end, thus enabling the vessel to be trimmed as the fuel is used. With this arrangement no cofferdams whatever are required in the vessel. The pump-room in this type of vessel should be located between the after-fuel tank and the boiler-room, thus separating the oil from the fires, and should contain the fuel-oil pumps and heaters as well as two cargo-oil pumps. A simple system of cargo-oil piping whereby both pumps can draw from the tanks and discharge overboard independently is sufficient. The summer tanks may be fitted with drop-valves, connecting them with the main tanks, or they may be piped for fuel oil, as conditions require. All tanks in these vessels should be fitted with heater coils.

" For the standard vessels intended to carry mixed cargoes of light gravity oils, the smaller would be of the forecastle, bridge and poop type and the larger of the shelter-decked type with expansion trunks carried up to the shelter deck. In both vessels rather larger fuel-tank capacity is required. On account of the danger in carrying naphtha next to fuel oil, cofferdams should be provided at each end of the cargo tanks. The cargo pump-room should be located amidships, thus dividing the cargo tanks into two groups. For safety, a cofferdam between the after fuel tank and the fire-room should be provided and the oil-burning apparatus installed in a separate enclosure in the fire-room wing. A fuel pump is required forward to transfer fuel aft from the forward tank. The cargo oil-piping system should permit of the pumping of different grades of oil from the forward and after groups of cargo tanks simultaneously and independently, without the two grades using any piping in common. The cargo piping must not extend into the fuel tanks. The summer tanks should be piped separately. Special precautions against gas must be provided, and the gas vents from the tanks fitted with automatic relief valves. Special ventilation for the pump-room and cofferdams must be furnished.

" The foregoing outlines briefly the minimum that could be expected in the standardization of tankers."

A.B.S. Rules for Ships Intended to Carry Oil in Bulk

(1) *General.* Vessels which are intended for the carriage of petroleum in bulk and to receive the classification mark (Oil Carrier) are to have an expansion trunk over each oil compartment with a capacity of not less than 6 per cent. of the capacity of the compartment with which they are connected. The oil holds are not to exceed 30 feet in length and are to be divided longitudinally by an oil-tight bulkhead which is to extend from the keel to the top of the expansion trunk. The attention of owners is drawn to the Panama and Suez Canal regulations for ships laden with oil in bulk.

(2) Cofferdams at least 3 feet wide, thoroughly oil-tight and well ventilated, are to be fitted at each end of each section of the vessel intended for the carriage of oil, so as to completely isolate that section from cargo and machinery spaces. All machinery, boilers and galleys must be completely isolated from the oil spaces and oil pump rooms. Where it is necessary to run a shaft tunnel through oil spaces, the tunnel is to be circular, isolated from the engine room, entered by a separate trunkway from the deck, and provided with a large ventilator at each end.

(3) All oil compartments are to be efficiently ventilated; the free escape of gases from all parts of the oil spaces must be secured by means of holes in every part, where otherwise there might be a chance of the gases being "pocketed." Special attention must also be paid to the effective ventilation of cofferdams, pump rooms and other spaces; efficient means are to be provided for clearing oil spaces of dangerous vapors by means of artificial ventilation or by steam. Where a double bottom is fitted at least four large ventilating pipes should be fitted to each double bottom compartment. The outlet and inlet of all ventilators above deck must be fitted with wire gauze protectors. Plans of the ventilating arrangements are to be submitted for approval.

(4) Pumping arrangements for spaces not intended for the carriage of oil, are to be entirely independent of the oil pumping system; the suction pipes in connection therewith should not pass through oil spaces; the pipes for the oil pumping system are not to pass through water spaces. Satisfactory arrangements are to be made for draining 'tween decks which form the crown of oil tanks. Plans of all the pumping and piping arrangements are to be submitted for approval.

(5) Cement will not be required on the bottom of spaces intended solely for the carriage of oil in bulk.

(6) Electric light is to be fitted throughout on the double-wire system. Switches and cut outs are not to be fitted in spaces where there may be accumulations of petroleum vapor or gas; lamps in such spaces are to be enclosed in air-tight glass globes and the wiring is to be lead covered where the insulation is of a character which is liable to injury by petroleum.

XIV

Oil Cargo

There are almost as many different kinds of oil as there are different kinds of dry cargo. Each oil has its peculiar properties and should be studied and handled accordingly.

Light oils which emit gas should be loaded with hatches down and plug hole open to admit of the escape of air. Such olis are generally carried as far forward as possible away from the fires. This also gives better trim conditions.

When loaded the things containing light oils should be screwed down at once.

As water is heavier than oil, a partly filled tank loaded with naptha or other light oils such as gasolene, benzine, or kerosene, may be completely filled by pumping in clean water which forces the oil up into the expansion trunk.

In discharging this sea water comes out first and care must be exercised to shut off the discharge at the right time, in a crowded harbor it may be necessary to send this water into a settling tank ashore.

Water should not be used under fuel oil, and with heavy oils carried as cargo it should be used only when no other safe method of stowage can be found. Use summer tanks for part tank load.

Oil cargoes are tested for temperature each day when the ullages are checked up, and this data is entered in the log.

Sounding. Use an ordinary sounding rod, chalked carefully. Let this down through the oil touching the bottom of the tank. On bringing it up, through light oils, the chalk will be found to have been washed off where the rod has been in the bottom water. This method will not work with heavy oils.

Another method of sounding for water is the use of the " water finder." This is a cylinder of brass about two feet long marked off in inches. A strip of litmus paper is fastened to the finder with brass sliding rings. Discoloration of the litmus strip shows the presence of water in the tank bottom, and this is measured by the gauge.

Flash point. The flash point of an oil is the temperature at which it gives off an explosive vapor.

The flash point of naphtha is 62 degrees F.

The flash point of fuel oil is about 180 degrees F.

These points vary and the flash point of any oil should be known to the master and officers of the vessel before loading.

Specific gravity. The specific gravity of an oil is the ratio between the weight of a cubic foot of the oil and a cubic foot of fresh water; where shown 60/60 it means that these densities are referred to that common temperature.

Hydrometers are used for this measurement. The Baumé-hydrometer gives the density of a fluid in degrees "Baumé"

Degrees Baumé and Corresponding Sp. Gr. of Oil, Lbs. per Gal., and Gal. per Lb.

Degrees Baumé	Specific Gravity at 60°/60° F.	Pounds per Gallon	Gallons per Pound	Degree Baumé	Specific Gravity at 60°/60° F.	Pounds per Gallon	Gallons per Pound
10.0	1.0000	8.328	0.1201	28.0	0.8861	7.378	0.1355
10.5	0.9964	8.299	0.1205	28.5	0.8833	7.355	0.1360
11.0	0.9929	8.269	0.1209	29.0	0.8805	7.332	0.1364
11.5	0.9894	8.240	0.1214	29.5	0.8777	7.309	0.1368
12.0	0.9859	8.211	0.1218				
				30.0	0.8750	7.286	0.1373
12.5	0.9825	8.172	0.1222	30.5	0.8723	7.264	0.1377
13.0	0.9790	8.153	0.1227	31.0	0.8696	7.241	0.1381
13.5	0.9756	8.125	0.1231	31.5	0.8669	7.218	0.1385
14.0	0.9722	8.096	0.1235	32.0	0.8642	7.196	0.1390
14.5	0.9688	8.069	0.1239				
				32.5	0.8615	7.173	0.1394
15.0	0.9655	8.041	0.1244	33.0	0.8589	7.152	0.1398
15.5	0.9622	8.013	0.1248	33.5	0.8563	7.130	0.1403
16.0	0.9589	7.986	0.1252	34.0	0.8537	7.108	0.1407
16.5	0.9556	7.959	0.1256	34.5	0.8511	7.087	0.1411
17.0	0.9524	7.931	0.1261				
				35.0	0.8485	7.065	0.1415
17.5	0.9492	7.904	0.1265	35.5	0.8459	7.044	0.1420
18.0	0.9459	7.877	0.1270	36.0	0.8434	7.022	0.1424
18.5	0.9428	7.851	0.1274	36.5	0.8408	7.001	0.1428
19.0	0.9696	7.825	0.1278	37.0	0.8383	6.980	0.1433
19.5	0.9365	7.799	0.1282				
				37.5	0.8358	6.960	0.1437
20.0	0.9333	7.772	0.1287	38.0	0.8333	6.939	0.1441
20.5	0.9302	7.747	0.1291	38.5	0.8309	6.918	0.1446
21.0	0.9272	7.721	0.1295	39.0	0.8284	6.898	0.1450
21.5	0.9241	7.696	0.1299	39.5	0.8260	6.877	0.1454
22.0	0.9211	7.670	0.1304				
				40.0	0.8235	6.857	0.1459
22.5	0.9180	7.645	0.1308	40.5	0.8211	6.837	0.1463
23.0	0.9150	7.620	0.1313	41.0	0.8187	6.817	0.1467
23.5	0.9121	7.595	0.1317	41.5	0.8163	6.797	0.1471
24.0	0.9091	7.570	0.1321	42.0	0.8140	6.777	0.1476
24.5	0.9061	7.546	0.1325				
				42.5	0.8116	6.758	0.1480
25.0	0.9032	7.522	0.1330	43.0	0.8092	6.738	0.1484
25.5	0.9003	7.497	0.1334	43.5	0.8069	6.718	0.1489
26.0	0.8974	7.473	0.1338	44.0	0.8046	6.699	0.1493
26.5	0.8946	7.449	0.1342	44.5	0.8023	6.680	0.1497
27.0	0.8917	7.425	0.1347				
				50.0	0.7778	6.476	0.1544
27.5	0.8889	7.402	0.1351	50.5	0.7756	6.458	0.1548

and this can be converted into specific gravity by the opposite table:

A temperature correction must be applied when the oil is above or below 60 degrees F.

For complete oil tables see Circular 57, Bureau of Standards, Department of Commerce, Washington, D. C.

Viscosity. Viscosity may be defined as the resistance to internal movement, or the internal friction of a liquid. It may be measured by observation of the ability of the liquid to oppose the movement of a body through it, or more commonly by noting the time required for a definite quantity of the liquid to pass through an orifice or short pipe under known conditions of temperature and head. In stating viscosity the name of the instrument used must be given, also the temperature at which it was run. Viscosimeters in use are the *Engler, Redwood,* and *Saybolt.*

The Engler Viscosimeter is specified for U. S. Navy fuel oil tests. It consists of an oil chamber, with platinum tube outlet, surrounded by water bath. For high temperatures an oil bath is used. The platinum outlet is 20 mm. long, with a bore of 2.9 mm. diam. at top and 2.8 mm. at bottom. A volume of 200 c.c. of the oil to be tested is allowed to flow out and the time is noted in seconds. The number of seconds required for 200 c.c. water to flow out at the temperature of 20 deg. C. (68 deg. F.) is then determined (50 to 52 sec. in the standard instrument). Viscosity is found by dividing the time required for the outflow of oil by the time of outflow of water.

Tank Barges are generally without summer tanks, except the largest ones in which the tank arrangement is like that of the power tanker.

Molasses Tankers. Vessels designed for the carriage of molasses have smaller tanks because of the greater density of the cargo. This is a special and restricted trade and is only mentioned here in passing.

Oil tank vessels are sometimes used for the carriage of molasses. To prepare for this cargo steam from 10 to 24 hours and flush with clean salt water. Clean corners and pipe lines. *Never use heater coils on molasses.* Keep all vents open.

To clean for oil cargo wash thoroughly with salt water. Do not use steam.

CHAPTER XII

PASSENGER VESSELS

I

General Remarks

The carriage of passengers is so important a part of sea trade that a special chapter is necessary for the setting down of the United States Navigation Laws governing the trade; and to outline the many duties connected therewith. Most of the regulations cover what is known as "Immigrant ships," and the officer in charge of vessel in this trade must thoroughly understand the scope and meaning of the law.

The regulation of a ship filled with several thousand passengers drawn from every strata of society calls for the most careful and circumspect conduct on the part of the officers. The Master especially is charged with duties calling for tact and consideration of the highest order.

The Passenger Act of 1882, with amendments, should be carefully studied.* Such matters as the number of passengers to be carried, the cubic capacity of passenger spaces, the number of life boats, life preservers, etc. are prescribed by this law and are certified to in the ship's *Certificate of Inspection.*

The Master will see to it that the limitations and requirements with respect to passengers are rigidly enforced.

Many other matters enter into the carriage of passengers that are not strictly matters of seamanship, but the whole question of *order* and *discipline* is one of seamanship, and in case of emergency, is of vital importance in the safeguarding of lives and property.

II

Station Bill

The following is taken from the Rules and Regulations of the Steamboat-Inspection Service, Department of Commerce, as amended to July 2, 1920.

* See U. S. Navigation Laws or *The Men on Deck.*

Station Bills, Drills, and Reports of Masters

It shall be the duty of the officer in charge of every steamer carrying passengers and all other vessels of over 500 gross tons propelled by machinery and subject to inspection to cause to be prepared a station bill for his own department, and one also for the engineer's department, in which shall be assigned a post or station of duty for every person employed on board such vessel in case of fire or other disaster, which station bills shall be placed in the most conspicuous places on board for the observation of the crew. And it shall be the duty of such master, or of the mate or officer next in command, once at least in each week, to call all hands to quarters and exercise them in the discipline, and in the unlashing and swinging out of the lifeboats, weather permitting, and in the use of the fire pumps and all other apparatus for the safety of life on board of such vessel, with especial regard for the drill of the crew in the method of adjusting life preservers and educating passengers and others in this procedure and to see that all the equipments required by law are in complete working order for immediate use; and the fact of the exercise of the crew, as herein contemplated, shall be entered upon the vessel's log book, stating the day of the month and hour when so exercised; and it shall be the duty of the inspectors to require the officers and crew of all such vessels to perform the aforesaid drills and discipline in the presence of the said inspectors at intervals sufficiently frequent to assure the said inspectors by actual observation that the foregoing requirements of this section are complied with. The master of every such vessel shall also report monthly to the local inspectors the day and date of such exercise and drill, the condition of the vessel and her equipment, and also the number of passengers carried, and any neglect or omission on the part of the officer in command of such vessel to strictly enforce this rule shall be deemed cause for the suspension or revocation of the license of such officer.

The *general* fire-alarm signal shall be a continuous rapid ringing of the ship's bell for a period of not less than 20 seconds, and this signal shall not be used for any other purpose whatsoever. The master of any vessel may establish such other emergency signals, in addition to the ringing of the ship's bell, as will provide that all the officers and all the crew of the vessel will have positive and certain notice of the existing emergency.

One copy of this section shall be furnished every vessel to which this section applies, which copy shall be framed under glass and posted in a conspicuous place on the vessel. (Sec. 4405, R. S.)

Lifeboat drill may be divided into two parts:

(a) Training of the crew of each lifeboat in the swinging out and lowering of boats, direction and stowing of passengers, use of oars and other equipment.

(b) Training of the entire crew as a unit in their duties when it becomes necessary to abandon ship. The efficiency of the crew as a unit can be attained only by frequent and thorough drills of the entire crew.

The duties connected with the stations for boats and fire may be summarized as follows:

1. Vessels over 500 gross tons, subject to inspection, or carrying passengers (any tonnage).

2. Must prepare a station bill assigning post and duty for every person on board in case of fire or disaster.

3. Bills must be placed in conspicuous places on board.

4. Boat and fire drill at least once each week.

5. Date and time of drill entered in ship's log book.

6. Drills to be performed in presence of U. S. Local Inspectors when required.

7. Master to make monthly report to U. S. Local Inspectors, stating date of drills, condition of vessel and her equipment, number of passengers carried.

8. Neglect of Master to strictly enforce above requirements of this rule shall be deemed cause for the suspension or revocation of his license.

The preparation of station bills differs slightly in different services. Where passengers are carried on large Transatlantic and Transpacific liners, the station bill embodies all of the requirements for safety. In freight ships, where the crew alone is to be considered a much simpler bill is needed, but the general principles are the same.

By assigning each member of the crew a station number, the bill need not be changed as men are discharged and shipped. Each man should be given a numbered bunk corresponding to his station number, if this can be arranged. These numbers should also appear against the name of the man on the ship's articles.

Fire Drill

The alarm of Fire will be the *Rapid Ringing* of ship's bell followed by 1 tap if fire is Forward, 2 taps if fire is Amidships and 3 taps if fire is Aft. All members of crew, excepting those specially excused on account of being on duty which cannot be avoided, must immediately proceed to their stations, stretch out the hose and otherwise see that the apparatus under their charge is ready. They must remain by same until further orders.

Men in charge of *bulkhead doors* will immediately close same and keep them closed until further orders.

Alarm blasts on the steam whistle (1 long and 4 short blasts) calls every member of crew (except those unavoidably on duty elsewhere) to the boat stations. The men must muster at their boats as quickly as possible and remain there, taking their orders from the officer or seaman in charge of the boat.

The ringing of the electric alarm bell means that for some urgent reason all members of crew must immediately leave their quarters and muster in an orderly manner on the lower deck awaiting further orders.

Muster List

The Muster List herewith assigns duties to the different members of the *crew* in connection with:

A. The closing of the watertight doors, valves, etc.	Carpenters, Deck, Engineer, Engine, Steward, Cabins.
B. The equipment of the boats and rafts, generally, to	Chief Officer and Junior Officer.
C. The launching of the boats attached to davits.	An Officer or Able Seaman.
D. The general preparation of the other boats and rafts.	Chief Officer and Junior Officer.
E. The muster of passengers.	Purser and Chief Steward.
F. The extinguishing of fire.	Chief Officer.

The Muster List hereby assigns to the members of the *Steward's Department* their several duties in relation to passengers at a time of emergency.

These duties shall include:

A. Warning the passengers.	Stewardesses.
B. Seeing that the passengers are dressed and have put on their life jackets in a proper manner.	Stateroom Stewards.
C. Assembling the passengers.	Chief Steward and Senior Assistant Stewards.
D. Keeping order in the passages and on the stairways and, generally, controlling the movement of the passengers.	Purser and Asst. Stewards.

The Muster List specifies definite *alarm signals* for calling all the *crew* to the *boat* and *fire stations.*

Boat Stations

1. Muster at stations. Put on life-belts.
2. See that the boat-falls are made fast.
3. Remove boat covers and boat-falls, pass out painters, and see that boat-falls are clear for running.
4. Cast adrift gripes.
5. Heave on boat-falls to take weight of boat.
6. Turn down chocks.
7. Cast adrift guys and heave out boat.
8. Man boat and lower away on both tackles.
9. Either lower boat right into the water or to the passenger deck rail to embark passengers as the Commander may direct.
10. When lowering the boat into the water, let go both boat-falls directly the boat touches the water. Release gear. The two men lowering the boat will slide down the falls into the boat as soon as she is in the water and the falls let go.
11. Where a second boat is to be launched from the same davits the second boat's crew will have her all prepared (cover off, gripes adrift, etc.) during the lowering of the first boat, and as soon as the first boat is away they will round up the falls and launch their boat.

Station Bill

Boat Numbers	Deck Department		Engine Department		Passenger Department	
	Boat Station	Fire Station	Boat Station	Fire Station	Boat Station	Fire Station
No.	Commander	In charge of ship	1st Asst. Engineer	In charge boiler room	Purser	Muster passengers and control dept.
	Storekeeper (A.B.)	Forward hand fire pump	Oiler		Surgeon	In dispensary
	Marconi Operator	Remain at post	Fireman No.	On duty remain at post	Stewardess No.	Warn passengers section
	Boat Handler No.	Fire station under the department you belong to			Steward No.	Bulkhead door section
	" " No.		Coalpasser No.	Off duty muster on lower deck	" "	Life belts in section
	" " No.		" "		Cook No.	Stretch hose in galley
No.	Quartermaster No.	Proceed to the bridge	Engineer			
	In charge Able Seaman No.	Muster under bridge	Oiler	Bulkhead door No.		
			Fireman No.	On duty remain at post	Steward No.	Bulkhead door section
	Boat Handler No.				" "	Life belts section
	" " No.		Coalpasser No.	Off duty muster on lower deck		
	" " No.		" "		Cook No.	Hose nozzle in galley

Note. Four pages showing part of a Station Bill are given here. Lack of space forbids publication of the entire bill. Study the Station Bill on board your vessel.

Station Bill—Continued

Boat Numbers	Deck Department		Engine Department		Passenger Department	
	Boat Station	Fire Station	Boat Station	Fire Station	Boat Station	Fire Station
No.	Licensed Engineer		Chief Engineer	In charge of department	Chief Steward	Assemble passengers, etc.
	In charge Able Seaman No.		Oiler Fireman No.	Off duty remain at post	Stewardess No.	Warn passengers
	Boat Handler No.					Bulkhead door section
	" " No.		Coalpasser No.	Off duty muster on lower deck		Life belts section
	" " No.		" "		Cook No.	Fire bucket fore square
No.	Quartermaster No. In charge	Proceed to bridge	Engineer	Bulkhead door No.		
			Oiler		Steward No.	Warn passengers section
	Able Seaman No.	Muster under bridge	Fireman No.	On duty remain at post		Life belts section
	Boat Handler No.					
	" " No.		Coalpasser No.	Off duty muster on lower deck		
	" " No.		" "		Cook No.	Fire bucket fore square

Station Bill—Continued

Boat Numbers	Deck Department		Engine Department		Passenger Department	
	Boat Station	Fire Station	Boat Station	Boat Station	Fire Station	Fire Station
No.	First Officer	Attend to stretching hose	Engineer		2d Cabin Steward	Assemble and control passengers
	In charge		Oiler		Stewardess No.	Warn passengers section
	Able Seaman No.	Muster under bridge	Fireman No.	On duty remain at post	Steward No.	Bulkhead door section
	Boat Handler No.					Life belts section
	" " No.		Coalpasser No.	Off duty muster on lower deck		
	" " No.		" "		Cook No.	Fire bucket fore square
No.	Able Seaman No. In charge	Keep promenade deck orderly	Engineer		Steward No.	Warn passengers section
					" "	Life belts section
	Able Seaman No.	Muster under bridge	Fireman No.	On duty remain at post		
	Boat Handler No.					
	" " No.		Coalpasser No.	Off duty muster on lower deck		
	" " No.		" "			Fire buckets fore square

Station Bill—Continued

Boat Numbers	Deck Department		Engine Department		Passenger Department	
	Boat Station	Fire Station	Boat Station	Fire Station	Boat Station	Fire Station
No.	Licensed Engineer	Carpenter to report to Chief Officer at fire	Engineer			
	In charge		Oiler		Steward No.	Fire extinguisher section
	Carpenter		Fireman No.	On duty remain at post	" "	Stretch hose section
	Boat Handler No.	Muster under bridge			" "	Hose nozzle section
	" " No.		Coalpasser No.	Off duty muster on lower deck	" "	Hydrant key section
	" " No.		" "		Cook	Fire bucket fore square
No.	Lookout (A.B.)	Muster under the bridge	Engineer			
	In charge				Steward No.	Fire extinguisher section
	Able Seaman No.	Muster on bridge	Fireman No.	On duty remain at post	" "	Hose nozzle section
	Boat Handler No.				" "	Stretch hose section
	" " No.		Coalpasser No.	Off duty muster on lower deck	" "	Hydrant key section
	" " No.		" "		Cook	Fire bucket fore square

N.B.—Captain will have Numbers of boats inserted in proper rotation; also the Numbers indicating the members of the Crew.

N.B.—Members of the Crew must recognize the man appointed to be in charge of the boat, whether officer or seaman. He must be recognized by the boat's Crew as being in charge.

General Instructions for Fire Drill

1. Upon hearing the signal for fire quarters, each member of the crew will take a station quickly, quietly, and without crowding or confusion.

2. Upon hearing the alarm, attend to your specific duty, which may be any of the following: (Rapid ringing of ships bell, see p. 375).

(a) Leading out and clearing away hose.
(b) Seeing that nozzles are coupled and secure.
(c) Opening valves to fire lines.
(d) Hand pumps clear for operating.
(e) Water tight doors closed.
(f) Fire extinguishers taken from racks and to stand by for instructions.
(g) Standing by with filled water buckets.
(h) Standing by with fire axes under direction of Chief Officer or Master.
(i) Standing by to assist passengers and distributing life preservers.
(j) Attending and turning on emergency lights distributed throughout the vessel.
(k) Starting fire pump under direction of engineer.

3. Attention is called to the fact that each master of a vessel may have individual ideas of the method of conducting drill and the assignment of crew. Also, it devolves upon each member of the force on board to learn thoroughly the method used on the particular vessel on which he serves and abide by the wishes of the master.

4. Upon the conclusion of fire drill—" Secure " is usually given by one stroke of ship's bell, and upon hearing this signal each member of the crew will stand by at his station for the " dismissed " signal.

General Boat Alarm Signal may be six short blasts of steam whistle or sounding on the siren.

General Instructions for Boat Drill

1. Upon hearing the signal for "abandoning ship," each member of the crew will take his station quickly, quietly, and without crowding or confusion.

2. Upon hearing the alarm, attend to your specific duty, which may be any of the following:

(a) Attending forward or after boat fall, clearing away same and making ready for running.

(b) Removing boat cover and casting off gripes.

(c) In boat and put on cap of automatic plug.

(d) Taking out or releasing boat chocks.

(e) Casting off forward or after guys after the boat is hoisted and rehooking after boat is swung out.

(f) In boat and bearing off when being lowered.

(g) Securing side ladder.

(h) In boat and casting off releasing hook lanyards or standing by releasing gear lever.

(i) Directing passengers and assisting in the distribution of life preservers.

(j) Casting off the lashings of life rafts.

(k) Attending painter of boat or raft.

3. Attention is called to the fact that each Master of a vessel may have individual ideas of the method of conducting drill and the assignment of crew. Also, it is encumbent upon each member of the force on board to learn thoroughly the method used on the particular vessel on which he serves and abide by the wishes of the master.

4. Upon the conclusion of boat drill "Secure" is usually given by one stroke of ship's bell, and upon hearing this signal the boats are hoisted, swung in and replaced in their chocks. The crew will then stand by for "dismissed" signal.

Miscellaneous Remarks on Duties at Fire and Boat Drill

1. If you do not understand your duties explicitly, request one of the Mates or instructors to explain them to you.

2. When leading out hose, see that there are no kinks.

3. See that the brakes are set on hand pump.

4. Do not invert fire extinguishers until ready for action.

5. Drain hose before coiling.

6. Be sure you know the proper method of belaying a fall and lowering away a boat by means of a turn on the davit cleat.

7. Proper method of adjusting the boat plug, and of handling releasing device should be understood.

8. Do not give commands to others but obey those given by the officer in charge of your fire squad or in charge of your particular boat.

9. If a signal is heard by you, quickly determine if fire or boat alarm.

The reader is referred to the chapters on Boats and on Handling a Steamer for further consideration of Fire, Abandoning ship, Collision, etc.

III

Baggage

The stowage of passenger baggage, marked " Not Wanted On Voyage " is a special duty and generally devolves upon the supervision of one of the officers who is designated " baggage officer," and has general charge of the baggage hold or trunk. In the S.S. *St. Louis*, during her prime as a passenger carrier, this duty fell to the Senior Second Officer, and such baggage was stowed in a deep trunk hatch filling up the space above the specie room. To get at the treasure it was first necessary to hoist out a thousand trunks or so. A special king post rig was available for hoisting this baggage out quickly and on approaching port, in fine weather, the greater part of it was got up on deck before coming alongside. It was then slid down on the dock for customs inspection on long skids.

IV

Mails

Mail steamers on Transatlantic and Transpacific routes are usually vessels of the first class and the handling of mail is placed under the supervision of one of the junior officers who has his station at the mail hatch on the day of sailing. Mail usually comes on board at the last moment and must be checked with great care. The sea post officer of the postal department, who travels with the vessel, where one is carried, is directly responsible and signs for the mail, having charge of it during the passage. In the Transatlantic Service the foreign mail bound for America is sorted during the passage across in the ship's post office, under the direction of this officer.

Ship's officers are responsible for the quick dispatch over the side, and should have charge of the slinging and handling of the mail sacks on deck. Where mail is being discharged into a mail boat, care should be taken to have nets under the slings.

V

Specie

Most first-class vessels have a specie room and from time to time transport great quantities of gold and silver. This is specially so of vessels in the Transatlantic Trade. The specie room is a strong box located near the bottom of the vessel. A good plan is to locate this room at the bottom of a trunk hatch, and after the specie is on board fill the hatch with the baggage not wanted on voyage. This makes it impossible to get at the treasure without hoisting out the entire cargo of baggage.

In slinging specie use a wire net, and have a stout treasure net suspended under the gangway.

Silver comes in pigs and is usually slid down wooden skids.

Gold is generally carried in kegs and should be slung in nets.

The ship's Purser usually signs for the specie himself. The Master, however, is directly responsible and where specie is carried should satisfy himself that all necessary precautions are being taken.

VI

Recent sea fires, *Georges Philippar* and *Morro Castle*, have resulted in stringent *fire patrol* regulations. None of these precautions can take the place of rigid fire drills and the readiness of all fire fighting equipment. The handling of a steamer, on fire, calls for quick action—SOS *at once*—and judgment as to disposition of all passengers in boats or on board.

CHAPTER XIII

BOATS

I

General—Types of Construction

For many years the small boat carried by merchant vessels was subject to neglect. Vessels went on long voyages with their boats bottom up lashed to skids, or perhaps the long boat was used as a convenient place for the chicken coop with its attendant filth. Tramp steamers worried around the world with boats sinking into their chocks and falls stiff and burned by smoke and sun or smeared with paint. Few merchant men knew how to pull an oar and the lowering and hoisting of boats in a seaway was seldom attempted. On many passenger lines boat stations were held in port while no passengers were on board as such reminders of possible disaster were supposed to have a bad effect on timid people.

These conditions were gradually amended* until the years of the World War when the importance of boats and boat equipment was driven home to all concerned. At the present time the importance of life boat equipment is better understood but much remains to be done to perfect boat, handling, rigging, and care. The writer feels strongly on the matter of boat work and would like to see standard sail equipment adopted, not just merely " sails." He would also like to see each vessel of the merchant service fitted with at least two handy rowing and sailing boats in which the officers and men might practice sailing during their off duty hours in foreign ports. There is no finer sport, and no greater opportunity for attaining perfection in this art.

Much is said in these pages about " efficiency," " turn round," etc. But the comfort and good will of the crew is an

* The International Conference on Safety of Life at Sea was held in London, Nov. 12, 1913, to Jan. 20, 1914. Boat conditions were thoroughly discussed and the present regulations were drawn up. (See Rules of U. S. Steamboat-Inspection Service.)

important factor in any scheme of enlightened management. When this can be added to and safety increased through practically no added expense, why not provide at least one *real* sailing boat? With one or two boats fit for sailing and rowing, the merchantman will approach the wisdom of the man-of-war where all work and no play has long been a thing of the past.

Boats may be conveniently classified with regard to their construction as follows:

Boats built of wood—	Boats built of metal—
Clinker built	Pressed from a single sheet
Carvel built	Built of strakes, riveted
Diagonal built	Crimped
	Welded or soldered.

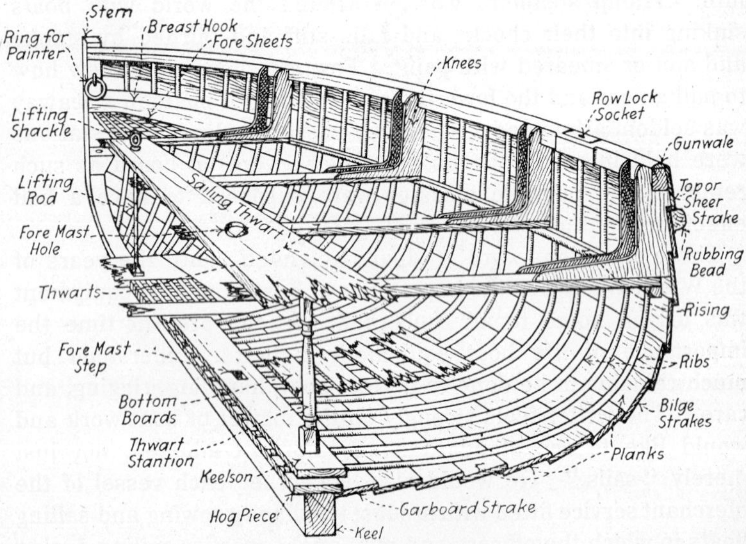

Section of a clinker-built boat.

Clinker-built. The planking is generally thin with the lower edge of the plank overlapping the upper edge of the plank next below, like the clapboards on a frame house. The edges are securely fastened together with copper rivets, plank to plank, and with longer rivets, planks to frames. It is a very light form of construction, flexible, and surprisingly strong. Small boats, wherries, dinghies, etc., are constructed on this principle. Many Class 1 lifeboats are so constructed, heavier planks being used for larger boats. The illustration shows the parts of the boat hull, corresponding in a general way to the structure of large wooden vessels.

Clinker built life boats, resting in smooth chocks, are often fitted with outside filling pieces in the wake of chocks. These bring the outside surface of the boat smooth against the chocks and prevent damage to the edges of the planking. Filing pieces are about a foot long and are smoothed down fore and aft.

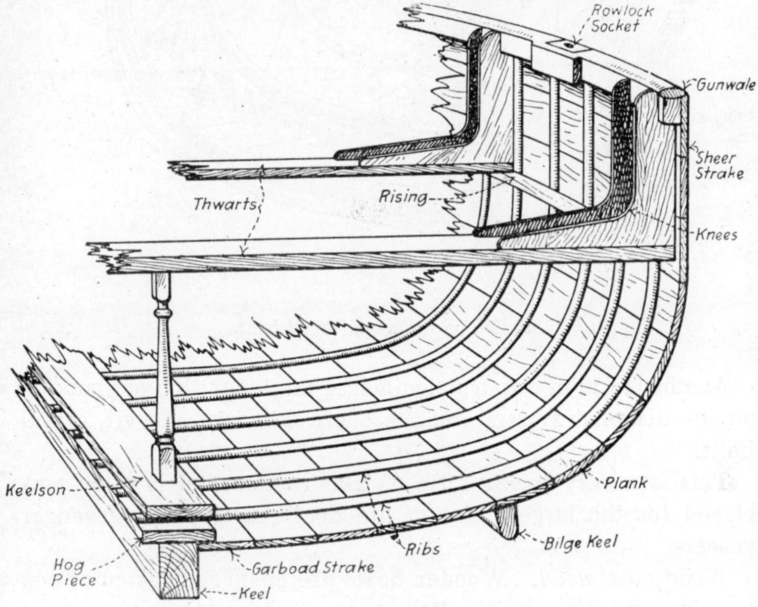

Section of a carvel-built boat.

Carvel-built. Here the planking lies flush, edge to edge and is made watertight by caulking. The planks are generally thicker, framing heavier, and boats of larger size. Whaleboats, cutters, and launches, are of this type of construction.

Diagonal-built boats. In this form of construction two layers of planking are worked in from the keel to the gunwale, striking away from the keel at an angle of forty-five degrees, the inner layer generally running from the keel aft, and the outer layer form the keel forward, the two layers crossing each other. A layer of waterproof fabric is laid between the planks.

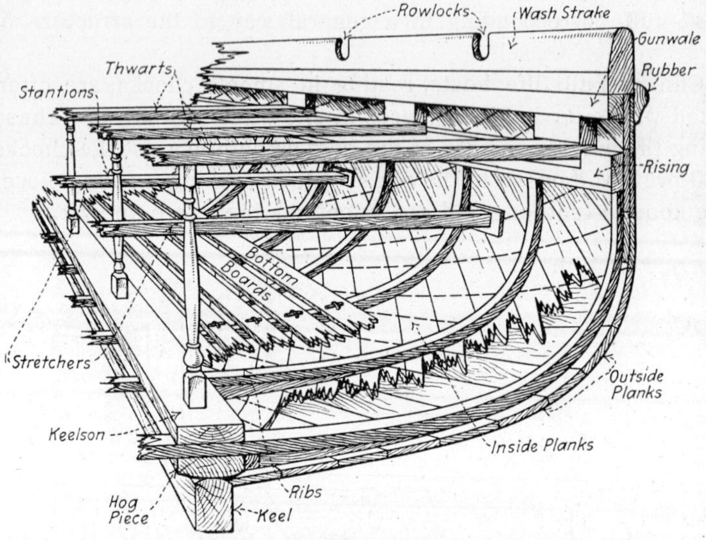

Section of a diagonal-built boat.

Another form of construction places the inner skin of planking on the diagonal system and the outer skin fore and aft, carvel built.

This is a very strong form of construction and is often employed for the largest size of life boats carried by passenger vessels.

Wood most used. Wooden boats are best constructed of *oak framing* and *long leaf yellow pine planking*, though a great variety of other woods are employed. *Mahogany* is used for some construction, is very durable and little effected by weather or wet. *Teak* is also an excellent wood for boat building, both teak and mahogany being employed as planking on *rock elm* or *oak* framing.

Where vessels trade in tropical climates, the teak or mahogany built boat is an economy because of its greater life.

Balsa wood is used for fenders and rafts. It is lighter than cork, and has many advantages for boat and raft construction.

Metal boats. These are generally life boats of the first class, large double ended deep bodied boats with high straight sides fitted with the required air chambers, and sometimes with high floors, over tanks, and self-bailing valves.

Open steel lifeboat, curved keel, reinforced type, equipped with power.

The metal boat is a necessity but not a thing to grow enthusiastic over. Like the boats with collapsible sides, and the pontoon rafts, it is something to cling to in time of disaster but a clumsy craft for sailing or rowing. The metal power life boat, however, is a very able boat.

II

The Parts of a Small Boat

Apron. Fitted inside of and strengthening the stem and sternpost.

Backboard. The piece of wood fitting across the stern sheets, literally a " backboard."

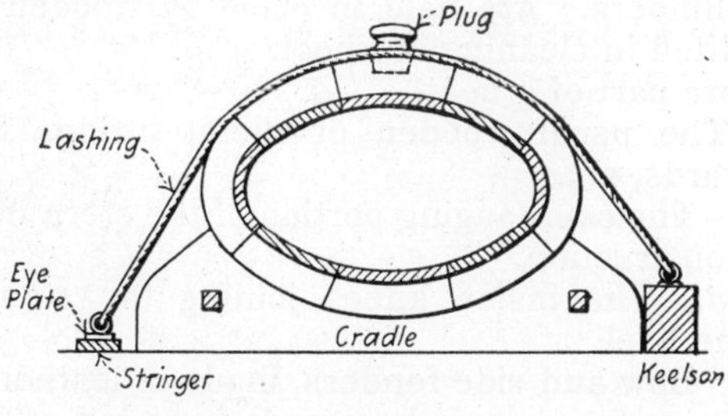

Water breaker. Method of carrying.

Barricoes. Also called " breakers." The small casks resting on cradels on the bottom boards and fitting under the thwarts. Used for carrying fresh water. Should be inspected each passage and water changed. Also should be fitted with a good spigot to avoid spilling, or with a leather *lip* at the bung.

Bilge. Flat part of bottom on either side of keel—extending to where frames turn upward, or " the turn of the bilge."

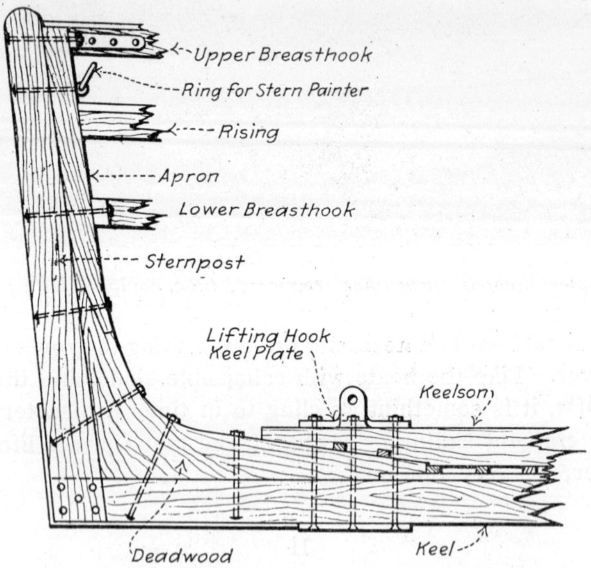

Framing at after part of a wooden boat.

Boomkin. Small boom projecting over the stern. Carries a lead block through which the mizzen sheet is rove. The boomkin should rig in and out.

Bottom boards. Loose boards fitted next the keelson. Correspond to limbers. Are held in place by wooden " buttons." Should be lifted in cleaning out boat.

Bow. Fore part of a boat.

Cleats. The usual wooden or metal fittings for belaying sheets, halyards, etc.

Counter. The overhanging portion of the stern in a square or oval stern construction.

Deadwood. The inside knees joining the stem and stern posts and the keel.

Fenders. Bow and side fenders, made of leather and stuffed with oakum, or of cork or balsa wood, and used as added buoyancy.

Floors. The inside planking running over the ribs.

Frames. The transverse timbers of a boat.

Garboard strake. The strake of plank on either side, next to the keel.

Gripes. These fittings are not exactly part of the boat, being long strips of sword mat, or roped canvas fitted with eyes and

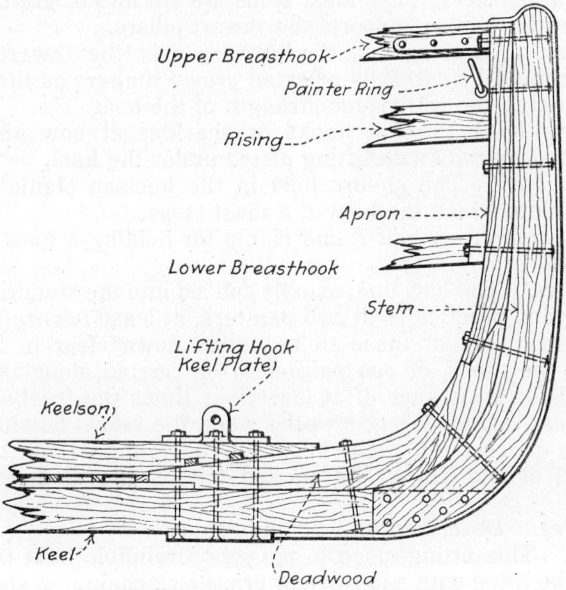

Framing at fore part of a wooden boat.

tails and used for griping boats into the strongback when swung outboard at sea. Gripes are fitted with a slip toggle for quick releasing. Iron clamps, chain and turnbuckles, fitted with releasing hooks are used for boats resting in chocks.

Gudgeons. The eyes on the stern post for the reception of the *pintles* on the rudder. Pintles and gudgeons form the hinge upon which the rudder swings. The lower pintle should be an inch *longer* than the upper one. In many boats the gudgeons are really on the rudder, being split rings, shipping over a bulb on the stern and swinging through suitable openings near the top and bottom of this bulb. This is easy to ship but not very reliable.

Gunwale. The " gunnell." The top strake of a boat, generally a square section, rounded on the outside with a rubbing streak, and fitting over the top ends of the framing. The built up or " box " gunwale is often used.

Head sheets. The small platform forward of the foremost thwart.

Hood ends. The ends of planking where same enters rabbets and is nailed to stem and stern posts.

Keel. The timber upon which the framing is erected.

Keelson board. The board covering the framing ends where they join the keel. The mast steps are cut into or are bolted to this board. It also supports the thwart pillars.

Knees. Fitted against the timbers over the thwarts. The knees should be carefully selected *grown* timbers as they add a great deal to the transverse strength of the boat.

Lifting hooks. Stout hooks or shackles at bow and stern connected by rods with lifting plates under the keel.

Mast step. The *square* hole in the keelson plank, or in a casting, into which the heel of a mast steps.

Mast clamp. A half-round clamp for holding a mast against a thwart.

Painter. The bow line, usually spliced into the stem ring bolt. It is a good practice to fit two painters, at least *twenty fathoms* in length. One of these to be coiled down clear in the fore sheets, the other, or *sea painter* to be carried along the deck, forward for a distance of at least four times the freeboard and *made fast.* If boats are lowered when the vessel has headway, the sea painter will help keep the boat under control. Sea painters should always be carried out on the emergency life boats.

Pintles. Described under " gudgeons."

Plug. This fitting, used to plug the drainhole next the keel, should be fitted with a lanyard of brass jack chain. A spare plug should be carried. Plug is always removed when a boat is hoisted, and inserted *before* lowering. In metal boats automatic check valves are used.

Poppets. The filling pieces used in cutters where box rowlocks are cut into the gunwale.

Rabbet. The groove in the stem and sternposts into which the hood ends fit.

Releasing gear. The special arrangements of hooks, cams, toggles, etc., by which a boat is released from her falls when waterbourn or near the water.

Rising. The narrow stringers on either side upon which the thwarts rest, also called *Wales.*

Rowlocks. The forked metal pieces in which the oars work while pulling. These are fitted to sockets in the gunwale and the ends should be fitted with chain or rope lanyards. Sunken rowlocks are those where boxes are cut into the gunwale, the forward side concave to prevent the lifting of the oars.

Rudder. The steering board hinged on the sternpost by pintles and gudgeons.

Sheer. The sweeping curve of the gunwale when compared with the straight waterline; low amidship, high at bow and stern.

Sheer strake. The upper strake just under the gunwale.

Slings. Chain and wire spans passing through ring bolts at top of stem and sternpost and down to link or lifting plates on the keel. *Steadying lines* run from the center of the slings to each side at the gunwale. A rig used in hoisting with a single davit.

Stem. The foremost timber in the framing of a boat.

Steering rowlock. A large swivel rowlock, mounted on a crutch with horizontal pivots, while crutch ships in a socket on the gunwale near the sternpost. Made to take a long steering oar, which should be fitted with a trailing line to prevent loss of oar if let go.

Sternfast. An after painter.

Stern post. The aftermost upright timber in the framing.

Stern sheets. That part of boat abaft the aftermost thwart.

Strakes. The continuous fore and aft lines of planking or plating.

Stretchers. Pieces of wood running athwart ship and fitting into chocks in the floor. The rowers brace their feet against the stretchers when pulling.

Tabernacle. A wooden or metal frame running from the thwart to the mast step for guiding the heel of mast when stepping in a seaway.

Thwarts. The cross seats on which the oarsmen sit. When one oarsman sits on a thwart, as in a whaler, the boat is said to be *single banked.* Where the rowlocks are abreast of each other, and two men sit on the same thwart the boat is said to be *double banked.*

Tiller. This is the lever by which the rudder is moved from side to side. It is the fundamental steering device, the *helm*, about which so much is said at sea. In learning the handling of large ships by first mastering the secrets of small boats, the use and meaning of the helm or tiller is driven home. Therefore *Starboard* actually means something, for the man receiving and the man giving the order *see*, in their mind's eye, that the tiller goes to starboard.

This reversal of names (an apparent thing) comes down from the time when the master shipman, knowing that he wanted the vessel's head to go to *port*, called out *starboard* to the man at the helm or tiller, and said thickheaded mariner jambed the tiller to starboard, as he was told.

The small boat is a great thing for getting the fundamentals of the sea.

Trailing lines. Small lines secured around the rising and to the loom of the oar by an eye splice forming a slip noose. When oars are allowed to " trail " the lines keep them from running overboard.

Transom. The board fitted to the after side of the sternpost in a " square-sterned " boat.

Wales. The light stringers upon which the thwarts rest, also called the *rising*.

Wash boards. Canvas or boards fitted on top of rails to increase the freeboard.

Yoke. The thwartship piece of wood or metal fitting over the rudder head to which the yoke lines are attached.

III

Classes of Boats

The *International Conference on Safety At Sea** divided standard lifeboats in two classes—those with rigid sides, called Class I boats, and those with partly collapsible sides, called Class II boats. Both classes were subdivided into three sections, and these rules have been made part of the regulations for safety at sea embodied in the famous Seamen's Act of 1915.

As these regulations are a part of the navigation law, and are the basic rules for all American lifeboat equipment, they have been included in the General Rules and Regulations regarding boats made by the Board of Supervising Inspectors, U. S. Steamboat-Inspection Service. These laws and rules, made according to law, should be studied carefully by the seaman who must master the management and care of his boats. The U. S. Steamboat-Inspection Service supplies the U. S. Rules free of charge.

Motor Boats

When motor boats are accepted, the volume of internal buoyancy and, when fitted, the external buoyancy, must be fixed, having regard to the difference between the weight of the motor and its accessories and the weight of the additional persons which the boat could accommodate if the motor and its accessories were removed.

All ocean steam vessels of more than 2,500 gross tons carrying passengers, whose route at any point lies more than 200 miles offshore, shall carry at least one motor-propelled lifeboat as a part of their required lifeboat equipment: *Provided*, That any vessel under the jurisdiction of the Steamboat-Inspection Service may carry one motor-propelled lifeboat as a part of the

* See footnote, page 385.

required lifeboat equipment, but on vessels carrying more than six lifeboats under davits, two of such lifeboats may be motor-propelled.

The engine for such motor-propelled lifeboats shall be of a reliable internal-combustion type, and shall be substantially and permanently installed inside the boat. It shall be of sufficient power to propel the boat when loaded to its full capacity at a speed of at least 5 miles per hour in smooth water without favorable current, and shall have an endurance of at least 24 hours under the above conditions.

Lundin housed power lifeboat towing Lundin decked lifeboat and open lifeboat. Radio equipment on power boat.

The motor shall be protected by a water-tight inclosure, the top of which shall be fitted so that it may be removed when necessary, and there shall be fitted in the top a mushroom ventilator.

The motor of each lifeboat shall be operated under service conditions for a period of not less than five minutes once at least in every seven days in order that it may be ready for service at any time. Such operation shall be a part of the lifeboat drill, and the fact of such operation shall be made a part of the report of such drill.

All fittings, pipes, and connections shall be of the highest standard and best workmanship and in accordance with the best modern practice.

The fuel for such motors shall be contained in substantial tanks of seamless steel, welded steel, or copper, securely and firmly fitted in the lifeboat and located where the greatest safety will be secured, and the storage of fuel other than in the lifeboat using it is prohibited.

In computing the cubical capacity of motor-propelled lifeboats the space required for the motor and fuel shall be excluded, and in fixing the air-tank requirements the weight of the motor and its accessories shall be carefully considered in the calculation and allowance made for the extra bouyancy required for such weights.

Capacity of Boats and Pontoon Rafts

First. The number of persons which a boat of one of the standard types or a pontoon raft can accommodate is equal to the greatest whole number obtained by dividing the capacity in cubic feet, or the surface in square feet, of the boat or of the raft by the standard unit of capacity, or unit of surface (according to circumstances), defined below for each type.

Second. The cubic capacity in feet of a boat in which the number of persons is determined by the surface shall be assumed to be ten times the number of persons which it is authorized to carry.

10 cu. ft. per person

Third. The standard units of capacity and surface are as follows:

Units of capacity, open boats, type 1A, ten cubic feet; open boats, type 1B, nine cubic feet.

Unit of surface, open boats, type 2A, three and one-half square feet; pontoon boats, type 2 C, three and one-half square feet; pontoon boats, type 1C, three and one-fourth square feet; pontoon boats, type 2B, three and one-fourth square feet.

3½ sq. ft. and 3¼ sq. ft. per person

Fourth. The board of Supervising Inspectors, with the approval of the Secretary of Commerce, may accept, in place of three and one-fourth, a smaller divisor, if it is satisfied after trial that the number of persons for whom there is seating accommodation in the pontoon boat in question is greater than the number obtained by applying the above divisor, provided always that the divisor adopted in place of three and one-fourth may never be less than three.

Equivalents for and Weight of the Persons

In test for determining the number of persons which a boat or pontoon raft can accommodate each person shall be assumed to be an adult person wearing a life jacket.

In verifications of freeboard the pontoon boats shall be loaded with a weight of at least one hundred and sixty-five pounds for each adult person that the pontoon boat is authorized to carry.

In all cases two children under twelve years of age shall be reckoned as one person.

Cubic Capacity of Open Boats of the First Class

First. The cubic capacity of an open boat of type 1A or 1B shall be determined by Stirling's (Simpson's) rule or by any other method, approved by the Board of Supervising Inspectors, giving the same degree of accuracy. The capacity of a square-sterned boat shall be calculated as if the boat had a pointed stern.

Sterling's / Simpson's Rule

Second. For example, the capacity in cubic feet of a boat, calculated by the aid of Stirling's rule, may be considered as given by the following formula:

$$\text{Capacity} = \frac{l}{12}(4A + 2B + 4C)$$

l being the length of the boat in feet from the inside of the planking or plating at the stem to the corresponding point at the stern post; in the case of a boat with a square stern, the length is measured to the inside of the transom.

A, B, C denote, respectively, the areas of the cross sections at the quarter length forward, amidships, and the quarter length aft, which correspond to the three points obtained by dividing l into four equal parts. (The areas corresponding to the two ends of the boat are considered negligible.)

The areas A, B, C shall be deemed to be given in square feet by the successive application of the following formula to each of the three cross sections:

$$\text{Area} = \frac{h}{12}(a + 4b + 2c + 4d + e).$$

h being the depth measured in feet inside the planking or plating from the keel to the level of the gunwale, or, in certain cases, to a lower level, as determined hereafter.

a, b, c, d, e denote the horizontal breadths of the boat measured in feet at the upper and lower points of the depth and at the three points obtained by dividing h into four equal parts (a and e being the breadths at the extreme points, and c at the middle point, of h).

Third. If the sheer of the gunwale, measured at the two points situated at a quarter of the length of the boat from the ends, exceeds one per centum of the length of the boat, the depth employed in calculating the area of the cross sections

A or C shall be deemed to be the depth amidships plus one per centum of the length of the boat.

Fourth. If the depth of the boat amidships exceeds forty-five per centum of the breadth, the depth employed in calculating the

Steel lifeboats nested under Steward davits. Covered box for boat fall. Davit swung out by means of screw.

area of the midship cross section B shall be deemed to be equal to forty-five per centum of the breadth; and the depth employed in calculating the areas of the quarter-length sections A and C is obtained by increasing this last figure by an amount equal to one per centum of the length of the boat, provided that in no case shall the depths employed in the calculation exceed the actual depths at these points.

Fifth. If the depth of the boat is greater than four feet, the number of persons given by the application of this rule shall be reduced in proportion to the ratio of four feet to the actual depth, until the boat has been satisfactorily tested afloat with that number of persons on board all wearing life jackets.

Sixth. The Board of Supervising Inspectors shall impose, by suitable formulæ, a limit for the number of persons allowed in boats with very fine ends and in boats very full in form.

Seventh. The Board of Supervising Inspectors may by regulation assign to a boat a capacity equal to the product of the length, the breadth, and the depth multiplied by six-tenths if it is evident that this formula does not give a greater capacity than that obtained by the above method. The dimensions shall then be measured in the following manner:

Length. From the intersection of the outside of the planking with the stem to the corresponding point at the sternpost or, in the case of a square-sterned boat, to the afterside of the transom.

Breadth. From the outside of the planking at the point where the breadth of the boat is greatest.

Depth. Amidships inside the planking from the keel to the level of the gunwale, but the depth used in calculating the cubic capacity may not in any case exceed forty-five per centum of the breadth.

In all cases the vessel owner has the right to require that the cubic capacity of the boat shall be determined by exact measurement.

Eighth. The cubic capacity of a motor boat is obtained from the gross capacity by deducting a volume equal to that occupied by the motor and its accessories.

Deck Area of Pontoon Boats and Open Boats of the Second Class

First. The area of the deck of a pontoon boat of type 1C, 2B, or 2C shall be determined by the method indicated below or by any other method giving the same degree of accuracy. The same rule is to be applied in determining the area within the fixed bulwarks of a boat of type 2A.

Second. For example, the surface in square feet of a boat may be deemed to be given by the following formula:

$$\text{Area} = \frac{l}{23}(2a + 1.5b + 4c + 1.5d + 2e),$$

l being the length in feet from the intersection of the outside of the planking with the stem to the corresponding point at the sternpost.

a, b, c, d, e denote the horizontal breadths in feet outside the planking at the points obtained by dividing l into four equal parts and subdividing the foremost and aftermost parts into two equal parts (a and e being the breadths at the extreme subdivisions, c at the middle point of the length, and b and d at the intermediate points).

Marking of Boats and Pontoon Rafts

The dimensions of the boat and the number of persons which it is authorized to carry shall be marked on it in clear, permanent characters, according to regulations by the Board of Supervising Inspectors, approved by the Secretary of Commerce. These marks shall be specifically approved by the officers appointed to inspect the ship.

Pontoon rafts shall be marked with the number of persons in the same manner.

IV

Equipment for Lifeboats

Note: The lifeboat and raft equipment is that given by the U. S. Inspectors. It is more ample than that given in the Seamen's Act.

All lifeboats on ocean steam vessels shall be equipped as follows:

A properly secured life line the entire length on each side festooned in bights not longer than 3 feet, with a seine float in each bight.

One painter of manila rope of not less than 2¾ inches in circumference and of suitable length.

A full complement of oars and two spare oars.

One set and a half of thole pins or rowlocks attached to the boat with separate chains.

One steering oar with rowlock or becket and one rudder with tiller or yoke and yoke lines.

One boat hook attached to a staff of suitable length.

Two life preservers.

Two hatchets.

One galvanized-iron bucket with lanyard attached.

One bailer.

Where automatic plugs are not provided there shall be two plugs secured with chains for each drain hole.

One efficient liquid compass with not less than a 2-inch card.

One lantern containing sufficient oil to burn at least nine hours and ready for immediate use.

One can containing 1 gallon of illuminating oil.

One box of friction matches wrapped in a waterproof package and carried in a box secured to the underside of the stern thwart.

A wooden breaker or suitable tank fitted with a siphon, pump, or spigot for drawing water, and containing at least 1 quart of water for each person.

Two enameled drinking cups.

A water-tight receptacle containing 2 pounds avoirdupois of provisions for each person. These provisions may be hard bread or United States Army ration. The receptacle shall be of metal, fitted with an opening in the top not less than 5 inches in diameter, properly protected by a screw cap made of heavy cast brass, with machine thread and an attached double toggle, seating to a pliable rubber gasket, which shall insure a tight joint, in order to properly protect the contents of the can.

Food or Provisions to be Carried in Lifeboats

Food which produces unusual or immoderate thirst, such as corned beef, salt fish, etc., will not be allowed, under any circumstances, as lifeboat provisions.

When hard bread only is carried in the lifeboat, there must be provided in addition thereto at least 10 United States Army emergency rations.

The United States Army emergency ration referred to above shall be prepared in accordance with the following formula: 45.45 per cent. chocolate liquor, 7.27 per cent. nucleo-casein, 7.27 per cent. malted milk, 14.55 per cent. egg albumen, 21.82 per cent. powdered cane sugar, and 3.64 per cent. cocoa butter. Percentage of moisture shall not exceed 3 per cent.

One canvas bag containing sailmaker's palm and needles, sail twine, marline, and marline spike.

A water-tight metal case containing 12 self-igniting red lights capable of burning at least two minutes.

A sea anchor.

A vessel containing 1 gallon of vegetable or animal oil, so constructed that the oil can be easily distributed on the water and so arranged that it can be attached to the sea anchor.

A mast or masts with one good sail at least and proper gear for each (this does not apply to motor lifeboats), the sail and gear to be protected by a suitable canvas cover. In case of a steam vessel which carries passengers in the North Atlantic and is provided with a radiotelegraph installation, all the lifeboats need not be equipped with masts and sails. In this case at least one of the boats on each side shall be so equipped.

All loose equipment must be securely attached to the boat to which it belongs.

Lifeboats of less than 180 cubic feet capacity on pleasure steamers are not required to be equipped as above.

Additional Equipment of Lifeboats

In addition to the equipment already required in lifeboats, there shall be provided a hand pump with a plunger of not less than 2 inches in diameter, and a discharge pipe of sufficient length to reach clear of the boat's side.

Equipment for Life Rafts

All life rafts on ocean steam vessels shall be equipped as follows:

A properly secured life line entirely around the sides and ends of the raft, festooned to the gunwales in bights not longer than 3 feet with a seine float in each bight.

One painter of manila rope of 2¾ inches in circumference, and of suitable length.

Four oars.

Five rowlocks properly attached.

One boat hook attached to a staff of suitable length.

One self-igniting life-buoy light.

One sea anchor.

A vessel containing 1 gallon of vegetable or animal oil, so constructed that the oil can be easily distributed on the water, and so arranged that it can be attached to the sea anchor.

A water-tight receptacle containing 2 pounds avoirdupois of provisions for each person. These provisions may be hard bread or United States Army ration. The receptacle shall be of metal and fitted with an opening in the top not less than 5 inches in diameter, properly protected by a screw cap made of heavy cast brass, with machine thread and an attached double toggle, seating to a pliable rubber gasket, which shall insure a tight joint, in order to properly protect the contents of the can.

A water-tight receptacle containing 1 quart of water for each person.

Two enameled drinking cups.

A water-tight metal case containing six self-igniting red lights capable of burning at least two minutes.

A water-tight box of matches.

All loose equipment must be securely attached to the raft to which it belongs.

Stowage of Boats—Number of Davits

The minimum number of sets of davits is fixed in relation to the length of the vessel; provided that a number of sets of davits greater than the number of boats necessary for the accommodation of all the persons on board may not be required.

Handling of the Boats and Rafts

All the boats and rafts must be stowed in such a way that they can be launched in the shortest possible time and that, even under unfavorable conditions of list and trim from the point of view of the handling of the boats and rafts, it may be possible to embark in them as large a number of persons as possible.

The arrangements must be such that it may be possible to launch on either side of the vessel as large a number of boats and rafts as possible.

Strength and Operation of the Davits

The davits shall be of such strength that the boats can be lowered with their full complement of persons and equipment, the vessel being assumed to have a list of fifteen degrees.

The davits must be fitted with a gear of sufficient power to insure that the boat can be turned out against the maximum list under which the lowering of the boats is possible on the vessel in question.

The *Schat* davits, a Dutch invention, have their base tilted at an angle of twenty degrees. The heel of the davit is held by a friction brake made tight by the weight of the boat. The upper half of the davit is inclined. When the brake is released by a lever the boat swings outboard by its own weight. The boat will swing outboard against a fifteen degree list. With a twenty degree list the action is similar to the old fashioned davit on an even keel. This gear is finding favor abroad. For rapid and easy swinging out it is hard to beat.

Many rules have been made by the U. S. Board of Supervising Inspectors, Steamboat-Inspection service, and these requirements, as stated before, are always available at the offices of the U. S. Local Inspectors.

The main requirements of interest to the seaman, under the heading of ship's boats, are as follows:

Lifeboats and rafts shall be stripped, cleaned, thoroughly overhauled and painted at least once in every year.

Lifeboats and rafts shall at all times be kept clear for launching.

The complete required equipment must be in the boats at all times, *and nothing else*.

Boat davit falls shall at all times be ready for use, they shall be protected from ice, shall never be painted.

All boat davit falls on boat *not swung out during boat drills*, shall be cast loose and overhauled.

Note: Boat drills should make use of all boats in rotation,

A life boat drill. Steward davits. Boats carried outboard against strongbacks.

swinging out a certain number on each side at each drill, entering this data in the log for future reference. Give *numbers* of boats *swung out* at each drill.

All boats must be marked with a number, plainly painted on each bow in figures not less than three inches high. No. 1 forward on Starboard side, No. 2, forward on Port side, and so on aft. Odd numbers to Starboard; even numbers to Port.

All lifeboats must have their cubic contents and *number of persons* such boat is allowed to carry plainly painted on each bow in letters no less than three fourths of an inch high. This same information must also be plainly marked or painted *on top* of at least two of the thwarts in letters and figures not less than three inches high.

When these required letters and figures are *painted* on lifeboats they shall be dark on a light ground, or light on a dark ground.

Life rafts shall have a plate affixed by the builder containing his name, number of raft, date of construction, cubical contents, number of persons allowed by U. S. rules.

Each boat shall be of sufficient strength to permit it to be safely lowered into the water with its full complement of persons and equipment.

Certificated Lifeboat Men must be carried as required by law. (See *Men on Deck* or U. S. Navigation Laws.)

V

Special Types of Boats

Many special types of life boats have been developed and much thought is being given to improvements along this line. Devices to be acceptable on board U. S. Merchant vessels must first be " approved " by the Board of Supervising Inspectors who have formulated certain tests for the various kinds of boats and equipment. These " approved " boats and apparatus are listed in the publications of the Steamboat-Inspection Service and the fact of such approval should be clearly known before taking on board new devices.

The Lundin decked lifeboats. The Lundin boat has received similar approval being rated as a Class 1A boat. The section of the revised statutes dealing with this boat is given below:

Lundin decked lifeboats shall be accepted as equivalent to Class 1A lifeboats and shall be rated and accepted as lifeboats under davits, and may be placed in nests of two under a single

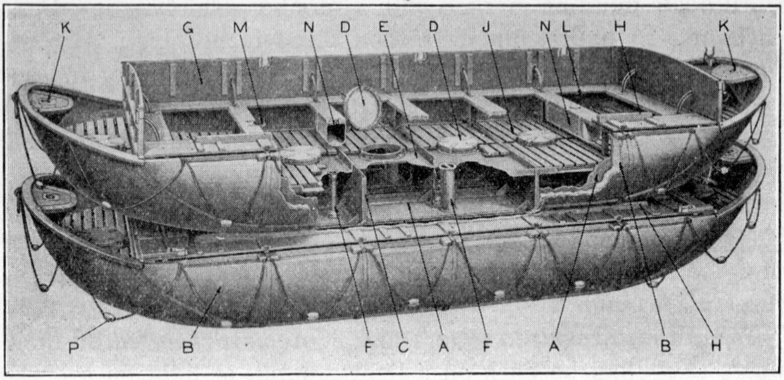

Lundin Decked Lifeboats.

A—Reinforced steel hull construction, steel keel plates.
B—Fenders, of Encysted Balsa covered with sheet steel.
C—Bulkheads dividing watertight compartments.
D—Manholes with watertight covers.
E—Self-Bailing Deck.
F—Scuppers with self-closing valves.
G—Folding weatherboards.
H—Wooden guards, chocking support for upper boat.
J—Removable gratings.
K—Mills releasing gear.
L—Handle and chain for releasing both Mills gears simultaneously.
M—Mast hasp.
N—Water tanks, with faucet.
P—Life line and floats.

pair of davits. They shall be fully equipped as lifeboats as required by these rules and regulations, and shall be measured in accordance with the following formula:

Cubic capacity = L × B × D × 0.9 cubic feet
Where L = length over all, in feet.
B = width over fenders, in feet.
D = depth from top of keel to top of gunwale, in feet.

Example

28 feet × 9.3 feet × 2.6 feet × 0.9 = 607.6 cubic feet.
Allow 10 cubic feet to a person, 607.6 ÷ 10 = 60 persons.

VI

Letter from Capt. A. P. Lundin

In response to a letter from the author, Captain A. P. Lundin, Chairman of the Board of the American Balsa Company, and inventor of the lifeboat that bears his name, very kindly has set down the result of his years of experience and study of the lifeboat problem. As vessels have reached a tremendous size, carrying thousands of persons, the problem of adequate lifeboat equipment and management calls for the most careful consideration. On a man-of-war, the whole crew are a well-drilled unit, while on a large passenger liner with ninety per cent. of the human beings on board unskilled, many very young, or old and feeble, and with women comprising a large proportion, the seamanship of boat handling that devolves upon the merchant sailor is of the most exacting kind.

It is "*women and children first, and passengers before the crew*" in time of disaster. The proud record of merchant seamen the world over attests the universal adherence to this rule of the sea. Captain Lundin's notes follow and will bear careful reading.

Although a great many improvements and new requirements have been made as regards lifeboats during the last four years or so, a glance at the average liner going in and out of any large harbor will suffice to convince one that from the viewpoint of highest efficiency and safety, there is still much to be desired.

The writer, whose business gives him ample opportunity to look over the various steamships, has often been impressed with the fact that the present method of stacking extra boats, such as flimsy wooden collapsibles with canvas sides, etc., in heaps on the deck, without systematic plan for getting them out, will make conditions worse, if anything, in case the ship sinks.

I firmly believe that efficiency in lifeboats on board ship, particularly in time of need, can only be obtained by an unremitting earnest study of the subject and by careful tests at sea, under conditions as nearly as possible like those prevailing when a disaster actually occurs.

For a number of years our company has carried on systematic experimental work, and briefly speaking, we consider that the whole problem resolves itself into these issues: *Lifeboats, Chocking and Stowing, Davits, Drills, Rafts.*

It is generally conceded that design, construction and tests of the ordinary open lifeboat presuppose favorable conditions, *i.e.*, smooth water and a normal or regulated load of persons carried; in other words, the ordinary

Boat Deck of S. S. " Olympic "—Welin Quadrant Davits.

open lifeboat has a certain buoyancy based on the principle that the boat will float, loaded to its full capacity and partly filled with water. For this reason an open lifeboat built of wood is required to have an air-tank capacity of 1 cu. ft. per person and when tests are made under normal conditions, viz. in smooth water, like in harbors, this works very well.

A metallic lifeboat is figured on the same basis, only with the difference that, being constructed of a material heavier than water and therefore sinkable of its own weight, the latter is required to have an air-tank capacity of $1\frac{1}{2}$ cu. ft. per person. Experiments and tests have shown that the stability and buoyancy factors are about equal in both types of boats. The trouble with both metallic and wooden boats of the standard type is that in most cases of disaster at sea, conditions are not the same as when such equipment was tested out. To begin with, even a moderately running sea becomes quite a swell when we are in a small boat, and in severe weather this is very much intensified. *Most experienced sailors know that small boats, if well handled and only moderately loaded, are quite safe, even in a rough sea.* The great trouble, however, lies in the fact that in most disasters at sea very little attention is paid to the rated capacity of each specific lifeboat; in other words nobody has time to ask whether a boat is rated for 30, 40 or 50 people. What actually takes place is this: Relatively few lifeboats are successfully launched and as many people as can possibly crowd in, pile into these, regardless of the rated capacity. Therefore, the comparatively small margin of safety in regard to the load for such open lifeboats, make them an unreliable proposition. Besides, even if the lifeboats successfully launched carry only the rated number of persons, many floating in the water will have to be picked up or will hang on to the sides and try to climb aboard, even at the risk of capsizing the whole boat load.

Then, when we consider a combination of abnormal load and a rough sea, it is easy to understand why so many lifeboats capsize, and the unfortunate part is that when such a boat is overturned, only the expert swimmers or those who have life preservers on, have any chance for their lives. In such cases the most able men or women try to crawl on top of the capsized boat and in so doing frequently right it again, but it is now half full of water and thereby the stability is still further greatly reduced so that it easily capsizes a second time and a third time, even with less than half the load with which it originally started.

Realizing all these conditions, we made a radical change in our designs which resulted in the Lundin Life Boats of three or four different types. In comparing these types with ordinary boats, we might say that by keeping the beam at the safe standard of about $\frac{1}{3}$ the length, we have a greater margin for stability, and our double bottom with its 3 to 4 cu. ft. of tank capacity per person, means a great deal more buoyancy than $1\frac{1}{2}$ cu. ft. tank capacity per person in ordinary open boats; moreover we have the added buoyancy and stability afforded by the fenders.

It is easy to see that our design increases the factor of safety tremendously. It has been our aim to construct a life boat which will not only take care of its rated capacity but *all the additional persons that may possibly crowd in.* Actual tests have shown that, with such an excess load, the Lundin decked lifeboat is a much safer proposition than the ordinary standard lifeboat with its normal load.

Of course there are a great many technical details covering this subject which might be discussed but I will merely keep to general principles.

It may safely be stated that it will take a tremendous amount of effort and weight to overturn a Lundin decked lifeboat. When a ship is sinking, it may happen that such a boat is overturned by hitting a smokestack, mast or spar of the ship, but if boats of the Lundin open type are overturned, they will remain so; at least, it will take just as much effort to right them as to capsize them. This is an advantage because the flat bottom will act as a raft, or refuge, for those who have been spilled out, and as many as the boat will hold, bottom up, can climb on without risking another spill.

Considering the lifeboat question as a whole, we know that a demonstration at sea, under actual conditions, will prove that a ship equipped with Lundin lifeboats for only *half* the number of people carried on board, would be far better off than one equipped according to the present method—*i.e.*, " boats for all," using all kinds of open and folding boats, placed all over the ship.

Chocking

Many ocean liners are so equipped and their boats so stowed that the possibility of being able to launch more than the outside and the upper of nested boats, is very remote. The lower boats and the inside ones are generally so chocked and griped down that it is not a matter of minutes but of hours before such boats could be released. In most cases boats so placed and chocked go down with the ship. One reason for this is that the lower outer boats in most cases are so-called pontoon boats, built of very light, flimsy material and not sufficiently strong to carry the open boats, without extra heavy chocks made up with the help of beams, stanchions, bolts, etc.

We have given particular attention to the chocking arrangement of what we call the Lundin system, which is based on the principle that not only the first boat shall be launched with as little effort and delay as possible, but also that the lower boat or boats will be readily accessible and can be swung out and lowered in the same manner; if the time should not be sufficient to launch the second boat, it will still be possible to make use of it by quickly releasing the gripes so that it will float off when the decks are awash.

This question of chock and gripe release arrangement in the Lundin system is a matter which you would fully appreciate if, when taking this subject under consideration you would first go on board some of the transatlantic liners and look at the way boats are fastened down, and then compare these methods with our chocking and releasing system.

Davits

The davit proposition has been considered a problem by itself, but this should not be so because it is simply a part of the lifeboat system and in order to make the lifeboat equipment really useful in time of need, the best possible davit equipment is imperative. I shall not here discuss the relative merits of davits.

What I wish to consider particularly is the arrangement of davits on board ship.

If you will go into this question, I am sure you will agree that it is preferable to have as many single-acting davits, instead of double-acting, as can be placed alongside the deck, and where necessary the boats nested two high, because in time of disaster it has been found that the boats most likely to be useful, *are those placed farthest outboard.* Therefore, I believe the principal advantage of what is called double frames is that by using such frames, sufficient longitudinal deck space is saved for one or more additional boats that can be placed outboard, rather than inboard of

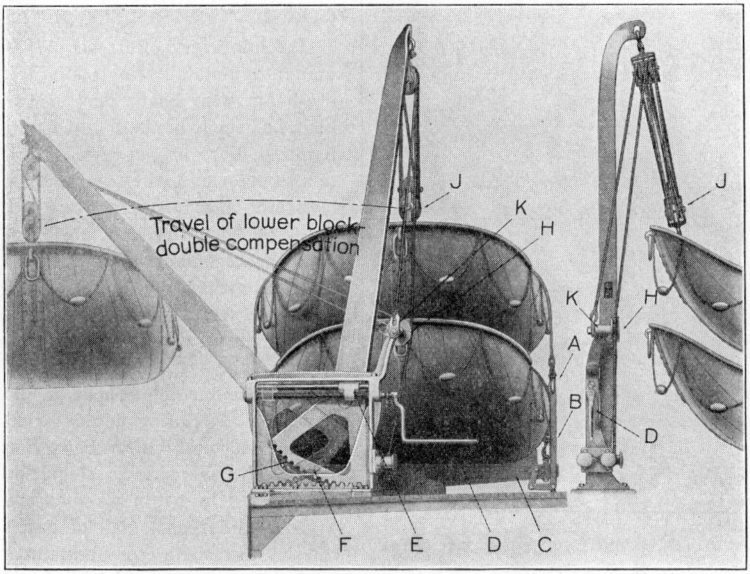

Welin Quadrant Davit and Nested Lundin Lifeboats.

The operation of this Lundin Lifeboat system is as follows (davit and chocking arrangement duplicated at other end of boats):

Release pelican hooks (A) and pull down levers (B) which through a connecting link tilt chocks (C) and the lower boat. This permits swinging out of upper lifeboat without hoisting. Davits are operated by turning crank handles (D) actuating travelling nuts (E) connected to davit arms. The travel of the arm on the quadrant (F) results in a moving pivotal point which gives a much greater outreach than would be possible for the same length of arm with a stationary pivotal point. The full weight of arm and supported boat is transferred to the deck through a flange (G) on the quadrant rolling in a slot in the base of the frame. The teeth of the quadrant prevent it from slipping. The falls run from lowering bollards over sheaves through non-toppling blocks (J). In the arrangement of double compensation the standing part of the falls is fastened to eyes (K); under single compensation, the standing part is fastened to the lower block.

other boats. It has been argued that by using double frames, there will be a certain lapse of time between launching of the boats, viz. where there are 8 units of lifeboats on each side with 6 double frames, it would not be possible to swing out more than 4 boats simultaneously; still I believe that practical tests will show it would be by far safer to sacrifice a few seconds and swing out only 4 boats at a time, than swing out and launch all the boats at once, particularly if there is any sea running and the ship rolling or pitching more or less.

I think every effort should be made to maintain single units of life-boats with boats one or two high, *i.e.*, single banked. In double banking there are always difficulties to overcome when it comes to launching the boats, and we still know of no better and more efficient arrangement to meet those difficulties than the double-acting Welin davits, although even this installation take considerable time before all the boats can be launched. More than one inner boat should never be allowed in double banking, the reason therefore being that in case of a ship sinking so quickly that as a rule not more than one lifeboat under each pair of davits can be launched, the remaining boats when only one high, can still be of service when released as the decks get awash. Of course, it is still worse when the boats are double banked with no mechanical equipment to launch the inside boats; this is sometimes the case on board passenger liners. *This ought to receive very serious consideration, particularly if a disastrous fire should occur on board such a ship.*

Hoisting and Lowering Control on S. S. "Olympic."

Each control unit serves two sets of Welin Quadrant Davits. Falls A and B lead to the two davits of the right hand set over sheaves at the base of davit frame. The boat is kept on an even keel by means of one equalizer, C, for each set of davits. The davits are swung outboard through crank handles operating the screws direct or through gears D.

I would state that there are a good many details about lifeboat equipment which might be considered of small importance, still—when it comes to a matter of life and death, and not only minutes but seconds count, very often the least friction or halt means much. I therefore urge ship masters and steamship owners to take this matter as seriously as it deserves and give due consideration to each and every detail. Such details as boat covers, releasing gear, gripes, boat falls, lowering bollards, and reels or tubs for the boat falls, etc., should be properly taken care of when the equipment is being installed, it can be done at practically no extra cost. A practical sea-faring man should be given supervision. I am sorry to state that there seems to be a disinclination to give these details sufficient attention.

Boat Drills

We must bear in mind that there is one important question in regard to lifeboat equipment which cannot be taken too seriously—and that is the boat drill, so that the men may familiarize themselves with the necessary

Three types of life boats:
A—Open steel life boat, standard type.
B—Broady class 2-A life boat—nested under standard boat.
C—Two Lundin decked life boats nested.
D—Welin quadrant davits with non-toppling blocks.

operations and in this connection I wish to point out that a great deal would certainly be gained if the various steamship lines would endeavor to standardize their equipment as much as possible, instead of fitting out each independent ship with different apparatus and different types of boats, etc. By standardizing such equipment it would obviate a great deal of unnecessary training of the individual men on each ship, particularly as the average sailor is more or less restless and often goes from one ship to another.

Another important question of the boat drill is to provide apparatus and equipment that will make the drill as easy as possible, there by encouraging the men rather than discouraging their actual efforts. For that reason provision should be made to hoist the boats after each drill by motor power instead of by hand. The best and most sensible way to do this would be to have one or two small electric winches on each side of the boat deck with ring bolts for snatch blocks to lead the falls to such winches. I do not favor independent controls for each pair of davits unless such controls are of the most perfect and up-to-date design which, as a rule, costs a great deal of money and also involves much expense in upkeep. Besides, whenever independent controls are used it is necessary to use wire instead of rope, and I am too old fashioned to look without a certain amount of suspicion on wire rope when used in connection with lifeboat work. It is all very true that wire is used very successfully not only in the operation of elevators and cranes, but also on board ship in handling cargo, but that is quite a different thing, for in such cases the wires are more or less protected or else stored away when the ship is at sea. Wire rope for boat falls is expected to stand a great deal longer than hemp or manila rope. It is also harder to see what takes place inside such wire falls when subjected to such severe conditions as on the high seas. Besides, I am absolutely sure that the wire ropes used for elevators, cranes, and cargo winches, etc., would not work anywhere as satisfactory if same were operated from the top deck of a ship on a stormy night out at sea, or in other words, under such difficult conditions as take place when it is necessary to abandon the ship. I foresee that lots of trouble would arise—there may be kinks, and the falls, as everybody knows, are apt to run foul and, of course, with the ordinary manila rope this could readily be taken care of by simply cutting the rope, whereas with wire rope it would be necessary to use an axe or to carry along heavy wire cutters adding further to the complications.

Rafts

Experience has shown that rafts may prove very useful on board ocean-going vessels, in the light of a temporary refuge, but if we look over the records of recent disasters at sea, we will find that whatever rafts were put to use, it was only for a comparatively short period of time. In most cases people who had been found floating about on rafts, were picked up by boats as soon as possible.

There are a few instances where rafts have actually saved lives but in those cases the disaster occurred close to shore and the refugees were not left to float about for long.

The main difficulty with rafts on ocean-going ships and liners is that people cannot be put on them before they are thrown into the water, *i.e.*, the raft is thrown overboard from the deck of a liner and perhaps a wave carries it a little distance from the ship. People with life-preservers properly adjusted, might risk jumping after it but, unless they could swim, they might not reach the raft when they landed in the water and only a strong, agile person—let us say a sailor, could hope to get on board and then, perhaps, could help others to get on if they floated near enough. In short the life-saving efficiency of rafts is entirely problematic and depends upon conditions. Where a ship sinks quickly, and hundreds of people are left struggling in the water with only life-preservers to keep them up, a few rafts floating about among them would be of great value, but so would any floating wreckage to which they could cling until picked up. However, where a ship is on fire, for instance, and *must* be abandoned before she sinks and the rafts can not be floated off but must be thrown from a high deck and the people to be saved on them must jump, or be pushed after them—it is doubtful whether this can be done successfully when there are women, children and old men to be saved.

It has been proposed to build very large rafts or detachable deck houses to take care of a great number of people. Of course, if a ship owner can afford to have special deck-houses made, or can arrange to stow rafts of enormous size in such a way that they could be launched before the decks are awash, this might work out all right, but deck houses as a rule must serve other purposes and therefore must have doors and windows and it will be very difficult to make these watertight when the deck house is to be used as a raft. Furthermore, very large units would be undesirable because if in a collision one were damaged, this would throw out a large proportion of the safety equipment. This same objection also applies to very large lifeboats, taking care of two or three hundred people.

Generally, speaking, I consider rafts useful in case of disaster in smooth waters, such as harbors, rivers or bays, and also out at sea, if it is calm and help is near at hand. In rough weather, those who seek refuge on a raft, will be washed off—unless they are strong and hardy *and the weather is warm*, so that the hands which cling frantically to the raft will not stiffen and lose their hold, and unless the rafts are scientifically constructed with considerable freeboard and stability in addition to the required buoyancy. This is very necessary, for when rafts are to be used as life-saving equipment, a great deal more attention should be paid to the details of their construction because *all life-saving equipment should be made as nearly fool-proof as possible.*

I believe that actual demonstrations out at sea will show that lifeboat equipment is indispensable and rafts are merely useful as a temporary refuge while waiting to be picked up by boats that are not filled to the utmost of their capacity.

I can not too strongly urge serious consideration of the lifesaving equipment on board ship. Let us take, for instance, one of the great skyscrapers in New York City, which is supposed to be built practically fireproof, yet no architect or constructor would dream of depending so absolutely on the fireproofness of his building that fire escapes could be dispensed with and no serious consideration given to means for getting the thousands of inhabitants out of the building quickly in case of fire or other accident. The elevators are of course the most important system in such a case and technical men and engineers give the most serious consideration to the problem of making this system as dependable as possible so that it can take care of most of the people to be removed from the building. Independent of the elevators are the staircases, and often there are ladders and platforms on the outside of buildings. In case of fire in such a building, the inhabitants are quickly and systematically removed to safety and nobody would think of staying in the building until the whole structure is on fire and then jumping out of a window into a net held by firemen—which is sometimes a last resort, but always risky.

Welin davits in action. Boats getting away from the sinking French Steamer "Sontay," torpedoed April 16, 1917. The "Sontay" sank in four minutes.—International Photo.

On board ship there is not only the ever present danger of fire but also the danger that the ship will sink, and therefore it seems strange that so many architects and shipbuilders did not consider lifeboats and floatage equipment of sufficient importance to give it serious consideration, although in mid-ocean the fire danger is much more horrible than on land, and the danger of sinking must be provided for also.

In time of disaster there should be no delay in starting the life-saving apparatus, people should not wait until the last moment before abandoning the vessel, and floating off on a raft, any more than they should stay in a burning building until the last minute and then all jump out of windows, no matter how many nets were spread to receive them.

More public attention to boats and boat equipment might make it fashionable, as it were, to travel on *safe* ships rather than in floating gilded palaces.

In these days of steam and oil, I know of no better exercise to train the seafaring man for all eventualities than the well-conducted boat drill. This is particularly desirable as we no longer have many sailing vessels on which young men who go to sea can be taught to become real sailors."

VII

Collapsible Boats

Collapsible boats are generally of the Englehardt type, a pontoon bottom with waterproof collapsible sides.

The following regulation with regard to the carrying of collapsible boats is issued by the U. S. Board of Supervising Inspectors, Steamboat-Inspection Service:

Capacity and Allowance of Engelhardt Collapsible Lifeboats

Engelhardt collapsible lifeboats may be carried as lifeboats and rated as class 2C.

When the Engelhardt collapsible lifeboat is allowed as a lifeboat, it shall be carried under the davits, with sides of boat fully extended, and only one Engelhardt collapsible lifeboat shall be allowed to be carried under one set of davits except that one nest of two Engelhardt collapsible lifeboats shall be allowed to be carried under one set of davits on each side of steam vessels of 2,500 to and including 5,000 gross tons, and one nest of three Engelhardt collapsible lifeboats shall be allowed to be carried under one set of davits on each side of steam vessels of over 5,000 gross tons, and when so nested the sides may be collapsed.

Engelhardt collapsible lifeboats shall be fully equipped as lifeboats as required by these rules and regulations.

The cubic capacity of Engelhardt collapsible lifeboats shall be determined in accordance with the following rule: Measure in feet and fractions of a foot the length and breadth outside of canvas extension and the depth inside at the place of minimum depth taken from the inside of the bottom planking of the bottom to the top of gunwale when extended. The product of these dimensions multiplied by 0.7 shall be deemed the capacity in cubic feet.

Special attention is called to Captain Lundin's observation on this type of boat carried in nests.

VIII

Radio Equipment

The motor lifeboat brings with it the logical use of radio equipment, especially on passenger liners where a great number of people may have to take to the boats and be shepherded by a motor boat. No doubt this will be " required " in the course of time. The radio phone, making possible direct communication by voice, in the event of a Morse operator not being in the boat, would seem the proper thing, assuming of course that the equipment is simple enough for an average person to set up and operate.

Kites

Captain Wilson-Barker, in his excellent book, "*Things a Sailor Needs to Know,*" cites the flying of kites from open boats by lads from the Schoolship *Worcester*. Kites may easily be sent up four or five hundred feet, flying signals, or even a light. Such kite equipment is easily designed, can be knocked down and put together in a few minutes. The writer has in mind the kites sold " knocked down " for a few cents: his small sons fly them. A really practical kite could be made with light waterproof fabric, and stowed in a tin case complete, line and all. Such a kite would give the boat, without wireless, a tremendously improved chance of being picked up.

IX

Boat Handling

Clearing away and lowering. The order having been given " *Clear away the boats!* " The officers in charge of boat sections will see that all men are up and at their stations, and that petty officers or others in direct charge of particular boats are at their appointed stations. It is well to arrange for whistle signals. *Avoid shouting.*

Under conditions of actual danger, when lowering boats, it is well to exercise the utmost caution. Unless the occasion is one calling for pell-mell speed, hold all sections on boat deck under strict control. Examine all boats carefully when cleared. See that chocks are down, gripes off, boat covers out of the way, ladders lowered, sea painters led forward (if under headway, or *aft* if making sternboard), that steady men are at their assigned places at the falls, and in the boat at bow and stern, with a cool hand at the releasing gear. See that boat gear is in order, *plug in.*

"*Swing out davits!*"

Have special care to drop life lines from the spans between the davit heads.

"*Lower handsomely!*"

"Avast lowering!" Boat has reached the passenger deck. Men in boat steady her at rail and take on board quota of passengers. *Women and children first.*

Mills releasing gear and Welin non-toppling block.

Never allow passengers to swarm up on the boat deck during this maneuver. Station men at the gangways to avoid this. Unless the vessel is actually going down fast, or listed so far over that boats will not come in to the rail, keep passengers away from the davits and falls.

When loaded:

"*Mind your painters!*" Take in slack of these, and stand by to pay out as boat goes down.

"*Lower handsomely!*" Boat is sent to the water, and released and turned over to the crew in charge.

Where one set of davits serve two or more boats it is necessary to round up on the falls, or hook other falls, or make use of those already hooked. In such work the greatest care must be taken to avoid fouling and confusion.

A vessel seldom goes down so fast that it does not pay to take time enough to do things right.

When a vessel goes down with a bad list, certain devices such as rollers and skids have been devised to enable the boat to ride down on the high side of the vessel. These are practical in application and afford a certain safeguard to the sides of a boat scraping over the skin of the ship. However boats should be of sufficient strength to withstand a good deal of knocking about in this fashion.

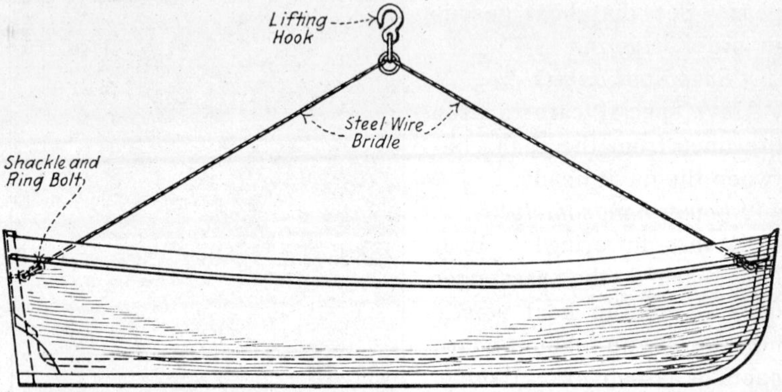

Slinging a boat by a crane or cargo boom. Always have a ring or shackle spliced or otherwise secured at the middle of span.

The lowering of quarter boats, and of running boats is a matter of routine and special precautions need not be assumed. Care should always be taken in lowering to have a sea painter out, unless in harbor, or in smooth water. With a high sided vessel this is most important as the releasing gear will cast the boat off as soon as water borne and she may drift away.

Hoisting boats. The hoisting of boats is less of an emergency measure, but calls for certain precautions.

See the davits steady, falls clear, and manned, or be certain that sufficient power is available on the winches to easily lift the boat. Have all hands but two or three come up over the Jacob's ladder.

"*All hooked forward?*" Always have them hook the forward fall *first* (unless under sternboard, then hook *aft* first).

"*All hooked aft?*"

"*Aye, aye, sir!*" From after fall. At once give the order:

"*Hoist away—lively!*" Have just enough slack on the fall to hook easily.

It is important to pick up a boat quickly when in a seaway to avoid getting it a foot or two out of the water and then having a big sea smash up under the boat, possibly with disastrous results.

Steward releasing gear, closed.

Steward releasing gear, open.

The swinging in and securing of a boat in a seaway is a good piece of work to test the seamanship of a crew. It should be done by way of practice whenever possible. Have life lines and buoys handy and hands stationed aft with a couple of buoys bent to heaving lines.

Oil. In all boat work in a rough sea the careful and skilful seaman will make use of his vessel as a lee, against wind and waves, when possible, and will also make use of oil to smooth the work wherever possible. With slow headway, oil sent through the forward pipes will help a wonderful lot in getting boats in and out of the water without accident. On long vessels oil reservoirs on the boat deck at sufficient intervals would not be a bad idea. When the boats *must* be used in rough weather the need for some such thing is always great, and the turning of a cock might work wonders, and save many lives and much valuable equipment.

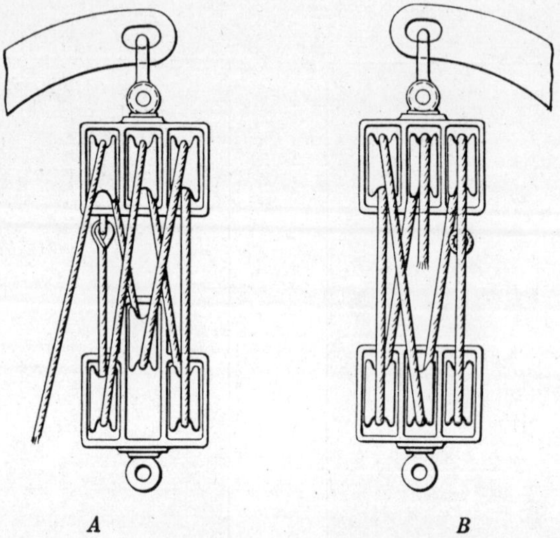

Two methods of reeving boat falls. A.—Non-toppling block. B.—Regular block. Note method of crossing falls in B, to prevent canting of upper block.

The Raymond Releasing Gear

The boat falls are rove off as a continuous fall so that as long as one end of the boat is suspended by the fall both ends of the fall remain under tension. This is very necessary as the *Raymond Releasing Hook* and the *Yankee Releasing Shackle,* both operate automatically as soon as the weight is taken off of

their respective falls. It is therefore necessary to reeve the falls as shown so that both hooks, or both shackles, whichever is used, are released at the same time, that is when the boat is fully afloat through her whole length.

This gear is especially useful for the quarter life boats.

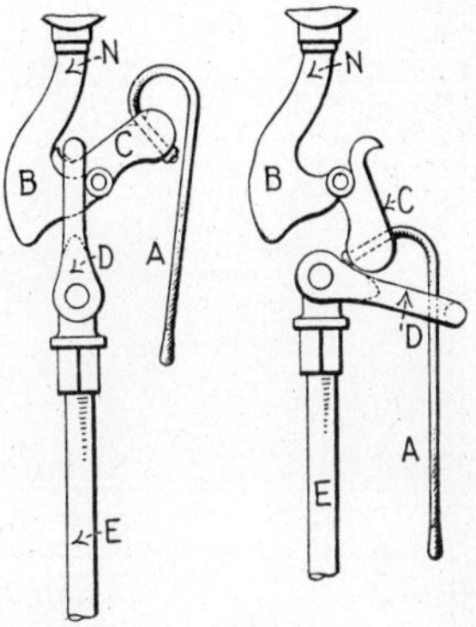

The Raymond Releasing Hook

The becket *A* is passed through the shackle *D* and the shackle rests in the turn of the releasing weight *C* forming the end of the hook *B*. The neck of the hook *N* is a swivel connection. When the hook is fast the becket *A* can be hitched about *N* for further security. When the boat is lowered, unhitch *A* and as soon as the boat is afloat the weight *C* falls, as shown in sketch, throwing the hook clear of the shackle. *E* is the lifting rod, shown with boat floating in the second figure and hook clear.

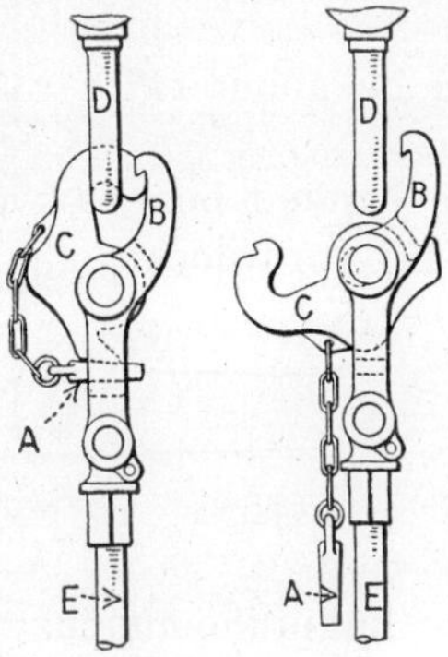

The Yankee Releasing Shackle

This works on the same principle as the releasing hook. When the weight of the boat is carried, shown in closed figure, the heavy side of shackle *C* is lifted up and engaged in the jog on *B* and held by the wedge *A*. In lowering pull out *A* and when *E* rises, the side *C* falls down, as it rotates about a pin on an oval opening, shown by dotted line in sketch, and the shackle on the lower block is released as shown.

X

Boats Under Oars

Oars. Oars are generally of ash. They should be of the best quality and carefully stowed in the boats. An oar improperly stowed will warp and take on a twist making it prac-

Boys of the Schoolship "Newport" out for boat practice in San Juan (Porto Rico) Harbor.

tically useless, as it turns out of the hands when pulling. The parts of an oar are shown in the illustration. In double banked boats stow oars blades forward. In single banked boats stow blades aft.

Oars for a double banked boat should be about twice the length of the thwart from which they are used.

The proper length of an oar for a single banked boat is two times the beam at rowlock plus the freeboard at rowlock.

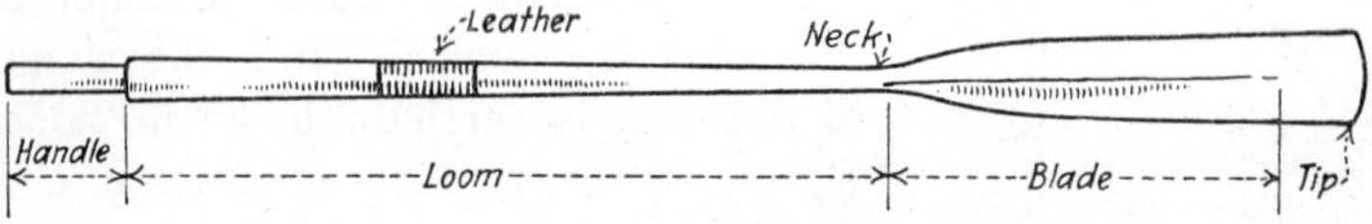

Rowing. Rowing is a fine art in the navy, but in the merchant service it is practically neglected, though the writer remembers seeing many fine oarsmen on merchant craft, men who were natural sailors and had mastered the art of boats in their youth, or through some lucky training. Schoolship boys are as a rule well trained in boat work. Navy seamen who are coming into the merchant service after their enlistments, many of them as junior officers, are bringing with them the splendid navy training in boat work. This should help to better standards and a better feeling with regard to boats and their usefulness.

Note. Some authorities refer to the parts of an oar as the loom (handle), the shaft (loom), and the blade. Mr. E. Scofield, Second Asst. Engineer of *S.S. Esparta,* United Fruit Co., calls attention to this point of seamanship. The Oxford Dictionary defines 'loom' as "the inboard part of the shaft of an oar." As soon as you put seamanship on paper such questions arise.

Rowing cannot be learned from books but the principal points to be observed are the following:

Rowing a whale boat. An emergency life boat crew. Half of crew are engineers off watch.

Sit square on thwart, facing aft.

Feet on stretcher, which should be properly placed. Many boats have two or three notches in the floor stringers carrying the stretchers so they can be shifted.

Hold oar with an easy grip, palms down. In whale boats many men find it easier to grasp the oar with the hand farthest from the loom, palm up. Some rowers in this type of boat swing the oar past the body; this looks good but don't help the boat through the water.

Start the stroke, blade of oar vertical, wrists straight body bent well forward. Lift handle dipping blade as the stroke begins, doing the pulling with the body.

End the stroke body bent back, and as the body comes upright pull it up against the oar, the last third of the stroke being due to this pull of the arms. This will finish the stroke with the body nearly upright.

Feather the oar at the end of the stroke. The elbows being down it is easy to drop the wrists as the blade leaves the water, and on the recovery the blade moves forward over the water with the upper edge forward, presenting no surface to wind or wave.

A whaler, finishing the stroke. Note the easy erect position of the oarsmen.

The whaleboat stroke should be as long and swinging as possible. An easy stroke with plenty of *beef* in it.*
The lifeboat stroke, corresponding to that of a navy cutter (double banked boats). Must be shorter due to the difference in length of loom in board.

A double banked boat. A ten-oared cutter. Middle of stroke. Note the " beef " on the oars.

In double banked boats oarsmen are apt to drop into a short nervous choppy stroke. Avoid this and keep stroke as long as possible. Lifeboats are apt to be very high sided unless loaded deep, and this should be taken into consideration in fitting them with oars.

* The *Gig stroke*, used to distinguish the boat of a commanding officer, is peculiar in that the oarsmen pause, for an instant, at the end of each stroke as their oars leave the water. It is a very tricky stroke and looks smart.

Catching crabs is a common practice, with some oarsmen. The oar dipping under on the recovery, suddenly wrenches from him, or the handle kicks ahead and knocks him from the thwart.

Don't overwork a green crew of oarsmen. Give them plenty of rest to start with. After a crew is seasoned it is surprising how long they can keep going without undue fatigue.

Fancy rowing is not good practice at sea. The feathering of the lower edge of the blade against the water is suitable for park lagoons and the like. At sea the practice is to bring the oar parallel to the surface of the water on the recovery.

Trailing lines should be fitted on all lifeboat oars as a precaution against loss when catching crabs, letting go, etc.

Sculling. Sculling is the art of sending a small boat through the water by means of a single oar over the stern or quarter. The sculler stands in the stern sheets facing aft. He holds the oar at the level of his chest palms inboard on either side of the handle, knuckles up. The oar resting in a stern notch is kept submerged and swung from side to side, alternately, by turning the wrists, the blade inclined, lower edge toward the side to which it is moving. This gives a continuous action like that of the tail of a fish. A little practice will give a man control of a boat by this method, the best for single rowing.

Japanese rowing sampans, carry their oars in crotches, the long sweeps trailing aft and the rowers working them from side to side as in sculling. These oars are very long and heavy and are constructed with an angle in the loom above the crotch, dropping the handle for about a foot on a long oar. The pushing of the oar outboard or inboard causes it to feather automatically. With five of these on a side a long sampan attains surprising speed with apparently little effort, the rowers standing, their bodies swaying from side to side.

The whole subject of rowing is one of fascination. We in the present day of motors are out of touch with the finer points of the great art. The ancient Mediterranean saw the galley in its prime, the *uniremes* of the Romans, and the *monêrês* of the Greeks, with only one rank of oars. Then came the *triacontoros,* with thirty men bending at the sweeps, the *pentêkontoros*, with fifty galley slaves sweating at the banks of oars. And in the great ship *Hiero*, built by no less a light than Archimedes, the ranks of oars were raised to forty, but the manner in which they were arranged has passed away with much of the ancient lore of Greece.

In the more modern galleys used in the Mediterranean from the 12th to the 18th centuries, oars were from forty to fifty feet long and were manned by from three to four men each.

But lack of space forbids more mention of these ancient things. Still, at any moment, the modern seaman may have taken his place at the oars, and a wholesome respect and understanding of this great tool of the sea is well worth while.

Steering. While all boats are fitted with rudders, still no boat can be properly handled in a heavy sea without the aid of a *steering oar.* The steering oar should be of selected ash, and for a long whaleboat it will be about eighteen feet in length. Handling a steering oar is a matter of practice alone. The operation is self evident. If a man is a boatman, has his sea legs under him, and knows how to handle the men who are rowing, he will soon master the use of the long sweep over the stern.

Handling of a single banked boat. The whaleboat is typical of this type. It usually carries six oars, the oarsmen sitting on alternate thwarts and on the side opposite the rowlock.

The smart appearance of such a boat, the fine quality of boatmanship to be attained through its use, and the extra ordinary buoyancy and ability of this boat in a heavy sea should make it mandatory on every vessel, two at least, one on each quarter, fitted as life boats for lowering in the event of a man overboard, or the necessity of going to the assistance of a vessel in distress.

The boat being lowered, see the men in their places, bow oarsman standing *on the bottom boards* (never allow a man to stand on a thwart), with his boat hook fending off the bow, all other men remain seated. Coxswain, at after thwart, with after boat hook. Tiller shipped, or yoke lines rigged. Oars are lying on thwarts, rowlocks are unshipped. The officer steps into the boat. Takes his seat, gets hold of yoke lines.

"*Shove off forward!*" Bow swings out, if there is current.

"*Shove off aft!*" Stroke oar (coxswain) gives boat a good shove with his hook and she rides clear of the ship's side.

"*Out oars!*" The oarsmen ship the rowlocks on the side on which they are sitting and lift the blade of the oars into these. That is, the men to port ship the rowlocks and place the blades for the men sitting to starboard. This prevents scrambling about the boat. Then each man takes the handle of his own oar and slides it outboard parallel with the water, and perpendicular to the line of the keel, blade parallel with the water. This is the position taken at the order "*Oars!*" when rowing.

"*Oars!*" A whale boat gig.

Boat being on the starboard side and wishing to go clear. "*Hold water starboard, give way port!*" the boat swings rapidly to starboard.

With a green crew it is well to give the command "*Oars!*" bringing all oars out of the water as before, and then the command "*Give way together!*" With a good crew and the officer watching the stroke, he can give the latter command at the proper time and start them off without coming to rest.

All commands should be preceded by the order "*Stand by!*" Except in close quarters where the whole crew are at attention and stand by orders may be dispensed with.

In approaching a landing or in coming alongside of a vessel at anchor, judgment must be used with regard to the strength and direction of the current, if any, the state of the sea, and the weight and carrying power of the boat. Be careful in making an approach to have the boat under complete control, do not come alongside too fast, if in doubt have the crew lay on their oars for a moment, then give 'way again if need be. Trail bow in plenty of time, and at the order "*Trail oars!*" the oarsmen allow their oars to trail, or if necessary, boat the oars, by giving the order "In bow!" and follow this by "*Boat your oars!*"

In coming alongside the bow and stroke oarsmen take care of the boat, get out the boat hooks and tend her at the gangway. The others remain seated unless ordered to do different. As soon as a boat comes alongside of a wharf or jetty, the oarsmen put out their fenders as they boat their oars.

To *point oars* in a boat is to use them on the bottom to shove her off if she is aground.

Some officers use the order "*'way enough!*" As a matter of fact it is simply giving information to the rowers and letting them act. The better plan is to give positive orders, managing the entire business from the standpoint of the officer in charge.

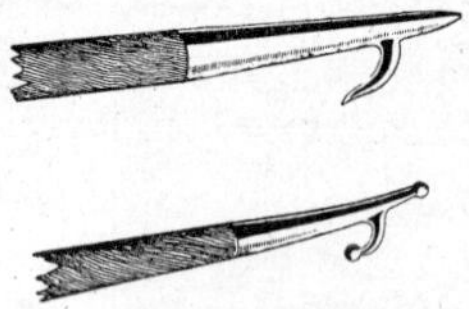

Boat hooks.

Handling a double banked boat. Here the commands are somewhat different due to the placement of the oarsmen.

Getting under way from a gangway or a wharf the procedure is as follows:

"*Stand by!*" Crew are at attention. The bow men take care of their painter or mind their boat hook, usually the man next the ship's side has the boat hook and his mate tends the painter.

"*Up oars!*" The men toss their oars, holding them upright trimmed with blades fore and aft, all oars being up but the bow and stroke oar next the gangway.

The boat is now ready, these orders having been attended to before the boat is so reported. Passengers then enter boat, lying at gangway with oars up.

"*Shove off forward!*" Bow oarsmen shove boat clear and let go sea painter, or haul in painter if boat's gear is used. After boat hook holds on a moment to give her a sheer away from the side if current is running. Then "*Shove off aft!*" and the after boat hook gives her a shove ahead clear of the side.

"*Let fall!*" The oars are dropped into the rowlocks in the position of "*oars.*"

"*Give way together!*" As soon as the bow and stroke oarsmen can do so they toss their oars, the bow oars *kissing* and let fall taking up the stroke.

In coming alongside the order "*In Bows!*" brings in the forward oars, the men toss and boat their oars, getting them in as expeditiously as possible. They then face forward with boat hook on side next ship and outside man ready to catch the gangway rope.

As the ship is approached lay on the oars if in doubt, but if certain of enough headway give the order "*Toss!*" At this command the oars come up smartly, tips "kiss," and blades are trimmed in line fore and aft as before.

"*Boat your oars!*" when alongside.

There are many fine points to boat handling under oars that can only be learned by constant practice.

Backing water to get sternboard, holding water, and backing and holding, or pulling and holding, enable the rowing boat to be taken into any place where there is room enough to work the oars. When running into a narrow passage as between boats in a basin, trail or toss, rather than to slide in the looms, as an error of judgment may cost you several oars besides looking rather bad.

Again be sure to boat oars properly. Blades aft in a whaler or single banked boat, and blades forward in a double banked boat. The reason is at once apparent when working the boats.

"*Stern all!*" that great command of the whaler, simply means back water. This should be preceded by "*Hold water.*" until the boat has lost her headway.

The following points should be kept in mind in handling boats under oars:

A laden boat holds her way much longer than a light boat.

In pulling across a current head up against the current and try to get a range on your required course.

In a river when pulling against the main stream, hug shore where current is liable to be less.

In a motor boat get compass bearing of ship or shore, *with boat headed on course.* This will take care of any deviation.

Do not go alongside of a vessel having sternboard, or when she is backing her engines.

In boarding a vessel, especially a man-of-war, have your boat pull off and lay clear of the gangway. If you will be on board for some time, ask permission to have your boat hauled out to the boom. When about to leave ask to have your boat brought to the gangway.

XI

Running Out A Line

The following from " The Deck and Boat Book " of the U. S. Navy summarizes what is to be said about this important use of boats:

1. Coil the greater part of the line in the stern sheets, but take end enough in the bow to make fast when you reach the landing. Pull away and let the ship pay out more line until you are sure of having enough in the boat to reach, then pay out from the boat. Always have plenty of good seizing stuff for making all secure, and if you are to stand by the line, have an ax ready for cutting in case you are ordered to do so.

2. If laying out with the tide, take less line in the boat than otherwise. If against the side, it will save work to take all the line in the boat, pull up and make fast, then bring the end back to the ship. With a long line to be laid out in a strong current, it will usually be necessary to have several boats—one to run away with the end, the other to underrun the line at intervals, floating it and pulling upstream with the bight.

3. If the line is to be secured to a post, put a bowline in the end before starting and throw this over the post. Bend on a heaving line and let the bow oarsman throw this, if hands are standing by to receive it, or jump ashore with it himself if necessary.

XII

Management of Open Boats in a Surf

The following rules on the management of open boats in a surf have long been accepted as standard practice:

Rules of the *Royal National Lifeboat Institution,* of *Great Britain*, on the Management of Open Rowing Boats in a Surf; Beaching Them, Etc.

In Rowing to Seaward

As a general rule, speed must be given to a boat rowing against a heavy surf.

Indeed, under some circumstances, her safety will depend on the utmost possible speed being attained on meeting a sea.

For, if the sea be really heavy, and the wind blowing a hard onshore gale, it can only be by the utmost exertions of the crew that any headway can be made. The great danger then is, that an approaching heavy sea may carry the boat away on its front, and turn it broadside on, or up-end it, either effect being immediately fatal. A boat's only chance in such a case, is to obtain such way as shall enable her to pass end-on, through the crest of the sea, and leave it as soon as possible behind her. Of course if there be a rather heavy surf, but no wind, or the wind off shore, and opposed to the surf, as is often the case, a boat might be propelled so rapidly through it, that her bow would fall more suddenly and heavily after topping the sea, than if her way had been checked; and it may therefore only be when the sea is of such magnitude, and the boat of such a character, that there may be chance of the former carrying her back before it, that full speed should be given to her.

Boat must have sufficient way upon her

It may also happen that, by careful management under such circumstances, a boat may be made to avoid the sea, so that each wave may break ahead of her, which may be the only chance of safety in a small boat; but if the shore be flat and the broken water extend to a great distance from it, this will often be impossible.

Keep boat between breakers

The following general rules for rowing to seaward may therefore be relied on:

1. If sufficient command can be kept over a boat by the skill of those on board her, avoid or "dodge" the sea if possible, so as not to meet it at the moment of its breaking or curling over.

Two important rules

2. Against a head gale and heavy surf, get all possible speed on a boat on the approach of every sea which cannot be avoided.

If more speed can be given to a boat than is sufficient to prevent her being carried back by a surf, her way may be checked on its approach, which will give her an easier passage over it.

On Running Before a Broken Sea, or Surf, to the Shore

The one great danger, when running before a broken sea, is that of *broaching-to.* To that peculiar effect of the sea, so frequently destructive of human life, the utmost attention must be directed.

The cause of a boat's broaching-to, when running before a broken sea or surf, is, that her own motion being in the same direction as that of the sea, whether it be given by the force of oars or sails, or by the force of the sea itself, she opposes no resistance to it, but is carried before it. Thus, if a boat be running with her bow to the shore, and her stern to the sea, the effect of a surf or roller, on its overtaking her, is to throw up the stern, and as a consequence to depress the bow; if she then has sufficient inertia (which will be proportional to weight) to allow the sea to pass her, she will in succession pass through the descending, the horizontal and the ascending positions, as the crest of the wave passes successively her stern, her midships, and her bow in the reverse order in which the same positions occur to a boat propelled to seaward against a surf. This may be defined as the safe mode of running before a broken sea.

But if a boat on being overtaken by a heavy surf, has not sufficient inertia to allow it to pass her, the first of the three positions above enumerated alone occurs—her stern is raised high in the air and the wave carries the boat before it on its front or unsafe side, sometimes with frightful velocity, the bow all the time being deeply immersed in the hollow of the sea, where the water, being stationary or comparatively so, offers a resistance, whilst the crest of the sea, having the actual motion which causes it to break, forces onward the stern, or rear end of the boat.

A boat will, in this position, sometimes aided by careful oar-steerage, run a considerable distance until the wave has broken and expended itself. But it will often happen, that if the bow be low, it will be driven under water, when the buoyancy being lost forward, whilst the sea presses on the stern, the boat will be thrown (as it is termed) end-over-end; or if the bow be high, or it be protected, as in most lifeboats, by a bow air-chamber, so that it does not become submerged, that the resistance forward, acting on one bow, will slightly turn the boat's head, and the force of the surf being transferred to the opposite quarter, she will in a moment be turned round broadside by the sea and be thrown by it on her beam-ends, or altogether capsized. It is in this manner that most boats are upset in a surf, especially on flat coasts, and in this way many lives are annually lost amongst merchant seamen when attempting to land, after being compelled to desert their vessels.

Hence it follows that the management of a boat, when landing through a heavy surf must, as far as possible, be assimilated to that when proceeding to seaward against one, at least so far as to stop her progress shoreward at the moment of being overtaken by a heavy sea, and thus enabling it to pass her. There are different ways of effecting this object:

Three important rules

1. By turning a boat's head to the sea before entering the broken water, and then backing in stern foremost, pulling a few strokes ahead to meet each heavy sea, and then again backing astern. If a sea be really heavy, and a boat small, this plan will be generally the safest, as a boat can be kept more under command when the full force of the oars can be used against a heavy surf, than by backing them only.

2. If rowing to shore with the stern to seaward, by backing all the oars on the approach of a heavy sea, and rowing ahead again as soon as it has passed to the bow of the boat, thus rowing in on the back of the wave; or, as is practised in some lifeboats, placing the after-oarsmen with their faces forward, and making them row back at each sea on its approach.

3. If rowed in bow foremost, by towing astern a pig of ballast or large stone, or a large basket, or canvas bag termed a "drogue" or drag, made for the purpose, the object of each being to hold the boat's stern back, and to prevent her being turned broadside to the sea or broaching-to.

Use of drogue

Drogues are in common use by the boatmen on the Norfolk coast; they are conical-shaped bags of about the same form and proportionate length and breadth as a candle extinguisher, about two feet wide at the mouth and four and a half feet long. They are towed with the mouth foremost by a stout rope, a small line, termed a tripping line, being fast to the apex or pointed end. When towed with the mouth foremost, they fill with water, and offer a considerable resistance, thereby holding back the stern; by letting go the stouter rope and retaining the smaller line, their position is reversed, when they collapse, and can be readily hauled into the boat.

Drogues are chiefly used in sailing-boats, when they both serve to check a boat's way and to keep her end on to the sea. They are, however, a great source of safety in rowing-boats, and the rowing lifeboats of the National Lifeboat Institution are now all provided with them.

A boat's sail bent to a yard, and towed astern loosed, the yard being attached to a line capable of being veered, hauled or let go, will act in some measure as a drogue, and will tend much to break the force of the sea immediately astern of the boat.

Trim of boat

Heavy weights should be kept out of the extreme ends of a boat; but when rowing before a heavy sea the best trim is deepest by the stern, which prevents the stern being readily thrown on.

A boat should be steered by an oar over the stern, or on one quarter when running before a sea, as the rudder will then at times be of no use. If the rudder be shipped, it should be kept amidships on a sea breaking over the stern.

Steering oar

The following general rules may therefore be depended on when running before, or attempting to land, through a heavy surf or broken water:

1. As far as possible avoid each sea by placing the boat where the sea will break ahead or astern of her.

2. If the sea be very heavy, or if the boat be very small, and especially if she have a square stern, bring her bow round to seaward and back her in, rowing ahead against each heavy surf that cannot be avoided sufficiently to allow it to pass the boat.

Five general rules

3. If it be considered safe to proceed to the shore bow foremost, back the oars against each sea on its approach so as to stop the boat's way through the water as far as possible and if there is a drogue, or any other instrument in the boat that may be used as one, tow it astern to aid in keeping the boat end-on to the sea, which is the chief object in view.

4. Bring the principal weights in the boat towards the end that is to seaward, but not to the extreme end.

5. If a boat, worked by both sails and oars, be running under sail for the land through a heavy sea, her crew should, under all circumstances, unless the beach be quite steep, take down her masts and sails before entering the broken water, and take her to land under oars alone, as above described.

If she has sails only, her sails should be much reduced, a half-lowered foresail or other small head-sail being sufficient.

Beaching or Landing Through a Surf

The running before a surf or broken sea, and the beaching or landing of a boat, are two distinct operations; the management of boats, as above recommended, has exclusive reference to running before a surf where the shore is so flat that the broken water extends to some distance from the beach. Thus on a very steep beach, the first heavy fall of broken water will be on the beach itself, whilst on some very flat shores there will be broken water as far as the eye can reach, sometimes extending to even four or five miles from the land. The outermost line of broken water, on a flat shore, where the waves break in three or four fathoms water, is the heaviest, and therefore the most dangerous, and when it has been passed through in safety, the danger lessens as the water shoals, until, on nearing the land, its force

Difference between steep beach and flat shore

is spent and its power harmless. As the character of the sea is quite different on steep and flat shores, so is the customary management of boats on landing different in the two situations. On the flat shore, whether a boat be run or backed in, she is kept straight before or end to the sea until she is fairly aground, when each surf takes her further in as it overtakes her, aided by the crew, who will then generally jump out to lighten her, and drag her in by her sides. As above stated, sail will, in this case, have been previously taken in if set, and the boat will have been rowed or backed in by oars alone.

Flat beach methods

On the other hand, on the *steep* beach, it is the general practice, in a boat of any size, to retain speed right on to the beach, and in the act of landing, whether under oars or sail, to turn the boat's bow half round towards the direction from which the surf is running, so that she may be thrown on her broadside up the beach, when abundance of help is usually at hand to haul her as quickly as possible out of the reach of the sea. In such situations, *we believe, it is nowhere the practice to back a boat in stern foremost under oars, but to row in under full speed as above described.*

Steep beach methods

The average merchantman will have only the problem of beaching or running before a sea to contend with. In the event of working a life boat up to a beach upon which the surf is running, remember that quite a bad surf will look harmless when seen from the sea. If the boat has been out for a considerable length of time and the crew are weak and perhaps impatient, use great care in going through. Stand off, if possible, until help arrives abreast the boat.

The writer has in mind the experience of a Coast Guard officer taking passage on a Pacific Coast steamer with his wife. It was necessary to abandon the vessel and this gentleman, being experienced, was placed in charge of a boat by the master of the vessel. The boat was filled with laborers and the officer had his wife with him. After a trying time he made the coast, having separated from the other boats during the night.

He made for a lighthouse and saw that the boat was observed. A heavy surf was running, although it did not look bad from the boat.

The laborers who were at the oars were tired and thirsty, they insisted upon going in at once. They saw the shore and would brook no delay.

" Unfortunately I never carry a gun," this gentleman said in explaining his experience. " They were rowing, there were no sailors in the boat, a few of the men only partly understood my frantic efforts to stop them.

" If I had had a gun I would have shot one, at least wounded him, and might have kept control of the boat.

" We went through the surf and were capsized a half hour before assistance arrived. My wife was drowned, though I succeeded in getting her almost to the beach three times.

" The laborers were all saved but were too dazed and frightened to render me any assistance."

Officers and petty officers in charge of life boats should be armed. It may be necessary at some time to carry out drastic measures of discipline for the safety of all concerned.

XIII

Riding Out a Gale in Small Boats

At times it becomes necessary to ride out heavy weather in small boats where vessels have been abandoned far from shore. Under such circumstances every precaution must be taken to make the boats more seaworthy. Canvas washboards rigged up forward are often very helpful. The boat should be kept trimmed and bailed.

The first thing to be done, of course, is to rig a sea anchor. The U. S. Regulations require that all boats be fitted with a sea anchor, also that they shall be provided with an oil tank constructed to distribute the oil and so fitted that it can be attached to the sea anchor, this tank must have a capacity of one gallon at least.

So far the best arrangement for this purpose, combining the sea anchor and the oil tank, is the Rouse Patent Sea Anchor. This device, the invention of Captain Frederick Rouse of New York, has proven of great value. The small 1½ gallon tank should hold out at least eight hours.

However any seaman worth his salt should be able to improvise a sea anchor, rigging boat spars to a bridle and weighting it with the boat anchor. In riding to a sea anchor pay out sufficient line, be certain that the line is well secured to the anchor, that the bridle will not slew and that the line is protected from chafe where it runs over the bow of the boat.

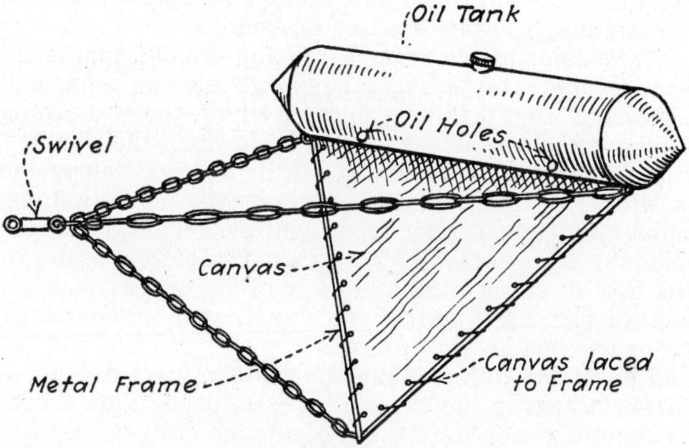

The Rouse Sea Anchor.

A tripping line is useless. If the sea anchor is to come in the sea will be sufficiently smooth to allow the boat to be hauled up to the anchor.

Where oil is to be used and the oil bag is not directly attached to the anchor, it might be well to rig a block and line for hauling the oil bag in when empty and sending it back after filling. This must be done, of course, as soon as the anchor is constructed.

XIV

Boarding a Wreck

The following concise directions are taken from " The Deck and Boat Book " of the U. S. Navy:

1. Whenever practicable, a vessel, whether stranded or afloat, should be boarded from to leeward, as the *principal* danger is that the boat may collide against the vessel or be swamped by the rebound of the sea, and the greater violence of the sea on the weather side of the vessel renders such accidents more liable to occur on that side.

2. *If a stranded vessel* is broadside to the sea, the chief danger in boarding to leeward is the possible falling of the masts, or that the boat may be stove by the wreckage alongside.

Under such circumstances it may be necessary to take a wrecked crew into a lifeboat from the bow or stern of the wreck. In boarding a wreck that is stranded on a flat shore, lifeboats usually anchor to windward and veer down from a safe distance until near enough to throw a line on board.

3. *In rescuing people* from a drifting wreck, approach from leeward, taking care to avoid wreckage floating alongside. If there is much wind it is best to lay well off, throw a strong line aboard, have the people secure the line around their bodies, one at a time, and jump overboard, for if the boat gets alongside of a wreck which is rapidly drifting to leeward, there is danger of swamping, and much difficulty in getting her clear of the side.

4. Should it be necessary to go alongside, it is preferable to run the bow or stern to the gangway or sea ladder, keeping her headed at right angles to the ship's keel, with oars out ready for pulling or backing away.

5. An exception to the usual rule of boarding a drifting vessel to leeward occurs in the case of a vessel of very low freeboard, such as small schooners etc. Board such craft on the weather quarter to avoid being stove in by her main boom chains, etc.

In the not unusual case of a passenger or other vessel foundering, with one or more vessels standing by, great judgment is necessary in order that lives may be saved. The best boat, or boats should be lowered, *all superfluous gear taken out,* with the exception, perhaps of sea anchor and oil. Extra coils of two and a half or three inch manila may be needed.

The rescuing vessels should try, in an open sea, to blanket the wreck, and to provide a " slick " by the careful distribution of oil from windward. (See page 711).

Where a line cannot be drifted down, it may be possible to put a line over the vessel by use of the Lyle gun, and in a sea of extra height, men may be dragged to the rescuing ship, to leeward by means of an endless line as in the case of the breeches buoy operated from the shore.

It is extremely difficult to do more than indicate certain possible operations. In such situations seamanship comes into its own and many years of preparation find their usefulness in the saving of life and property.

Where radio is working, an understanding can be arrived at between the wreck and the rescuers. Otherwise use the International Code, or flag semaphores, though the code is far more definite and reliable over considerable distances. Be certain that *both* sides understand the manner of rescue to be adopted. *In any event it might be well for the master of the rescuing vessel to always assume direction.* If this rule were universally understood a great deal of hesitation and confusion would be saved, even though the skipper of a liner might have to take orders from the captain of a tramp.

XV

Man Overboard

A quarter boat ready for instant lowering. A. Knotted life lines. B. Boat pad to prevent chafe against strong back. C. Slip or pelican hook to release gripes. Old fashioned davits, swung out. Boat griped against strongback.

When a man falls overboard the things to be done *at once* are as follows:

A. Stop engines *or he may be cut up by the screws.* Give helm *away* from the side from which he has fallen, *i.e.*, if man goes over on *starboard*, *port* your helm.

B. Drop buoys from wings of bridge, these are the buoys to which water lights are attached.

C. Order lee life boat cleared away.

D. Keep sharp lookout on surface of water in position of the wake at time of making turn.

E. At night don't bother to keep lookout for man, head for buoys and get boat out.

F. Put searchlight in commission and sweep vicinity of buoys, keeping lookout with night glasses.

In any well regulated ship a lifeboat's crew is designated in each watch. These men should be mustered at night at the beginning of the watch and should be in readiness for a call.

Much of the above should be done at once, especially the directions under A.

With the helm hard over, the vessel will pass directly over the place, or very near it at least, where the man was dropped. With the water light going this can readily be seen. Start engines ahead slow, and *when the course has been regained,* or nearly so, stop.

Then stand by to lower away life boat.

The usual precautions in lowering are to be observed.

In reporting man overboard it is well to add which side.

" Man Overboard—*Port!* " or

" Man Overboard—*Starboard!* "

This will give the officer on the bridge the necessary information for turning.

As soon as anyone goes overboard, whoever sees him should at once release a life buoy, and if he sees the man *throw the buoy at him.*

When falling overboard *strike out away from the ship.*

At sea in a fog, boat leaving ship should carry a compass, though return to vessel can usually be made by sound signal.

In an extra heavy sea, vessel going into it, it is best to stop, form a lee, and send boat back under lee of vessel. When sea is too high to admit of lowering boat, work vessel back to point where man went overboard and throw line to him. If necessary lower a man to him, put rescuer into a life jacket.

Use oil where it can be done. (See page 711).

XVI

Sailing Boats

A fine sport.

Boat rigs for the life and working boats of vessels have gradually simmered down to the following:

The *standing lug.*

The *sprit sail.*

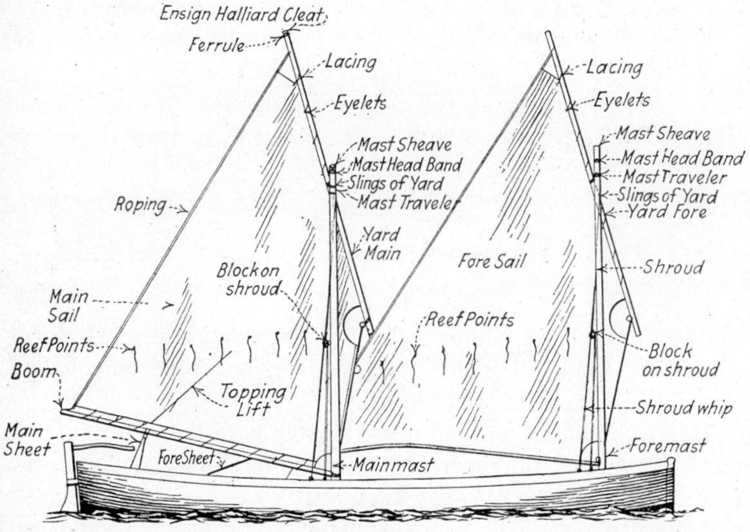

Standing lug.

These sails, with the addition of a jib, are used singly or on two masts. For large boats two masts are generally stepped because of greater ease in handling.

The standing lug. The standing lug rig on two masts with a "lug foresail," hauling aft without a boom, is the simplest rig that still presents easy handling and quick reefing features. The rig is self explanatory from the illustrations. When reefed down very little sail is exposed, and when under stress the use of a jib and trysail on the fore and trysail on the main can be provided for.

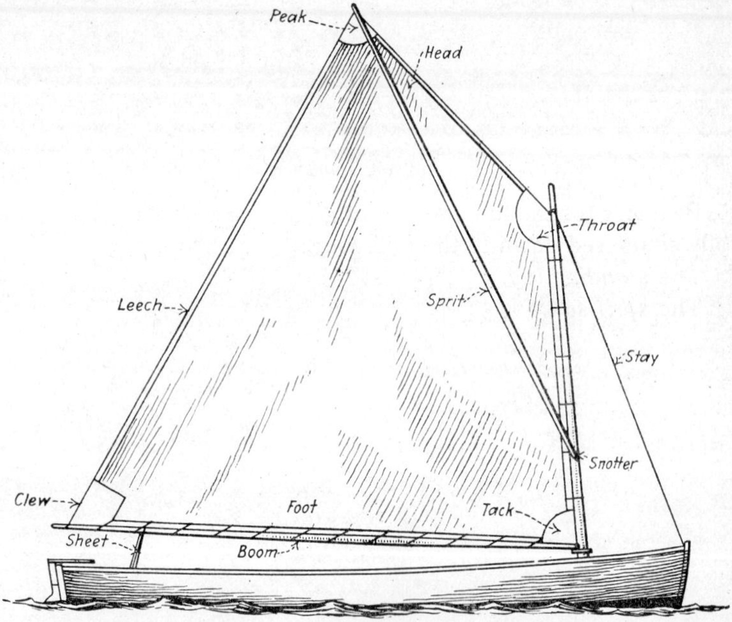

Sprit sail rig.

One of the main points about life boat sailing gear is to get something that will make up smooth, will not become balled up, and can easily be understood.

Masts should be marked near the step with the letters FORE and AFT cut into the mast, so that it will not be stepped with the lead of shrouds and sheaves wrong.

The sprit rig. This is a very handy rig for small boats. It has certain advantages in the way of spreading the sail, but is not over handy in setting because of the shipping of the sprit. The advantages of the sprit are a very flat sail. The sprit takes all of the sag out of a sail and sets it like a board. The writer was fortunate enough to have a very fine gig rigged with two masted sprit sails. Being a whale boat with a six inch keel, very few boats, or yachts for that matter, could pass her.

The sprit is supported on the mast by a strop called a "*snotter*". This consists of a short rope with eyes spliced in each end. One end is passed around the mast and through the other eye, the heel of the sprit then rests in the hanging eye. The sail is then "peaked" by pushing up on the snotter, then sheet aft, *after* the head is up.

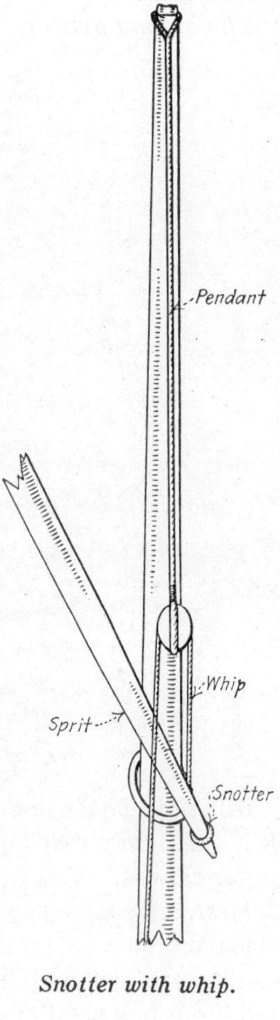

Snotter with whip.

With a heavy sprit rig a pennant and block are fitted to the mast head, and the heel of the sprit is stepped in an eye seized to a stout mast ring, the whole thing is lifted by a whip as shown in the drawing.

When the snotter has a tendency to work down make it long enough to get a round turn about the mast.

Sheet. Care should be taken to reeve the sheet properly.

Booms. In life boats it is recommended to do away with booms as they add so much more to the complication. When a long passage must be made under sail booms can easily be improvised by using oars, lashing them together.

Fore sail should be attached to fore mast, and both masts plainly marked.

Sloop rig. This rig is handy for a special sailing boat and is given for reference.

Schooner rig. Useful for a larger boat. Given for reference.

The cat rig. Mast stepped far forward with a single gaff and boom mainsail.

The Falmouth lugger. A very handy little rig. Standing lug and mizzen.

The sliding gunter. A good rig, handy, foolproof (almost).

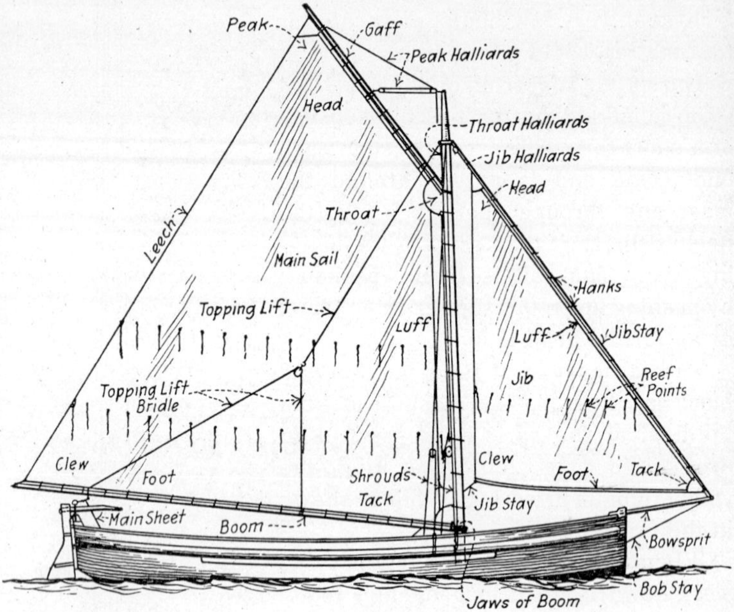

Sloop rig.

Handling boats under sail. The successful boat sailor must, in a small way carry out the principles of handling larger craft under canvas.

First. He must pay special attention to the weather. If about to leave the vessel for a sail, know what to expect. Give heed to storm warnings, find out what winds prevail, if in a foreign port, and if out in a small boat on the open sea watch the weather and note the wind and sea with the greatest care. Sailing ship men do this as a matter of habit. Steamship sailors are liable to be a trifle careless about the wind.

Second. See all gear properly set up, shrouds taut, masts stepped and secured, and stayed, and all running gear rove properly, and in order.

Third. Have boat in sailing trim, usually a few inches by the stern. Dispose weights in bottom of boat. Have all hands sit down preferably on bottom boards.

Wind aft. This is a dangerous point of sailing in a rough sea and great care should be taken to watch the helm or any shift of wind, as the boat may *yaw* about. Many advocate run-

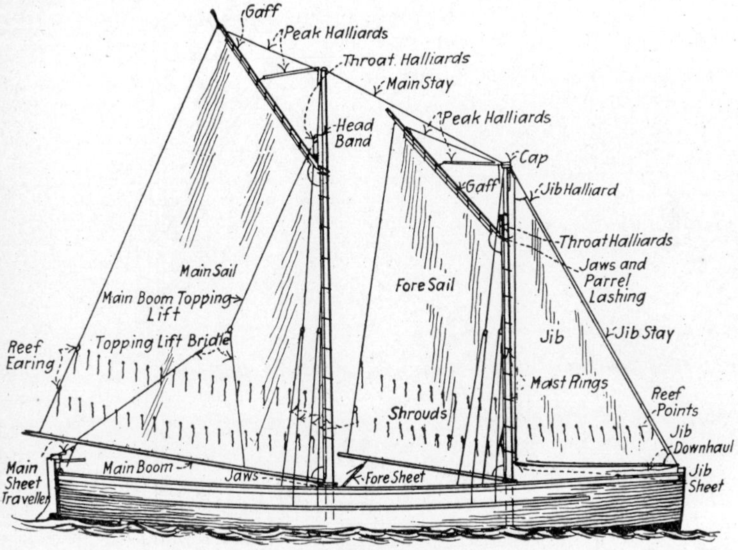

Schooner rig.

ning off the course one side and then the other, somewhat after the manner of the historic *zigzag* of war time days, *and nights*.

When going before the wind be on the lookout against *gybing*, that is the topping up of the main boom, the sail bellying forward of the mast, and the boom slapping up against it.

Keep the weight well aft in running.

Wing and wing. Boat running before the wind, fore and mainsails spread on opposite sides, the fore sail sheet held out with an oar or a boat hook.

Running large. Sailing with wind free on either side. This is usually the best point of sailing of a ship's boat, wind somewhere on the quarter, and all drawing.

Squalls. Heavy wind puffs under above conditions of sailing are best met by dropping the peak, or if no boom is fitted, by letting fly the sheets. This latter is to be done only in the event of a very bad squall.

When sheets have been let fly cast off halyards and haul down at once. Never *belay* a sheet no matter how fine the weather may *appear* to be.

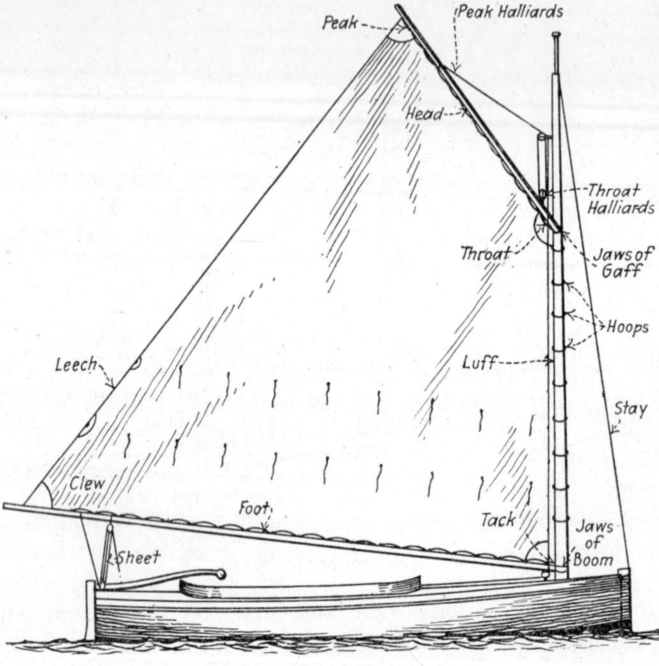

Cat boat.

Sailing on the wind. When the boat cannot make her course it becomes necessary to sail as close to the wind as possible, tacking by various stages in working to windward.

In sailing *close hauled*, as it is called, do not trim sheets too flat, and trim the boat so that she will have a small tendency to come up into the wind, necessitating a small amount of weather helm. The sails should be kept *full* and *by* that is the forward cloths just about to tremble. In rough water give the boat a good full and she will go better and gain more than by pinching her into the wind.

Tacking (a two masted boat). Give boat a good full, get as much way on her as possible. Order the men standing by sheets, to be ready—"*Ready about*" is the proper order. Then "*Ease down the helm!*"—"*Let fly fore and jib sheets!*" "*Haul main boom slowly amidships!*"

As soon as the boat comes up into the eye of the wind, if she is slow, have the jib held out flat at a small angle with the keel, *to windward*. This will help turn her head around on the new tack. Do not hold out the jib like a bag. This only stops the way of the boat. If the boat should begin to make sternway. *Shift* over helm.

Sliding gunter.

As soon as she is around, "*Trim aft fore and jib sheets!*" and ease off main boom.

When a boat or ship gets into the wind and will not go about she is said to be *in irons*. *Box* her around with the jib.

Tacking a single sticker put down helm and *go about*.

Wearing. If in a heavy sea and on the wind with a laden boat it may be necessary to *wear*, or to *gybe*, as it is called in a small boat. With considerable wind, brail up or lower the mainsail.

Then put the helm *up*, her head falls away from the wind, ease the jib sheets, and the fore sheet, as the wind comes aft and shifts on the new weather side, haul over the main boom and sheet it aft to bring her up into the wind. Keep head sheets loose until wind is forward of beam then trim aft all sheets.

With plenty of sea room wearing is the proper thing to do with a laden boat.

A good boat, in smooth water should sail to within five points of the wind. Yachts will go to four, square riggers to six.

In sailing on the wind, the back draft of the fore, is liable to shake the luff of the mainsail. Where a jib is carried and trimmed flat, this is the best guide for a helmsman sitting well on the weather quarter of his boat. A small wind vane is very useful however and a strip of bunting at the main truck comes in very handy, especially in light winds.

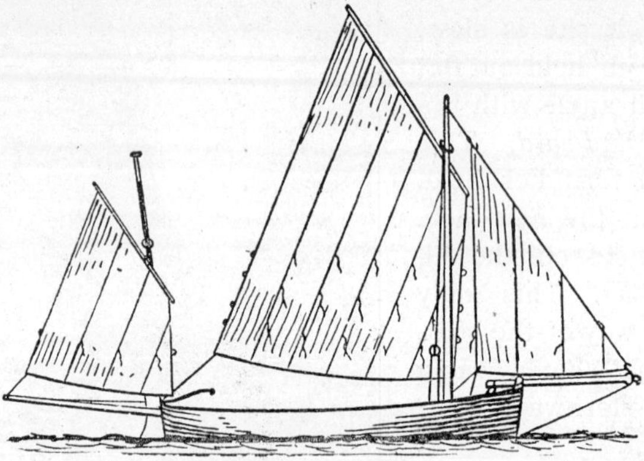

Falmouth lugger.

Squalls when on the wind. These are best met by putting down the helm and *luffing* up into the wind. Then sail can be shortened if desired.

Reefing. Luff up into the wind, lower the yard (standing lug) gathering in the sail. Pass tack lashing, pass reef points around *joot* of sail, not around boom, hoist away.

Reef foresail first, then main.

If weather looks doubtful do not hesitate to reef in plenty of time. The reef can always be shaken out, but if you wait too long trouble may ensue.

Conclusion. These notes on boat sailing have been made as brief as possible. No book can teach the art of sailing. It must be acquired by practice. The steamship officer should at least be required to *sail* an open boat. On the bridge at night the ights of a sailing craft will have a new meaning to him. Given the direction of the wind, and he will *know* within a few points of how she may be heading. He will also know just where she *cannot* sail and this will be a great help to him in avoiding her as he must, under the Rules of the Road, Article 20, keep out of the way of all sail vessels.

When sailing keep every one seated. All gear clear for running.

The following questions and answers from the *Bluejacket's Manual* of the U. S. Navy give the main points to be observed in bringing a boat under sail alongside of a gangway. Similar tactics will make a good landing at a wharf.

Q. What precautions in coming alongside under sail?

A. It requires care, judgment and experience. Never attempt to go alongside under sail if a boat or other obstruction that the mast could touch overhangs the gangway. Don't go alongside under sail in rough weather when the rolling motion of the boat would cause the masts to strike the gangway platform. Under these circumstances unstep the masts and bring the boat alongside under oars.

Q. What is the best method of coming alongside under sail when the ship is riding to a windward tide?

A. Approach the gangway from abaft the beam. Tend all gear and shorten sail when boat has sufficient way to reach gangway. Bow and stroke oarsmen tend boat hooks, and other men perform their duties in shortening sail.

Q. If the ship is riding to the wind?

The sprit is a very handy rig.

A. Approach gangway from about abeam. Tend all gear. Bow and stroke oarsmen stand by with boat hooks. When there is enough way to make the gangway, command: "In jib and foresail." Let go jib tack and sheet; smother jib into foremast. Lower foresail or brail it up. At the same time put tiller hard down; haul main boom amidships or a bit on weather quarter. This throws the boat's head into the wind; hauling the main boom to windward deadens her headway when desirable. When alongside command "In mainsail"; stow sails and unstep if desirable. This is the surest and safest method; but with skill in handling, all sails may be taken in together, the tiller put hard down, and the boat rounded up to gangway. This requires more skill and judgment. It should not ordinarily be attempted.

Q. If there is any current, how make allowances for it?

A. Head for a point further forward or aft as the case may be.

In coming alongside of a wharf or jetty with the wind directly on to the landing. Get in sail in plenty of time and come in under a jib or luff into the wind and drift down, lowering sail in plenty of time.

CHAPTER XIV

COMPASS—LEAD—LOG—PILOTING

I

Compass

The compass, as everyone knows, dates back to the earliest times. The following interesting data on the invention of the compass and upon the origin of its cardinal divisions is taken, in part, from an article in *Shipping* of September, 1917.

There is unquestionable evidence contained in a document of the year 1269 that at that time a pivoted compass was in use by navigators and a description of this instrument is contained in the 'Epistola de Magnete,' of Petrus Peregrinus de Maricourt, written at Lucera and addressed to Sigerus de Fauconcourt. Several manuscripts of this remarkable treatise are in existence, notably at the Oxford Library. It seems that about 1450 someone wrote that the compass had been invented at Amalfi by a certain Flavius and about a century later a so-called historian wrote that the name of that Flavius was Gioja. No evidence exists that Gioja ever lived, although he is supposed to have made such a portentous invention. Another superstition regarding the compass is that which ascribes the discovery of the properties of the magnetic needle to the Chinese, European mariners being supposed to have acquired the compass from them through the Arabs. But this supposition entirely overlooks the fact that the existence of magnetism was known to European culture at the time of Aristotle and we have no means of ascertaining whether or not this knowledge was not made use of in practical navigation. The Chinese never shone as navigators, although they are supposed to have at one time journeyed by sea as far as the Persian Gulf. But their compass was a very crude affair, and although their method of suspending the needle made it more sensitive than the European, their compass card (divided in 24 points) was so defective that there is no reason to believe it could ever have been used by Europeans, for the reason that if there had existed at that time any interchange of ideas between the West and the Far East the Chinese would not have clung so long to so crude a compass as they were using. On the other hand, Indians and Arabs as early as the sixteenth century were using compasses of European make and there is no evidence that they ever used the Chinese card. Therefore the story of the compass being of Chinese origin must also be relegated to the junk pile of unfounded allegations. There is on the contrary every reason to suppose that the compass was but a natural evolution brought about by the combination of the magnetic needle with the 'Rosa Ventorum,' known to the Ancients. This 'Rose of the Winds' is known to be much older than the compass. It goes back to the days of the Temple of the Winds at Athens, which was built by Andronicus Cyrrhestes. The Rose contained eight cardinal points dividing the heavens according to the prevailing winds. These points were Tramontano, Greco, Levante, Scirocco, Ostro, Africo or Libeccio, Ponento and Maestro. The north point was indicated by a broad arrowhead or spear, as well as by a T (initial of Tramontano). In time after the Rosa Ventorum had been adapted to indicate the swing of the magnetic needle, the symbol used to designate the Tramontano evolved into a fleur-de-lys. This was about 1492. The Rosa Ventorum also had a cross at the east and it is noteworthy that the compasses of British ships carried this cross until the eighteenth century. The subdivision of the Rosa Ventorum into 32 points, or rhumbs, is generally believed to have been the invention of Flemish mariners. It is certain that a compass divided substantially on modern lines was known to Chaucer about 1391. All the expressions used to denote the accessories of the mariner's compass denote the predominance as mariners formerly held by the Southern races. Thus the word 'binnacle,' used to describe the stand holding

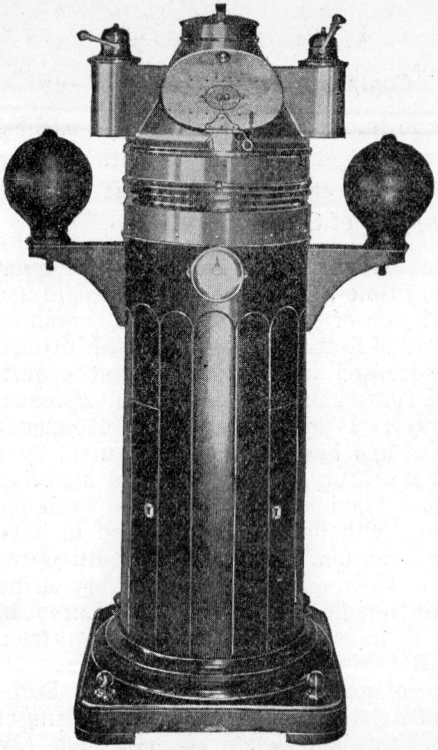

A modern binnacle.

the compass, is a corruption of the word 'bittacle,' which in turn was derived from the Portuguese 'abitacolo,' the house in which the compass was housed. Compasses improved very little in efficiency until the early part of the nineteenth century. So little reliance could be placed upon the compasses then in use that in 1820 Peter Barlow reported to the British Admiralty that half of the compasses used in British warships were mere lumber and only fit to be destroyed. He suggested instead of the prevailing method of single suspension, a pattern having four or five parallel straight strips of magnetized steel fixed under a card. This method was eventually adopted and remained the British Admiralty standard until the Thomson (Lord Kelvin) compass came out in 1876.

The construction of the compass, in principle at least, is simple. A magnetized bar of steel, or iron, called the *needle*, is balanced on a pivot so that it will rotate freely in the horizontal plane, coming to rest in the line of the magnetic meridian at any particular place where it is free from other disturbances. On board ship the compass needle is deflected from the magnetic meridian by the *unequal* attraction of the surrounding iron and steel in the hull and fittings of the vessel. This deflection is called *deviation.* Compasses are *adjusted*, by placing certain magnets in such positions, about the needle, that they act in a direction *opposite to* and *of equal force* to the deflecting iron in the vessel. A perfectly adjusted compass would lie in the plane of the magnetic meridian on all headings of the vessel. Such a compass would have no deviation. The subject of compass errors and their correction is one of navigation and is fully treated in the many excellent works on that subject. The seaman is concerned with the fact that there is such a thing as *deviation*, and should always take it into account in laying courses when piloting.

In addition to *deviation*, the compass is generally pointing to one side or the other of true north by an angle known as the *magnetic variation of the place.** At different points on the

* History furnishes some interesting instances of the early ignorance of the existence of magnetic variation. On September 13, 1492, consternation prevailed among the sailors on board Columbus's ship, the *Santa Maria*, when it was noticed, for the first time, that the compass needle, instead of pointing a little East of the North Star, as it had done all along since their leaving European shores, though, to be sure, by a gradually diminishing amount, then pointed somewhat West of the North Star, and continued to

earth's surface, the needle, pointing roughly to the magnetic pole, which does not coincide with the true pole at the axis of the earth's rotation, forms an angle with the true meridian. This angle is shown on sea charts by means of the *compass rose* and by lines of equal variation, for some certain year, together with a notation of the annual increase or decrease for that locality.

By means of the deviation table, giving the deviation for all headings, and the variation taken from the chart and corrected, the *compass error* is found, and from this, the true bearing of an object, or the true course made by compass, can be obtained.

The method of applying the error, of checking it by bearings of terrestrial or celestial objects and bodies, is part of the science of navigation—perhaps the most important part of navigation. *Bowditch—The American Practical Navigator*—explains the groundwork of these fascinating calculations.

do so as the ship passed to the Westward. Columbus on his first voyage not only discovered a new world, but also an important scientific fact. Before that time the variation of the needle from the true North was considered due to the imperfection in the mechanical construction of the magnetic needles, and was not before recognized as a distinct error. Incidentally it may be stated that during this first voyage Columbus passed through one place, a little West of Fayal, in the Azores, where the needle pointed to the true North, and a few years later Sebastian Cabot observed another such place somewhat farther to the North, the observations of the two thus roughly locating for the first time an *agonic* line.

The earliest observations on land of the fact that the magnetic needle does not point exactly " true to the Pole " appears to have been made by George Hartmann, a maker of compass sundials, who, in about the year 1570, found that at Rome the needle pointed 6 deg. East of true North. About 125 years later, after observations of the declination of the needle from the true North and South line began to multiply, it was found that at London between 1580, the date of the first declination observations at that place, and 1634 the needle had changed its direction of pointing from 11½ deg. East to 4 deg. East, or a change to the Westward of 7 deg. Thus another important phenomenon was discovered, the cause of which remains without adequate solution up to the present time, though some of the best minds through the intervening years have studied it. This phenomenon is the so-called secular variation of the earth's magnetism, by the action of which changes of varying magnitudes are continuously occurring in the distribution of the earth's magnetism. The continual observation and study of these changes and the correction of magnetic charts, as, for example, the lines of equal magnetic variation supplied to navigators, follow as a consequence.

Having stated the fundamental errors of the compass, we can go a step further in elaborating upon its present design.

The simple bar or needle has been superseded by swinging two or more needles, in parallel, on either side of the pivot. To the needles is attached the *compass card* carrying the divisions about which the seaman is most concerned.

Dry compasses consist of a segmental circle of paper mounted on an aluminum ring, suspended from the central boss containing a jeweled cup by thirty-two silk threads. The needles suspended below the card, are single wires and depend from the card ring by a second series of silk threads. This brings the weight of the needles down low and makes the card very steady. The pivot supporting the jeweled cup held in the boss of the card, rises from the bottom of the *compass bowl*, and the bowl, in turn, is carried on a ring, ring and bowl supported by *knife edge bearings* placed at right angles to each other. These bearings are called *gimbles;* the ring is the *gimble ring*.

The bearings on the bowl, resting on the ring, are fore and aft, those on the ring, resting on the *binnacle* (the compass box), are athwartship. So, no matter how the ship may heel or pitch, the compass pivot remains vertical and the compass card horizontal.

In the dry compass the parts of the card are made as light as possible to avoid friction on the pivot.

To *dampen* the oscillation of the bowl in a seaway, with vessel moving, a chamber in the bottom of the bowl is partly filled with a viscous oil—a sort of sluggish friction brake. The action of this is self-evident.

The *Liquid Compass* differs in construction. The needles are formed by bunching magnetized wires in the form of small cylinders, and the card, of metal, is carried by these bundles of magnets. The boss is carried by a central hub, also of metal, and also attached to the magnets. There are usually four bundles of magnets, two in each side of the pivot. This rather rigid and heavy arrangement is *floated* in a mixture of glycerine and water or of alcohol and water, or alcohol alone. Hollow air chambers in the hub supply buoyancy, the whole thing *almost* floats, so that the cup, under the center of the hub, bears down lightly upon the pivot rising from the bottom of the bowl. The bowl is covered with a heavy glass, all air is excluded, and the compass swings freely in the liquid. An expansion chamber provides for temperature changes.

The liquid compass has reached a high state of perfection, and has many things in its favor. In the United States Navy all magnetic compasses are of the liquid type.

The seaman should study the construction of his compasses; he should know how to adjust them. The binnacle should be kept locked and the key in charge of the master. When a compass is to be adjusted, under favorable conditions, the master, or navigator, must attend to it themselves, or the compass is placed in charge of a compass adjuster. The writer remembers, as a youngster, trying to read the *Admiralty Manual on Compass Adiustment,* a thick red book filled with a frightful amount of mathematics. Recently the following advice on compass adjustment printed in *The Oracle* of the Oriental Navigation Co. came to his attention and is given here because it states truths in such clear language that seamen who read it may profit by its simplicity.

" While the compass is a delicate instrument, and while it is well to have it attended to by an expert occasionally, there is a tendency among some officers to regard it as a mystery only to be approached by shore adjusters. This is undesirable both because it is unnecessary and because a good officer in training to command will naturally want to be master of his tools rather than afraid of them.

" Suppose you have taken an ore cargo in Rio, and your compass is out. Choose early morning or late evening on a clear day (the sun changes bearing too rapidly around mid-day), work out a table of azimuths for this time, or if you prefer plot three on co-ordinate paper and fair a curve through them. With your pelorus or with a shadow pin bring the sun on the correct azimuth for the time; the ship will then be heading north magnetic. Open your binnacle base and you will see two carriers with magnetized wires in them whose ends are painted red and blue. Remove all those lying athwartship of the vessel. Your ship being on north magnetic for at least two minutes, note the compass. Place the wires in the thwartship carrier with red ends to same side of binnacle the 0° of compass points to—E, deviation, red ends to starboard;—W, red to port,—and run the carrier up until needle is amidships. If possible use enough wires so that carrier will be about half way up for this. Now steady in the same way on East Magnetic, and remove wires from the fore-and-aft carrier. Do the same as before: if E'ly deviation, put in wires red ends forward; Westerly, red ends aft. Bring 0° to lubber's line by moving carrier.

"Now steady on N. E. Magnetic, slack up the nuts on the two soft iron spheres and move them equally in or out until the N. E. point coincides with the lubber's line. Secure everything, and swing ship for residuals. Plot the remaining deviation and if you have done a good job it ought to be a smooth, wavy curve not over 3° out.

"Some time later, when in a seaway, note if the card swings badly with the roll of the ship. If so, remove the compass carefully and in the center of the binnacle you will find a rod hanging by a chain. Pull this rod up enough to 'damp' the swings of the compass, but remember that too much will make your card sluggish in good weather. Incidentally this rod should be capsized in its tube whenever the magnetic equator is crossed.

"If your azimuths are correct and your helmsman is good, the whole job can be done in half an hour. Once you have done it and checked your work with a deviation table, you can laugh thereafter at the high-priced adjuster, and feel secure of your courses."

The writer of the above, Lieut.-Commander R. T. Merrill, an official of the Oriental Navigation Company, and a navy officer of wide experience, has summed up the *final act* of a rather complicated subject. Seamen are advised to study Lecky's *Wrinkles* and to carefully con their *Bowditch*, before opening the door of the binnacle—also, there are many methods of carrying the magnets, but of course the resultant positions are similar to those described.*

Having taken a rapid survey of the magnetic compass we will now get down to the seamanship end of the business, the use of the divisions on the card—alike for all compasses, in so far as the different systems are alike.

First, *outside of the card*, and marked on the bowl, is the

* It is considered preferable for a compass and correctors to remain in a compensating binnacle when the ship is to be laid up for several months. The effect of the compensation is to neutralize the effect of the iron of the ship, so that there should be less effect upon the compass than if the binnacle were not compensated.

No effect should be produced on the quadrantal correctors if spherical in form and properly made. Should any effect occur, it can be at once detected by loosening the securing nuts of the quadrantal correctors and rotating each sphere half a turn, at the same time observing whether the compass is affected.—U. S. Hydrographic Office.

lubber's line, a sharp black vertical mark in the true fore and aft line of the vessel. This indicates the ship's head and the point where the lubber's line cuts the rim of the compass card is the *Compass heading* at that particular time.

No doubt in the very old days, when an ancient mariner cocked his weather eye at the north star, a point or two "*to windard o' the bowline,*" and told off the course, the lubber's line, painted on the rim of that new-fangled contraption, the compass, was a truly contemptible thing only fit for weak-minded land lubbers. This, lubber's line like a few hundred other old things still sticks with us at sea.

II

Boxing the Compass

But the spirit of change is on us and many people finding it a slow process to learn to *box* the compass by points and quarter points, are clamoring for *degrees.* "Throw overboard this old stuff" they say "and give us something *easy and scientific.*" This seems to be the cry. In fact there is a great deal of change going on, even the old lubber's line is being tampered with as we will see later on in dealing with the *gyroscopic compass.*

But in adopting new things, in the matter of the sea, it is safer to first be certain that the old ones are really no longer of any use. Everything at sea is so different, so damned *unnatural* to a landsman, that some of the most *natural* things *to a sailor,* are looked down upon by lawyers, editors and the like, who have a genius for getting themselves into snug places of authority ashore.

Let us examine the points of a compass. The compass card with its thirty-two points is divided as follows:

Cardinal points	North	*Intercardinal* points	North east
	East		South east
	South		South west
	West		North west

"*Three name*" points,	North, north, east	South south west
	East north east	West south west
	East south east	West north west
	South south east	North north west

"*By*" points North by east
North east by north
North east by east
East by north
East by south
South east by east
South east by south
South by east
South by west
South west by south
South west by west
West by south
West by north
North west by west
North west by north
North by west

These points, worked out by seamen through the ages, are not as they are without much logical reason behind it all. For a time we have had with us a school of men both in the government and merchant services who have taken a careless view of many fundamental matters connected with the sea. To most of these men the seaman, untaught so far as schooling within four steady walls is concerned, is looked upon as being somewhat out of date. On the other hand, under sea conditions, methods that appear to be rough and ready are often the most valuable.

Our writer in *Shipping*, of September, 1917, the article being unsigned, had something more to say about compasses that will bear repeating:

"Reference has been made to the elimination of cardinal points and their substitution by degree-subdivision. This latter method is undoubtedly more scientific, but it has the defect of giving no direct indication of relative direction. To seamen, a designation of 135 deg. for S. E., for instance, does not appear sufficiently plausible. Furthermore, the method of steering by degrees alone might psychologically, prove dangerous in the mercantile marine for certain reasons which we shall explain. The fundamental principle underlying point-division is based upon a fact peculiar to man's naive method of thinking and reasoning. We naturally think of 'dividing' as meaning exactly the same as 'halving.' If a child is told to divide an apple among three persons, he will first halve it, and then halve one of the halves. And even after he has realized the fact that the three portions are unequal, his further efforts to render the division more equitable will, as a rule, result only in further halvings. And man, actuated by this same principle, when asked to determine in what direction the sun appears to be in the heavens, will first ascertain it to be, say, between S and E. Then he will consider whether it be nearer to S or nearer to E; in this way he establishes the position of SE. Then he will proceed to find out if it is nearer to SE or S, and will fix SSE as a further point of departure; and so on. The division of the compass-card into points corresponds perfectly with the above-described mental process of obtaining subdivisions by continued halvings. Its chief advantage is likewise in close relation thereto. This advantage consists in its extreme plausibility and the splendid view it gives of *the system of directions.* This view is rendered still more striking by means of graduated signatures, the main points looming up very conspicuously, while the auxiliary points grow less and less prominent in proportion to their relative degree of importance; all of which is requisite in practical seamanship, as, for example, steering by unstable card, or with poor light, or turning through certain desired angles, etc. To this we must add the close connection of this division with the importance which seamen attach to the traditional cardinal points, and to a nomenclature by which one can know at once in which quadrant, and whereabouts in that quadrant, a given direction is to be looked for. The absence of just this direct indication is what practical seamen object to in the division of the compass into degrees, particularly the graduation from 0 deg. Merchant seamen have objected to degree-graduation because the helmsman cannot follow it and needs the guidance of point-division in order to keep his course. It must not be forgotten that the mariner refers to nearly all the occurrences relating to wind, weather, and navigation in terms of compass-points and the merchant navigator, in spite of what scientists may say, cannot do without the terms N, E, S, W, and desires, moreover, to see them represented in the compass.

To box the compass the points are named in succession from North around to North, either way. Or from any other point and around.

To box the compass *by quarter points*, the divisions are named progressively until we get to a " by " point running in the *opposite* direction. Then we start with three quarters and work down to one quarter. An inspection of the table will show how this is done.

The *pelorus* or dumb compass is a compass card mounted at some convenient place and is used for taking bearings of objects when the compass itself cannot be employed. The pelorus is set to the course and the vessel held as steady as possible while taking these bearings. The pelorus is marked in points and in degrees.

Boxing by Points	Boxing by ¼ Points
North	N ¼ E
North by east	N ½ E
North north east	N ¾ E
North east by north	N by E
North east	N by E ¼ E
North east by east	N by E ½ E
East north east	N by E ¾ E
East by north	N N E
East	N N E ¼ E
East by south	N N E ½ E
East south east	N N E ¾ E
South east by east	N E by N
South east	N E ¾ N
South east by south	N E ½ N
South south east	N E ¼ N
South by east	N E
South	N E ¼ E
South by west	N E ½ E
South south west	N E ¾ E
South west by south	N E by E
South west	N E by E ¼ E
South west by west	N E by E ½ E
West south west	N E by E ¾ E
West by south	E N E
West	E N E ¼ E
West by north	E N E ½ E
West north west	E N E ¾ E
North west by west	E by N
North west	E ¾ N
North west by north	E ½ N
North north west	E ¼ N
North by west	E, etc., etc. Through
North	S & W to N.

III

Relative Bearings

Relative bearings are bearings with relation to the vessel and are most important in connection with maneuvering to avoid collision. The relative direction of the wind, with reference to a sailing vessel, is most important *particularly to the officer in charge of a steamer*, who, under the rules of the road, must so handle *his* vessel as to keep clear of the sailer.

A vessel is heading North and the wind is from the following points:

Wind	Relative direction of wind with respect to vessel
North	Ahead
N by E	One point on starboard bow
N N E	Two points on starboard bow
N E by N	Three points on starboard bow
N E	Broad on starboard bow
N E by E	Three points forward, starboard beam
E N E	Two points forward, starboard beam
E by N	One point forward, starboard beam
E	Abeam
E by S	One point abaft, starboard beam
E S E	Two points abaft, starboard beam
S E by E	Three points abaft, starboard beam
S E	Broad off starboard quarter
S E by S	Three points on starboard quarter
S S E	Two points on starboard quarter
S by E	One point on starboard quarter
South	Astern

And so on around the port side to north.

Relative bearings of any object, vessel, lighthouse, etc., are also roughly located in the same way. Insist upon quick accurate bearings from lookouts when reporting. A lookout aloft will sing out*

"Sail ho!"

Officer: "Where away?"

Lookout: "Broad on port bow." Etc.

Too much emphasis cannot be placed on the importance of this subject of the compass and relative bearings. *Know the compass*—every sailor should have the compass engraved upon his brain, together with the action of the helm. Men who have many lives in their charge have special responsibilities. We all take the surgeon and his work very seriously. If he makes a mistake *one* person perishes. If the watch officer, on a liner, makes a mistake, a few hundred lives, at least, are liable to pay for his error.

*A good plan, suggested by Capt. W. J. Bernard, is to mark the points from the bow on the rim of the crow's nest to guide lookouts in reporting bearings accurately.

A Few Compass Problems

You are heading north. You sight a sail broad on your port quarter. How does she bear? Ans. S W.

You are close hauled on the starboard tack (in a square rigger, sailing six points from the wind) heading North. You put your helm up and haul the wind one point abaft the weather beam. How will you be heading then? Ans. N W by N.

A fore and after will lie (in theory at least) about four points from the wind. You are close hauled on the port tack, your schooner heading S W by S. What is the direction of the wind? Ans. S by E.

You go about. How will you be heading? Ans. S E by E.

Endless problems can be stated for practice. Such problems are always coming up when vessels meet. The wide-awake officer of the watch will always work them out in his mind even when no apparent danger exists.

We will state one more problem.

You are on the bridge of a steamer at night, making fifteen knots to S S W (course 202.5 degrees). Your smoke is rolling ahead of you three points to port and about one half as fast as you are going through the water. *Of course you have figured out the direction and force of the wind immediately upon taking over the watch.* You have looked at the sea and have seen the white caps a point on your starboard quarter. You know the wind is blowing a fresh full sail breeze from North by East, about 5 to 6 by the Beaufort Scale.

On the bridge there *seems* to be a pleasant light breeze three points on the starboard quarter.

You suddenly catch a glimpse of green light in a fold of the smoke blowing off ahead on the lee bow. A large sailing ship is off somewhere on your port bow slamming along with all sail set, anywhere from ten to twelve knots through the water. She has the right of way. How may she be heading?

Ans. You have seen her green light, broad on your port bow (S S E), therefore she may be running to S W, or going close hauled on starboard tack heading N W by W, or anywhere in between these points. That is, roughly, her possible heading under the conditions given is confined to the seven points of the compass indicated. *Also she is certainly crossing your bow.* What would you do?

Ans. Starboard helm at once and pass astern of her.

Officers of sufficient training will have had many such problems come to them in the course of their experience. Often there is

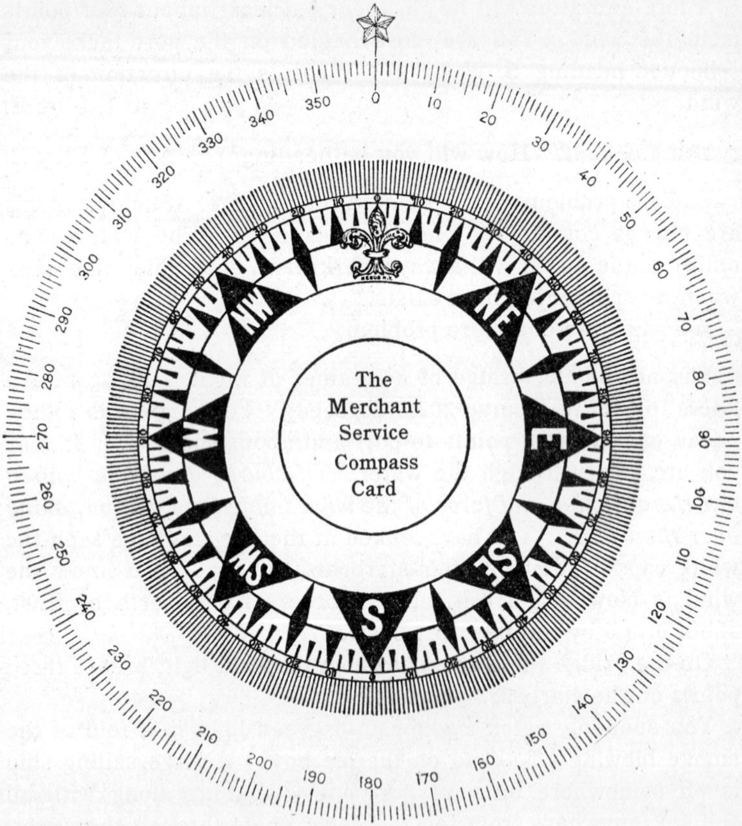

Outside circle the "scientific" compass card. Good for navigation; not much good for seamanship.

no time to note bearings, call the captain, etc. The watch officer must *act at once.*

But, to arrive at such decisions the watch officer must absolutely know his compass and how to work out relative bearings in his mind, seeing the possible direction of another craft quickly and correctly. Smoke rolling ahead has been the cause of many collisions. Some day the motor ship may do away with this.

Compass Graduations by Degrees

The method of graduation from North to East and West, ninety degrees each way, from South to East and West, ninety degrees each way, is well understood. The letters N, E, S, and W, and their combinations, must always be given. That is N E is N 45 degrees E. S W is S 45 degrees W. North, East, South and West are given direct without naming degrees.

The approved method in the newer navigation is to divide the horizon into 360 degrees, with 0 at North and to name the directions right-handed, as follows:

North	0	degrees
N E	45	"
East	90	"
S E	135	"
South	180	"
S W	225	"
West	270	"
N W	315	"

IV

*The Gyro Compass**

The gyro compass has come to stay and seamen should have a better understanding of its many points. The following interesting and instructive data on the gyroscopic compass is contributed by Mr. C. D. Jobson of the Sperry Gyro Company.

The gyro-compass obtains its directive force from the rotation of the earth, and always points to the true or geographic north.

* The Sperry Gyro Company conducts a special school for those who are interested in the use and care of their compass, gyro stabilizers, etc. Address the Company at Manhattan Bridge Plaza, Brooklyn, N. Y.

It has no variations and as magnetism does not effect it, it consequently has no deviation; therefore, as a compass, it is a valuable aid to navigation.

A balanced rotating gyroscope with three degrees of freedom will always point in the same direction or will maintain its "fixity of plane," unless affected by an outside force. Therefore, if a gyroscope with three degrees of freedom has a weight

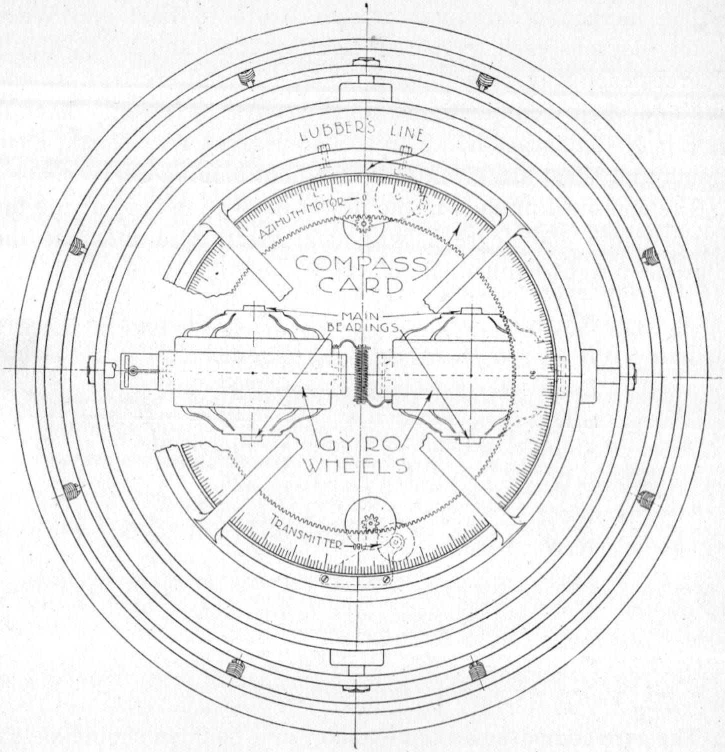

Sperry gyro compass—master compass.

hung from it, as the earth rotates the gyroscope points in the same direction holding the weight and relative to the earth this weight is raised and gravity immediately began to pull it down—this force of gravity exercises an outside force on the gyroscope and the resultant of the two forces will be the direction the gyroscope will travel. The action of gravity continues until the weight comes to rest held by gravity, at which time the axis of the gyroscope will be parallel with and pointing to the geographic north and south and will be rotating in the same direction. In other words, a gyroscope with a weight hung on it will line itself up with the axis of the earth and rotate in the same direction as the earth and can consequently be used as a compass.

First Successful Gyro Compass

Elmer A. Sperry's first compass was installed on the *Princess Anne* of the Old Dominion Line in 1911, and after very good success was removed and installed on the U. S. S. *Delaware* the same year. It proved so successful that the United States Navy immediately purchased ten compasses, and after they were installed the entire United States Navy was equipped, and the British, French, Italian, Russian, Spanish, Danish, Japanese, and other navies of the World immediately followed suit, and today there are over 1200 Sperry Gyro-Compasses in the naval service of the world.

Master gyro compass stand. Binnacle bowl lowered. Note—correction dials. See page 471.

After the European War the demands for gyro-compasses in the navies having been satisfied many ships of the Merchant Marine are being equipped with the Sperry Gyro-Compass. Among them the *Mauretania, Aquitania, Martha Washington, Bergensfjord, Panhandle State,* etc., etc.

The Sperry Gyro-Compass consists of the master compass, switchboard and repeater panel, motor generator, storage battery, steering repeater compass, bearing repeater compass and alarm bell. The motor generator is run from the ship's electric supply and regenerates the proper voltage to run the gyroscopes in the master compass, same being controlled through the switchboard; the storage battery is used in an emergency to run the motor in case the ship's supply fails. The steering and bearing repeater compasses are small electric compasses that are controlled by the master compass in the same manner that a master clock controls any number of repeaters.

The gyro steerer on the ship's bridge called "Metal Mike" is used to steer the proper courses. The steering repeater installed at the steering wheel is used to take bearings, i.e., to obtain a bearing or the position of another ship, lighthouse, or in fact any object relative to the position of the ship taking the bearing. Also the position of the sun can be taken, and by the use of azimuth tables the true course can be found, which is a check on the compass.

Steering repeater.

Messrs. Martienssen and Anschutz Kaempfe have invented a gyro-compass. This compass only has two degrees of freedom and is floated in mercury; also the gyroscopes run in a bowl of hydrogen put in at a pressure. The use of this compass has been confined purely to German warships.

The following data on the gyro compass is by Mr. Bradley Jones and is used here with his permission.

Latitude Error

Since the action of the gyroscope depends on the balance between two forces, one being the momentum of the gyroscope's rotation and the other being the unbalancing caused by the earth's rotation; any change in either of these will cause a change in the conditions of balance. The gyroscope's speed being kept constant its momentum will remain unchanged. On the contrary the effect of the earth's rotation varies with latitude. While the earth rotates at uniform speed, an object at the equator travels around at a speed of approximately 25,000 miles in the 24 hours or a little more than 1,000 miles per hour; while an object at say 60° lat. travels at only half that speed. This is due to travelling on a smaller diameter circle. Thus the conditions governing the precession of a wheel at the equator will not be the same at any other latitude.

As there is a definite and constant relation between the compass reading at varying latitudes, it is easily possible to calculate a table of corrections which may be applied when the latitude is changed. Or the compass lubber-line may be adjusted, for an average latitude and any errors disregarded. A vessel plying between New York and England might be adjusted for 45° say and since at 35° the error would only be .5° W and at 55° only .6° E; it may be disregarded in most cases safely.

If a vessel travels east or west it may be considered to be

either aiding or decreasing the effect of the earth's rotation. If it travels north or south; that is either as true directions or as components of direction, the balancing becomes further complicated by having to consider forces acting in three directions on the gyroscope system. Any error resulting from not properly compensating for this, is termed the 'north (or south) steaming error.' In foreign makes, this is taken care of by a set of tables.

In the American designed compass, while it is entirely possible to use tables to correct for these errors, provision is made for correcting both of these errors by *shifting the lubber-line.* Two graduated dials are set to correspond with the latitude, and speed respectively and these dials automatically shift the lubber-line and compensate for the respective errors. It should be borne in mind that by this means the errors are not eliminated, as the axle of the gyroscope does not actually point north and south, and while shifting the lubber-line so that it no longer coincides with the fore-and-aft line of the ship enables one to correctly interpret the ship's course. In the 'repeaters' which automatically copy the action of the main or 'master' compass in various parts of the ship, by a simple arrangement it is feasible to have true directions shown.

With the gyroscope there is of course, no troublesome swinging of the ship, to determine deviation. There is no need to determine the effect of the cargo on the compass needle for unlike the magnetic type it is unaffected by the nearness of iron or steel. It can easily be believed, as the makers claim, that the cost of the newer type is soon offset by saving in fuel and wages by steering straighter, truer courses. Perhaps even more important is the psychological effect, for with the manifold cares and anxieties incidental to their safely guiding their ship to its destination, what a relief it is to the navigators, no longer to be forced to depend on the magnetic needle with its variations and susceptibilities to error by any chance bit of iron or steel but to have for their use an instrument on whose readings they may always depend.

V

The Lead

To ascertain the depth of water on entering or leaving a port, or in any case where there is supposed to be less than twenty fathoms, soundings are taken by the *hand lead.* A quartermaster being stationed in the lead chains for the purpose. Hand lead lines are marked as follows:

At 2 fathoms from the lead, with 2 strips of leather.

At 3 fathoms from the lead, with 3 strips of leather.

At 5 fathoms from the lead, with a white cotton rag.
At 7 fathoms from the lead, with a red woolen rag.
At 10 fathoms from the lead, with leather, having a hole in it.
At 13 fathoms from the lead, as at 3.
At 15 fathoms from the lead, as at 5.
At 17 fathoms from the lead, as at 7.
At 20 fathoms from the lead, with 2 knots.
At 25 fathoms from the lead, with one knot.
At 30 fathoms from the lead, with three knots.
At 35 fathoms from the lead, with one knot.
At 40 fathoms from the lead, with four knots. And so on.

Heaving the lead on the Schoolship Newport.

These are known as the "marks." The numbers omitted, as 1, 4, 6, 8, etc., are called the "deeps," and they are spoken of together as the "marks and deeps of the lead line."

All lead lines should be marked when wet.

Soundings by the hand-lead are taken while the vessel has headway on, the leadsman throwing the lead forward, and getting the depth as the vessel passes, while the line is nearly perpendicular. He communicates to the officer the soundings obtained, thus:

If the depth corresponds with any of the marks, he calls, for instance "*By the mark 5!*" If the mark is a little below the surface, he calls, "*Mark under water 5!*" If the depth is greater, or one half more than any of the marks, he calls, "*And a quarter,*" or "*And a half 5!*" If the depth is a quarter less, he calls, "*Quarter less 5!*" If he judges by the distance between any two of the marks that the depth of water is 4, 6, 8, 9, 11, 12, 14, 16, 18, 19, or 21 fathoms, he calls, "*By the deep 4,*" etc.

On the hand-lead line there are nine "marks" and eleven "deeps."

Soundings should be given in a sharp, clear and decided tone of voice. In steamers, this is certainly the best plan, for while the old-fashioned "song" is being drawled out, the vessel may run ashore.

Hand leads generally weigh 7 or 14 lbs., though the following weights are also made, 4, 6, 8, 10, and 16 lbs.

An expert leadsman will grasp the line about two fathoms from the end (a small wooden toggle is sometimes seized into the lay of the line) and by swinging it back and forth a few times, keeping the line taut as the lead rises horizontal, he will get it over his head, and with two full turns, will send the lead and line along at a tangent, parallel with the ships side and almost parallel with the water. The coiled line must run out of his other hand without kinks. As the lead plunges, he grasps the running line with the hand used in heaving, and pulls in rapidly, until he feels the lead on the bottom. When the line is up and down, he bends over, plumbs the lead on the bottom and get the *feel*, hard, sticky, etc., as he reads the sounding and sings out to the bridge. The lead is swung overhead in the opposite way in which a wheel would turn if going ahead. It is released at the bottom of the swing and shoots ahead close to the water. Only considerable practice will make a good leadsman.

In coming into port do not expect good casts when the vessel is going above six or seven knots. Casts of eight to nine fathoms can then be made with reliability. When going faster the fourteen pound lead is used and an extra good leadsman is needed.

The markings of all lead lines should be examined from time to time, the lines being measured when wet. Always have at least three lead lines and five or six leads ready at hand in the bridge chest. The white rags at five and fifteen fathoms should be white cotton bunting. The red rags at seven and seventeen fathoms should be red woolen rag. On a dark night the feel will give the mark; if the hands are too cold take the rag to the lips.

American hemp, Italian hemp or braided cotton cord is generally used for lead lines, though any pliable signal halyard stuff will do. A hand lead line is usually 60 fathoms in length.

Too much care cannot be given to the position and fitting of the lead stands. These should be under or forward of the bridge on each side and far enough below the side light boxes so the lead will not strike them when swung overhead. Have a breast band fitted if the lead is to be used for any considerable time, and have the leadsmen protected from the wet with a tarpaulin apron. A second hand should stand by to haul in the line after each cast. Often a small snatch block is handy for this purpose. The leadsman if assisted will only have to coil his line for the next cast as it comes aboard.

Heaving the lead is so important that practice at sea is desirable. Where boys are carried they should be given regular practice in heaving, using a small canvas bag filled with water. This keeps them busy and does no harm if it flys over the rail, or comes down on their heads when they first try to swing it clear around.

In taking the chains at night it is well to know the height of the rail above water, in calling the depths. Wherever possible have two men in the chains on both sides, check one against another. Left-handed leadsmen should be developed.

The *blue pigeon* has kept many ships off the ground, and no modern device has yet been perfected that will take the place of its direct and reliable readings. No shipmaster should be at sea long without the certain knowledge that he has some *able seamen* in his crew who are dependable leadsmen. Remember a good leadsmen always calls out the character of the bottom, as *hard*, *soft*, *sticky*, etc., when he makes a cast; this information is of great value in coming to an anchorage.

The *coasting lead* is a heavy lead used in depths of from twenty-five to one hundred fathoms. It weighs from twenty-five to fifty pounds and is cast by carrying the lead well forward, and passing the line along the rail aft. On a sailing ship the lead line may be carried around the stern, the lead cast from the lee bow, and the final depth taken on the weather quarter. The markings are 20 fathoms, fish line with 2 knots; 30 fathoms, fish line with 3 knots, etc. A line with one knot marks each 5 fathoms between.

The deep sea lead (*dipsea* lead) is seldom used. It weighs 50 lbs.—the line is 120 fathoms or over. Markings same as coasting lead.

All leads are hollowed on the bottom and are *armed* with tallow or soap to bring up specimens of the sea bottom. This is specially so of the leads used with the sounding machine where a line of deep soundings may be taken on approaching a coast in thick weather. Then the character of the bottom is of great help in determining the approximate position of the vessel.

The Drift Lead. While at single anchor, it is good practice always to have a lead somewhat heavier than the hand-lead, say from fourteen to twenty pounds, over the side, and resting on the bottom, with a man to attend it. Of course, this is only necessary in a stiff breeze, or at night. By this you will have instant notice if the vessel drags her anchor.

VI

The Sounding Machine

The *sounding machine* now generally used at sea was first developed by the late Lord Kelvin. The machine consists of the following parts:

The *frame* carrying the *drum* upon which the *sounding wire* is wound. *Handles* are hinged to the journal of the drum and this in turn is controlled by a *friction brake.* When a sounding is to be taken the handles are thrown out, the lead is armed, a *depth recording tube* is placed in the brass holder, *open end down*, the lead is steadied over the stern, and the brake is released. As the lead plunges down, the vessel going ahead, a brass *finger pin* is held over the wire just forward of the roller of the after fair lead over which the wire runs. The *feel* of the wire, at the *sudden slack* when it strikes bottom, are attained by practice. Immediately after making bottom, the handles are wound in (this connects them) and the lead is brought back on board by means of the drum. A dial on the machine shows the actual amount of wire run out. Should the finger pin be lost a piece of wood will do just as well in feeling the run of the line. This method of feeling when bottom has been made is most important in getting good soundings and is only had by practice.

It is a good plan to save the tubes taken with *short casts* and to use them *for practice* in deeper water whenever this may be necessary. The time taken up in practice will be well spent when casts have to be made at night coming on the coast during bad winter weather, with snow and sleet. At times like this only experienced men are worth anything at the sounding machine. The writer has seen the most remarkable soundings sent to the bridge by amateurs, a hundred fathoms and over *with very little water under the ship.* The machine is allowed to run out after the lead has struck bottom, and if the vessel is not going very fast the lead lies on the bottom, the sounding tube is horizontal and fills with water, recording great depths. It is a good practice to always have a responsible officer at the sounding machine when important casts are to be taken. In the old days in the American Line the junior officer of the watch had this job.

Depth recording devices consist of some means to measure the *pressure* of the water when the lead is on the bottom. Knowing the pressure, a scale can be prepared which will show the head of water, or the depth. The method in general use is to fit a glass tube, closed at the upper end, and to measure the distance the water is forced *up* into the tube against the air which is compressed above it. This measure is made in different ways. Tubes are coated on the inside with a chemical composition (chromate of silver). This is reddish, and the action of the salt water turns the coating white, giving a very satisfactory mark of the distance the water pressure has forced salt water into the tube.* The tubes are two feet long, the scale, a two-sided graduated ruler, is calibrated to translate this distance into fathoms. As the depth increases the graduations become smaller and of course less accurate.

Each cast uses up a tube, and to prevent this waste (?) tubes with the inside surface made opaque by grinding have been used. The rise of the water can readily be seen on the ground glass. The closed end of the tube can be opened and the tube dried out. As a practical matter, the ground glass tube is not an economy. Time is too valuable to be taken up in drying tubes, although a few such tubes for emergency use are advisable on

* The mark should be sharp and perpendicular to the length of the tube A sounding with a slanting mark should be regarded with suspicion.

board ship. The writer has examined different depth scales and care must be taken to have a scale that will read correctly with any particular tube. This is not always the case. Tubes must be accurately made and of *exactly* the same inside diameter throughout.

The following practical and valuable notes on the degree of dependability and the use of sounding tubes are taken from reports of the U. S. Coast and Geodetic Survey.

"Although of undoubted value as a navigational instrument, the sounding tube is subject to certain defects which, operating singly or in combinations, may give results so misleading as to seriously endanger the vessel whose safety is entirely dependent upon an accurate knowledge of the depths.

"Efforts have been made from time to time by the Coast and Geodetic Survey to utilize tubes for surveying operations. The results obtained, however, have been so unsatisfactory that the general use of such tubes for surveying work has been discouraged.

"In *practical* tests, *carefully made by surveying parties,* where up-and-down casts of the lead were taken with tubes attached to the lead, *errors in the tube amounting at times to as much as 25 per cent. of the actual depths have been noted. Errors of 10 to 12 per cent. of the actual depth were quite common.*

"It is also worthy of note that in the great majority of cases the tubes gave depths *greater* than the true depths, which, in actual use in coastwise navigation, would usually have resulted in the conclusion that the ship was farther offshore than was really the case."

To Test a Sounding Machine

"Before undertaking the sounding necessary to make any particular landfall the vessel should be stopped for an up-and-down cast of the lead in order to test the accuracy under the prevailing conditions of the tubes which are to be used. For this purpose it is not necessary to get bottom; simply run out 60 to 80 fathoms of wire and then see how closely the tubes register that amount. A number of tubes can be sent down at one time, and it is then possible to select one or two which register most nearly correct.

"It is well to keep a permanent record of the results of each tube tested. By so doing the navigator will soon obtain valuable information as to the performance of the various tubes and the degree to which they may be trusted. Such a record should, of course, take into account the various conditions affecting the result."

A " Home Made " Sounding Tube

" It is interesting to note that sounding tubes which give good results can readily be made from plain glass or metal tubes aboard ship—gauge glasses, for instance. One end of the tube is closed with a cork and sealing wax. A narrow strip of chart paper of uniform width, on which a line has been ruled with an indelible pencil, is inserted the entire length of the tube. The paper is held in place by bending the projecting lower end upward along the outside of the tube and securing it with a rubber band. The height in which the water rises in the tube will be indicated by the blurring of the pencil line.

" If the air column in the tube is 24 inches long, the sounding may be read from any scale graduated for tubes of that length. If of a different length, a special scale must be prepared; its graduations, compared to those of the 24-inch scale, will be proportional to the comparative lengths of the two tubes.

" If certain precautions are taken, these tubes will give results which compare favorably with commercial tubes. The paper should be inserted uniformly in the tube, and its upper end, or a mark from which the measurement is taken, should coincide with the top of the air column. Metal tubes have the advantage of uniform bore, but if metal tubes are used the paper, in order to insure uniformity, should be fastened at the upper end when that end is being sealed and then stretched lightly at the bottom. The depth should always be read from the dry portion of the paper, as the wet portion is subject to considerable change in length."

Depth recorders depending upon spring pressure working against a piston, are sometimes used. A marker rides on a scale and the readings are direct. Such devices are all right when handled by experts, but are liable to get out of order at sea.

Other types of depth recorders *trap* the water at lowest depth and measure the sounding by the *amount* of water they bring up. Such instruments are far too complicated for use at sea. The chemically coated glass tube seems to be the best thing so far.*

Sounding machines are generally placed aft, a few paces from the taffrail, the frame of the machine screwed to deck plates

* " Physical Laws Underlying The Scale Of A Sounding Tube," by Walter D. Lambert, Geodetic Computer, U. S. Coast and Geodetic Survey, goes into this matter very thoroughly. It is a very valuable forty-five page pamphlet. Price five cents. Sold by Superintendent of Documents, Government Printing Office, Washington, D. C.

fitted for its reception. When lying in port for any length of time it is well to unship the sounding machine and stow it in the after wheelhouse, getting it out when preparing for sea.

Many sounding machines work from the bridge deck, the sounding wire leading out over the side through a swivel block carried on the end of a sounding spar. This should be at least three fathoms from the side of the vessel and fitted with a lift, and forward and after guys. The block is swiveled to a traveller and is hauled in and out along the spar so that the lead may be got at when hauled up. This arrangement has much to recommend it and enables the officer on the bridge to keep an eye on the casts without leaving his post.

The following practical instructions for the sounding machine are general. Officers should study the particular machine on board and become familiar with all of its parts and their operation.

"1. The work of taking a cast is to be done by two men, under the superintendence of an officer. For brevity, the men will be referred to as brakesman and leadsman. The regular post of the brakesman is at the starboard side of the sounding machine. The regular post of the leadsman is beside the taffrail fair-lead.

"2. The men go to their posts, and without further orders the brakesman puts on the two handles and fixes them securely by means of the screws. At the same time the leadsman sees that the lead is properly armed, and takes it along to the fair-lead. The officer examines the tube and places it in the guard-cylinder.

"3. The brakesman standing on the starboard side of the machine sees that the arm is prevented from turning by means of the catch. He then takes hold of the handle and puts the brake on by turning the handle in the direction for winding in the wire. When the brake is sufficiently tightened, the brakesman calls out 'brake on.' The leadsman then lets down the sinker without a jerk till it hangs upon the rope. The brakesman then, holding the handle in one hand, releases the arm and pays out by turning the handle until the link (connecting the plaited rope to the wire) has passed over the fair-lead. The leadsman then calls out 'on brake'; at which order, the brakesman engages the arm in the catch. The brakesman then reports 'brake on,' and the leadsman allows the sinker to hang free.

"4. The brakesman now, having seen that the index of the counter is at zero, takes the brass finger-pin, and holding it lightly by its handle, presses it against the wire and waits for the officer to give the order 'let go.'

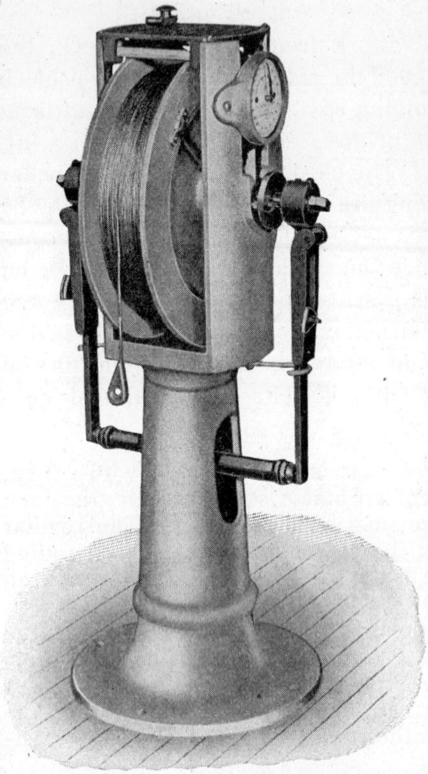

The Hand sounding machine.

"5. The brakesman instantly turns his handle in the direction for paying out until the drum with wire rotates freely. While the wire is running out he holds the handle in one hand and the finger-pin pressing against the wire in the other hand. The brakesman watches the counter, and if the bottom has not been reached before coming to 250, *he commences to apply the brake as soon as he sees the index of the counter at 250, so as to stop before 300 is reached.* As Soon as the brakesman feels the wire slacken, he at once begins turning the handle in the direction for hauling in, until the brake is tightened up and the egress of the wire stopped. He then releases the arm D and commences to wind in.

"6. The leadsman winds with his left hand and guides the wire to the drum with a piece of waste canvas in his right hand. The brakesman, winding with both hands, watches the counter from time to time during the winding in, and when the link is 5 fathoms from the fair-lead, he calls out 'hand the lead.'

"*Note.*—When the speed exceeds ten knots it is desirable to have another man to help in the winding. He is to stand looking aft, and to work with both his hands on the port handle, the leadsman working on the same handle with his left hand.

"7. The leadsman instantly leaves the machine, goes to the taffrail, and steadies the link and cord by his hand as they come up, and guides the link over the fair-lead; while the brakesman continues slowly winding in until the link reaches the wire drum; and placing it properly on the wire drum he winds in one turn more; then, taking care that the link is a little above the middle of the after side of the drum, so that its weight may help to keep the wire stretched, he puts on the brake. Meantime the leadsman hauls by hand on the sinker. The leadsman then takes the lead on board, shows the tube to the officer, examines the arming for specimen of bottom, shows it to the officer, and prepares the arming for a fresh cast, and then goes forward to the machine and stands by for another sounding.

"8. The reading on the counter shows approximately the number of fathoms of wire run out. This may be something more than twice the depth for speeds under 11 knots; or it may be almost as much as three and a half times the depth if the speed be 15 or 16 knots. The proportion of wire to depth differs not only with the speed of the ship, but also with the roughness of the sea and with the depth itself.

"Cautions and Explanations

"9. The wire will break *at a kink* under a very moderate pull or a very slight jerk. Without a kink, and with proper care, the wire can scarcely be broken in practice with the machine. No wire should ever be lost in service, unless by some extremely rare accident, not foreseen, and therefore not provided against.

"10. Absolute security against kinks would be had if the wire could be prevented from ever slacking. It does slacken somewhat the moment the lead touches the bottom, but not to a dangerous degree if the ship is going at anything more than 5 knots, and if the brake is instantly applied, when, by the wire's yielding to the brass pin, the commencement of slacking is shown. The brake should be instantly applied, so as to slow the motion of the wheel, but not with force enough to stop the wheel suddenly. There is much more danger of losing the wire through a kink in taking an up-and-down cast than in a flying cast with the ship running at 12 or 14 knots. *Whenever a cast is taken at any speed less than 5 knots, it is advisable to manage the brake so as to moderate the speed of egress according to judgment, letting the wheel run around at something like three turns per second.* If the ship's speed is more than 5 knots, observe all the rules laid down in the instruction preceding.

"11. When taking the last cast of a series of soundings, wipe off wire with a greasy rag as it comes in over the rail."

Soundings taken at random are of little value in fixing or checking position and may at times be misleading. In thick weather, when near or running close to the land, in shoal water, or in the vicinity of dangers, soundings should be taken continuously and at regular intervals, and, with the character of the bottom, systematically recorded. An exact agreement with the soundings on the chart need not be expected, as there may be some little inaccuracies in reporting the depth on a ship moving with speed through the water, or the tide may cause a discrepancy, or the chart itself may lack perfection, but the soundings should agree in a general way and a marked departure from the characteristic bottom shown on the chart should lead the navigator to doubt his position and proceed with caution; especially is this true if the water is more shoal than expected. By laying the soundings on tracing paper, according to the scale of the chart, along a line representing the track of the ship, and then moving the paper over the chart parallel with the course until the observed soundings agree with those on the chart, the ship's position will, in general, be quite well determined.

The value and importance of soundings, especially in thick or foggy weather, can best be shown by an example: In Lake Superior, on the steamboat course from Devils Island to Duluth, when 50 fathoms or more are obtained by sounding, the master knows at once that he is to the northward of his course, and, owing to strong local disturbance, liable to strand on the north shore. The value of this information can not be overestimated. Again, in approaching Boston, almost due north of Race Point and a little to the northward and eastward of Stellwagen Bank, a hole has been found of nearly 100 fathoms, the adjacent soundings being between 50 and 60 fathoms This hole is so sudden and pronounced that it would be almost impossible to make a mistake about it, and in coming into Boston in thick weather makes a very good "fix," and is invariably looked for by captains making this trip in foggy weather.

Motor sounding machines have come into use, doing away with the labor of winding in the wire after each cast. The motor is carried in the base of the machine, all very compact and up to date.

The Fathometer. The operation of the Fathometer System is based upon the principle that the velocity with which sound travels through water is substantially constant. Consequently a measurement of the time interval required for a sound to travel to the bottom of the sea and return to the ship as an echo is a true measure of the depth. The Fathometer Indicator automatically measures these time intervals and converts them into depth readings which are visually indicated on a clock-like dial. The Fathometer Indicator, Amplifier and Oscillator Control are usually placed either in the pilot house or chart room of the vessel.

Fathometer Indicator. The Fathometer Indicator controls the operation of the Oscillator which produces the sound waves. It receives the electrical impulses produced in the Hydrophone by the returning echoes and translates the time interval elapsing between the emission of the sound and its return as an echo into a visual indication of the depth on the Fathometer dial.

Thus by noting the figure on the depth scale opposite the flash of light, the depth of water is determined as easily as time is shown on a clock. Automatic repetition of the soundings 24 times a minute ensures frequent and accurate depth measurements upon which safe navigation so often depends.

Amplifier. The Amplifier which accompanies the Indicator transforms the sound echoes as received from the Hydrophone into electrical impulses of sufficient strength to cause a flash of red light at the proper place on the Fathometer dial to indicate the depth beneath the vessel's keel.

Oscillator. The Impact Oscillator which delivers sounds of great intensity for a small fraction of a second is usually installed in the double bottom water tank. The sound so produced is transmitted through the ship's skin to the bottom of the sea, from which it returns to the ship as an echo. After the sound is sent out, the spring driven plunger, the impact of which against the oscillator diaphragm produces the sound, is returned to its original position in preparation for the next sounding. Such adjustments of the current required to operate the oscillator are made with the oscillator control which is installed in the wheel house or chart room near the Fathometer Indicator.

Hydrophone. The hydrophone sound receivers are suspended in a small water filled tank mounted against the ship's skin at a short distance from the impact oscillator. When the Fathometer is in operation the echo returning from the bottom passes through the ship's skin to the sound receiver. The echo produces a short, sharp pulsation of the current in the electric circuit of the hydrophone and is amplified sufficiently to produce the momentary flash of red light on the clock-like time measuring dial of the Fathometer Indicator.

Operation. To start the Fathometer the navigator turns the switch on the Fathometer Indicator and the depth is indicated on the dial. As long as the equipment is left in operation, it will indicate the depth continuously. This is in marked contrast to the many minutes required to obtain a single sounding with mechanical methods of obtaining depth measurements.

In the 1930 issue of the United States Coast Guard Pilot for the Atlantic Coast, Section C, Page 279, attention is directed to the value of echo depth sounding as an aid to navigation, as follows:

"*Soundings.* In thick weather, when near or approaching the land or danger, soundings should be taken continuously and at regular intervals . . . , systematically recorded. By marking the soundings on tracing paper, according to the scale of the chart, along a line representing the track of the ship and then moving the paper over the chart parallel with the course until the observed soundings agree with those of the chart, the ship's position will in general be quite well determined. Echo sounding instruments, the use of which is increasing rapidly, provide the mariner with a most valuable aid to navigation." *

VII

The Submarine Sentry

The submarine sentry is a sort of inverted kite resembling in shape a hod used for carrying bricks. It is fitted with a span and a trigger projecting downward which releases the span and the letting up of pressure on the towing wire sounds an alarm. Speed also is limited to about fourteen knots.

VIII

The Log

The measurement of speed through the water is essentially an operation of seamanship, as much as the steering of the vessel. The recording of distance run and direction made good falls within the sphere of navigation, although it is seamanship applied to navigation.

Perhaps the oldest method of measuring, or estimating, the speed of a vessel through the water is to observe the water rushing by and to note objects, such as weed, waves, etc. The practiced eye, accustomed to see from a certain position, will gauge speed with a remarkable degree of accuracy. In coming alongside of other vessels, entering harbor, docking, and in maneuvering to avoid collision at sea, this method of measuring speed comes to the fore. Under such circumstances no one thinks of consulting logs. Taffrail logs are generally hauled in

* The Submarine Signal Co., of 160 State Street, Boston, Mass., will gladly supply those readers who inquire with folders describing their apparatus.

by that time (in or near port), and all the faculties are concentrated on the big job of handling the vessel itself. It is simply another instance of getting back to first principles. Where very slow movements of a ship are being made, as in docking, some masters turn a small stream of water overboard near the bridge, this instantly advises them of any change in speed or whether going ahead or astern.

The *dutchman's log* consisting of a chip, thrown overboard near the bow and drifting aft past certain marks on the rail, was a very practical means of measuring speed in the times of slow old tubs taking half a year or more to double the cape on the long passage to the East Indies.

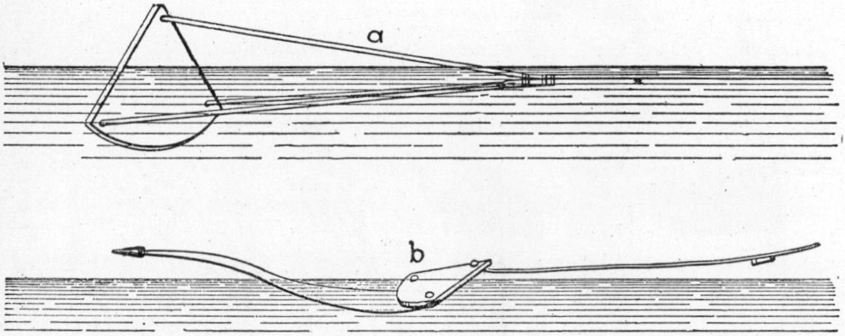

Chip log. A, with chip upright. B, plug jerked out of socket for hauling in.

The *chip log*, still used on sailing craft, is a very accurate means of measuring speed up to say fifteen knots. It is a splendid check on the performance of the taffrail log or of some newer logs that record speed in miles per hour on a dial. When the chip log and line are properly marked, *line wet* in marking, and the sand glass has been compared with the chronometer and found to be accurate, the whole business is simple and certain.

The apparatus consists of the *chip*, a quadrantal sector of wood, weighted with lead on its circular side and fitted with a bridle, and a socket and toggle. The toggle is held in the socket by friction and is released when a jerk is given the line on hauling in. The radius of the quadrant should be about six inches.

The *log-line* is made of signal halyard stuff, 150 fathoms long. One end is secured to the chip and the other to a reel on which the line is wound. The line is marked at 15 fathoms from the chip end by a piece of bunting. This part of the line is called *stray line*. From this piece of bunting the line is marked at every 47 feet 3 inches by a piece of fish line held between the strands of the log-line, the line being marked by a knot in the fish line for every division (47 feet 3 inches) from the bunting. Thus at 94 feet 6 inches from the bunting the piece of fish line has two knots in it, etc. These main divisions, called *knots*, are further subdivided into five equal parts by pieces of white bunting between the strands to indicate two-tenths of a knot.

Heaving old-fashioned chip log.

The *log-glass* is a sand glass similar to an hour glass constructed to run for 28 seconds. A 14-second glass is also used.

Three men are needed to " heave the log." One heaves the chip-log and tends the log-line, one holds the reel, and one tends the log-glass.

To find the speed by the chip-log, hold the reel well up by its handles and unwind some of the stray line. Insert the toggle in its socket and heave the chip overboard, allowing the line to run out freely. As the first piece of bunting, which marks the end of the stray line, passes over the taffrail call out " *turn* " and invert the log-glass sharply. Just as the last particle of sand passes from the top to the bottom of the glass call out "*mark*" and seize the log-line, which has been running out freely. The subidivisional mark which is now at the taffrail indicates the speed of the vessel in knots and tenths. For instance, if the cord having six knots is at the rail, the vessel is making six knots per hour. This can be demonstrated as follows:

Principle of Construction. When the chip hits the water it ceases to partake of the motion of the ship and becomes stationary in the water. Between the first mark and the interval of time is 28 seconds (the time it takes the sand to run from the top to the bottom of the glass). In this interval of time the vessel moves 6 times 47 feet 3 inches (as shown by the log-line). Now in feet $\frac{6 \times 47.25 \times 60 \times 60}{28}$ is the distance that the vessel would move in one hour at the same rate.

$$\text{Or } \frac{6 \times 47.25 \times 60 \times 60}{28 \times 6080} = 6 \text{ knots per hour.}$$

The 28-second glass is used for low speeds. For speeds over 6 knots a 14-second glass is used and the reading of the log-line is doubled.

To haul in the line after a reading is obtained, give the line a sharp tug. This will release the toggle and the chip will lay flat on the surface and can be hauled in hand over hand and reeled up.

Of course everyone knows that a *knot* is 6080 feet, and when we speak of a *mile* at sea we always mean a knot. The knot, mile, and minute of latitude (mean) are all the same, that is 6080 feet in length.*

Speed by revolutions. Many vessels gauge their speed by the revolutions of the propeller, or propellers, in the case of twin and triple screw craft. An accurate measure of the revolutions

* In the United States the sea mile or nautical mile or knot, used for the measurement of distances in ocean navigation, has a length of 6,080.27 feet; in France, Germany, and Austria the nautical or sea mile has a length of 6,076.23 feet; in England the nautical mile, corresponding to the "Admiralty knot," is 6,080 feet. The geographic mile, which is the length of one minute of longitude of the equator of the terrestrial spheroid, is 6,087.15 feet long. The statute mile, used principally in measurements on land, is 5,280 feet.—Questions and Answers, No. 1, U. S. Hydrographic Office.

is kept by the counters, the *pitch* of the screws is known, that is we know the distance they would travel through a solid medium in one revolution, and the *slip* or the percentage the screw falls short of its theoretical advance is estimated.

Given

Pitch of screws
Revolutions (total or per minute)
Percentage of slip

We can easily figure out speed and distance. Revolution speed tables are usually prepared for a vessel and the whole matter simmers down to *guessing* what the slip is under certain conditions. Wind, sea, draft, trim and condition of the bottom of the vessel all effect the amount of slip. If some accurate method of determining the exact slip were available, this method of measuring distance through the water would be ideal.

Devices fitted for counting and recording the speed at which the shaft and propeller is turning are called *tachometers.* The recording dials on the bridge are most useful in indicating *at once* the changes in speed and direction of the engines and gives the master information he needs in maneuvering his vessel.

One of the most practical devices giving visual indication of the direction and action of the engines is the McNab direction indicator, operated by a pneumatic pump, a positive means of keeping the bridge informed as to the action of the engines.

The principle of pneumatic action is also used in the Cumming's Log, where after every fifty revolutions of the propeller, a small valve at the engine room counter opens to the vacuum of the main condenser and actuates the counter on the bridge.

The Navigator Log employs the well-known principle of the *pitot* tube. Here the difference in pressure on two sides of a diaphragm records the speed. The *Sal Log* is a similar device.

The navigator log is a Swedish invention. The log is simple in operation. The business end of it protrudes vertically from the bottom of the vessel and consists of a hollow tube with two passages. Near the end of the tube are two holes, one facing the direction in which the ship is traveling, and the other opening on the side at 90 degrees. A passage through which the water flows leads from each hole to the mechanism immediately inside the hull.

The hole facing towards the ship's bow registers the water pressure produced by the speed of the vessel, while that on the side gauges the hydrostatic pressure, or that resulting from the draft of the ship. The pressures record themselves upon a membrane in an indicator located in the engine-room, which measures the difference between the speed and draft pressure of the vessel and thus determines her speed. From the engine-room indicator there is conveyed to a second indicator on the bridge by means of an electric current a registration of every knot traveled by the ship. The officer on duty is thus able to tell not only how fast his ship is traveling, but also the total number of knots the ship has traveled since the indicator was set.

The log is said to begin to act as soon as the vessel is set in motion and to indicate with the greatest precision both the speed of the vessel, as well as the distance traveled. It further begins to register at very low speed (1 to 1½ knots), and acts independently of all external conditions, such as changes of temperature, the draft of the vessel, the rolling and pitching of same, etc.

The apparatus is well protected and easy to instal. When once in place it requires little attention. Nor does it call for frequent adjustments, refilling, winding, etc.

The Nicholson log was another one of the pitot tube devices, but depended upon mechanical means for its readings. It is seldom used today.

IX

The Taffrail Log

The *taffrail log* consists of a rotator trailing astern at the end of a length of log line (cotten plaited stuff) an indicator mounted on a pivoted fork resting on the taffrail. The rotation of the small screw or rotator is communicated to the recording device on the rail. It is a simple device, its operation can be readily seen from the bridge. The log line may become fouled and the log should be streamed on the side opposite from the ash ejector, as this will effect its readings. Gulf weed is a prolific source of trouble. The moment a change in distance is noted, at the hourly reading, the log should be hauled in and examined, unless the engine speed has been altered during the interval and accounts or it. A scrap of rag twined about the

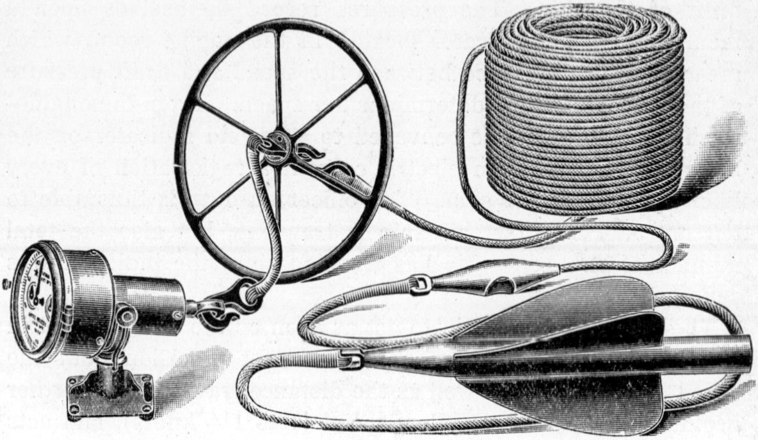

The Bliss Star taffrail log.

line near the rotator or a bit of yarn or weed will generally be found.

The speedier a vessel the longer the line will have to be. The log line for a vessel of 150 feet should not be less than 200 feet. On fast craft longer lines are needed. The pitch of the rotor blades can easily be altered and care should be taken to put the log overboard and calibrate it over a measured distance in waters reasonably free from current.

Dial of a taffrail log.

At very slow speed the log is liable to lag and the rotor will hang down with the log line floating; unsatisfactory readings are generally the result. In a sailer it is well to use a Bliss taffrail log where slow speeds are frequent.

Certain logs, such as the Walker Cherub, ring a bell at intervals. The Walker log does this each sixth of a knot. A handy table should be computed and hung in the wheelhouse so that the time interval between "bells" will give the rate of speed at a glance.

This relation between speed and time can easily be plotted in the form of a curve and pasted to a card (varnished) to be hung in the wheelhouse. A stop watch is handy for measuring the interval of time.

A. Recording dial. B. Rotator. C. Bunch of Gulf weed on line, D. This often happens and must be looked after when log slows up.

Most logs for the higher speeds are fitted with a fly wheel or governor, as the line is otherwise liable to be filled with turns, then speed up the recording clock and untwist itself, and again lie idle while the line accumulates another set of turns. The governor prevents this action and does much toward making the taffrail log fairly reliable.

The log should always be streamed as soon as the pilot is dropped, or at least before taking the departure, so that it is working freely when the readings are taken. As soon as the vessel stops, no matter when or for how long, haul in the log. When the log is hauled in while the vessel has way upon her, unhook the inboard end of the line and trail this over the *opposite* quarter while hauling in the rotator. Otherwise the hauling in of the rotator fills the log line with additional turns and makes it awkward to coil. When the rotator is on board haul in the free end and coil down. Always hang up the line to dry before stowing away, clean rotator and wipe off the log.

For night reading an electric connection should be made near the log. A log dial made luminous would seem to be desirable.

Some logs are streamed from a spar near the bridge wing.

The *harpoon log.* This was a contraption towed astern and fitted with vanes revolving from its tail and connected to recording mechanism in the log. To get the readings the "harpoon" was hauled in each watch. Now only an interesting relic.

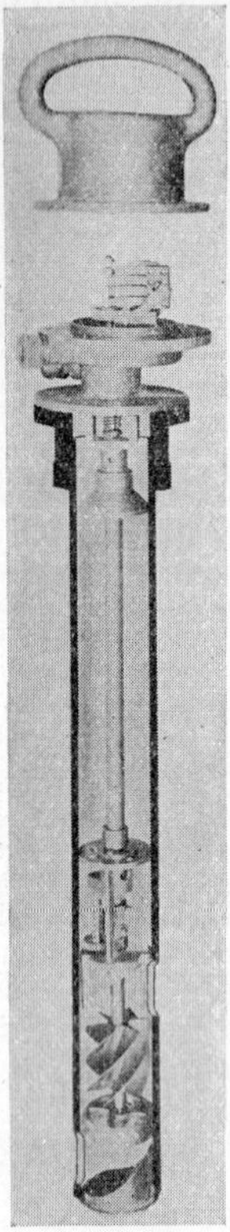

Sperry log rotator.

The Sperry Log and Shoal Water Alarm

The sperry log consists of a rotator placed in a vertical tube projecting through the bottom skin of the vessel. Suitable valves are provided for the withdrawal of the tube. The action of the log is seen from the sketch. Water enters the vertical tube placed on or near the center line of the vessel and at the "turning point" of the length of hull. The small propeller records the passage of water through the tube and this, in turn, is measured by an electric counter and transmitted to the bridge.

The *shoal water alarm* consists of an automatic comparison between the speed made by the log and the revolutions made by the propellers. As a vessel slows up in shoal water the speed of ship, for a given speed of propellers, decreases. This relation of propeller speed and ship speed is practically constant under all speeds in deep water.

By means of cams, laid out to correspond to varying relations between speed and R.P.M. of propellers, two contacts are held at a certain distance apart under normal deep water conditions. When the water shoals this ratio is changed, the contacts close, and an alarm bell rings.

The dial diagrams are self explanatory.

Like all things on board ship, the Sperry log must be taken care of and handled with intelligence in order to obtain reliable results.

X

Piloting

Piloting, and coming in with the land, is another part of seamanship where the navigator and the sailor exercise their skill at the same time. No seaman will close in with a coast until he has informed himself fully as to the conditions prevailing. The sailing directions, the charts, the buoy and light lists, and the tide tables should be consulted and carefully digested, not by the master alone, but by one or more of the ship's officers.

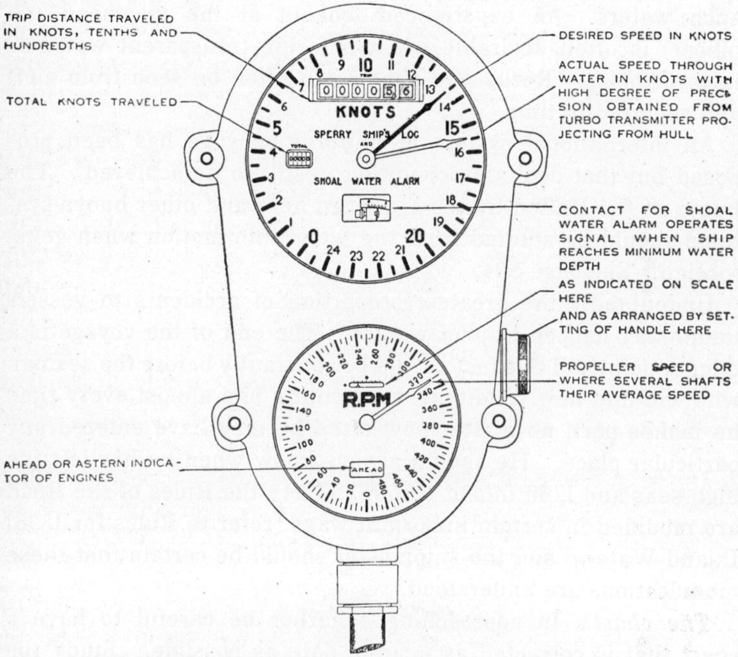

Bridge dials. Sperry log and shoal water alarm.

It is well to talk over the situation and be certain that those who are to be in charge of the bridge are familiar with the conditions.* Where complete data is not available, the greatest care should be taken to get soundings, check all bearings, and *see* all marks laid down on the charts. Where buoys, other marks, kelp, etc., are met with that are not found on the chart proceed with caution.

The greatest care should be taken in going into shallow waters for the first time. It is an excellent plan to proceed into

* "Officers spend much time in perfecting themselves in deep sea navigation where the ship is not endangered, but do not always acquire the maximum knowledge available before piloting into port where the danger really exists."—Lieut.-Commander R. R. Mann, U. S. Navy, in *Proceedings, U. S. Naval Institute*, Nov., 1919.

such waters near the low stage of the tide, except, of course where high tide is needed to get in over bars.*

Tidal currents are liable to take dangerous directions across channels, often depending upon the winds prevailing at any certain time, and great care should be exercised in going into such waters. An experienced lookout at the masthead (an officer) is often desirable when entering transparent water as in the tropics. Rocks and shoals can often be seen from aloft and reported in time.

An international system of uniform buoyage has been proposed but that desirable condition is still to be achieved. The buoys of the United States are given here and other buoys systems should be studied from the latest information when going foreign. See page 504.

Undoubtedly the greatest proportion of accidents to vessels under way happen in pilot waters. The end of the voyage is a danger point and this fact should be constantly before the seaman who will find new conditions confronting him almost every time he makes port, no matter how often he may have entered any particular place. He should always know when he has left the high seas and is in *inland waters.* Here the Rules of the Road are modified in certain important ways (refer to Rules for U. S. Inland Waters) and the shipmaster should be certain that these modifications are understood.

The chart. In approaching a harbor be careful to have a chart that is corrected as near to date as possible. Study the chart with the greatest care. It is well to consider a harbor by means of a small scale chart in order to get an idea of its general surroundings, then concentrate on the large scale chart. Study channels, bars, shoals, tides, currents, buoys, lights, anchorage, wharves, harbor regulations, wind conditions, etc. Work out all bearings and courses to be steered. Read all notes and directions *even if a pilot is expected.*

XI

Data on Charts

The following information in regard to charts is adapted from the U. S. Hydrographic Bulletin No. 10. It is of the utmost importance to the seaman and should be thoroughly studied.

*If possible see all ballast tanks full before entering shallow waters. The reason is self-evident.

"The charts in general use by navigators are constructed on the Mercator projection. All the meridians are parallel straight lines, and the degrees of longitude are all equal. The parallels of latitude are at right angles to the meridians, and the degrees of latitude increase in length from the lowest to the highest parallel in the same proportion as the degrees of longitude decrease on the globe. The property which makes it so useful for purposes of navigation is that the track of a ship, as long as she steers the same true course, appears upon the chart as a straight line.

The Mercator chart

"The course is the direction in which the ship passes from one place to another, referred to the meridian which lies truly North and South, or to the position of the needle of the compass by which the ship is steered; the former is called the *true course* and the latter the *compass course.*

Courses true and compass

"To find the course draw a straight line connecting the point of departure and the point of destination; transfer the direction of this line to the center of the nearest compass rose by means of a parallel ruler, and read the angle that this line makes with the true meridian upon the divisions of the compass rose. The course to be steered by compass is found by applying to the true course the value of the variation of the compass, as found from the lines of equal variation given on the chart, and then the value of the deviation of the compass which is due to the iron in the ship's hull, and is different for different directions of the ship's head. Thus, the true course between Chicago Lighthouse and Big Point Sable is N. 20° 30′ E. or 20° 30′, the magnetic course is N. 18° 10′ E. or 18° 10′; the mean variation being 2° 20′ E., and the course to be steered by compass, assuming the deviation on the magnetic course N. 18° 10′ E., to be 5° W. is N. 23° 10′ E., or 23° 10′.

"The latitude scales, which bound the charts on the east and west, are to be used for measuring distances between places. If the places are on the same meridian, their distance apart is most readily estimated by finding the difference of latitude in minutes. Distances between points situated on lines that make an angle with the meridians may be measured by taking between the points of the dividers a small number of subdivisions near the middle latitude of the line to be measured, and stepping them off on that line. All distances measured by means of the latitude scale are in nautical miles which can be readily converted into statute miles by multiplying by 1.15.

Measuring distances

"The value of a chart must manifestly depend upon the character anu accuracy of the survey on which it is based, and the larger the scale of the chart the more important these become.

Accuracy of a chart

"To judge of a survey, its source and date, which are generally given in the title, are a good guide. Besides the changes that may have taken place since the date of the survey in waters where sand or mud prevails, the earlier surveys were mostly made under circumstances that precluded great accuracy of detail; until a plan founded on such a survey is tested it should be regarded with caution. *It may indeed be said that, except in well-frequented harbors and their approaches, no surveys yet made have been so minute in their examination of the bottom as to make it certain that all dangers have been found.* The fullness or scantiness of the soundings is another method of estimating the completeness of the survey, remembering, however, that the chart is not expected to show all soundings that were obtained. When the soundings are sparse or unevenly distributed it may be taken for granted that the survey was not in great detail.

Soundings

"Large or irregular blank spaces among soundings mean that no soundings were obtained in these spots. When the surrounding soundings are deep it may fairly be assumed that in the blanks the water is also deep; but when they are shallow, or it can be seen from the rest of the chart that reefs or banks are present, such blanks should be regarded with suspicion. This is especially the case in coral regions and off rocky coasts, and it should be remembered that in waters where rocks abound it is always possible that a survey, however complete and detailed, may have failed to find every small patch or pinnacle rock.

"A wide berth should therefore be given to every rocky shore or patch, and *instead of considering a coast to be clear, the contrary should be assumed.*

Reading a chart

"*Chart reading* aims to give such explanation concerning the various symbols and standards as will establish easily remembered relations between these graphic representations and the physical features which they represent. Briefly stated, the standards governing charts are the following:

"The 'shore line' is the boundary between water and land at high water. This boundary is shown by a continuous line wherever data is sufficient to plot the same with any degree of accuracy; otherwise a dashed line is used, indicating 'approximate' delineation.

"*Vertical* lettering is used for any feature dry at high water and not affected by the movement of the waters.

"*Leaning* lettering is used to describe such features as are parts of the hydrography.

"Very often, on smaller scale charts, a small reef can not be

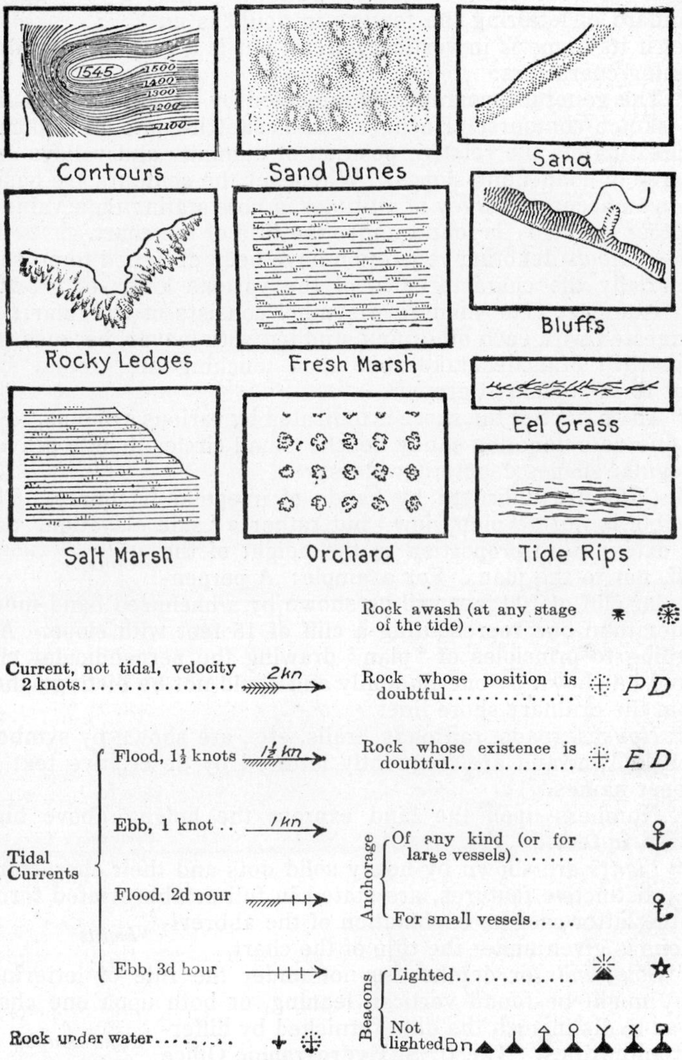

Chart symbols.

distinguished from a small islet; the proper name for either might be '.......... Rock.' Following the standard of lettering the feature in doubt is an islet if its name is in vertical letters, but is a reef if lettered in leaning characters.

Reefs or Islands

" The general topography is indicated by hachures, contours, or sketch-contours. Hachures and sketch-contours indicate approximately the relative position of summits and valleys and degree of connecting slopes. Whenever the contours are based upon an accurate survey of altitudes, a note stating their value—contour interval—is found under the title of the chart.

" *Symbols* denoting vegetation have been designed to present pictorially the characteristics of the various kinds of growth. For example: The mangrove symbol consists of irregular ribs connected with each other and studded with leaves, because the mangrove branches take root upon touching the ground and thus form a chain of growth.

" The nature of the shore is indicated by various symbols, rows of fine dots denoting sandy beach; small circles denote gravel; irregular shapes denote bowlders.

" *Cliffs* are indicated by bands of irregular hachures. The symbol is *not* a ' plan view,' but rather a ' side elevation,' and its extent is in proportion to the height of the cliff, not to the plan. For example: A perpendicular cliff of 100 feet will be shown by a hachured band much wider than one representing a cliff of 15 feet with slope. According to principles of ' plan ' drawing the perpendicular cliff could be shown by one line only and could not be distinguished from the ordinary shore line.

Cliffs

" *Houses*, roads, railroads, trails, etc., are shown by symbols well known, and are frequently lettered by descriptive text or proper names.

" Numbers upon the land express the height, above high water, in feet.

" *Lights* are shown by heavy solid dots and their characters, *i.e.*, distinctive features, are stated in full or abbreviated form; in the latter case an explanation of the abbreviations is given under the title of the chart.

Lights

" *Soundings* or depths are not under the rule of lettering; they might be found vertical, leaning, or both upon one chart so as to distinguish the data furnished by different authorities. The U. S. Hydrographic Office shows the soundings by means of vertical block figures, considered the clearest type. These figures denote fathoms or feet, always stated in the title of the chart.

Hydrography

" The extent of fairway and water areas restricting navigation to limited draft, is indicated by a system of lines, called ' fathom

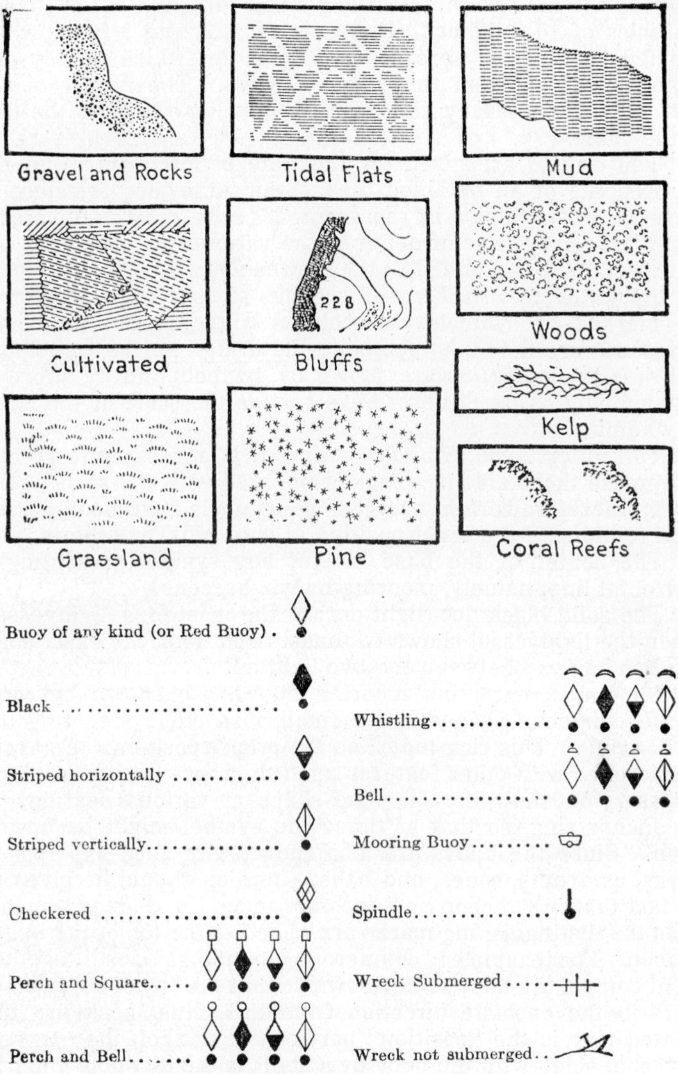

Chart symbols.

lines.' They are lines connecting equal depths, generally showing the limits of areas of depth of 1 fathom, 2, 3, 5, 10, and multiples of 10 fathoms. The areas of 1, 2, and 3 fathoms are stippled so that they are covered by a tint which readily distinguishes them from the deeper waters. The *nature of the bottom* is indicated by abbreviations, explained under the title of the chart.

"The *depths* are given for the time of low water, and the least depths of all obtained during the survey are selected, so that the hydrography is represented in its most unfavorable condition. Increases of depth at the various stages of tide can be ascertained and added to the figures upon the chart.

"*Reefs, ledges, sunken rocks,* rocks awash, and foul ground are marked by symbols. Discolored water, ripples, currents, and weeds are noted, by symbol or lettering.

"*Aids to navigation* are shown by symbols and by abbreviations, or by as much descriptive text as the scale of the chart may admit.

"To render these symbols distinct it is necessary to greatly exaggerate these aids in size, as compared with the scale of the chart; therefore certain parts of the symbols have been agreed upon to indicate the exact position of such aids, as follows:

"The center of the base line of any symbol presenting a horizontal line, namely, mooring buoys, beacons.

"The solid black dot (light dot) at the mast of a lightvessel. When the lightvessel shows two masts and dots, the exact position lies halfway between the two light dots.

"All *buoys*, excepting mooring buoys, are shown by compressed diamond-shapes and a small open circle, denoting the anchor ring. This ring indicates the proper position. To avoid interference with other features upon the chart it is often found necessary to show the diamond-shape at various bearings to the anchor ring, so that at times the symbol might be upside down. Since the buoys are also shown with such superposed marks, as drums, cones, and balls, attention should be given to the fact that the anchor ring does *not* touch the diamond-shape, while the distinguishing marks are *joined* to the top of the buoy-symbol. For example: Numerous soundings close together might compel the buoy to be shown so that the top of the symbol bears in the opposite direction from the actual position; the isolated ring is the 'position' part of the symbol, the opposite ring (connected with the buoy by a staff) is the distinctive mark.

"The *buoy symbol* is shown 'open'—in outline—for buoys of any color other than black; black buoys are shown by 'solid' shape. If the buoy system shown upon the chart consists of the black and one other color only, the explanation under the title will ascribe such color to the 'open' symbol. Thus upon one chart it may be found to denote 'red buoy' while upon another chart it may be stated as 'white' or 'green;' the meaning of the 'open' symbol *varies*, the meaning of the 'solid' symbol is always the same—'black.'

"Upon any chart containing buoys of various colors besides black the color will be found stated by abbreviation or in full alongside each symbol.

"The buoy symbol, surmounted by a small dot surrounded by rays, denotes a 'lighted' buoy; surmounted by a crescent (points downward) denotes a 'whistling' buoy; surmounted by a half disk with dot *above* the same denotes a 'bell' buoy.

"A line drawn between the upper and lower points of the diamond-shape (longer axis) denotes 'vertical stripes;' a line drawn between the side points (shorter axis) denotes 'horizontal stripes;' both lines drawn denote 'checkered' buoy.

"*Ranges* are shown by lines of dashes and by continuous lines, the latter are only shown as far as a ship may follow the range in safety. The bearings are given as 'true' and are expressed, upon later charts, in degrees of a protractor divided into 360, starting at North and following the hands of a clock. Older charts, still giving bearings by easterly or westerly deviations from North or South, are being corrected in this respect as rapidly as the facilities of the Hydrographic Office permit. For example: 'N. 15° E.' becomes simply '15°,' 'S. 15° E.' becomes '165°,' 'S. 15° W.' becomes '195°,' etc.

New methods

"The *compasses* upon the charts are divided in accord with this new system. The outer rose, divided into degrees, is the 'true' compass, the inner rose, divided into quarter points is, the 'magnetic,' and set upon the variation for the epoch stated in the central legend.

"Upon charts of small scale and greater territory, coast charts, and ocean charts, 'variation lines' are given because the magnetic conditions differ greatly in the various localities represented upon one chart.

Magnetic variation

"The 'variation lines' are lines connecting such localities as show the same amount of variation of a magnetic needle from the true meridian. The amount of this variation is stated on each, or on every fifth line.

"The *Variation Chart of the World*, No. 2406, shows these lines for every full degree of variation; W. denotes westerly variation—*i.e.*, the magnetic needle points westward of the true meridian. E. denotes easterly variation. All W. lines are continuous lines; all E. lines are composed of dashes. In the absence of any other source for obtaining the 'variations,' the ship's position can be plotted upon this Chart of the World and the amount of variation can be ascertained to sufficiently accurate degree from the nearest variation line.

"The magnetic variation of the compass from the true meridian does not remain the same, but changes slightly or considerably in any locality. The movement of the north end of the magnetic needle is to eastward or to westward and the amount of this movement is expressed as 'annual change.' An eastward change *decreases* westerly variation and *increases* easterly variation; a westward change increases westerly and decreases easterly variation. Figures in parentheses on the chart represent the 'rate' or annual change in the variation of the compass, the plus sign indicating a yearly increase and the minus sign a yearly decrease in the value of the variation for the locality so designated. When using the chart at a time not within the epoch 1915 (for which year the Variation Chart was compiled) it will be necessary to apply the annual rate of change.

"For *example*, a mariner uses this chart in 1917; his position is spotted halfway between 5° W. and 6° W. variation lines, giving 5° 30′ W. variation for 1915. He then finds that the position falls near (plus 2′), showing an annual westward movement of the needle. Thus the needle will point 4′ farther to the left in 1917 than shown for 1915, increasing the variation from 5° 30′ W. to 5° 34′ W.

"To avoid confusion and obviate the errors often made in connection with the use of variation lines the following summary should be firmly impressed upon the mind:

Caution

"The lines or curves simply *connect* equal values; they do not represent by their direction the direction or pointing of the needle. Along a line which runs northwestward upon the chart the variation might be easterly. By coincidence only may the direction of the line and the bearing of the magnetic north be the same.

"The value of 'variation' is the amount of arc separating the true north and the magnetic north.

"The value of 'rate' is the amount of arc covered by the change in the pointing of a magnetic needle in one year's time; thus, along a 'rate' curve running in a northeasterly direction upon the chart the compass needle may steadily have a westward movement.

"*Fathom curves a caution.*—Except in plans of harbors that have been surveyed in detail, the 5-fathom curve on most charts may be considered as a danger line, or caution against unnecessarily approaching the shore or bank within that line on account of the possible existence of undiscovered inequalities of the bottom, which only an elaborate detailed survey could reveal.

In general surveys of coasts or of little-frequented anchorages the necessities of navigation do not demand the great expenditure of time required for so detailed a survey. It is not contemplated that ships will approach the shores in such localities without taking special precautions.

"The 10-fathom curves on rocky shores is another warning, especially for ships of heavy draft.

"A useful danger line will be obtained by tracing out with a colored pencil or ink the line of depth next greater than the draft of the ship using the chart. For vessels drawing less than 18 feet the edge of the sanding serves as a well-marked danger line.

"Charts on which no fathom curves are marked must especially be regarded with caution, as indicating that soundings were too scanty and the bottom too uneven to enable the lines to be drawn with accuracy.

"Isolated soundings, shoaler than surrounding depths, should always be avoided, especially if ringed around, as it is doubtful how closely the spot may have been examined and whether the least depth has been found.

"*The chart on largest scale* should always be used on account of its greater detail and the greater accuracy with which positions may be plotted on it.

"*Caution in using small-scale charts.*—In approaching the land or dangerous banks regard must always be had to the scale of the chart used. A small error in laying down a position means only yards on a large-scale chart, whereas on one of small scale the same amount of displacement means a large fraction of a mile.

"*Distortion of printed charts.*—The paper on which charts are printed has to be damped. On drying distortion takes place from the inequalities of the paper, which greatly varies with different paper and the amount of original damping, but it does not affect navigation. It must not, however, be expected that accurate series of angles taken to different points will always exactly agree when carefully plotted on the chart, especially if the lines to objects be long.

"*Notes on charts.*—The source of a chart and the authority upon which it is based should be considered. The mariner will naturally feel the greatest confidence in a chart issued by the Government of one of the more important martime nations which maintain a well equipped office for the especial purpose of acquiring and treating hydrographic information. He should be especially careful that the chart is of recent issue and bears corrections of a recent date—facts that should be clearly shown on the face of the chart. Notes on charts should always be read with care, as they may give important information that can not be graphically represented."

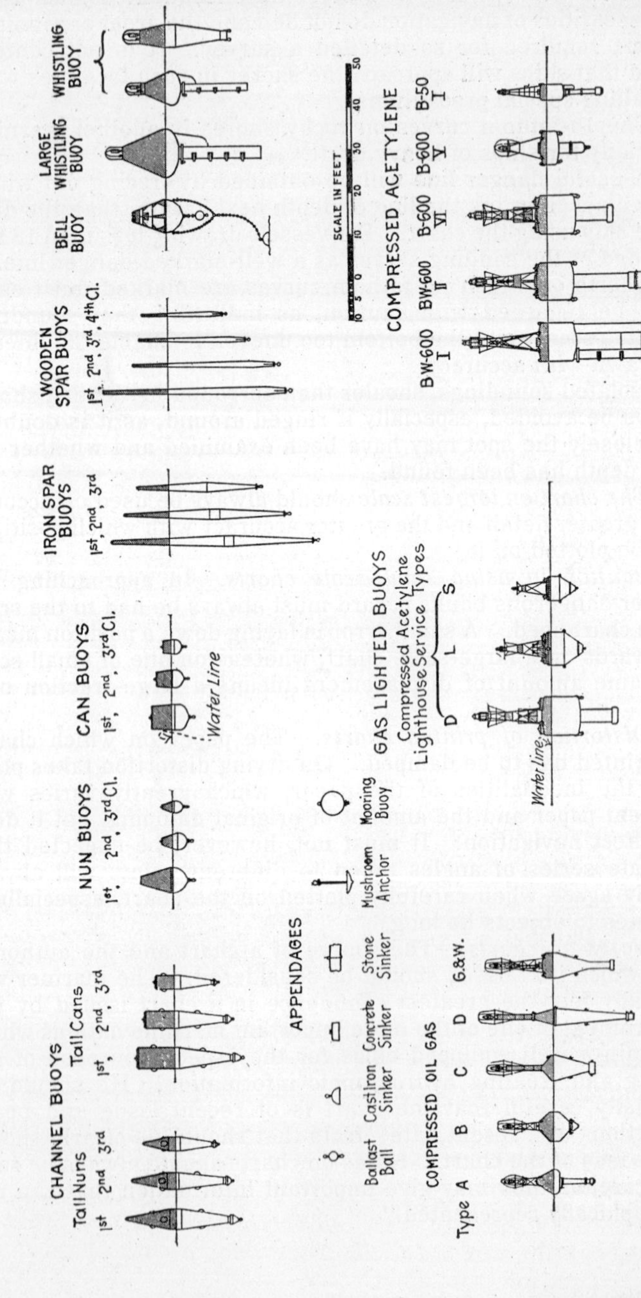
CHANNEL BUOYS
Tall Nuns
1st 2nd 3rd
Tall Cans
1st, 2nd, 3rd
NUN BUOYS
1st, 2nd, 3rd Cl.
CAN BUOYS
1st, 2nd, 3rd Cl.
Water Line
IRON SPAR BUOYS
1st, 2nd, 3rd
WOODEN SPAR BUOYS
1st, 2nd, 3rd, 4th Cl.
BELL BUOY
LARGE WHISTLING BUOY
WHISTLING BUOY
APPENDAGES
Ballast Ball
Cast Iron Sinker
Concrete Sinker
Stone Sinker
Mushroom Anchor
Mooring Buoy
GAS LIGHTED BUOYS
Compressed Acetylene
Lighthouse Service Types
D L S
SCALE IN FEET
10 5 0 10 20 30 40 50
COMPRESSED ACETYLENE
BW-600 I
BW-600 II
B-600 VI
B-600 V
B-50 I
COMPRESSED OIL GAS
Type A B C D G.&W.
Water Line

U. S. Buoys.

XII

Buoys and Lights

While buoys are valuable aids, the mariner should always employ a certain amount of caution in being guided by them. It is manifestly impossible to rely on buoys always maintaining their exact position, or, indeed, of finding them at all. Heavy seas, strong currents, ice, or collisions with passing vessels may drag them from their positions or cause them to disappear entirely, and they are especially uncertain in unfrequented waters, or those of nations who do not keep a good lookout on their aids to navigation. Buoys should therefore be regarded as warnings and not as infallible navigation marks, especially when in exposed places; and a ship's position should always, when possible, be checked by bearings or angles of fixed objects on shore. The lights shown by gas buoys can not be implicitly relied upon; the light may be altogether extinguished, or, if intermittent, the apparatus may get out of order.

Whistling and bell buoys are sounded only by the action of the sea; therefore, in calm weather they are less effective or may not sound.

The U. S. System of Buoyage

In conformity with section 4678 of the Revised Statutes of the United States, the following order is observed in coloring and numbering the buoys along the coasts, or in bays, harbors, sounds, or channels,viz.:

1. In approaching the channel, etc., from seaward, *red buoys* with *even numbers*, will be found on the starboard or right side of the channel.

2. In approaching the channel from seaward, *black buoys* with *odd numbers*, will be found on the port or left side of thechannel.

3. Buoys painted with *red* and *black horizontal stripes* will be found on *obstructions*, with channel ways on either side of them.

4. Buoys painted *white* and *black perpendicular stripes* will be found in *mid-channel*, and must be passed close-to.

5. Buoys painted *white* mark the limits of anchorages.

All other distinguishing marks to buoys will be in addition to the foregoing, and may be employed to mark particular spots, *a description of which will be given in the printed list of buoys.*

Perches with balls, cages, etc., will, when placed on buoys, be at turning points, the color and number indicating on which side they shall be passed. Lighted buoys are generally at turning points. Study charts and buoy list for characteristics.

Nun buoys, properly colored and numbered, are usually placed on the starboard side, and can buoys on the port side of channels.

Spar buoys conform to the regular coloring. They are first or second class, and are often anchored close by the more important metallic buoys, as stand-by marks.

Day beacons, stakes and spindles (except such as are on the sides of channels, which will be colored like buoys) are constructed and distinguished with special reference to each locality, and particularly in regard to the background upon which they are projected.

The removal, damage or destruction of any buoy or beacon is punishable by heavy penalties.

" *Lighthouse tenders* when working on buoys in channels or other frequented waters may display a red flag (international signal-code letter ' B ') and a black ball at the fore, as a warning to other vessels to slow down in passing."

The foregoing regulation has been approved by the War Department and the Steamboat-inspection Service; passing vessels will facilitate the work of the Lighthouse Service by a proper observance of the signals.

Lights.—Before coming within range of a light the navigator should acquaint himself with its characteristics, so that when the light is sighted it will be recognized. The charts, sailing directions, and light lists give information as to the color, character, and range of visibility of the various lights. Care should be taken to note all of these and compare them when the light is seen. If the light is of the flashing, revolving, or intermittent variety, the duration of its period should be noted to identify it. If a fixed light, a method that may be employed to make sure that it is not a vessel's light is to descend several feet immediately after sighting it and observe if it disappears from view. A navigation light will usually do so while a vessel's light will not. The reason for this is that navigation lights are, as a rule, sufficiently powerful to be seen at the farthest point to which the ray can reach without being interrupted by the earth's curvature; they are therefore seen the moment the ray reaches the observer's eye on deck, but are cut off if the light is lowered. A vessel's light, on the other hand, is of limited intensity and does not carry beyond a point within which it is visible at all heights.

Care must be taken to avoid being deceived on first sighting a light. The glare of a powerful light is often seen beyond the distance of visibility of its direct rays by the reflection downward from particles of mist in the air. The same mist may cause a white light to have a reddish tinge, or it may obscure a light except within short distances. A fixed light when first picked up may appear flashing, as it is seen on the crest of a wave and lost in the hollow.

Caution

Some lights are made to show different colors in different sectors within their range. In such lights one color is generally used on bearings whence the approach is clear and another covers areas where dangers are to be found. By consulting the chart or books the explanation of the color of the ray in which you find yourself is found.

When *looking for a light,* the fact must not be forgotten that aloft the range of vision is increased. By noting a star immediately over the light a good bearing may be obtained by pelorus or compass. All the distances given in the light lists and on the charts for visibility of lights are calculated for a height of 15 feet for the observer's eye. For a greater or less height of eye the table of distances of visibility due to the height published in the light list should be consulted. To obtain the distance of visibility take the square root of the height in feet of the light and multiply by 1.15, which will give the distance in miles the light can be seen at the sea level; add to this the square root of the height in feet of your own eye above the sea level multiplied by 1.15 and you will have the distance in miles the light will be visible to you.

The intrinsic power of a light should always be considered when expecting to make it in thick weather. A weak light is easily obscured by haze and no dependence can be placed on its being seen."

XIII

Data on Lighthouses

Lighthouses, since the time of the Egyptian Pharos,* have been a symbol of civilization. No land is wholly bad where sea-coast lights are religiously maintained—the altar lights of integrity burning before the sacrament of commerce.

It is astonishing how little most seamen *know* about the great lighthouses of our coasts. The following data on lighthouses is taken from Government reports.

* The first lighthouse of which we have authentic record is the great Pharos of Alexandria. This famous light of the ancients, built about 258 B. C., was a huge tower of solid masonry on which a large bonfire was maintained nightly.

Illuminating apparatus consists of a source of light placed in an optical apparatus. Usually, for the purpose of concentrating the light and directing it toward the horizon or in horizontal beams to sweep the horizon, there is an arrangement of lenses, prisms, and reflectors in various combinations. The lenses act as refractors of the light, and the prisms may act as refractors or reflectors, or both. The system of reflectors is named *catoptric*, of refractors *dioptric*, and the combination of the two *catadioptric*.

To vary the characteristics of lights there are flashing and occulting mechanisms by which lens panels or screens are revolved, or the light is periodically obscured by shutters, or in the case of gas or electric lights the supply of gas or current is cut off. Lights are also distinguished by the number of lights or by showing either a fixed color over definite areas, or a colored flash, this being effected by the use of colored glass. The source of light for the greater number of lights is a special form of kerosene oil wick lamp, but in recent years other more powerful lamps and illuminants have been introduced; the oil-vapor lamp burning vaporized kerosene oil under an incandescent mantle gives a much more powerful light; oil gas is extensively used, particularly for lighted buoys; acetylene gas is used for lighted buoys and unattended lighted beacons; electric arc lights, electric incandescent lights, and coal-gas lights are used in special instances.

Lights are classed and names printed as follows:

" PRIMARY SEACOAST LIGHTS.
" Secondary Lights.
" RIVER, HARBOR, AND OTHER LIGHTS.
" *LIGHT VESSELS.*
" *Other Floating Lights.*

Unwatched lights.—' *U* ' after the name of a light on the Light List or chart indicates that the light is unwatched. In addition, *all gas buoys are unwatched.* Gas buoys can not be implicitly relied upon, as they may become extinguished or, if intermittent, the apparatus may get out of order and some time may elapse before they can be reached to repair or relight. The same is true in a less degree of unwatched lights on fixed structures.

Too much reliance must not be placed on lighted buoys maintaining their exact positions; it is safer, when possible, to navigate by bearings or angles to fixed objects on shore, and by the use of soundings.

The characteristics of the lights are indicated in the light list by abbreviations, as follows:

Lights Which Do Not Change Color	Characteristic Phases	Lights Which Do Change Color. (Showing Alternately White and Red in Various Combinations)
F. = Fixed	A continuous steady light	Alt. = Alternating.
Fl. = Flashing	(*a*) Showing a single flash at regular intervals. (*b*) A steady light with total eclipses.	Alt. Fl. = Alternating flashing.
F. Fl. = Fixed and flashing.	A fixed light varied at regular intervals by one or more flashes, usually of greater brilliance. A flash is preceded and followed by a diminution of light or an eclipse.	Alt. F. Fl. = Alternating fixed and flashing.
Gp. Fl. = Group flashing	Showing at regular intervals groups of flashes.	Alt. Gp. Fl. = Alternating group flashing.
Occ. = Occulting	A steady light suddenly and totally eclipsed at regular intervals.	Alt. Occ. = Alternating occulting.
Gp. Occ. = Group occulting.	A steady light suddenly and totally eclipsed by a group of two or more eclipses.	

W. = White; R. = Red; G. = Green.

A *flash* is always shorter than the duration of an eclipse.

An *occultation* is shorter than, or equal to, the duration of light.

Lights are characterized as flashing or occulting solely according to the relative durations of light and darkness, and without reference to the type of illuminating apparatus employed or relative brilliancy.

In *approaching* a light of varying intensity, such as fixed varied by flashes, or alternating *white* and *red*, due allowance must be made for the inferior brightness of the less powerful part of the light. The first-named light may, on account of distance or haze, show flashes only and the true characteristic will not be observed until the observer comes within the range of the fixed light; similarly the second named may show as occulting white until the observer comes within the range of the red light. Also, where there are two fixed lights, one *white* and one *red*, the latter may be obscured, and the station may appear to show only a fixed white light.

At short distances and in clear weather flashing lights may show a faint continuous light.

Period of a flashing or occulting light is the time required to go through the full set of changes in the light. This total time is given in the light list column ' Name. Character and period of light,' and the details are stated in the column ' Remarks.'

The durations of light and darkness given are those for which the apparatus is designed, and may vary slightly with irregularities in the working of the apparatus or because the apparent duration of a flash may be reduced by great distance or haze.

A light in which the flash or occultation is caused by revolving lenses or screens may apparently differ from the given period when observed at short distances from a rapidly moving vessel nearly abeam, the period and duration being increased or diminished according as the vessel is moving with or against the direction of revolution of the apparatus.

Visibility of lights.—The distances given in the Light List at which lights may be seen in clear weather are computed in nautical miles for a height of the observer's eye of 15 feet above the water level. These distances may at times be increased by abnormal atmospheric refraction, and of course may be greatly lessened by unfavorable weather conditions, due to fog, rain, haze, or smoke. Weak lights and colored lights are easily obscured by such conditions.

Under certain atmospheric conditions, especially with the more powerful lights, the glare of the light may be visible beyond the computed geographic range of the light. When approaching a light it evidently may be seen earlier from aloft.

The table below gives the approximate geographic range of visibility for an object which may be seen by an observer whose eye is at sea level; in practice, therefore, it is necessary to add to these a distance of visibility corresponding to the height of the observer's eye above sea level. In some instances the actual or luminous range given in the Light List may be less than the geographic range because the light is not of sufficient power to be seen to the limit of the geographic range.

Distances of Visibility for Objects of Various Elevations above Sea Level

Height, in Feet	Distance, in Nautical Miles	Height, in Feet	Distance, in Nautical Miles	Height, in Feet	Distance, in Nautical Miles
5	2.55	70	9.56	250	18.07
10	3.61	75	9.90	300	19.80
15	4.43	80	10.22	350	21.38
20	5.11	85	10.54	400	22.86
25	5.71	90	10.84	450	24.24
30	6.26	95	11.14	500	25.56
35	6.76	100	11.43	550	26.80
40	7.23	110	11.99	600	27.99
45	7.67	120	12.52	650	29.14
50	8.08	130	13.03	700	30.24
55	8.48	140	13.52	800	32.32
60	8.85	150	14.00	900	34.29
65	9.21	200	16.16	1,000	36.14

Example.—Minots Ledge Light, seen just at the horizon, what, under ordinary conditions of the atmosphere, is its distance from the observer?

Height (according to Light List), 85 feet, distance visible (according to table)	10.54 nautical miles.
Add distance corresponding to height of observer's eye above sea level, 15 feet . . . . =	4.43 " "
Distance of light	14.97 " "

Distances corresponding to heights not included in the above table may be found approximately by the formula $D = 8/7 \sqrt{H}$, in which H = the elevation, or height, in feet, of the object above sea level, and D = the corresponding distance of visibility, in nautical miles. The formula is based on the mean curvature of the earth and is corrected for ordinary atmospheric refraction, and should be used only for moderate distances and elevations.

Candlepowers of lights are stated approximately in English candles, but the intensity of a light as seen from a vessel may be greatly lessened or the light may be made invisible by unfavorable conditions due to fog, haze, rain, or smoke.

Light sectors.—In some conditions of the atmosphere white lights may have a reddish hue; the mariner therefore should not trust solely to color where there are sectors, but should verify the position by taking a bearing of the light. On either side of the line of demarcation between white and red there is always a small sector of uncertain color; in flashing lights with revolving illuminating apparatus this sector increases with the width of the flash panels and is therefore usually greatest in the case of the more brilliant flashing lights. It should also be remembered that the edges of a sector of visibility can not be cut off sharply.

When a light is cut off by adjoining land, and the arc of visibility is given in the Light List or Chart, it must be remembered that the bearing on which the light disappears will, in many cases, vary with the distance of the vessel from which observed. When the light is cut off by a sloping point of land or hill, the light may be seen over a wider arc by a ship far off than by one close-to.

Lightvessels en route to or from station, or off station, will fly the International Code signal letters ' QE ' (signifying ' light ship is not at anchor on her station ').

" *Relief lightvessels* may be placed at any lightvessel station. Relief lightvessels will in all cases, when practicable, exhibit lights and sound signals having the characteristics of the regular station vessel relieved. Relief lightvessels have all visible parts from the bow to the middle of the foremast, and from the middle of the mainmast aft, painted red; all visible parts between the fore and main masts, including the middle third of each lantern mast, white except stack, which is black. The daymarks (oval grating or lantern galleries) at the mastheads have five vertical stripes, of equal width, three red and two white, and on the springstay, midway between the two masts, there is an oval grating daymark, with one white and two red vertical stripes. The word 'RELIEF' is in large black letters on the bulwarks on the middle of each side.

The Navesink Light

At the entrance to New York harbor the most brilliant lighthouse in America shines every night. The Navesink Light at Sandy Hook holds this foremost position, swinging a beam of 11,000,000 candle-power out across the sea once every ten seconds. It is well worth a trip to this famous lighthouse to see the remarkable Fresnel prism head. Two tons of optical glass built in the form of a cylinder about six feet high are mounted so beautifully that one can rotate the system with the slight pressure of a finger. This heavy head floats in a container of mercury and thus rotates with practically no friction. The two-ton head is revolved slowly all night long by the gradual dropping of a small weight through the height of the tower.

XIV

Tides

Tides. Where tide tables are available all information can usually be obtained. When these tables are not at hand the chart will show the *establishment of the port* That is, the interval between the moon's meridian passage, and the time of high water. Appendix IV Bowditch also gives many geographical positions throughout the world, the range of the tide and, the *lunitidal interval* for high and low water. The following is taken from Bowditch's Navigator and explains the use of these figures.

" *Establishment.*—High and low water occur, on the average of the twenty-eight days comprising a lunar month, at about the same intervals after the transit of the moon over the meridian. These nearly constant intervals, expressed in hours and minutes, are known respectively as the *high water lunitidal interval* and *low water lunitidal interval.*

"The interval between the moon's meridian passage at any place and the time of the next succeeding high water, as observed on the days when the moon is at full or change, is called the *vulgar* (or *common*) *establishment* of that place, or, sometimes, simply the *establishment.* This interval is frequently spoken of as the *time of high water on full and change days* (abbreviated 'H. W. F. & C.'); for since, on such days, the moon's two transits (upper and lower) over the meridian occur about noon and midnight, the vulgar establishment then corresponds closely with the local times of high water. When more extended observations have been made, the average of all the high water lunitidal intervals for at least a lunar month is taken to obtain what is termed, in distinction to the vulgar establishment, the *corrected establishment* of the port, or *mean high water lunitidal interval.* In defining the tidal characteristics of a place some authorities give the corrected establishment, and others the vulgar establishment, or 'high water, full and change;' calculations based upon the former will more accurately represent average conditions, though the two intervals seldom differ by a large amount.

"Having determined the time of high water by applying the establishment to the time of moon's transit, the navigator may obtain the time of low water with a fair degree of approximation by adding or subtracting $6^h\ 13^m$ (one-fourth of a mean lunar day); but a closer result will be given by applying to the time of transit the *mean low water lunitidal interval,* which occupies the same relation to the time of low water as the mean high water lunitidal interval, or corrected establishment, does to the time of high water."

Knowledge of the times of high and low water and of the amount of vertical rise and fall of the tide is of great importance in the case of vessels entering or leaving port, especially when the channel depths are less than or near their draft. Such knowledge is also useful at times to vessels running close along a coast in enabling them to anticipate the effect of the tidal currents in setting them on or off shore. This is especially important in fog or thick weather.

In navigating coasts where the tidal range is considerable, caution is always necessary. It should be remembered that there are generally indraughts to all bays and bights, although the general run of the stream may be parallel to the shore. On coasts where there is much diurnal inequality in the tides, the amount of rise and fall can never be depended upon, and additional caution is therefore necessary.

It should also be remembered that at times the tide falls below the level of low-water ordinary springs. This always occurs on the coasts of Europe at the equinoxes, but in other parts of the world, and especially in the tropics, such periodic low tides may coincide more frequently with the solstices. Wind or high barometer may produce it at any time, and the amount varies with locality. When the moon's perigee coincides with the full or new moon the same effect is often produced.

The turn of the tidal stream offshore is seldom coincident with the time of high and low water on the shore. In some channels the tidal stream may overrun the turn of the vertical movement of the tide by three hours, forming what is usually known as tide and half tide, the effect of which is that at high and low water by the shore the stream is running at its greatest velocity.

The effect of the tidal wave in causing currents may be illustrated by two simple cases:

(1) Where there is a small tidal basin connected with the sea by a large opening.

(2) Where there is a large tidal basin connected with the sea by a small opening.

In the first case the velocity of the current in the opening will have its maximum value when the height of the tide within is changing most rapidly, *i.e.*, at a time about midway between high and low water. The water in the basin keeps at approximately the same level as the water outside. The flood stream corresponds with the rising and the ebb with the falling of the tide.

In the second case the velocity of the current in the opening will have its maximum value when it is high water or low water without, for then there is the greatest head of water for producing motion. The flood stream begins about three hours after low water, and the ebb stream about three hours after high water, slack water thus occurring about midway between the tides.

Along most shores not much affected by bays, tidal rivers, etc., the current usually turns soon after high water and low water.

The swiftest current in *straight* portions of tidal rivers is usually in the *middle* of the stream, but in *curved portions the most rapid current is toward the outer* edge of the curve, and here the water will be deepest. *The pilot rule for best water is to follow the ebb-tide reaches.*

Countercurrents and eddies may occur near the shores of straits, especially in bights and near points. A knowledge of them is useful in order that they may be taken advantage of or avoided.

A swift current often occurs in the narrow passage connecting two large bodies of water, owing to their considerable difference of level at the same instant. The several passages between Vineyard Sound and Buzzards Bay are cases in point. In the Woods Hole passage the maximum strength of the tidal streams occur near high and low water.

Tide rips are generally made by a rapid current setting over an irregular bottom, as at the edges of banks where the change of depth is considerable.

Current arrows on charts show only the most usual or the mean direction of a tidal stream or current; it must not be assumed that the direction of a stream will not vary from that indicated by the arrow. The rate, also, of a stream constantly varies with circumstances, and the rate given on the chart is merely the mean of those found during the survey, possibly from very few observations.

No seaman should content himself with anything but a complete knowledge of the practical effects of the tide. Only a summary can be given here, but further study of actual effects is of the utmost importance.

The word *tide* is often used in a confusing sense referring to the vertical movement and also the horizontal movement of waters. The best practice is to refer to the latter effect of the tidal wave as *tidal currents.*

The tide rises until it attains a maximum elevation for any particular day. This is *high water,* or *high tide.* It then falls to a minimum level called *low water* or *low tide.* The period at both extremes, when for a short time no change in level takes place is referred to as the *stand.*

The tidal current generally flowing in from the sea during the period preceeding high water is called the *flood*, and the opposite movement following high water is called the *ebb*. The period between flood and ebb, or ebb and flood, is known as *slack water*, when there is no current. This approximately coincides with the period of stand, referred to above. It is the best time to handle vessels around docks, except in cases where the current can be utilized to advantage.

Set and *drift* are terms applicable to tidal currents, in describing their direction and velocity.

The *range* of the tide is the difference in level between high and low water, and is generally tabulated as the mean range, or mean rise and fall. The terms *spring range* and *neap range* are defined below.*

At the times of new and full moon, the relative positions of the sun and moon are such that they exert a maximum effect on the tide in the same direct. These tides are *spring tides;* they have a greater range than any other tides of the lunar month.

At the first and third quarters of the moon, the positions are such that the high tide due to one body occurs at the time of the low tide due to the other; the two actions are opposite and we have *neap tides* or the tides of smallest range. Tidal currents, depending upon the range of the tide, are greatest at the spring tides and least at the neap tides.

The effect of the moon's being at full and change (full moon and new moon) is not felt at once in all parts of the world, the greatest range of tide does not generally occur until one or two days thereafter; thus, on the Atlantic coast of North America the highest tides are experienced one day, and on the Atlantic coast of Europe, two days, afterwards, while on the Pacific coast of North America they occur nearly at full and change.

The nearer the moon is to the earth the stronger is its attraction, and as it is nearest in perigee, the tides will be larger then on that account, and consequently less in apogee. For a like reason the tides will be increased by the sun's action when the

* The distinction between "rise" and "range" of the tide should be understood. The former expression refers to the height attained above the datum plane for soundings, differing with the different planes of reference; the latter, to the difference between successive high and low waters.

earth is near its perihelion, about the 1st of January, and decreased when near its aphelion, about the 1st of July.

Strong prevailing winds, abnormal barometric conditions, and the state of the sea, may cause changes in the height of tides. The effect of atmospheric pressure is to create a difference of about two inches in the height of tide for every tenth of an inch of difference in the barometer.

The *tidal day* is the variable interval between two alternate high waters. It averages 24 hours 50 minutes. The amount by which the tidal day exceeds twenty-four hours is called the daily retardation. When the sun's influence is such as to cause a reduction in the lunitidal intervals, reducing the length of the tidal day, thus causing the tides to occur earlier than usual, there is said to be a *priming* of the tide. When the same influence of the sun causes a lengthening or delay there is said to be a *lagging* of the tide.

The theory of tides fills volumes. Every now and then some new and startling proposition is put forth. The subject is one of great interest to seamen as well as to scientists. A sailor may well use up some of his eight hours below in reading along these lines. In Washington they have tide predicting machines that foretell the tides, but in spite of this seeming perfection there is still a great deal to be found out about the mysterious rise and fall of the waters of the world, the effect of the tides upon the rotation of the earth and many other things relating to the past and future of the spheroid upon which we live.

XV

Bearings

Bearings are among the oldest and simplest methods of locating the position of a vessel when within sight of land. Books on navigation treat of this subject fully and only the briefest mention will be made of it here.

Cross bearings of two or more objects, so situated that the lines of bearing will *cut* at a good angle (a right angle is best) are taken by compass and plotted, being certain to allow for the proper error.

The bearing and distance of a known object. Distance found in a number of ways such as measurement of horizontal angle of the lantern of a light, height known. Distance found by inspection of Table 33 Bowditch. Distance found by noting the time and interval between the flash and report of a gun, at some known station, taking the bearing at the same time. (Sound travels at the rate of 1090 feet per sec. at freezing temperature (approx.).) At sea the use of sound measurements may often be employed, estimating the distance a wreck lies off shore, etc. The following table from *Trautwine's Engineer's Pocket Book* is of interest to the seaman:

The velocity of sound in quiet open air, has been experimentally determined to be very approximately 1,090 feet per second, when the temperature is at freezing point, or 32° Fahrenheit. For every degree Fahrenheit of increase of temperature, the velocity increases by from ½ foot to 1¼ feet per second, according to different authorities. Taking the increase at 1 foot per second for each degree (which agrees closely with theoretical calculations) we have

at	− 30°	Fahr.	1,030	feet per sec.	= 0.1951	mile per sec.	= 1	mile in	5.13	sec.
"	− 20°	"	1,040	" "	= 0.1970	" "	= 1	"	5.08	"
"	− 10°	"	1,050	" "	= 0.1989	" "	= 1	"	5.03	"
"	0°	"	1,060	" "	= 0.2008	" "	= 1	"	4.98	"
"	10°	"	1,070	" "	= 0.2027	" "	= 1	"	4.93	"
"	20°	"	1,080	" "	= 0.2045	" "	= 1	"	4.88	"
"	32°	"	1,092	" "	= 0.2068	" "	= 1	"	4.83	"
"	40°	"	1,100	" "	= 0.2083	" "	= 1	"	4.80	"
"	50°	"	1,110	" "	= 0.2102	" "	= 1	"	4.78	"
"	60°	"	1,120	" "	= 0.2121	" "	= 1	"	4.73	"
"	70°	"	1,130	" "	= 0.2140	" "	= 1	"	4.68	"
"	80°	"	1,140	" "	= 0.2159	" "	= 1	"	4.63	"
"	90°	"	1,150	" "	= 0.2178	" "	= 1	"	4.59	"
"	100°	"	1,160	" "	= 0.2197	" "	= 1	"	4.55	"
"	110°	"	1,170	" "	= 0.2216	" "	= 1	"	4.51	"
"	120°	"	1,180	" "	= 0.2235	" "	= 1	"	4.47	"

If the air is calm, fog or rain does not appreciably affect the result; but winds do. Very loud sounds appear to travel somewhat faster than low ones. The watchword of sentinels has been heard across still water, on a calm night, 10½ miles; and a cannon 20 miles. Many lightships now send out a radio signal at the instant of the sound signal. (See Characteristics of Light Vessels.) The time interval, radio signal ahead of sound signal, give a close measure of the distance off. Figure this out for yourself.

The *bearing of a known object* and *the angle between* the known objects. This case needs no explanation.

Two bearings of a known object with the *course and distance run between bearings.* Simply a matter of plotting.

Sextant angles between three known objects. These are set on a three armed protractor or are plotted on tracing cloth or transparent paper and afford an ideal method of locating a vessel in pilot waters See Bowditch Art. 152.

Vertical and horizontal danger angles, are treated fully in Art. 155 Bowditch.

The bow and beam bearing. Sometimes called the *four point bearing.* Note when an object is broad on the bow. Note log. When broad abeam note log. Interval run is distance off when abeam. Knowing the bearing this gives an excellent fix. Be certain that you will clear all dangers for if you find you are in to close by this simple method you will also learn this fact *too late.*

Doubling the angle on the bow. When the angle on the bow at the second bearing is double what it was at the first bearing, the distance run in the interval is the distance off at the time of taking the second bearing. Plot this and continue the line of the course to get the distance off when abeam *before getting there.* This of course, refers to cases where the first bearing is less than four points on the bow. A good method is to take the object at two points on the bow and four points on the bow.

When the first bearings is 26½ degrees on the bow, (2⅓ points—nearly) and the second bearing is four points, the distance run will show the distance off when abeam.

These bow and beam bearings all depend upon accuracy in steering and correctly measuring the distance traveled *over the ground.* Currents along a coast may seriously falsify the results.

Never hug a coast line too close.

Let the other fellow take chances.

If you are expecting to pick up a light and do not see it when expected, slow down, take a cast of the lead, watch weather carefully and stand to seaward again if need be until conditions improve.

If about to make a coast on the starboard hand and you sight a light to port, starboard helm at once unless you are certain it is a steamer. If you do not sight the side lights, find out what the light is *while your own stem is pointing to seaward.* If making land to port do the opposite.

Don't be reckless with the lives of others. Be wide awake to the possibility of disaster and you will avoid it.

The above notes on piloting are made brief for the simple reason that no person in charge of a vessel should have such responsibility without actual practice in taking all of the bearings enumerated. Bowditch treats of this subject fully.

Ranges are specially important to the seaman. By selecting suitable ranges on the shore, fore and back range marks far enough apart to be sensitive, he can keep informed of the holding of his ground tackle in heavy weather and of his actual progress up or down stream when drifting with a current. In places like the Magellan Straits where strong tidal currents are met with at some stages of the tide, ranges are of the utmost importance. Sailers entering or leaving port can often make good use of a range in casting or coming to anchor.

A bearing and a range make a fine fix when such conditions are plainly marked on the chart. A range and a tangent on a point will often do when the point is marked by a sharp enough rise.

Piloting through Fog

The danger of running in fog has been very much reduced through special devices and methods of transmitting and receiving signals. The seaman of today must be familiar with many things unheard of less than a score of years ago. Submarine bells, more reliable than those of the air, radio compasses, not to mention radio itself, the radio telephone, piloting cables, and ingenious applications of the relative speed of sound through air and water or through water alone, comparing it with the instantaneous messages received by electric impulse.

Still, with all of these things to guide him, many of the most dangerous places in the world are as they were since the beginning and seamen must be more than ever able to so pilot their larger and more important craft by careful use of the lead, the log, and by careful steering. Lookouts must be more awake than ever, officers and men more familiar with the dangers to be met with through greater draft and speed.

Speed in a fog is not a matter of guesswork. It should be *moderate.*

The United States Supreme Court, in the case of the *Colorado,* defines moderate speed in a fog as

" such a rate of speed as would enable her to come to a standstill, by reversing her engines at full speed, before she should collide with a vessel which she should see through the fog."

The English courts agree upon this definition of the term " moderate speed " as applied to steaming in a fog, and the rest of Article 16—" having careful regard for the existing circumstances and conditions " sounds well on paper.

Undoubtedly when it is so thick that the bridge lookouts cannot see the bow lookout, the rendition of the learned court means that moderate speed is to stop and drift.

Most fog collisions occur in pilot waters and the greatest care must be exercised in the use of all fog signal apparatus. Seamanship of a high order is necessary under such trying conditions as often prevail in Long Island Sound where traffic is heavy and the fog comes thick. The astonishing freedom from disasters, through collision, is due largely to good seamanship and a sense of *feel* developed by men who " eat " fog many days and nights during the year. The main thing necessary is to keep your reckoning *and* your head. (See Rules of the Road, Chapt. 16).

Space will not permit of the exposition of the underlying principles of the fog signaling devices now in use, but a brief description is in order.

Sound is conveyed in a very capricious way through the atmosphere. Apart from wind, large areas of silence have been found in different directions and at different distances from the fog signal station, in some instances even when in close proximity to it. The apparatus, moreover, for sounding the signal often requires some time before it is in readiness to act. A fog sometimes creeps imperceptibly towards the land, and is not observed by the people at a station until it is upon them; whereas a ship may have been for many hours in it, and approaching the land. In such a case no signal may be made. When sound has to travel against the wind it may be thrown upwards; in such a case a man aloft might hear it when it is inaudible on deck. Under certain conditions of the atmosphere, when the fog signal is a combination of high and low notes, one of the notes may be inaudible.

The mariner should not assume:

(*a*) That, because he fails to hear the sound he is out of hearing distance.

(*b*) That, because he hears a fog signal faintly, he is at a great distance from it.

(*c*) That, because he hears the sound plainly, he is near it.

(*d*) That, because he does not hear it, even when in close proximity, the fog signal has ceased sounding.

(*e*) That the distance from the intensity of the sound on any one occasion is guide to him for any future occasion.

Taken together, these facts should induce the utmost caution in closing the land in fogs.

XVI

*Submarine Bells**

Although the sound-carrying properties of water have long been known, and experiments were made more than a century ago, it was not until about the year nineteen hundred that submarine bell signalling became possible. Some patents were obtained in this country in 1887, and the following year two Englishmen named Neale and Smallpage applied for British patents for a system almost identical in many respects with the system eventually adopted, but their apparatus was not a success, and their financial resources were not sufficient to enable them to make additional experiments. A few years later, Mr. A. J. Moody, of Boston, Mass., took up the subject, but ill-health compelled him to surrender the work to Mr. J. B. Millet, of the British Institution of Naval Architects, who went into the matter with great enthusiasm, and conducted extensive experiments which resulted in placing the system on a satisfactory and practical basis. The difficulties which he had to overcome were the designing of submarine bells of various types to suit the requirements of different localities, the perfection of a reliable apparatus for receiving the signals, the discovery of the best location in the ship for the receiving apparatus to be placed, the accurate location of the sounds and avoidance or stopping of the engines, when signals were being received or transmitted. Sound transmitted through water will not rise and be wasted in the air.

* Adapted, by permission, from an article by Lawrence Irwell in the September, 1920, National Marine.

A lightship fitted with the apparatus may be actually agitated by it, yet the passengers on a passenger ship will see nothing of it, although twenty to forty feet below the surface the bell may be ringing its appointed signals. This type is usually pneumatic, and is operated by compressed air. Another type of signal is one that is attached to the buoys which are a familiar sight along the coast of some European countries—little less familiar, however, along the coast of our country. These buoys must not be confounded with the well-known bell buoy which, with its inverted bath-shaped going and four swinging hammer, gives its melancholy warning with every oscillation caused by the movement of the sea.

The automatic submarine signalling bell is of an entirely different type. Suspended from the buoy is a contrivance like a sea-anchor, and through this is fastened the apparatus which actuates the bell below. The difference in flotation between the buoy and the sea-anchor causes a difference in the vertical motion of the two bodies, and it is this difference which produces the power for striking the bell. The mechanism consists simply of a combination of rachets and pawls by which the motion of the waves acting upon the buoy compresses a spring to a certain point when it is automatically released, and causes the clapper to strike the bell. The inventor has left nothing to chance, for the force of the blow being dependent on the spring, and not on the wave-motions, is always the same whatever the weather. The only difference the weather makes is that the rougher the sea, the more frequently the bell strikes, sometimes as often as every five seconds. An absolutely dead calm alone silences the bell. Even eight waves, each six inches high, per minute will give six strokes. It is indeed seldom that the sea is so deficient of motion, however still it may look, that this bell will not sound.

The submarine bell of every lightship has its own distinctive signal so that there can be no mistake as to what bell it is. For example, a lightship bell might strike three strokes at intervals of two and a half seconds between each stroke and then an interval of fifteen seconds. An actual case is that of the Maas lightship off the Hook of Holland which sounds groups of four strokes at two-second intervals, with an interval of twelve seconds between the groups. Other lightships, again, have groups of alternating numbers so that any ship captain on hearing the bell can ascertain his position without difficulty.

Another method of communicating with vessels consists of a heavy tripod above the apex of which the bell projects. It is sunk at the desired location and is connected by means of an electric cable usually with a lighthouse ashore, the keepers of which can sound the bell for as long a time as may be desired—for hours or days continuously.

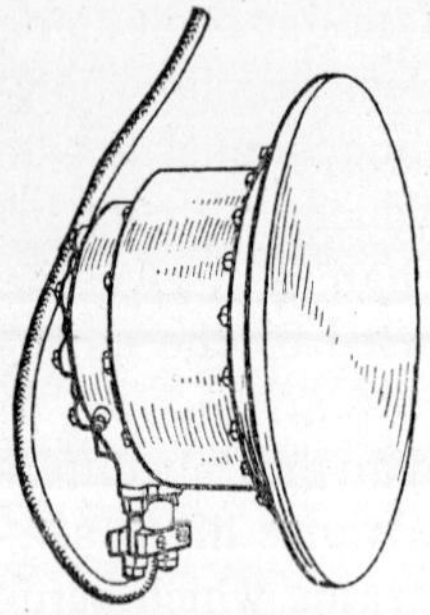

The oscillator.

The apparatus carried by steamships consists of an oscillator fitted into the ship, and is useful for three distinct and important purposes, viz.: signalling approach in time of fog so as to avoid collision; summoning aid in case of disaster. The latter use has to a limited extent been superseded by wireless; exchanging communications by code between war ships when other means of signalling, either by lights or by wireless, would be inadvisable for strategic reasons.

Even a vessel which does not carry bell-signalling apparatus can take advantage of the signal bells, or any one can hear any submerged bell that may be ringing within sound by placing his ear against the skin of the ship below the water-line. Without the receiving apparatus, however, it is impossible to ascertain accurately the direction from which the sound reaches him. An unequipped vessel in distress can summon assistance by swinging the ship's bell overboard so that it rings by striking the ship some distance below the surface of the water. This method of communication was used considerably in pre-wireless days, and it is still used to summon aid in storm or fog by fishermen who go out in their dories from the large fishing schooners near the banks of Newfoundland.

The receiving apparatus consists of two boxes filled with common salt and water and containing specially devised microphones. These boxes are fixed one on each side of the skin of the ship's hold. The exact spot at which they are placed to obtain the best result varies according to the size and shape of the hull, but as a general rule their position is somewhat back from the fore-foot just before the full width of the ship is reached, or near the bilge and where the plates begin to curve from the bottom to the sides. A receiving box is necessary on each side because the sound, though it may strike the side of the ship, cannot pass through it and out at the other side. Each microphone is electrically connected with an indicator on the bridge, or charthouse, and by means of a couple of telephone receivers, the officers can listen for the bells. As these receivers are in duplicate, two persons can listen at once. The indicator is provided with a switch which connects either or both microphones, so that the listener can ascertain from which side the sound is travelling; when both sides sound equally plain, the bell heard is dead ahead, whether it is a ship's collision bell or any other. The stronger the sound is on either side, the weaker it must be on the other, and by listening and comparing carefully, any one can, with a little experience, locate the bell to within a quarter of a point of the compass.

Distance by Submarine Signal

When two ships equipped with this apparatus are proceeding in a fog, the apparatus is kept in constant operation and has a range from ten to twenty miles. Through the exchange of submarine oscillator signals, which are syncronized with the radio signals, the distance and position of one ship can be determined by the other and if any other ships equipped with similar apparatus are within range, this ship will also receive the same signals, and upon determining their direction from the transmitting ship, can avoid collision. The direction and distance determining feature also enables a vessel to determine its distance and bearings from lighthouses or vessels similarly equipped.

In operating the direction and distance finding apparatus, signals are sent out simultaneously by the oscillator and by the radio apparatus from the transmitting ship, and the receiving ships through measuring the difference between the time the submarine signal is received and the radio signal is received can determine their distance from the transmitting ship very accurately. In other words, sound from the submarine apparatus travels through water at the rate of 4,708 feet per second and radio waves through the air at the rate of 186,000 miles per second, and when signals are sent from both simultaneously the difference in time in the receipt of the submarine signal and the radio signal can be measured and the distance of the transmitting ship computed from the result.

In addition to its uses as a navigation aid, the submarine oscillating apparatus also lends itself quite readily to both telegraphing and telephoning through the water. Telegraphic signals can be exchanged for distances from twenty-five to seventy-five miles, depending upon the water characteristics, and telephone conversation can be carried on from five to twenty-five miles, depending upon the depth and characteristics of the water. It is, therefore, possible and not improbable that we will shortly be able to telephone from one ship to another through the water as well as through the air.

XVII

Radio Compass Bearings

The *Radio Compass** is an invention growing out of the war, one of the things that were developed to detect the direction of enemy submarines, aircraft and cruisers through the location of their radio calls. It consists essentially of a pivoted vertical coil forming the direction finding part of the receiving apparatus.

Dr. Kolster of the Bureau of Standards, Department of Commerce, discovered the principal of the radio compass; officials of the Navy Department worked out its practical application.

Dr. Kolster, while experimenting with the electromagnetic wave, the wave sent out by a radio station, or by a "wireless station" as they are still incorrectly termed at times, discovered that when these waves struck, or cut as the electricians term it, a coil of wire at right angles to them, an electric current flowed through the coil, but when the coil was parallel to the wave, no current flowed through. Imagine a spiral spring lying on the

* The two most widely used systems of Radio Compass to-day are the *Bellini-Tosi*, which is the system usually employed by the British, and the *Kolster* which is the type used by the United States Navy. In both a pivoted vertical coil, is rotated by the operator.

beach parallel to the shore line and the waves coming and striking on the side, or lying at right angles to the shore line and the waves coming in and striking it on the end, and the principle involved is perfectly clear. Striking, or cutting, at right angles as stated, the electric current flows through the coil, but striking the coil parallel currents of equal phase and amplitude, that is of similar force and character, start through the coil from each side and neutralize or offset each other.

With this principle, or theory, of the radio wave to work on officials at the Boston and Philadelphia Navy Yards were instructed to experiment and work out an apparatus to determine the direction from which a radio wave as coming and the location of the station sending the wave. These experiments began in 1916.

The radio compass as now constructed is very simple. Two forms of coil are used. In one the wire is wound about the face of a five-foot frame in the form of a square, in the other the wire is wound around a rectangular box-like frame. The coil, in either form, is attached to the top of a steel shaft. Two wires lead from the coil through the shaft and are attached to a sound receiver worn by the operator. Attached to the shaft in the operating room is a wheel which the operator uses in turning the coil. Below the shaft is a dial divided into 360° the 0°–180° line in the true meridian.

Below the hand wheel of the shaft is a direction pointer revolving within the compass dial.

When a ship desires to get its bearing from the radio compass station, or its position in longitude and latitude, it sends a prearranged signal for one minute. As the signal comes in the operator slowly turns the coil of wire and listens to the sound of the signal. In the flat, or pancake form of coil as it is named by the Navy, the signal is loudest when the frame is edgewise to the wave. In this position the wave is striking, or cutting, the wire and flowing through to the sound receiver. When the frame is facing the wave the wire is struck simultaneously on both sides, the current does not flow through and there is no sound in the receiver. As the operator turns the coil there is a position at which he gets the loudest click and it then begins to weaken until he reaches the position at which there is an absence of sound. As it is easier to determine the position of absence of sound than the position of loudest sound the operator notes the bearing of the ship on his dial when no sound can be detected.

When the rectangular or box form of coil is used the position of loudest sound is when the coil is directly broadside to the wave, and the position of absence of sound is when one of the two open ends of the coil is directly facing the wave and the wire is being cut by the wave on both sides at the same instant.

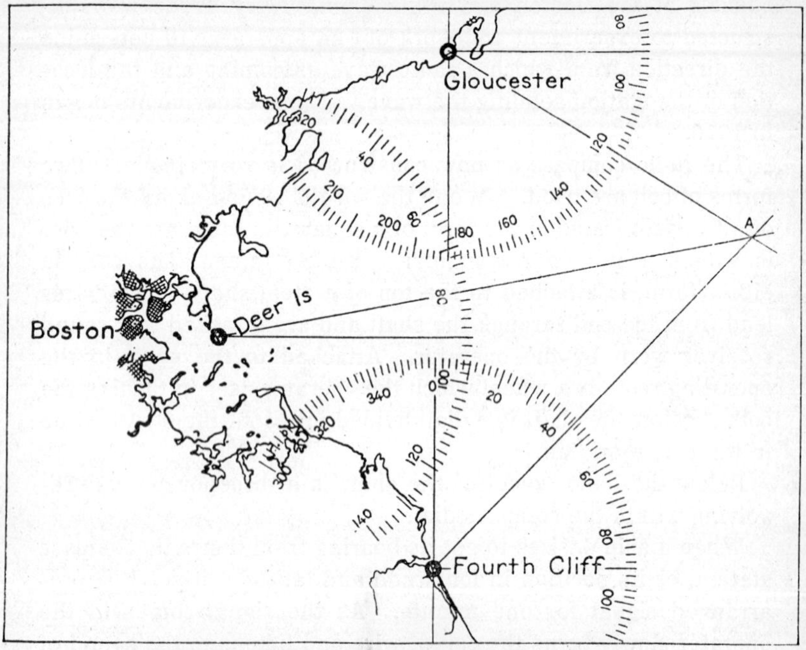

Plotting position by radio compass bearing. Vessel at A.

In May, 1919, the *U. S. S. Chicago* left Boston for Charleston to test out the radio compass stations. The following is an extract from her report.

" The results were very satisfactory, and the stations uniformly efficient. They prove, beyond doubt, the great value of the system both to the Navy and to merchant shipping. The average error of radio bearings was less than one mile. Up to distances of forty miles from the entrances to the various ports the navigators can generally rely on the information furnished being correct within a few hundred yards. From 40 to 75 miles away about three miles error should be allowed for and from 100 to 150 miles 3 to 6 miles error should be allowed for."

The board further stated that it considered it perfectly feasible to navigate reliably, exercising the usual caution, from Cape Hatteras to Boston in thick weather and practically to make each of the port entrances without difficulty, due to the radio compass stations.

The Navy (1921) maintains Radio Compass Stations along the Atlantic and Pacific coasts on the Great Lakes. Radio Compass Stations are designed to aid navigators, especially in thick weather, and have come to be recognized as one of the first aids to navigation.

Because of the large amount of radio traffic handled on commercial wave-length of 600 meters, the workings of the radio compass service were greatly interfered with when operating on that wave-length. Accordingly, the Radio Compass Stations issue radio compass bearings on 800 meters only. Vessels to make use of this service, must have their transmitters tuned to 800 meters wave-length.

Accuracy of Radio Bearings*

Mr. Elmer Collins, Nautical Expert, U. S. Hydrographic Office, has pointed out that long distance radio bearings must be plotted on great circle lines or considerable error will ensue.

The following information was furnished by the Director of the U. S. Naval Communication Service under date of October 10, 1919:

"The reliance that can be placed in bearings furnished by

* While the Navy Department states that at the present time radio compass bearings have reached a high degree of accuracy, it must be understood that the Government incurs no liability for any consequences resulting from any inaccuracy in the taking or transmission of radio compass bearings. These bearings are provided free of charge, as aids to navigation, to be used at the discretion of the master of the vessel.

shore radio compass stations will be governed by the following conditions:

" (*a*) When two sets of bearings are received which do not agree, a third set should immediately be requested.

" (*b*) In thick weather bearings should be requested at least every half hour.

" (*c*) Bearings that pass over intervening land or that are tangent to the shore line are not as reliable as those that have a clear sweep over the sea.

" (*d*) Navigators receiving a set of bearings should immediately investigate the approximate fix indicated and determine whether or not they are being furnished with bearings from the stations that should be most reliable.

" (*e*) When the position of the ship as indicated by the radio bearings differs materially from the position by dead-reckoning, a second set of radio bearings should be requested in order to check the first radio position."

Radio compass instructions are issued by the Hydrographic Office.

XVIII

The Direction Cable

" The Audio Piloting Cable System "

The system is operated as follows: an insulated electric conductor or cable is laid along the line of the fairway in river mouths, harbor entrances, etc. A source of audio frequency alternating current is impressed upon the cable. One terminal of the generator producing the alternating current to energize the cable is connected at the shore end to a ground connection. The other terminal of the generator is connected to the insulated conductor or cable. The extreme end of the cable for example at a point at the entrance of a harbor is grounded to a metallic plate or is electrically connected to the steel armor, which serves as a protective sheath to the cable. It is a fundamental law of electricity that any conductor carrying an electric current produces a magnetic field around the conductor. The current producing the magnetic field can be direct, pulsating or alternating. Michael Faraday, the eminent English scientist, in the year 1831, pointed out to the scientific world that if a coil of wire connected to an electrical indicating instrument was brought in the proximity of another loop or conductor carrying an electric current, that the signals produced in the transmitting loop or conductor would actuate an instrument connected to the receiving loop. Upon this discovery is based the invention of the Direction Cable.

A cable is laid in the center of the ship channel. Through the listening devices on board, the ship gives off a sound of certain pitch that cannot be mistaken for any other sound. The ship hugs the cable from harbor line to the dock. On the bridge and in the captain's cabin listening devices like telephone receivers are placed and attached by wires to the hull of the ship. The ship follows the course of the cable. Any variation away from the cable is indicated by visible indicators which show in feet the distance away from the cable and the ship is then put back over the cable by the steering rudder in the usual manner.

By the ear receivers the indicators may be confirmed at all times. Vessels going into port will use one cable; those coming out another. The sound on each is different and there can be no confusion and therefore no collision.

Along the cable at mile intervals a section is insulated with lead. Through this no sound can come and therefore the man on listening duty can tell instantly how far the ship has progressed, and by the cable chart in front of him can tell where the cable turns and where the ship must be steered to follow the curve of the cable and the center of the channel. The new device, according to those who have tested it and recommended its use, is as reliable as the telephone. It will work in all conditions of water and weather, it is said, and no amount of electricity in the air or powerful wireless currents about the ship can effect it in any way.

XIX

Pilots

In concluding this chapter on piloting it may be well to say a word or two about pilots themselves. No seaman will question the sterling worth of his fellow workers, the pilots, in such services as those off Sandy Hook, and up and down the Atlantic seaboard, the San Francisco Bar Pilots, those of the River Hoogly, and many others in the great ports of the world. But men are to be found in many places who have set themselves up as pilots. The late Captain Ned Clements of Seattle, in speaking of Alaskan waters, used to warn the youngster who inclined that way—" Don't go to Alaska as a pilot on your first voyage. I did," the Captain was wont to say, and then he would spin a yarn out of place in the pages of a book on seamanship.

But the master mariner going into strange ports should look upon all pilots with suspicion, at least he should stick to the bridge himself, see to it that leadsmen are in the chains, and know where the vessel is at all times.

Shipping and Engineering, a Shanghai publication in an issue of recent date, has the following to say about the Celestial pilots of the Yangtze River:

" The Chinese plying pilot is generally a native who has been discharged from one of the river-boats or a quartermaster who has been employed as such on the river, or as a leadsman, perhaps, to a foreign pilot. He has a smattering of the river and by means of oiling the palm of some Chinese compradore or shipping clerk, gets thrust forward as a competent pilot who will do a job cheaply and if asked for references can always produce somebody's papers which have been loaned for the occasion for a consideration. Should an accident happen to the vessel whilst in charge of these incompetent natives, the pilot goes free; not so the master, who usually loses his job, although the vessel was in charge of a Chinese pilot appointed by the owners, or agents."

W. H. LaBoyteaux in his *Handbook for Masters* (a very excellent work of 100 pages) defines the responsibility of the Pilot and Master.

" The American and English laws differ somewhat in respect to compulsory pilotage, but in neither country is the pilot deemed to be in complete command, nor is the master relieved from all responsibility.

"The duties of the pilot are never completely those of a master, nor under the American law is the authority of the master ever superseded by that of the pilot. The master remains at all times in full charge of his vessel, and upon him always rests the responsibility for her safety."

CHAPTER XV

THE BRIDGE

I

Design

Undoubtedly the bridge of a modern vessel is the most important part of her superstructure. With the vast increase in size and a general doubling of ocean speed, the station of the officer of the watch becomes, more than ever, the brain of the vessel. A twenty thousand tonner with a poorly designed " brain," a place where the officer in charge is not at his best, is like any big fellow with a foggy headpiece.

In the first place the bridge should be an ideal lookout situation, with unobstructed vision, all around the horizon. It should be up high enough to give a clear view of both stem and stern. Where this is impossible docking bridges, fore and aft, or perhaps aft alone, should be provided, these to be within sight of the navigating or maneuvering bridge.

The bridge should be well sheltered. But the question of shelter is one that very few officers agree upon. Some like to be housed in entirely, steam heated and foot warmed. This is very comfortable but many believe it carries with it a false sense of security—a lack of actual knowledge of wind and weather without. With a few *million* tons of *large* sailing craft on the sea, this question of what the wind is doing (free of charge) is of high importance. Many coast vessels keep their watch in the wheelhouse entirely, the bridge being practically eliminated. With large wheelhouses this is not a bad plan, but to the mind of the writer it involves too much standing and sitting around. An officer should be actively on his feet, keeping awake by walking back and forth in the fresh air, his eyes sweeping the horizon, the surface of the water,* noting the direction of the wind and sea, and a number of other things about the ship. The watch

* Hundreds of derelicts and other dangerous obstructions are reported in the hydrographic bulletins each month.

officer outside on the bridge is liable to be more active and able than the chap inside. If the reader should fall overboard (it is being done every day) undoubtedly he would prefer to have a watch officer out in the open to stop the vessel, toss over a buoy and call away the lifeboat, rather than to have some one first run into the wheelhouse and call the officer.

A great many designs have been developed with regard to bridges but the following points should be kept in mind.

An officer generally stands at the weather wing of the bridge. This is the most sheltered part, gives the best idea of what is going on ahead, and *on the weather bow and beam.* From the weather wing he can look anywhere from dead aft around the weather side to well abeam to leeward.

This ideal condition is only possible with a bridge running *straight* across the breadth of the vessel.

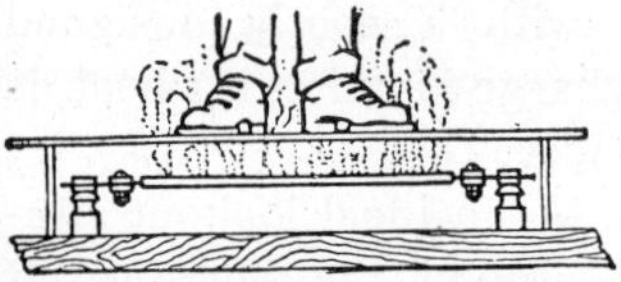

Not a bad idea for the helmsman during the North Atlantic winter.

The helmsman should always be on the same deck with the watch officer. He should always, except in the finest weather, be sheltered in a wheelhouse and made as comfortable as possible. He should be within *sight* and *hearing* of the watch officer no matter where the latter may be while on the bridge. The wheel should be so placed that the officer in charge can *see* that his commands are being correctly understood and carried out.

The wheelhouse should stand back from the path across the bridge, should have a circular front, glassed in with sliding shutters, and from the wings, quarters and middle of the bridge, dictaphone connection should be made with a loud speaking telephone opening into the top of the wheelhouse over the head of the helmsman. The officer will then get his command into the wheelhouse correctly and *at once.* The system should provide for a reply audible at these points on the bridge.

So much for the wheelhouse. This should be large, kept warm, and communicate with the chart room aft of it and with the master's quarters below. The master should have a bunk in the chart room, and should always sleep there, *all standing,* when making the coast.

As to the bridge itself, it should be fairly wide, but not too wide. Six or eight feet is ample, as a bridge that is too wide will fill with wind eddies and keep things uncomfortable by back drafts.

The old plan of fitting canvas dodgers is good and these should be strongly made and triced to a stout wire jackstay. Newer vessels sometimes carry glass shutters in place of canvas. At any rate it is very necessary that the officer in charge have a clear view ahead *over* the dodger or shutter. Where a vessel is plunging into heavy rain or sleet, the problem becomes more difficult. The *Kent-Chadburn Clear View Screen* is being placed on many vessels. It consists of a circular disc of plate glass, mounted on a horizontal pivot in the fore and aft line. A small motor gives the disc a rapid circular motion and all water and sleet is thrown off by centrifugal action, giving the observer a clear view through the revolving disc. The balance of the glass disc must be perfect and the glass of high quality. The observer cannot tell that the disc is revolving and can look into the dirtiest kind of weather with his eyes wide open.

Kent-Chadburn Clear View Screen.

During the war the vast importance of good lookouts at sea developed an excellent type of wind shield. Here the wind impinging on the bridge, or other lookout, is split in a horizontal line, part of it shoots under the bridge and the upper portion curving on a convex plow turns back upon itself carrying the main wind current slightly forward and up over the head of the

The convex wind shield on a poorly designed bridge.

observer leaving him in the calm center of this miniature tornado. Where the curves are well designed a match will burn held over the edge of the shield. It is a very excellent method of sheltering a watch officer or a lookout and still keep him in the open where he can move about and see things.

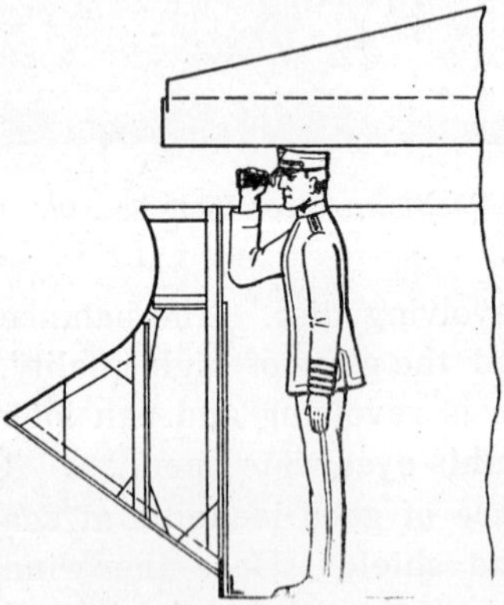

The correct curve on the wind shield—not on the officer.

When the vast importance of bridge design is realized, not only as a matter of comfort, but as an important factor in the safety of life and property, these points, grown out of experience on bridges, good, bad and indifferent, will be taken into account by gentlemen who design bridges while bending over the exposed position of a drafting board. The writer recalls one bridge in particular where he would have given a great deal to have caught the designer in the above position, especially after a cold watch off Cape' Pillar in the month of June.

The bridge with a semicircular front looks nice but has many practical disadvantages for the watch officer who likes to do his four hours duty walking back and forth, or to do his main peering into the night from the weather wing.

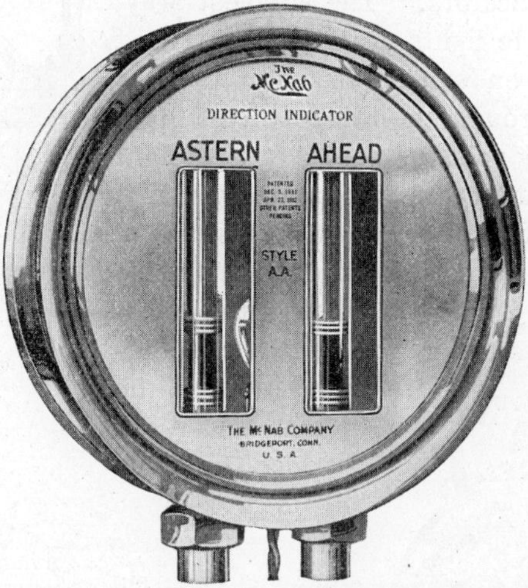

McNab Engine Direction Indicator. The appropriate spindle moves with each stroke of the engine. The action is caused by an air pump attached to the engine.

The bridge either straight, or circular, with a wheelhouse cutting across the center of the bridge (a favorite design with the Germans) is just as bad. Close the weather door of the wheelhouse and the weather wing of the bridge becomes useless.

The opinion of the writer is that the weather wing of the bridge is the most advantageous lookout on a vessel.

The best position of engine indicators, revolution indicators and the like is at the center of the bridge and possibly in the wheelhouse. On a wide bridge it is a fine thing to have the engine indicators led to the wings of the bridge. When docking most masters are either on one wing or the other of the bridge.

The ideal position for engine room telegraphs is at both quarter points of the bridge. They are then within jumping distance at all times, do not interfere with the weather or lee stations at the bridge wings, but of course this means a double set of telegraphs—not much of an item on a five-million-dollar liner.

Docking telegraphs should be at or near the wings of the bridge. A good position for docking telegraphs is on the after side of the bridge.

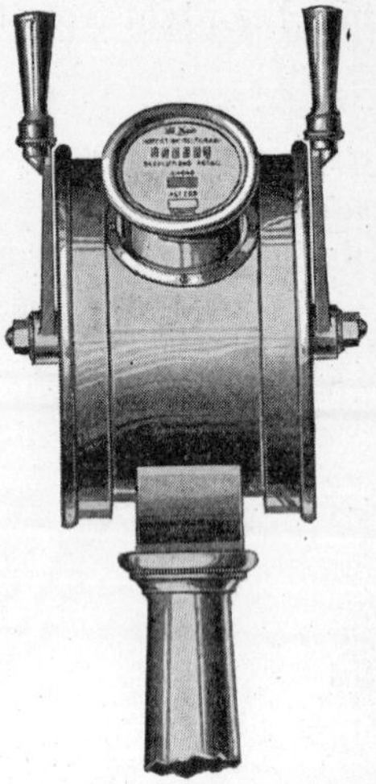

A handy rig. Revolution counter. R.P.M.'s and direction of engines on telegraph stand.

The bridge should be provided with running light indicators. The simplest way, where the side lights are carried in light boxes at the ends of the bridge is to have a pinhole through the bridge to the light box. A fine point of red or green light then shows that the lights are working. Some sort of audible alarm is also good. This should lead into the wheelhouse where the quarter-master standing by, or the junior officer, can at once see to the lights if they go out. Of course the masthead lights are generally visible from the bridge direct.

Telegraph on a turbine steamer. Lower dial maneuvering turbines.

Upper dial ahead only.

Telegraphs are generally of the mechanical type and are shown in the illustrations. These should always be tested before leaving or entering port. The electric telegraph dial has much to recommend it.*

Telephones are becoming more general and have a wide application on board ship; those of the loud speaking variety are best. Docking orders, etc., are less liable to be misunderstood, however, if given by telegraph. Engine room orders must be so given, except, of course when control is from the bridge direct.

* U. S. Navy telegraphs carry, on the ahead side, after FULL SPEED, the designation FLANK. This calls for the extreme speed possible to the vessel. Used when a vessel, in formation, is ordered to the flank, or in emergencies.

II

Keeping Watch

The Officer of the Watch, the Master not being on the bridge, is in direct command of the vessel. If a derelict suddenly shows underfoot, he must act, must handle the situation. At night, under many different combinations of wind and weather, he has great responsibility resting upon him. For many weeks and even months nothing may happen, then, all of a sudden, he is confronted with situations that require the clearest judgment, the quickest action. Throughout this book, such situations are stressed, but the best advice the watch officer can assimilate, is this—*Keep wide awake at all times, day and night.* Realize your responsibilities. Know the Rules of the Road with *absolute certainty.* Impress upon yourself the tremendous moral responsibility that rests with you every moment you are on the bridge. Your charge is a direct personal responsibility; *never forget this.*

When a watch officer comes down from "mount misery" as they call it in the bally trans-Atlantic trade, he has earned his pay for half a day at least. His *duty* then consists of taking excellent care of himself. He must rest and recuperate for the coming four hours of duty that lie ahead after his eight below. Taking such good care of oneself is a rather pleasant duty and this is one of the many reasons why going to sea in these days is such a fine thing to do. Many of us ashore, between the tyranny of office work, the suffering in subways, and the necessity for "relaxation" never find time to read any of the great books by which a man, while still alive, may gain some vision of the heaven and hell through which we all pass upon our strange voyage. Now, thanks to better conditions, every man jack on board has the marvelous gift of time at his disposal, in this respect being far better endowed than many of the most fortunate men ashore.

Night Order Book. Every well regulated vessel has a book on the bridge which is consulted at night by the officer about to relieve the watch, and signed and initialed by him. The Master writes out the *Night Orders* each evening. When he takes the bridge himself, in thick weather or when close to the land, the writing of night orders is usually omitted.

The *Standing Orders* are the usual precautionary admonitions, re fog, heavy rain and passing vessels, or weather changes. These should all be causes for immediately calling of the Master.

The *Special Orders* relate to course, change of course, lights expected to be sighted, time the Master wants to be called, etc.

" Call me immediately upon any unusual occurrence whatever," is a good " order."

Marine Superintendents might look over the night order book when ships are in port.

In cases of stranding or collision it is an important record.

III

Relieving Watch

The watch on the bridge is not relieved until the course has been passed.

This is a rule that should be strictly observed on all vessels. If an emergency arises, when the two officers are on the bridge, some confusion may exist as to who is in charge. It is well to insist upon a rapid and business-like turning over of the watch. The following procedure is recommended.

Call relief at least twenty minutes before eight bells. This gives him some time to get awake. Some officers, under the three-watch system, prefer to be called at seven bells. (In the old days a chap " caulked off " to the last minute and did his waking up—if he ever woke up—while on the bridge.)

Quartermaster in calling the watch should always state the weather and temperature.

Come to bridge at least five minutes *before* eight bells. Read the Captain's orders, and sign them. Look over log, note state of barometer, etc. Get in tune with things, speed, etc.

The officer of the watch should stand to windward, and as soon as his relief comes he should give the following information.

Vessels in sights—point them out. Vessels met with during watch, if any—just a general statement. Weather changes, and any other orders or instructions with regard to the vessel, her speed, behavior if weather is heavy, steering, lookouts, etc.

The officer in charge then " passes the course."

" North 30 east," or simply, " Course is 30."

" Thirty, sir! " the relief replies and steps to the weather side in *front* of the officer being relieved.

The instant that takes place the relief is in charge and if in crowded waters, fog, snow, rain, etc., and a sudden emergency comes up, there is no question as to who is in charge.

If close to vessels or in the midst of a difficult maneuver, the officer of the watch should stay in charge until the maneuver is completed before turning over the watch.

After the watch is relieved, the lookouts should make their reports to the new officer of the watch, and all routine duties should then go forward.

As soon as relieved the officer who has just left the bridge should write up the log book before going below. If a junior watch officer is carried the senior reads and initials the log.

IV

Bridge Routine

The discipline and life of the ship above decks centers on the bridge. A sloppy bridge is usually an indication of a sloppy vessel. Lax conduct, slovenly manners and dirt are a certain sign of a lubberly outfit. The master is directly responsible for the tone of his vessel.

Officers and men should come to the bridge properly dressed. If uniform is worn this should be strictly according to regulation. Where civilian clothes are worn officers and men should be as neat in appearance as if ashore. Absolute cleanliness should be insisted upon. All fittings about the bridge should be kept in order, bridge washed down and paintwork wiped in the morning watch.

All instruments, glasses, telescopes, lead and log lines, should be cared for by the quartermasters.

Red and blue lights, rockets, bombs, and line carrying gun are usually under charge of the quartermasters. The buoys with waterlights should also be in their charge. The officer specially charged with the upkeep of the lifeboat equipment, generally has one or two quartermasters to assist him.

The navigator has charge of the chart room. No unauthorized persons should be permitted in this room. The bridge, as required by law, must be kept free from access by persons not directly connected with the navigation of the vessel. Customs officers and certain other government officials are permitted on the bridge. These rules are posted in all ships and should be strictly observed.

On liners the master should insist that all officers and men coming on the bridge " salute the bridge." A little ceremony, but a big thing. Insist upon no skylarking by the youngsters. All conduct centers upon the dignity and seriousness of the watch officer, who takes his cue from the master.

In passing orders by messenger do so as follows:

" Give my compliments to Mr. Smith, and tell him to prepare to come to anchor in half an hour."

Quartermaster, salutes, " Aye, aye, sir," and approaching the Chief Mate, salutes, and delivers message as follows:

" Captain Black's compliments, sir, and prepare to come to anchor in half an hour."

On a liner great care should be taken in these little ceremonies. Salutes always returned and insisted upon.

The great thing is to know just how far to carry this feature and at the same time maintain a just balance between common sense and ceremony.

On many large freighters the same sort of consideration and discipline is carried out. It is a necessary part of sea routine where men are thrown together for months at a time and some sort of organized courtesy is a great help.

The master who is not too familiar gets on best. It is a fine art to be friendly and severe at the same time. Never reprimand an officer in public. Do it in the privacy of your quarters—and do the job up brown. After that treat him with the greatest courtesy in public.

The master who interferes with the routine work of the ship is usually a fool. If things don't go right, get the Chief Mate and lay him out. Many of the wisest ship commanders do it all through this unfortunate individual, giving him "the work" for things that happen, even when he is ashore, and "should have left proper orders, etc."

This sort of thing adds to the quality of the respect shown the "old man."

But—and this is important—back up the Chief Mate, and through him all officers, in the proper performance of their duty.

The Master who comes on board and kicks about a dirty gangway to the poor dub stationed there, simply makes a grouch out of himself. But the Skipper who comes over the side, says nothing, and ten minutes later the wrath of ages descends in the person of the Chief Mate, that skipper is a genius, and when he does bawl out orders, should the ship and all hands, perhaps, be in danger, every word he says is listened to with respect and rapid action follows.

One of the best master mariners the writer was ever shipmates with, never set foot on the bridge except to enter or leave port, or in fog, or other danger. If ice was reported he was on the bridge in an instant. The result was that whenever the old man was up, everyone was on edge. He came aboard a half hour before sailing and left when the lines were fast. Every man jack on board was proud of the skipper.

Too many Masters, through a mistaken sense of their duty, or because of pressure from behind, try to show how active they are by meddling in the work of the mates.

The Master has so much to do by reason of his responsibility that the wise ones see everything out of the corner of their eyes, do all their kicking through the Mate, training him in turn, to become a good skipper. This gives the master time to attend to the larger issues which make for the prosperity of shipping.

V

Steering

A very interesting paper appeared in *International Marine Engineering* of March, 1919, on the steering of ships and this is printed, below, as it sums up much of the data with which seamen should be familiar. The article is unsigned, but whoever wrote it has said much in very few words.

" All ships must possess the power to maneuver, but exactly to what extent will depend on the type of the vessel and the use for which it is intended. Although all vessels possess the power to maneuver, it can hardly be said that the majority of ships are really easy to handle. It is true they are handled, and handled effectively, but nevertheless captains often wish that they had more control over their vessels than is given them, even by twin screws and the ordinary rudder.

" It will not be without interest to examine what takes place when helm is given to a ship. As the rudder at first goes over, the ship for the moment continues on her course and there is a sudden concentration of water between the rudder and the deadwood aft. This sets up an increase of pressure on both the rudder and the deadwood, which pushes away the stern of the ship in the opposite direction to which the rudder is turning. The ship also moves bodily outwards. The instantaneous effect, therefore, is to move the ship along a course, which is curved in the opposite way to that in which the ship is required to turn finally. In a short time the ship takes up a definite but not really steady swing. This swing is helped by the pressure on the bow, the excess pressure on the deadwood aft being reduced. Shortly after this, the vessel settles down to a steady swing, the pressures on the bow and the rudder turning her, but the pressure on the deadwood aft is now on the opposite side to what it was oiginally, with the result that it retards the turning of the vessel. Equilibrium must eventually be established when the center line of the ship takes up a definite angle to the direction in which the center of gravity of the ship is traveling. This angle is called the drift angle. The distance between the original course of the vessel and the position of the ship when she is moving in exactly the opposite direction to her original one is called the tactical diameter of the vessel. If this is to be small, the deadwood aft should be well cut away.

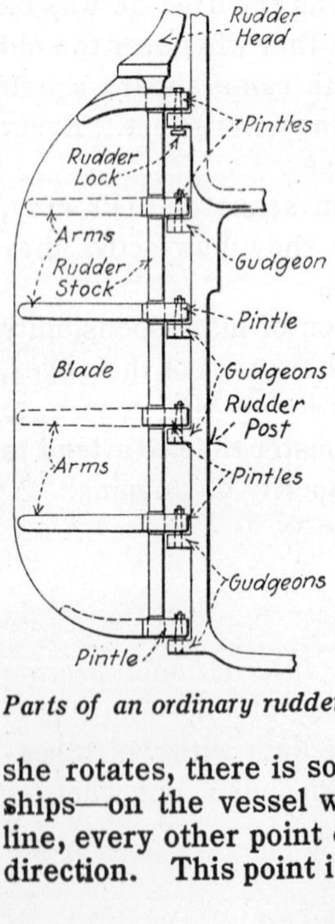

Parts of an ordinary rudder.

" When the ship settles down on her turning circle, about the center of which she rotates, there is some point—usually well forward of amidships—on the vessel which only has a motion along the center line, every other point on the vessel really moving in some other direction. This point is called the pivoting point, and the resistance of the various parts under water to turning depends on their distances from this pivoting point. Since the pivoting point is forward of amidships, it follows that the aft deadwood is more effective in reducing turning than the forward deadwood.

"When the rudder is first put over, the center of pressure on it is below the center of pressure of the force opposing the lateral motion of the ship and in consequence the vessel at first heels towards the center of the turning circle. When steady motion is established, centrifugal force acts on the vessel through a point generally above the waterline and certainly above the center of lateral resistance. This force is more powerful than the pressure on the rudder, with the result that the vessel heels outwards. Although this is very generally true, it would be possible to conceive of a case where the pressure on the rudder was so great and relatively high, and the center of gravity of the ship, through which the centrifugal force acts, so low, that the ship might heel inwards on the turning circle instead of outwards.

"It is, of course, well known that wind will affect the steering of a ship. If she is moving with the wind on the beam, the center of pressure of the wind force on the above-water portion may be forward or abaft the center of lateral resistance of the under-water portion. In any case, helm will have to be carried one way or another to correct the tendency of the wind to turn the ship. This will always decrease the speed of the vessel. In one particular case, it so happened that the center of pressure of wind was abaft the center of lateral resistance, the deadwood aft was cut away, bringing the latter point further forward, making matters worse, so that a good deal of helm had to be carried with a beam wind.

"It is generally understood that wind can affect the speed of a ship a good deal. If the wind is directly ahead, it will retard the motion of a ship considerably by direct pressure, although it will not affect the helm. If it is on either bow, it will not only retard the speed on account of its direct pressure, but also by the fact that helm will have to be carried to keep the vessel straight. With wind directly on the beam, helm will always practically be carried, and the speed of the ship will be retarded on this account, although the wind pressure has no direct effect.

"Rudders are divided into several classes. The most common form is the ordinary merchant ship rudder, in which the whole area of the rudder is abaft the axis of rotation. For many years the most common type of rudder in war vessels has been the balanced rudder. This takes several different forms. It may be completely balanced and supported by the rudder head and a bottom pintle, or it may be completely balanced and also completely underhung and supported from two points on the rudder stock. There is another form of rudder, described as semi-balanced, in which a small portion only of the rudder area is forward of the axis, the rudder being pivoted on the rudder-head and one or more pintles, the portion of the rudder below the bottom pintle being completely underhung.

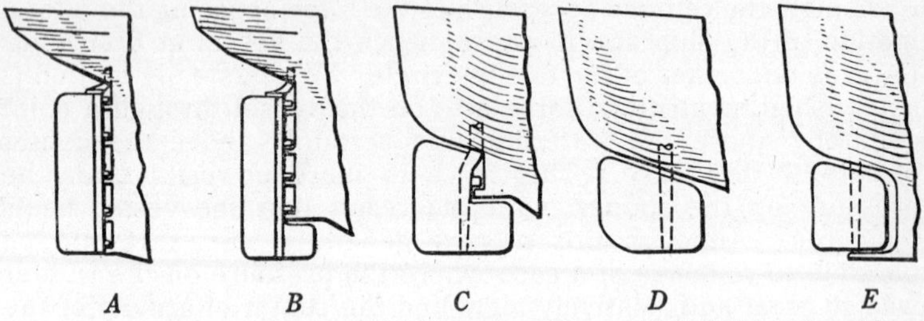

A, ordinary rudder. B, C, semi-balanced rudders. D E, balanced rudders.

"The ordinary merchant ship form of rudder remains in general use because it is easily handled, although it is not so economical in form as some of the other types; speeds of merchant vessels being generally small, does not make the rudder unmanageable in size. The steering gear for it has to be larger and heavier than the more effective rudder of the balanced or semi-balanced type; all of its area being abaft the axis, the twisting forces acting on it are much greater than with the latter types. For vessels with cruiser sterns—which includes practically all war vessels—the balanced type of rudder becomes almost a necessity, although in the last few years certain merchant vessels fitted with cruiser sterns have still been given the ordinary merchant type of rudder, and it is doubtful if there is any reason to depart from this form in general practice. If particularly rapid maneuvering is required, there may be some reason for it.

"There is no very accurate way of working up the strength of rudders from first principles, as the forces acting on them have never been very accurately determined. Formulæ are used for this purpose in certain cases which are admittedly comparative. For the majority of merchant vessels the necessary rudder sizes are all given in the rules of the classification societies. It can hardly be said that a rudder is particularly effective in controlling a ship; in fact, if specially delicate maneuvering is required in a vessel, twin screws must always be fitted to assist the rudder. Whether more effective methods will be devised for controlling the motion of a ship must be left for the future to decide, but any improvement on the present system would certainly be sure of a warm welcome."

The *turning circle* of a vessel should be known to the master and all officers who are in charge of the bridge, and it is well to measure this when the exact data is not available from correct records made during the steaming trial.

A sighting object, a mark buoy or barrel, is weighted and fitted with a pole painted white and carrying a small brightly colored flag. This mark is thrown overboard and the vessel steams off a mile or so, turns and approaches the mark, keeping it about a quarter mile inside of the proposed circle. At a given

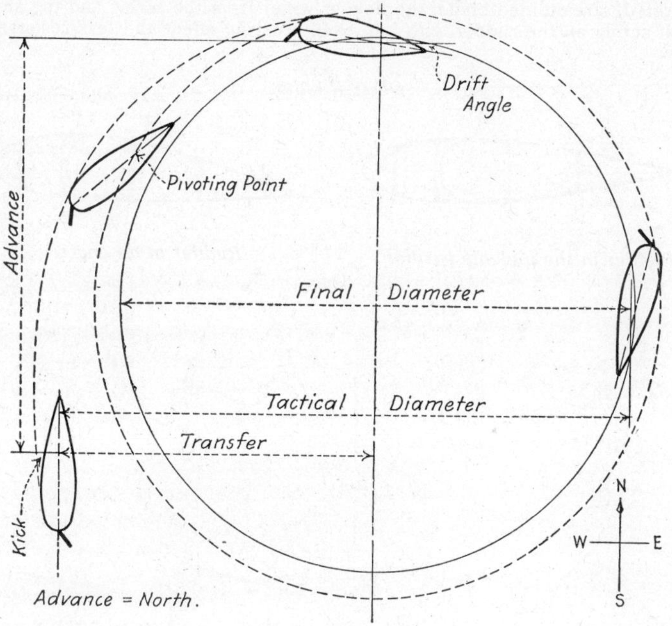

A turning circle.

signal the helm is put over hard, the mark being about two points forward of the beam, turning, let us say, on port helm with the mark buoy to starboard. The course, the time, and the bearing of the mark buoy are simultaneously recorded and two observers, forward and aft, angle on the buoy. After the vessel's head has turned four points, blow a whistle and record course, time and bearing of buoy. Do this every four points until the vessel is back again on her original course.

With these bearings (from the bridge) and the horizontal angles between the buoy and the forward and after observers, their distance apart being carefully measured, the turning circle can easily be plotted to scale and measured.

Oertz Rudder. This construction takes advantage of streamlining in the steering of ships. It has given satisfactory results by an appreciable increase in speed and a corresponding saving in fuel consumption over rudders of the conventional design. The *S.S. Alderamin,* fitted with the Oertz rudder, gained 11.67% in time of passages and saved 14.10% in fuel over passages made by a conventional ruddered sister ship, on parallel runs.

The rudder consists of a fore part, streamlined rudder post, and a thick, socketed, streamlined blade, the flow of water from the screw and the ship's wash acting on the rudder with improved steering effect and less resistance.

Oertz Rudder.

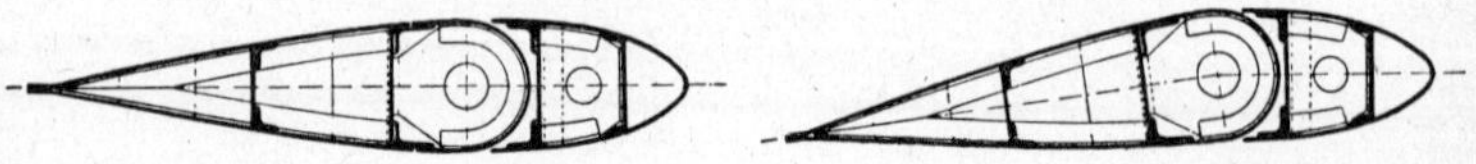

Rudder in the midship position. ***Rudder at an angle.***

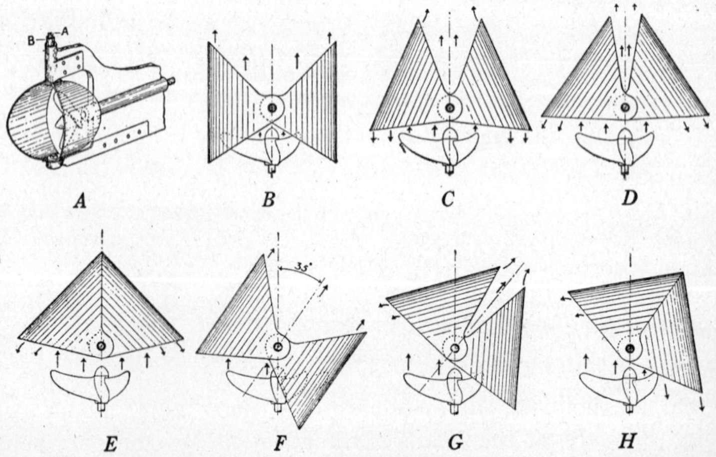

The Kitchin Reversing Rudder. A, control for opening and closing blades. B, Rudder head for steering.

The *Kitchen Reversing Rudder* performs incredible things in the way of maneuvering a small single screw vessel. The rudder consists of two semi-circular blades, and is best shown by the illustrations. The usual helm action is used for ordinary steering with the added advantage that the form of the rudder causes the *entire* propeller stream to be directed either to one side or the other, *F*. When going ahead the rudder stream passes through the opening in the steering semicircles, these are somewhat contracted causing a slight nozzle action in the propeller stream tending to increase the speed, *A* and *B*.

But the most astonishing effect is found when the two parts of the rudder are brought together, and the propeller stream, reacting on the rudder, turns forward, *E*; the vessel then goes astern. While going astern the rudder action is available for steering, *H*.

Many combinations of steering and reversing, *H*, or partly reversing the propeller current *C* and *G*, can be made, giving the vessel a wide range in maneuvering.

The opening and closing of the rudder blades is effected by a separate mechanism adding somewhat to the complication of the steering gear.

But for tugboats, and other small craft, its marvelous steering qualities may overcome this apparent drawback.

Steering gear is generally considered to consist of the wheel, on the bridge, the means of communicating the motion of the wheel to the valves of the steering engine, the steering engine or motor, and the machine upon which this operates to effect the turning of the rudder, in other words the tiller or helm.

So we have—

Wheel
Communicating device to engine
Steering engine
Helm
Rudder

The wheel located in the wheelhouse on or near the bridge generally consists of a small brass or mahogany wheel, or a combination of both. It acts the same on all ocean vessels. To *Starboard* the *helm*, turn the wheel to port—and ship's head goes to port. To *port* the *helm*, turn wheel to starboard. That is the wheel is turned in the *opposite* direction to the helm command. This has caused endless confusion, but like many things, including original sin, it seems here to stay. The Navy has cleaned out the whole situation, for themselves at least, by an official *fiat* that the commands for steering shall be

Right rudder	in place of Port
Left rudder	in place of Starboard

When the order " Right rudder " is given the steersman turns the wheel to right, and the ship's head goes the same way.

Captain W. A. Sprague, master of the *Planter E. P. Nones* in a letter to the author makes the following common sense suggestion.

" Any man who has been going to sea long enough to qualify as a helmsman has learned instinctively the port and starboard hand of a vessel. Then what simpler method of conning the wheel than to give the command, ' Starboard the wheel! ' indicating that the wheel is to be turned to starboard, and likewise the vessel's head goes to starboard."

If this were carried out, the terms *Starboard* and *Port*, so necessary in many ways at sea, would be retained and the burden of thinking of the new system would be on the officer and not the man. Also, the officer would only have to call out his direction having in mind his desire to turn the vessel the same way.

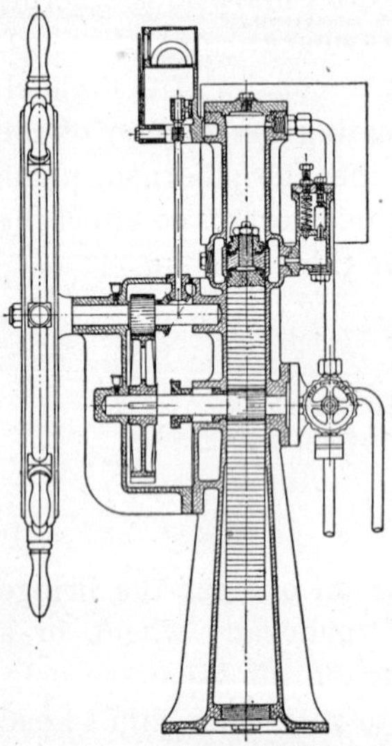

Section through wheel and telemotor stand.

After a while the word wheel could be dropped and we would again have the simple sea terms *port* and *starboard.*

But seagoing began before the modern day of wheels, and when the wheel came in the shellbacks of that ancient period looked upon it with little favor and still insisted upon their helm.*

Boat practice is a great educator for the helm method of conning the wheel, and so far as we now know, this relic of the past will stick with us in the merchant service for a few hundred years more, or at least until such time when steering is done by radio from the home office and the skipper and mate are simply called the first and second lookouts.

The disadvantage of having two kinds of helm orders under the same flag is a serious one, especially in war when so many merchant seamen must enter naval service. Only one mistake would be a dear price for the new idea.

* Direct helm orders—RIGHT and LEFT—referring to the way the steering wheel (upper semi-circle) is moved, the way the rudder blade is moved, and the way the ship's head moves, are now compulsory on all ships.

Communication between wheel and steering engine may be by some direct method, such as rods or wires, or by an hydraulic device called a *telemotor*. This is used very extensively and works with ease. The Brown hydraulic telemotor consists of two hydraulic cylinders, one located in the wheelhouse and one aft near the steering engine, connected by copper tubing.

The piston in forward cylinder is displaced by the wheel working through the gearing as shown. This displacement is communicated to the piston in after cylinder and the movement communicated by suitable levers to steam valve on the steering engine. As soon as the wheel is released the springs will return after piston to neutral position and this displacement will in turn be communicated to the forward piston returning it also to neutral position.

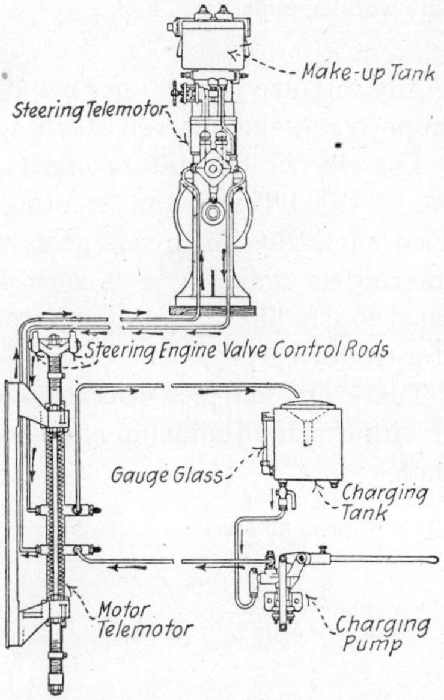

Diagram of telemotor gear. (Wheel not shown.)

Should the zero position of the steering wheel not correspond with the zero position of the helm, the wheel should be put to the zero position this is all that is required in some makes of telemotor, in others it is necessary to open a by-pass valve which is kept open until the helm reaches the neutral position.

The pump for charging the system with liquid is shown in diagram.

Troubles. The most frequent source of trouble in the hydraulic telemotor has been due to air in the system. Instructions issued with the various makes of telemotor for getting rid of air should be consulted.

Leaks in the piping connections are another source of trouble.

The fluid pressure in a telemotor need never exceed 250 lbs. per square inch.

Piping should not be run where there are great variations in temperature. Sharp bends, or pockets which are likely to form air traps should be avoided.

Mixture. In tropical climates the system should be filled with clean fresh water but in colder climates a mixture of water with glycerine or telemotor oil should be used. The best mixtures follow—

Per cent glycerine in mixture......	25	33	50	60
Safe working temp., deg. F........	+13	+10	−20	−30

Any mixture over 60 per cent glycerine is too thick to operate properly. Telemotor oil starts to congeal at about 15 deg. F.

The *electric telemotor* consists of an electrical control between the "wheel" and the steering engine. The term wheel is used advisedly for in this gear, the *Benson Electric Telemotor*, steering is done by a "*controller handle*" from what looks suspiciously like the familiar pedestal mounted on the front end of a trolley car.

There are fourteen contact points on the contact disc, seven on either side of midship and correspond to the following rudder angles:

Contact Number	Degrees of Travel	Total Rudder Angle
1	3	3
2	3	6
3	3	9
4	5	14
5	10	24
6	10	34
7	10	44 (hard over)

The controller handle may be put hard over one way and back again and then brought to rest at say number 4, Starboard (or right) and the rudder will then come to rest at that point, for obviously the rudder can not go over and back as fast as the controller, so it finds its way to the position of the controller direct without going through the motions made in getting there.

It is all a matter of electric wiring, relay cabinets, and motors. The action is as follows:

When the controller lever is placed on any contact on the controller disc an electrical circuit is completed through a contact in the follow-up disc to a controller ring in the follow-up casing and from there to one of the remote control relays selected by the direction in which the lever is resting. This immediately closes the primary circuit through the motor, starting it running in that direction. As the motor runs it operates the cross head (on the rudder head) and also the follow-up disc. When the follow-up disc reaches the position corresponding to the controller lever the circuit is open through the relay causing the motor and the crosshead block to stop at that position. At the same time the single pole relay closes and places a dynamic brake on the motor to insure its stopping instantly at the right place. It stays in this position until the controller lever is shifted by the (steersman, let us say), when the operation is repeated.

"Great Jupiter! is this seamanship?" someone may say, but every change has brought with it similar exclamations.

Steering engines, are generally steam engines, but with the increase in motor vessels electric steering motors will become more numerous. The steering engine is most often a stationary

A quadrant steering engine.

engine operating a moving gear, a *tiller*, a *quadrant*, or some arrangement of a *cross head* with arms working on a right- and left-handed screw, or else it turns a *drum*.

The *Brown steam tiller* is a device in which the engine is mounted on the tiller and swings from side to side, a cog wheel actuated by the engine, engaging the cogs of a stationary semicircular rack, or quadrant, bolted to the deck. Steam is led to the tiller from a point directly over the axis of the rudder stock. This device does away with chains, rods, ropes, etc.

Quadrant steering engines are the reverse of the Brown engine. The engine is stationary and the quadrant rack is directly keyed to the rudder head. This is a good gear where space is limited.

Right and *left screw gear* works with two steering arms pivoted to two nuts (right and left) working at opposite ends of the same shaft the screw having opposing threads. The ends of the steering arms are pivoted on a cross head attached to the rudder head. When the screw shaft revolves the nuts come together or move apart, imparting a turning motion to the cross head by means of the steering arms. It is a simple system and works well. Many hand steerers are built on the same plan.

Drum steering engines simply work a drum and this, by means of wires or chains, works a tiller or quadrant. The quadrant is preferable to the tiller as the same leverage is maintained throughout the swing of the rudder.

Hydraulic steering gears are coming into favor. The use of a cross head, two steering arms, pivoted to the plungers of the hydraulic engine, works out very well. The pressure is supplied by an electric driven pump. The direction and speed of this pump is controlled from the bridge by telemotor. In the Hele-Shaw gear, oil is used instead of water.

In all steering engines and gears provision should be made for ready uncoupling and for instant shipping of the hand gear. All such gears of good design are fitted with buffers, friction couplings, dash pots, and the like for taking up severe rudder shocks. This saves the rudder as well as the gear.

No definite rules can be laid down at the present time with regard to steering gear. Use common sense. Study the gear in each new ship. Practice the crew in shifting from power to hand and back, and try out the gear at sea under hand power. On entering or leaving port always be certain that the second mate has the hand gear clear and understands its use.

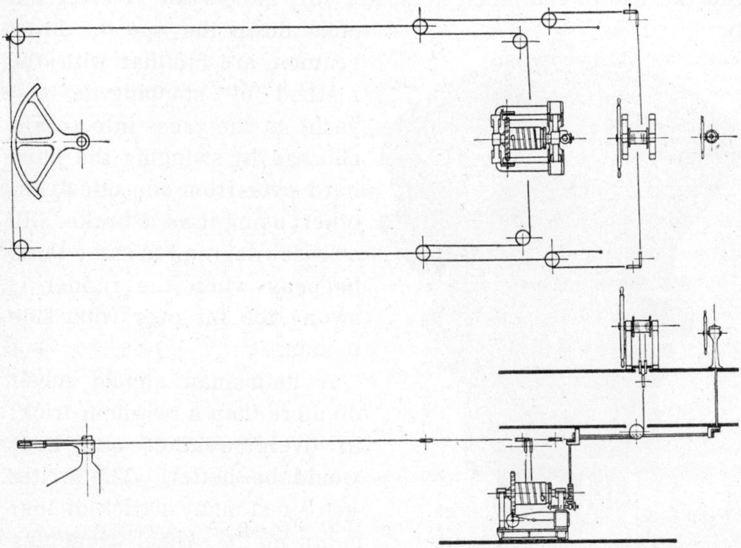

Drum steering engine. Hand gear. Note that hand gear is always ready with this rig. Lock hand gear and work engine. Stop engine, unlock hand gear and steer by hand.

Do not allow the after wheelhouse to be used for stowing deck gear. Be certain that everything in it is secure against shifting even with a severe shock, such as a collision. Sometimes heavy spanners, spare tillers, etc., are held to the bulkhead, close to the steering engine, in such a way that they may be dislodged and fall into the gear, perhaps at a time when the working of the gear would be vital to the safety of the vessel.

Before winding up the subject of steering it may be well to say a word or two about the actual process of steering a ship. Green helmsmen are apt to give the vessel too much helm, to pay too much attention to the lubber's line and not enough to the ship's head. Steering is of such great importance and good helmsmen are so valuable that great attention should be given to steering and to the training of men to do this work. Like heaving the lead, steering is one of the few real sailor's jobs that are left. Tooling along a forty-thousand-ton liner is some sport and requires a good man, even with the best of gear. Wind and sea make a great difference in the steering quality of a vessel and the use of too much helm not only affects her steering but pulls down the speed. Most seamen are familiar with the method of stopping a fast yacht as she races into an anchorage by swinging the helm hard over from one side to another, using it as a brake. In a lesser degree the same thing happens when the rudder is swung too far over from side to side.

An electric helm indicator.

A helmsman should never do more than a two-hour trick; in lively weather one hour would be better. The writer has stood many a trick of four hours at the wheel droughing down the coast through the Florida Straits, steering and keeping a lookout while the Mate on deck did a turn or two with a paint brush, or a hose. Those were great days at sea.

But while times are easier today, still new things bring with them a demand for better work. Devices are now perfected to keep a record of the steering, to trace on a cylinder the very track of the vessel each minute of the day. Other devices record the performance of the helmsman.* Many a chap has

* A recent series of tests on a large modern steamship showed surprising results in regard to different helmsmen. It was found that the best helmsmen made 85 movements of the steering wheel per hour, and the worst 565. A device, therefore, which records the steering operations, and thus enables investigation of them, has possibilities of great practical usefulness. Such a device is available in the *Russell-Ranken steering recorder*, which records graphically, without need of subsequent plotting or calculation, every movement of the helm, at the same time registering the hour, the minute, half-minute and quarter-minute. It shows the amount of helm to port or starboard, the length of time taken to operate the rudder, and the length of time it remained in a stationary condition.

cut snakes in the wake while the old man was napping and the mate earning his pay with a brush, and no one was the wiser although it was an expensive process even in the old days when coal was two dollars a ton.

VI

Notes On Signals

The most important signals at sea are those of the *radio telegraph* and the *radio telephone*. The first involves a knowledge of some code while the latter merely requires a knowledge of the language spoken by the sender.

The *International Morse Code*, or a modification of it called the *Continental Code*, is used in submarine cable messages and in radio messages. This latter code consists of the Morse alphabet and numerals together with a special set of conventional signals particularly adapted to radio transmission.

The Morse Code

Alphabet		Numerals	
A ·—	N —·	1 ·————	6 —····
B —···	O ———	2 ··———	7 ——···
C —·—·	P ·——·	3 ···——	8 ———··
D —··	Q ——·—	4 ····—	9 ————·
E ·	R ·—·	5 ·····	0 —————
F ··—·	S ···		
G ——·	T —		
H ····	U ··—		
I ··	V ···—		
J ·———	W ·——		
K —·—	X —··—		
L ·—··	Y —·——		
M ——	Z ——··		

The recorder may be connected to either the controlling shaft of the steering engine or to the rudder-post, and, depending upon which of the plans is adopted, the position of the instrument may be either aft in some suitable position, or on the bridge.

The instrument is a combination of three main features, viz.:

1. A slide carrying the marking device, and attached either to the rudder-post or to the intermediate fore and aft shafting between the engine and steering gear.
2. A clock, having combined with it an automatic recording apparatus.
3. A clockwork mechanism operating the paper.

Punctuation

Period	·· ·· ··
Comma	·—·—·—
Interrogation	··— —··
Hyphen or dash	—····—
Parentheses (before and after the words)	—·— —·—
Quotation mark (beginning and ending)	·—··—·
Exclamation	— —··— —
Apostrophe	·— — — —·
Semicolon	—·—·—·
Colon	— — —···
Bar indicating fraction	—··—·
Underline (before and after the word or words it is wished to underline)	··— —·—
Double dash (between preamble and address, between address and body of message, between body of message and signature, and immediately before a fraction)	—···—
Cross	·—·—·

The *Morse Code* (leaving off the "International"), can be used for signalling in many ways. Flash lanterns (blinker), whistles, searchlights on the clouds, and in fact any dot and dash method may employ this code. It is so important that no youngster going to sea nowadays should neglect to thoroughly learn the alphabet and numerals and the few conventional signals necessary to send and read messages. Often a knowledge of this code is the means of saving life.

The International Code

This refers to the flag and distant signals and the many combinations by which seamen may communicate with each other regardless of language. It is truly an *international* method of communication.

There is no substitute for the *Code Book.*

This note is simply to impress upon the mind of the seaman the fact that it is his duty to study this book and know it thoroughly.

Know—

How to make a hoist.
How and when to use *Repeaters.*
How to interpret a signal made by another vessel.
How to reply, and how to take a signal from the book.
How to recognize the character of a hoist by the number of flags, one, two, three and four flag hoists.

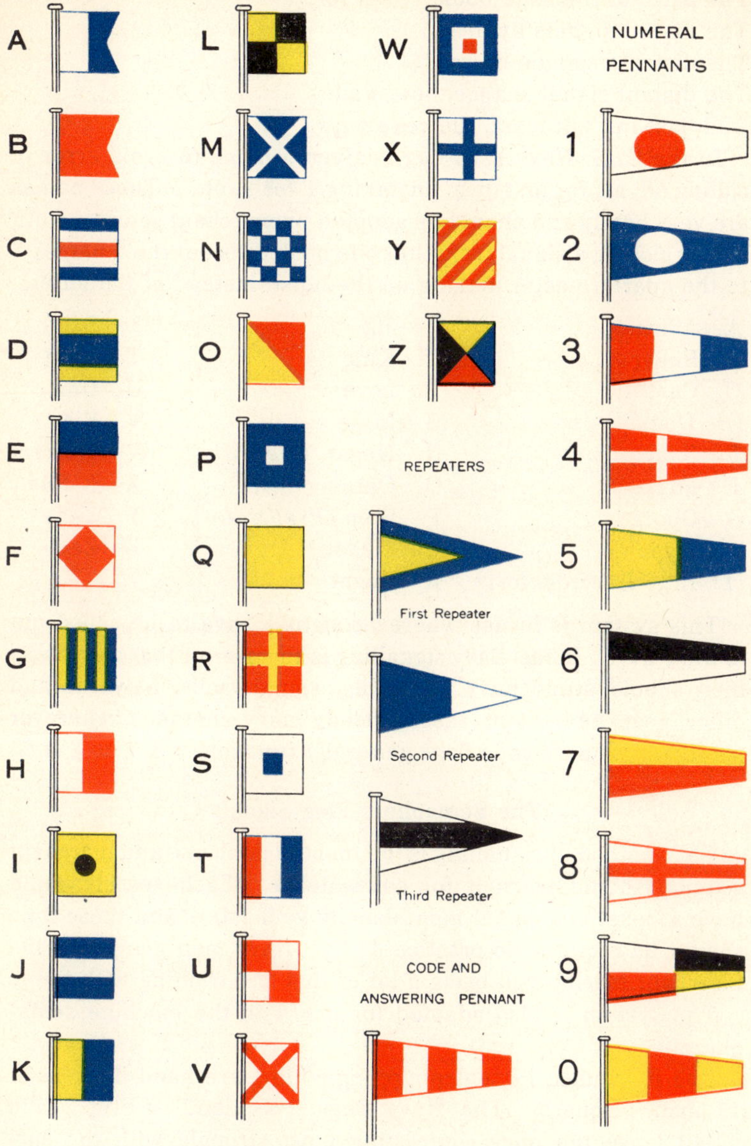

International Code Flags and Pennants.

The parts of the code book—what for.
The urgent signals by heart.
The distress signals by heart.
The distant signal shapes, how made.
And, last but not least, the *code flags*.

In the U. S. Navy each flag is given a name to avoid error in calling off, as, for instance, mistaking T for V, etc. These names are very handy and should be adopted by merchant seamen. An officer picking a signal from the code book calls out the "names" to the quartermaster making up the hoist, instead of the letters.

A—Affirm	J—Jig	S—Sail
B—Baker	K—King	T—Tare
C—Cast	L—Love	U—Unit
D—Dog	M—Mike	V—Victor
E—Easy	N—Negat. (*Negative*)	W—William
F—Fox	O—Option	X—X-Ray
G—George	P—Prep (*Preparatory*)	Y—Yoke
H—Hypo	Q—Queen	Z—Zed
I—Int. (*Interrogatory*)	R—Roger	

This system is in use wherever signals have to be called out in the Navy. In fact navy signalling is so superior that merchantmen should study navy signalling, signal racks, halyards and other gear and adopt these speedy navy methods wherever possible. Square code flags generally run from 3′ x 3′ to 8′ x 8′.

The Semaphore Flag Signals

This method of signalling is the most rapid in use and merchant seamen should learn it for convenience. Each vessel should have at least two signal men, usually youngsters and these men should be required to practice daily. Navy men going into the merchant marine will bring a lot of this fine training with them.

The system is also adapted for use with the machine semaphore.

The flags used in semaphore signalling, are hand flags 12 or 15 inches square. The Navy flags, "Option," "Prep" and "Sail," use the ones contrasting most strongly with the surroundings of the sender.

Make all motions sharp and distinct to avoid confusion. A

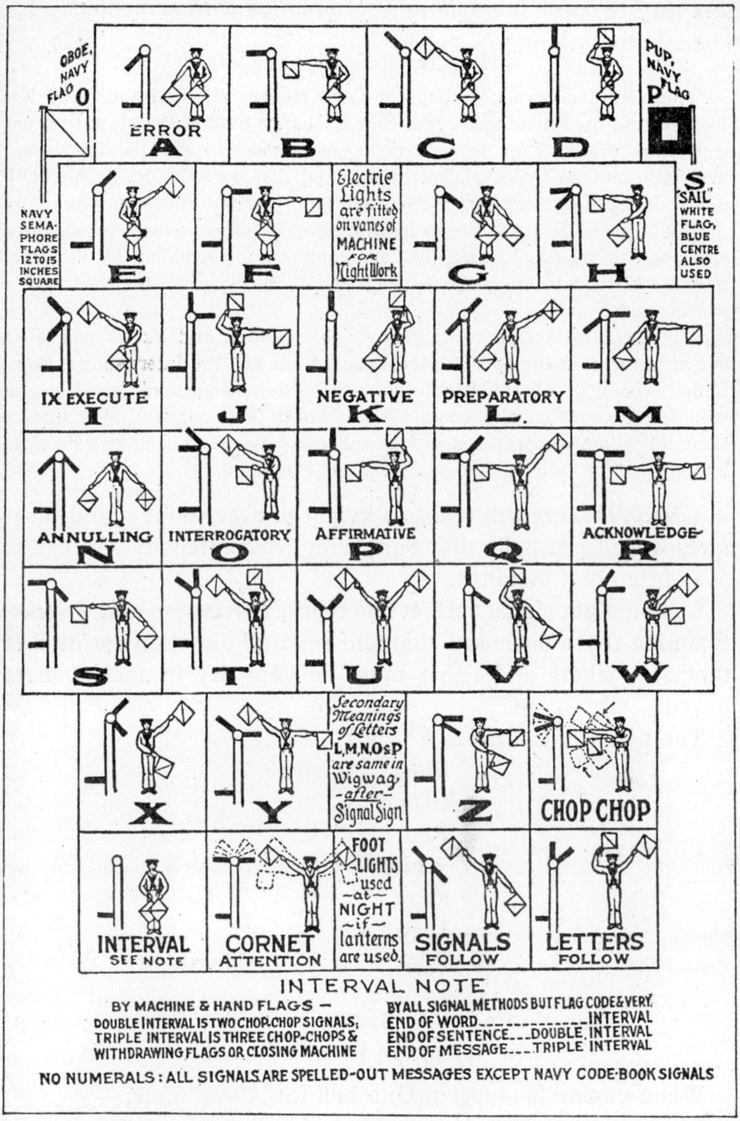
OBOE, NAVY FLAG O
ERROR
A
B
C
D
PUP, NAVY FLAG P
S "SAIL" WHITE FLAG, BLUE CENTRE ALSO USED
NAVY SEMAPHORE FLAGS 12 TO 15 INCHES SQUARE
E
F
Electric Lights are fitted on vanes of MACHINE FOR Night Work
G
H
IX EXECUTE
I
J
NEGATIVE
K
PREPARATORY
L
M
ANNULLING
N
INTERROGATORY
O
AFFIRMATIVE
P
Q
ACKNOWLEDGE
R
S
T
U
V
W
X
Y
Secondary Meanings of Letters L, M, N, O & P are same in Wigwag -after- Signal Sign
Z
CHOP CHOP
INTERVAL SEE NOTE
CORNET ATTENTION
FOOT LIGHTS used -at- NIGHT -if- lanterns are used.
SIGNALS FOLLOW
LETTERS FOLLOW
INTERVAL NOTE
BY MACHINE & HAND FLAGS —
DOUBLE INTERVAL IS TWO CHOP-CHOP SIGNALS;
TRIPLE INTERVAL IS THREE CHOP-CHOPS & WITHDRAWING FLAGS OR CLOSING MACHINE
BY ALL SIGNAL METHODS BUT FLAG CODE & VERY.
END OF WORD .... INTERVAL
END OF SENTENCE ... DOUBLE. INTERVAL
END OF MESSAGE ... TRIPLE INTERVAL
NO NUMERALS: ALL SIGNALS ARE SPELLED-OUT MESSAGES EXCEPT NAVY CODE-BOOK SIGNALS

slight pause should follow each character or letter. *The quickest way to learn semaphore is to practice with someone.*

Miscellaneous Signal Data

The Weather Bureau stations at Cape Henry, Virginia; and Sand Key, Florida; and the Philadelphia Maritime Exchange Station at Delaware Breakwater, are equipped for day and night communication with passing vessels. The International Code is used by day and the Morse Code, flashlight, by night. Messages to or from vessels will be forwarded to destination.

The stations at Point Reyes light, California; North Head, Washington; and Tatoosh Island, Washington, are equipped for signaling by the International Code, and are prepared to transmit by telegraph the messages of passing vessels.

All U. S. Coast Guard Stations on the Atlantic and Pacific coasts are equipped for signaling by the International Code and the International Morse Code (wig-wag). On the Atlantic coast those stations north of Cape Hatteras, with few exceptions, and on the Pacific coast those stations near lines of communication, are prepared to transmit messages of passing vessels either by telegraph or by telephone and telegraph combined.

Coston rockets will rise to a height of over 400 feet and throw a shower of red balls that burn with great intensity and can be seen at a great distance.

Coston night signals are of two types, *Percussion* and *Friction.* Examine those on board ship and read *all* directions printed on them. Rockets and lights must be kept dry in special metal boxes.

The lights in use are:

Blue	Lights	
Green	"	
Red	"	
White	"	
Fog	"	
Distress	"	
Pilot	"	(blue light)

Signals from Pilot House to Engine Room (if Telegraph Breaks Down)

When engine is stopped, One bell for *Ahead Slow.*
When running ahead slow, Jingle for *Full Speed Ahead.*
When running full speed ahead, One bell for *Slow Down.*
When running ahead slow, One bell for *Stop.*

When stopped, Two bells for *Astern.*

When running astern, jingle bell for full speed *Astern.*

When running astern, One bell for *Stop.*

When running full spead ahead, Four bells for *Full Speed Astern.*

When running ahead slow, Three bells for *Full Speed Astern.*

Salutes are given at sea by dipping the ensign. Merchant craft dip to men of war, hauling the ensign down two thirds, if at the gaff, or to the rail, if at a flagstaff. The ensign should be hauled down in plenty of time so that the intention to dip may be observed by the vessel saluted and reply made while vessels are still nearly abreast.

Always haul down and hoist the ensign slowly and without jerks. Never send it aloft to be broken out.

Vessels in foreign ports should dress ship on occasions of ceremony, on national holidays of the country and of course on the prescribed American holidays—the Fourth of July, Washington's Birthday, etc.

VII

Yacht Routine

Colors, Etc. Yachts in commission should hoist their colors at 8 o'clock a. m., and haul them down at sunset, taking time from the senior officer present.

Before colors in the morning and after colors at sunset, the ensign and distinguishing flags should be shown when entering port, and should be hauled down immediately on coming to anchor.

At all other times yachts should fly a blue night pennant at the main, from colors at sunset until colors the next morning.

No guns should be fired for colors except by the yacht giving the time, nor from colors at sunset until colors the next morning, nor on Sunday.

Absence flags and meal pennants are not considered colors.

On Decoration Day and occasions of national mourning the ensign only should be half-masted. On the death of the owner of the yacht, both the Club flag and his private signal should be half-masted, but not the ensign. When mourning is ordered for the death of a member of the Club, the Club flag only should be half-masted. This rule should apply to yachts both at anchor and under way.

Flags should always be mast-headed before half-masting them, and should be mast-headed before hauling them down. Saluting with the ensign at half-mast should be done by mast-heading first.

Officer in Command of Anchorage. The senior officer present should be in command of the anchorage, should give the time for colors, make and return salutes, visits, etc.

His yacht should remain the station vessel until a senior to him in rank arrives and assumes the command of the anchorage.

Pennants, Private Signals, Etc. Flag officers should always fly their pennants while in commission.

Yachts, when the owner is not on board, should fly at the main starboard spreader, during daytime, a blue flag, rectangular in shape. This flag should never be flown when under way.

Single-masted vessels should fly the private signal of the owner when entering a home port, or when approaching other yachts at sea; at other times the Club flag, except when with the squadron.

Meal Pennants. A white flag, rectangular in shape, should be flown at the main starboard spreader on schooners, and at the starboard spreader on single-masted vessels, during the meal hours of the owner.

A red pennant pointed in shape should be flown at the fore-port spreader on schooners, and at the port spreader on single-masted vessels, during the meal hours of the crew. A white light should be displayed on starboard spreader after sunset and during owner's meal hours.

Lights. Commodore. From colors at sunset until sunrise the Commodore should show, when on board, two blue lights, perpendicularly, at the stern; when absent, one blue light should be shown.

Vice-Commodore. The Vice-Commodore should show lights as provided for the Commodore, substituting red lights instead of blue.

Captains. Captains, when on board, should show a white light under the main boom; when absent this light should be extinguished.

Salutes. All salutes should be returned in kind.

The following rules should not apply to yachts leaving for, or returning from a day's sail.

Yachts should salute vessels of the United States Navy by dipping the ensign once.

The Commodore, on entering port to join the squadron, should be saluted, on coming to anchor, by the yachts present. On all other occasions the Commodore should be saluted, on coming to anchor, by the officer in command.

Junior flag officers should be saluted, on coming to anchor, by the officer in command unless the latter be a senior in rank, in which case they should salute him.

Captains should on all occasions salute the officer in command.

The salute from yachts entering port should be made by dipping the ensign once, or by firing a gun or letting go anchor.

The senior officer, when leaving the anchorage, excepting temporarily, should indicate the transfer of command to the next in rank by firing a gun on getting under way. All other yachts should salute the officer in command.

All visits should be made according to rank.

Yachts, passing one another, should always exchange salutes by dipping the ensign once, juniors saluting first. Steam whistles should never be used to make salutes.

The salute to yachts entering port, entitled to a salute, should be made by dipping the ensign once, or by firing a gun, when they let go anchor.

An official salute to a foreign club should be made by firing a gun, with the flag of the foreign club at the fore on schooners and steamers, and at the main on single-masted vessels; or, in the absence of such flag, by half-masting the Club flag and firing a gun. When the salute has been returned, or a reasonable time for its return allowed, the flag should be hauled down, and the Club flag hoisted again.

The salute from or to yachts arriving after sunset, or on Sunday, should be made immediately after colors on the following morning.

When a flag officer makes an official visit, a gun should be fired, with his pennant at the fore on schooners and steamers, and at the main on single-masted vessels, while he remains on board.

A yacht, acting as judges' boat, should not be saluted during a race.

The quarter-deck should always be saluted by lifting the cap on coming on board or from below.

With the Squadron. Yachts should report to the commanding officer on joining the squadron, and should obtain his permission before leaving it.

When under way with the squadron, firing guns and signalling should be avoided, except when joining or parting company, or when repeating signals.

Passing at Sea. When squadrons of different clubs meet at sea, salutes should be exchanged only by the commanding officers.

Salutes from single yachts at sea should only be answered by the flag-ship.

Single-masted vessels should fly the private signal of the owner when under way with the squadron; when at anchor, the Club flag.

When a foreign yacht arrives, the senior officer present should send on board, without regard to rank, a tender of the civilities of the Club.

Entering a Foreign Port. Yachts should salute on entering port in the home waters of a foreign club, where any of its fleet are lying. After the tender of civilities has been made, owners of the entering yachts should visit the officer in command of the anchorage. All other visits should be made according to rank,—visits to their equals in rank being made by the owners of the entering yachts.

The time for colors in the home waters of a foreign club should be given with its senior flag officer present.

The term " foreign " should be understood as applying to all other clubs outside of the waters in which a club is stationed.

Boat Service. The order of entering and leaving boats is, juniors enter first and leave last.

Flag officers and the Fleet-Captain should fly their pennants, and Captains their private signals, when in their boats; members, the Club flag. After sunset a white light should be shown at the bow.

Passing one another, juniors should salute seniors by raising the cap.

Every boat approaching a yacht at night should be hailed.

The answer of the Commodore when intending to board, should be "Commodore;" for Junior flag officers, and fleet-captains, "Flag;" for captains and members, "Ay, ay;" for captains returning on board, the name of their yacht; for visitors, "Visitors;" for sailing-masters, etc., "No, No," using the port side; for passing boats, "Passing."

Church Pennant (white triangular, with blue cross) is the only flag ever displayed above the ensign, and only during divine service, with Yacht at anchor.

The above section may seem out of place in *Standard Seamanship*—but every sailor in the merchant marine would like to be a yacht owner some day, and every yacht sailor aims to be a deep-water sailor—so we try to be of use to all.

VIII

The Log Book

The writing up of the log book is an important part of the work of an officer. Great care should be exercised in performing this duty as the original entries (without erasures) are of great value when points of law are being decided with respect to the ship or voyage. Care should be taken to enter everything having to do with the state of the weather and the work of the vessel, the relief of lookouts, the names of men on lookout, etc. The watch officer should practice the art of concise writing, sticking to facts. The log book entries should always be signed.

The Official Log is generally another book kept by the Master in which certain entries are made according to law. Men are "logged" in this book. Deaths are recorded, etc. Below are the exact entries required as stated in the U. S. Navigation Laws. These entries must be made by the Master himself, or at his direction.

First. Every legal conviction of any member of his crew, and the punishment inflicted.

Second. Every offense committed by any member of his crew for which it is intended to prosecute, or to enforce a forfeiture, together with such statement concerning the reading over such entry, and concerning the reply, if any, made to the charge, as is required by the provisions of section forty-five hundred and ninety-seven.

Third. Every offense for which punishment is inflicted on board, and the punishment inflicted.

Fourth. A statement of the conduct, character, and qualifications of each of his crew; or a statement that he declines to give an opinion of such particulars.

Fifth. Every case of illness or injury happening to any member of the crew, with the nature thereof, and the medical treatment.

Sixth. Every case of death happening on board, with the cause thereof.

Seventh. Every birth happening on board, with the sex of the infant, and the names of the parents.

Eighth. Every marriage taking place on board, with the names and ages of the parties.

Ninth. The name of every seaman or apprentice who ceases to be a member of the crew otherwise than by death, with the place, time, manner, and cause thereof.

Tenth. The wages due to any seaman or apprentice who dies during the voyage, and the gross amount of all deductions to be made therefrom.

Eleventh. The sale of the effects of any seaman or apprentice who dies during the voyage, including a statement of each article sold, and the sum received for it.

Twelfth. In every case of collision in which it is practicable so to do, the master shall, immediately after the occurrence, cause a statement thereof, and of the circumstances under which the same occurred, to be entered in the official log-book. Such entry shall be made in the manner prescribed in section forty-two hundred and ninety-one, and failure to make such entry shall subject the offender to the penalties prescribed by section forty-two hundred and ninety-two. (R. S., 4290; Feb. 14, 1900.)

Miscellaneous Log Book Data

Bell Time

The twenty-four hours are divided on board ship into seven parts, and the crew is divided into two parts or watches, designated Port and Starboard Watches. Each watch are on duty four hours, except from 4 to 8 p. m., which time is divided into two watches of two hours each, called Dog Watches, by means of which the watches are changed every day, and each watch gets a turn of eight hours' rest at night. *First Watch*, 8 p. m. to midnight; *Middle Watch*, midnight to 4 a. m.; *Morning Watch*, 4 to 8 a. m.; *Forenoon Watch*, 8 a. m. to noon; *Afternoon Watch*, noon to 4 p. m.; *First Dog Watch*, 4 to 6 p. m.; *Second Dog Watch*, 6 to 8 p. m. In the French service there are no Dog Watches, but there are two watches of 6 hours each.

The British custom is to strike the bells 1, 2, 3, in the two hours of the second day watch.

The Bell is Struck Every Half Hour to Indicate the Time

1 Bell,	12.30 a. m.	1 Bell,	12.30 p. m.	
2 Bells,	1.00 "	2 Bells,	1.00 "	
3 "	1.30 "	3 "	1.30 "	
4 "	2.00 "	4 "	2.00 "	
5 "	2.30 "	5 "	2.30 "	
6 "	3.00 "	6 "	3.00 "	
7 "	3.30 "	7 "	3.30 "	
8 "	4.00 "	8 "	4.00 "	
1 Bell,	4.30 "	1 Bell,	4.30 "	First Dog Watch
2 Bells,	5.00 "	2 Bells,	5.00 "	
3 "	5.30 "	3 "	5.30 "	
4 "	6.00 "	4 "	6.00 "	
5 "	6.30 "	5 "	6.30 "	Second Dog Watch
6 "	7.00 "	6 "	7.00 "	
7 "	7.30 "	7 "	7.30 "	
8 "	8.00 "	8 "	8.00 "	
1 Bell,	8.30 "	1 Bell,	8.30 "	
2 Bells,	9.00 "	2 Bells,	9.00 "	
3 "	9.30 "	3 "	9.30 "	
4 "	10.00 "	4 "	10.00 "	
5 "	10.30 "	5 "	10.30 "	
6 "	11.00 "	6 "	11.00 "	
7 "	11.30 "	7 "	11.30 "	
8 "	12.00 noon.	8 "	12.00 night.	

Formula for Recording State of Weather

B denotes Blue Sky, *i.e.*, clear or hazy atmosphere.
C " Cloudy—detached opening clouds.

D denotes Drizzling Rain.
F " Fog—FF Thick Fog.
G " Gloomy—dark weather.
H " Hail.
L " Lightning.
M " Misty or Hazy—so as to interrupt view.
O " Overcast—*i.e.*, whole sky covered with an impervious cloud.
P " Passing showers.
Q " Squally.
R " Rain—continuous rain.
S " Snow.
T " Thunder.
U " Ugly with a heavy appearance of the weather.
V " Visibility of distant objects.
. Dot under any letter, an extraordinary degree.

By the combination of these letters all the ordinary phenomena of the weather may be recorded with certainty and brevity.

BCM—Blue sky, with detached opening clouds, but hazy round the horizon.

GV—Gloomy dark weather, but distant objects *remarkably* visible.

Numerals for Recording State of Sea

0 Calm.	5 Rather Rough.
1 Very Smooth.	6 Rough.
2 Smooth.	7 High.
3 Slight.	8 Very High.
4 Moderate.	9 Tremendous.

IV

Preparing For Sea

Under the law the Master is held responsible for the seaworthy condition of a vessel about to proceed on a voyage.* He

* The executive committee of the Board of Supervising Inspectors, Steamboat-Inspection Service, at a meeting held on October 9, 1915, amended the general rules and regulations, ocean and coastwise, and for lakes, bays, and sounds, relative to the covering of hatches. The amendments were approved by the Secretary of Commerce on October 12, 1915, and now have the force

must satisfy himself that everything is in order, hatches battened down and all secure. In fact the whole business of going to sea hinges on this important point of responsibility. The Chief Mate is charged with the direct responsibility and the following reminders are printed here as a matter of importance.

A heavy sea coming on board off Cape Pillar. Photograph taken by Captain H. C. Hostler on board the S. S. Santa Rosalia, a U. S. Steel Products Company steamer.

of law. The rule for ocean and coastwise vessels has been amended so as to read as follows:

"It shall be the duty of the Master of any vessel under the jurisdiction of the Steamboat-Inspection Service to assure himself, before proceeding to sea, that all the cargo hatches of his vessel are properly covered and the covers secured. The covers of all exposed hatches shall be made water-tight by the use of pliable gaskets or by heavy canvas tarpaulins, thoroughly covering the hatch cover and firmly secured by iron or steel bars extending from side to side or end to end of the hatchway, which bars shall be securely fastened by toggles or wedges made of hardwood or by the use of efficient screw fastenings. *Failure by the Master of any vessel to observe this regulation shall be sufficient cause for suspension or revocation of his license on a charge of inattention to his duty.*"

The rule for vessels navigating lakes, bays, and sounds has been amended so as to read as follows:

"It shall be the duty of the Master of any vessel under the jurisdiction of the Steamboat-Inspection Service, and which is carrying cargo, to assure himself before leaving port that all the cargo hatches of his vessel are properly covered and the covers secured." The remainder of the rule being the same as above.

Before leaving, if alongside, the engines may have to be turned over. The Engineer in charge should notify the Chief Mate and the necessary adjustments must be made to lines, gangways, hoses, or any other connection between the vessel and the wharf. *Watch out for floating logs near propeller.* Have a hand standing by engine, telegraph and bridge.

The order to " single up " is usually given shortly before leaving. All extra lines are taken on board. Rat guards may be taken off and only the single parts of bow and stern lines and a few springs kept out. It is a good plan, where no men are available on the dock, to carry the splice inboard and a bight around the bollards on the dock. The lines can then be let go and hauled in from the vessel's deck. Sometimes a slip toggle can be used, the toggle being attached to a heaving line. Great care must be taken with the lines leading from the quarter not to get them foul of the propellers.

Hatches must be put on and caulked if off for a wet passage, and treble tarpaulins battened down.

Booms should be shipped in the cradels and lashed or clamped in place. Topping lifts should be unrove, or at least unhooked and carried into the eyebolts on the mast table. It is well to unreeve all manila cargo gear and stow it below on a voyage of any length, at least on a voyage across the Atlantic. Where gear is left standing abaft the funnels it should be covered with smoke covers.

All handling lines should be triced up to dry or coiled on gratings and then stowed below when thoroughly aired.

If tow boats are to be used, fenders should be handy.

On the bridge it is necessary to have all of the navigating gear in order. The whistle should be tried and *freed from water* before getting into the stream. The long blast on pulling out usually does this. The telegraphs should be tried on all points, the hand leads and lines should be coiled in the chains and men ready to heave them if necessary. The log should be ready to stream, and the signal number bent on the halyards and ready. All proper flags should be mastheaded.

As soon as the vessel gets way on her haul down the blue peter, and the jack, if these flags are flown.

Never fly torn flags, especially the ensign. It may be soiled and old, but never have it frayed. Torn flags are an abomination associated with flagstaffs ashore where they often stay up until they fall apart. It is a good idea to have the Quartermasters uncover when they haul down the ensign at sunset and hoist it at eight bells in the morning, it instills respect for the flag.

Always be certain to have a long boat line ready for the pilot and his ladder handy on the lee side.

Be sure the running lights are working before it gets dark. Have spare oil lights ready.

On approaching port a great many things must be attended to. Warn the first assistant in time so that all ashes can be got out before getting into restricted waters. Have the steward throw overboard all galley waste and get salt water tank filled while the water is clean.

Have handling lines up and coiled down clear fore and aft.

Have heaving lines handy.

Prepare lead lines and stands. Have leadsmen in the chains.

Have signal letters bent on.

Have pilot ladder and boat line ready, on lee side.

Have gangway ready.

Have cargo gear rove off if weather permits.

Have anchors ready to let go.

Have steam on the windlass and winches ready for lifting booms and handling anchor. Have steering gear clear.

See that the capstans are working.

Find out, if possible, which side is to be next the wharf, if going alongside. What hatches are to work.

Haul in log when past the last mark, lighthouse lightship, buoy, etc.

See precautions about hauling in log page 491.

Know the customs and quarantine regulations. Be certain that the vessel observes all local rules. Consult with Pilot and Harbor Master when in a strange port.

Set all watches for the night and have liberty arranged beforehand, so there will be no misunderstanding when the vessel gets in.

All these things should be looked after from the bridge. The Officer of the Watch never leaves the bridge, unless relieved by the Master.

CHAPTER XVI

RULES OF THE ROAD AT SEA

I

Foreword

A great deal has been written on the rules of the road at sea. David Wright Smith, in " The Law Relating to the Rule of the Road at Sea " cites more than two hundred and fifty cases to illustrate the many ways in which vessels may come to grief through ignorance, misunderstanding, or unavoidable accident when meeting on the sea. It has become the fashion to treat the *International Rules of the Road at Sea* to a sort of literary vivisection, interlarding them with notes and " explanations " that, to the mind of the present writer, seem to do anything but clarify them. The best brains available were bent upon the task of producing the present *International Rules,* and as they stand today they are remarkable for their clear language, unmistakable in meaning and economical in words.

Ninety per cent of collisions at sea grow out of careless disregard for the rules, or out of plain ignorance of them or of their meaning. A man who will not study the rules and know them, and keep on refreshing his memory, will find no short cut method to help him out.

The U. S. *Inland Rules* of the United States have wisely followed the exact wording of the *International Rules* except in a few places where conditions necessitate a change.

The *Pilot Rules*, promulgated by the Board of Supervising Inspectors of Steam Vessels, supplement the *Inland Rules*. Their most important departure from the *International Rules* is the adoption of the *danger* or *four whistle* signal. This signal should be carefully studied under its proper place in the *Pilot Rules*. It should really have a place in the *International Rules*. (See page. 614)

To avoid confusion in the mind of the reader, and to present the whole body of the rules of the road, the following plan is followed in *Standard Seamanship:*

Where the *International* and *Inland Rules* are identical the text is leaded and is captioned—International and Inland Rules.

Where *International Rules* are different from *Inland Rules,* or are not contained in *Inland Rules*, the text is printed solid and is captioned—International Only.

Where *Inland Rules* are different, or are not contained in *International Rules* the text is in italics and is captioned—Inland Only.

The whole of the two sets of rules is printed in this way and in proper sequence so that the student may know, at a glance, when he is reading rules applicable to both high seas and U. S. inland waters, or to either one alone. At the same time he may conveniently note their points of difference. Also, and this is important, the book is not cluttered up with a lot of repetition.

The *Pilot Rules* are printed separately, at the end, together with the situation diagrams published by the Government.

Rules of the road cannot be learned from a book.

These vital rules are only learned at sea, where the constant passing of vessels, both sail and steam, drives home to the young sailor the meaning of the rules. He must *memorize* the rules from the book, and *visualize* them at sea. The quartermaster, cadet, junior officer, in fact any one on the bridge, should carefully observe the manner in which the Master, or officer of the watch, acts in accordance with the rules. Then, when the day, *or night*, comes for him to take over his first watch, he will act with experience drawn from observation. On this important occasion the conscientious man has a feeling of great responsibility resting upon him.

Innumerable diagrams have been drawn to show the many situations that may arise at sea and these, in theory at least, are correct, but the present writer is of the opinion, and many officers concur with him, that such paper diagrams, red, green and yellow spots, and inch square smudges of black (representing night at sea) are utterly worthless. If a man has not enough intelligence to understand the full meaning of the Rules of the Road, as printed, " having careful regard to the existing circumstances and conditions," he had better remain off the bridge of a ship.

Therefore the young mariner is urged to study these important but simple rules with a better appreciation of their beautiful clearness. He should know them word for word.

The writer was under a skipper once who had a habit of bobbing up on the bridge and asking the officer of the watch a sharp embarrassing question or two on the rules. An officer who could not answer correctly *a second time* was certain to find other employment. As a matter of fact, nine men out of ten, so this ancient skipper said, were stuck at the first question. It is a good way for the "old man" to be certain that his watch officers keep brushed up on the rules. It is the duty of the Master to satisfy himself that all his watch officers are proficient in the Rules of the Road.

Many excellent works have been written in the Rules of the Road, works going into much detail in setting forth the "cases" wherein learned jurists have dissected some thrilling moment when ships have crashed at sea. W. H. LaBoyteaux in an exceedingly important and interesting volume of two hundred and forty odd pages called "*The Rule of the Road At Sea*" cites some three hundred and more cases. This is a recent book, published in 1920, and is about the best thing along these lines. As important supplementary reading, for masters and watch officers, it should be very valuable.

It is mighty interesting to read of the mistakes and mishaps of others, but it is exceedingly unpleasant to sit in a stuffy court room and have your own mistakes raked over the coals of judgment.

Lawyers write these useful books but it is pretty tough to listen to them talk for days at a time. Every time a vessel goes to sea the captain and each officer who stands a watch is liable to wind up in the clutches of this legal inquisition. His only safety lies in keeping wide awake every moment of the time, with the rules of the road, the maneuvering power of his own vessel, *and of other vessels both sail and steam,* constantly in mind.

The reader will now be left alone with the rules. Study them thoroughly, then read them over at least once a month from end to end; make it your monthly *office.*

II

The Rules

International Only

I.—Enacting Clause, Scope, and Penalty

Be it enacted by the Senate and House of Representatives of the United States of America in Congress assembled, That the following regulations for preventing collisions at sea shall be followed by all public and private vessels of the United States upon the high seas and in all waters connected therewith, navigable by seagoing vessels.

Art. 30. Nothing in these rules shall interfere with the operation of a special rule, duly made by local authority, relative to the navigation of any harbor, river, or inland waters.

Inland Only

I.—Enacting Clause, Scope, and Penalty

Whereas the provisions of chapter eight hundred and two of the laws of eighteen hundred and ninety, and the amendments thereto, adopting regulations for preventing collisions at sea [i. e., international rules], apply to all waters of the United States connected with the high seas navigable by sea-going vessels, except so far as the navigation of any harbor, river, or inland waters is regulated by special rules duly made by local authority; and

Whereas it is desirable that the regulations relating to the navigation of all harbors, rivers, and inland waters of the United States, except the Great Lakes and their connecting and tributary waters as far east as Montreal and the Red River of the North and rivers emptying into the Gulf of Mexico and their tributaries, shall be stated in one act: Therefore,

Be it enacted by the Senate and House of Representatives of the United States of America in Congress assembled, That the following regulations for preventing collisions shall be followed by all vessels navigating all harbors, rivers, and inland waters of the United States, except the Great Lakes and their connecting and tributary waters as far east as Montreal and the Red River of the North and rivers emptying into the Gulf of Mexico and their tributaries, and are hereby declared special rules duly made by local authority:

Sec. 3. *That every pilot, engineer, mate, or master of any steam vessel, and every master or mate of any barge or canal boat, who neglects or refuses to observe the provisions of this act, or the regulations established in pursuance of the preceding section* [*see section 2, page 581*], *shall be liable to a penalty of fifty dollars, and for all damages sustained by any passenger in his person or baggage by such neglect or refusal: Provided, That nothing herein shall relieve any vessel, owner, or corporation from any liability incurred by reason of such neglect or refusal.*

Sec. 4. *That every vessel that shall be navigated without complying with the provisions of this act shall be liable to a penalty of two hundred dollars, one-half to go to the informer, for which sum the vessel so navigated shall be liable and may be seized and proceeded against by action in any district court of the United States having jurisdiction of the offense.*

International and Inland Rules

Preliminary Definitions

In the following rules every steam vessel which is under sail and not under steam is to be considered a sailing vessel, and every vessel under steam, whether under sail or not, is to be considered a steam vessel.

The words " steam vessel " shall include any vessel propelled by machinery.

A vessel is " under way," within the meaning of these rules, when she is not at anchor, or made fast to the shore, or aground.

II.—Lights, and So Forth

The word " visible " in these rules when applied to lights shall mean visible on a dark night with a clear atmosphere.

Article 1. The rules concerning lights shall be complied with in all weathers from sunset to sunrise, and during such time no other lights which may be mistaken for the prescribed lights shall be exhibited.

Steam Vessels—Masthead Light

Art. 2. A steam vessel when under way shall carry—(a) On or in front of the foremast, or if a vessel without a foremast, then in the fore part of the vessel, at a height above the hull of not less than twenty feet, and if the breadth of the vessel exceeds twenty feet, then at a height above the hull not less than such breadth, so, however, that the light need not be carried at a greater height above the hull than forty feet, a bright white light, so constructed as to show an unbroken light over an arc of the horizon of twenty points of the compass, so fixed as to throw the light ten points on each side of the vessel, namely, from right ahead to two points abaft the beam on either side, and of such a character as to be visible at a distance of at least five miles.

Steam Vessels—Side Lights

(b) On the starboard side a green light so constructed as to show an unbroken light over an arc of the horizon of ten points of the compass, so fixed as to throw the light from right ahead to two points abaft the beam on the starboard side, and of such a character as to be visible at a distance of at least two miles.

(c) On the port side a red light so constructed as to show an unbroken light over an arc of the horizon of ten points of the compass, so fixed as to throw the light from right ahead to two points abaft the beam on the port side, and of such a character as to be visible at a distance of at least two miles.

(d) The said green and red side lights shall be fitted with inboard screens projecting at least three feet forward from the light, so as to prevent these lights from being seen across the bow.

Steam Vessels—Range Lights

(e) A steam vessel when under way may carry an additional white light similar in construction to the light mentioned in subdivision (a). These two lights shall be so placed in line with the keel that one shall be at least fifteen feet higher than the other, and in such a position with reference to each other that the lower light shall be forward of the upper one. The vertical distance between these lights shall be less than the horizontal distance.

Inland Only

(f) All steam vessels (except seagoing vessels and ferryboats), shall carry in addition to green and red lights required by article two (b), (c), and screens as required by article two (d), a central range of two white lights; the after light being carried at an elevation at least fifteen feet above the light at the head of the vessel. The headlight shall be so constructed as to show an unbroken light through twenty points of the compass, namely, from right ahead to two points abaft the beam on either side of the vessel, and the after light so as to show all around the horizon.

International and Inland

Steam Vessels when Towing

Art. 3. A steam vessel when towing another vessel shall, in addition to her side lights, carry two bright white lights in a vertical line one over the other, not less than six feet apart, and when towing more than one vessel shall carry an additional bright white light six feet above or below such lights, if the length of the tow measuring from the stern of the towing vessel to the stern of the last vessel towed exceeds six hundred feet. Each of these lights shall be of the same construction and character, and shall be carried in the same position as the white light mentioned in article two (a), excepting the additional light, which may be carried at a height of not less than fourteen feet above the hull.

Such steam vessel may carry a small white light abaft the funnel or aftermast for the vessel towed to steer by, but such light shall not be visible forward of the beam.

International Only

Special Lights

Art. 4. (a) A vessel which from any accident is not under command shall carry at the same height as a white light mentioned in article two (a), where they can best be seen, and if a steam vessel in lieu of that light two red lights, in a vertical line one over the other, not less than six feet apart, and of such a character as to be visible all around the horizon at a distance of at least two miles; and shall by day carry in a vertical line one over the other, not less than six feet apart, where they can best be seen two black balls or shapes, each two feet in diameter.

(b) A,vessel employed in laying or in picking up a telegraph cable shall carry in the same position as the white light mentioned in article two (a), and if a steam vessel in lieu of that light three lights in a vertical line one over the other not less than six feet apart. The highest and lowest of these lights shall be red, and the middle light shall be white, and they shall be of such a character as to be visible all around the horizon, at a distance of at least two miles. By day she shall carry in a vertical line, one over the other, not less than six feet apart, where they can best be seen, three shapes not less than two feet in diameter, of which the highest and lowest shall be globular in shape and red in color, and the middle one diamond in shape and white.

(c) The vessels referred to in this article, when not making way through the water, shall not carry the side lights, but when making way shall carry them.

(d) The lights and shapes required to be shown by this article are to be taken by other vessels as signals that the vessel showing them is not under command and can not therefore get out of the way.

These signals are not signals of vessels in distress and requiring assistance. Such signals are contained in article thirty-one.

International and Inland

Lights for Sailing Vessels and Vessels in Tow

Art. 5. A sailing vessel under way and any vessel being towed shall carry the same lights as are prescribed by article two for a steam vessel under way, with the exception of the white lights mentioned therein, which they shall never carry.

Inland Only

Lights for Ferryboats, Barges, and Canal Boats in Tow

Sec. 2. *That the supervising inspectors of steam vessels and the Supervising Inspector-General shall establish such rules to be observed by steam vessels in passing each other and as to the lights to be carried by ferryboats and by barges and canal boats when in tow of steam vessels* (*and as to the lights and day signals to be carried by vessels, dredges of all types, and vessels working on wrecks by* [*or*] *other obstruction to navigation or moored for submarine operations, or made fast to a sunken object which may drift with the tide or be towed*) *not inconsistent with the provisions of this act, as they from time to time may deem necessary for safety, which rules when approved by the Secretary of Commerce are hereby declared special rules duly made by local authority, as provided for in article thirty of chapter eight hundred and two of the laws of eighteen hundred and ninety. Two printed copies of such rules shall be furnished to such ferryboats* (*barges, dredges, canal boats, vessels working on wrecks*) *and steam vessels, which rules shall be kept posted up in conspicuous places in such vessels* (*barges, dredges, and boats*).

International and Inland

Lights for Small Vessels

Art. 6. Whenever, as in the case of small vessels under way during bad weather, the green and red side lights can not be fixed, these lights shall be kept at hand, lighted and ready for use; and shall, on the approach of or to other vessels, be exhibited on their respective sides in sufficient time to prevent collision, in such manner as to make them most visible, and so that the green light shall not be seen on the port side nor the red light on the starboard side, nor, if practicable, more than two points abaft the beam on their respective sides. To make the use of these portable lights more certain and easy the lanterns containing them shall each be painted outside with the color of the light they respectively contain, and shall be provided with proper screens.

International Only

Lights for Small Steam and Sail Vessels and Open Boats

Art. 7. Steam vessels of less than forty, and vessels under oars or sails of less than twenty tons gross tonnage, respectively, and rowing boats, when under way, shall not be required to carry the lights mentioned in article two (a), (b), and (c), but if they do not carry them they shall be provided with the following lights:

First. Steam vessels of less than forty tons shall carry—

(a) In the fore part of the vessel, or on or in front of the funnel, where it can best be seen, and at a height above the gunwale of not less than nine feet, a bright white light constructed and fixed as prescribed in article two (a), and of such a character as to be visible at a distance of at least two miles.

(b) Green and red side lights constructed and fixed as prescribed in article two (b) and (c), and of such a character as to be visible at a distance of at least one mile, or a combined lantern showing a green light and a red light from right ahead to two points abaft the beam on their respective sides. Such lanterns shall be carried not less than three feet below the white light.

Second. Small steamboats, such as are carried by seagoing vessels, may carry the white light at a less height than nine feet above the gunwale, but it shall be carried above the combined lantern mentioned in subdivision one (b).

Third. Vessels under oars or sails of less than twenty tons shall have ready at hand a lantern with a green glass on one side and a red glass on the other, which, on the approach of or to other vessels, shall be exhibited in sufficient time to prevent collision, so that the green light shall not be seen on the port side nor the red light on the starboard side.

International and Inland

Fourth. Rowing boats, whether under oars or sail, shall have ready at hand a lantern showing a white light which shall be temporarily exhibited in sufficient time to prevent collision.

The vessels referred to in this article shall not be obliged to carry the lights prescribed by article four (a) and article eleven, last paragraph.

Lights for Pilot Vessels

Art. 8. Pilot vessels when engaged on their station on pilotage duty shall not show the lights required for other vessels, but shall carry a white light at the masthead, visible all around the horizon, and shall also exhibit a flare-up light or flare-up lights at short intervals, which shall never exceed fifteen minutes.

On the near approach of or to other vessels they shall have their side lights lighted, ready for use, and shall flash or show them at short intervals, to indicate the direction in which they are heading, but the green light shall not be shown on the port side, nor the red light on the starboard side.

A pilot vessel of such a class as to be obliged to go alongside of a vessel to put a pilot on board may show the white light instead of carrying it at the masthead, and may, instead of the colored lights above mentioned, have at hand, ready for use, a lantern with green glass on the one side and red glass on the other, to be used as prescribed above.

Pilot vessels when not engaged on their station on pilotage duty shall carry light similar to those of other vessels of their tonnage.

A steam pilot vessel, when engaged on her station on pilotage duty and in waters of the United States, and not at anchor, shall, in addition to the lights required for all pilot boats, carry at a distance of eight feet below her white masthead light a red light, visible all around the horizon and of such a character as to be visible on a dark night with a clear atmosphere at a distance of at least two miles, and also the colored side lights required to be carried by vessels when under way.

When engaged on her station on pilotage duty and in waters of the United States, and at anchor, she shall carry in addition to the lights required for all pilot boats the red light above mentioned, but not the colored side lights. When not engaged on her station on pilotage duty, she shall carry the same lights as other steam vessels.

International Only

Lights, Etc., of Fishing Vessels

Art. 9. Fishing vessels and fishing boats, when under way and when not required by this article to carry or show the lights hereinafter specified, shall carry or show the lights prescribed for vessels of their tonnage under way.

(a) Open boats, by which is to be understood boats not protected from the entry of sea water by means of a continuous deck, when engaged in any fishing at night, with outlying tackle extending not more than one hundred and fifty feet horizontally from the boat into the seaway, shall carry one all-round white light.

Open boats, when fishing at night, with outlying tackle extending more than one hundred and fifty feet horizontally from the boat into the seaway, shall carry one all-round white light, and in addition, on approaching or being approached by other vessels, shall show a second white light at least three feet below the first light and at a horizontal distance of at least five feet away from it in the direction in which the outlying tackle is attached.

(b) Vessels and boats, except open boats as defined in subdivision (a), when fishing with drift nets, shall, so long as the nets are wholly or partly in the water, carry two white lights where they can best be seen. Such lights shall be placed so that the vertical distance between them shall be not less than six feet and not more than fifteen feet, and so that the horizontal distance between them, measured in a line with the keel, shall be not less than five feet and not more than ten feet. The lower of these two lights shall be in the direction of the nets, and both of them shall be of such a character as to show all around the horizon, and to be visible at a distance of not less than three miles.

Within the Mediterranean Sea and in the seas bordering the coasts of Japan and Korea sailing fishing vessels of less than twenty tons gross tonnage shall not be obliged to carry the lower of these two lights. Should they, however, not carry it, they shall show in the same position (in the direction of the net or gear) a white light, visible at a distance of not less than one sea mile, on the approach of or to other vessels.

(c) Vessels and boats, except open boats as defined in subdivision (a), when line fishing with their lines out and attached to or hauling their lines, and when not at anchor or stationary within the meaning of subdivision (h), shall carry the same lights as vessels fishing with drift nets. When shooting lines, or fishing with towing lines, they shall carry the lights prescribed for a steam or sailing vessel under way, respectively.

Within the Mediterranean Sea and in the seas bordering the coasts of Japan and Korea sailing fishing vessels of less than twenty tons gross tonnage shall not be obliged to carry the lower of these two lights. Should they, however, not carry it, they shall show in the same position (in the direction of the lines) a white light, visible at a distance of not less than one sea mile on the approach of or to other vessels.

(d) Vessels when engaged in trawling, by which is meant the dragging of an apparatus along the bottom of the sea—

First. If steam vessels, shall carry in the same position as the white light mentioned in article two (a) a tri-colored lantern so constructed and fixed as to show a white light from right ahead to two points on each bow, and a green light and a red light over an arc of the horizon from two points on each bow to two points abaft the beam on the starboard and port sides, respectively; and not less than six nor more than twelve feet below the tri-colored lantern a white light in a lantern, so constructed as to show a clear, uniform, and unbroken light all around the horizon.

Second. If sailing vessels, shall carry a white light in a lantern, so constructed as to show a clear, uniform, and unbroken light all around the horizon, and shall also, on the approach of or to other vessels, show where it can best be seen a white flare-up light or torch in sufficient time to prevent collision.

All lights mentioned in subdivision (d) first and second shall be visible at a distance of at least two miles.

(e) Oyster dredgers and other vessels fishing with dredge nets shall carry and show the same lights as trawlers.

(f) Fishing vessels and fishing boats may at any time use a flare-up light in addition to the lights which they are by this article required to carry and show, and they may also use working lights.

(g) Every fishing vessel and every fishing boat under one hundred and fifty feet in length, when at anchor, shall exhibit a white light visible all around the horizon at a distance of at least one mile.

Every fishing vessel of one hundred and fifty feet in length or upward, when at anchor, shall exhibit a white light visible all around the horizon at a distance of at least one mile, and shall exhibit a second light as provided for vessels of such length by article eleven.

Should any such vessel, whether under one hundred and fifty feet in length or of one hundred and fifty feet in length or upward, be attached to a net or other fishing gear, she shall on the approach of other vessels show an additional white light at least three feet below the anchor light, and at a horizontal distance of at least five feet away from it in the direction of the net or gear.

(h) If a vessel or boat when fishing becomes stationary in

consequence of her gear getting fast to a rock or other obstruction, she shall in daytime haul down the day signal required by subdivision (k); at night show the light or lights prescribed for a vessel at anchor; and during fog, mist, falling snow, or heavy rain storms make the signal prescribed for a vessel at anchor. (See subdivision (d) and the last paragraph of article fifteen.)

(i) In fog, mist, falling snow, or heavy rain storms drift-net vessels attached to their nets, and vessels when trawling, dredging, or fishing with any kind of drag net, and vessels line fishing with their lines out, shall, if of twenty tons gross tonnage or upward, respectively, at intervals of not more than one minute make a blast; if steam vessels, with the whistle or siren, and if sailing vessels, with the fog-horn, each blast to be followed by ringing the bell. Fishing vessels and boats of less than twenty tons gross tonnage shall not be obliged to give the above-mentioned signals; but if they do not, they shall make some other efficient sound signal at intervals of not more than one minute.

(k) All vessels or boats fishing with nets or lines or trawls, when under way, shall in daytime indicate their occupation to an approaching vessel by displaying a basket or other efficient signal where it can best be seen. If vessels or boats at anchor have their gear out, they shall, on the approach of other vessels, show the same signal on the side on which those vessels can pass.

The vessels required by this article to carry or show the lights hereinbefore specified shall not be obliged to carry the lights prescribed by article four (a) and the last paragraph of article eleven.

Inland Only

Lights, Etc., of Fishing Vessels

Art. 9. (*a*) *Fishing vessels of less than ten gross tons, when under way and when not having their nets, trawls, dredges, or lines in the water, shall not be obliged to carry the colored side lights; but every such vessel shall, in lieu thereof, have ready at hand a lantern with a green glass on one side and a red glass on the other side, and on approaching to or being approached by another vessel such lantern shall be exhibited in sufficient time to prevent collision, so that the green light shall not be seen on the port side nor the red light on the starboard side.*

(*b*) *All fishing vessels and fishing boats of ten gross tons or upward, when under way and when not having their nets, trawls, dredges, or lines in the water, shall carry and show the same lights as other vessels under way.*

(*c*) *All vessels, when trawling, dredging, or fishing with any kind of drag nets or lines, shall exhibit, from some part of the vessel where they can be best seen, two lights. One of these lights shall be red and the other shall be white. The red light shall be above the white light, and shall be at a vertical distance from it of not less than six feet and not more than twelve feet; and the horizontal distance between them, if any, shall not be more than ten feet. These two lights shall be of such a character and contained in lanterns of such construction as to be visible all round the horizon, the white light a distance of not less than three miles and the red light of not less than two miles.*

Lights for Rafts or other Craft not Provided For

(d) Rafts, or other water craft not herein provided for, navigating by hand power, horse power, or by the current of the river, shall carry one or more good white lights, which shall be placed in such manner as shall be prescribed by the Board of Supervising Inspectors of Steam Vessels.

International and Inland

Lights for an Overtaken Vessel

Art. 10. A vessel which is being overtaken by another shall show from her stern to such last-mentioned vessel a white light or a flare-up light.

The white light required to be shown by this article may be fixed and carried in a lantern, but in such case the lantern shall be so constructed, fitted, and screened that it shall throw an unbroken light over an arc of the horizon of twelve points of the compass, namely, for six points from right aft on each side of the vessel, so as to be visible at a distance of at least one mile. Such light shall be carried as nearly as practicable on the same level as the side lights.

Anchor Lights

Art. 11. A vessel under one hundred and fifty feet in length when at anchor shall carry forward, where it can best be seen, but at a height not exceeding twenty feet above the hull, a white light, in a lantern so constructed as to show a clear, uniform, and unbroken light visible all around the horizon at a distance of at least one mile.

A vessel of one hundred and fifty feet or upwards in length when at anchor shall carry in the forward part of the vessel, at a height of not less than twenty and not exceeding forty feet above the hull, one such light, and at or near the stern of the vessel, and at such a height that it shall be not less than fifteen feet lower than the forward light, another such light.

The length of a vessel shall be deemed to be the length appearing in her certificate of registry.

International Only

A vessel aground in or near a fairway shall carry the above light or lights and the two red lights prescribed by article four (a).

International and Inland

Special Signals

Art. 12. Every vessel may, if necessary in order to attract attention, in addition to the lights which she is by these rules required to carry, show a flare-up light or use any detonating signal that can not be mistaken for a distress signal.

Naval Lights and Recognition Signals

Art. 13. Nothing in these rules shall interfere with the operation of any special rules made by the Government of any nation with respect to additional station and signal lights for two or more ships of war or for vessels sailing under convoy, or with the exhibition of recognition signals adopted by shipowners, which have been authorized by their respective Governments and duly registered and published.

Steam Vessel under Sail by Day

Art. 14. A steam vessel proceeding under sail only, but having her funnel up, shall carry in daytime, forward, where it can best be seen, one black ball or shape two feet in diameter.

III.—Sound Signals for Fog, and So Forth

Preliminary

Art. 15. All signals prescribed by this article for vessels under way shall be given:

First. By " steam vessels " on the whistle or siren.

Second. By " sailing vessels " and " vessels towed " on the fog horn.

The words " prolonged blast " used in this article shall mean a blast of from four to six seconds duration.

A steam vessel shall be provided with an efficient whistle or siren, sounded by steam or by some substitute for steam, so placed that the sound may not be intercepted by any obstruction, and with an efficient fog horn, to be sounded by mechanical means, and also with an efficient bell.

International Only

In all cases where the rules require a bell to be used a drum may be substituted on board Turkish vessels, or a gong where such articles are used on board small seagoing vessels.

International and Inland

A sailing vessel of twenty tons gross tonnage or upward shall be provided with a similar fog horn and bell.

In a fog, mist, falling snow, or heavy rain storms, whether by day or night, the signals described in this article shall be used as follows, namely:

Steam Vessel under Way

(a) A steam vessel having way upon her shall sound, at intervals of not more than two minutes, a prolonged blast.

Inland Only

Steam Vessel under Way

(*a*) *A steam vessel under way shall sound, at intervals of not more than one minute, a prolonged blast.*

International Only

(b) A steam vessel under way, but stopped, and having no way upon her, shall sound, at intervals of not more than two minutes, two prolonged blasts, with an interval of about one second between.

International and Inland

Sail Vessel under Way

(c) A sailing vessel under way shall sound, at intervals of not more than one minute, when on the starboard tack, one blast; when on the port tack, two blasts in succession, and when with the wind abaft the beam, three blasts in succession.

Vessels at Anchor or Not Under Way

(d) A vessel when at anchor shall, at intervals of not more than one minute, ring the bell rapidly for about five seconds.

Vessels Towing or Towed

(e) A vessel when towing, a vessel employed in laying or in picking up a telegraph cable, and a vessel under way, which is unable to get out of the way of an approaching vessel through being not under command, or unable to maneuver as required by the rules, shall, instead of the signals prescribed in subdivisions (a) and (c) of this article, at intervals of not more than two minutes, sound three blasts in succession, namely: One prolonged blast followed by two short blasts. A vessel towed may give this signal and she shall not give any other.

International Only

Small Sailing Vessels and Boats

Sailing vessels and boats of less than twenty tons gross tonnage shall not be obliged to give the above-mentioned signals, but, if they do not, they shall make some other efficient sound signal at intervals of not more than one minute.

Inland Only

Rafts or Other Craft Not Provided For

(f) All rafts or other water craft, not herein provided for, navigating by hand-power, horse-power, or by the current of the river, shall sound a blast of the fog-horn, or equivalent signal, at intervals of not more than one minute.

International and Inland

Speed in Fog

Art. 16. Every vessel shall, in a fog, mist, falling snow, or heavy rain storms, go at a moderate speed, having careful regard to the existing circumstances and conditions.

A steam vessel hearing, apparently forward of her beam, the fog signal of a vessel the position of which is not ascertained shall, so far as the circumstances of the case admit, stop her engines, and then navigate with caution until danger of collision is over.

IV.—Steering and Sailing Rules

Preliminary

Risk of collision can, when circumstances permit, be ascertained by carefully watching the compass bearing of an approaching vessel. If the bearing does not appreciably change, such risk should be deemed to exist.

Sailing Vessels

Art. 17. When two sailing vessels are approaching one another, so as to involve risk of collision, one of them shall keep out of the way of the other, as follows, namely:

(a) A vessel which is running free shall keep out of the way of a vessel which is closehauled.

(b) A vessel which is closehauled on the port tack shall keep out of the way of a vessel which is closehauled on the starboard tack.

(c) When both are running free, with the wind on different sides, the vessel which has the wind on the port side shall keep out of the way of the other.

(d) When both are running free, with the wind on the same side, the vessel which is to the windward shall keep out of the way of the vessel which is to the leeward.

(e) A vessel which has the wind aft shall keep out of the way of the other vessel.

International Only

Steam Vessels

Art. 18. When two steam vessels are meeting end on, or nearly end on, so as to involve risk of collision, each shall alter her course to starboard, so that each may pass on the port side of the other.

This article only applies to cases where vessels are meeting end on, or nearly end on, in such a manner as to involve risk of collision, and does not apply to two vessels which must, if both keep on their respective courses, pass clear of each other.

The only cases to which it does apply are when each of the two vessels is end on, or nearly end on to the other; in other words, to cases in which, by day, each vessel sees the masts of the other in a line, or nearly in a line, with her own; and by night, to cases in which each vessel is in such a position as to see both the side-lights of the other.

It does not apply by day to cases in which a vessel sees another ahead crossing her own course; or by night, to cases where the red light of one vessel is opposed to the red light of the other, or where the green light of one vessel is opposed to the green light of the other, or where a red light without a green light, or a green light without a red light, is seen ahead, or where both green and red lights are seen anywhere but ahead.

Inland Only

Steam Vessels

Art. 18. Rule I. *When steam vessels are approaching each other head and head, that is, end on, or nearly so, it shall be the duty of each to pass on the port side of the other; and either vessel shall give, as a signal of her intention, one short and distinct blast of her whistle, which the other vessel shall answer promptly by a similar blast of her whistle, and thereupon such vessels shall pass on the port side of each other. But if the courses of such vessels are so far on the starboard of each other as not to be considered as meeting head and head, either vessel shall immediately give two short and distinct blasts of her whistle, which the other vessel shall answer promptly by two similar blasts of her whistle, and they shall pass on the starboard side of each other.*

The foregoing only applies to cases where vessels are meeting end on, or nearly end on, in such a manner as to involve risk of collision; in other words, to cases in which, by day, each vessel sees the masts of the other in a line, or nearly in a line, with her own, and by night to cases in which each vessel is in such a position as to see both the side-lights of the other.

It does not apply by day to cases in which a vessel sees another ahead crossing her own course, or by night to cases where the red light of one vessel is opposed to the red light of the other, or where the green light of one vessel is opposed to the green light of the other, or where a red light without a green light or a green light without a red light, is seen ahead, or where both green and red lights are seen anywhere but ahead.

Rule III. *If, when steam vessels are approaching each other, either vessel fails to understand the course or intention of the other, from any cause, the vessel so in doubt shall immediately signify the same by giving several short and rapid blasts, not less than four, of the steam whistle.*

Rule V. *Whenever a steam vessel is nearing a short bend or curve in the channel, where, from the height of the banks or other cause, a steam vessel approaching from the opposite direction can not be seen for a distance of half a mile, such steam vessel, when she shall have arrived within half a mile of such curve or bend, shall give a signal by one long blast of the steam whistle, which signal shall be answered by a similar blast given by any approaching steam vessel that may be within hearing. Should such signal be so answered by a steam vessel upon the farther side of such bend, then the usual signals for meeting and passing shall immediately be given and answered; but, if the first alarm signal of such vessel be not answered, she is to consider the channel clear and govern herself accordingly.*

When steam vessels are moved from their docks or berths, and other boats are liable to pass from any direction toward them, they shall give the same signal as in the case of vessels meeting at a bend, but immediately after clearing the berths so as to be fully in sight they shall be governed by the steering and sailing rules.

Rule VIII. *When steam vessels are running in the same direction, and the vessel which is astern shall desire to pass on the right or starboard hand of the vessel ahead, she shall give one short blast of the steam whistle, as a signal of such desire, and if the vessel ahead answers with one blast, she shall put her helm to port; or if she shall desire to pass on the left or port side of the vessel ahead, she shall give two short blasts of the steam whistle as a signal of such desire, and if the vessel ahead answers with two blasts, shall put her helm to starboard; or if the vessel ahead does not think it safe for the vessel astern to attempt to pass at that point, she shall immediately signify the same by giving several short and rapid blasts of the steam whistle, not less than four, and under no circumstances shall the vessel astern attempt to pass the vessel ahead until such time as they have reached a point where it can be safely done, when said vessel ahead shall signify her willingness by blowing the proper signals. The vessel ahead shall in no case attempt to cross the bow or crowd upon the course of the passing vessel.*

Rule IX. *The whistle signals provided in the rules under this article, for steam vessels meeting, passing, or overtaking, are never to be used except when steamers are in sight of each other, and the course and position of each can be determined in the daytime by a sight of the vessel itself, or by night by seeing its signal lights. In fog, mist, falling snow or heavy rain storms, when vessels can not see each other, fog signals only must be given.*

Supplementary Regulations

Sec. 2. *That the supervising inspectors of steam-vessels and the Supervising Inspector-General shall establish such rules to be observed by steam vessels in passing each other and as to the lights to be carried by ferryboats and by barges and canal boats when in tow of steam vessels, not inconsistent with the provisions of this act, as they from time to time may deem necessary for safety, which rules when approved by the Secretary of Commerce are hereby declared special rules duly made by local authority, as provided for in article thirty of chapter eight hundred and two of the laws of eighteen hundred and ninety. Two printed copies of such rules shall be furnished to such ferryboats and steam vessels, which rules shall be kept posted up in conspicuous places in such vessels.**

* See Pilot rules, page 597.

International and Inland

Two Steam Vessels Crossing

Art. 19. When two steam vessels are crossing, so as to involve risk of collision, the vessel which has the other on her own starboard side shall keep out of the way of the other.

Steam Vessel Shall Keep Out of the Way of Sailing Vessel

Art. 20. When a steam vessel and a sailing vessel are proceeding in such directions as to involve risk of collision, the steam vessel shall keep out of the way of the sailing vessel.

Course and Speed

Art. 21. Where, by any of these rules, one of two vessels is to keep out of the way the other shall keep her course and speed.

Note—When, in consequence of thick weather or other causes, such vessel finds herself so close that collision can not be avoided by the action of the giving-way vessel alone, she also shall take such action as will best aid to avert collision. [See articles twenty-seven and twenty-nine.]

Crossing Ahead

Art. 22. Every vessel which is directed by these rules to keep out of the way of another vessel shall, if the circumstances of the case admit, avoid crossing ahead of the other.

Steam Vessel Shall Slacken Speed or Stop

Art. 23. Every steam vessel which is directed by these rules to keep out of the way of another vessel shall, on approaching her, if necessary, slacken her speed or stop or reverse.

Overtaking Vessels

Art. 24. Notwithstanding anything contained in these rules every vessel, overtaking any other, shall keep out of the way of the overtaken vessel.

Every vessel coming up with another vessel from any direction more than two points abaft her beam, that is, in such a position, with reference to the vessel which she is overtaking that at night she would be unable to see either of that vessel's side lights, shall be deemed to be an overtaking vessel; and no subsequent alteration of the bearing between the two vessels shall make the overtaking vessel a crossing vessel within the meaning of these rules, or relieve her of the duty of keeping clear of the overtaken vessel until she is finally past and clear.

As by day the overtaking vessel can not always know with certainty whether she is forward of or abaft this direction from the other vessel she should, if in doubt, assume that she is an overtaking vessel and keep out of the way.

Narrow Channels

Art. 25. In narrow channels every steam vessel shall, when it is safe and practicable, keep to that side of the fairway or mid-channel which lies on the starboard side of such vessel.

Right of Way of Fishing Vessels

Art. 26. Sailing vessels under way shall keep out of the way of sailing vessels or boats fishing with nets, or lines, or trawls. This rule shall not give to any vessel or boat engaged in fishing the right of obstructing a fairway used by vessels other than fishing vessels or boats.

General Prudential Rule

Art. 27. In obeying and construing these rules due regard shall be had to all dangers of navigation and collision, and to any special circumstances which may render a departure from the above rules necessary in order to avoid immediate danger.

Sound Signals for Passing Steamers

Art. 28. The words " short blast " used in this article shall mean a blast of about one second's duration.

When vessels are in sight of one another, a steam vessel under way, in taking any course authorized or required by these rules, shall indicate that course by the following signals on her whistle or siren, namely:

One short blast to mean, " I am directing my course to starboard."

Two short blasts to mean, " I am directing my course to port."

Three short blasts to mean, " My engines are going at full speed astern."

Precaution

Art. 29. Nothing in these rules shall exonerate any vessel, or the owner or master or crew thereof, from the consequences of any neglect to carry lights or signals, or of any neglect to keep a proper lookout, or of the neglect of any precaution which may be required by the ordinary practice of seamen, or by the special circumstances of the case.

International Only

Art. 30. Nothing in these rules shall interfere with the operation of a special rule, duly made by local authority, relative to the navigation of any harbor, river, or inland waters.

Inland Only

Lights on United States Naval Vessels and Coast Guard Cutters

Art. 30. *The exhibition of any light on board of a vessel of war of the United States or a Coast Guard cutter may be suspended whenever, in the opinion of the Secretary of the Navy, the commander in chief of a squadron, or the commander of a vessel acting singly, the special character of the service may require it.*

International and Inland

Distress Signals

Art. 31. When a vessel is in distress and requires assistance from other vessels or from the shore the following shall be the signals to be used or displayed by her, either together or separately, namely:

In the daytime—

First. A gun or other explosive signal fired at intervals of about a minute.

Second. The international code signal of distress indicated by N C.

Third. The distance signal, consisting of a square flag, having either above or below it a ball or anything resembling a ball.

Fourth. A continuous sounding with any fog-signal apparatus.

At night—

First. A gun or other explosive signal fired at intervals of about a minute.

Second. Flames on the vessel (as from a burning tar barrel, oil barrel, and so forth).

Third. Rockets or shells throwing stars of any color or description, fired one at a time, at short intervals.

Fourth. A continuous sounding with any fog-signal apparatus.

III

U. S. Pilot Rules

Pilot Rules for all Harbors, Rivers, and Inland Waters of the United States, Except the Great Lakes and Their Connecting and Tributary Waters as far East as Montreal and the Red River of the North and Rivers Emptying into the Gulf of Mexico and Their Tributaries.

Preliminary

In the following rules the words *steam vessel* shall include any vessel propelled by machinery.

A vessel is *under way*, within the meaning of these rules, when she is not at anchor, or made fast to the shore, or aground.

Risk of collision can, when circumstances permit, be ascertained by carefully watching the compass bearing of an approaching vessel. If the bearing does not appreciably change, such risk should be deemed to exist.

Signals

The whistle *signals* provided in these rules shall be sounded on an efficient whistle or siren sounded by steam or by some substitute for steam.

A *short blast* of the whistle shall mean a blast of about one second's duration.

A *prolonged blast* of the whistle shall mean a blast of from four to six seconds' duration.*

One short blast of the whistle signifies intention to direct course to own starboard, except when two steam vessels are approaching each other at right angles or obliquely, when it signifies intention of steam vessel which is to starboard of the other to hold course and speed.

* Under the provisions of par. (a), sec. 4, of act of Congress approved June 9, 1910, "a blast of at least two seconds shall be deemed a prolonged blast within the meaning of the law," when given by vessels propelled by machinery and not more than 65 feet in length, except tugboats and towboats propelled by steam.

Two short blasts of the whistle signify intention to direct course to own port.

Three short blasts of the whistle shall mean, "My engines are going at full speed astern."

When vessels are in sight of one another a steam vessel under way whose engines are going at full speed astern shall indicate that fact by three short blasts on the whistle.

Rule I. If, when steam vessels are approaching each other, either vessel fails to understand the course or intention of the other, from any cause, the vessel so in doubt shall immediately signify the same by giving several short and rapid blasts, not less than four, of the steam whistle, the *danger signal.*

Rule II. Steam vessels are forbidden to use what has become technically known among pilots as "*cross signals*," that is, answering one whistle with two, and answering two whistles with one.

Rule III. The *signals for passing,* by the blowing of the whistle, shall be given and answered by pilots, in compliance with these rules, not only when meeting "head and head," or nearly so, but at all times, when the steam vessels are in sight of each other, when passing or meeting at a distance within half a mile of each other, and whether passing to the starboard or port.

The whistle signals provided in the rules for steam vessels meeting, passing, or overtaking, are never to be used except when steam vessels are in sight of each other, and the course and position of each can be determined in the daytime by a sight of the vessel itself, or by night by seeing its signal lights. In fog, mist, falling snow or heavy rain-storms, when vessels can not so see each other, fog signals only must be given.

Situations

Rule IV. When steam vessels are *approaching each other head and head, that is, end on, or nearly so,* it shall be the duty of each to pass on the port side of the other; and either vessel shall give, as a signal of her intention, one short and distinct blast of her whistle, which the other vessel shall answer promptly by a similar blast of her whistle, and thereupon such vessels shall pass on the port side of each other. But if the courses of such vessels are so far on the starboard of each other as not to be considered as meeting head and head, either vessel shall immediately give two short and distinct blasts of her whistle, which the other vessel shall answer promptly by two similar blasts of her whistle, and they shall pass on the starboard side of each other.

The foregoing only applies to cases where vessels are meeting end on or nearly end on, in such a manner as to involve risk of collision; in other words, to cases in which, by day, each vessel sees the masts of the other in a line, or nearly in a line, with her own, and by night to cases in which each vessel is in such a position as to see both the side lights of the other.

It does not apply by day to cases in which a vessel sees another ahead crossing her own course, or by night to cases where the red light of one vessel is opposed to the red light of the other, or where the green light of one vessel is opposed to the green light of the other, or where a red light without a green light or a green light without a red light, is seen ahead, or where both green and red lights are seen anywhere but ahead.

Rule V. Whenever a steam vessel is *nearing a short bend or curve in the channel,* where, from the height of the banks or other cause, a steam vessel approaching from the opposite direction can not be seen for a distance of half a mile, such steam vessel, when she shall have arrived within half a mile of such curve or bend, shall give a signal by one long blast of the steam whistle, which signal shall be answered by a similar blast, given by any approaching steam vessel that may be within hearing. Should such signal be so answered by a steam vessel upon the farther side of such bend, then the usual signals for meeting and passing shall immediately be given and answered; but, if the first alarm signal of such vessel be not answered, she is to consider the channel clear and govern herself accordingly.

When steam vessels are moved from their docks or berths, and other boats are liable to pass from any direction toward them, they shall give the same signal as in the case of vessels meeting at a bend, but immediately after clearing the berths so as to be fully in sight they shall be governed by the steering and sailing rules.

Rule VI. When steam vessels are running in the same

direction, and the vessel which is astern shall desire to pass on the right or starboard hand of the vessel ahead, she shall give one short blast of the steam whistle, as a signal of such desire, and if the vessel ahead answers with one blast, she shall put her helm to port; or if she shall desire to pass on the left or port side of the vessel ahead, she shall give two short blasts of the steam whistle as a signal of such desire, and if the vessel ahead answers with two blasts, shall put her helm to starboard; or if the vessel ahead does not think it safe for the vessel astern to attempt to pass at that point, she shall immediately signify the same by giving several short and rapid blasts of the steam whistle, not less than four, and under no circumstances shall the vessel astern attempt to pass the vessel ahead until such time as they have reached a point where it can be safely done, when said vessel ahead shall signify her willingness by blowing the proper signals. The vessel ahead shall in no case attempt to cross the bow or crowd upon the course of the passing vessel.

Every vessel coming up with another vessel from any direction more than two points abaft her beam, that is, in such a position, with reference to the vessel which she is overtaking that at night she would be unable to see either of that vessel's side lights, shall be deemed to be *an overtaking vessel;* and no subsequent alteration of the bearing between the two vessels shall make the overtaking vessel a crossing vessel within the meaning of these rules, or relieve her of the duty of keeping clear of the overtaken vessel until she is finally past and clear.

As by day the overtaking vessel can not always know with certainty whether she is forward of or abaft this direction from the other vessel she should, if in doubt, assume that she is an overtaking vessel and keep out of the way.

Rule VII. When two steam vessels are *approaching each other at right angles or obliquely so as to involve risk of collision,* other than when one steam vessel is overtaking another, the steam vessel which has the other on her own port side shall hold her course and speed; and the steam vessel which has the other on her own starboard side shall keep out of the way of the other by directing her course to starboard so as to cross the stern of the other steam vessel, or, if necessary to do so, slacken her speed or stop or reverse.

If from any cause the conditions covered by this situation are such as to prevent immediate compliance with each other's signals, the misunderstanding or objection shall be at once made apparent by blowing the danger signal, and both steam vessels shall be stopped and backed if necessary, until signals for passing with safety are made and understood.

Rule VIII. When a *steam vessel and a sailing vessel* are proceeding in such directions as to involve risk of collision, the steam vessel shall keep out of the way of the sailing vessel.

Rule IX. Every steam vessel which is directed by these rules to *keep out of the way* of another vessel shall, if the circumstances of the case admit, avoid crossing ahead of the other.

Rule X. In *narrow channels* every steam vessel shall, when it is safe and practicable, keep to that side of the fairway or mid-channel which lies on the starboard side of such vessel.

Rule XI. In obeying and construing these rules due regard shall be had to all *dangers of navigation and collision,* and to any *special circumstances* which may render a departure from the above rules necessary in order to avoid immediate danger.

Sound Signals for Fog, and So Forth

Rule XII. In fog, mist, falling snow, or heavy rainstorms, whether by day or night, signals shall be given as follows:

A steam vessel under way, except when towing other vessels or being towed, shall sound, at intervals of not more than one minute, on the whistle or siren, a prolonged blast.

A steam vessel when towing other vessels shall sound, at intervals of not more than one minute, on the whistle or siren, three blasts in succession, namely, one prolonged blast followed by two short blasts.

A vessel towed may give, at intervals of not more than one minute, on the fog horn, a signal of three blasts in succession, namely, one prolonged blast followed by two short blasts, and she shall not give any other.

A vessel when at anchor shall, at intervals of not more than one minute, ring the bell rapidly for about five seconds.

Speed to be Moderate in Fog, and So Forth

Rule XIII. Every steam vessel shall, in a fog, mist, falling snow, or heavy rainstorms, go at a *moderate speed*, having careful regard to the existing circumstances and conditions.

A steam vessel hearing, apparently forward of her beam, the fog signal of a vessel the position of which is not ascertained shall, so far as the circumstances of the case admit, stop her engines, and then navigate with caution until danger of collision is over.

Posting of Pilot Rules

On steam and other motor vessels of over 100 gross tons, two copies of the placard form of these rules (Form 803) shall be kept posted up in conspicuous places in the vessel, one copy of which shall be kept posted up in the pilot house.

Diagrams

The following diagrams are intended to illustrate the working of the system of colored lights and pilot rules:

First Situation

Here the two colored lights visible to each will indicate their direct approach " head and head " toward each other. In this situation it is a standing rule that both shall put their helms to port and pass on the port side of each other, each having previously given one blast of the whistle.

Second Situation

In this situation the red light only will be visible to each, the screens preventing the green lights from being seen. Both vessels are evidently passing to port of each other, which is rulable in this situation, each pilot having previously signified his intention by one blast of the whistle.

Third Situation

In this situation the green light only will be visible to each, the screens preventing the red light from being seen. They are therefore passing to starboard of each other, which is rulable in this situation, each pilot having previously signified his intention by two blasts of the whistle.

Fourth Situation

In this situation one steam vessel is overtaking another steam vessel from some point within the angle of two points abaft the beams of the overtaken steam vessel. The overtaking steam vessel may pass on the starboard or port side of the steam vessel ahead after the necessary signals for passing have been given, with assent of the overtaken steam vessel, as prescribed in Rule VI.

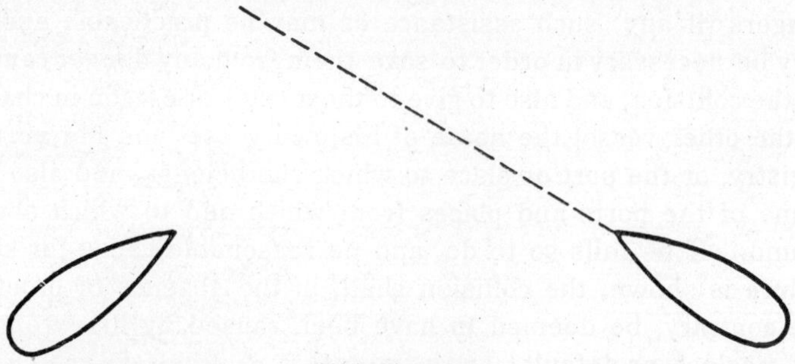

Fifth Situation

In this situation two steam vessels are approaching each other at right angles or obliquely *in such manner as to involve risk of collision,* other than where one steam vessel is overtaking another. The steam vessel which has the other on her own *port* side shall hold course and speed, and the other shall keep clear by crossing astern of the steam vessel that is holding course and speed, or, if necessary to do so, shall slacken her speed or stop or reverse.

IV

Special Rules

U. S. Local Inspectors of Steam Vessels

Act of September 4, 1890, in Regard to Collision at Sea, that Went into Effect December 15, 1890

By the President of the United States of America

A proclamation

Whereas an act of Congress in regard to collisions at sea was approved September 4, 1890, the said act being in the following words:

"*Be it enacted by the Senate and House of Representatives of the United States of America in Congress assembled,* That in every case of collision between two vessels it shall be the duty of the master or person in charge of each vessel, if and so far as he can do so without serious danger to his own vessel, crew, and passengers (if any), to stay by the other vessel until he has ascertained that she has no need of further assistance, and to render to the other vessel, her master, crew, and passengers (if any) such assistance as may be practicable and as may be necessary in order to save them from any danger caused by the collision, and also to give to the master or person in charge of the other vessel the name of his own vessel and her port of registry, or the port or place to which she belongs, and also the name of the ports and places from which and to which she is bound. If he fails so to do, and no reasonable cause for such failure is shown, the collision shall, in the absence of proof to the contrary, be deemed to have been caused by his wrongful act, neglect, or default.

"*Sec. 2.* That every master or person in charge of a United States vessel who fails, without reasonable cause, to render such assistance or give such information as aforesaid shall be deemed guilty of a misdemeanor, and shall be liable to a penalty of one thousand dollars, or imprisonment for a term not exceeding two years; and for the above sum the vessel shall be liable and may be seized and proceeded against by process in any district court of the United States by any person; one-half of such sum to be payable to the informer and the other half to the United States.

"*Sec. 3.* That this act shall take effect at a time to be fixed by the President by Proclamation issued for that purpose."

And whereas it is provided by section 3 of the said act that it shall take effect at a time to be fixed by the President by proclamation issued for that purpose:

Now, therefore, I, Benjamin Harrison, President of the United States of America, do hereby, in virtue of the authority vested in me by section 3 of the said act, proclaim the fifteenth day of December, 1890, as the day on which the said act shall take effect.

In testimony whereof I have hereunto set my hand and caused the seal of the United States of America to be affixed.

Done at the city of Washington this eighteenth day of November, in the year of our Lord one thousand eight hundred and ninety and of the Independence of the United States the one hundred and fifteenth.

[*Seal.*] Benj. Harrison

By the President:

James G. Blaine, *Secretary of State*

Rule Relating to the Use of Searchlights

The Board of Supervising Inspectors, at their annual meeting of January, 1905, adopted the following rule relating to the use of searchlights:

Any master or pilot of any steam vessel who shall flash or cause to be flashed the rays of the searchlight into the pilot house of a passing vessel shall be deemed guilty of misconduct and shall be liable to have his license suspended or revoked.

Rule Prohibiting Unnecessary Sounding of the Steam Whistle

[Authority: Act of Congress approved February 8, 1907]

The Board of Supervising Inspectors, at their annual meeting of January, 1907, adopted the following rule.

Unnecessary sounding of the steam whistle is prohibited within any harbor limits of the United States. Whenever any licensed officer in charge of any steamer authorizes or permits such unnecessary whistling, upon conviction thereof before any board of inspectors having jurisdiction, such officer shall be suspended from acting under his license as the inspectors trying the case may deem proper.

Rule Prohibiting the Carrying of Unauthorized Lights on Steam Vessels

[Adopted by the Board of Supervising Inspectors on February 16, 1910, and approved by the Secretary of Commerce on March 9, 1910. Authority: Section 4450, Revised Statutes]

Any master or pilot of any steam vessel who shall authorize or permit the carrying of any light, electric or otherwise, not required by law, on the outside structure of the cabin or hull of the vessel that in any way will interfere with distinguishing the signal lights shall, upon conviction thereof before any board of inspectors having jurisdiction, be deemed guilty of misconduct and shall be liable to have his license suspended or revoked.

V

Notes on Rules of the Road

Death through negligence, misconduct, etc.

" Every captain, engineer, pilot or other person employed on any steamboat or vessel, by whose misconduct, negligence, or inattention to his duties on such vessel the life of any person is destroyed, and every owner, charterer, inspector, or other public officer, through whose fraud, neglect, connivance, misconduct, or violation of law the life of any person is destroyed, *shall be fined not more than ten thousand dollars or imprisoned not more than ten years, or both. . . .*"

Act March 3, 1905, Sec. 282; 35 St. at Large 1144.

Rules of the Road are mandatory.

" I do not want any option in these rules. The minute that you permit a sailor to have an option, whether he will or will not do a certain thing, you introduce confusion in the rules. I want to see these rules, as far as they can be made, as rigid as steel, so that there shall be no doubt what the Conference of Nations mean. They say, ' Obey these rules, and you will be saved from the danger of negligence; disobey them, and the courts will impose upon you the penalties of disobedience to the rules adopted by the nations of the world.' "

Delegate Goodrich (United States) in the International Conference Rule of the Road Committee.

Rules apply to all vessels alike.

" The size, importance or speed of a vessel does not give her special rights over small, less important or slower vessels. All are equal under the rules and obligated to the same strict observance of them. Passenger steamers have no special rights."

The Bellingham, 138 Fed. 619.

Obedience to rules.

" Obedience to the rules is not a fault even if a different course would have prevented the collision, and the necessity must be clear and the emergency sudden and alarming before the act of disobedience can be excused. Masters are bound to obey the rules and entitled to rely on the assumption that they will be obeyed."

Bilden V. Chase, 150 U. S., 674, 699.

The rule of special circumstances.

" In obeying and construing the rules, due regard must be had to all the dangers of navigation and collision, and to any special circumstances which may render a departure from the rules necessary in order to avoid immediate danger."

Close shaving must be avoided.

" . . . if the rules are carried out according to the spirit of them, I am sure every one will agree with me in saying that it is necessary for the keeping-out-of-the-way vessel to maneuver so as to leave the way free for the other vessel in time, not only in time to avoid a collision, but, as far as possible, in time to avoid even the risk of a collision. Close shaving is to be avoided."

Prot. of Proc., p. 524.

When a vessel is " under way."

A vessel lying dead in the water is under way, if not at anchor or made fast to the shore or aground, and is an overtaken vessel in respect to any vessel approaching from any direction more than two points abaft her beam.

The George W. Elder, 249 Fed. 956, 958.

Screening lights.

" Great care should be exercised to see that the inboard screens of the colored running lights are placed exactly as required by the rules, and that the lights are set in their proper positions. If so placed, the rays will cross at the proper distance ahead of the ship.

" Extraordinary care should always be exercised in screening and watching the running lights when placed in the rigging. In the case of lights so located, it is difficult to fix the inboard screens sufficiently rigid on a line with the keel and in perpendicular so that they will not show across the bow; but failure to have such lights conform in these and in all other respects with the regulations is a source of danger. The difficulty should, therefore, increase the caution. Side lights so located on sailing vessels are particularly apt to cause trouble, and being subject to change under sail pressure, are likely to convey to an approaching vessel the impression that the sailing vessel has changed her course."

La Boyteaux.

Anchor lights.

" Anchor lights should be placed strictly in accordance with the rule. *They should not be placed in too close proximity to the masts, nor where they will be obscured in any direction by the masts, spars, sails or rigging.*

" Sails and all gear should be so stowed that they will not obstruct the anchor lights in any way.

" The forward light for vessels of 150 feet or upwards in length must be located in the forward part of the vessel. The forestay is the usual and probably the best place."

La Boyteaux.

Speed in fog.

" The discretion of the navigator in the matter of speed in a fog must be exercised not wholly as a matter of individual judgment or individual views as to what is moderate speed, but also with due regard to the interpretation of the term ' moderate speed ' by the maritime courts and to the general standards of good seamanship established by those courts in applying the term ' moderate speed.' "

The Sagamore, 247 Fed. 743, 749.

Vessel may be stopped in fog.

" . . . if a steam vessel in a fog cannot be continuously navigated at such a slow speed as will comply with the requirement of Article 16, she must, in the absence of exceptional dangers of navigation, such as may arise from narrow waters or current, be stopped from time to time to take off her way."

The Eagle Point (C.C.A.), 120 Fed. 449, 454.

Precautions.

" The general consensus of opinion in this country is to the effect that a steamer is bound to use only such precautions as will enable her to stop in time to avoid a collision, after the approaching vessel comes in sight, provided such approaching vessel is herself going at the moderate speed required by law."

U. S. Supreme Court.

*Circumstances affecting speed in fog.**

Amongst the circumstances and conditions for which careful regard must be had in determining what shall constitute moderate speed, the following were mentioned in the discussion before the conference:

The density of the fog and the condition of the weather for hearing fog signals;

Whether the vessel is in narrow waters or on the broad ocean;

Whether on fishing grounds or in frequented or unfrequented waters;

The possibility or probability of meeting other vessels;

The readiness with which a vessel (if laden or in ballast) is able to maneuver;

The quickness with which she can be brought to a standstill with the reserve of steam available for that purpose;

Her position with respect to heavy tideways, strong currents or other dangers.

The rate of speed constituting " moderate speed " under the requirement of this rule, therefore, will depend entirely upon the location of the vessel, the probability of meeting other vessels, the density of the fog, her ability to maneuver or bring herself to a standstill quickly, and any and all other surrounding circumstances and conditions affecting her own safety or the safety of others.

This rule permits only such speed in a fog as a vessel may maintain without danger to herself or without endangering others.

La Boyteaux.

The first thing that a mate on the bridge does when he hears a fog horn is to blow his own, and he always answers the signal

* Steamers equipped with wireless apparatus and also those equipped with submarine signalling apparatus should make full use of these systems to safeguard to the utmost navigation in a fog. Navigators whose vessels are so equipped must not, however, rely upon information secured through the use of such apparatus to disregard the positive requirements of the rule in respect to moderate speed or the stopping of the engines upon hearing a fog signal forward of the beam.

at once. The man on the other vessel cannot possibly hear him, because his ears are deafened by the noise of his own horn, and he is, therefore, not aware of the presence of the other vessel until it is too late, and at the subsequent trial he will swear, and truthfully too, that he never heard the fog horn, although it was blown as often as his own. All officers should be warned that if they blow their horn immediately after hearing another one they will not be heard. They should wait at least half a minute before they answer a distant call, in order to allow those on board the other vessel to regain the full use of their ears.

Nautical Magazine.

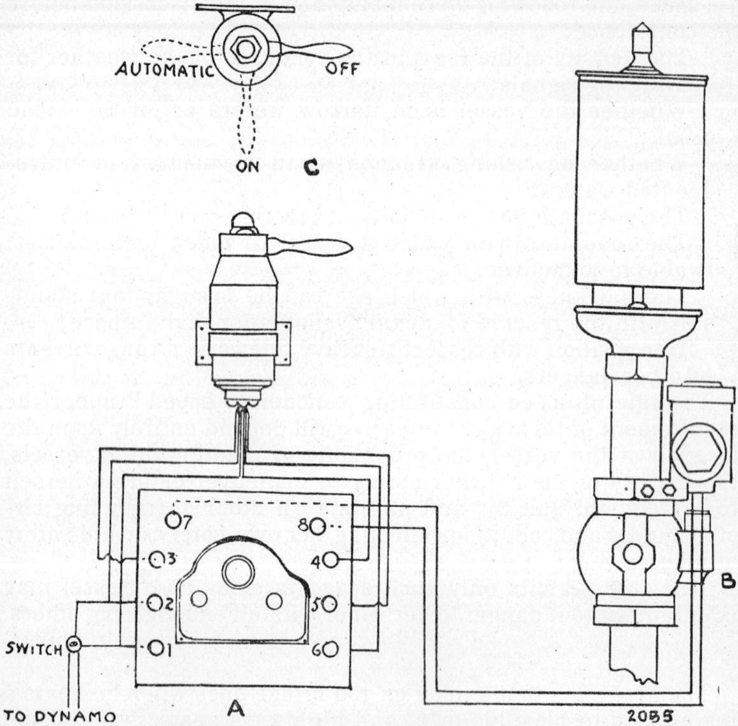

Automatic fog signal arrangement.

Sailing craft in fog.

Moderate speed for a sailing craft is such speed as will enable her to be kept properly under command, *but no more.*

The provision "having careful regard for the existing circumstances and conditions" is intended as a warning that strict attention and consideration must be given by mariners to all conditions, *the density of the fog,* etc., the state of the weather, the proximity of the land or rocks, *the position of the vessel in respect to the possibility or probability of other vessels being in the vicinity;* and, in fact, to any and all circumstances which could in any manner affect the handling of the vessel.

Sailing vessel and steamer.

" Where a sailing vessel and a steamer are proceeding in a direction that may involve collision, the duty of the former is to hold its course, while the latter keeps out of its way. The observance of the rule is no more strictly required of one than of the other. The rule creates a mutual obligation, whereby the sailing vessel is required to hold its course in order that the other may know its position, and not be led into erroneous maneuvers in endeavoring to comply with the requirements of the rule. The rule is imperative, and admits of no option or choice."

Europa, 116 Fed. 696, 698.

Sailing vessel and steamer.

" Meeting a sailing vessel proceeding in such a direction as to involve risk, it was her [the steamer's] duty to keep out of the way, and nothing but inevitable accident, or the conduct and movements of the ship can repel the presumption that she was negligent, arising from the fact of collision. But this duty of the steamer implies a correlative obligation of the ship to keep her course, and do nothing to mislead."

The Scotia, 14 Wall. 170, 181.

Sailing vessel cannot hold on blindly.

" As a privileged vessel [sailing vessel], she was bound to maintain her course so long as it was possible for the burdened vessel to avoid her, at least in the absence of some distinct indication that the burdened vessel was about to fail in her duty. We are of the opinion that the schooner had notice of the intention of the tug [the burdened vessel] to hold her course, and thus create a situation where disaster was inevitable unless the schooner gave way, at a time when there was ample opportunity to have avoided a collision had she acted promptly and with ordinary skill and prudence. . . . The tug gave no indication of changing her course, and the situation was one calling for the utmost caution on the part of the schooner. . . . The tug, by her own negligence, of course, had brought about a situation where a collision could be avoided only by the prompt intelligent action of the schooner. Can there be a doubt that it was her duty so to act? Was she justified in holding her course with stubborn determination when it was demonstrated that such action could only result in a collision? We think not. The law provides that in obeying and construing the rules of navigation 'due regard shall be had to all dangers of navigation, and to any special circumstances which may render a departure from the above rules necessary in order to avoid immediate danger.' The rules are not to be blindly followed to certain disaster. It behooves every navigator to avoid a collision if he can do so and for manifest error, except in the jaws of collision, he must be held responsible. He cannot plead that his was the privileged vessel to relieve him from consequences which were induced by his own lack of prudence and common sense."

The Gladys (C.C.A.), 144 Fed. 653, 657.

Steamers' Whistles

It seems surprising that so little attention has been given to so important a part of the vessel's equipment on which her safety, and that of perhaps hundreds of lives, may depend, but it is a fact that many steamers are at present trading on the coast the whistles of which are by no means sufficient to indicate their proximity to other ships in fog or to indicate to another vessel in sight the course she is about to take.

The fault does not lie so often with the power of the whistle as with the method adopted for draining off the water condensed while the whistle is out of use or for rapidly disposing of the condensed steam which, in cold weather, is deposited in the whistle or connections long before a clear blast can be sounded. Probably the cause of a great deal of unsuitability in whistles is due to the fact of their having been installed without regard to the boiler pressure they are to work with and many cases have been observed where an inefficient whistle, under a bench test, has sounded perfectly, though remaining as bad as before when reinstalled on board the ship.

The principal, and most dangerous, defect of steam whistles is, however, the refusal to sound a clear blast until the water accumulated in the pipe has been blown out or the whistle been thoroughly warmed by being repeatedly blown, and faults of this description are very prone to mislead another ship and prompt her to take a course that might land both vessels in serious difficulty.

It is no uncommon sight on the Whangpoo to see a steamer approaching another attempt to give a short blast on her whistle to indicate that she is taking the starboard side of the channel and be unable to produce more than a gasping cough that can hardly be heard on her own forecastle head. The officer in charge, naturally, does not regard this as an efficient signal to the other ship and repeats the blast to get a clear and audible sound from his whistle. But it is quite probable that the man in the approaching ship has seen the jet of steam from the first blast and concludes that some noise in his own vicinity has prevented the sound being heard. On seeing the second jet, and perhaps hearing that blast, he concludes that two whistles have been blown and that the other ship is altering her course to port, regulating the course of his own vessel to that belief. It does not need much imagination to realize that here is the making of a first-class disaster for the occurrence of which it would be wrong to blame either officer. If blame attaches to anyone, it must certainly be to the builder who installed such a whistle, the surveyor who permitted it to pass or the marine superintendent who neglected to have the defect rectified when pointed out to him.

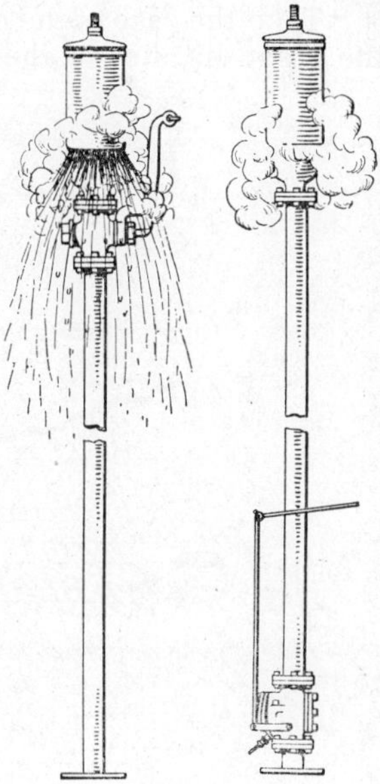

A B

A, water, no sound. B, whistle sounds when clear of water.

Unfortunately, there can be no hard-and-fast rule as to efficiency of steam whistles, but it should certainly be insisted upon that every whistle is capable of blowing a loud and clear blast the first time the lanyard is pulled instead of being seized with a prolonged fit of coughing and spluttering that lasts until the water has been blown out and the whistle warmed.*

The instant readiness of the steam whistle or siren to give a clear blast indicating the course the vessel is about to take may seem a small matter to the uninitiated, but its failure to do so at a critical moment in crowded waters such as the Whangpoo or Yangtze might cause grave confusion in the mind of the captain or pilot of an approaching vessel and, by misleading him in his interpretation of the other vessel's premeditated action, lead him to take a course that would bring about the very accident to avoid which the signal was given.

Shipping and Engineering (Shanghai), Aug. 6, 1920.

* Whistle pipes should connect directly to the boiler. A straight lead will keep them drained. This also prevents freezing in cold weather. *Leading the pipe to the whistle inside the stack casing is good practice.*

Whistle steam pipes should be provided with drains. The whistle installation is one of the most important details of ship construction.

The Four Whistle Signal and the Halifax Disaster*

"Take the case of the collision between the ships which caused the great disaster to the City of Halifax, Nova Scotia, on Dec.

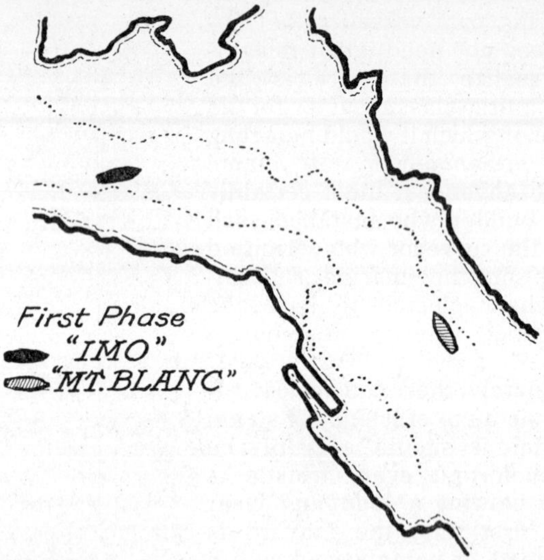

6, 1917. It will be remembered that the Norwegian steamer '*Imo*' of 5043 gross tons was leaving Bedford Basin, Halifax, bound to sea and collided with the French steamer '*Mt. Blanc*' of 3121 gross tons laden with TNT, and other explosives, bound in for Bedford Basin. The collision took place in the Narrows and was due entirely to a misunderstanding of signals. There was plenty of room for the vessels to have passed each other, and the vessels were also plainly visible to each other.

"At the official inquiry the captain of the '*Mt. Blanc*' said that he was on the starboard side of the passage about one hundred and twenty feet from the Dartmouth shore; that the '*Imo's*' starboard side was visible to him about two points on his port bow distant about half a mile and that she was headed across his course, viz. toward the Dartmouth shore. (*First Phase.*) He gave one short blast to indicate that he was

* Printed by courtesy of *The National Marine*, and Lieut. James Otis Porter, U.S.N.R., formerly Executive Officer of the Massachusetts Schoolship *Nantucket*.

going to starboard, and slowed his engines. The '*Imo*' replied with two short blasts, crossing his signals, contrary to all rules. It is fair to say however that survivors of the *Imo* say

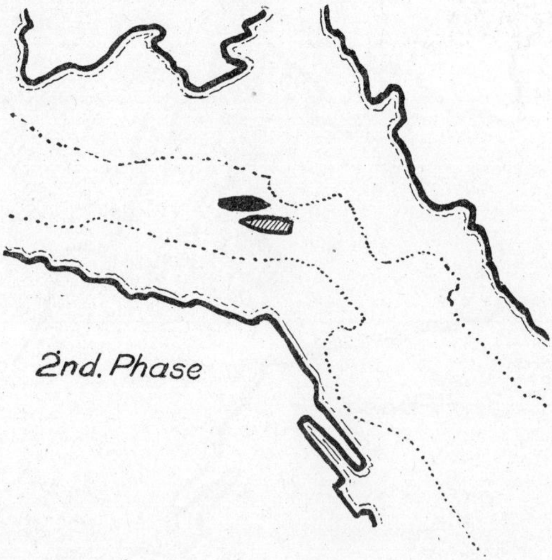

that the *Mt. Blanc* gave two blasts.* She did not, but they thought she did. If she had it would have created a very awkward situation, and right there was where a four whistle danger signal by the *Mt. Blanc* on the *Imo* would have prevented the accident. The *Mt. Blanc* was swinging to starboard and *Imo* to port and rapidly approaching each other. In the meantime the captain of the *Mt. Blanc* stopped his engines. When the ships were about one hundred and fifty feet apart he gave two blasts. The ships were now fifty feet apart nearly parallel each having the other to starboard. (*Second Phase.*) The *Imo* reversed her engines† and gave three blasts and the *Mt. Blanc* also gave three blasts and reversed,‡ with a starboard helm, in order to take the blow as far forward as possible. (*Third Phase.*)

"The master of the *Mt. Blanc* was asked while on the witness stand at the inquiry if he understood the *Imo's* two whistles, *viz.* in answer to the first one he gave? He said, 'I thought she was whistling wrong, but as she signalled first I could not change.'

* See above on water in whistle.

† Bow swings to starboard.

‡ Bow swings to starboard.

"Right there was the place and time when the four whistle signal would have prevented the collision. It would have warned the captain of the *Imo* that he must have misunderstood the *Mt. Blanc* and that he could not hold his course without danger of disaster."

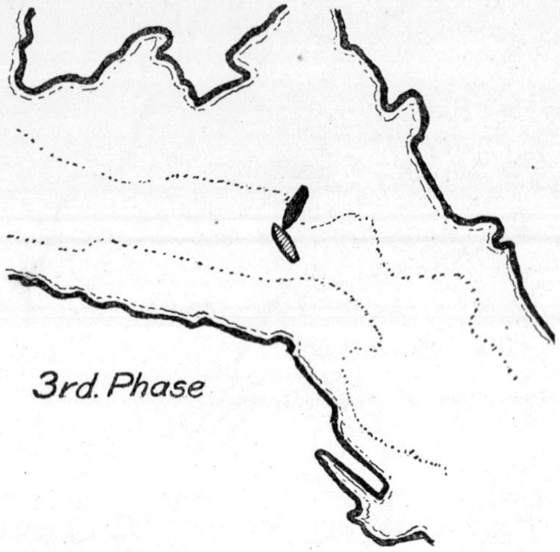

Wireless phone.

The use of whistle signals is unsatisfactory, but seems to be the best thing we have, for the present, at least. When the wireless phone comes into general use it should be of great help in these matters. "I am steering to starboard" would not be misunderstood.

The two whistle signal.

As this is used when going contrary to the general rule that vessels should pass each other on the port hand, it should only be employed when absolutely necessary. Such cases arise very frequently in the crowded waters about New York, but it is well to always go to starboard if possible.

Local routes.

When running along a coast at night or in thick weather always have in mind the local conditions. A vessel passing the mouth of a large river, or the entrance to a port, may expect other craft to come upon her broad on either beam. A knowledge of trade routes, especially those frequented by sail (see pilot charts) is of great importance.

Backing.

Vessels backing observe the same steering rules as when going ahead. But a backing vessel that must give way is often unable to do so because of her poor steering ability and the rule of special circumstances comes into play.

Foreign Inland Rules.

Consult " Pilots," sailing directions, and chart notes.

Light towers.

On sailing craft, wherever possible, the side lights should not be carried in the rigging, where the condition of the shrouds, either slack to leeward or taut to windward, may greatly effect the screening of the lights. On large vessels light towers are usually fitted on the forecastle head. These not only provide a well-placed and rigid position for the side lights, but also protect them from damage by gear and from the wash of heavy seas.

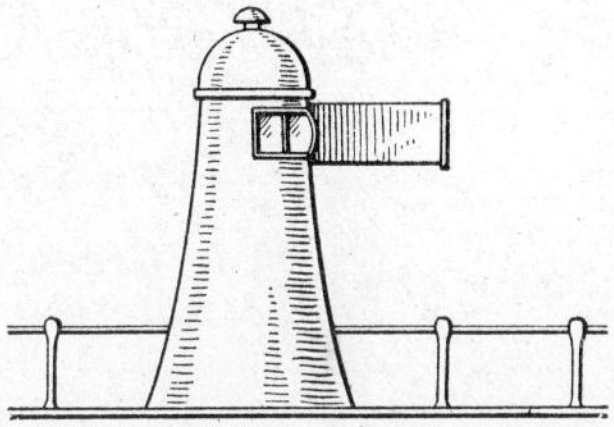

A light tower or lighthouse.

Shapes.

The various shapes prescribed by the rules of the road are generally made of painted canvas stretched on metal frames. As these shapes are seldom used it is often found that they are out of order when needed. They should be stowed in a special compartment of the bridge signal chest.

Depth of fog.

Fog often lies in comparatively thin layers. Send a hand aloft and also get a lookout down as far as possible as at times the range of view will be widely extended from such positions.

Crow's nest signals.

On some ships it is the custom to have the crow's nest lookout provided with a horn. One short blast—vessel on starboard bow. Two short blasts—vessel on port bow. Three short blasts—vessel ahead.

Course signals.

Vessels coming close together in a fog, *but not in sight of each other,* must not use the direction signals. As soon as they sight each other these signals may be used, although the general rules for steering hold. In the case of a sailing vessel, her signals, on the fog horn (a distinctive sound) will indicate the tack she is on and her general direction. Wind is usually light in a fog.

These verses by Thomas Gray are a good aid to memory—so far as they go. They are changed to *direct* helm orders.

Two Steamships Meeting

When you see Three Lights ahead—
Right rudder, and show your Red.

Two Steamships Passing

Green to Green, or Red to Red—
Perfect safety, Go ahead!

Two Steamships Crossing

If to your Starboard Red appear,
It is your duty to Keep Clear;
To act as judgment says is proper,
To Right, or Left, or Back, or Stop her.
But when upon your Port is seen
A Steamer's Starboard light of Green,
There's not so much for you to do,
The Green light must keep clear of you.

General Caution

Both in safety and in doubt
Always keep a good look-out.
In danger, with no room to turn,
Ease her—Stop her—Go astern.

Sailing Ships

If close hauled on the starboard tack,
No other ship can cross your track;
If on the port tack you appear,
Ships going free must all keep clear;
While you must yield when going free,
To sail close hauled or on your lee.
And, if you have the wind right aft,
Keep clear of every sailing craft.

CHAPTER XVII

GROUND TACKLE

I

Foreword

The *ground tackle* of a vessel consists of *anchors* and *cables** (generally *chain* cables). The *windlass*, or *anchor engine*, as some call it, is used for heaving up the anchor or *weighing* anchor. The *hawse pipes* are located near the stem and provide a lead for the anchor chain, and, in the case of *stockless* anchors, they provide stowage for the *shank* of the anchor, the *flukes* resting snug against the vessel's side. A hawse pipe is sometimes fitted in the stern for a stern anchor.

Coming up through the hawse pipes the anchor chain usually passes through *riding chocks* fitted with heavy *pawls* used for the purpose of taking the stress off of the windlass when riding at anchor in heavy weather. *Stoppers*, of various design, are also fitted in many vessels between the hawse pipes and the windlass and are used for the same purpose.

The chain passes over a sprocket wheel on the windlass known as a *wildcat*. This engages the chain, link by link, and serves to apply the power of the windlass engine to the chain when heaving in. When *letting go*, the wildcat is thrown out of connection and revolves freely, except for its control by a friction band operated by a brake lever, or a screw and wheel.

On merchant vessels the chain, after passing over the wildcat, generally drops directly into the chain locker located immediately below. *Chain lockers* are usually built just forward of the collision bulkhead, or just abaft of it. They are deep compartments divided by a stout wooden bulkhead to separate the starboard and port anchor chains. Inspection of various drawings in the book (pp. 254, 344), will show the position of the

* Destroyers use wire cables. Fishing schooners use hemp cables, and generally use old-fashioned anchors.

chain locker. It is not necessary to *tier* the chain, that is to stow it, when heaving in. This is done by the shape of the locker; the chain, confined by the sides of the locker, falling and resting in irregular short fakes, one on top of another.

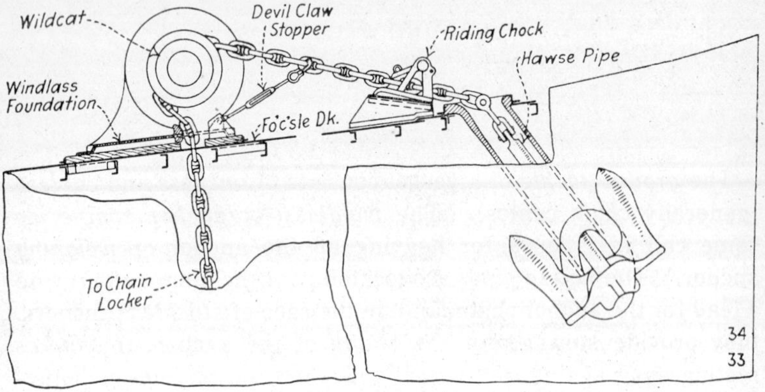

Diagram showing stowage of stockless anchor, and deck arrangements for working chain cable.

Sometimes additional *controllers*, or *compressors*, are fitted under the deck *chain pipes* or *naval pipes* leading to the chain locker. These lock, or control, the chain abaft of the windlass.

The deck chain pipes, abaft of the windlass, should be provided with effective watertight stoppers. Where hawse pipes lead into a 'tween deck, or under a forecastle head, conical canvas stoppers, stuffed with tarred oakum, are often fitted. These are pulled into the pipes, big end outboard. They are hove tight by means of rope tails usually taken to the gypsey heads of the windlass. These fittings are known to sailors as *jackasses*. They are the most effective method of making hawse pipes water tight, especially in deep water sailing ships with old-fashioned ground tackle, where the anchors stow on the *bill boards*, and chains are unshackled and hauled in when off soundings.

Ground tackle is in many respects the most vital part of a vessel's equipment. Her safety frequently depends upon the good design and sound construction of this important gear. Proper ground tackle has saved many ships and lives, and on the other hand, poor ground tackle, or ground tackle *poorly managed,* has often been the prime cause of disaster. The seaman must know his ground tackle, understand its use, its limitations, and the many elements that enter into its effective operation.

The writer recalls an experience in the Bay of Gibraltar, in 1897, when the New York Schoolship *St. Mary's*, anchored outside of the squall line. During a heavy blast from the north, the ship dragged her two bower anchors, with one hundred fathoms of chain on each anchor, yards braced sharp up, and sheet anchors about to let go, when the old ship slid off into deep water in the Straits. Making sail in the squalls and trying to keep control of the ship with all of her bower chain overboard was no fun. But this was practical training. The skipper, Lieut. Comm. W. H. Reeder (in those days a lieutenant commander in the U. S. Navy was an officer with about twenty-five years of regular sea service behind him) gave the boys on board an example of splendid seamanship. It is pleasant to recall that stirring time when the old *Mary's* dragged past the coal hulk *Three Brothers,* once a famous Yankee ship, then, and perhaps still, a coal hulk in *Gib.** We went so close our boat booms were only saved by quick work.

For half a day forty boys at a time manned the capstan bars, working in the heavy chain inch by inch, while the other sixty sailed the ship, or gave a hand dragging chain along the gun deck to the lockers located at the foot of the mainmast. As the boys at the capstan fell out from time to time, oatmeal water was fed to them, and a youngster with a fife, sitting on the drum head of the capstan, livened up the scene which was wild enough, with the roaring wind and slatting canvas.

After this the skipper gave quite a lecture on always studying local conditions before coming to anchor.

No matter where you anchor, never for a moment rest in security. A nice muddy bottom may seem safe, but the mud may only be a soft silt without holding power overlying a hardpan bottom, also without holding power, especially if your anchor plows through the soft mud almost upright. The writer can tell a story of just such conditions in the harbor of Pensacola, but space here will not permit, remember—always watch the weather.

* The *Three Brothers* was broken up a few years back.

Before going on with the specific details of ground tackle, it may be advisable to impress upon the reader the importance of knowing the exact state of and method of handling the gear in the vessel in which you happen to be. Books are all right, but a book cannot supply you with all the things you should know about the ground tackle you are shipmates with. Merchant craft anchor so seldom, compared with navy vessels, that many seaman make voyage after voyage directly from dock to dock, never using their anchors. This is all the more reason why the merchant seaman should make a special study of his ground tackle.

The young seaman should remember that ground tackle is always spoken of by sailors as *ground* TAYKEL (phonetic spelling). The *ay* is sounded as in *may*. Philologists may find fault with this, but nevertheless it is the way seamen talk.

II

Anchors

After centuries of development the anchor finally reached a stage where no further improvement seemed possible. This form of anchor, generally known as the "old-fashioned" anchor is shown in the drawing with the names of parts marked upon it. A similar formation of arms and flukes seems to be of very early origin. Medals, found in the Catacombs of Rome, depict an anchor closely resembling that of the present day. The use of an eye in the crown, no doubt for bending a tripping line, was a concession to its excellent holding power. Of course in those days anchor was weighed by hand with perhaps some form of purchase.

Anchors of early Christian era.
Medals found in Catacombs, Rome.

The anchors of Columbus were distinguished by their long shank, straight arms and sharp triangular flukes. Heavy wooden stocks were lashed, or wedged, by hoops. These were excellent anchors for sandy bottom.

The essential things to be kept in mind in anchor design are as follows: It must bite quickly, hold firm, even when the vessel swings around on her cable, and it must be easy to *break out*, when weighing anchor. It must also present the least chance of fouling, as a foul anchor (the chain leading around the stock or an arm) will not hold.

Anchors with long shanks and small sharp flukes take hold better in sandy bottom. A soft bottom will afford better hold to an anchor with a large fluke or palm. The most general design is one in which the shank, arms, stock, etc., are about as shown in the illustration. The old-fashioned anchor with the metal stock is of a heavier type and that shown is the design used in the navy. The balls at the end of the stock are to prevent it from sinking into the bottom when canting.

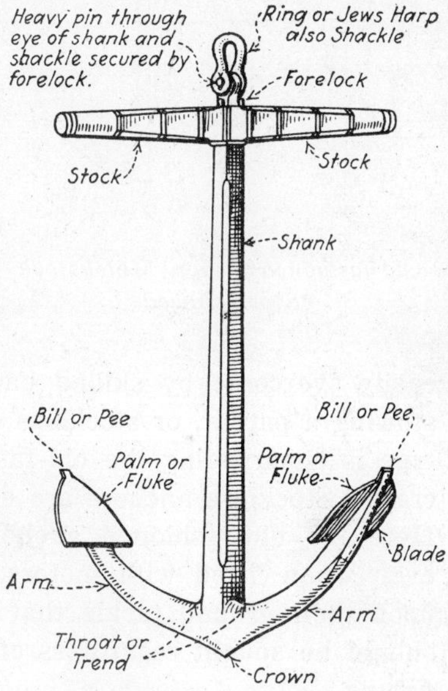

An old-fashioned anchor—wooden stock.

When an old-fashioned anchor is let go it strikes bottom crown first. The vessel should have sternboard, or headway, so that the chain, as it pays out, will not fall on top of the anchor and foul the stock. As the anchor strikes bottom it will fall over on its side and rest on the crown and the lower end of the stock. The pull of the chain, when the brake is put on the windlass, will cause the stock to lie horizontal and *cant* the anchor, one arm will point down, and the bill, or pee will bite. The palm or fluke will then work down into the bottom. A heavy pull will cause a well-designed anchor to bury itself in the bottom. When weighing anchor, the pull becomes up and down and the lifting of the shank will cause the curved arm to work around in a circle bringing the bill and fluke up through the bottom.

The old-fashioned anchor with its single arm holding the bottom is more easily adjusted to different directions of the cable. If a vessel swings through a wide angle the stock may cause the holding arm to come out, but at once the canting action of the stock will again cause the other, or the same arm, to engage the bottom as when letting go. When swinging gradually the stock will keep the arm pointed vertical and it will pivot around with the ship. The curved shape of the arm will prevent it from working out of its grip.

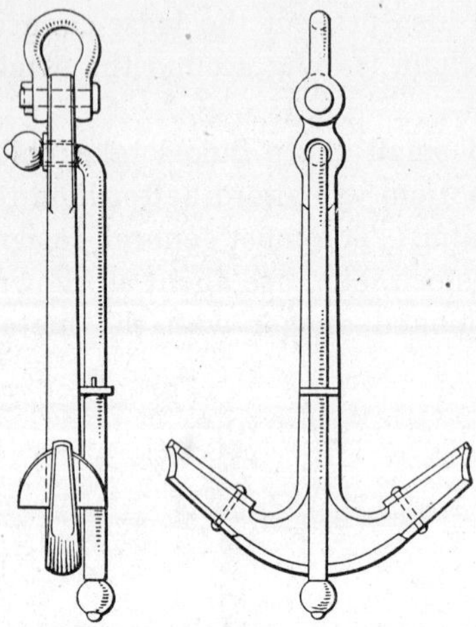

Old-fashioned anchor. Metal stock Stock stowed.

The old-fashioned anchor has some disadvantages. Difficulty in stowing, and ease of fouling from improper letting go, are among the most objectionable features. Both, however, are easily overcome by skilled handling. But the time saved in stowing a patent, or stockless anchor, is so important that this type is superseding the old-fashioned anchor in most modern craft. Stockless anchors are even being fitted in sailing craft. Here the old-fashioned anchor should be retained. Sailers, even when fitted with motors, are so much more dependent upon their ground tackle that the very best holding qualities should be sought regardless of time or trouble in *catting* and *fishing*.

This greater dependence of sailing craft upon their ground tackle is recognized by the rules of the classification societies. A 5,000 ton (equipment tonnage) sailer is required, according to A.B.S. Rules, to carry bower anchors weighing over 8,000 lbs., while a steamer of the same size must only have 6,000 lb. bowers. The greater amount of tophamper carried by sailers is also a factor in this greater weight of anchors. As a general thing, the preponderance of weight in sailing ship anchors over steamer anchors, in vessels of the same tonnage, is as four is to three.

The Patent, or Stockless Anchor*

This anchor is most used in steam and motor vessels. In a general way it consists of the following parts: The *shank* and the *arms*, having motion about the shank as shown in the drawings. The *crown* or *head* is the part between the arms where they pivot on the shank. The *flukes* are large, in fact the arms are all fluke. *Tripping palms* are cast at the base of the arms to make the fluke bite. Practically all stockless anchors are assembled as follows: The bare shank, without anchor shackle, is passed up through the hole in the crown or head of the anchor between the flukes. It is then secured in various ways against backing, or falling out, usually by pins, under the heel of the shank, through the heel of the shank, or through locking pieces which close up the hole in the crown. All of the best anchors however are so built that shoulders, on the shank, of various shapes engage recesses in the head so that the shank cannot pull through. The Baldt anchor is assembled in the same way and is held by a ball and socket joint. An inspection of the drawings will show that great similarity exists between the standard form of stockless anchors. Sketches of the foremost makes in the United States are given as a matter of interest. The *Gruson-Hein*, a German anchor, carries its flukes in close to the stock, giving somewhat the effect of a single split anchor arm, an advantage when swinging. One objection to the double fluke anchor is the tendency to cant or *step up*, as greater pressure comes on one fluke and then on the other, while a vessel swings or when the anchor drags through uneven ground. Also one fluke may strike a rock and the other one lift out of the bottom, causing the anchor to capsize. The wider apart the flukes the more this canting effect will be emphasized.

Stockless anchors have been designed carrying a single fluke, and a wide head, which performs the duty of the old-fashioned stock. Mr. A. W. Jansen, late safety engineer at the navy yard, New York, has developed such an anchor.

All well-designed stockless anchors are provided with projections or *tripping palms* on the head, so that these take hold

* Where weight of anchors is specified in A.B.S. tables, $1/4$ the weight given must be added if stockless anchors are used.

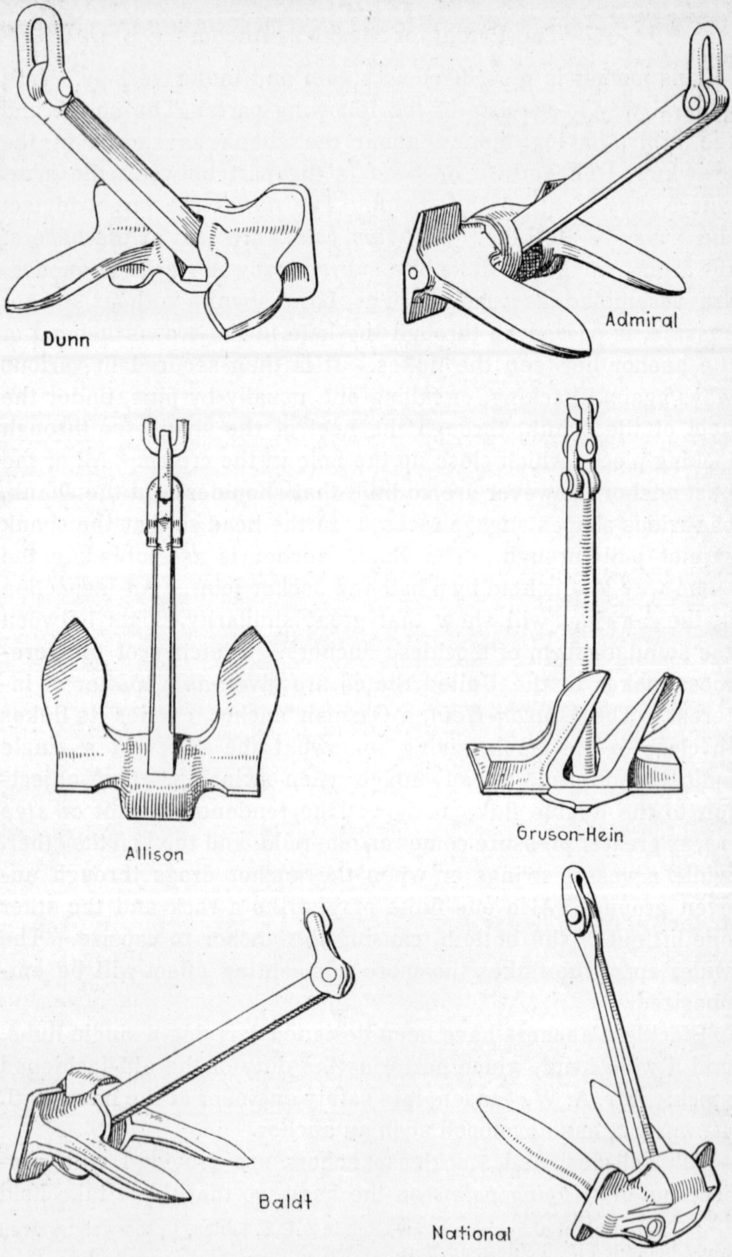

Types of stockless anchors in general use at sea.

and turn the flukes down into the ground when a pull comes on the cable. The drawings indicate this clearly.

The flukes are given motion through ninety degrees, forty-five degree on either side of the shank.

The *Eells* Anchor differs in design from other stockless anchors and presents many features of interest.

The following extract from tests of an Eells anchor is of interest as it not only demonstrates the excellent holding power of this anchor but gives a good idea of how an anchor test may be made.

The method used in conducting the tests was as follows:

The anchor to be tested was shackled on to the starboard chain and then dropped, the chain being run out to the desired scope and then shackled on to the port chain on which a testing link with a Watson and Stillman 100 ton gauge attached, had been placed between the hawsepipe and windlass, port wildcat being locked and compressor on. With starboard wildcat open and chain slack so that no resistance was offered, the engines were put astern at various speeds in order to obtain the results as set forth below.

After one anchor had been tested it was hove up and put on deck while the other anchor was being tested in a similar way. Two anchors were used, one a regular stockless type weighing 3,145 lbs. and one " Eells " weighing 2,375 lbs.

Approximate dimensions of steamer with which tests were made are as follows: Length 150 feet,—breadth 34 feet,—draft mean 17 feet, with engines of 1200 horsepower.

Following is a record of the tests in the order in which they occurred.

First test: 11 A.M. off Stapleton, S.I. in 42 feet of water, soft mud bottom; strong ebb tide running. Regular stockless anchor 38 fathoms of chain outside. Engine $\frac{1}{3}$ speed astern, anchor dragging, no strain on chain.

Second test: 12 noon, same place and conditions. Eells anchor scope of chain as above. Engines $\frac{1}{3}$ speed astern for about four minutes, anchor holding, engines put $\frac{2}{3}$ speed astern, anchor dragging, strain on chain $3\frac{3}{4}$ tons.

Third test: 2:45 P.M. $\frac{1}{4}$ mile outside entrance buoy to Ambrose Channel in 6 fathoms of water, hard sand and gravel bottom, 12 knot breeze, flood tide, slight sea, steamer pitching slightly. Eells anchor 53 fathoms scope, Engines $\frac{1}{3}$ speed astern for few minutes, then $\frac{2}{3}$ speed astern with gauge registering 6 tons strain and anchor holding, then engines full astern and anchor beginning to drag.

Fourth test: 4:15 P.M. Same place and conditions. Regular stockless anchor same scope of chain. Engines ⅓ speed astern, anchor holding, then engines ⅔ speed astern anchor commencing to drag when gauge registered a strain of two tons.

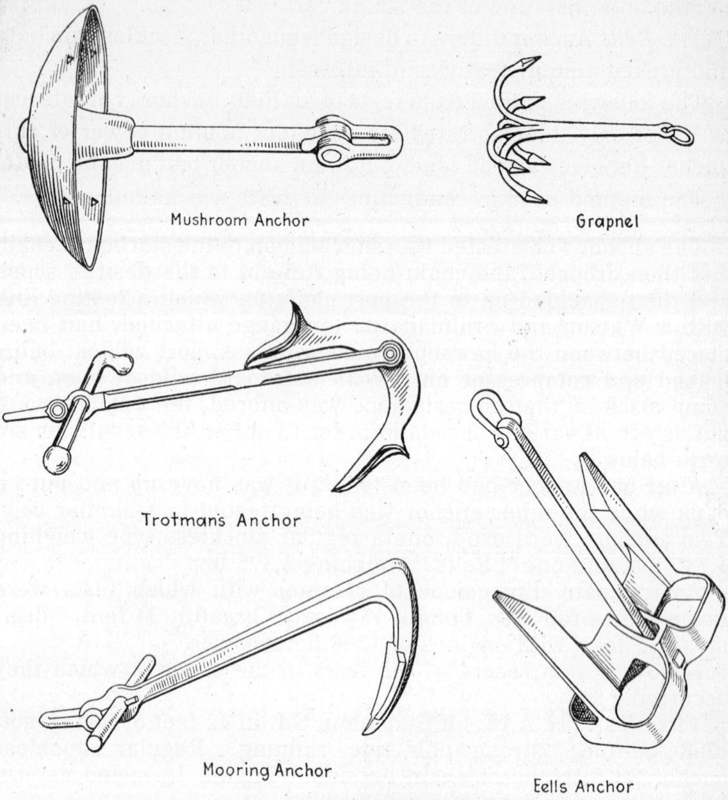

Types of special anchors.

Fifth test: 7:00 P.M. On lower spit of Red Hook Flats in 6 fathoms of water, hard clay bottom, calm, sea smooth, strong flood tide, stockless anchor scope of chain as above. Engines started astern and gradually worked up to full speed, anchor holding registered strain on chain 6½ tons. Engines stopped and backed full speed three times, anchor commencing to drag on third attempt.

Sixth test: 8:15 P.M. Same place and conditions. Eells anchor, same scope of chain. Engines gradually worked up to ⅔ speed astern, anchor then commencing to drag when gauge registered a strain of 6 tons on chain.

Considering the previous tests it was concluded that the last test of the Eells anchor was not a fair test; but in view of the fact that it was getting dark no additional test could be made.

This anchor is used to a great extent by wrecking companies, and seems to be well fitted for use as a stream anchor or a kedge because of its superior holding power. Anchors of the largest size, however, are built on this design.

Trotman's anchor is notably free from fouling as the upper arm lies close to the shank. It is really an old-fashioned anchor and has much to recommend it for use by sailers.*

The *single arm mooring anchor* is also free from fouling. It is a good anchor to put down as a permanent mooring; for ship use it is uncertain as the anchor may cant, *fluke up*, and the vessel drag for an indefinite distance.

In anchor design extra large palms are not always an advantage as they are more liable to become *shod* and loose much of their holding power. This is specially so in clay bottom.

Classification of Anchors

Anchors are classed as follows:

Bower anchors, the main working anchors of a vessel, are carried on or near the bow and are generally referred to as the Starboard and Port anchors.

The *spare bower* anchor may be lighter in weight than the regular bowers, according to the rulings of the A.B.S. It is usually carried on deck, or on the forecastle head, where it can be put over the side by a boom and tackle from the foremast head.

Sheet anchors are not generally carried by merchant craft, but are found in many naval vessels. These are usually carried abaft of the bower anchors and are provided with extra hawse pipes on either bow. In the old days the sheet anchors were carried on the rail well aft and just over the sheaves for the fore sheets. Sheet anchors are only let go in extreme emergencies when bower anchors drag or are carried away.† It is now the practice to carry only one sheet anchor.

Stem anchors are coming into use and are very easily stowed in the stem hawse pipes fitted on some of the latest battleships

* The Great Eastern carried ten bower anchors. Eight of them are said to have been 7,000 lb. Trotman anchors.

† Called *L'ancre desperance* by the French.

and liners. These are heavy anchors, as large as, or larger than, the bowers. The stem anchor takes the place of the sheet anchor referred to above.

These anchors constitute the main dependence of the vessel when anchoring is necessary during heavy weather. Bower and stem anchors range from a ton to fifteen tons in weight. However the very largest working anchors are seldom over ten tons.

Stream anchors are about one half as heavy as the bower anchors and are used for stern mooring in congested waters. These anchors are useful in many ways when an anchor has to be carried out and it is not necessary to use the bowers. The stream anchor may be stowed in a stern hawse pipe and may be handled by an after windlass, connected with the after capstan engine.*

Kedges are about half as heavy as the stream anchor according to A.B.S. Rules. These are used for ordinary kedging work when a vessel may have to be moved about without power other than deck capstans and winches. It is well to carry at least two kedges.

Grapnels make good boat anchors and are useful in many ways on board ship. If a wire or anchor chain runs overboard (the first often happens) a grapnel will bring it up if water is not too deep. One wire saved will pay for all the grapnels in the ship. The weights most common range from twenty to a hundred pounds.

Boat anchors are usually of the old-fashioned type with metal stock and should run to about a hundred pounds for a large life boat.

* There is no clearly defined practice relative to the use of stern anchors. The Germans have used them in many of their large naval vessels. On these ships a single anchor carried in a hawse pipe well aft, either at the side or on the centerline, has frequently been fitted. The British have followed a similar practice in such vessels as the *Eagle* and *Argus*, *Furious*, *Courageous* and *Glorious*, as well as in some light cruisers and monitors. Most of the capital ships in the United States Navy carry small stern anchors weighing 5,000 or 6,000 pounds. They are not, however, carried in hawse pipes, but are stowed on deck and handled by means of crane or davit. In some of the United States gunboats, stern anchors are carried stowed on chocks on the weather deck aft. In such cases a collapsible anchor crane has frequently been fitted, so located as to plumb the stowage position, and of such outreach as to swing the anchor well clear of the vessel's side.—*Marine Engineering.*

Mushroom anchors are useful in securing mooring buoys, and in anchoring navigational buoys. They are seldom found on board ship. They range up to about five tons in weight and are hard to foul.

Mooring clumps are concrete mooring weights fitted with heavy iron eyes.

The classification societies require that anchors shall be severely tested both as to material and construction.

When anchors have satisfactorily passed the American Bureau of Shipping* requirements they are to be clearly stamped by the manufacturer as follows:

Ordinary Anchor

A. The Number of Certificate. (Furnished by the Surveyor)	7147
B. The Initials of the Surveyor who witnesses the Proof Test	X.Y.Z.
C. Month and Year of Test	3, 17
D. Proof Test applied (lbs.)	76440
E. Signifying that the Testing Machine is recognized by the Committee of the American Bureau of Shipping	A.B.
F. The Weight of Anchor (excluding Stock) (lbs.)	4200
G. The Weight of Stock (lbs.)	1050

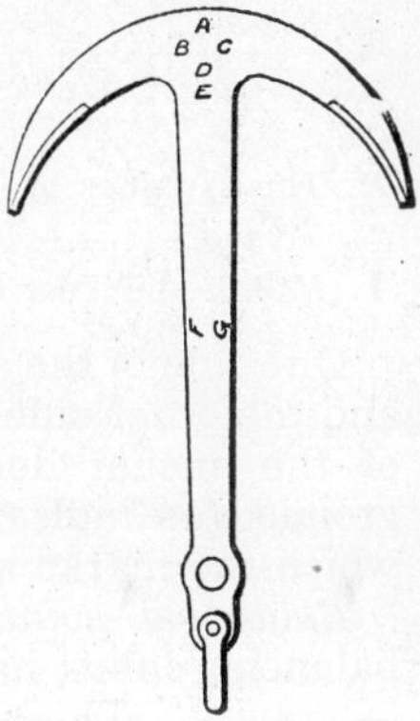

* *Anchors* are to be made of forged wrought iron, forged open hearth ingot steel, or cast steel; the shackles may be of wrought iron or of forged steel unwelded.

Anchor stocks are to be in weight equal to one-fourth that of the anchor.

Stockless anchors may be adopted, subject to the Committee's approval and the addition of one-fourth to the weights for ordinary anchors; the weight of the head is not to be less than three-fifths of the total weight of the anchor.

No vessel can be classed with the letter (E) unless the anchors have been tested and the weights are in accordance with requirements as to tonnage of vessel.

All anchors are to be tested under the inspection of a Surveyor to this Bureau in a machine recognized for such purposes by the Committee of the American Bureau of Shipping.

Prior to testing the actual weight of the anchor is to be ascertained.

—*Rules of A.B.S.*

Stockless Anchor

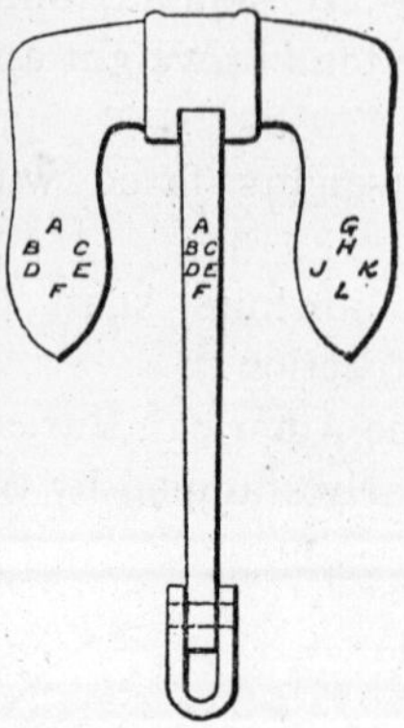

A. The Number of Certificate. (Furnished by the Surveyor) 7147

B. The Initials of the Surveyor who witnesses the Proof Test .... X.Y.Z.

C. Month and Year of Test 3, 17

D. Proof Test applied (lbs.) 76440

E. Signifying that the Testing Machine is recognized by the Committee of the American Bureau of Shipping .... A.B.

F. The Weight of Anchor (lbs.) 4200

G. Signifying that the Anchor Head has been tested by a Surveyor to the American Bureau .... A.B.

H. The Weight of Anchor Head (lbs.) 2520

J. The Initials of the Surveyor who witnesses the Drop Test .... X.Y.Z.

K. The Number of Drop Test Certificate. (Furnished by the Surveyor) 4914

L. Month and Year of Drop Test 3, 17

One side of the anchor should be reserved for the above marks, and the other side be used for the makers' name. If the design of the anchor does not admit of the marks being placed or grouped as indicated, a boss should be cast on each arm, on which the marks should be stamped.

Balancing point. All anchors should, if not provided with balancing links, have a mark on the stock indicating the center of gravity. This will save much time in hoisting out an anchor by a single purchase, as in kedging.

III

Cables

As important as the anchors themselves are the cables, or chain cables, to give them their full name, which attach to the anchor. In large vessels these are always made of stud link chain of either forged or cast steel. The characteristics of these cables are shown in the sketches. The stud in forged chain is forced into the link after it is formed and merely serves to keep the sides of the link from coming together under an excessive stress. It is said to add about 15 per cent to the ultimate strength of the chain. Studs also seem to keep the

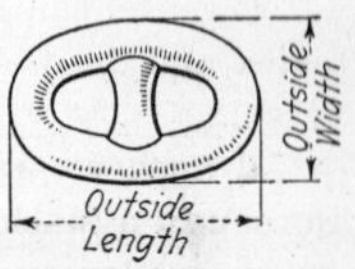

A stud link.

chain free from kinks. Chain is tested in two ways, *proof* and *breaking*.

A *proof test* (about 70 per cent of the required breaking test), is applied to each fifteen fathom *shot* of chain. The full *breaking test* is only given to selected experimental lengths of three links each cut from each fifteen fathom shot.

Chain cable ranges in size up to four inches* (the diameter of the metal in a link). The A.B.S. tables give the requirements for 3¾ inch chain as follows:

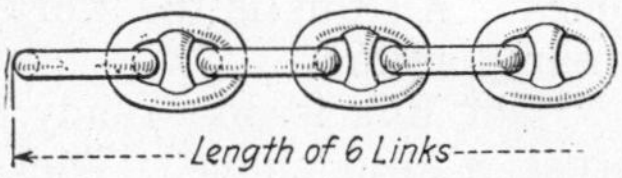

Wrought iron and steel
    Breaking 588,320 lbs.
    Proof 425,370 lbs.
Cast steel
    Breaking 824,000 lbs.
    Proof 588,500 lbs.
Weight per fifteen fathoms 12,025 lbs.

It will be noted that this is *some* chain.

The reason why so much care is taken in testing chain cable is self-evident.

The size of chain required for the various tonnages is determined by the rules of the A.B.S. and must be strictly adhered to in order that a vessel may get her rating for equipment. Seamen who are interested in this matter should get the Rules of the American Bureau of Shipping. These can be obtained from the Bureau (the price is $5.00) or may be consulted in any public library.

The following account of how an anchor chain is made is taken from an article by F. A. Collins which appeared in *Collier's Weekly*.

" The links (of a modern anchor chain) are a foot, or perhaps a foot and a half long. Such chains are forged and every detail of the work is carefully safeguarded. Every link must pass the most exacting tests. Link by link the great chain must be patiently built up. The iron used for the chain comes in long bars. The diameter of the bars is determined only after accurate

* 4¼ inch chains have been made.

calculations of its tensile strength. The bars are first cut in uniform lengths depending upon the size of the link. One end of the bar is then heated until it is more or less pliable, when it is slightly bent over. The enormous force necessary to bend the bar is supplied by a powerful machine operated by hydraulic power. When both ends of the bar have been turned it is placed under a hammer which swedges out the curved ends to a point. To keep the link from slipping it is placed in a die cut in a place block. All this is the work of a few well-directed blows of the steam hammer.

" The link is now ready for the bending machine which is to press it into shape. The bar is heated and placed upon an ingenious device that twists it into shape. The tons of pressure required are exerted by an hydraulic press and the bar takes the form of a link in a few seconds. A crew of three men is required for the work. Two men lift the bar and hold it in position while a third operates the hydraulic mechanism. It is, however, important that the work be done as quickly as possible before the metal cools. In fact it is necessary to heat the links several times during the process of bending and welding, and as the old forms of furnaces would be too slow, oil furnaces are used.

" Twenty or thirty of these giant links are placed in a furnace at one time and removed as quickly as they come to the proper heat. The workmen are obliged to use tongs 3 or 4 feet in length in placing the links in the furnace and removing them, for the heat is intense. The use of the oil furnace saves an immense amount of time in chain forging.

" Now that the link has been scarphed and bent it is ready for welding. The two flattened ends have been bent over until they overlap but without joining. Again the link is placed in the oil furnace and heated to the proper temperature, when it is placed beneath the hammers of the welding forge. Two husky workmen grasp the link with long tongs and swing it quickly to the welding machine while a third works the levers controlling the hammer. The end of the chain to which the new link is to be attached hangs just above the hammer. The heated ends are slipped through the last link of the finished chain, placed under the hammer and a few strokes welds the two ends together in a complete link. By so slow and painstaking a process is the great chain lengthened out link by link.

" After the welding the link is once more reheated in an oil blast furnace. This is a very delicate operation since it is an easy matter to carry the heating too far and a few seconds' miscalculation may burn the iron. The link has already been fastened to the chain, and if it is burned it is necessary to cut it away and replace it with a new link. A special form of oil blast furnace is used for this stage of the work. The end of the massive chain, which is coiled up near by, is carried over and suspended by a pulley directly above the furnace, where it is lowered into place. So intense is the heat that the workmen use plyers and welding devices mounted at the end of arms 4 feet or more in length. Even these are handled with thick gloves. Only workmen of long experience are entrusted with this delicate part of the work.

" The link is now ready for its final shaping. The pounding it has received has forced it out of shape, and it is important that the links be uniform. It is again heated and placed in a steel die cut to the proper form. Another powerful hammer driven by hydraulic power now descends upon it and quickly forces it into the die, giving the link its true form. After a few strokes the link is taken from the die and the stud is inserted. The small cross bar found in these heavy chains prevents the links from becoming tangled up and relieves the strain. The cross bar is heated and set in place, when a single blow with the steam hammer makes it firm. It is unnecessary to weld this piece into position as carefully as the ends of the bar are joined in forming the link itself.

" The link is finished by hand. Once more, and for the last time, it is softened by heat. The finishing consists in cutting away all the rough edges of the link and the slight rough projection at the ends. A smoother or rounded die is then held by hand over the rough parts of the link and a few smart blows with a hand hammer quickly smooths out all inequalities. This is the only part of the hammering which is now done by hand. Formerly all the hammering and welding was hand work which rendered the process much more laborious. The great sledge hammer blows of the steam hammer not only do the work much more quickly but the links thus formed are stronger than those forged by hand power alone. With the assistance of the steam hammer there is practically no limit to the size of a chain which may be forged.

" 3⅝" chain is the heaviest form used in the United States Navy, and is usually attached to the largest anchors. Each link when complete weighs 112 pounds. To handle these links a gang of four skilled workmen are required, a chainmaker, a hammer man, a tongs man and a hoist man. The work of each man is indicated by his name, and each becomes something of a specialist in his line before he is entrusted with a great chain."

Stream chain is close link, without studs and is used for the stream anchor or on small or medium-sized vessels.

Cast steel chain has been developed in recent years, one link being cast into another with good success. The stud is cast directly into the link forming an integral part of the chain. The chain may be cast in two ways. The whole is cast as a continuous chain, or the process is made up of two steps. Whole links are cast; then, after these have been inspected and cleaned, connecting links are cast between the whole links.

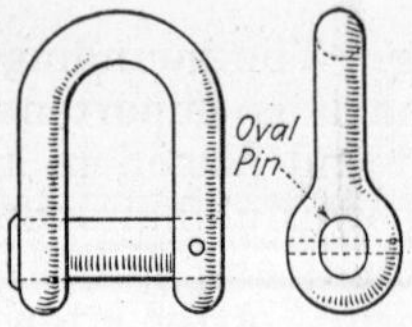

Anchor shackle.

Anchor shackles are wider than *joiner shackles*, but in every instance the strength must be equal.† Shackle pins are held in place by a *forelock pin*, usually of hickory. Sometimes a steel pin is used and this is prevented from coming out by setting it with a pellet of lead hammered down over the head of the pin. When a steel or iron pin is used it should be tinned to prevent rusting in.

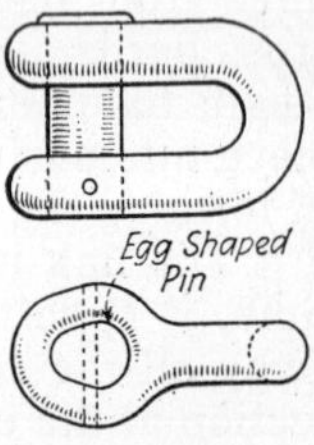

Joiner shackle.

Swivels are provided to prevent the accumulation of turns in the cable. In merchant service practice a swivel is placed at three or four links from the anchor, where it will never come to the wildcat and where it can be examined when the anchor is housed in the hawse pipe. Only one swivel is used. In the merchant service all shots of chain are fifteen fathoms, throughout the length of the cables.

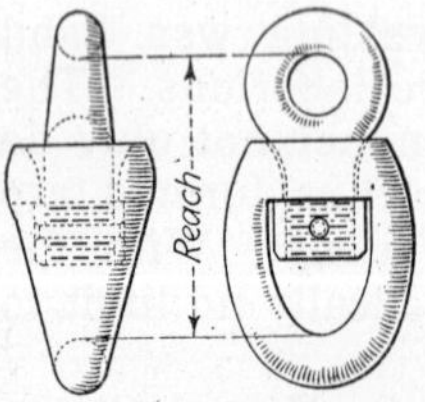

A swivel.

In the navy outboard swivel shots of five fathoms are used next the anchor. These are 1/8″ larger than the rest of the cable.

Marking of Chain Cables

This is a most important matter and merits careful attention. The merchant service custom is to mark chain cable by turns of wire alone. The navy custom of painting the links white should be used by merchant seamen.

* In the British navy a shot of cable is 12½ fathoms.

† The U. S. Navy uses a smooth shackle for joining. This is the *Kenter Shackle*. It is not used in the merchant marine. See Knight's Modern Seamanship.

	Merchant Service	Navy
15 fathoms	One turn of wire on first stud from each side of shackle.	One white link, next to shackle.
30 fathoms	Two turns of wire on second stud from each side of shackle.	Two white links, next to shackle.
45 fathoms	Three turns of wire on third stud from each side of shackle.	Third stud link on each side of shackle white, and three turns of wire on each painted links.
60 fathoms	Four turns of wire on fourth stud from each side of shackle.	Fourth stud link on each side of shackle white, and four turns of wire on painted links.
75 fathoms	Five turns of wire on fifth stud from each side of shackle.	Fifth stud link on each side of shackle white, and five turns of wire on painted links.
90 fathoms	Six turns of wire on sixth stud from each side of shackle.	Sixth stud link on each side of shackle white, and six turns of wire on painted links.

Where links are painted, these should be dried off and touched up with fresh paint as the chain comes in when conditions are favorable for this. Put plenty of dryer in the paint.

Chain cables are *ranged* in a number of ways.

If at anchor on a clean sandy bottom, with plenty of room to swing, kick the vessel astern with the engines, if tide and wind are not sufficient, and pay out chain to the bitter end. Clean the locker, and if time permits paint it. If the bottom is sharp clean sand it will do no harm to let the vessel ride around her cable before heaving in. Scrub off when heaving in slowly. Place an anchor buoy over your anchor when doing this sort of work.

When in dry dock range the cable on the bottom of the dock. Lower anchor carefully, place on skids, and paint. The cable should be ranged in long fakes, all markings and shackles overhauled, and all links sounded with a hammer. If a link does not seem to ring true go over it carefully for defects.

A record should be kept in the *maintenance book* (more about this later on) showing just when and where the cables have been ranged. When ranging in a dry dock try to paint or mastic them before stowing.

Swivels should be greased and all shackle pins should be backed out, examined and coated with white lead and tallow before assembling.

Securing the Chain Cables in the Locker

Some seamen prefer to have the ends of both cables shackled together and connected through the bulkhead separating the chain lockers. This is a bad practice. The *bitter end* of each chain should be passed through a link in the bottom of the locker and then up to the top of the locker to another link near the scuttle. Bring the chain up in a corner of the locker and stop it along the corner with small stuff to prevent it fouling the bight of the chain. The upper end should be lashed, or secured by a stout slip hook.

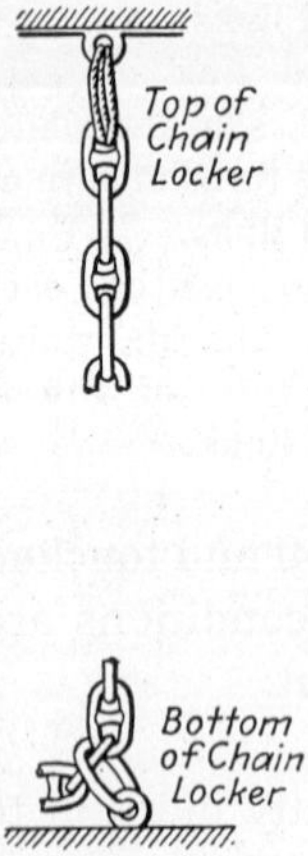

Securing chain in locker.

When it becomes necessary to slip the cable, the bitter end can be cast loose without trouble, the stops will break.

Chain cables vary in length according to the size of the vessel.

The longest cables listed by the A.B.S., for an equipment tonnage of 26,500 tons, are 330 fathoms. This length of cable is required for all vessels down to twelve thousand tons and then goes down by thirty fathom increments. The cable listed is of course divided between the two bower anchors, 165 fathoms on each anchor.

Cables are attached to the anchors as follows:

1st. *Bending* or *anchor shackle* (bow of shackles always on anchor side) into *anchor shackle*, or *Jew's harp*. As this is very heavy, the bending shackle has to be wide.

2d. *Extra heavy open link.*

3d. Stud link (or open link).

4th. Swivel, bow toward anchor, swivel eye inboard.

5th. Stud link (or open link).

6th. Shackle (bow toward anchor). This shackles into first shot of the cable.

Note. Other methods are in use but this is recommended.

End links, long end links (long link with stud to one end), and *enlarged stud links* are used in connecting swivels and shackles.

The combination of links, swivel and shackles is called a *swivel piece.*

Mooring swivels are used to connect two cables to a single swivel and this is shackeled to the chains leading into the hawse pipes from which the vessel is riding.

A *cable's length* is 100 fathoms.

According to A.B.S. Rules. Chains are marked as follows:

After being weighed the shackles and the end links of each shot, and every 15 fathoms in the case of chain which is in one continuous length without joining shackles, are to be clearly stamped by the manufacturers as follows:

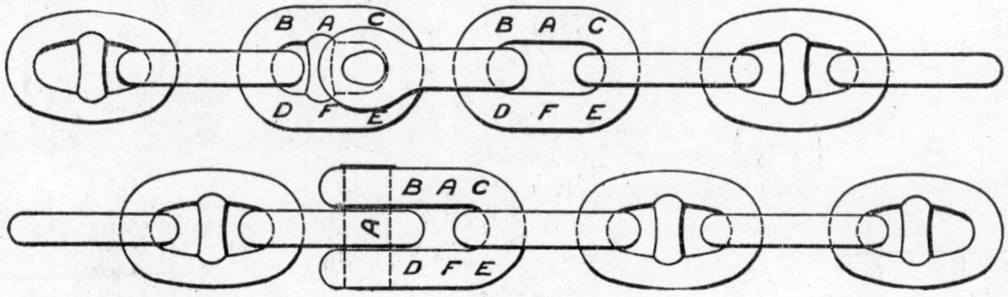

A. The Number of Certificate. (Furnished by Surveyor) 8442
B. The Initials of the Surveyor who witnesses the Test.......... X.Y.Z.
C. Month and Year of Test.................................. 3, 17
D. The Breaking Test (lbs.).................................. 211680
E. The Proof Test applied (lbs.).............................. 151200
F. Signifying that the Testing Machine is recognized by the Committee of the American Bureau of Shipping............... A.B.

IV

The Windlass

The *windlass* is a winding engine having a horizontal axle to which is keyed the worm or spur gear for applying power and the *barrels, gypsies,* and *wildcats* for hauling in rope or chain. These things have been mentioned briefly in the foreword to the present chapter. The illustration gives a good idea of the relation of these parts and the method of control.

To let go an anchor, the wildcats are unlocked and the brakes are applied. This holds the wildcats rigid with respect to the frame. The stoppers are then released, wherever they may be, either forward or abaft the wildcats and the chain is ready for letting go. The anchor, in the case of a stockless type, is let fall by releasing the pressure on the brake band, allowing the wildcat to revolve and lower the chain. This is a good method of letting go as it gives control over the run of chain. The chain can be held as soon as the anchor strikes bottom and only allowed to pay out as the vessel rides away from her anchor.

Parts of a Windlass.—A, Brakes wheels on wildcats. B, Reversing control on engine. Operates the slip eccentric. C, Chain riding in the grip of wildcats (sprockets). D, Main driving gear. E, Gypsie heads. F, Brake bands. G, Locking rings. H, Horizontal beam for shipping hand levers. I, Ratchets for pawls of hand power mechanism.

To heave, in the wildcat is locked to the axle or shaft of the windlass, the brake band is released and steam, or other power, applied to the worm or pinion.

In heaving up an anchor by hand, long brake beams are fitted in the cross head and these engage the turning gear by means of pawls. Heaving in by hand is a long, tedious job. Where the windlass is situated beneath a forecastle head the hand power is usually applied by a worm or pinion attached to the vertical shaft of a forecastle capstan. Power is then applied by means of capstan bars. This is the best method of heaving in by hand.

The following directions apply to the Hyde steam windlass with forecastle deck capstan. This type is a worm gear windlass. The directions are as given by the maker.

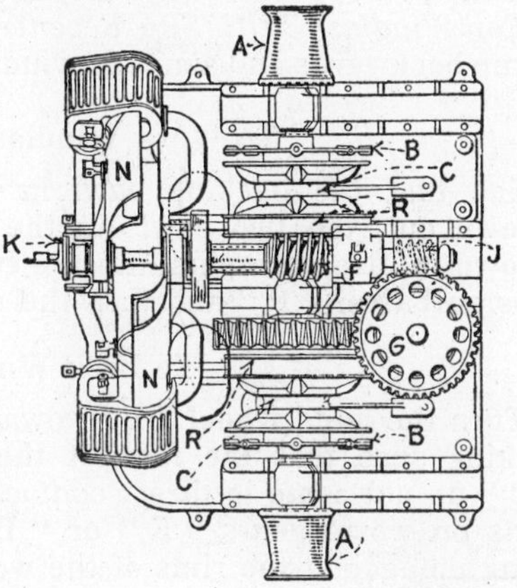

To Work Windlass by Steam Ahead and Heave in Chain

For Windlass With Reverse Valve. Lock the Windlass. Start ahead by opening the throttle in steam pipe, and push the hand lever "L" of the reverse valve "K" forward and control the running of the engine by means of the lever or by the throttle valve as is most convenient.

For Windlass With Slip Eccentric. Lock the Windlass. See that eccentric is set for running ahead, open the throttle valve and control by throttle.

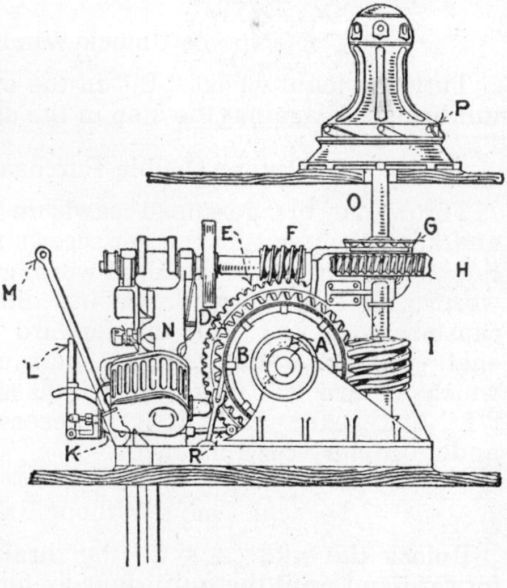

On either style of windlass, if it is not desired to run the capstan at the same time, throw out the pawls in the capstan worm gear "H" by turning the hand wheel "G" to the right hand, until it brings up. When running ahead, it is better to keep the backing pawl in the engine worm gear "E" thrown out, avoiding the noise it otherwise makes.

To Stop the Windlass

Windlass With Reverse Valve. Bring the reverse lever " L " back to central position if only stopping for a short time, but if stopping permanently, also close the throttle valve.

Windlass With Slip Eccentric. Close the throttle valve.

To Reverse Windlass for Veering Chain. See that the backing pawl in the engine worm gear " E " is thrown in, and the two pawls in the hand worm gear " D " are thrown out, then

For Windlass With Reverse Valve. The throttle being open, pull the reverse lever " L " aft, and control as before.

For Windlass With Slip Eccentric. See that eccentric is set to run backwards and start the windlass by opening throttle valve.

To Work Windlass by Hand

See that the backing pawl in engine worm gear " E " is thrown out, the two pawls in the hand worm gear " D " are thrown in, drop the pins into the two holes in the lower part of capstan barrel " P " and turn the capstan " with the sun."

To Lock Windlass

Turn the hand wheel " B " towards you, or from forward aft, making sure that the face of the projections on the wildcat " C " do not come in direct contact with the face of the projections on worm gears " E " or " D," but that they go by and bring up against the rims of the worm gears in such a way that one projection will engage the other as in a clutch.

To Unlock Windlass

Turn the hand wheel " B " in the opposite direction until the nut brings up against the stop in the shaft.

To Obtain Double Purchase on Windlass

Throw out the go-ahead pawls in engine worm gear " E " and keep them out by the set screws provided for that purpose. See that the pawls in the hand worm gear " D " and the capstan worm gear " H " are thrown in. Start the windlass, and the capstan worm " J " on the forward end of the engine crank shaft will drive the upright shaft or capstan spindle " O " which in turn will drive the windlass through the hand worm " I " and gear " D." It is unnecessary to use this purchase under ordinary circumstances.

To Veer Chain Without Using the Engine

Unlock the wild cat " C " by turning the hand wheel " B " forward and until the nut brings up on stop in shaft, and control the wild cats by means of the friction brake levers " M."

To Run Capstan by Steam

Throw in the pawls in the capstan worm gear " H." See that the pins are in the holes in the lower part of the capstan barrel " P " and run the engines ahead as when running the windlass, at the same time having the wild cats thrown out.

If it should be desired to run the capstan constantly, without working the windlass, the go-ahead pawls in the engine worm gear " E " may be thrown out and kept out by set screws provided for that purpose.

To Run Capstan by Hand

Pull out the two pins in the lower part of capstan barrel " P." Holes will be found in the base to hold these pins while not in use. Use as an ordinary hand capstan, turning head " with the sun " for speed, and " against the sun " for power.

Use of Pins in Capstan

The pins or toggles connecting capstan to shaft are only removed when capstan is to be worked by hand.

Use of Friction Bands

Ride only by friction bands " R " and with windlass unlocked. It is then ready to pay out chain at an instant's notice. Windlass should be locked only when heaving in chain. Do not use oil on the friction bands. Keep the turnbuckles free from rust so they can be screwed up at any time.

Working the Pawls

To throw out the backing pawl in the engine worm gear " E " and the two pawls in the hand worm gear " D," pull the pawl lifter cam away from its seat one-eighth of an inch and give it half a turn to the left.

To throw the same pawls in, turn the pawl lifter cam to the right or in the opposite direction.

To throw out the pawls in the capstan worm gear " H," turn the hand wheel " G " to the right or " with the sun " until it brings up.

To throw these pawls in, turn the hand wheel " G " to the left, " against the sun " or in the opposite direction from above, until it brings up.

Directions for Keeping Windlass in Order

Oil holes will be found in the wild cats, in the nuts, and in the rims of the worm wheels.

Turn windlass by hand occasionally, to insure the oil working under the rims of worm wheels. Use sperm oil on all parts of windlass that are exposed, or where ordinary oil would " chill."

Careful study of the foregoing instructions and drawings will give the seaman a very good idea of the operation of a modern windlass no matter what kind of anchor engine he may be shipmates with. Always study the windlass in your ship, *know* how to work it on the darkest night. Do this no matter what your station may be. A Second Mate, Boatswain or Quartermaster, may be called upon to use the windlass, and generally would only be required to do so under extraordinary circumstances. The Chief Mate and Carpenter *must* know it thoroughly.

A final word may be said about *hand gear.* Try it out with your crew on the first fine afternoon at sea. Release the wild cats, come up on the brakes (chain and anchors secured, of course) and give the windlass a good turning over, throwing the gear in and out a few times to make sure that every one understands its use.

This same practice should extend to the hand steering gear as well. Here it would be just as well to steer for a half hour by hand.*

* Anchor Engines are severely tested in the Navy. The following from U. S. Navy Specifications may be of interest here:

The Anchor Engine should be tested on or before the official trial of the vessel by hoisting and lowering two bower anchors simultaneously, in 30 fathoms of water or in the greatest depth of water obtainable in the vicinity of the building yard, continuously at the approximate rate of 6 fathoms of chain per minute. If the depth of water is less than 30 fathoms, weights shall be attached to the anchors to compensate for the lesser depth, the weight, however, not to exceed the weight of the anchor. The operation of the windlass and any heating of thrust and worm bearings should be noted. The windlass brake and locking device should be tested.

In the case of steam windlasses the duration of the test should be one hour.

In the case of electric windlasses the test should be divided into three divisions, viz., the wildcats being labeled " A," " B," and " C," the test shall be run continuously with all motors operating together as follows: " A " and " B "—one-half hour; " B " and " C "—one-half hour; " C " and " B "—one-half hour.

The tests of evaporating and distilling plant, of refrigerating machines, of steering and anchor gear, and the bilge test of circulating pumps should be made before trials in free route.

Anchor Engine Trials. With the vessel at sea in a depth of water exceed-

V

Coming To Anchor

Coming to anchor involves many problems of pilotage and ship handling. The method of letting go will be described here.

Having determined to come to anchor send word to the Chief Mate at once.* (If entering port anchors should always be "ready to let go.")

The men being at their stations, the commands are as follows:

"*Stand by starboard anchor* (or port), *stand clear starboard chain!*"

"*Aye, aye, sir!*" (All ready for letting go.)

"*Let go!*"

Then follow this command, or precede it, with instruction as to the amount of chain to *veer*.

"*Forty-five fathoms at the windlass!*" (or thirty fathoms at the water), or whatever *scope* of chain is desired. Many officers prefer to name the shackle at the windlass, especially at night. The Carpenter should work the brake and watch the chain as it goes out, calling the shackles to the Mate who will be on the forecastle head watching the *trend* of the chain. As the chain runs out the Mate should indicate the trend to the Master on the bridge by the direction of his arm. At night he may call out, "*Chain up and down!*" as an indication that the vessel has

ing 60 fathoms, one of the anchors shall be backed out until the 60-fathom shackle is at the water's edge and the anchor clear of the bottom. The anchor shall then be hove in at a speed of at least 6 fathoms per min. and the results noted. Two of the anchors shall then be backed out simultaneously, one to 60 fathoms and the other 55 fathoms, so that two shackles will not be on the wildcat at the same time. The anchors shall then be hove up together at 6 fathoms per min. and the results noted. The single-anchor test shall be made twice, using a different windlass each time (also a different motor in case of electric windlasses). The two-anchor test shall also be made twice, using different pairs of windlasses for the two tests (using both motors in case of electric windlasses). The deep-sea tests shall be carried out under such conditions as will not cause fouling of the anchors and chains. All useful data shall be taken during both series of tests, such as speed of hoisting and lowering, temperature of bearings and worm gearing, etc. For electric windlasses there should be included the horsepower developed by the motors, and speed of motors. If there is only one wildcat the windlass test shall be conducted by hoisting and lowering one anchor instead of two.

* The Chief Engineer should also be advised, an hour ahead of time if possible.

not sufficient way, either ahead or astern. Or he may sing out "*chain ahead!*" or "*chain leading aft!*"

Team work in this respect is most valuable, especially at night.

The Mate will control the run of the chain and should be careful not to let it go out too fast, nipping it on the wildcat with the brake.

When the chain will not pay out and the desired scope has not run out. The Mate should advise the Master: "*Won't take chain, sir,*" or "*Chain not veering, sir!*"

In coming to anchor a certain amount of sternboard is desirable and only practice can determine how much. Vessels of heavy tonnage must be handled with greater care than smaller craft. Going astern, or ahead too fast may put a dangerous stress on the cable should the anchor bite into hard ground and get a sudden hold. Such stresses are dangerous as they tend to weaken, if not part, the chain.

Where an old-fashioned anchor is carried and let go from the bill board, be careful to have the stoppers off and the windlass ready with wild cat under control of the brake. Do not have the wild cat bound too tight, but keep enough control over the brake to easily nip the chain as soon as the anchor fetches bottom. In letting go from the bill board the anchor is said to be let go "stock and fluke." It is held by the *ring stopper* on the cat head and the *shank painter* on the bill board. More modern rigs provide a tripping device as shown in sketch, letting go with one movement.

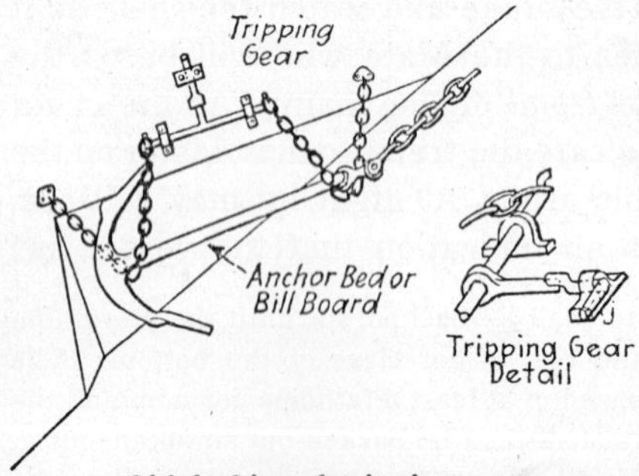

Old-fashioned tripping gear.

Should it be necessary to come to anchor while the vessel has considerable way upon her, or is being swept along on a tide, veer as much chain as is safe, nipping the cable gradually. In a steamer the engines may control this and overcome the speed while the chain is running out. When at rest heave in to the desired scope.

Coming to anchor on a sailing ship under unfavorable conditions is a test of seamanship. Where canvas cannot be set aback to check her way, the veering of chain is almost always necessary. Large yachts, running up to their moorings, are stopped by throwing the rudder hard over from side to side, shifting the helm before the yacht has a chance to swing. The rudder when hard over acts as a brake. A sailer should always, if possible, approach her anchorage by luffing up into the wind.

When coming to anchor in deep water, say anything over ten fathoms, use great care in veering chain, as the weight of chain alone will cause it to run overboard after the anchor has reached bottom. If allowed to run it may pile up on the anchor and cause it to foul.

Scope of Chain

A safe rule to follow in coming to anchor is to allow five fathoms of chain to each fathom of depth in holding ground known to be good. When blowing veer more chain, ten or twelve to one. The "five to one" rule should always be the minimum scope unless there is not sufficient room to swing, when mooring must be resorted to.

In bad weather, with poor holding ground, use judgment in giving the vessel more scope.

Coming to anchor and handling ground tackle will be treated further in the chapters following, on management of steamers and sailers.

VI

Weighing Anchor

When weighing anchor on a steamer or motor vessel ease the windlass by careful use of the engines and helm if necessary. The stations for weighing are similar to those for letting go. The Chief Mate should indicate the trend of the chain and call out the shackles as the chain comes in. Call out when at the water's edge in the day time or when on the windlass, at night.* Always have a hose ready and wash off the chain as it comes in.

"*Short stay!*" is reported when the anchor cable is in line with the fore stay.

* A cargo light on the forecastle head is very handy at night, especially if the anchor comes up foul.

"*Up and down!*" when the vessel is right over her anchor and ready to "*break out.*"

"*Anchor aweigh!*" when the anchor leaves the bottom. This is generally indicated by the windlass engine picking up the chain with greater ease.

If the anchor refuses to *break out* it is sometimes advisable to lock the windlass and give the vessel a kick ahead with the engines. This will usually trip the anchor and bring it free. If the hold is very hard stopper the chain before working the engines.

"*Foul anchor!*" is reported as soon as in sight, or if the anchor is clear it is well to report "*Clear anchor!*"

To clear a foul anchor some means must be found to cant the anchor clear, or to hang the anchor and clear by surging or slacking the chain. No definite rules can be laid down. Some officers have a wire clearing pendant already fitted. This is provided with a large fish hook and is handled on the forecastle by the capstan. It is generally easy enough to hook on with this, leading the pendant down through the bow chock. Then heave up and take the weight of the anchor. After that be guided by the manner in which the anchor is fouled.

The worst instance of fouling that the writer can remember occurred when the *Schoolship Newport* picked up a waterlogged spar buoy, some thirty fathoms of close link chain, and a mushroom anchor, all incorporated with the ship's own chain and anchor. This happened in the Hudson River with a strong tide running ebb, assisted by the current of the stream and a brisk north wind.

Very often such things happen at a time when the power to maneuver the vessel is limited and to let go a second anchor is next to impossible. Fortunately stockless anchors are very free from fouling and this is perhaps their best recommendation.

A final word about weighing. Never break out an anchor with a shackle on the windlass, if the hold is hard. Ease the shackle off and break out with the engines as recommended above.

When an anchor is buoyed, pick up the buoy as soon as possible. This should be fitted with a slip rope, so it can be hauled on board, after the turns have been taken out of it.

Weighing from a Mooring

When two anchors are down, circumstances permitting, veer chain on the anchor to which the vessel is riding strongest, sheer over toward the leeward anchor and heave in. When this anchor is up, hold your sheer and heave in on the second anchor.

When anchored in a crowded harbor always keep steam on the windlass.

VII

Stowing Anchors

Most anchors of the stockless type stow in the hawse pipes and require no special gear. Care must be taken in heaving in to not bring a heavy stress on the anchor after it is snug. Generally no special means for securing the anchor are necessary.

Stowing an old-fashioned anchor. Showing fish davit, guys, fish tackle. fish hook, balancing band. Fish fall (leading aft along deck), bill board. The sailor is about to " pass " the shank painter.

Some ships make sure of the anchor by passing a heavy steel bar through the chain just over the inside end of the hawse pipe. This bar should be fitted with a lanyard and lashed to deck bolts.

The practice is not very safe as the other method, of locking the chain by a devil's claw stopper, leaves the anchor free to let go without first lifting it by the windlass.

Old-fashioned anchors usually stow on the bows. The best practice is to stow them on an anchor bed or *bill board.** In sailing craft the anchor is lifted by means of a long fish pendant fitted to the foremast head in schooners and to the foretopmast head in square riggers. Many vessels carry a special fish davit for lifting the anchor. Steamers fitted with old-fashioned anchors almost all make use of a fish davit.

As soon as an old-fashioned anchor comes up to the water's edge, the fish tackle is overhauled, the fish hook is hooked in the *balancing link*, the fish tackle is rounded in, and as it picks up the anchor, the windlass is backed and the chain *surged*† to allow the anchor to rise to its bed.

Cat heads (the small projection or davit fitted on the bow to lift the anchor) are seldom met with nowadays. In the old days two falls were used. The *cat fall*, reeving through shieves in the cat head and fitted with a *cat hook* on the lower block. This was a threefold purchase. The cat hook took hold of the ring of the anchor. The fish tackle was generally a twofold purchase and was extended out over the bow by the *fish boom*, pivoted in a gooseneck on the forward side of the foremast. The *fish hook* was hooked under the fluke of the anchor. Both of these ancient contraptions lifted the anchor up to its bed on the bill board, where it was secured, as stated before, by ring stopper (to cat head) and shank painter (to bill board).

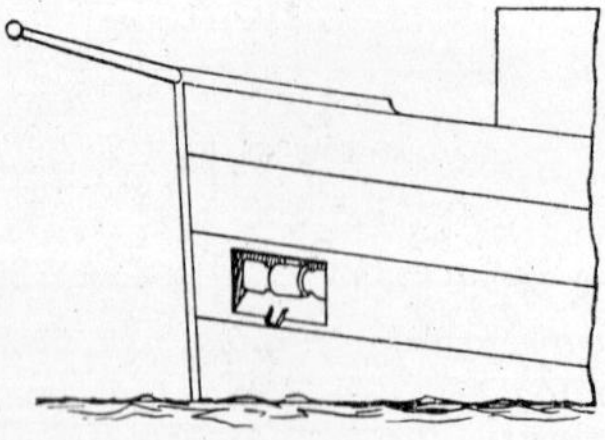

An anchor pocket.

In sailing craft on deep water voyages, it is the fashion to unshackle the chains and bring them in to the windlass, after the vessel is well off soundings. The anchors are *roused in* by deck tackles and securely lashed.

On the Great Lakes many of the large ore and grain carriers stow

* In old wooden ships an iron-shod board that protected the ship from injury by the bill of the anchor.

† To *surge* a chain or hawser is to slack it off.

their anchors in *anchor pockets* or *stowing boxes* as shown in the sketch. This avoids trouble where vessels are *scarphed*, bows and quarters in close contact alongside of wharves. It also is useful in protecting the anchors when working through narrow canal locks.

VIII

To Lay Out An Anchor

This operation is seldom necessary in the merchant service. In men of war it is practiced frequently when ships must moor in more or less dangerous ground and in places unprovided with permanent moorings. Naval vessels generally carry special gear for this work.

However when an anchor is to be placed some distance away from the vessel the occasion is liable to be one of necessity and the work must be done with dispatch. Kedge and stream anchors are easily handled in ship's boats having a square stern, but in the average high-sided double-ended life boat great care must be taken in slinging the anchor. Large stream anchors are best handled by the use of two boats securely lashed side by side with stout spars.

Carrying out an old-fashioned anchor with two boats. A stockless anchor would be slung with flukes horizontal, close under boats, and anchor shackle up near gunwales.

When a bower anchor is to be carried out use two boats side by side. Sling the anchor between them and coil five fathoms of the wire hawser in the boats. Making certain that the bight of wire leading back to the vessel is securely lashed with strong new ratline stuff. Have an axe handy to cut this BEFORE letting go. The wire is payed out by the ship when bringing the anchor into its desired place.

At best an anchor cannot be carried out with ship's boats unless weather and sea are moderate, and then every precaution must be taken to avoid accidents. The rails of life boats are not strong and cross spars must be well chocked to carry the weight down into the bilge of the boat.

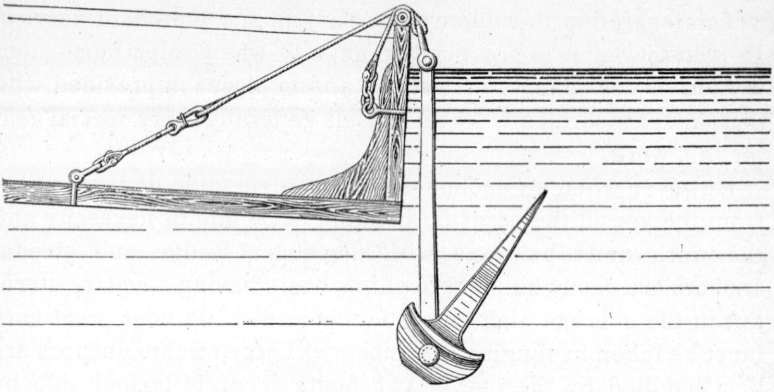

A stockless stream or kedge slung over stern of boat. Cable not shown.

Means must be provided for slipping the anchor, either by the use of a pelican hook or by means of a strong toggle and a heavy rope strap. If the anchor is a large one, make a strap of a number of turns of light flexible wire rope and use a strong steel bar for the toggle.

An anchor layed out in this fashion should be provided with a strong trippling line, clove hitched and stopped, about the crown. When a stockless anchor is used be careful not to place the tripping line so that it will interfere with or jamb the motion of the arms.

Keep as much gear off of the anchor as possible.

Keep the anchor up between two boats with shackle in sight until ready to let go. This is the most certain rig for all purposes.

If only one boat is available the anchor must be slung under the boat by a *bridle.* The bridle is passed around the belly of the boat in the wake of extra spreaders and chocks, and the anchor is slung by a *hanging line* made fast to the bridle. A

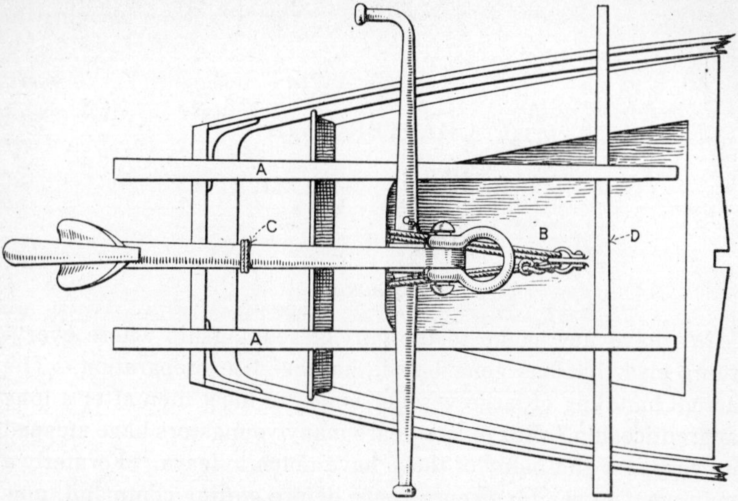

Stream anchor carried in large square stern boat. A, A, Skids. D capstan bar. B, Stock lashing. C, Shank lashing. Cable not shown, Anchor is dropped by lifting forward ends of AA.

third line called the *lowering line* is also hooked into the balancing band, or sling, on the anchor and serves to lift it from the ship and to lower it down under the boat until the bridle and hanging line take the weight. When the anchor is let go in this way considerable gear goes down with it.

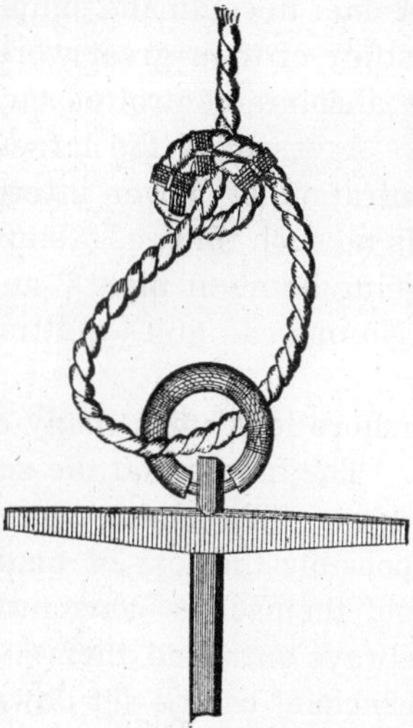

An inside clinch.

When laying out an anchor always attach a buoy to the anchor. When a weighing or tripping line is used bend the buoy rope to this line at a point far enough from the anchor so that the buoy rope will bring the bight of the tripping line to the surface at high tide. This is useful when about to get the anchor.

When securing a rope hawser to an anchor use a clinch as shown in the sketch. Some prefer a round turn and two half hitches, the end secured by stout seizings. The clinch, however, cannot jam.

CHAPTER XVIII

HANDLING A STEAMER

I

Foreword

We have now come to the part of seamanship where everything else that has gone before has been in preparation. The actual handling of large vessels comes to most men after a long apprenticeship. But in late years many youngsters have stepped up very fast and many of these have much to learn. Formerly a man went to sea for twenty years before getting command, now the trick is often done in one fourth of the time. Youngsters are not four times as clever; we are simply living in a more rapid age. Opportunities for advancement are very great, and the *obligations* going with the *opportunities* have increased tenfold at least.

The officers on the bridge and the Master in command simply have to buckle down to the constant study of their great work. Nowhere, except at sea, do men have absolute control of such vast forces as we find on board ship. A vessel of the largest class combines within itself a concentration of power utterly unknown ashore. When afloat there is no such thing as " shutting down the works," there is no " going home at night " and forgetting things until the next day. No one can quit—quitting at sea is mutiny.

Sympathetic, well-meaning people ashore look upon many of the customs at sea as harsh and cruel. The fact is that the sea itself is absolutely relentless in its laws. The finest vessel afloat would meet with disaster and possibly the loss of many lives, if the men on board did not hold themselves constantly responsive to the great dangers that always surround them.

In ship handling only the broadest principles can be set down. Vessels built from the same plans differ in their ways. Every cargo brings with it alterations in the trim and stability of the same vessel. The progress of the voyage, with bunker weights constantly diminishing, causes further alteration in the qualities of handling. Wind and sea conditions are always changing, and as a vessel progresses from the time of her last docking her bottom becomes coated with marine growths and her maneuvering power becomes less and less. This condition was brought home to the writer with great force during the first voyage of the S. S. *American*, Captain George McDonald, on her two passages through the Magellan Straits. Outward bound we were clean, going to the westward, and made all anchorages. Homeward bound a foot of grass trailed from her plates and all anchorages were missed, often by a small fraction of an hour. Only the finest seamanship prevented the vessel from meeting with disaster while afloat off Field's Anchorage during a night of constant snow and willi waws.

The varying quality of fuel also has much to do with the handling of vessels.

Certain *hull appendages* are found on the wetted bottom of merchant vessels and effect the handling. These are *rudder* and *rudder post, shaft struts* or *bossing* (sometimes called *spectacle frames*), the *bilge keels*, and in rare cases *bar keels.*

The changing elements make ship handling anything but a precise business. Also, no two men will do a similar piece of work in the same way. They may follow general principles but each individual will have many ideas and wrinkles of his own. Also, no shipmaster worth his salt imagines he knows it all and every one of them learns new things, and is on the lookout for them, on every voyage.

II

Anchoring

Before coming to an anchorage, if time permits, ascertain all facts available about the conditions that exist. The seasonal characteristics, storms, tides, bores (look out for these in the large river anchorages), the character of bottom, depths, room to swing, bearings, ranges, lights, etc., are a part of the art of piloting and have a direct bearing upon the selection of an anchorage.

When coming into an anchorage during the high stage of the tide be specially careful not to touch. Have leadsmen in both stands, sounding as you go in, and anchors always ready. It is also a good precaution to have a lead line in the running boat, or motor launch. Where there is any doubt send a boat ahead of the ship and sound as you go in, keeping the boat so far ahead that you can easily stop if the water shoals.

Such precautions are looked upon with great favor by the underwriters who have to foot all bills for carelessness. No one will criticize a master for seamanlike precaution. When he gets his ship into trouble, however, a thousand critics stand ready to tell him what he should have done. The *Standard Seamanship* does this for him *in advance.*

Many harbors are effected by currents during different stages of the tide. Your vessel may be going over the ground at a good rate of speed, even though she has very little way upon her through the water. Watch bearings ashore and pick up natural ranges where possible.

Having selected an anchorage, be certain that the vessel has sufficient room to swing. Anchoring in a crowded harbor calls for great judgment. Note, if possible, the manner of anchoring of other vessels, whether riding to single anchors or whether moored. Figure out their position at different stages of the tide. Note whether they are *tide rode* or *wind rode.**

The navy has developed the use of the *mooring board*, but this method of plotting the moorings of vessels with relation to each other is a refinement hardly necessary for merchant craft. It is a good plan, however, to strike off a circle on the chart *about the point of dropping anchor*, using the scope of chain as radius. This will show the limits of swing at all stages of the tide.

Riding at Single Anchor

A vessel riding at single anchor should have as much cable out as is necessary. Never ride to a short scope unless compelled to do so because of lack of room. Have at least five times as much chain out as there is depth. Remember that it is always better to veer chain as the weather makes up *before* the anchor begins to drag.

* *Tide rode* swinging to the tide. *Wind rode* swinging to the wind. Often a vessel will be both tide rode and wind rode at the same time.

A vessel at single anchor should normally ride with a sheer away from her anchor. That is, if the port anchor is down give the vessel a small amount of port helm. This steadies the vessel and prevents her from yawing about. Under severe conditions of wind and sea a vessel at anchor should be steered, giving her a small sheer.

Riding to port bower. Sheer with port helm.

As the tide slacks and the wind makes up, perhaps from a different quarter, a vessel may *break her sheer.* That is, she will swing off before the new forces and may carry a long bight of loose chain with her. A vessel riding to a weather tide may be taken by the wind and carried across her anchor at slack water, tripping or fouling it.

Tending ship at anchor is an art somewhat neglected on steamers. The sailer must tend ship. The steamer may almost always avoid serious trouble by use of the engines.

When a vessel is about to break her sheer, it may be advisable to heave in, if riding to a long scope, and then veer chain again on the making up of the new tide.

An officer should always be on deck at the turn of the tide. As this time is known he can easily be called before she begins to swing. In heavy weather many Masters insist upon an officer's anchor watch. This is reasonable, as the conditions are generally such that quick action is necessary by someone who has been awake and knows how the vessel is riding.

A *drift lead* should always be over the side in heavy weather or tide.

Where a vessel lies to an anchor for long periods, it is a good plan to heave in at slack water and *sight* the anchor at frequent intervals. Also, note the way in which the vessel turns at each tide by recording the headings in the log book. This will give some idea of what is happening to the anchor and the chain. An old dry compass, with cover off the card, and two loose threads leading up to a support, gives an actual idea of the state of the two chains.

Get *bearings* or *ranges* whenever possible while on an anchorage. See Page 520.

III

Backing an Anchor

When riding to a single anchor, weather making up, it may sometimes be necessary to add to the holding power of the anchor that is down by backing it with a second anchor. This however is an extreme case and might only be resorted to after both anchors had failed to hold the vessel and engines were either out of order or unable to stem the storm.

A spare bower or stream anchor would be got up, a length of the heaviest wire in the ship rove through one of the anchor shackles outside of the hawse pipe, and carried inboard to the anchor. Lower the anchor and heave in on the wire. Then lash or shackle the anchor to the cable. If sufficient wire cable is available veer this overboard from the bow chock as the cable with the backing anchor is veered. Vessels are often blown ashore when hurricanes and other great storms sweep over them. With three anchors down, one of them a backing anchor, and steam up, engines going ahead, almost any storm can be weathered. It is a good plan to consider such possible work in advance and have the gear ready for use. It may never be used—but you never can tell.

IV

Mooring

Mooring is often necessary in congested anchorages and in such narrow anchorages as Port Churruca and others in the Magellan Straits. In coming to a mooring it is well to put down the anchors in a line with the main strength of the tide, and if possible have one anchor laid out in the direction from which the most severe storms are expected. Often, however, these things are uncertain and the best all 'round arrangement is resorted to.

The method of mooring is to come up to the point of dropping the first anchor, to let go and ride along, veering chain in the meanwhile until the point of dropping the second anchor is reached. This is then let go and as the second cable is veered, the first is hove in until the vessel rides on a span one anchor ahead and one astern.

When the tide or wind swings her across the lines of the mooring she will bring a great stress on the anchors (see composition of forces) and it is often necessary to veer chain. Sometimes it is possible to veer chain on one anchor and ride from the other.

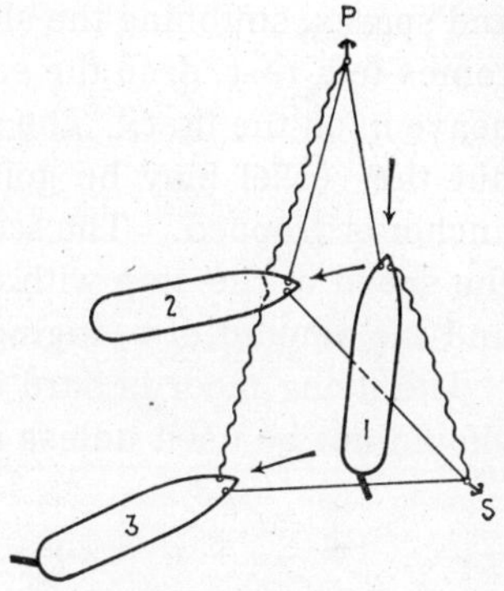

Mooring.—1, Riding to port anchor. 2, Riding to both anchors. 3, Slacking off port cable and riding to starboard anchor. Cables clear.

The reader will see at once that many combinations of mooring anchors and buoys are possible.

Where a vessel is to ride to a mooring for some time it is advisable to place a mooring swivel shackle outside of the hawse to take care of possible turns.

Clearing hawse where a vessel gets turns in her cables is an operation that cannot always be avoided. One chain (the cable with the least stress upon it) is secured below the turn by a clear hawse pendant brought in over the bow chock to the forecastle head capstan or the gypsie head of the windlass. This is hove taut, and the chain is unshackled on board, passed out through the hawse pipe, after hooking or shackling it to a hawser that has been passed down through the pipe and dipped around the standing cable. This hawser (dipped in the opposite direction of the turns in the cable) is hove upon and takes the loose end of the second cable clear of the riding cable and hauls it on board.

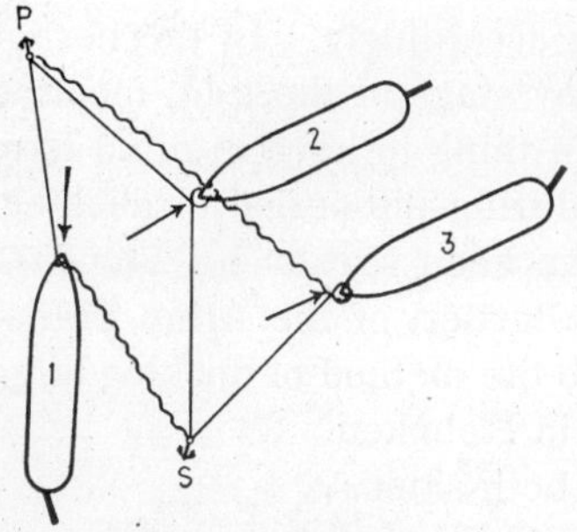

Mooring.—1, Riding to port anchor. 2, Riding to both anchors. 3, Riding to starboard anchor. (Port cable slacked off.) Half turn in cables. A half turn in cables is also called an "elbow."

All of this in one operation aided by a lot of *intelligent pursuasion.*

The best plan is to tend hawse and never let the cable get more than a half turn, or elbow, before taking it out at the following swing of the tide.

A *flying moor* is a fancy stunt that youngsters look upon as smart. The vessel slams up to her mooring at a fair speed, drops her hook and lets the cable go out with a shower of rust and sparks, snubbing the ship with the windlass brakes. As she comes to a rest, drop the second anchor, veer chain on this, and heave in on the first. The method is the same as a regular moor but the vessel may be going four or five knots when the first anchor is dropped. The scope of chain to let run before checking the speed of the ship with the windlass is a matter of judgment and the amount of swinging room available.

The flying moor is hard on all parts of the ground tackle and should not be used unless necessary.

V

Coming Alongside

This evolution is performed very frequently by merchant seamen and presents no special difficulty on smooth-sided vessels with ample power. Only where the vessel is large and tide or wind conditions are severe and tugs are not available, is there much danger.

The best ship handlers always make it a point to know exactly what conditions are to be expected at all stages of the tide and they choose their time for docking accordingly. In the harbor of New York many men dock at any stage of the tide, meeting conditions as they exist. The main thing to have in mind is to know what conditions will prevail during the period of docking.

The following practical notes have been written for *Standard Seamanship* by Captain Robert A. Bartlett of the Army Transport Service. These notes relate to the method of docking large liners at the Army Transport Base in Hoboken.

Have slip clear of all lighters on both sides.

If pier is covered have five or six camels or floats secured along the dock, to keep the vessel away from the string piece and to permit discharge water to go overboard clear of the dock.

Hoist a signal at the end of the dock to be used. A red flag is convenient and warns off other vessels also, preventing any misunderstanding as to which dock and which side is to be used.

At the corner cluster piles have a large paunch mat fender

securely lashed to the piles. The piles should be secure. When the cluster piles at the dock end are not suitable use a strong camel lying at the corner of the dock and well secured against slipping by wire springs. The dock corner will act as a turning point for the vessel when she springs around into the slip.

The best time to dock at the Hoboken piers is at slack water high, just before the beginning of the ebb tide.

Place the vessel heading up stream bringing her to a stop about one hundred and twenty feet out from the bulkhead line, the bow a little beyond the middle of the slip, the docking pier on the port hand. Vessel to be put alongside on the north side of the pier, that is on the side against which the tide will presently be running.

A tug is sent to the port bow and takes two 12-inch manila lines, running them half way up the dock. The Docking Master has his crew ready to place these lines on posts and to shift them ahead as required. These lines are referred to as No. 1 and No. 2. They lead to capstans on the forecastle.

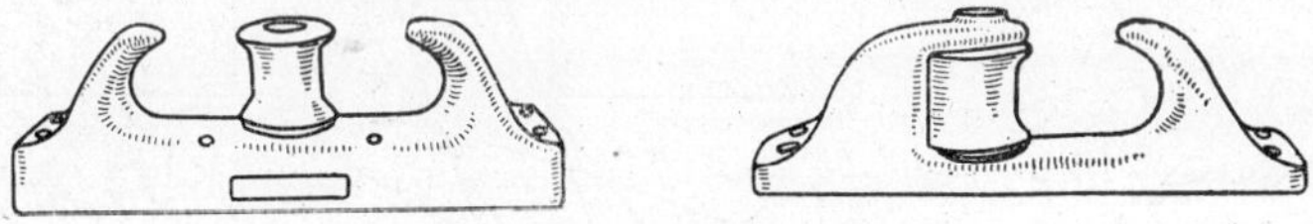

Types of roller chocks.

The tug then takes a third line from the port bow as a tow line. If the tide or wind is strong a second tug is put on the port bow with a towline.

The tugs, and lines 1 and 2, cant the bow into the slip and the vessel's side against the camel or fender.

From eight to ten tugs take hold against the port quarter and start working her up against the beginning of the ebb. The ship is worked ahead very slowly with the engines. As she works into the slip and the tide makes up stronger the forward tugs on the port quarter drop off and stand by to take lines from the starboard quarter if needed.

Springs are put over as she works into the slip and if a heavy wind is blowing from the north a 12-inch line is sent from the starboard quarter to the corner of the pier to the north.

The whole operation is simple and depends upon everyone understanding the method and attending strictly to business. The Captain and the Dock Master are the only ones giving orders.

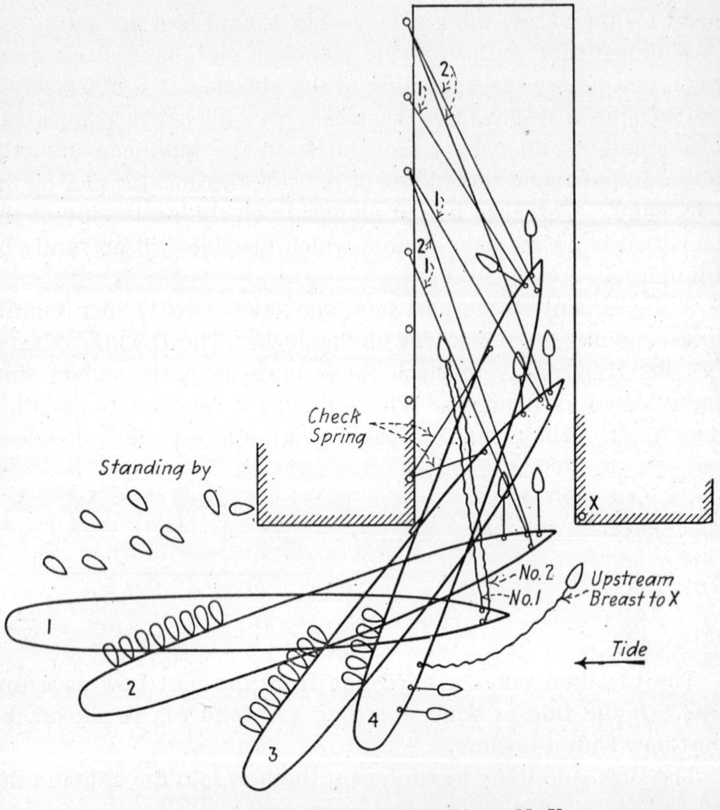

Docking a large liner, North River, N. Y.

Use docking telegraphs fore and aft on the vessel, and signals to the dock. The Chief Mate, on orders from the bridge, shifts the bow lines.

Docking with a flood tide bring the vessel up the river and turn her with the aid of tugs. This should be done just before the tide begins to run strong, or just before slack water high, if there is not too much water in the slip at low tide.

The principle is to always have the tide make against the side of the dock to which the vessel is to lie. It is very difficult to hold a vessel against a dock with the tide running in under the dock at its outer end and pushing her off.

The vessel should always stem the tide.

A roller head fair lead.

With a heavy wind and a high light vessel the wind may take hold and modify the effect of the tide.

Always come alongside slowly.

Use heaving lines in leading out warps and springs from the quarter chocks. Never send the line until all is ready, as the lines may easily foul the propellers.

Large vessels can leave the piers at any stage of the tide. The stern is held up against the tide by tugs, either pushing or pulling, or both. When the tide is setting the vessel away from her berth great care must be taken to have two or three powerful tugs on the up-tide quarter already taking a pull as the vessel backs out. If being set down against the pier the vessel will not pivot so fast on the corner piles or the camel, and the pushing tugs come in and take hold as she leaves the slip. Be certain that the tugs are ready at their station at the bulkhead before backing out into the stream.

Long liners must be turned by tugs as the North River is not wide enough for them to swing alone.

From ten to twelve tugs are needed to dock a large vessel under the above conditions.

Captain Bartlett has outlined the conditions under which the longest* ships are handled in one of the worst docking ports of the world. Where vessels enter a tideless basin, or one without current, the problem of handling is greatly simplified.

The *spring* is the most useful means of handling a vessel along side of a dock. Spring lines lead at a slight angle with the keel and are used to " spring in " or " spring out " the bow or stern, or where two spring lines are used at the same time

* Among merchant ships the *Queen Mary* with a length between perpendiculars of 1,004 feet, and a beam of 118 feet, is the largest. Her registered tonnage of 80,772 presents a special problem in handling alongside. This has been done without too much difficulty. Largest ships listed on Page 8.

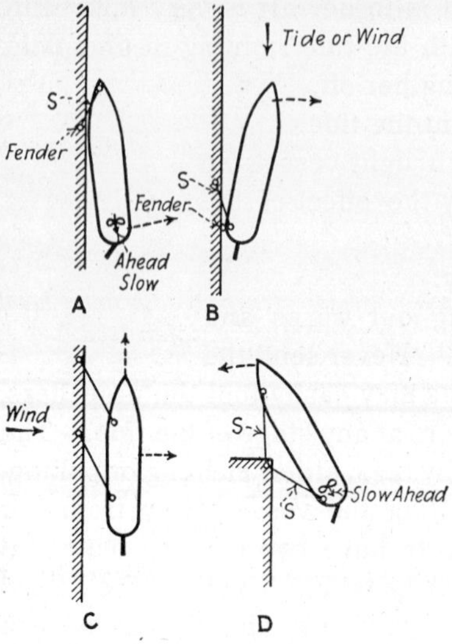

A, Working stern clear with engines. B, Tide and wind send bow out. C, Springing off parallel to dock. D, Winding around corner of dock. S, Spring lines.

the vessel can be bodily moved in or out or pivoted depending upon the direction of the springs and the motion given the vessel with the engines. Diagrams of the action of the spring are not very satisfactory, but at least they serve to show some of its uses. *Surging* and *Rendering* are terms used by seamen when slacking off heavy lines under stress, to prevent lines from parting or to assist in maneuvering. Be careful that *wet* lines do not get out of hand.

Springs are always used in tying up at a dock and these, in conjunction with *breast lines*, and *bow* and *stern lines* constitute the regular mooring lines of vessels alongside of a dock or wharf.

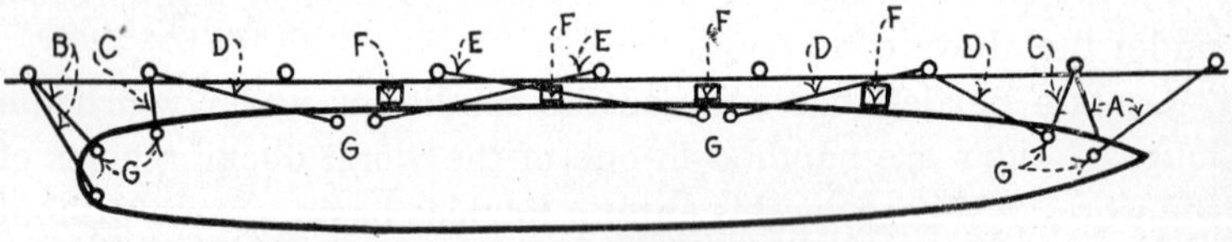

Tying up a large vessel.—A, Bow lines. B, Stern lines. C, Breast lines. D, Springs. E, Cross springs. F, Camels or fender logs.

Fire Warp

Many officers when placing their ships alongside of a wooden shed, or one filled with combustible materials, make it a practice to lead a fire warp from the inshore end of the vessel to a corner of the wharf. This is held in beckets just below the rail, or may simply rest on the string piece of the wharf. It is led to the forward capstan if bow in, or to an after capstan or winch, if stern in. The fire warp should be a flexible wire rope.

Should a fire start ashore, engines probably being out of commission, or boilers cold, the fire warp will throw the vessel clear of the slip, all other lines being cast off. The vessel can then drift clear and anchor, or be picked up by a tug.

VI

Going Alongside Another Vessel

The art of placing a fairly large craft alongside of another vessel while in a tideway is not generally understood by seamen. The fact that merchant vessels as a rule do not have to perform this evolution, except on rare occasions, leaves the matter very much in doubt in the minds of many. One branch of the navy, the Naval Auxiliary Service, has long been a fine school for ship handlers. Here the colliers and supply vessels are ordered about by some crusty old admiral and the young skippers just go where they are told. The excellent training received by the collier masters has been reflected in their records during the World War.

Commander E. V. W. Keen, of the Naval Reserve Force has written a most interesting and valuable set of notes for *Standard Seamanship*, covering the handling of a collier, single screw, and bringing her alongside of a battleship. Of course his instructions are applicable to the bringing alongside of any two vessels. Commander Keen has translated his helm instructions into merchant service practice.

General Remarks

No definite rules can be made for the successful handling of a steamer while going alongside another ship, wharf, or in mooring to a buoy, which will not bear adverse criticism. Opinions among seamen differ very much in this respect. Some advocate one procedure, and some, another. It is a known fact that different steamers, under similar conditions, act differently. Therefore the following suggestions, the result of practical experience, are to be taken accordingly.

Going alongside another ship at anchor in a harbor, river or narrow channel is one of the difficult jobs a shipmaster has to do now and again. In the Naval Auxiliary Service, it becomes more or less easy, as you are continually called upon to perform this duty at all hours, under favorable and unfavorable conditions, and practise in this, tends to perfection.

The type or class, of vessel discussed here is the average cargo vessel of low power, about 7000 tons displacement, length 410 feet, draft, loaded 24 feet, speed 9½ knots, horsepower 1400, with right-handed screw propeller. It is surprising how far a vessel of the above type will travel before coming to a standstill, even with little headway and engine going full astern. The distance required by the steamer, mentioned above, running half speed, 5 knots ahead in slack water, to come to a standstill, with engine full astern is about 1100 to 1300 feet or *over three times the vessel's length.* Running at full speed 10 knots, between six and seven times the vessel's length.

Caution

When you have a narrow channel, or congested harbor to navigate, which is usually the condition under which you will go alongside another ship, keep as little headway on as possible. Bear in mind, that should your order for half, or full speed ahead, not be answered as soon as reasonably expected by you (due no doubt to some hitch which may arise while handling the engine) no serious damage may result. But the result may be quite different if you have a fair amount of headway on and there is some unexpected delay in answering your signal for half or full *astern.*

Turning Effect—Rudder and Screw

Most single screw steamers are fitted with what is termed, a right-handed propeller, meaning that while in motion ahead, it turns from port to starboard, or like the hands of a watch. A right-handed screw, turning over slowly ahead, with rudder amidships, and other influences eliminated, such as wind, tide, etc., has a tendency to cause the ship's stern to travel to starboard and bow to port. As the speed is increased this tendency to cause the ships stern to travel to starboard is diminished. *The screw going ahead has its greatest turning effect upon bow and stern while turning over slowly.* In backing, this condition is reversed, the screw turning counter-clockwise. The ship's stern will travel to port, bow to starboard, and as the speed is increased the bow and stern will travel to starboard and port that much faster. *The screw in going astern has its greatest effect upon bow and stern while turning at full speed.**

Backing—Rudder Has Little Effect

The greatest turning effect on the ship's head is that of the rudder, when the screw is going full speed ahead. When the

* Note this—Greatest turning effect of screw.
Going ahead—slow.
Going astern—fast.
Author

screw is going full speed astern, the rudder has little effect. This effect can be changed slightly by varied conditions of draft and, too, there are times when it is possible to back your ship in a straight line due to wind, sea and tide. But in the majority of cases you will invariably find that the rudder has little effect in backing and that your bow, irrespective of rudder, will swing fast to the starboard and stern to port.

Effect of Wind and Tide

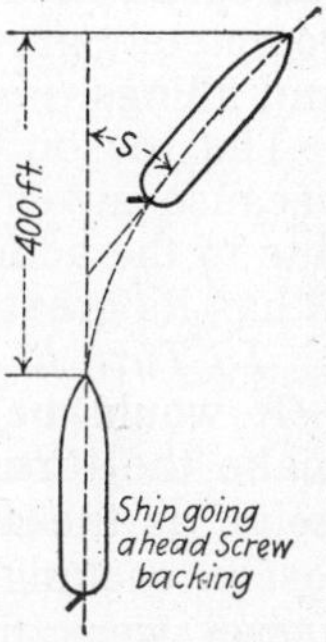

Vessel going ahead slowly, engine full astern, ship's head will go to starboard from 30° to 50° (angle S.) while traveling 400 to 600 feet, helm hard astarboard. If it is possible first go to port by putting the helm hard astarboard full ahead until she starts to swing and then stop her. In backing the propeller will swing bow to starboard and straighten her out.

Wind, sea and tide effect all maneuvers. The latter has the greatest effect upon a vessel fully laden. In maneuvering, or entering a narrow channel, it is advisable to stem rather than travel with it. There are times when a sea may have a great effect upon a light ship, this when in open water.

Wind has its greatest effect upon a light vessel and it is surprising how quickly a steamer (light draft), having no headway, will fall off from the wind. If on even draft, fore and aft, exposed surfaces equal, she will bring the wind abeam. If down by the stern, say 8 or 9 feet, she will bring the wind abaft the beam. If in open water the engine be reversed while the vessel has little headway with head to wind, she will, in a short time, turn stern to wind by falling off to starboard. A vessel fully loaded or light, no wind, in a fair sea and stopped she will gradually seek her own position and in most cases it will be the trough of the sea, and when in this position, by reversing engine her stern will sooner or later head into the sea.

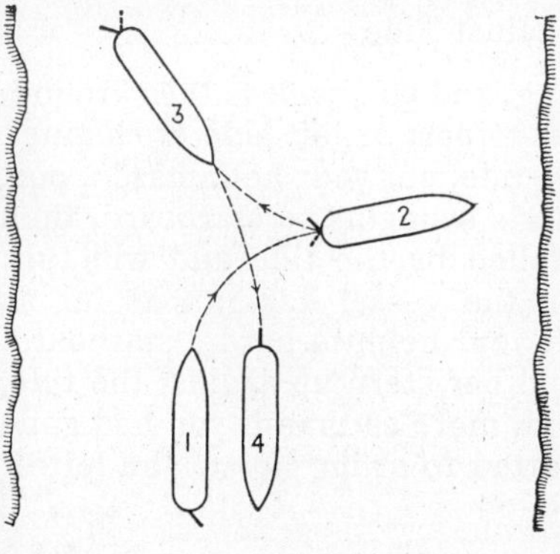

Backing and Filling (Steamer)

To turn a vessel in a limited space slack water, endeavor to get all the way you possibly can off the vessel before you put your helm over. Assuming the vessel is nearly stopped, put your helm hard a port and go full speed ahead.

(1) When she starts to swing, and before she gets much headway, stop her and let her run as far as prudent (if in a strange harbor, be sure to study the chart well, noting all immediate danger). (2) Keep your lead going and have both anchors ready for letting go, then go full astern helm amidships. When she has lost her headway, put helm hard a starboard. After backing as far as you may go, put your helm hard a port and go full speed ahead. (3) Repeat this maneuver till the vessel turns completely around, which usually is after two or three backings and fillings.

The reason for going full speed ahead, and then astern, is because a vessel under these conditions swings much faster, due to the action of the water from the propeller on the rudder. It has its greatest effect in deep water.

To Turn to Port—Right-hand Screw—Using Port Anchors

It would be quite difficult, under the above conditions, to make the turn to the port, that is going ahead on a starboard helm, as the angle gained in going ahead would be practically lost in backing. It would, however, be the way to turn if your vessel were fitted with a left-handed propeller. Of course, there are times when one is compelled to swing to the port and make the turn. If this is the case proceed as above with your helm hard a starboard and having run as far as prudent let go the port anchor veer 10 to 15 fathoms of chain (perhaps less, no definite amount can be stated you must be guided by the amount of water and kind of bottom), then go full astern.

In veering chain, you will note that it leads well astern and that the stern is swinging fast to starboard. When the vessel brings up on the chain, it may drag the anchor, if you have a clear bottom, no cables to hook on to and plenty of room astern, let her drag until she is straightened out, then stop, heave in and proceed on your way.

Turning Against Tide

If at anchor, strong tide running, and you want to turn around, heave up anchor and steam over to port or left side of channel. Arriving there and stemming the tide, put your helm hard a port and full ahead until the bow starts swinging to starboard, then stop. The vessel is now controlled by the tide and will turn dead athwart the river. When the vessel has run as far as prudent, go full astern and shift your helm to hard a starboard. This will have a tendency to hold her stern up against the tide, and she will come quickly around, more so than if you had gone over on the other shore and started to swing her to the left or with starboard helm.

Going Alongside of Another Vessel

Suppose you are entering port, and as you pass the flagship you receive signals to go alongside the U. S. S. . . . . immediately. Conditions are as follows: a strong spring flood tide, wind light, sea smooth. The U. S. S. . . . . is two miles further up the river and wants you to come alongside his port side and is ready for you. Notify the First Officer and Chief Engineer of your instructions to go alongside, "*Our* starboard side to *their* port side." The First Officer will have all hands take stations. See that anchors are ready for letting go, lines up and neatly coiled ready for use both fore and aft, steam on capstan engine, and winches turned over, fenders in position over the side. Be sure and have a large fender placed at the break of forecastle and well down on your starboard side as in all probability this location will be where you fetch up. Have a 5-inch manila line, of about 120 fathoms, ready as a running line. Lead this out through your forward chock to the foreshrouds, have a heaving line bent on. Have fenders ready for immediate use, heaving lines up and in charge of those who are to use them. Be certain that everything is ready.

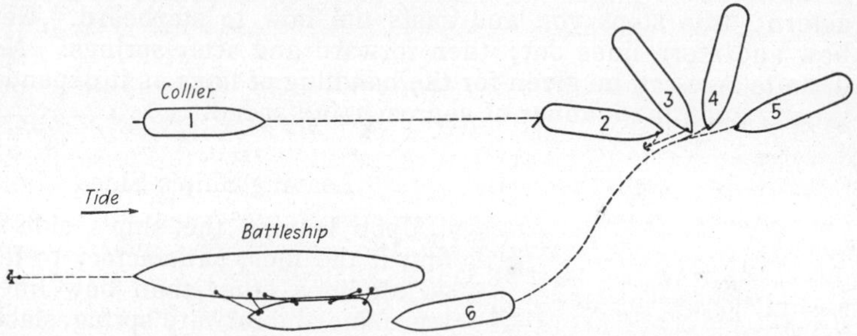

Proceed as follows: Try to keep in the center of river and endeavor to get most of the headway off the vessel and still have her manageable. Continue up river passing the U. S. S. . . . . on her starboard side, distance of about 500 ft. (1). When your bow is abreast of her bow stop your engine and let the tide carry you. By the time your bridge is abreast of her stern (if previously traveling very slowly) it will be noted that your headway is dead. Remember you are still traveling over the ground at a fair speed with the tide. Assuming that the river is clear ahead or that you have at least 3 or 4 ship lengths of clear water, put your helm hard aport (2), give a kick ahead full speed. When she starts to swing, go full astern, let go your starboard anchor and stop your engine (3). Veer chain gradually to 8 or 10 fathoms (in 6 fathoms of water. At this stage it is not your intention to give her enough chain to hold the ship, but just enough to break her around so as to head the tide. The greatest strain will occur when your ship is at right angles to the tide (4) and diminishes as your angle is reduced.

Having swung almost head to tide and when the tide is about 2 or 3 points on your starboard bow (5) (ship still swinging) you may veer chain and gradually bring her up. This may require between 60 and 70 fathoms of chain. If you feel that giving her that amount of chain may result in bringing you too close to some object astern of you, or the tide may be very strong and the strain on anchor engine and chain too great, go ahead on your engine. Assuming your ship has stopped and you have swung ahead to tide, put your helm amidship and start to heave up. Use your engine to take strain off capstan and steer your ship so as to follow the lead of your anchor chain. Get anchor away, and up. Head up for the stern of U. S. S. .... When within 200 feet of his stern, port your helm and bring his flag in line with your bridge (6). Then straighten her up and run parallel, keeping about 30 feet off, and watch your port helm. *Do not let the tide catch you on your port bow and carry you in.*

Having run your distance put helm astarboard and go full astern; this stops you and casts the bow to starboard. Get bow and stern lines out; then forward and after springs. No definite rule can be given for the handling of lines as it depends greatly upon the manner of approach and speed.

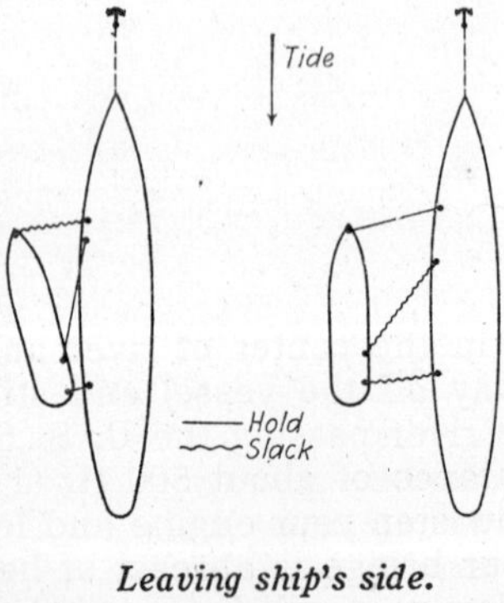

Leaving ship's side.

Leaving Ship's Side

Upon leaving the ship's side I find it the most satisfactory to let go all lines other than bow line, stern line and forward spring, slack bow line gently until ship brings up on spring. Hold bow line, and stern will gradually swing off. When off far enough take in stern line. Helm is amidship. When all clear aft, go slow ahead. Let go bow line, and as ship comes ahead haul aboard the spring. Be careful not to get spring in propellers.

On Heaving Lines

As a rule there are few seamen who can handle a heaving line with any degree of perfection. As a successful landing, under adverse conditions, often depends upon getting a heaving line on board, it is only natural that some instruction should be given to those who are to use them. Take a few coils of 15 or 18 thread manila and cut into 16 to 19 fathom lengths, and limber it up so that it is quite pliable. At one end seize a small canvas bag large enough to hold about a pound and a half of sand. (Write the ship's name on a piece of canvas, place this in the sand when sewing up the bag—when disputes arise over the ownership of heaving lines, rip open bag and claim your own.)

Set aside a half hour each day for practice in heaving. Create some rivalry, have a heaving line match once a week granting some inducement for perfection. With a few weeks of this practice we found that we could cut our heaving lines into twenty-five fathom lengths. Some men prefer a heavier sand bag with the longer length of line.

Single Screw Vessels

Commander Keen has shown very clearly what may be expected in the handling of a single screw, right-handed propeller, vessel of average tonnage under various conditions.

The action of a vessel with right-handed screw under a variety of circumstances is best illustrated by reference to the following table adapted from *Applied Naval Architecture* by W. J. Lovett.

Of course a left-handed screw will give opposite results under similar conditions.

But no matter how a screw will work in theory, the only safe guide is the study of the particular vessel under consideration.

The most unsatisfactory conditions may arise when a vessel is compelled to back due to wind or current and the lessened effect of the rudder. In going astern a vessel will give a tendency to back up into the wind, regardless of the helm even in a slight breeze.

Careful study of the above table and a comparison with the actual conditions found upon your ship will result in valuable data.

Know what the vessel will do under certain conditions, *then be careful not to try and make her do something else.* Handling a ship, or a woman, the same rules seem to apply.

Study of the rules set down will help toward gaining an understanding of the action of vessels, but too much stress cannot be given to the fact that all vessels differ and each one must be mastered by actual practice.

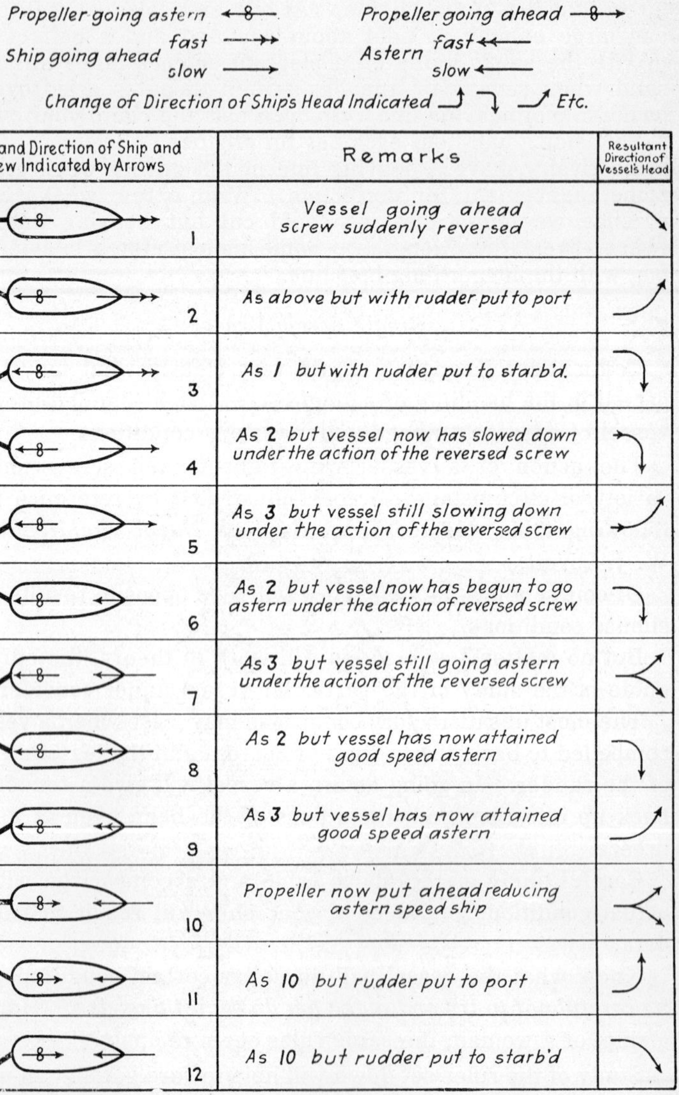

Maneuvering table, single screw right-handed.

VII

Twin Screw Vessels

A twin or triple screw vessel has many advantages over the single screw in the matter of maneuvering. Going astern the screws, turning in opposite directions, have less effect in deadening the steering power of the rudder.

Twin screws may be placed in two ways. The starboard screw may be right handed and the port screw left handed. Then the upper blades turn away from each other.

Or, the right and left-handed screws may be shifted and we have the upper blades turning toward each other.

The first method of fitting twin screws is the most common. It is the best arrangement for maneuvering, seeming to give more effect to the rudder than when the screws are inboard turning.

The turning effect of the blades of a screw in the lower half of the circle of their rotation is through denser water and the blade meets with greater resistance. This resistance is transferred to the end of the shaft and, in turn, to the hull itself. It is for this reason that a right-handed screw, turning backward, throws the ship's stern to port, and head to starboard.

In a twin screw vessel when going ahead, the ship will pivot rapidly when the outboard screw on the turning circle goes full ahead and the inboard screw is stopped, or reversed. The greater the distance between the shafts the more pronounced the turning effect.

The action of twin screws in turning is so simple that not much thought is needed to understand the effects due to different combinations of their action with the rudder and the forward or sternward motion of the vessel.

Steering. The steering of a vessel by twin screws has been accomplished on a number of occasions and is managed by controlling the revolutions of the engines.

Steering by rudder on a twin screw vessel is often effected by the rolling of the vessel. First one screw is low and shoves with more power, then the other is in the low position and gets in an extra push. This combined with the natural yawing of the ship will often cause her to steer badly. The writer remembers the very marked effect of the rolling of the old *St. Louis*, her screws kicking her from one side to another, making it very difficult with a quartering sea to steer a course within two or three degrees on each side.

Backing. In backing the effect of the rudder is less than when going ahead but ample turning power rests in a manipulation of the relative speed of the screws, or in stopping one and going astern on the other.

Turning from a stop. Here it is necessary to work the vessel around with her screws, backing on one and going ahead on the other. As the backing screw is less effective than the going ahead screw, it is well to turn over the ahead screw at a slower speed. Also, the effect of wind, trim, tide, and depth of water must be considered when performing this maneuver. In making such a turn with the screws the rudder should be held amidship.

Turning, going ahead. The helm is used as with a single screw vessel, while the screw, on the inside of the turn, is stopped or reversed.

Stopping. Twin screws are much more effective in stopping than single screws. A full-powered vessel should stop, twin screws going full speed astern, in about six to seven lengths.

In this connection it may be of interest to note that a vessel 660 feet long, 23,500 tons displacement, 35,000 I.H.P., with maximum speed of 23.5 knots will require seventeen and a half minutes to go from dead stop to full speed and will travel a distance of approximately 35,400 feet while working up to top speed. Reversing her engines she will come to a stop from full speed in a fraction over four minutes and will travel approximately 4,300 feet, or six and a half times her length.

Roughly a vessel can be stopped from full speed, with engines reversed, in one fourth of the time it takes to work her up to full speed.

The average results also show that she will run over six times her length unless a heavy head wind or sea knock down her speed.

Triple screw vessels handle like twin screws.

Quadruple screw vessels handle like twin screws.

Turbine vessels having multiple screws are fitted with special backing turbines on the maneuvering screws.

Cavitation is caused by a propeller revolving so fast that the head of water pressure cannot supply solid water for it to work in and the blades cut across the suction column of the propeller instead of working in it. This produces heavy vibrations and consumes additional power without effective thrust.

A somewhat similar condition prevails when a propeller revolves in still water, that is the vessel is so deeply laden, or burdened by a tow, that the propeller spins around without a corresponding forward movement into solid water. This is often seen on tug boats, it is called "*dispersal of the thrust column*" and of course results in vibration and loss of efficiency.

Many steamers shift berth, and in fact some make considerable passages with the propeller two thirds submerged. This effects their handling to a considerable extent. Usually tramp steamers of moderate tonnage are sent out in this condition, which sailors term "*flying light.*"

Horse Power

Before leaving this question of maneuvering it may be well to say a word about horsepower. To the average man there seem to be as many kinds of horsepower as there are breeds of this almost extinct domestic animal.

The following short definitions may help to clear up the matter.

A horsepower, by the way, is 33,000 foot-pounds of work performed per minute. That is, 33,000 pounds lifted one foot in a minute. Or 550 pounds one foot in a second. Or one pound 33,000 feet in a minute, and all proportions in between.

Indicated Horsepower is the power developed in the cylinders of an engine. It is measured by an indicator device, the pressure during the stroke being traced on a card. This calculation neglects all losses arising from friction in the machinery.

Shaft Horsepower is the brake horsepower measured on the shaft. It is the actual amount of twist given the shaft in units of foot-pounds and time.

Effective Horsepower is the actual power expended in moving the hull through the water. It is the tow-rope power, the final power applied after all losses in engine and shaft and slip of propeller.

Notes on Docking

No rule can be given as to the number of hawsers to be used in coming alongside. A moderate-sized vessel should have at least five lines at each end ranging from seven inch to ten inch. The largest vessels use twelve-inch manila handling hawsers.

Wire hawsers may be used at times but as a rule are not put out until the vessel is to be tied up.

When the end of one line is on a bollard a second one can readily be placed so that either line may be let go first. Take the eye of the second line up through the eye of the first and over the head of the bollard. If you have never seen this done just figure it out for yourself.

Where possible pass the eye of the working lines out through the chocks and up on the rail. Bend on heaving lines and have all ready for use. Most men bend the heaving line on the eye. It is better to bend it on just inside of the splice so the line can be lifted over a post and the heaving line unbent without trouble.

A vessel coming into a berth alongside of a dock or wharf will always try to get her bow line ashore first. It is well to also get a stern line out by passing the *heaving line* forward. If a long ship, bend two heaving lines together. This is safer than to put a long stern line out—this might fall overboard and drift aft into the propeller.

Docking telegraphs and docking bridges keep the Second Mate, stationed aft, in touch with the bridge. On a small vessel he should take a station where he can see the bridge at all times.

Entering a vessel in a dock slip bow first is comparatively simple. Getting a vessel alongside of a dock with wind or tide holding her off, lead forward and after springs aft, go slow ahead on engines for a few turns; this will cause her to come in sideways. Shorten in on bow and stern lines and get out breasts to hold her close.

To back into a slip is often a more serious job, depending upon conditions. Take advantage of all forces rather than to work against them. Get stern line out and up the slip and to after capstan or warping winch as soon as possible. It is often possible to first put a vessel alongside of the bulkhead, stern pointing across the slip, and to wind her around the corner of the dock by means of a strong spring leading forward, engines slow astern, and by heaving in on the stern line. Be certain to have a bow line out and a check spring leading forward. Never kick the engines too hard astern. The rudder, in this maneuver, is practically useless. It is assumed that no tugs are available.

Off shore breasts are often of great use when the vessel is going into a slip where they can be used.

Where there is no great amount of tide and wind, there is very little need of doing more than just having the slightest way on the vessel. Drift her into her berth slowly. Have cork or basket fenders handy.

In cold weather when lines refuse to hold on the drum of a capstan a little sand will help them grip. When a line rides down on the barrel, slack or surge it to bring it up. If there is a heavy pull on the line use great care in surging. Work the turns around by hand a little at a time. Many lines are parted by starting the loose turns too far and then holding them suddenly when the hawser surges. Always keep clear of a hawser working under heavy stress; many a leg has been broken by neglecting this precaution. Always have an *able seaman* tending hawsers under stress.

In making fast lines have the bight slightly more taut than the standing part where an end and a bight lead to a dock bollard.

Parcel all lines with strips of old canvas where they work over the edges of docks, etc. Marl this down with spun yarn.

Camels are heavy fender floats usually consisting of four squared logs bolted together.

Spur shores are heavy spars resting against the side of a vessel, the ends usually fitted into wooden *saucers*. The ends are held up by one or more lanyards made fast to the deck or rail. The shore end of spur shores are usually fitted with rollers to accommodate the shore end to different stages of the tide. Two breast tackles lead from the heel of the spur shore to the string piece of the wharf. These are used to haul the shore hard against the side of the vessel. Two or more are usually employed when a vessel is to lie so that she will have room for coal or other lighters between her and the wharf.

Dolphins are clusters of mooring piles driven in mooring basins and used for the purpose of tying up vessels. Lines of dolphins are found to be very convenient in congested basins. They admit of easy and stationary mooring. Oil pipe lines are sometimes led out to dolphins and vessels taking aboard fuel oil can do so in this manner.

In docking and handling ship two requisites should never be neglected. All officers should be provided with whistles, all sailors should carry sharp knives.

Tending lines alongside of a dock is most important. Where the range of tide is considerable this is necessary. The safety of the vessel may depend upon the faithful performance of this duty.

Where a vessel discharges or loads rapidly this duty should be constantly in mind. When taking in bunker coal under chutes, watch the lines. Where the vessel has to be shifted to aid in trimming under the chutes, special springs should be fitted and led to deck winches. Always watch the gangway while shifting and have some on watch, especially at night.

The " KEEP CLEAR OF PROPELLERS " signs should always be put out on a twin screw vessel. Where lighters are liable to be knocking about near the quarter at night have these signs fitted with a deck portable light hung over them.

Rat guards should always be put out where required. Sometimes this is of great importance where the shore is infested with the pests, or local quarantine regulations demand it.

VIII

Towing

In deep sea towing operations with a ship's own gear these important points are to be observed.

First the line to be used. This must be amply strong to withstand sudden jerks when the towing vessel and the vessel in tow bring upon the cable suddenly through the motion of the sea and the momentum of one of the vessels as against the lack of movement of the other. It must be understood that these stresses are liable to be excessive—more than any *taut* chain or wire, or fiber rope can stand. The art of towing successfully depends upon a careful regard for this and in adopting every means at hand to overcome, or to lessen, the sudden stresses due to the heavy forces involved.

The chain cable makes an ideal towline because of its weight and because of the degree of control over its length by the windlass of the vessel in tow. Where the windlass is in good order and the vessel to be towed can unshackle one anchor (after first getting it on board), the towing craft can haul on board this chain and secure it with suitable lashings.

A chain cable hanging between two objects forms a curve known to mathematicians as a *catenary.* On a long tow this curve will sag or flatten, depending upon the distance between the ends, and as this distance is dependent upon the pull at the ends of the heavy chain we have an ideal method of equalizing sudden stresses between the two vessels.

Towing by chain cable presents certain difficulties to the towing vessel. Getting the chain slung over the counter of the towing ship is not so easy. Towing by a bridle is desirable making certain that the connection of the bridle to the chain cable will not part. To make this connection leave the anchor shackle on the end of the cable and pass as many turns of new flexible wide as possible forming a large towing eye pass the parts of the bridle through this eye. The bridle should be long to prevent excessive stress due to the angle of pull. The bridle referred to here is on the towing vessel.

The towing eye and bridle should be held at the center of the span by means of two bights, one from each quarter. When dropping the tow these are cast off and then the span itself is let go. All stanchions and other obstructions must be removed, and care must be taken to avoid short nips and chafe. The ends of the bridle should lead as far forward as possible, generally to the quarter bitts, and after a turn around these to the bitts next forward.

Leading a towing line through a central chock on the taffrail may make steering difficult.

Where a vessel is to be towed by wire cable, or manila hawser, a shot or two of chain cable in the middle of the tow lines adds the necessary *sag* to give spring to the line. This is specially so with wire hawsers.

The length of tow lines should be regulated by the conditions prevailing. By slacking out or hauling in the length of sea running may be taken advantage of and both vessel will find themselves retarded or accelerated at the same time in that way saving stress upon the tow line.

In a general way, of course, the longer the line the easier the tow, but the limit to this is evident when actually handling a tow.

Sometimes it is necessary to tow a vessel without using her bower chain. It may be desirable to keep both anchors ready for letting go.

In this case pass a new flexible wire through both chain pipes, lowering the anchors (stockless) to do this. Pass as many turns as possible without interfering with the run of the chains. Frap the turns outside of the hawse pipes, form a long bridle, bring this up on the forecastle head and shackle or bend the towing line into this. Then drop over forward and secure the anchors with a stout tackle fitted on each side with a slip toggle or with a strong manila strap that can be cut away when they have to be lowered. The anchor shackles can be snug against the hawse pipes and the tackles, leading up and aft, will prevent swaying of the anchors.

The above observations are only general. Special conditions impose different methods. In matters of this kind the seaman proves his skill by adapting the most simple and secure measures with the means he has at hand.

Mr. Spencer Miller, Chief Engineer of the Lidgerwood Company, has prepared the following valuable data on towing and the use and utility of the Miller-Lidgerwood Automatic Tension Engine. These notes are given here through the courtesy of the above company.

The Automatic Tension Engine for Deep Sea Towing

Deep sea towing, even with many types of steam towing machines, is towing by jerks. The hawser stresses vary 500 to 600 per cent. Hawsers must be of enormous strength to withstand the maximum stresses incident to towing by jerks, and of great length to minimize the jerking.

The Automatic Tension Engine maintains a uniform tension or stress in the hawser (within ten per cent) and light short hawsers are used. The ships can be towed within 800 to 1000 feet even in a heavy seaway. This gives to a towed barge the practical equivalent of a propeller of its own.

In this steam towing apparatus the stress in the towing hawser is maintained practically uniform. The towing hawser cannot be over-strained whatever be the sea conditions.

The 13″ x 13″ engine will require a 1″ diameter steel hawser through which it will transmit a constant stress of 18,000 pounds to the towed ship. It need not exceed 1000 feet in length.

The automatic tension engine.

Under no possible combination of sea, weather and towing speed can the hawser stress exceed 18,000 pounds.

Any jerk exceeding 18,000 pounds will instantly lower the steam pressure and cause the engine to pay out hawser. Surges on hawsers seldom last over 3 seconds, and are followed by a slackening of hawser. The instant the hawser stress falls (to about 17,000 pounds) the steam pressure is raised and the hawser wound upon the drum until the stress is again (about) 18,000 pounds.

The hawser stress can be reduced at will by a turn of the regulating hand wheel. In practice the attendant adjusts the working stress to harmonize with the towing speed. If too much hawser is being wound upon the drum the hand wheel is turned one way to reduce the towing stress, and conversely, if the drum is seen to be losing hawser, the wheel is turned in the other way to increase the stress. If the towing ship slackens its speed the attendant reduces the hawser stress. Any man of the grade of oiler can be taught to operate the Automatic Tension Engine in a few moments.

What a Pull of 18,000 Pounds Has Done and Will Do

With an 18,000 pound hawser stress, the U. S. Battleship *Wyoming* (26,000 tons) was towed at 4⅓ knots with a 1″ (dia.) steel hawser, using the automatic tension engine.

With an 18,000 pound hawser stress, the U. S. Destroyer *O'Brien* (1,174 tons) was towed 9½ knots with a 1″ (dia.) steel hawser, using the automatic tension engine.

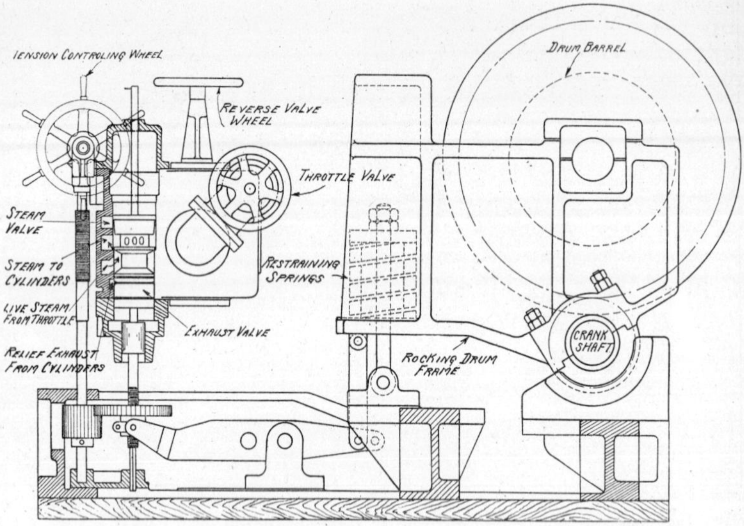

Diagram of automatic tension engine working parts.

An 18,000 pound hawser stress is enough to tow:

S. S. Colon	5,667 gross tons	6½ knots
S. S. Panama	5,667 gross tons	7 knots
S. S. Allianca	4,000 gross tons	7½ knots
U. S. S. Maumee ...	14,500 tons (without propeller) ..	8 knots
Oil Barge Navahoe ..	7,718 gross tons	6 knots

Manila vs. Wire Hawser

It is well known that manila hawsers are far superior to steel wire hawsers in the point of elasticity. Steel wire hawsers are cheaper for same strength, they last longer, are lighter, less bulky, easier to handle—all factors of importance on shipboard. Nevertheless, largely because of the greater elasticity, manila hawsers hold their own in well-earned popularity. Elasticity is recognized as a factor of prime importance.

For deep sea towing of large vessels long steel wire hawsers are practicable *only* in connection with means to overcome their deficiency in elasticity.

Use of Anchor Chain

Frequently steamship captains couple steel hawsers to the anchor chains of the towed ship. This greatly increases the sag or dip, and supplies a substitute for the elasticity of a manila hawser.

This is objected to as greatly increasing the resistance to towing and the wearing of the links. Anchor chains should not be used except in an emergency—such as a big ocean liner towing a disabled vessel. *Success in towing at present then depends almost entirely upon the exercise of good judgment and careful seamanship.*

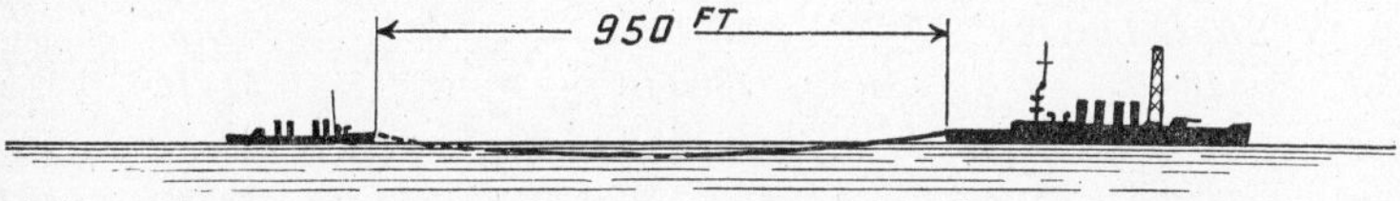

U. S. S. Tennessee (later U. S. S. Memphis) Towing U. S. S. Preble.
Towing line 180 ft.—1⅛" anchor chain.......... wt. 2450 lbs.
780 ft.—10" circ. manila rope....... wt. 2540 lbs.
960 ft. wt. 4990 lbs.
Hawser stress, 18,000 lbs.—Normal sag, 35 ft.
Towing line failed at 10 knots.

Experiments in towing. In 1908 certain towing experiments were made in the Pacific from San Francisco to San Diego, the sea was smooth one-half the time and a moderate following sea the other half. Three cruisers towed three destroyers of 592 tons full load, one of these was the *Perry*.

130 fathoms of 10" manila hawser were used, shackled to 30 fathoms of anchor chain. These tow lines *failed* at 10 knot speed. Elements estimated to possess an ultimate strength of 50,000 lbs. broke.

The report says, " chain should not be used at all." " The great weight of chain carries the hawser way down in the water, and increases the resistance."

The accepted plan for towing gear for battleships employs anchor chains coupled to wire hawsers. This plan (wholly justified because of military reasons) undoubtedly provides an increased range of elastic extension in the hawser. It is frequently used, sometimes failing which indicates that it does not furnish an *adequate* range of elastic extension. Even used in connection with manila hawsers, whose elasticity is perhaps ten times that of wire, it has repeatedly failed in practice. In fact, whenever it has succeeded superior seamanship was exercised in handling the towing ship, the speed of towing very low, or else sea and weather conditions were favorable.

The Conventional Steam Towing Machine

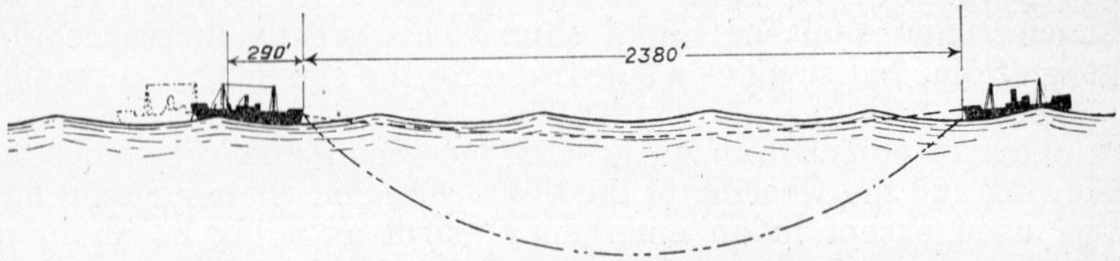

S. S. Iroquois Towing the Barge Navahoe, 2700 Foot Tow Line.
Length of Hawser 2700 Feet.

Hawser Stress Lbs.	*Span, Air Line*	*Sag or Dip*
10,000	*2380 ft.*	*514 ft.*
30,000	*2650 ft.*	*205 ft.*
50,000	*2660 ft.*	*124 ft.*
80,000	*2670 ft.*	*78 ft.*

The conventional steam towing machine as a contribution to the art of deep sea towing is well illustrated by the Standard Oil Tanker *Iroquois* regularly towing the Standard Oil Barge *Navahoe* and indicates that there remains much to be desired.

The *Iroquois* has a gross tonnage of 9201 tons, 2500 indicated horsepower, and a maximum speed (alone) of 12.79 knots. The Barge *Navahoe* has a gross tonnage of 7718 tons and is equipped with sail power.

Both the *Iroquois* and *Navahoe* have commercial steam towing machines, near the stern of the former and the bow of the latter. Towing is done with two parallel 7″ (circ.) steel wire hawsers of (about) 342,000 lbs. ultimate strength.

These towing machines have two 18″ x 20″ steam cylinders and a winding drum to hold 500 fathoms (3000 feet) of 2¼″ (diameter) or 7″ (circ.) steel hawser. This hawser weighs about 13 tons alone. Each towing machine weighs about 27 tons.

In rough water these hawsers are paid out to 450 fathoms (2700 ft.) and the speed of towing is only 5 to 6 knots.

To tow the Barge *Navahoe* 6 knots in smooth seas, should not require stress in both hawsers of more than 18,000 lbs., that is to say, 9000 lbs. stress per hawser, but this assumes that the hawser itself was not dragging through the water.

Calculating the sag or dip of each 7″ (circ.) hawser at 10,000 lbs. stress shows the hawser sagging down below the water 300 to 500 feet. The sag of these two hawsers produces an increased resistance to towing estimated at 12,000 pounds which is wholly wasted. Such a sag or dip could not be thought of along the Grand Banks of Newfoundland nor along most of our own coasts. It cannot be accepted as a solution of the problem of deep sea towing.

With 10,000 lbs. stress in hawser and 342,000 lbs. ultimate strength, we have a factor of safety of 34, indicating that the hawser gets some serious overstrains even though two steam towing machines are used.

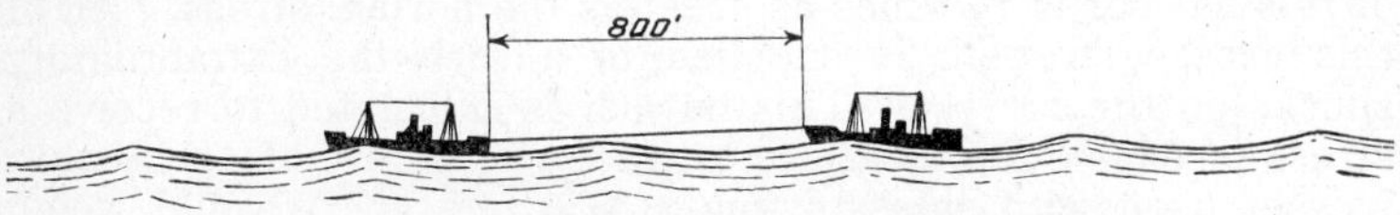

Towing a Barge with the Automatic Tension Engine.

The Theory of the Conventional Steam Towing Machine. There is a great deal of misconception respecting the conventional steam towing machine; one is that it maintains a uniform tension in the hawser, paying out rope under an increased stress and winding it in under diminished stresses. Nothing is further from the truth, for according to the statements of the manufacturers the variation in stress may be 500 per cent or even 600 per cent.

In the usual steam towing machines, the operations follow in rapid sequence, as follows:

A heavy wave strikes the towed barge (steam pressure 10 to 20 lbs. on the towing machine). An extra stress is produced in the hawser. This overhauls the towing engine and its drum; this in turn by suitable mechanical connection opens the steam valve. This is followed by a great increase in the flow and pressure of the steam in the cylinders (up to 125 lbs. at times) which greatly increases the hawser stress. The purpose and intent of the design is to build up the steam pressure (and consequently the hawser stress) to prevent paying out too much hawser.

The theory of the automatic tension engine is that the ship cannot be restrained by the hawser to an appreciable degree, hence it is more practicable to give it the hawser it demands and not permit the hawser stress to increase. This and this alone permits the use of small short towing hawsers.

An examination of indicator cards taken by Mr. Wilkie, Chief Engineer of the *Iroquois* and printed in Mr. Kemble's paper (Naval Architects & Marine Engineers, June 1909), shows that the steam pressure in the cylinders of the towing machines varied from a minimum of 10 lbs. to a maximum of 125 lbs.—quite sufficient to show that with the conventional steam towing machine the hawser stress varies all of 600 per cent. This is towing by jerks.

Big Hawsers

The usual steam towing machine demands a hawser of the same weight, same strength, and practically the same length as before. The hawser that towed the *U. S. S. Maumee* (14,500 tons) eight knots was 2¼" in diameter, its ultimate strength was 342,000 lbs. The normal stress to tow the *U. S. S. Maumee* eight knots would be about 18,000 lbs. The ultimate strength of this hawser is 19 times as great as the normal stress. All of this excess strength is supplied to absorb the extraordinary shocks on the hawser. This hawser is calculated to receive a stress of 85,000 lbs. at times—a factor of safety of 4. Such a hawser used with ships towing at 850 feet apart would weigh 6800 pounds and have a normal sag of 40 feet when towing 18,000 lbs. Frequently the distance between ships is increased sufficient to drag the hawser on the shallow bottoms of much of the waters along our coast. This explains why many hawsers give out near the middle of their length.

A light hawser 1¼" in diameter with an automatic tension engine under the same conditions would sag only 12 feet and in the case of the *U. S. S. Prometheus* and *U. S. S. Maumee* would be wholly out of the water at all times. It would never slacken enough to strike the water, because the automatic tension engine has an available speed of take-up exceeding the speed with which hawser may slacken.

It has been said that the hawser on the commercial steam towing machine does not fail at the drum, but at some other point. This may be accounted for in three ways:

1. Dragging on bottom
2. Chafing on rollers and chocks
3. Bending on small drums

The rope winding on the drum, and paying off from the drum, is alternately bent (bending stress about 20 tons) and straightened, this rapidly weakening the wires of the hawser. When a surge comes on the hawser, the steam towing machine starts to pay out (under reduced steam) easily, the stress being perhaps 20,000 lbs. The steam pressure builds up rapidly, after some of the hawser has been paid out, to the strain of perhaps 100,000 lbs. It is, therefore, clear that the part of the hawser, partly destroyed by the bending, is off the drum at the time the maxmum stress occurs. This is one fact, but we have another serious difficulty incidental to big heavy hawsers sliding on chocks, rails, guards, etc. It is the great weight of the big hawsers that is responsible for the serious chafing and accounts for a large part of the wear. Bending and chafing cause the destruction—and that part of the rope off the drum is chafed worse than the part that is on, and hence is the first to give way.

Towing with the Automatic Tension Engine

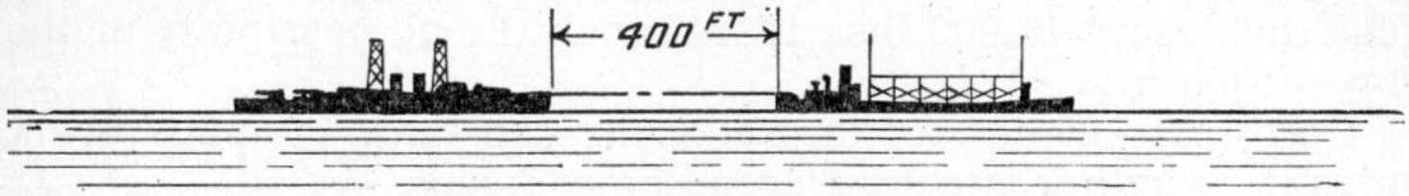

U. S. S. Cyclops Towing U. S. S. Wyoming—Using Automatic Tension Engine
Towing line—400 ft.—3″ circ. wire rope—wt., 2520 lbs.
Hawser stress—18,000 lbs.—normal sag—2 ft.
Towing speed—$4\frac{1}{3}$ knots.

The automatic tension engine on the U. S. Collier *Cyclops* towed the battleship *Wyoming* (26,000 tons) at a speed of $4\frac{1}{3}$ knots, using only 100 fathoms of 1″ diameter steel hawser. The calculated tow line pull for this speed is 9,000 pounds plus the resistance due to the drag of the propellers. The hawser stress was never greater than 18,000 lbs.

September 9th, 1915, the turbine propelled destroyer *O'Brien* 1174 tons (full load), was towed $9\frac{1}{2}$ knots by the U. S. Collier *Cyclops* using the same automatic tension engine and a 1″ diameter wire rope. The test lasted four hours, tension in line 17,000 to 18,000 pounds.

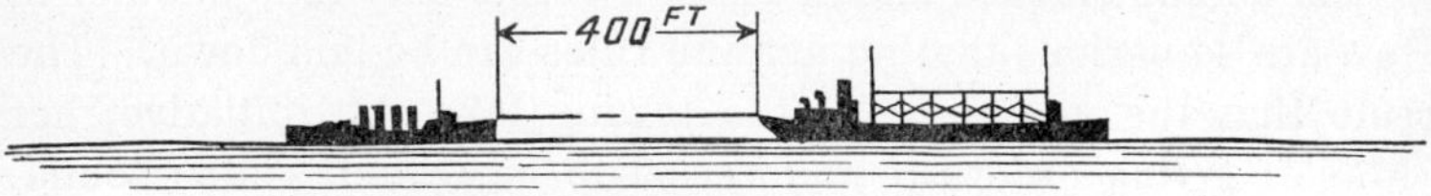

U. S. S. Cyclops Towing U. S. S. O'Brien—Using Automatic Tension Engine.
Towing line, 400 ft.—3″ circ. wire rope—wt., 2520 lbs.
Hawser stress, 18,000 lbs.—normal sag, 2 ft.
Towing speed, $9\frac{1}{2}$ knots.

This might be contrasted with the failure in towing of the *Perry* (one half of the weight of the *O'Brien*) practically at the same speed, using 130 fathoms of 10″ manila hawser, coupled with 30 fathoms of anchor chain.

Again the *U. S. S. Vermont*, 16,000 tons, was towed by the *U. S. S. Delaware* using 300 fathoms of 2″ diameter steel hawser and 45 fathoms of chain, $3\frac{1}{2}$ to 5 knots; contrast this with the *U. S. S. Wyoming*, 26,000 tons, towed by the *Cyclops* $4\frac{1}{3}$ knots using less than 100 fathoms of 1″ diameters steel hawser and the automatic tension engine.

If the *Cyclops*, with its present equipment, was at sea with a disabled ship of the size of the *Vermont*, the *Cyclops* could easily tow it to safety at a speed of 5 to 6 knots. The hawser could be short for the required range of elastic extension resides in the engine. As the automatic tension engine pays out hawser for every stress exceeding 18,000 pounds and takes it up with less than (say) 17,000 lbs., there would be no possibility of the hawser parting.

The stress in hawser is practically constant. It pulls every instant—whether pitching, 'scending or rising.

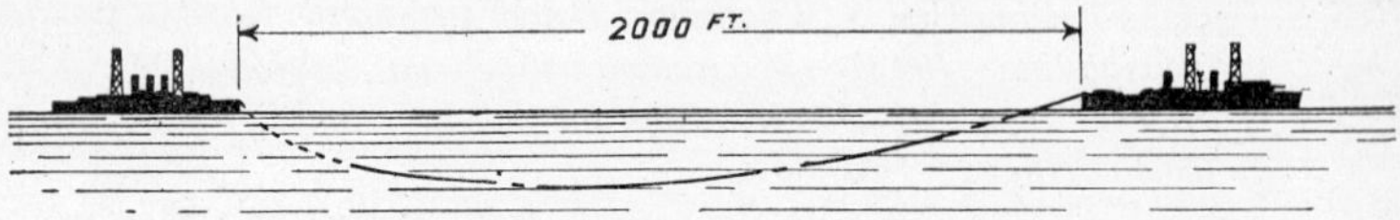

U. S. S. Delaware Towing U. S. S. Vermont.

Towing line	*270 ft.—2¼″ anchor chain........*	*wt. 14230 lbs.*
	1800 ft.—6″ circ. wire rope........	*wt. 10500 lbs.*
	2070 ft.	*24730 lbs.*

Hawser stress—18,000 lbs.—normal sag—200 ft.
Towing speed—5 knots (Maximum).

Neither the automatic tension engine nor its 1″ diameter steel-hawser (a3″ rope) has ever failed in any sea. It is jerk-proof.

Taking a Vessel in Tow

The circumstances under which a vessel may take another in tow are so various that no definite rules can be laid down. The rule that the vessel to do the towing take the initiative, her Master giving orders to the vessel to be towed, seems sound. Still, even here it may at times be necessary for the other Master to assume charge.

Before attempting to take another vessel in tow be certain that both Masters understand what is to be done and prepare for the operation before actually attempting to put a line across and connect by chain cable or otherwise.

Where both vessels are fitted with radio the plan of procedure can easily be agreed upon.

To get a line across, either use the Lyle gun, or drift a buoy down on the helpless vessel if the other craft can get to the weather side. Of course under moderate weather conditions a boat would be put overboard and communication made in that way.

A strong manila hawser should be put across *after* both vessels are ready with their bridles or other towing gear, and know just what is to be done.

When the tow line is finally across and all is ready, the general opinion is that the vessel to do the towing should point four or five points away from the tow and bring the stress on the line straightening out the two vessels and starting the tow. This brings the tow line into action without giving it a direct load at once, the pull being expended in turning the tow and starting her through the water at the same time.

Stowage of Wire Lines

Wire towing and handling lines are generally kept on reels. Experience has demonstrated the danger of kinks and the unsatisfactory stiffness of wire when handling by hand. When not on reels the wire should be ranged along the deck, preferably fore and aft, in long clear fakes. Have *chain stoppers* fitted at the bitts where the wire is to belay.

Coiling of Manila Hawsers

The point to be remembered here is the quite general abuse of manila hawsers. Long lengths of hawser are coiled down close to the chocks or pipes through which it is to be payed out. Often the hawser is *flemished down*, that is, coiled flat and close together. A second tier of the same rope may be flemished on top of the bottom coil, riding between the lower rings of the coil. The close coil may often be necessary and the flemish coil looks nice, but when a hawser is payed out from a coil of this kind the end should be free. When the end is made fast, as to a tug, for instance, the line will either be filled with extra turns, as it goes out, or it will loosen up. In this connection it must be remembered that in taking turns out of the line, extra twist is put into the strands. Both conditions cause kinks, and do damage to the rope. Remember—*Kinks Kill Ropes*.

Manila hawsers should be carried on upright reels, where possible, these being fitted with canvas covers. This keeps the lines handy, prevents turns, and protects them from damp and dust.

When getting ready to pay out a hawser, coil down in large *figure-of-eight* coil, or if necessary, fake down, lapping the coils to avoid fouling. Pass out the hawser on a heaving line which will allow the end to revolve and take out the turns.

The *figure-of-eight* coil allows the hawser to run out without turns.

Casting Off A Tow

Where this is done without compulsion, the vessel towing slows down and as both vessels lose way the cable or hawser is rounded or hove in on the vessel being towed and when the two craft are reasonably close (do not get dangerously close), the line is cast off. Care should be taken not to cast off a long towline that may foul the propeller. A manila line may easily drift into the screw even though it is not turning over.

Abandoning a Tow

There is a well-recognized rule which warrants the master of a vessel in abandoning a tow, but it is a prime requisite that *the peril must be extreme* and that there must be sound reason for belief that to *hold fast to the tow would only cause the loss of both. Above this is the ethical law that human resource and ingenuity shall first have been invoked to the utmost to transfer the crew of the abandoned vessel.*

Wire Towing Hawsers

The American Bureau of Shipping has set the following requirements for the strength of towing and warping hawsers made of wire. These required wires are often referred to as the *insurance lines.*

Circumference of Steel Wire Rope	Breaking Test in Lbs.	Circumference of Steel Wire Rope	Breaking Test in Lbs.	Circumference of Steel Wire Rope	Breaking Test in Lbs.	Circumference of Steel Wire Rope	Breaking Test in Lbs.
1″	6,000	2½″	29,500	4½″	96,100	6¾″	216,400
1¼″	10,000	2⅝″	32,700	4¾″	107,000	7″	232,700
1½″	14,500	2⅞″	39,200	5″	118,720	7¼″	249,800
1⅝″	15,600	3″	42,700	5¼″	131,000	7½″	267,200
1⅞″	17,800	3¼″	50,100	5½″	143,600	7¾″	285,300
2″	18,800	3½″	58,200	5¾″	157,000	8″	303,900
2⅛″	21,200	3¾″	66,700	6″	170,900	8¼″	327,000
2¼″	24,000	4″	76,100	6¼″	185,500	8½″	347,200
2⅜″	26,700	4¼″	85,700	6½″	200,700	8¾″	367,300

The use of special flexible steel wire rope will be approved provided it is of not less strength than the ordinary steel wire rope.

Towing Regulations

Towing of barges has become an increasingly important method of transportation and certain rules are set down for the regulation of this business. Under some conditions these long tows are a danger as well as a nuisance. Tows in inland waters are limited to four vessels including the tug or towing vessel. This of course also limits deep sea towing as the tow must traverse inland waters first. The regulations follow.

1. Tows of seagoing barges navigating the inland waters of the United States are limited in length to four vessels, including the towing vessel or vessels.

2. Hawsers are limited in length to 75 fathoms, measured from the stern of one vessel to the bow of the following vessel; and should in all cases be as much shorter as the weather or sea will permit.

3. In cases where the prescribed length of hawser is, in the opinion of the master of the towing vessel, dangerous on account of the state of weather or sea, hawsers need not be shortened to that length until reaching the localities named below:

(*a*) Tows bound for Hampton Roads or beyond, before passing Thimble Light.

(*b*) Tows bound up the Chesapeake, to the northward of Baltimore Light.

(*c*) Tows bound up the Delaware, between Fourteen Foot Bank and Cross Ledge lighthouses.

Hawsers may also be lengthened in the same places, under the same circumstances, when tows are bound out.

4. In case of necessity, on account of wind or weather, hawsers of vessels navigating between Race Rock and Gay Head may be lengthened out in the discretion of the master of the towing vessel; but this paragraph shall not apply to Narragansett Bay north of Beavertail Light.

5. In all cases where tows can be bunched it should be done.

(*a*) Tows navigating in the North and East Rivers of New York must be bunched above a line drawn between the Statue of Liberty and the entrance to Erie Basin. When tows are entering Long Island Sound from the westward, the lines may be lengthened out to the prescribed length after passing Fort Schuyler; and when bound for New York from Long Island Sound tows must be bunched before passing Whitestone Point.

(*b*) Tows must be bunched above the mouth of the Schuylkill River, Pa.

6. Section 15 of the act approved May 28, 1908, provides:

That the master of the towing vessel shall be liable to the suspension or revocation of his license for any willful violation of regulations issued pursuant to section 14 in the manner now prescribed for incompetency, misconduct, or unskillfulness.

7. Any violation of these regulations shall be reported in writing as soon as practicable to the Board of Local Inspectors of Steam Vessels most convenient to the officer or other person who may witness the violation.

The use of oil when towing is illustrated under the subject of Handling a Steamer in Heavy Weather.*

* In order to get an equipment rating from the *American Bureau of Shipping* vessels must carry towline ranging from ninety fathoms in length for a thousand-ton vessel (equipment tonnage), 150 fathoms in length for a 17,700 ton vessel and over. The size and kind of towline is also specified. From

Running Short of Bunker Fuel

The subject of towing brings to mind that nightmare of bad luck, or poor management, known to steamer-sailors as *fuel fever.* The author recalls a passage from Hilo toward Coronel, later on directed toward Callao, when the *S. S. American*, bucking head winds and current, and with grass trailing from her bottom, struggled toward the South American shore. She arrived at the Peruvian port with swept bunkers. In this instance good seamanship, and judgment, overcame adverse conditions. Had she held a day longer on the route to Coronel she never would have fetched Callao by burning coal.

Captain E. L. Yates writes as follows in the *Oracle* of the Oriental Navigation Co.—

" Most men will, at some time in their experience, have been up against the gruelling anxiety of fuel shortage. Before the war, if a shipmaster or chief engineer arrived at a home port with more than two or three days' fuel left in his bunkers, he was either keel-hauled or sacked by his owners for having bought too much expensive fuel abroad in comparison with the prices ruling for same at the home ports. As a consequence of the fears of losing their berth through this cause, many chances were taken which would otherwise be avoided if a little more latitude were allowed them.

"A famous passage or run where fuel fever has dragged the sweat out of the bodies of masters and chief engineers is that from Cape Verde Islands to Grand Canary. The distance is only a matter of 850 miles, but vessels on a voyage from the River Plate to Europe usually go carefully into the question of bunkers on board the day previous to passing Cape Verde, and if the quantity remaining is too bare to make the 850 miles, they usually put into St. Vincent, Cape Verde, for an extra day's fuel.

"These islands lie in the direct track of the North-East Trade winds, and often enough the winds have appeared comparatively moderate when the vessel is in the vicinity of St. Vincent and many a man has figured on such conditions continuing as far as Grand Canary, but probably after clearing north of the Cape Verde you run into a half gale of head winds and heavy sea with the ship bobbing three times in the same hole, and many a ship

1,000 to 10,300 tons the sizes run as follows: Hemp (manila) from 10 inch to 17 inch and from 90 fathoms to 140 fathoms. Wire 3¼ inch to 6½ inch. The vessel may be equipped with either one. From 11,200 tons to 26,500 tons the hawser must be of steel wire running from 6½ inch to 8¾ inch and in length from 140 fathoms to 150 fathoms.

Sailing craft are required to have similar towing lines. The largest sailing craft, about 5,000 equipment tons will carry a towline 120 fathoms long and either of 13½ inch manila or 4½ inch steel wire.

has done one third of the distance against these conditions and found he has just enough fuel left to run back. If he runs back he gets the sack and if he foolishly tries to push on, hoping for better weather ahead, he runs out of fuel short of his coaling port and is towed in by one of the fortunates who have plenty of fuel and are always hoping for a salvage tow with its consequent prize awards."

Captain Lecky in *Wrinkles in Practical Navigation* (pages 675–6) gives several examples on the relation between coal consumption, speed, and distance.

The courts have held a vessel *unseaworthy* which did not bunker 25 per cent more fuel than her anticipated requirements.

IX

Coaling at Sea

Under certain conditions it may be necessary to transfer coal from one vessel to another while under way at sea. The following illustrations supplied through the courtesy of the Lidgerwood Company serve to make clear the general method of procedure.

The Marine Cableway

This apparatus, the first marine cableway, was installed on the U. S. Collier *Marcellus,* and tested during the fall of *1899*, delivering coal to *U. S. S. Massachusetts.*

It was designed to transfer from collier to warship (300 feet between ships) 15 tons of coal per hour in moderate sea and weather. It actually transferred over 22 tons per hour, in a sea heav-

Collier Marcellus rising on a sea.

Collier Marcellus plunging.

ier than moderate, with 400 feet between ships.

In the rough sea test with the ships head-on to the sea, the forecastle of the *Massachusetts* being washed at every plunge, a little over 20 tons were handled in an hour. When the course was changed, quartering on the sea, the results were the same. With the ships steered in the trough of the sea the rolling did not affect the working. The towing speed was five to six knots, load, 840 pounds; conveyor speed, 1200 feet per minute; actual capacity, 22 tons per hour.

The first picture shows the Collier *Marcellus* rising on a sea. The second one shows her plunging. Note the equal tension on towline and cableway under both conditions.

The *Cyclops—South Carolina* Trials

This test was made on April 12, 1913. The contract called for a delivery of 480 tons of coal in a period of eight hours. The mechanism was operated for six hours under most unfavorable conditions of weather and was pronounced a success. The maximum amount of fuel transferred within an hour was 83 tons. The test was conducted for four hours, or long enough to convince the naval board that the system would answer all the purposes of the service. The transfer of coal from the Cyclops to the South Carolina at sea in a driving rain with the collier rolling 20 degrees was preceded by a dock trial.

Under this improved system of coaling at sea all of the gear is installed on the collier.

It will be noted that in this trial the collier had the battleship in tow, or at least with a nominal tension on the towing cable.

The plant includes an automatic tension engine, which maintains a tension on the main cable sufficient for carrying the load from ship to ship. There are two conveying engines for hauling the load, and even the mast necessary to erect on the coal-receiving ship is carried, when not in use, on board the collier.

The regular winches and regular gear of the battleship are used to lower the bags to the battleship's deck, making it possible for a collier to tie up to any battleship and coal. The fuel is delivered at the rate of five or six bags, carrying 700 to 800 pounds on each trip, or a total delivery of 3,500 or 4,000 pounds. The rate of delivery is from 50 to 60 seconds in a distance of 500 feet between the collier and the battleship, which in the recent test were steaming at the rate of from 7 to 8 knots.

More coal was transferred than ever before, and justified the opinion, freely expressed by naval observers who witnessed the test, that the cableway as easily capable of a delivery of 100 tons per hour. It was also observed that the best record was in the last hour of the test, which showed that the machine did not have a fatiguing effect upon the men.

In the test, the tension of the engine was 17,000 to 18,000 pounds and never showed the slightest disposition to slacken nor unduly tauten the main cable.

On the warship end a " let-down system " is employed. The warship end of the main cable is attached to a bridle, the ends of which bridle are attached to the deck of the battleship, well aft. A block and fall raises the end of the main cable, as well as the joining point of the bridle. By this means the carriage and cable are raised and lowered at the warship end.

X

Bunkering Fuel Oil at Sea

In bunkering fuel oil to a battleship at sea the battleship is taken in tow by the fuel ship. A short " A " frame is mounted near the bow of the battleship, guyed back and well secured. One end of a supporting cable for the oil hose is anchored to this " A " frame. The other end of the supporting cable is wound on the drum of the tension engine on the fuel ship. It is desirable to carry the supporting sheave for this cable on the fuel ship well forward, and consequently quite high. The oil hose is then passed across from the fuel ship, being supported from the cable by hangers properly spaced. The supporting cable being well above the deck of the fuel ship a clear lead for the oil hose can readily be obtained to the oil pump. The last supporting hanger will be about over the bow of the battleship, the oil hose dropping from there to the deck, and running to the bunker coupling.

A steel supporting cable of 1″ diameter, at a tension of about 18,000 lbs. will support above the sea a 5″ hose, with the ships a distance of 400 feet apart. While the automatic tension engine is used to pay out and take in the hose supporting cable, its most important function is to maintain a uniform tension in this supporting cable, and prevent any lashing of the hose in moderate or rough seas.

In any seaway sufficient to cause pitching of the vessels the distance between them continually increases and decreases. If both ends of the supporting cable were fixed or if the conventional steam towing machine were used this action of the ships would produce repeated variations in the tension of the supporting cable, which would in turn cause corresponding changes in the deflection. The result would be a continual lashing up and down of the oil hose, greatly impeding the flow of oil, reducing the hourly capacity, with a strong probability of parting both the hose and the supporting cable.

U. S. Collier Cyclops Transferring Fuel Oil to Battleship in Tow.

The automatic tension engine absolutely prevents any variations of the tension in the supporting cable, and consequently keeps the deflection constant and eliminates the lashing of the oil hose. The engine is adjusted to maintain uniformly whatever tension is necessary in the supporting cable. If the pitching of the ships increases the distance between them the tension engine automatically pays out more supporting cable, if the distance decreases, it automatically takes in cable, no change of tension is permitted in the cable, and therefore there is no variation in the deflection, and no lashing of the oil hose.

Receiving Oil Hose on Board Battleship.

The illustrations show a test made of this apparatus between the *U. S. S. Wyoming* and the U. S. Collier *Cyclops* at sea, August 26th, 1915. The hose was passed from ship to ship along the supporting cable, coupled up, and oil was flowing in eight minutes. At no time did the hose touch the intervening water.

To sum up its uses the automatic tension engine is the essential element in the marine cableway for

Coaling Warships in a Seaway, whether installed on battleships or colliers.

The automatic tension engine is useful as a heavy boat hoisting machine. It will hoist boats without the shocks commonly incident to the use of the ordinary hoisting machine.

Supporting an Oil Hose between two ships fuel bunkering at sea. The desirability in a heavy sea of this engine to maintain a uniform tension in the hose supporting line, to prevent the hose from lashing up and down in a seaway, will be readily appreciated.

Life Saving at Sea. The addition of the automatic tension engine to a ship carrying the ordinary breeches buoy apparatus enables passengers to be rescued from wrecks in seas far too heavy to permit the use of life boats.

Towing at Sea. The automatic tension engine is ideal for towing. See section on towing. Pages 680 to 688.

Salvage Work. The difficulty of raising sunken ships when the sea is rough is well recognized. The ability to compensate for the motion of the salvage ship in a heavy sea by automatically controlling the tension in the lines attached to the sunken vessel gives to the automatic tension engine special usefulness.

Handling Guns and Supplies. The automatic tension engine on a ship can maintain a line in suspension between the ship and shores to which vessel cannot approach closely, and where boat landings are difficult. Guns, ammunition and supplies can be landed by a trolley carriage running over this line.

Warping Ship. The automatic tension engine used as a warping winch absolutely regulates and controls the tension in the warping lines. The danger of parting the lines is reduced and far smaller lines can be used.

Commander H. C. Dinger, U.S.N., in a valuable paper printed in the *Proceedings of the U. S. Naval Institute* of September, 1919, advocates fueling at sea by towing abreast rather than astern.

We quote from this paper as follows:

" It is a comparatively easy operation to take a vessel in tow and maintain her position—a steady almost exact position —well clear of the side. With a vessel maintained in this position, coal can be transferred by bags from boom ends, or by means of movable pipes from fuel vessels fitted with coaling towers.

" As far as is known, the first actual oiling of vessels at sea in rough weather was done by the U. S. S. *Maumee* in May, 1917, when a division of destroyers was oiled on the way across the Atlantic.

" The gear used was as follows:

" A 10-inch manila line was led from the bow of the fuel vessel, taken outboard and stopped along the rail; a 2-inch messenger was bent on the end. Two 6-inch breast lines were provided with heaving lines. Two 3-inch lines of oil hose were connected to the oil line, and were supported on a wooden carrier suspended from boom end, the line supporting this carrier being led to a winch, and tended by winch man.

" The manner of coming alongside, taking lines, etc., is indicated in the instructions prepared for the occasion, quoted as follows:

" Prepared on U. S. S. *Maumee* for Guidance of Destroyers Oiling at Sea

" 1. *Gear.* All supplied by fuel ship.

" *10-Inch Bow Spring.* This line is led from the bow of the fuel ship and stopped along the rail; a 2-inch messenger is bent on about 50 feet from end and stopped along to end. This line should be taken in on destroyer bow through bitts just forward of bridge. Take messenger to capstan and assist handling by hand; cut stops as they come to bitts. Take turn around base of gun mount as indicated on sketch and secure end to bitts on opposite side. Be sure that hawser is secure around base so that it will not ride up on mount. As soon as end is secured notify fuel ship, which will then heave in to place destroyer in proper position. Put lashings around and over bitts to prevent hawser jumping.

" 2. *Breast Lines, 6-Inch.* Forward, take in through bitts forward of forward gun, then to bitts forward of capstan. Do not secure to capstan as it may be damaged. This line *must* be securely fastened as a very heavy strain may come on it.

" 3. *After Line.* Take through bitts in wake of deck house, secure, and stand by to tend.

" 4. *Hose.* The hose, two lines, are led together through a wooden carrier supported from boom. Near end of hose, there is a wooden yoke to which is attached a handling line. The hose should be handled on board destroyer with this line, not with end of hose. Rail should be broken down and clear where hose is taken on board. Get ends of hose and hose yoke on destroyer, secure yoke and then put ends of hose in tanks. Pumping will start as soon as destroyer reports ready.

" 5. *Handling of Destroyer.* Come along on parallel course, speed about 8 knots, distance about 50 feet from fuel ship; slow down to keep abreast fuel ship, ease in or out as necessary, but do not drop aft too far and get under counter. When 10-inch spring is fast, drop down on it slightly and let fuel vessel take in on breast lines till desired position is reached, about 40 feet from side, then maintain about 4 knots, just keeping slight or occasional strain on 10-inch spring. Destroyer will then ride to 10-inch spring and forward breast. Do not head out suddenly as this will break away the forward breast. Speed up if necessary to take strain off 10-inch spring and keep from swinging in too close.

" The breast lines keep the destroyer in and prevent hose being carried away. Destroyers can come abreast and make connections in moderate sea without danger if precautions mentioned are adhered to. The principal danger is coming too close and throwing stern in. There is a suction under counter and destroyer should keep out of this. A speed of about 5 knots is maintained by fuel ship. This is necessary in order to steady fuel vessel and enable her to steer a straight course. The fuel vessel must steer a straight course; rolling is not objectionable, but yawing is,—hence sea should be abeam or slightly forward of beam.

" 6. Before coming alongside destroyer should have her forecastle clear, rail clear for hose, have lashings ready, capstan ready and men instructed where the lines are to be led. Lines must be *very* securely fastened.

" In smooth weather one destroyer can be taken on each side, and in calm, destroyers can make fast and receive oil as in port.

" The first time that this was tried was in a moderate sea, as the attached photograph will indicate. The destroyers were each oiled in about two hours, and oil was delivered at from 30,000 to 40,000 gallons an hour. In some cases destroyers were connected up and oil being pumped on board in 15 minutes from the time the destroyer passed the stern of fuel vessel, this being done with a vessel that had never previously gone through the operation. With practice, a destroyer could no doubt connect up in 10 minutes.

"In rough sea the fuel vessel makes a lea, taking sea a little forward of beam. In smooth weather a destroyer can be taken on each side while steaming 8 to 10 knots, one vessel connecting up while the other is having oil delivered. When towing abreast, both vessels are entirely and instantly under full control of their engines and helm. Lines can be cast adrift without danger of fouling screws. The whole operation can be viewed by the captain from the bridge of each vessel, and the two vessels are in direct verbal communication *all* of the time that they are close to each other. In towing astern or from the quarter, this is not the case, and unless the officer in control of either vessel can see fully what the other is doing, difficulties are likely to be presented.

"With fuel vessels thus arranged as mentioned above, a fleet can maintain the sea indefinitely. Fueling cannot be attempted in very rough weather, but a fairly smooth sea can usually be found in the course of several days, except in specially tempestuous waters.

"The method employed with destroyers can be used for much larger vessels, though perhaps it could not be done in as rough a sea."

XI

Handling a Steamer or Motor Vessel in Heavy Weather

A vessel with power presents no special difficulty in heavy weather unless cargo has shifted, or she is loaded too deep, or is unseaworthy because of other defects.

The usual precautions should be taken on the approach of heavy weather. Look after all hatch covers, ventilator openings, lashings, boats, and loose gear. On the approach of extra heavy weather, stays and shrouds should be examined and booms securely lashed to their beds. If cargo gear is rove off, either send it down or lash it securely to the masts.

See that oil tanks are working and that they are filled. Have oil bags ready on the bridge with a supply of oil for immediate use.

See that steering gear is in order, that relieving gear, if fitted, is ready to be thrown in.

See that anchors are secure, and that all openings to chain locker are water tight.

Sound all tanks and bilges. Know the condition of trim of the vessel. Avoid half empty or *swash* tanks.

If just leaving port make certain that no loose skids, or spars are about the decks. The well decks will fill up and such heavy gear, washing about, may be very dangerous. *Rig life lines.*

Awnings, if bent, should be unbent, or at lease secured by extra gasgets. Sails, if bent should be fitted with preventer gear and securely furled, but ready for use if needed.

See that all ports are securely closed, in the forecastle and poop as well as in the deck cabins.

Where heavy steel doors are fitted to the forward and after ends of the superstructure have these closed and securely fastened.

Have fiddley tarpaulins ready and batten down in the event of extra heavy weather.

A water spout breaking over the ship might flood the engine and fire rooms.

Most of these precautions pertain to extra heavy weather, to typhoons in the China and Indian Seas, or to hurricanes off the West Indies.

Even a vessel of second rate ability, if properly handled, will ride through the worst weather that is liable to come along. Do not be afraid to take precautions.

Heaving To

The method of procedure during extra heavy weather, when a vessel cannot make way against the wind and sea without shipping dangerous quantities of water, admits of two general divisions.

Heaving to, head *toward* the sea and steaming slowly *against* the storm, or at least making way enough to keep steerage on the vessel.

Heaving to with the quarter toward the wind and slowly moving *away* from the storm.

Very often the method of heaving to must be determined by the position of the vessel with regard to the storm center. She will then be headed with the wind on the bow or quarter so as to soonest avoid contact with the center.*

Other conditions may prevail. It may be necessary to head in a certain direction, regardless of storm center or the easy riding of the vessel. A course may have to be made to avoid dangerous shoals or the land.

*See Chapter 20—Weather at Sea.

Some vessels will lie best with the wind on the bow, others seem to make better weather of it with the wind on the quarter. Short vessels as a rule take more kindly to a heavy sea. They dip and roll with the sea but ship less water than long craft that cut into the crests or sink into them depending upon how they are riding.

In most long vessels the favorable position for extra heavy weather is found by bringing the sea aft and stopping engines, or only turning them over slowly, and by streaming oil in the wake. Backing the engines slowly has also been tried with success.

Engines Disabled. Sea Anchors

A vessel slowly steaming before a storm may maintain her position when engines are disabled by the drag of the propellers, and if need be by putting a sea anchor over the stern. A storm staysail rigged on the foremast serves as an extra precaution against broaching to.

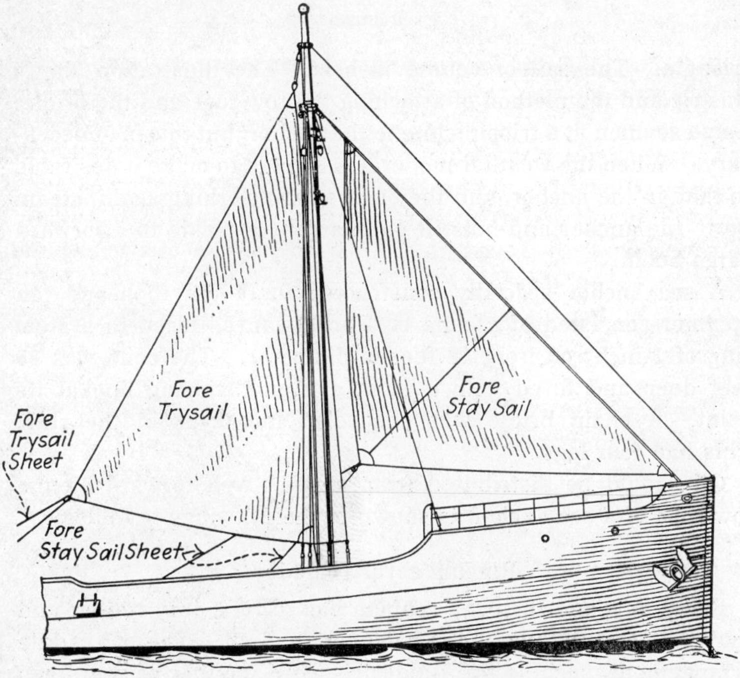

Sail is still very useful at times. A similar rig is fitted on mainmast.

With head to the sea, the usual practice is to improvise a drag or sea anchor. Formerly an iron ring and canvas cone was carried but this rig is no longer required. A sea anchor can easily be constructed by any experienced seaman. Spare cargo booms, a few lengths of stream chain and a spare storm staysail, or a stout tarpaulin, folded and stopped across in the form of a

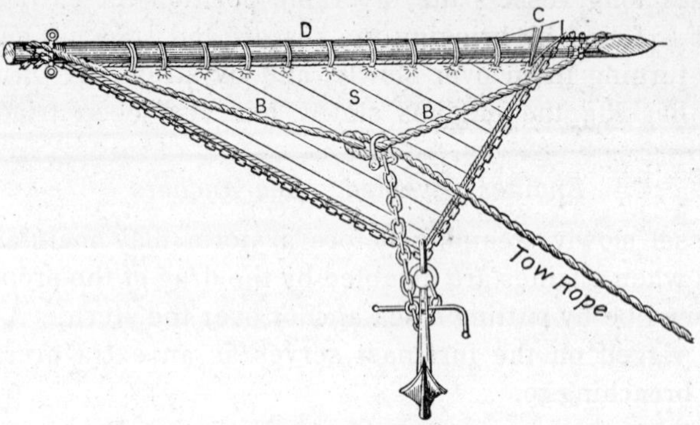

A sea anchor.

triangle. The sail of course is best. The illustration shows this rig and the method of attaching the tow rope and the bridle. Some seamen fit a tripping line to the anchor, but this is unnecessary. When the weather moderates enough to make it desirable to take in the anchor, and the engines are working again, steam up to the anchor and hoist it on board by a tackle to a forward cargo boom.

A sea anchor specially constructed for a ten thousand ton steamer consisted of a cone of No. 00 canvas laced to a steel ring of 1-inch rod iron, 18 feet in diameter. The cone was 25 feet deep and fitted with a stout eye and tripping line at its point. A chain bridle was shackeled into eyes in the ring. This had four legs.

Oil should be distributed from a point well forward on the tow rope of a sea anchor as shown in the drawings to follow.

Rigging a Jury Rudder

Every now and then the seaman has to rig a jury rudder and by " the seaman " we mean engineers and all. The old paddle arrangement, such as the rudder rigged a number of years ago on the *S. S. Ramsdal* (1,535 gross tons), Capt. O. A. Hirsch, worked very well for a small craft. With the big ten thousand tonner, and over, a more substantial rig is needed. With drills and cutting tools available and steel booms, a very substantial jury rudder can usually be devised. The sketch is an imaginary rig shown for the purpose of guiding the seaman in making a rough design should his rudder let go in mid-ocean. At least he should make every effort to provide a strong and workable rig.

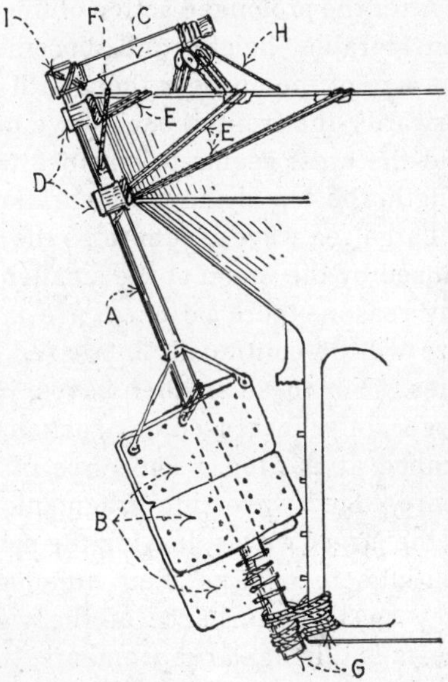

A—is a steel cargo boom cut to the required length. (Consult the blue prints for dimensions.) B—cargo hatch covers, or metal doors. C—length of boom, or other stout metal fitting, such as a strongback. D—upper bearings made to size by improvising pipe or other large round fittings. Bolted through holes cut in transom, and reinforced by wire lashings—E. F—a lashing, or pendant, to take the weight of the rudder. G—Heel lashing, of wire rope. A figure-of-eight lashing passed by sending down a man on a bowline, and heaving taut with a handy billy from the deck, after each turn is passed. H—steering tackles to deck winches. I—Rudder head lashing to reinforce the bolts and bands connecting the tiller C to the rudder stock A.

The work of preparing a jury rudder should be carefully planned. To bring a vessel in from mid-ocean under such a rig, without paying some other craft a fortune in salvage, would just about make the reputation of the Master and Chief Engineer who did the trick.

Note: Steering by drags is well known. Bridles from the quarter chocks usually afford too little leverage. Captain Levi J. Plesner, a master mariner qualified in sail and steam, has suggested the use of heavy cargo booms, well stayed, providing at least forty-eight feet of leverage for the steering bridle, enough to make a drag effective. With this idea in mind a seaman, knowing the forces involved, can figure the required strength of booms and gear.

XII

*Use of Oil to Calm the Sea**

Sea Waves. Sometimes there are three or four distinct series of waves existing on the sea within the same area at the same time, each series having a different direction from the others. Frequently the slopes of two or more happen to end at the same place and they unite to form a larger wave.

After the prolonged action of the wind, when the waves rise to a considerable height and become sharper and sharper, the passage of the air over them with high velocity bends the crests forward; the front of each wave becomes steeper than the back, and the crest seems to advance faster than the trough until, at length, the top of the wave curls over and breaks.

Large sea waves seem to be the result of a building-up process caused by the union of the smaller with the larger waves. If, by any reason, there be one wave larger than those around it, its size will be continually increased at the expense of the smaller ones. For these smaller waves, in passing over the crest of the larger, offer increased obstruction to the wind and become dart-shaped at the top. The force of the wind easily breaks these sharp-edged waves into fragments which go to increase the size of the larger waves, leaving the small ones yet smaller. So they continue to enlarge their dimensions and the depth to which they cause disturbance of the water until, with their foaming crests and irregular movements, they produce the confusion of a stormy sea.

Objects floating on the surface of such a sea are not carried along by the waves, except when they are struck by the loose masses of water from the breaking crests. A ship, one moment in the hollow of a large wave, is the next riding on its crest, and wave after wave rushes under her without driving her out of her course. In tidal estuaries, with the waves rolling in from the sea against the current of ebb tide, all mariners have often noticed floating objects continuing to pass out to sea against the inward passage of the waves.

So that these waves at sea, rushing along with a speed of many miles per hour, do not carry the water along with them. In fact

* Adapted from the bulletins of the U. S. Hydrographic Office.

the wave is the advancement of a mere form, and the motion of the particles of water is very different from the wave motion. Imagine a case in which the water has been suddenly heaped up by a gust of wind. The weight of the particles of water in the heap causes them to push forward the particles in front of them to a place farther on and there they come to rest, but the process of displacement continues from one to another successive mass of water until the displacing force is spent. As the particles of water crowd upon one another in going out of their old places into the new the crowd forms a temporary heap on the surface of the water, and, as each successive mass is displacing the mass in front of it, there is always one such heap moving along at the place where the displacement is going on, and made up always of another and another set of traveling particles. This moving crowd constitutes a true wave. The velocity of the wave is the velocity with which the heap is seen to move. Its form is the form of the heap. Its length is the distance from crest to crest, and its height is the distance from the level of the crest to the level of the hollow.

The tendency of the moving air to draw the water along when wind blows over the sea is much stronger than casual observation would suggest. There is no such condition as friction between air and water. So great is the adhesion between the two, that, when wind blows over water, the lowest layer of air remains in contact with the water, and it is to the tendency of the upper layers of air to draw this lowest one along that the effect of the wind to draw the surface of the water along is mainly due. A storm wind will exert a force of 51 grams per square meter upon the surface of the sea, and, when we consider that the particles in this surface are moving in their orbits, in the direction in which the force is exerted, with a velocity of about 1 meter per second, it will be apparent how powerful an effect the wind must have in causing the distortion of the crests of the waves.

To sum up, then, with a view of seeing what should be done to calm the violence of waves at sea, it is to be noted, first, that capillary waves, whose size and height depend upon the surface tension of the water, are the forerunners and upbuilders of regular sea waves; and, secondly, that as long as the wave mechanism is not disordered, that is, as long as the particles of water are allowed to move in their undisturbed orbits or paths, there is no breaking of the waves and vessels ride from hollow to crest without shocks and without shipping any water. Therefore, a substance, in order to be of use in subduing the violence of waves, should be capable (1) of spreading rapidly over the surface of the sea, (2) of making the tension of the exposed surface less than the surface-tension of water by as great an amount as possible, and (3) of forming, as a shield to the wave mechanism, a continuous surface film, whose particles are distinct from the particles of water and therefore do not share their orbital motion.

When a film of oil is spread over the surface of the water the heaping-up action, which, in the case of the water film, results in the formation of ripples, can not take place.

In the following table of surface tensions, given in grams per linear meter at 20° C., the liquids are named in that order which corresponds to the quickness with which they spread on the surface of a body of water:

Liquid	Specific Gravity	Tension of the Surface Separating the Liquid from		Sum	The Excess of the Tension Separating Air from Water over the Sum Stated in Column 5, or the Relative Spreading Force
		Air	Water		
Soapsuds	....	2.68	0.00	2.68	5.57
Sperm oil	....	3.39	.79	4.18	4.07
Oil of turpentine	0.887	3.03	1.18	4.21	4.04
Rapeseed oil	....	3.35	1.56	4.91	3.34
Linseed oil	....	3.34	1.70	5.04	3.21
Benzoin	....	3.12	1.97	5.09	3.16
Ricinus oil	....	3.83	1.62	5.45	2.80
Oil of almonds	....	3.52	2.07	5.59	2.66
Oil of olives	.914	3.76	2.10	5.86	2.39
Petroleum	.798	3.23	3.83	7.06	1.19
Water	1.000	8.25	.00	....	....

Of the substances named, petroleum spreads less rapidly than any of the others, its tendency to spread being only about one-half that of olive oil, one-third that of linseed oil, one-fourth that of sperm oil, and one-fifth that of soapsuds. This explains, in large part, why seamen have found it inferior to the other oils, especially those of animal and vegetable origin, for calming the sea.

According to theory, of all the liquids named, soap water is the best agent for preventing the growth of waves, both on account of its superior spreading power and the reduction of the surface tension that it brings about.

With respect to the oils, the table indicates that oil of turpentine is the best for spreading and reducing the tendency of the wind to form waves and increase their size. Moreover, oil appears to have a great advantage over soap water, since it weighs less than water and does not mix with it. These qualities enable it, when spread over the surface of water traversed by waves, to maintain itself as a distinct layer whose particles do not take up the orbital motion that the particles of water have in sea waves. Much of the efficacy of oil is due to the formation of this distinct layer with a definite surface cohesion between the particles of oil, for, as already pointed out, the wave mechanism is then to some extent protected from derangement, since in a sea wave the particles of water in the crest are moving forward in their orbits, or in the direction in which the wind is blowing when they reach the surface, and the tractive effect of the wind being brought to bear upon them at this point, causes the breaking of the crests and the consequent danger that is experienced in a stormy sea.

Brief Rules for the Use of Oil to Protect Vessels in Stormy Waters

[From the prize essay submitted to the Hamburg Nautical Union by Capt. R. Karlowa of the Hamburg-American Steamship Company. In the illustrative figures, the flowing lines represent the spreading oil and the arrows denote the direction of the wind and sea.]

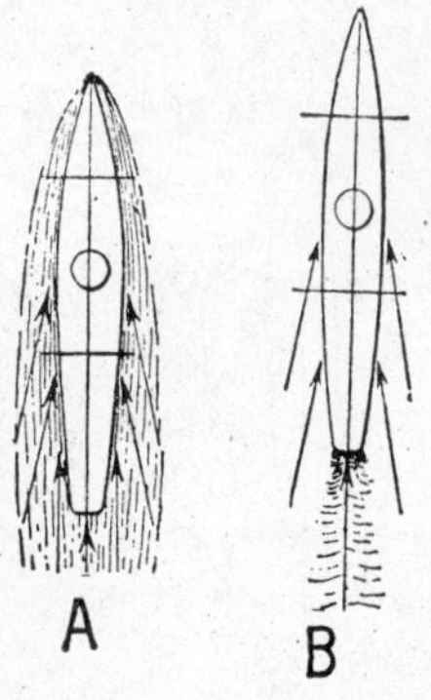

Scudding before a gale, figure A, distribute oil from the bow by means of oil bags or through waste pipes. It will thus spread aft and give protection both from quartering and following seas.

If only distributed astern, figure B, there will be no protection from the quartering sea.

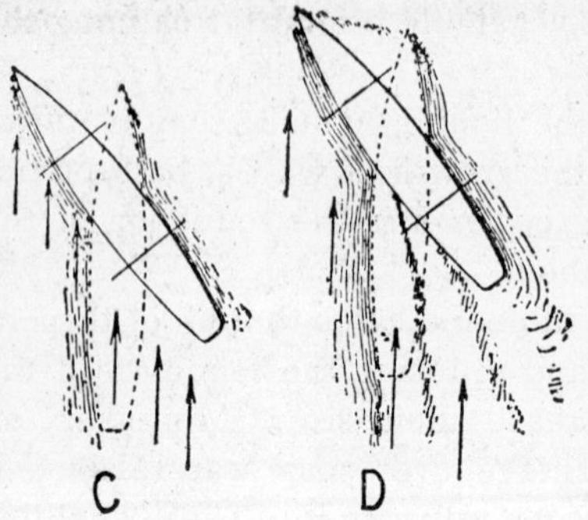

Running before a gale, yawing badly, and threatening to broach-to, figures C and D, oil should be distributed from the bow and from both sides, abaft, the beam.

In figure C, for instance, where it is only distributed at the bow, the weather quarter is left unprotected when the ship yaws.

In figure D, however, with oil bags abaft the beam as well as forward, the quarter is protected.

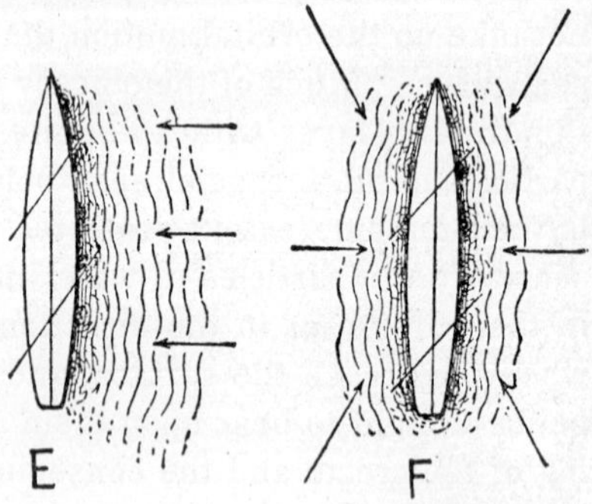

Lying-to, figure E, a vessel can be brought closer to the wind by using one or two oil bags forward, to windward. With a high beam sea, use oil bags along the weather side at intervals of 40 or 50 feet.

In a heavy cross sea, figure F, as in the center of a hurricane, or after the center has passed, oil bags should be hung out at regular intervals along both sides.

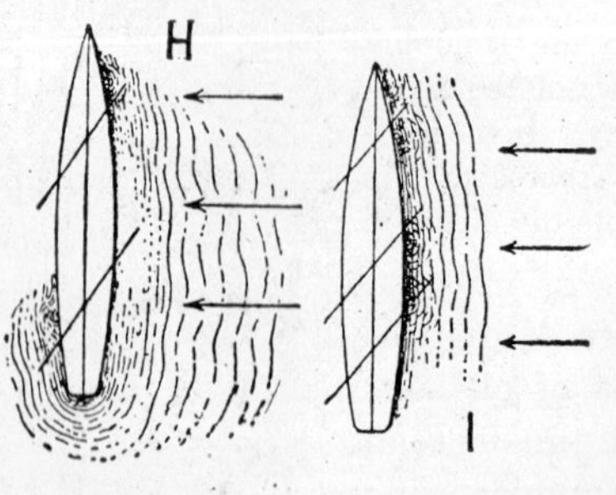

Drifting in the trough of a heavy sea, figures H and I, use oil from waste pipes forward and bags on weather side, as in figure I.

These answer the purpose very much better than one bag at weather bow and one at lee quarter, although this has been tried with some success, see figure H.

Steaming into a heavy head sea, figure G, use oil through forward closet pipes. Oil bags would be tossed back on deck.

Lying-to, to tack or wear, figure J use oil from weather bow.

Cracking on, with high wind abeam and heavy sea, figure K, use oil from waste pipes, weather bow.

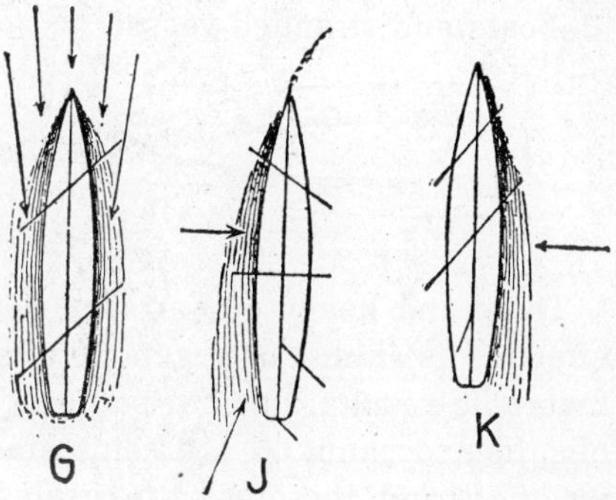

A vessel hove to for a pilot, figure L, should distribute oil from the weather side and lee quarter. The pilot boat runs up to windward and lowers a boat, which pulls down to leeward and around the vessel's stern. The pilot boat runs down to leeward, gets out oil bags to windward and on her lee quarter, and the boat pulls back around her stern, protected by the oil. The vessels drift to leeward and leave an oil-slick to windward between the two.

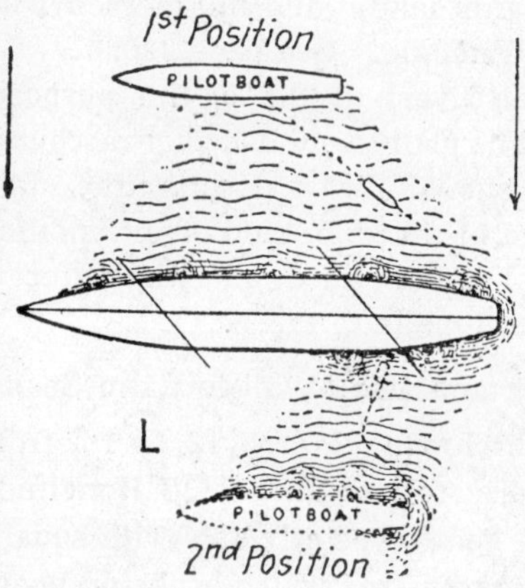

Towing another vessel in a heavy sea, oil is of the greatest service, and may prevent the hawser from breaking. Distribute oil from the towing vessel forward and on both sides, figure M. If only used aft, the tow alone gets the benefit.

At anchor in an open roadstead use oil in bags from jibboom, or haul them out ahead of the vessel by means of an endless rope

M

rove through a tailblock secured to the anchor chain, figure N.

In addition to the above, there are other cases where oil may be used to advantage, such as lowering and hoisting boats riding to a sea anchor, crossing rollers or surf on a bar, and from lifeboats and stranded vessels.

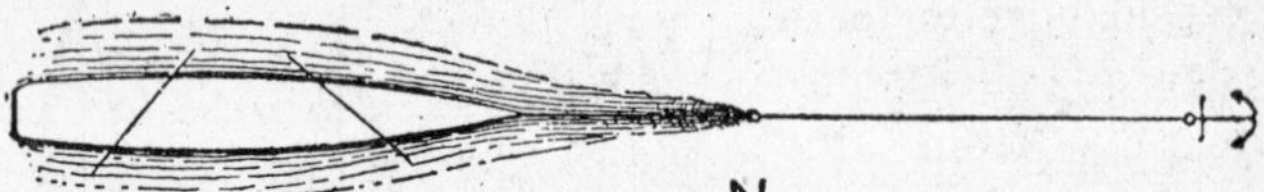

Thick and heavy oils are the best. Mineral oils are not so effective as animal or vegetable oils. Raw petroleum has given favorable results, but not so good when it is refined. Certain oils, like cocoanut oil and some kinds of fish oil, congeal in cold weather, and therefore are useless, but may be mixed with mineral oils to advantage.

The simplest method of distributing oil is by means of canvas bags about 1 foot long, filled with oakum and oil, pierced with holes by means of a coarse sail needle. See page 220.
The waste pipes forward are also very useful for this purpose.

The Hydrographic Office will be glad to publish short accounts of the use of oil. The reports should always describe the state and direction of the seas, speed of the ship, kind of oil, method and place of applying the same, amount used, and what effect it had. The following reports were made to the H. O.

Maneuvering before a Storm, and Use of Oil to Calm Seas

S. S. Monmouth, Captain Birchman—March 12 to 16, from latitude 43° 57′, longitude 39° 23′, to latitude 45° 30′, longitude 20° 28′, while running before a heavy westerly gale with squalls of hurricane force and high dangerous sea which broke on board on both sides, used oil with good effect from four bags, one on each side forward and one on each side on lower bridge suspended from spars extending 15 feet from the vessel's side. Oil was also used from the closet pipes.

Schooner *John A. Matheson,* Captain Matheson—I have frequently used oil to calm the sea when in charge of fishing vessels, fishing for cod. Several hogsheads are distributed about the deck, into which cod livers are thrown and in heavy weather holes are bored in the hogsheads and the oil runs out through the scuppers.

S. S. Teesbridge, Captain Shaw, from Baltimore, December 21, 1905, to Hamburg, January 9, 1906—While running before a southwest gale, with seas continually breaking over the vessel, used fish oil for sixteen hours from the forward waste pipes with good results, as no more water came aboard. Used about 1½ gallons of oil an hour.

S. S. Ohio, Captain Oliver, from Rotterdam to Baltimore—January 10, 1906, engines stopped, ship hove to, with winds of hurricane force from northwest; used oil from forward, amidships, and aft on each side for twenty-four hours to good advantage, and believe had it not been for the timely use of oil seas would have swept the decks.

S. S. Sloterdyk, Captain Van der Heuvel, from Rotterdam to New York—Used oil for three hours with very good results, as wherever the oil reached the water was calm and smooth, while in the distance the sea was angry and turbulent. Always carry oil for use in stormy weather and use an oil made from the residue of whales and codfish, which is efficient and cheap. No special apparatus is used for distributing the oil, but use the following methods: When the ship can be kept head to the sea, a 24-pound butter can with oil is placed in the bowl of each forward closet and the flushing water kept running freely. If the sea is moderate, one hole is punctured in the can and the oil allowed to drip; if the sea increases, two or three holes are made. If the ship falls off a couple of points, the oil is distributed from the forward bow closets and from a closet amidships. This method is followed when the wind is not too strong, otherwise the oil flies over the side of the ship and does not reach the water close enough to do any good. When the ship's head continues to fall off, headway is stopped and the ship permitted to drift; then oil is distributed on both sides forward and amidships, if possible.

Thomas (United States Army transport), Capt. E. V. Lynam—Left Guam April 24, 1905, for Manila; weather threatening. April 26, at 3.40 p. m., hove to in the trough of the sea, which was very heavy, and ran fish oil from water-closet pipes fore and aft. The oil streak spread to windward about 300 yards and no seas broke within it, though they did so ahead and astern. Went ahead slowly on course at midnight, using oil forward and aft on both sides, ship riding easily and taking no water. Hove to again from 8 p. m. 27th to 4 a. m. 28th, and experienced tremendous seas, but only some light spray came aboard. The ship rode easily, as before, while hove to and using oil on weather side. Very heavy rain made it impossible see how far the oil streak extended. [Report by Third Officer H. M. Davie.]

Tugela (British steamship), Capt. J. Marchbanks, reports as follows: April 11, 1905, bound east, in latitude 46° north, longitude 41° west, experienced a fresh northwest gale. Used oil to save our deck load. My experience is that with the sea abaft the beam it is much better to give a double pressure of oil from the forward closet pipe (weather side) and use bags from midship section of steamer and also one at the break of the poop. This method I have found will enable me to run much longer and with less danger of a sea breaking aboard. At 4.30 p. m., wind and sea increasing, I resolved to heave steamer to. Oil was freely used and steamer's speed reduced, with the result that for about one-fourth of a mile around the sea was comparatively smooth, and with little difficulty the vessel was brought to the wind. The average speed of steamer while running was 9 knots. The oil used was a cheap quality of colza thinned down with about 30 per cent of kerosene. The bags used were ordinary canvas bags made on board, with small holes pricked in the bottom. By using this style of bag the flow can much more easily be regulated. The amount of oil expended while running before the gale was 1¼ gallons per hour. After heaving to I found it better to use only the forward closet pipe, as this was quite sufficient to prevent any water from breaking aboard, and the expenditure of oil was reduced to about one-half gallon per hour. This method was very efficient in smoothing the seas and greatly reduced the risk of losing the deck cargo or sustaining any other serious damage.

Invermark (British bark), Captain Bolderston—September, 1903, to the westward of Tasmania, got a succession of gales with high dangerous seas. On the first rise of the barometer wanted to put the vessel on the port tack, but was afraid she would be damaged, as that would have brought the sea on the port beam. Filled oil bags and put them over and wore ship. Although the vessel lay in the trough of the sea for eighteen hours she only took a little lee water. There was a smooth oily wake for 200 yards to windward, notwithstanding that ahead and astern the sea was breaking heavily. Arrived in port without damage and deck load of lumber intact.

American (Dutch steamship), Capt. E. Marktschlaeger—March 5, 1905, while bound east, latitude 41°, longitude 56° 54′, during a northerly gale with very high rolling seas, used storm oil through forward waste pipe with good effect. March 7, same, during a northwest gale. March 9 to 11, during a gale from southwest, west, and northwest, used oil on both bows through waste pipes with apparently good results. At 8.30 p. m., the 11th, latitude 47° 40′ north, longitude 21° 15′ west, with a whole gale and furious high sea, we had to stop on account of a break in the engines and used plenty of storm oil to heave to; also while lying broadside to the sea, with bags forward, amidships, and aft, causing a smooth sea a safe distance from the ship. [Report by Chief Officer Sytor.]

Mildred (schooner), Captain Kindler—While serving on board the bark *William Ritson*, that vessel was caught in a typhoon in the Indian Ocean and was on her beam ends for twenty-four hours, when by some accident a tin of coal oil got adrift and had a hole punched in it, allowing the oil to run out and spread on the water. As soon as the bark drifted to leeward of the oil the water began to act on the rudder and the vessel came up to the wind and righted. After that, used all kinds of oil, but the most satisfactory was cod-liver oil, which was used drop by drop. The use of oil saved the bark.

S. S. Sirrah (Dutch), Capt. K. Ru. On Oct. 2, 1920, at 12.01 a. m., in lat. 56° 10′ N., lon. 22° 45′ W., wind NW., force 4, barometer 30.07. At 2 a. m. the wind shifted to east, force 0; barometer falling steadily. Later the wind shifted to southeast, increasing in force, and at noon its force was 7 and the barometer read 29.48. Ship's course, 65°. The clouds, winds, and barometer indicated stormy weather. At 2 p. m., steering more northerly so as to pass to the northward of the storm center. The wind shifted to ESE. with heavy seas; barometer falling; steering with full, half, and then slow speed. At 10 p. m., wind force 9, barometer 28.89; heavy rough sea. Ship taking much water aboard, became unmanageable, and fell in the trough of the sea. Stopped the engines and spilled oil on the decks in three places, using 2 gallons in four hours, after which the ship lay with the wind and sea three points abaft the starboard beam, and but little water came aboard aft. The barometer fell until 4 a. m. of the 3d. The wind shifted slowly to eastward. We drifted until noon, when the wind was east and barometer rising. Later the wind shifted to N.E., force 1; barometer still rising. Started engines at slow, then half, and finally full speed. The storm center passed to southward. " When you are in a storm and can not keep head on to the sea, stop your engines and use oil from the weather side and you are safe. You may have a little water on the after part, but that is all, as the seas break at a distance from the ship and not aboard." [Report by Chief Officer N. de Herta.]

Crossing Bars

Crossing a bar with a flood tide, to pour oil overboard and allow it to float in ahead of the boat, which would follow with a bag towing astern, would appear to be the best plan. As before remarked, under these circumstances the effect can not be so much trusted.

On a bar, with the ebb tide running, it would seem to be useless to try oil for the purpose of entering.

Crossing a dangerous bar with a short vessel attempt to ride over on the rest of the sea. When a long vessel *must* cross a bar, or is being driven down on a bar, the safest maneuver seems to be the following:

Just before getting to the bar bring the vessel parallel with the bar and in the trough of the sea. This can be done with a sea anchor over the bow. The sea anchor must be put over board in plenty of time. Have an extra long scope of the best towing hawser bent to the sea anchor. Put this over and check with a short scope. Work the vessel into the trough. As the anchor begins to haul the ship's head up ease off on the tow line. This should be just before she rides over. The vessel will roll over the bar, keel parallel to the bar.

When over check the tow lines and bring the vessel's head to the wind. Anchor when safely inside, or, if engines are working, proceed to a safe anchorage.

The maneuver may, of course, be simplified by use of the engines to bring the vessel parallel to the bar.

A sailing craft may execute this maneuver by use of an after sail to bring her into the wind, assuming that she is running down onto a bar under shortened canvas.

If the vessel has no way upon her except the drift to leeward, toward the bar, she may touch lightly on the outside edge of the bar but the next sea will pick her up and lift her over. All of this is predicated upon a heavy swell running over the bar, the absence of rocks, and favorable wind. And the absolute need of going over, or of being driven over.

Storm Oil

On and after January 1, 1915, all U. S. merchant vessels of more than 200 gross tons propelled by machinery and navigating the oceans or gulfs shall carry a supply of oil for the purpose of smoothing the sea or quelling the force of the waves in case of emergency or necessity in the following quantities:

Vessels of over 200 and not over 1,000 gross tons, 30 gallons.

Vessels of over 1,000 and not over 3,000 gross tons, 40 gallons.

Vessels of over 3,000 and not over 5,000 gross tons, 50 gallons.

Vessels of over 5,000 gross tons shall carry at least 100 gallons.

This oil shall be accessible and available at all times, and the location of the supply and the means and methods of its distribution shall be determined by the master of the vessel.

XIII

Stability

The question of stability, the power a vessel has of righting herself when heeled over from any outside cause, is generally considered under the question of stowage. On the other hand stability is of vital importance in the many problems arising in the handling of craft, in the gradual consumption of fuel and in the filling and emptying of ballast tanks.

A vessel is always acted upon by the resultant of two forces. The force of her own weight, that is, *gravity*, and the flotation force of the water she displaces, that is, *buoyancy*. The two forces may conveniently be plotted as acting through two centers. The *center of gravity* and the *center of buoyancy*.

In a submarine the center of gravity will lie below the center of buoyancy. In a surface vessel of average build and loading the center of buoyancy will lie below the center of gravity.

The center of gravity is of course the center of the mass of the vessel. The center of buoyancy is the center of the submerged portion of the vessel. When weights are not shifted to produce heeling the center of gravity remains in the same place, but as a vessel heels over the *shape* (not the volume) of her submerged section changes, and the center of buoyancy shifts toward the side upon which she is lying.

Gravity acts *downward*, buoyancy acts *upward*.

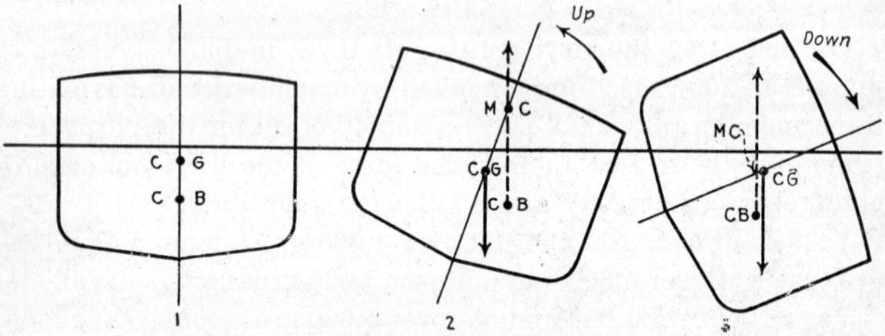

C.G, Centre of Gravity. C.B, Centre of Buoyancy. M.C, Meta Centre.

The *meta center* is a point on the center line of the vessel where a line from the center of buoyancy, passing straight upward, cuts this center line. The meta center is located only when the vessel heels over to one side or the other by some external force. The *metacentric height* is the distance from C.G. to C.M.*

The *righting moment*, tending to put the vessel on an even keel is the amount of the buoyant force, acting upward times the horizontal distance between the vertical lines passing through the center of gravity and the center of buoyancy.

The figures show the action of these three centers and explain all we need to know about the mysterious meta center. In the first figure the vessel lies on an even keel and there is no righting

* Elaborate inclining experiments are made to determine the position of the center of gravity, metacentric height, etc. Usually carried out at wet dock in shipyard. See Applied Naval Architecture, by W. J. Lovett.

moment. In the second figure she is heeled over to starboard (we will assume we are looking forward) and the center of buoyancy shifts to starboard of the center of gravity. The two forces, gravity and buoyancy, form a *couple* and the righting moment is readily seen.

In the third figure the vessel has gone over so far that the center of buoyancy has passed to port of the center of gravity. The meta center has passed down below the center of gravity and to port of it, and we no longer have a righting moment, but the two forces now act as an *upsetting* couple and over she goes.

In loading or ballasting, when the weights are carried very low, we have a greater metacentric height for any draft, and a very strong righting moment. The vessel is then said to be stiff. She comes back from a roll with a sharp upward jerk. She is hard to upset, but on the other hand she is liable to be very hard on the machinery or spars or cargo. A very stiff ship will almost snap the masts out of herself in a heavy sea running on her bow or quarter, let alone her beam.

By carrying the weights up and reducing the extreme righting moment we make her more *sea kindly*. The vessel has an easier roll, a more equable motion. On the other hand when the weights are too far up and the metacentric height is reduced, she becomes tender or sluggish, rolls over and recovers slowly, and may be very dangerous in a seaway. Water shipped on the well deck may carry her down and a combination of a heavy sea fore and aft and a third one breaking over her when she is down may shift the cargo or actually carry her beyond her righting power and capsize her. This is an extreme case, of course.*

* Of late years there has developed a tendency to require captains to know something of the stability of their ships. In some cases blue prints of curves of metacentric heights and other ship's properties have been furnished captains. In one case a captain inquired, "What am I to do with this?" "I don't know, but be sure to receipt for it," was the enlightening reply.

Recent British books on naval architecture assert that many captains understand stability and suggest that a captain, being supplied with the heights of the metacenter, should be able to determine the metacentric height. Considering that the metacentric height desirable for a large ship is about one foot, while the height of the metacenter from the keel is likely to be 25 or 30 feet, is rather a rigid requirement. There is no question that some captains can learn to figure change of location of the center of gravity due to

The above considerations will show how necessary it is to use great care in proportioning weights when loading heavy cargoes such as sugar. Here the filling completely of lower holds would make a vessel crank. By carrying weights up this is over come, but the proportioning must be such that weight is not carried too high.

Seamen who have the loading of a vessel in charge are usually men of some experience. Common judgment in the placing of weights and the distribution of measurement cargo is all that is needed in the modern vessel. Engines, boilers and oil or water tanks control stability and trim to a large extent.

Most trouble arises in light voyages where ballast is not taken in sufficient amount for reasons of economy.

Vessel of good beam and high freeboard are often designed with small metacentric height in order to make them less crank. Here too, other methods of reducing excessive rolling are generally employed.

Rolling

Rolling, aside from its discomforts (to passengers especially) results in bad steering, reduced efficiency of propellers, especially with twin screws, one screw racing and the other slowed as she rolls from side to side. Other losses such as increased skin friction, and decreased efficiency of the fires under boilers, water swashing in boilers and tanks, and wear and tear on gear and damage to cargo and vessel are all directly due to excessive rolling.

Bilge keels are generally fitted, these being shaped to the average streamline of the vessel and affording direct outside resistance against rolling. They also, of course, add just so

loading and stowage, and perhaps all ought to; but the exact determination of metacentric height is difficult for the naval architect, and an error of half a foot might occur in a captain's computation without much blame to him.

It is suggested that a more certain and a fairer way is to require the naval architect to determine the metacentric heights for all conditions of loading and stowage for the ship in ordinary service, and to give this information to the captain in the form of directions for loading, taking account of weight and bulk of cargo and locations of various kinds to keep within proper requirements. In case the captain has any question concerning stability it would be better for him to cable information and ask instructions.

—*Marine Engineering.*

much to the resistance of the hull, whether rolling takes place or not.

The use of *anti-rolling tanks*, notably those of Frahm, have also been tried with moderate success.*

The *gyro-stabilizer* developed by Mr. Elmer A. Sperry has proven the most successful wave-quenching device produced up to the present time. Here the stabilizing gyro is placed in the center line of the vessel and near the midship point of her length. Mr. Robert B. Lea, of the Sperry Gyroscope Company describes the action as follows:

" Many gyroscopical phenomena are the result of the operation of Newton's First Law of Motion, which states that all matter is pig-headed by saying ' a body continues or perseveres in a state of rest, or of uniform motion in a straight line except in so far as it may be deflected therefrom by an externally applied force.' This law, when applied to a rotating wheel, may be expressed by stating that the wheel tends to maintain the direction of its plane of rotation, and axis, in space.

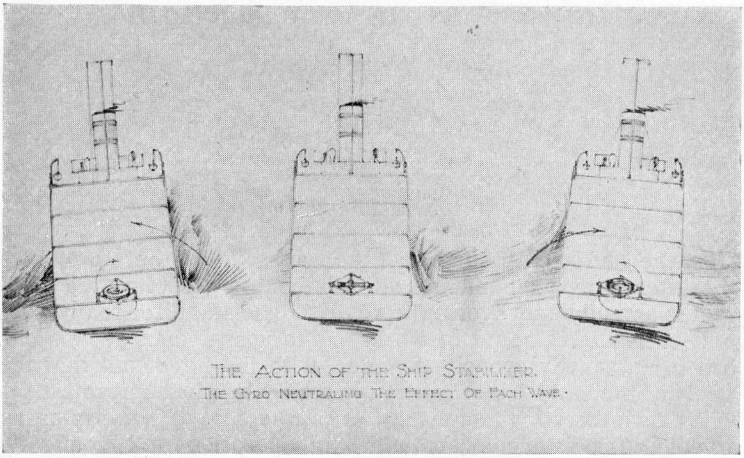

The sketch above shows the stabilizer in relative position and size on a large passenger liner. The arrow indicates the reaction of the gyro when neutralizing wave effort.

" The theory of the ship stabilizer calls into play this characteristic of any rapidly revolving gyroscope or wheel to maintain its axis of spin or plane of rotation rigidly in any direction.

* The use of " blisters " or outside bilge tanks has also proven successful in adding to stability at sea.

So persistent and powerful are the inertia forces in this wheel that it opposes with great effort any disturbing forces, resisting them (up to the limit of its power) with an equal and opposite magnitude. In a ship the disturbing forces are the waves.

"The revolving gyroscope, being dislodged from its vertical plane of rotation by the action of the waves endeavoring to roll the ship, immediately opposes and neutralizes this action with an equal force by tilting or 'precessing' in the proper direction, fore or aft, in a plane at right angles to the disturbance. Practically all the power to stabilize the vessel comes directly

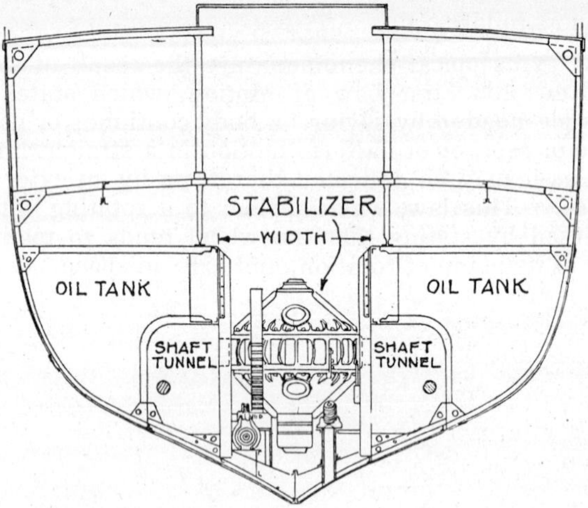

A gyro-stabilizer in place.

from the source of disturbance, the waves. We, therefore, have the interesting phenomenon of stabilizing a vessel by the force that is actually endeavoring to roll it. The stabilizer really does only a smaller amount of work on the vessel than each wave, but in an exactly opposite manner, with the net result that the effort of the wave is neutralized and the ship does not roll.

"This interesting fact means, of course, that with the spinning wheel, no greater power (with the exception of the slightly increased power for bearing friction) is required to stabilize the ship, than to let the wheel run idle. The gyro merely performs the function of passing the forces 'around the corner'; that is, taking in the forces on one side and passing them out as equal but opposing forces at right angles. In opposing the roll of the ship, the gyro is oscillated, or, as it is technically known, 'precesses' slowly fore and aft (the reaction, of course, being athwartship), the speed being governed by suitable control apparatus, so that the gyro will make just one complete oscillation while the tendency of the ship to roll persists.

"In accomplishing this result we seize hold of the fact that the ever-changing period of the waves, acting upon the constant period of the vessel first, builds up a large angle of roll and then as the waves become out of synchronism, undoes their work by opposing and crushing out the roll. Any one wave can impart only a very slight roll, the matter of stabilization, therefore, becomes more one of proper control than of exerting large neutralizing forces; our problem being merely that of installing a small wheel capable of taking care of the few degrees roll (three to five degrees) which any one wave can impart to the vessel."

Advantages of the gyro stabilizer are summed up as follows.* Calculations being made from a model 1/26th the size of the vessel. Vessel: Length 520 ft., beam 65 ft., draft 16 ft. Displacement 11,000 tons.

"It appears that at a speed of 15 knots the effective horsepower would be increased from 3,000 to 3,300 when the ship is rolling through an arc of 25 degrees, and to 3,600 when rolling through an arc of 45 degrees, corresponding to an increase in effective horsepower of 10 per cent and 20 per cent respectively. It is to be noted that this does not include the loss of power due to decrease in propeller efficiency for a twin screw ship, when the propellers alternately approach the surface, if not actually coming out of the water.

"These results confirm experience at sea that loss of speed is found to occur when ships are rolling heavily. Under these circumstances it appears that the power and weight devoted to the means for stabilizing a ship are more than amply repaid by the saving effected in the power required to drive her."

Much more might be written about this very interesting development in modern ship handling. The amount of extra water displaced by a heavily rolling ship, the alternate shifting of the buoyant forces, and the all tend to added economy when eliminated under gyro stabilization.

In the Sperry gyro-stabilizer the main gyro is controlled by a small control or *pilot gyro;* this feels the beginning of a roll instantly and sets the main gyro working in opposition to it at once. It is the brains of the mechanism. The pilot gyro closes

* From a paper by Commander Wm. McEntee, C.C., U.S.N. on comparative tests of bilge keels and gyro-stabilizer, read before the American Society of Naval Architects and Marine Engineers.

a contact to the *precession control unit*, this releases the brake and starts the precession motor geared to a circular rack on the gyro case in the proper direction to tilt the main gyro on its vertical axis and thereby bring into play the counter force that prevents the ship from rolling. A thirty ton gyro wheel was used to stabilize the 10,000 ton *U. S. S. Henderson.*

Sea Waves

The *period of a wave* is the time, in seconds, between the passing of successive crests, taken from some stationary point. A vessel steaming into a sea will *apparently* cut down this period, or if steaming away from the sea will lengthen it. This is known to physicists as *Doppler Effect*, and has a wide usefulness in the vast field of wave-length investigations. It is simply mentioned here in passing.

The *period of roll* is the time in seconds required for a complete roll from the extreme angle of roll on one side to the extreme angle of roll on the other. The *double period* is the time required to roll from extreme starboard (let us say) back to extreme starboard.

For any given condition of stability this period will be the same no matter what the angle of roll.* That is, a vessel with a seven-second period will require seven seconds to roll ten degrees and also seven seconds to roll twenty or thirty degrees.

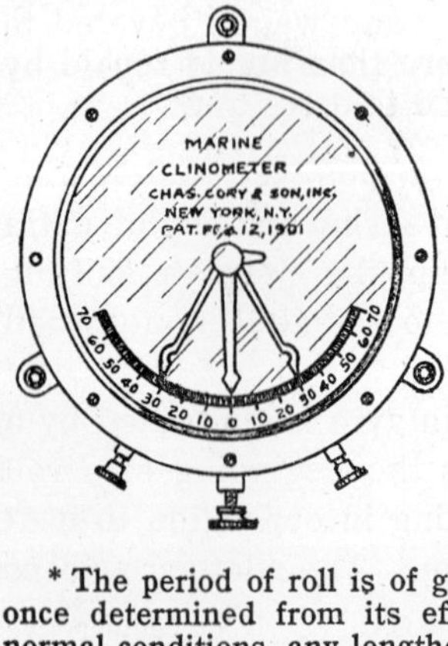

But, as the angle of roll increases her rapidity of roll increases directly with the distance through which she rolls. The greater roll, in the same time, carries with it an increase of momentum that may make it very dangerous. The speed of the roll is greatest at the middle of the roll, when the vessel is upright. The ship is simply a huge floating pendulum.

To measure the angle of roll, *clinometers* are fitted at convenient

* The period of roll is of great importance. Lack of stability may be at once determined from its effect on rolling. Knowing the period, under normal conditions, any lengthening, and if the rolling becomes sluggish and lags at the end of the roll, will indicate lack of stability.

If tanks cannot be filled to correct this, return to nearest port and shift cargo weights lower down. Report by radio, or cable owners at once.

points. These usually have indicating arms that are carried out on each side by the recording pendulum and show the maximum roll. The indicators may be moved to the center of the scale by small milled heads located outside of the clinometer case. It is very essential that a sensitive clinometer be fitted in the engine room to guide the engineers in the filling or emptying of boilers, tanks, bunkers, etc. The angle of heel and stability is also of importance when loading fast cargoes, or when purchasing extra heavy weights with the vessel's own gear.

When the period of the waves and the period of rolling are synchronous, or nearly so, the waves may add to the rolling at each swing until dangerous conditions arise. Of course good seamanship would call for measures to put the vessel out of the trough of the sea where such rolling would take place.

The period of roll is less when a vessel is moving through the water, the reduction however is slight.

Large liners may have a period of roll of from ten to twelve seconds.

Pitching is of less importance than rolling so far as it effects the safety of the vessel. A light vessel pitching into a heavy sea may strain herself. The writer recalls the fore hold stanchions buckling under pitching stresses on a vessel going light into a heavy head sea.

Heaving is the vertical motion of a vessel, increasing and decreasing her draft.

The resultant motion of a vessel, due to rolling and pitching, and heaving is the combined effect of sea and wind, and her own machinery, all acting together upon the whole structure.

The growth of sea waves is treated of under calming the sea with oil.* The following definitions are of interest here:

The generally accepted theory of wave formation at sea is the *trochoidal* theory. This defines the form of a sea wave as a trochoid, a curve traced by a point inside of a circle rolling along on a straight line. The path of a point on a wheel rolling on a level road is a trochoid. In the case of a sea wave the circle is supposed to roll along on the *under side* of a straight line. The line in this instance is the level of the sea.

* Page 706.

Every particle of water influenced by the wave has a fixed circular orbit, around which it moves with uniform velocity, completing the circle in a time equal to the period of the wave.*

The following is taken from the Manual of Seamanship of the British Admiralty:

"The size of waves varies in different localities, and with different forces and directions of the wind. The longest wave recorded is one of 2,600 feet and with a period of 23 seconds.

"The longest waves are usually encountered in the South Pacific with lengths varying from 600 to 1,000 feet, and periods of from 11 to 14 seconds. Waves of from 500 to 600 feet in length are occasionally met in the Atlantic, but more commonly the lengths are from 160 to 320 feet, with periods of 6 to 8 seconds.

"The variation of length with the force and direction of the wind is not yet fully understood.

"The ratio $\frac{\text{height}}{\text{length}}$ decreases as the length increases.

"For the longest waves the ratio varies from 1/50 to 1/30, and for waves 300 to 400 feet long the ratio appears to vary from about 1/25 to 1/20. For waves 100 to 200 feet long the ratio may vary from 1/10 to 1/20. For small waves such as those near the coast line the ratio of height over length may be as great as 1/5 to 1/6."

The Speed of Waves. A definite idea of the speed with which waves may travel is of use to the officer handling a vessel. This is specially so when running before the sea in a sailing ship, or in a low powered steamer, or auxiliary.

The speed of large waves may be taken to roughly approximate half the speed of the wind that causes them. In a moderate sea the speed of the waves often exceeds the speed of the wind.

In long stretches of sea as the route from the Cape of Good Hope to Australia, waves traveling at the express speed of thirty knots are not uncommon. This is one of the reasons why sailors who have "*run their easting down*" on this classic sea way have a wholesome respect for the great blue-black combers with their snarling crests of silver white that crackle and curl in the wake of a stormy night. Such waves have an eight-second period, if we may append a scientific fact to something coming very close to romance.

In the Atlantic waves with a speed of twenty knots and a six-second period are not uncommon.

*The *Period* is the time between the passing of successive wave crests measured from a stationary point.

In shallow waters waves are distorted and piled up. Here the waves of translation with broken crest and ugly masses of moving water add to the dangers of ship handling.

Waves piling and breaking on a beach are an instance of the effect of shoaling water.

It is quite possible for two series of waves to be in motion at the same time. Each may have its origin at widely different points. When the two are in coincidence we have a piling up of a great wave, one upon another. Seamen can do a great service by carefully studying and observing the characteristics of sea waves—indeed no one else can do this except those men who actually live upon the sea and observe it under all conditions.

The *height of waves* is taken from hollow to crest. Mount the rigging and when in the hollow, vessel in the trough, and ship upright, sight across the crest to the horizon and measure the height of eye above the waterline. This will approximate the height of the wave.

The highest waves observed at sea are in the neighborhood of forty feet. These are only possible when there is plenty of sea room, or " fetch " for them to make up in. Waves of from fifty to sixty feet in height are possible but rare.

Mr. Thomas Stevenson, of lighthouse fame, worked out an empirical formula that approximates the possible maximum height of waves, the same being considered as a function of the " fetch," or distance from which they may originate. This is as follows:

Height of wave (in feet) equals the square root of the " fetch " in nautical miles multiplied by the constant 1.5.

Or, the distance from which a great wave comes is equal to its height divided by 1.5, and the quotient squared.

This formula seems to give wave heights in excess of those actually observed.

Waves formed by the action of the vessel itself are the *bow waves* and the *wake.* These are of considerable force and are very important when steaming through crowded waters or through canals. Speed in canals is limited because of their erosive action, where the banks are sand. The water of the wake has a speed imparted by the skin of the vessel, and in single screw ships the propeller works in this water, adding somewhat to its propulsive effect.

On the other hand the wake movement detracts slightly from the effective action of the rudder.

Rollers are the great waves piling up on a shelving beach.

The *Bore*, or *eager*, is a high crested wave, advancing up river with the flood tide. It is liable to do considerable damage if met with unawares. Seamen who put into strange rivers or estuaries should remember this when handling or mooring their vessels. *Sailing Directions* provide ample information. The Bore is met with in such rivers as the Amazon, Hoogly, Ganges, Indus and in the Tsientang Estuary. The term is sometimes used to describe the "meeting of the tides" in the Bay of Fundy.

Convoys

Convoys are a strictly naval measure and are only employed in time of war. Many merchant service officers have had experience in running in convoy and the few notes here are of a supplementary nature. Conditions under which a convoy may be formed are military conditions and these need not be set down here.

The zig-zag course, a whole convoy changing course at a given moment and in a given direction, and the S course where courses are constantly changing through the working of automatic shifting devices displacing the lubber's line progressively from side to side, were worked out and are a part of our knowledge in this form of work.

The *towing spar*, trailing astern from vessels in convoy forms a mark for following vessels to keep ahead of them and is often the only guide on a dark night or when running in thick weather.

Smoke boxes are carried by merchant craft in war time and their use is now familiar to many.

Paravanes are devices streaming out at an angle from either bow attached to strong wires shackled to chains leading through eyes riveted to the forefoot. These are held out from the vessel's side by underwater kites and carry a sharp cutting knife that shears off mines which are carried out clear of the track of the vessel by the wire cables trailing the kites.

Without a doubt the paravane was one of the most useful and ingenious devices invented during the war. It was invented by Lieutenant Burney, R.N. who is said to have received $150,000 from the British Government for his service, in addition to other honors of a less substantial nature.

The "kites" or "fishes" are torpedo-shaped water planes fitted with fins and rudder. They can be regulated for any desired depth or distance from the vessel depending upon the speed, length of wire, and set of the rudders.

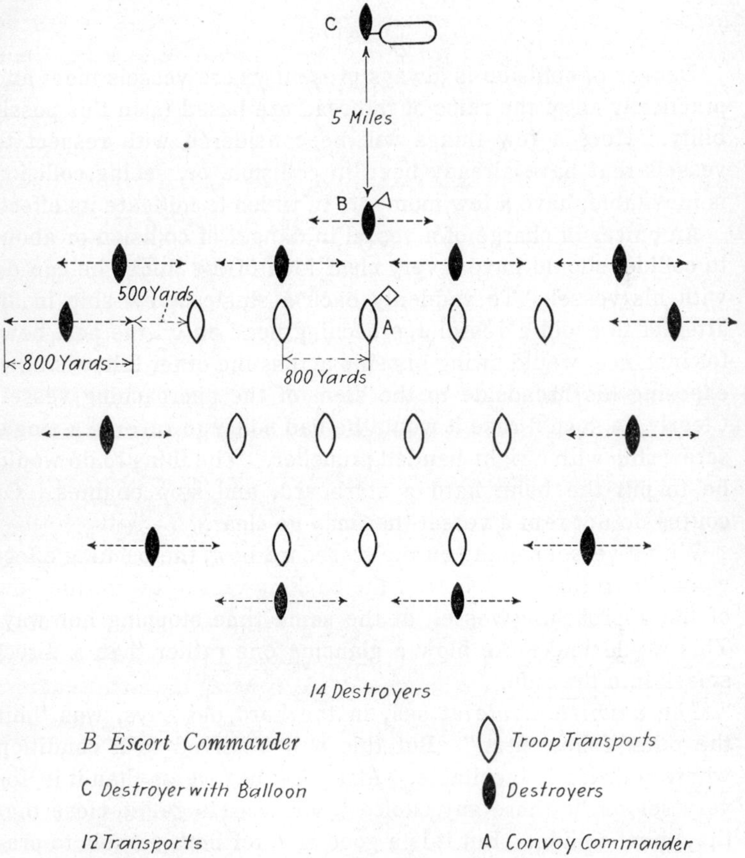

Instructions when in Convoy. Masters of vessels in convoy are supplied with instructions which should be complete and should be strictly followed. A ship master who does not fully understand such instructions should insist upon complete instructions. As master of his ship he has certain obligations imposed upon him by law. He must see the authority of the naval commander and must receive full instruction governing his own vessel as a part of the convoy. Such orders and instructions are given in detail by the naval commander.

XIV

Collision

Danger of collision is always present where vessels meet and practically all of the rules of the road are based upon this possibility. Here a few things will be considered with respect to vessels that have already been in collision, or, seeing collision is inevitable, have a few moments in which to mitigate its effect.

An officer in charge of a vessel in danger of collision or about to collide, should have a very clear idea of the things he can do with his vessel. To suddenly back a single screw ship in an attempt to avoid a vessel approaching head on on the port bow, for instance, would swing his ship across the other fellow's bow, exposing his broadside to the stem of the approaching vessel. Clearly, in such a case it would be bad policy to reverse a single screw ship with a right-handed propeller. The thing to do would be to put the helm hard a starboard, and stop engines. Of course do not ram a vessel that may go clear.

With a vessel coming on the starboard bow, the backing effect would be to throw the bow of the backing vessel toward the bow of the approaching vessel, at the same time stopping her way. This would make the blow a glancing one rather than a direct smash into the side.

The unwritten rule at sea, in the hard old days, was "hit the other fellow first." But this only referred to a condition where collision is inevitable. Also it sounds worse than it is, for very seldom is there any choice when vessels get so close that they must collide. But it is a good rule for both vessels to present their bows to each other, or to swing in that direction, making the blow a glancing one.

Having collided with another vessel, your bow into his side, *do not back out.** If a heavy sea is running the question of

* "With a double lookout peering into the fog ahead, the *Monroe* was creeping under half speed northward, and the *Nantucket*, heavily laden with freight, was nosing her way toward Norfolk.

steaming into the gap made by the stem may be governed by the tearing and rending of one ship against another and backing out may be necessary. But where the striking vessel can do so *without further damage* to the vessel struck, she should plug the hole until satisfied that both vessels have their bulkhead doors closed and pumps working. Where a large hole is cut into the side of a vessel, opening two holds, it is well if possible to transfer passengers over the bow of the striking vessel. *The vessel struck should stop her engines at once.* This is a safe rule to follow.

In such a case bow of one vessel into side of another, it may be necessary to get out heavy stern lines from the striking vessel to the vessel struck to prevent the two craft from slewing broadside to in the sea and further opening up the gap. The quickest and clearest headed seamanship is needed under such conditions. Boats should be swung out on *both* vessels, passengers mustered, life belts issued ready for anything that may arise. Insist upon quiet, maintain order and discipline.

Many lives have been lost and much property has been sunk through lack of cool understanding in such emergencies.

A shipmaster who meets with a collision (as every one may) and who acts quickly and with cool judgment, saving lives and property, may turn a disaster into a personal triumph.

In the event of a collision both vessels must stand by. See page 604.

The full report of a collision must also be entered in the official log book. Always note *all* changes of course, speed and weather with *exact time.*

" The two vessels, moving slowly through the dense fog, were gradually drawn toward each other.

" Without warning, the crash came—in the grayblack mist that shut even the waves from view, the feeble gleam of the *Nantucket's* searchlight scarcely touched the dripping side of the *Monroe* before the knife-like bow of the south bound vessel cut into the other's side with a crashing and ripping of steel plates that threw the stricken ship aback, and the *Nantucket*, with her bow crushed in, BACKED out of sight into the fog.

" The order was shouted for lifeboats, but so soon did the *Monroe* roll over on her side and plunge beneath the waves that many who were fortunate enough to reach the deck safely were left afloat to be picked up by boats sent out from the *Nantucket*. Others, unable to leave their staterooms were caught like rats in a trap with no chance whatever to save themselves."

—*Master, Mate and Pilot*

The Italian Lloyd S. S. Florida in the Morse Dry Dock, N. Y., after ramming and sinking the S. S. Republic in January, 1909. Jack Binns, wireless operator of the latter vessel became famous when he sent out his C.Q.D. after the collision. The photograph shows the tremendous impact of such a collision.

As collision cases generally end up in the admiralty courts, the Master who violates any part of the law must be prepared to have his violation set up against him as a presumption of fault. The reader will do well to consult Hughes, On Admiralty, in connection with this important question of the legal aftermath of collision.

Concrete vessels seem to be a dangerous proposition when we think of the possibility of collision. Like crockery pots—they either don't break, or they sink.*

Cut down by a straight stem.

Straight Stem versus Inclined or Clipper Stem

The undoubted danger of fitting all vessels with a sharp straight stem that, in the event of collision, cuts directly down to

* Newport, Oct. 29, 1920.—The concrete steamer *Cape Fear* was sunk in the deepest part of Narragansett Bay tonight in a collision with the Savannah Line steamer *City of Atlanta*. At a late hour nineteen of the crew of thirty-four of the sunken vessel were unaccounted for.

The *Cape Fear* sank in three minutes about half way between Castle Hill on the Newport shore and Rose Island, going down bow first in 125 fathoms.

the water's edge,* has lately received some attention. The straight stem, aside from its simple construction, has nothing to specially recommend it. A considerable forward rake of the stem piece would improve the appearance of most vessels. The need for carrying upward of the knife edge stem is also far from apparent. By widening the forecastle head, and making the bow, well above the water line and inclining forward, rounded instead of sharp, the danger due to collision would be greatly minimized. A more comfortable vessel would be the result and considerable reserve buoyancy and storage and working space would be gained in the forecastle. Perhaps naval architects may someday do this.†

Water-tight doors‡ are generally built after two plans. Either they are hinged and swing to against gaskets of rubber or other material and are set close by means of *dogs* and *screws,* or they

* On the 25th of April, 1908, the S. S. *St. Paul* and H. M. cruiser *Gladiator* were both making their way in the waters of the Solent. The wind was blowing in squalls, and every now and then flurries of snow shut off vision except for a short range of a few hundred feet. Finally, the driving flakes blinded the men on the bridges of the nearing liner and the fighting craft and, before either vessel could be swung clear, the straight stem of the *St. Paul* crashed at an oblique angle into the starboard broadside of the warship, ripping the *Gladiator's* shell plating *right down to the very bottom of her moulded structure.* As a result, a hole 50 feet long, extending to within a few inches of the bilge, was opened in the cruiser's side through which the sea poured in a flood and carried the craft to the bottom in a few minutes.

† The above suggested practice of raked stems rounded above the water line, with wide flaring bows is now general in fast vessels. 1937 sees many marine advances over 1922.

‡ The International Convention Rules for watertight doors, in vessels carrying more than 200 passengers, make it necessary to have, either doors which close by their own weight or by power pressure, and in any case operated from the bridge. Actually it is not often possible, in practice, to make all the watertight doors in the machinery spaces slide vertically so that they will close by their own weight. The result is that power-operated doors must be fitted, so that the Convention Rules do, in effect, require a power-operated, centrally-controlled system of watertight doors in passenger steamers.

In a passenger vessel, therefore, the choice remains between solid bulkheads and centrally-controlled, power-operated doors, and the advantages of doors are so obvious as compared with the inconvenient system of unpierced bulkheads that, in these days of high wages and short working hours, it follows that the moderate expense of installing an efficient power system would quickly be exceeded by the wages bill where solid bulkheads were fitted. It appears certain that all liners will in future have their bulkheads pierced for watertight doors, and that such doors will be centrally controlled and operated by power.—" Engineering."

are sliding doors and are held in contact by wedge-shaped cams and are also close fitted or made watertight by gaskets.

The method of control, either by hand or motor should be understood by all, and on large passenger liners and transports a complete system of signals, showing the state of the watertight doors should be led to the bridge and engine room.

Doors operated by power are all of the sliding type and are vertical or horizontal sliding doors. Operating doors from the bridge should carry with it an adequate alarm before closing or else very unhappy results might ensue to some unfortunate trying to get through just as the door closes.

Where watertight doors are fitted frequent drills should be held and the doors should all be operated *before* starting on a voyage. All doors should be kept closed unless their being open is essential. At all times the Master, Chief Mate, and Officer of the Watch should be informed as to just what doors are open. When running in a fog have all doors closed, or at least have some-one ready to close doors that are open should a collision occur.

Men of war carry large collision mats, heavy canvas thrum mats fitted with *hogging lines* from the lower corners to lead under the keel, and *distance lines* from the upper corners to stretch the mat fore and aft.

Such mats should be very heavy, of two or three thicknesses of canvas and with the thrum surface next the ship's side.

Spare tarpaulins or sails may be used if a hole is to be stopped on a merchantman. Use great care to have the mats and the lines properly secured before passing it over the side. A bight of stream chain lashed at the lower edge of the mat has been found of great use in placing a collision mat. A patent collision mat has recently been devised. This consists of a number of steel pipes set close together and parallel to each other and all securely stopped to a heavy mat. The device is secured over the hole, pipes parallel to the water and unrolled downward against the inrush of water. This seems to be a very practical thing. The inventor is Mr. John L. Hyland of New York.

Ice and Derelicts

Collision with these dangers to navigation is always a possibility and should be uppermost in mind. Collision with derelicts is end on, and usually at top speed, and of course is liable to have serious consequences, such as fire, damage to engines, and a general shaking up and breaking up of all concerned, depending upon the solidity and mass of the derelict.

In colliding with ice still greater dangers are to be expected as a vessel may rip open a considerable length of her side. This happened on the *Titanic*.

The notes below are taken from H. O. Reprint No. 2. They sum up the

Signs of the Proximity of Ice

Ice Blink. Before field ice is seen from deck the ice blink will often indicate its presence. On a clear day over an ice field on the horizon the sky will be much paler or lighter in color and is easily distinguished from that overhead, so that a sharp lookout should be kept and changes in the color of the sky noted.

On clear nights, especially when the moon is up, the sky along the horizon in the direction of the ice is markedly lighter than the rest of the horizon. This effect can be noted before the ice is sighted.

Visibility in Daylight. On a clear day icebergs can be seen at a long distance, owing to their brightness; during foggy weather they are first seen through the fog as a black object. In thick fog the first sight of a berg is apt to be a narrow streak of dark at the water line.

Echoes. They can sometimes be detected by the echo from the steam whistle or the fog horn. In that case, by noting the time between the blast of a whistle and the reflected sound, the distance of the berg in feet may be approximately found by multiplying by 550. The absence of echo is by no means proof that no bergs are near, for unless there is a fairly vertical wall, no return of the sound waves can be expected.

Noise. The presence of icebergs is often made known by the noise of their breaking up and falling to pieces. The cracking of the ice or the falling of pieces into the sea makes a noise like breakers or a distant discharge of guns, which may often be heard a short distance.

Absence of Swell. The absence of swell or wave motion in a fresh breeze is a sign that there is land or ice on the weather side.

Animal Life. The appearance of herds of seal or flocks of murre far from land is an indication of the proximity of ice.

Temperature Air. The special temperature studies made during the ice patrol of 1914 showed that no definite temperature effects of the air can be attributed to the presence of icebergs. Also that if there are temperature effects of sea water due to icebergs they are not distinguishable from the irregular variations observed.

Temperature Water. In the ice zone ice is more likely to be found in cold water than in warm. So when encountering water below 40° in spring and below 50° in early summer, it is well to be on guard for ice. In foggy weather it is advisable to keep in water above 50° while crossing the ice zone, thereby avoiding both ice and fog.

Calf Ice. A reliable sign of icebergs being near is the presence of calf ice. When such pieces occur in a curved line, as they may do, especially in calm weather, the parent berg is on the concave side of the curve.

No ship captain can afford to trust any of the above-named signs to the exclusion of a good lookout.

A remarkable optical phenomenon was observed one day by the ice patrol of 1914 when an iceberg which was ordinarily below the horizon was seen raised above it, at one time inverted and at another time erect. This phenomenon was observed near the Gulf Stream.

Bilging

Bilging is the rupturing of the shell of a vessel at any point below the water line and at once effects her stability and her buoyancy. This may be due to collision, or to some internal cause such as an explosion, of boilers or cargo. It also results from grounding on rocks, or other vessels sunken in a fairway. In war time, and for a considerable time afterward, bilging may be caused by contact with mines.

In the event of bilging the closing of watertight doors is in order. The following should be done at once:

Start pumps. Sound wells.

Watch heel and trim. If a hole is not too far below the water-line a vessel may be heeled over to bring the hole above or nearer the surface. The higher up the less water will flow through in a given time. This maneuver depends somewhat upon the state of the sea.*

Watch draft gauges if fitted to keep tabs on the action of pumps.

When possible examine all bulkheads next to flooded compartments and if possible strengthen them by shores, should it seem necessary.

*If state of sea permits, lower boats on side of hole and unhook. Lower boats on other side, fill with water and hoist clear. Otherwise fill these boats with a hose. Only do this if there is no immediate need of the boats. Also trim with tanks.

When a cargo hold is bilged the *permeability* of the cargo should be taken into account. If the vessel is stowed with light freight of non-permeable character, it will add to her buoyancy by displacing water. Also consider *floodable length*. See page 26.

On the other hand if she is close stowed, with grain, let us say rice, the swelling of the cargo becomes of the utmost moment in considering her safety.

Hatch covers on vessels of standard design are built on the principle of the alligator's jaw, which is powerful to crush anything but just strong enough to open up. The hatch is powerful against water pressure *on top* but practically useless against pressure from underneath.

Hatches have been designed to work both ways, and all hatches on a bulkhead deck should be of such construction that they become an integral part of the deck, and both deck and hatches should be so designed that in the event of bilging the deck will not lift and the hatches cannot fly off when the water rises in a hold and the air pressure under deck becomes equal to the water pressure under the bottom.

Such construction would reduce the danger from bilging to a very great extent. Hatches could be made of steel fitting into gaskets and these could be screwed down from below. A small hatch cap would admit the men for securing the hatch, and would also admit of a complete filling of the hatch square, if need be, and this hatch cap, in turn, could be screwed down like a man hole. The whole thing could be lifted by the cargo booms in one hoist and deposited, end up at the side of the hatch away from the winches. Such hatches might be hinged and fold back against the hatch openings and be worked by special gears from the winches. All of this of course is nothing new—however it is not being done at present.

Marine underwriters should have some interest in seeing hatches on the bulkhead deck properly constructed from the standpoint of safety, both against bilging and fire. The present wooden deck hatch covers are unsafe.

XV

Stranding

Practically every seaman, at some time or another, puts his vessel aground, or at least is on board of some such unfortunate craft. The writer recalls quite a few stirring incidents of this kind. It was great fun, in a way, especially to watch the Skipper. Later on the fun was not so apparent when his own ship touched on the bar off the foot of Duval Street, at Key West.

The procedure when stranding is simple. Know the state of the tide—if falling act without hesitation and at once. Start to pump out tanks, sound along sides and get the location of the point of contact with bottom, sound the wells, and if conditions permit, prepare to put all boats overboard without delay, lightening the vessel of many tons of weight, if she is a big ship with large boat equipment. Place handy weights in boats.

Sometimes a vessel may back off at once. At other times, if grounded amidship on a reef, fill tanks forward, pump out aft, and go *ahead* full speed.

The most serious condition, of course, is taking the beach at high tide, and in an exposed position with regard to the wind and sea.

If the vessel is fast lay out anchors *at once* to prevent her going further on the beach. If tugs are standing by use tugs to carry out the bower anchors with best wire hawsers bent.

If grounded in sand care must be taken not to fill the condenser with sand by continuing the use of the engines. The writer recalls the grounding of the old American Liner *St. Louis*, in the Solent, near Hurst Castle. This fortunately happened near low water but on a falling tide. The backing of the engines began to pile the sand up under the bottom, so this was stopped. Later on as the tide rose she slid off under her own power although the bow was lifted ten feet above her normal water line. The trouble came through a yacht luffing across the bow, the helm was jambed hard a port to avoid the yacht and the steering gear stuck with the helm hard over. She piled high and dry with the engines kicking full speed astern.

Sand in Condenser

This is generally impossible if the main injection valve is placed on the hull at or above the turn of the bilge. Many ships are provided with two main injection valves at bottom and side of the ship. On such a ship, if she take the ground, all that is necessary is to close the bottom injection and open the side.

On ships not provided with double injections there is frequently a connection made from one of the auxiliary pumps, such as the ballast pump or auxiliary feed pump to the water end of the condenser. This can be used temporarily for injection purposes. Some ships are provided with hose connections on water ends of condenser whereby circulating water may temporarily be provided through the fire hose. If the outboard delivery happens to be below the waterline, water may be allowed to flow by gravity through the condenser into the bilges temporarily and pumped overboard from the bilges. Should none of these means be available a temporary exhaust pipe could be used, made of canvas or sheet metal, discharging into condenser through the engine room trunk.

Innumerable cases of stranding are on record. The American Liner *St. Paul* spent eleven days on the sands off the Jersey Coast in midwinter, 1896, piling up early in the morning of January 25 in a fog and sliding off on February 4. While the many attempts were being made to haul the vessel off into deep water a telephone line was connected to the stranded ship, being the first instance of this use of the telephone.

Another famous case of stranding in recent years was that of the North German Lloyd Liner *Prinzess Irene* on Lone Hill Bar, Fire Island. Three days after grounding on April 7, 1911, she was hauled off with little damage. The discussion in the press resulted in the following important letters advocating and explaining a method of freeing ships from the sand that has the weight of engineering use behind it. It should be known to seamen more generally. Piles are sunk into hard sand and lifted clear again by the use of a water jet; the same use of water to clear the skin of a ship from friction and to float her is feasible and easy of application.

On the Rocks

This situation demands special caution. If the vessel is held fast and is being pounded by the sea, it is often good judgment to flood her, to hold her still until the weather moderates and she can be lightened, by pumping or hoisting out cargo. Season, weather changes expected, and the condition of her bottom, all must be considered. Get out anchors if possible.

Treatment of Ships Ashore

Suggests That Water Be Forced Through Pipes Along Their Keels

To the Editor of The New York Times:

I wish to make public a suggestion that may possibly be of use in the case of stranding of vessels as in the recent case of the *Prinzess Irene*. If I understand it, when a steamer runs ashore, on a sandbar or beach, the sand, after the motion of the vessel has ceased, takes such a strong hold on the surface of the hull that it is extremely difficult to pull the vessel off. I suppose this action of the sand to be something like that when a pile is driven in a river bottom. If I am correctly informed, immediately after a pile is driven it can readily be withdrawn, but after the sand, or earthy material, has settled about it, and displaced the water on its skin, and taken hold on the pile, it requires a number of times as much force to withdraw the pile as was used to drive it.

My suggestion is that perforated pipes be run along the keel of a vessel on each side, and connected with the ship's pumps, so that, in case of stranding, water could be forced out of the perforations, and this water, in passing upward along the hull, between the sand and the hull, would, I think, be found to disturb the sand and to materially lessen its hold on the hull. I am led to think this by the fact that piles are driven by forcing water through them to the lower end and then allowing it to escape, the action of the water disturbing the sand so that the piles can sink.

Edwin J. Prindle.

New York, April 16, 1911.

This brought forth the interesting letter by Mr. Picard, printed in next column, telling of a very successful use of the water jet to free ships held by sand.

Cites Case in Which Ship's Pumps Were Rigged to Disperse the Sand

To the Editor of The New York Times:

It may interest your readers to know, in connection with the suggestion offered by Mr. Edwin J. Prindle in your columns some days ago to float stranded ships on a sandy coast by " forcing water through perforated pipes running along the keel of a vessel on each side," that it would be practically impossible to accomplish, for any one who knows the circumstances of the sea and shipbuilding; however, the idea has already been put in practice with success, but in a different way. Twenty years ago an English squadron cast anchor outside of Port Said, previous to entering the Suez Canal, and through some inexplicable error one of the men of war was run full speed high and dry on one of the sand shoals of the roadstead. The efforts of all the tugs sent to her assistance and some of her sister ships put together could not budge her.

I do not remember how long she remained stranded until the engineers conceived the plan to use the ships' and other pumps in connection with a battery of pipes lowered vertically on either quarter, right under her stern post, and the operation to float her was started.

The water pumped through the beds of sand soon began to tell, for, in conjunction with the hauling of other craft, her own efforts on her kedge anchors she moved inch by inch easily, the pipes being displaced alongside the board as she was freeing herself into deep water, until she finally floated unhurt.

The deed was highly praised at the time and recorded in all the nautical papers of the world; it was the first time the scheme had been put in practice.

G. S. Picard.

New York, April 26, 1911.

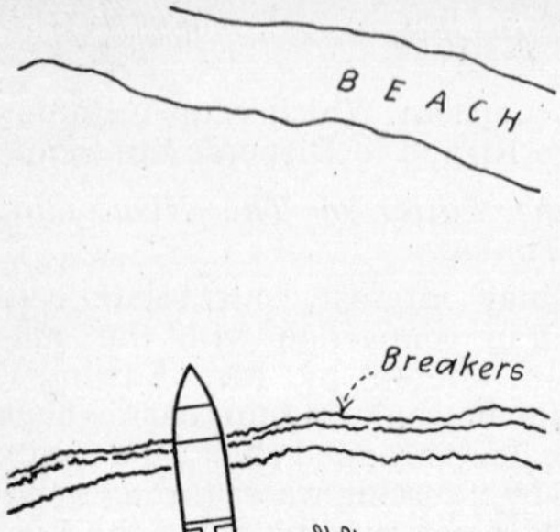

The Case of the *S. S. Arakan*

On August 29, 1920, the Dutch steamer *Arakan* fetched up on the California beach six miles north of Point Reyes. This happened at four bells in the mid watch. As this was a very successful salvage operation the story of its details is taken from an excellent account in the *Pacific Marine Review* of October, 1920.

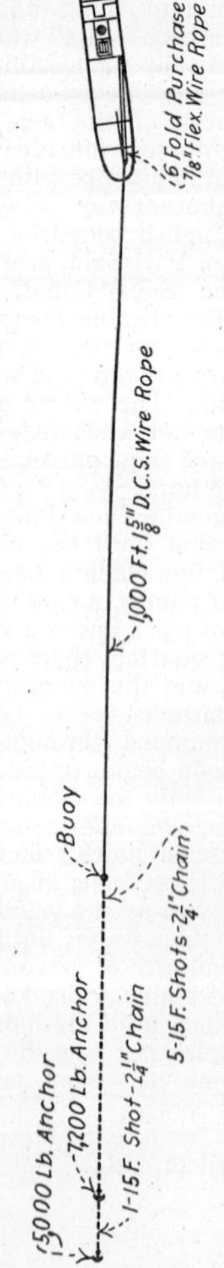

"When tugs and salvage vessels arrived at the scene they found the *Arakan* nearly broadside on to the beach and hawsers were passed aboard from both tugs. The tugs pulled all night and by morning the *Arakan* had been fairly well straightened out. As the vessel was steaming ahead at a seven-knot clip when she struck, she was well up on the beach, straddling a hump of sand, with the surf breaking against the starboard side. *The accident happened during high tide,* and when the water fell there was but sixteen feet of water amidships, the stem was barely afloat, and the stern was buried in four feet of sand. As time passed, the big ship snuggled down in a bed of sand amidships estimated at about eight feet. *The strain was terrific on the hull and the plates in the bottom buckled badly and the boilers and engines became useless.*

"The prompt work of the tugs kept the ship from pounding to pieces and permitted the operations to be conducted successfully afterwards. Captain Cecil M. Brown* appeared at the wreck on Monday afternoon at 4:30 o'clock aboard the tug *Chief*. He hoped to get aboard the *Arakan*, but, owing to the rough surf, dashing against the steel hull and breaking clear over the bridge, the plan had to be abandoned. In the meantime the *Sea Queen* and *Sea King* had returned to San Francisco and the tugs *Sea Fox* and *Restless* had taken the lines from the *Arakan*.

* Of the Board of Marine Underwriters, San Francisco.

"Captain Brown released the *Chief* that night and waited for the arrival of the *Homer*.* She encountered a heavy fog at the harbor entrance and had to feel her way to the wreck, by following the breaker line. She anchored in a position 1000 feet from the *Arakan* on Tuesday at 4 a. m. In the meantime the steamer had started to broach to the beach again and there was a battle of the tugs for many hours before the hull lined out straight from the beach.

This picture, taken from an aeroplane, the "Arakan" gripped by the sand of Point Reyes, Cal. She is the only vessel ever to touch on Point Reyes and come off again.

"Immediately after the arrival of the *Homer*, Captain Brown came aboard and consulted with Captain Seike. It was decided to begin laying the moorings, including the big anchors, immediately. Simultaneously it was agreed that it would be best to run out the anchors of the *Arakan* and Captain Brown and Captain Langren shifted to the wreck. Brown put the engine room crew to work repairing two of the boilers and steam connections in order to have the necessary steam for working the ship's winches. This was done in a few hours and Langren ran the anchors. The port hook was carried back astern forty-five fathoms by the *Restless*, but the rough sea on the starboard side made necessary the use of the pontoon from the *Homer*. Previously this pontoon had been used to carry to the wreck the huge blocks, wire and other gear from the *Homer*.

"While this work was conducted aboard the *Arakan*, Captain Seike proceeded to lay his big anchors. These were laid in

* Salvage steamer.

tandem, each being marked by a small mooring. Longshoremen brought from San Francisco came aboard the *Arakan* in the afternoon and prepared to jettison such cargo as was deemed necessary by Captain Brown. They started work at 7 p. m. on Tuesday, but belayed at 8 o'clock because it was deemed best to refrain from lightening ship until all the purchases could be secured and a simultaneous pull exercised.

" Captain Seike completed laying the moorings on Tuesday just before midnight and all was in readiness to run the big five-inch wire from the main mooring to the *Arakan*. The tugboatmen refused to undertake this work until the morning because there was considerable danger that the hawsers might become fouled. Captain Langren ran the wire at 4 a. m. and Theodore Wicks, who was aboard the *Arakan* and in charge of the *Homer* share of the job, promptly made the end fast to one of the big blocks and started to take in the slack. At 7 a. m. this slack had been taken in and all was taut. The purchase on the ship's anchors had also been taken in and then the stevedores started to spill copra cake into the sea.

" Captain Brown, who kept in close touch with the operations, decided that a few hundred tons of cargo over the side would suffice, and when 350 tons of cake had been jettisoned he ordered all hands to belay. The purchases on anchors and moorings had been fleeted and at 10:30 a. m. there was a total strain estimated at better than 350 tons. Captain Brown was so certain that the ship would float at noon—high tide—that he flashed a message ashore to that effect.

" All about the scene was expectancy. The tugs *Alert* and *Intrepid* were stationed in readiness to take a tow when the ship slid off. No move was made until 11:30. The weather had cleared, until but little fog was in evidence. The tide rose constantly and then the hull began to grind a bit and rock as the huge pressure of the sea became manifest. The winchman took in just the slightest bit of slack that was now noted in the big five-inch line. Then the anchor chains were tautened a bit more. The tide was due to rise a few inches more at 11:45, when all of the lines began to sag a bit. The winchmen used a bit more of steam and then all realized that the ship was actually shifting from her sand cradle out toward the deep water. The ship moved faster, and just fourteen minutes before the noon hour and sixteen minutes after the full power of the purchases was effected, the *Arakan* was floating safely, ready to tow to San Francisco."

Here it will be noted that the *Arakan* was pulled off by her own winches. *Water jets might have been useful.*

The Floating of the *S. S. Ecuador*

The following letter by Capt. C. F. Deprê appeared in the Grace Log and contains several excellent points of seamanship.

" Speaking of shipwrecks, puts me in mind of one very serious stranding of the Pacific Steam Navigation Co. in 1900.

" On the 10th of July, 1900, a telegram was received at the head office, Valparaiso, that their *S. S. Ecuador* had run ashore at 6 a. m. on the day previous at Morgilla Beach, some fifteen miles south of Lebu and ninety miles north of Corral.

S. S. Ecuador ashore at Morgilla Beach. This picture was taken by Captain, Deprê at the time of the wreck.

" The ship struck the outside breakers just before dawn, and being light, as she only had 300 tons of cargo on board, was pushed shorewards bodily by the heavy seas. By midday the crew were landed by rocket apparatus, which had been set up by a boat's crew from the ship who had risked the landing. By evening all hands were on shore, and went to some nearby farm houses for the night.

" Mr. George Sharpe, the West Coast manager at Valparaiso, and Captain Harris, the Marine Superintendent, made a hurried trip south, and, after looking over the conditions, decided that an effort should be made to get the vessel off, as the hull was not damaged and engines and boilers were intact. I volunteered for the position of taking full charge of the salvage of the ship and got together a crew for the work.

" August 10th, or thirty days after the ship stranded, we started from Valparaiso for the wreck. The party consisted of Captain Depré, 20 A. B., 2 O. S., 2 firemen, 6 carpenters, 1 diver, 1 cook, 1 steward's boy, 34 all told. We arrived on board the wreck at 4 p. m., 16th of August, and at once set to work to clear up the wreckage, and sent the ship's crew to Valparaiso, where the Court of Enquiry was held at the British Consulate, and verdict given that the ship was set in during the night, and that no one was to blame for the accident.

" The plan to get the ship off was as follows: The company's tug *Assistance* was to bring down two anchors and 180 fathoms of 2-inch cable for each anchor. The anchors to be laid out seawards, and then 3-inch wires shackled on to the end of the cable chain, each about 1800 yards long, and to be hauled in by ropes floated to the ship on balsas fitted with sails and six empty barrels lashed to the sides of each, to give it more floating power. As the wind was nearly always from the south, the *Assistance* went well to the southward when sending the line. When we received the small line floated in by the balsa, we hove in until we received a 5-inch Manila hawser which brought in the wire.

How Wire Was Floated

" The wire was floated in on empty barrels lashed at intervals of about forty feet, and was a most successful way of floating in the wire without allowing it to drag on the bottom. After the two wires were received on board and set up with big purchased tackles, which were secured to the foot of the iron main-mast, and when spring tides came round, we pulled on the tackles for an hour before and after high-water, and we slowly pulled the ship's head around from N. N. E. to West, and on the 10th of October we made the first attempt to pull her out, but owing to a big sea running, we had to stack away the wire and allow her to fall in on the beach again. Another unsuccessful attempt was made on the 24th of October. Our third and successful effort was made on the 15th of November at night, and we pulled the ship off the outside breakers about midnight.

" At daybreak we hove up to our north anchor and proceeded under steam to Lebu, where we took in 100 tons of bunker coal and 400 tons in the hold as ballast, and sailed for Valparaiso twenty-four hours later. We arrived at Valparaiso on the 17th of November, at 6 p. m., and moored the ship awaiting dry dock. On the 19th of November, we entered the dry dock and found over 3000 rivets loose and the rudder post cracked, which had to be repaired.

" The ship was just three weeks in dry dock making repairs, and on the 10th of December took up her usual sailing to Port

Montt and way ports. Her starting out was most opportune for the company, as they were just starting to extend the line to San Francisco, and would not have been able to do so had the *Ecuador* not been floated and ready to take her run. The vessel was 118 days on the beach, and it was indeed wonderful that she suffered such small damage.

"In conclusion, I may say that I was specially promoted to command the ship I was successful in floating, and remained in command of her over a year, when I was promoted to a larger ship."

Here, as in the *Arakan*, the vessel came off with her winches working on a suitable purchase and without the use of tugs.

The salving of the *Arakan*, lying with engine disabled and on an exposed beach taken at full speed during high tide speaks well for the seamanship of the salvors. It also shows that a vessel need never be given up so long as she holds together.

The recent case of the refloating and refitting of the British ship *Andrina* run ashore on the sandy beach at Policarpe on the coast of Tierra del Fuego in the spring of 1899, and successfully floated off in February, 1918, by man power alone, is fresh in mind. She was five hundred meters farther up the beach when pulled off than when she struck. And after nineteen years of rest on the beach, $40,000 worth of cargo was salved by the seamen who took her off, re-rigged her and sailed her to New York to be refitted. She is now at sea under the Chilian flag, named the *Alejandrina*.

Vessels under certain conditions are freed from the grip of the sand by "*rocking them off*." Anchors are laid out to seaward and the making up of the sea helps the pull of the anchor cables, or any other means available, to move the vessel clear.

From the cases cited it will be seen that very many factors enter into the freeing of a vessel that has grounded. The *U. S. S. Vicksburg* ran on a sharp rock. She was floated off by cementing the rock into her bottom and by blasting it off outside of the hull. Hydraulic cement is most useful under many conditions where repairs have to be made to hulls. This is generally known as Portland Cement, and a considerable supply should be part of the ship's stores. It is most useful in many ways.

In lightening a ship by throwing cargo overboard, or *jettisoning* cargo, that part which floats is called *Flotsam*, the part which sinks is called *Jetsam*, and cargo that sinks but is marked by a buoy is called *Ligan*.

In grounding it is well to use any means at hand to loosen the grip of the bottom while at the same time kicking ahead, or astern, on the engines. In the experience mentioned at the beginning of this section, the writer put the Schoolship *Newport* hard and fast amidship of her length on a coral reef in Key West Harbor. A very brisk breeze was blowing at the time a point or so on the port bow. Soundings were taken at once locating the reef, all boats were made ready to lower, the fore yards were braced up sharp by starboard braces, the fore topsail (single) was loosed, sheeted home and hoisted flat. Then at a given word, boats were lowered, fore topsail was boxed around by port braces, and the engine kicked hard astern as she began to heel and pivot. The vessel slid off the bottom without damage. Just then two powerful navy tugs steamed alongside. It was a rather agreeable thing to inform the youngster in command of the tugs that assistance was not required, " thank you!"

Remember these things—
If your vessel runs aground.
Know state of tide.
Sound all around.
Form a plan—be careful.
Have all forces act *together*.
Lay out anchors if it can be done—*at once*.
If bow on, try to keep stern free.
When tide and wind are right, trim tanks, drop weights. Work *all* freeing agencies together.

When in a bad fix don't hesitate to take assistance when you need it. Make no bargains, if possible, unless you are certain to make a good one—then get it in writing. The shipmaster should always remember that his business on the sea is that of a merchant, out to make money for his owners, and by the same token he is looked upon as fair prey for anyone who can get the best of him in a matter of business. As soon as a vessel meets with trouble this unpleasant but important side of seafaring comes to the fore.*

* The *Handbook for Masters* by W. H. LaBoyteaux has a fine chapter on " First Aid to Stranded Vessels."

XVI

Fire

The fire drill and the fire mains and connections have been taken up in previous chapters. Here the larger questions of ship handling when fire is discovered on board will be considered. A fire when alongside, where shore assistance is at hand, need not be specially considered. The usual methods of fire fighting are employed, fire boats, fire engines, and fire hydrants from the shore, supplement the equipment of the vessel. The saving of life is less difficult, though very severe fire losses have been suffered alongside of wharves. Many will remember the burning of the German liners at Hoboken some years ago and the terrible loss of life. Ports were so small that men caught below decks could not get through to safety and perished miserably in the flames. A good precaution, already mentioned, is to run a wire *fire warp* along any dock filled with inflammable material. Should fire start on the wharf, and the engines not be in commission, or tugs not be handy, the vessel has a chance to work clear of the wharf. All fire hose couplings on ship and shore should be of standard size.

The *general fire alarm* on board ship is a rapid ringing of the ship's bell. Other fire alarms are fitted in all living and working compartments and are of the same character, namely, a rapid ringing of an alarm gong.

Fire stations (see the general *Station Bill.* Page 381.)

Upon the discovery of fire, sound the alarm and order all hands to fire stations. On a passenger vessel swing out boats (unless weather forbids). *Consider the fire to be serious unless certain of the contrary.* Every fire may soon spread and with certain cargoes the danger is extreme.

Close all openings to hold or compartment where fire is located. Start all smothering agencies. Be certain that men have left hold or compartment before turning on steam or carbon dioxide gas. Where a sprinkler system is used the water can be turned on at once, if it is not automatic.

Weather and sea permitting, place the vessel directly under the wind. Avoid excessive rolling, or wallowing in the sea. Moderate speed may be preferable to this, as it shakes up the fire and adds to its intensity.

On a sailer clew up the courses and shorten sail, but do not allow her to roll more than is necessary.

Smoke helmets and masks should be out, as part of the fire drill routine and used before sending men into the holds.

Where a fire gains headway rapidly and is located in a lower hold it is sometimes possible to extinguish it by opening sea cocks and flooding the hold through the bilge suctions. Knowing the condition of stability this can be done and the hold pumped out when the fire is extinguished. The kind and permeability of the cargo in the hold should be considered when attempting this. A master would be justified, under certain favorable conditions of the sea, to lower his freeboard until practically awash—always keeping his pumps in hand and watching the weather.

The cargo diagram, the nature of cargo, or bunker coal, on fire, and the kind and location of inflammable materials surrounding the fire are all to be considered.

When fire starts all dangerous cargo, even some distance from the fire, should be made ready to throw overboard. Adjacent holds should be filled with gas—as this will usually not harm the cargo—or with steam, after the hold on fire has been filled.

When fire starts it is well to radio facts to owners and if it cannot be controlled make for nearest safe port, stating route and speed.

When in shallow waters and with fire gaining on extinguishing efforts, carefully select position for scuttling ship at last recourse. Hard clean sand bottom, if available. Sheltered location. Vessel just awash at high tide, out of fairway, as near port as possible. These are the most desirable points to have in mind.

Bring ship to, take soundings, anchor by short scope, open sea cocks, turn condenser discharge into bilges, open injection valves, draw fires, blow off steam, get boats ready, save ship's valuables, papers, etc. Lift hatch covers, if necessary to allow escape of air, and open all sluice gates to equalize the water level. Get accurate bearings of vessel on chart, and note same—have them checked by an officer, as masts and upper works may be carried away and vessel may drop from sight after abandonment.

Causes of Fire on Board Ship

Fire may start in so many ways that to attempt to enumerate would be useless. One general rule can be set down. *Fire always starts because some one has been careless.*

It may be the fault of the cargo, its improper condition, or because it contains some forbidden dangerous ingredient. Poor or careless stowage, oily waste hidden near some inflammable stuff. Defective electrical insulation. Sparks down a ventilator. Poor ventilation, as in the case of a coal cargo.

The spontaneous combustion of bituminous coal in holds or bunkers may happen on any voyage. It is careless and improper to stow other inflammable cargo over coal or near it, unless this cannot be avoided. (See instructions for stowing coal cargo, page 310.)

Lightning may strike the vessel and set her on fire. This is an act of God, and no one can be blamed.

Prevention of Fire

Take the utmost precaution in stowage, in the carrying of lights into holds, in the closing of ventilators in the wake of sparks. Smoking in holds should be forbidden at all times. Officers must look after this themselves. There is very little fire, pilfering, or other irregularity, on a vessel where the officer personnel is strictly on the job in the interest of the ship.

The regulations for the stowage of dangerous cargo should be strictly adhered to (see page 272).

Fire Detectors

A number of very satisfactory systems of fire detection have been devised. The systems may be divided as follows:

Thermostatic alarms, carrying an alarm at the rise in temperature.

Smoke pipe lines, carrying smoke into a detecting cabinet.

The first system may operate in a number of ways. The *Mount Thermostatic Wire System* carries an alarm to any point or points desired, the cargo and other compartments being wired and connected to thermostats that complete the alarm circuits at any desired rise in temperature.

The *Aero Automatic Fire Alarm* consists of a small tube extending around the mouldings of passageways and staterooms and in suitable corners of the holds where it will be protected from damage by cargo. A rise in temperature expands the air in the tubes leading to a detection cabinet. A diaphragm is moved by the expanded air, a circuit is closed and a bell rings, etc.

In both of the above systems the hold or compartment must also be piped with the usual smothering lines for the admission of steam, or CO_2 gas.

In the second system a series of air pipes lead from smoke collectors in the holds to a detection cabinet in the wheelhouse. These pipes are constantly being exhausted by a small fan. A wisp of smoke is easily seen, or if the exhaust is in a closed wheelhouse the smell of smoke is noticeable.

This is a very sensitive system. It takes about five minutes for the smoke to come from the farthest hold to the bridge on a vessel of average size.

As smoke is usually formed some time before the temperature rises to an appreciable extent, this system has much to recommend it.

It has an added advantage in that the smoke detecting lines are also available for carrying steam or CO_2 gas into the holds.

This is the *Rich System*, and the makers claim it has the further advantage of enabling the state of a hold to be determined by stopping the steam, or gas, and trying for smoke. If the fire is still going evidence is soon forthcoming. If out no smoke will appear and it is reasonably safe to open up hatches if necessary.

Automatic sprinklers are being fitted in many ships. In order to avoid freezing in cold weather, the *dry pipe system* is used. This is, the pipes are filled with air under pressure and when this is released by the melting of the releasing links of the sprinkler heads, water rushes through the pipes to the seat of the fire.

This system may be adopted to the distribution of CO_2 gas, either liquid or under pressure.

The *Lux System* carries the liquid gas to the discharging head where it vaporizes. The distribution of the pipes is shown in the sketch. The pipes may be as small as ½″ in diameter. The liquid gas is immediately brought to the nozzle by the pressure of the containers. Immediately upon its release it vaporizes, causing a drop in the temperature of the room in which it is released.

A very interesting pamphlet is issued by the Department of Commerce detailing the Proceedings of a Conference on Automatic Sprinklers on Vessels held at the Department in May, 1916. This can be had by addressing the Department.

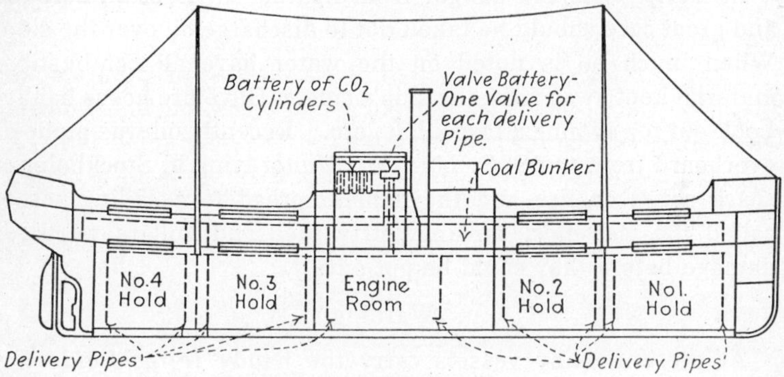

Lux Fire extinguishing system.

The *Grinnell Automatic Sprinkler* is designed for shipboard use so that no matter what happens to a sprinkler head no water will be discharged on the cargo unless the pipe line has first been filled through a separate thermostatic control. That is, in the event of a fire a thermostatic control fills the pipes, and then the sprinkler heads work in the usual way, those near the fire opening up and discharging on the flames.

Carbon Dioxide

Carbon dioxide is not dangerous to life except that it asphyxiates from lack of air. It is not an explosive gas. Its presence can be determined by lowering a candle into the area where it is supposed to be. If the candle goes out, it is not safe for a person to breathe the air. Carbon dioxide is perfectly stable, and can be kept indefinitely without changing its properties. A man can live for a limited time in an atmosphere containing 10 to 15 per cent. It does not require 100 per cent to extinguish a fire.

At 30 to 40 per cent the fire will go out. It is not injurious to merchandise. One of the 20-pound cylinders, which are about 4 feet high and 8 inches in diameter, would take care of at least 320 cubic feet of air, and probably as much as 400 to 500 feet, and a 50-pound cylinder would take care of not less than 800 cubic feet of air, and probably 1,000 to 1,200 cubic feet.

Floating Oil

In many ports the danger from floating oil is often serious, and great care should be taken not to discharge oil over the side. When much oil is noted on the water have all combustible material kept away from the ship's side. Have fire hoses handy. Look out for awnings, tarpaulins, etc. Recently oil was pumped overboard from the S. S. *Lordship Manor* lying in Stockholm, a spark set it on fire and the flames spread to a sailing vessel called the *Advance*, causing thirty thousand dollars worth of damage before they could be put out.

Warning

At present many vessels carry the handy *tetrachloride* fire extinguishers. Use great caution in discharging these while confined in a small state room or compartment. The fumes are about as powerful in extinguishing the life of man as they are in putting out a fire. Two men were recently killed in the Portsmouth Navy Yard when they attempted to put out a fire in a submarine, using this handy extinguisher.

Generally a fire aboard ship originates in the coal bunkers and may keep on going for weeks at a time. The writer recalls such a fire starting a few days out of St. Lucia and continuing for some six weeks well up into the Pacific. The decks during that time were so hot that planks were scorched.

Fire in a wooden ship may also be a long dragged out affair. Often crews abandon ships on the strength of thick smoke, or a harmless explosion. This was supposed to have been the cause of the abandonment of the brig *Marie Celeste*, found afloat with her hatches off, a fowl roasting in the galley, and all hands gone, the ship sailing along in fine weather with no one on board.

The following experience of the wooden ship *Twin Brothers* shows the endurance of even a wooden craft when a coal fire starts.

The *Twin Brothers*, engaged some years ago is the wheat trade between San Francisco and Liverpool. The vessel was returning from the latter port with a thousand tons of coal in the hold as ballast. Just after she rounded Cape Horn it was discovered that the coal was on fire.

There was a steam pump on board, and after closing the lower hatches the crew flooded the hold until the ship had settled about four feet lower in the water. No one was frightened and every one was confident that the ship would be safely brought into port at San Francisco. Call was made at Valparaiso, but not a man deserted the ship.

The vessel was seventy-two days in reaching San Francisco from the Horn, and all that time the coal burned, and little streams of smoke could be seen coming through the cracks in the deck. Arriving at San Francisco the *Twin Brothers* sailed out on the mud flats and was flooded until she settled almost even with her upper deck. This extinguished the fire.

The appearance of the vessel after all this was pretty fair evidence what a ship may survive in the way of fire damage. In a dozen places the bottom had burned through, and all that was between the crew and the deep sea was the thin sheet of copper bottom. The weight of the coal and the pressure of the water kept about equal strain on both sides of the copper sheathing, and it had not broken through, although it was little thicker than an ordinary tin pan.

Sulphur Fires

Statement of Capt. Arthur N. McGray before Commerce Dept. Conference on Fire at Sea, Washington, May 3, 1918.

"A number of fires occurred in the bulk sulphur cargoes of the steamers *Herman Frasch*, and *Frieda* during my command of those ships. Theoretically, the best means of extinguishing a sulphur fire is for a shovel brigade to heap on more sulphur and smother the fire. This plan, however, works poorly in practice, as it is impossible to know exactly what is happening underneath, and the confinement of the gases, which generate very rapidly when sulphur begins to fuse, presents an explosive menace which it were well to avoid. I have used steam jets from the standard fire-smothering equipment of the ship on several occasions, but to little or no purpose. The liberal use of water has been the only adequate answer I have discovered so far, but on two occasions this involved entering a hold filled with strong sulphurous fumes in order to direct the hose effectively. The risk to be incurred appeared greater than I felt justified in ordering officers or crew to accept, so the only road open was to personally handle both hose and nozzle. I was impressed at this time with the fact that it was not my ship itself which was burning or which was in imminent danger, but that it was the cargo within the vessel."

Morro Castle. This disastrous fire has emphasized, as nothing else, the need for seamanlike precautions, and the necessity of a well drilled competent crew. No mechanical devices can take the place of control of passengers through organization, once a fire has started.

Smoke helmets are carried by many vessels. Practice in the use of the apparatus is very desirable. Such helmets, as gas masks are often very useful when ammonia or other fumes get loose about the holds or compartments. This sort of apparatus should be carefully looked after by the chief mate.

XVII

Ship's Business

Salvage. Salvage is to the merchant seaman what prize money is to the naval seaman (unfortunately for the American naval seaman it is, "*was*"). Here the possibility of a tidy sum, even a fortune, always stands before him off somewhere in the mystery and adventure that lies ahead. To quote from "Hughes On Admiralty."

" The right of salvage depends on no contract. A salvor who rescues valuable ships or cargoes from the grasp of wind and wave, the embrace of rocky ledges or the devouring flame, need prove no bargain with its owner as the basis of recovering a reward.

" He is paid by the courts *from motives of public policy*—paid not merely for the value of his time and labor in the special case, *but a bounty in addition, so that he may be encouraged to do the like again.*"

And while quoting from Hughes, it may be just as well to strongly recommend this standard work on Admiralty to all seamen, deck and engineers. It is a book on the law of admiralty so clearly written and so filled with useful information that no seafarer should fail to own it and study it. Hughes goes into the law and adjusting of salvage awards which need not trouble us here. We merely bring up the question of salvage to further impress upon the mind of the seaman the *valuable* side of seamanship, of ship handling, and of a clear knowledge of the forces and materials of his ancient profession.

Salvage operations are also those in which wrecked property is recovered. The Master, at least, should have a definite idea of how vessels are salvaged. Of the limits to which a diver can work, of the pumps, cranes, floats, cofferdams, and the like that may be employed to float and recover ships and cargoes.

Data for the Master

In Case of Disaster. 1. Take all necessary measures for relief, recovery and preservation of property.

2. Advise owners at once by cable.

3. Cut down all unnecessary expense.

Forced Sale. The immediate sale of wrecked or damaged property, without orders from owners, is only legal or justifiable, if destruction is impending for the vessel from perils beyond the control of the master and which tend to increase quickly from *lapse of time.*

If a vessel is on the rocks, bilged, full of water, exposed to the waves so that she is almost certain to break up from hour to hour, the master may act on his own responsibility.

If the cargo is in danger of rotting, or when a refrigerator plant breaks down—then a prompt sale may be the only method of saving anything.

Expense to Save Insured Property. It is a grave error on the part of a master to neglect to save property known to be insured, even when the attempt to do so will cost some money, under the mistaken idea that such expense will not be recoverable in case of failure.

The master, acting as agent for the assured, is empowered to do all he can for the preservation of the property in his charge, and the underwriters are bound to pay their portion of the expense whether the property be saved or not.

Repairs in Port. As soon as a vessel has been relieved of

immediate danger, she must be repaired as speedily and as economically as possible.

When repairs may not be made:

If absolutely beyond repair.

If the estimated cost of the repairs, at the place, and under the circumstances, would in gross exceed her value after repairs.

Repairs at Sea. Loss or injury of spars, sails, rigging, rudder, etc., should be made good at sea by experienced seamen. Such jury rigs may often serve until a vessel arrives at a home port, or a port where repairs can be economically made. Spare gear, spars, wire blocks, etc., should always be carried. Masters and engineers effecting repairs at sea find favor with the underwriters.

Responsibility of Master. The master is the responsible manager in a port of distress, as in all other circumstances and places. He cannot be relieved of this responsibility so long as he is competent to attend to business.

In all cases the master should enter a protest before the American Consul, who will appoint a committee of three to assist and advise the master. One member of the committee will be the local representative of the American Bureau of Shipping.

The powers of the committee are limited to giving advice. It remains for the master to decide whether he will follow their advice. If he follows bad advice, a total loss to his owners or underwriters may ensue, or at any rate an enormous average may be incurred.

The master must remember that no underwriter, agent, surveyor, or consignee, has the right to *order* him to take any measure at all. Only his *owner* has that *right.* Others can only recommend.

The following hints may be useful.

Energetic Action. Take energetic action immediately on getting into trouble to get out of it as quickly as possible, though it involves sacrifice of anchors, masts, deck load or jettison of cargo. If ashore, on a falling tide, very prompt measures in dropping weight may be necessary.

Salvage Agreements. Have salvage agreements in writing, if possible.

Discharge of Cargo at Port of Disaster. Cargoes should not be discharged at a port of disaster without the clearest necessity.

Surveys. The master should see that reports of surveys distinguish between repairs attributable to the perils insured against, and other repairs due to wear and tear, or to original defects, natural decay or depreciation of the vessel. This will enable the average adjusters to make a correct statement.

Disbursements. The master should see that disbursements are charged to their correct uses such as, salvage expense, general average expense, and repairs. Particular average expenses and repairs, and special charges for items that do not come under any of these heads.

These divisions of expenditure should be kept carefully distinct, especially when repairs are undertaken by contract. In this care the contractor should be required to apportion the total into the above division coming under his work. This will help in the preparation of the average statement.

The particulars of expenditure cannot be too complete.

Give the fullest possible information.

Funds. A master may obtain funds as follows:

A. By draft on his owners.

B. By a bottomry bond on ship and freight.

C. If absolutely necessary by a bottomry or respondentia bond on ship, freight and cargo.

D. By the sale of a *portion* of the cargo. Cargo should be sold as follows:

1st. Any damaged goods condemned by the surveyor as unfit to go forward and recommended by them to be sold.

2d. Cargo that will bring the highest price at the port of distress, compared with its value at the port of destination.

E. If the ship be condemned and the cargo forwarded by another vessel, the master can give a respondentia bond on the cargo alone, but only for that portion of the whole expense for which the cargo alone is responsible. In this case the sale of the vessel will supply funds for her proportion of the expense.

Ship's Papers

To round out the preceding sections it may be well to briefly indicate the kind and nature of the documents carried by a merchant vessel. A book on seamanship is not the place to go into the matter of ship business fully. The reader is advised to consult *Hughes on Admiralty*, referred to above. *Ocean Shipping*, by *Annin, Handbook for Masters by La Boyteaux, Marine Insurance* by *Huebner*, and the writer's *The Men on Deck*. These books cover the law, the method of doing ship's business and the regulations and responsibilities of the master.

The *Ship's Papers* are—

The Register—her evidence of nationality. Gives name of master, and all necessary data as to home port, size, owners, etc.

Certificate of Classification carried by vessels complying with the requirements of the American Bureau of Shipping. The continuance of classification of any vessel is conditional upon full compliance with the rules.

Periodical surveys must be carried out every four years and special surveys whenever required.

To maintain class a surveyor must be called whenever vessel is dry docked, caulked, or repaired. In case of damage at any time vessel must be surveyed. Violation of any condition of the rules renders class void. See page 36.

Certificate of Freeboard shows the assigned position of the load line disc which must be permanently marked, the particulars given in the Certificate must be entered in the Official Log and the Certificate of Freeboard must be framed and placed in a conspicuous place. This is also issued by the American Bureau of Shipping.

Certificate of Inspection is issued by the U. S. Steamboat Inspection Service and states that the Inspectors approve the vessel and her equipment throughout. It also must be framed and placed in a conspicuous place.

Tonnage Certificate for Panama and Suez Canals.

A Seaworthy Certificate is issued by a Classification Surveyer and attests the good condition of the vessel. See page 766.

Sea Letter. A document issued to unregistered vessels owned by citizens of the United States and issued by the Customs authorities. It certifies to the nationality and ownership of the vessel.

The Articles of Agreement—these recount the voyage and its duration. The names and ratings of all members of the crew and their compensation, and the time of the commencement of their service. The *Crew List* is a separate paper.

Clearance—the official permission to sail from her port of departure. Shows that all port dues and charges have been paid, port of destination, etc.

Bill of Health—shows condition of the health of all on board, port of destination, etc. Bill of health, in duplicate, should be obtained from U. S. Consuls abroad.

Charter Party—contract between owner of vessel and charterer, or shipper. Carried where the vessel is under charter.

Manifest—a detailed account of the cargo on board, names of the consignee, consignor, ports of loading and discharging same, marks, etc.

Bills of Lading—the bill, signed by the master, or owner, or agent, receipting for the lading of the goods on board ship, in good condition. It promises to deliver them safely at the place agreed upon, perils of the sea, excepted.

Passenger List—contains names and destination of passengers. A part of manifest.

Stores List—contains detailed account of ship's stores must be complete when entering port, showing all unbroken and broken stores.

Invoice. This document must contain a detailed account of the cargo, stating the number of packages, value, charges, freight, insurance, marks and numbers. Also the name of the vessel, her master, port of destination and name of consignee.

The Log—gives history of the voyage to date. A log that is not written up each watch is useless. The *smooth log* is a copy of the *rough log*. The latter is the original and valuable record. The *Official Log* is supplied by the Government. See page 766.

Ship's Business Definitions

Charter Party. A mercantile lease of a vessel; a specific contract by which the owners of a vessel let the entire vessel to another person, to be used by him for transportation for his own account, either under their charge or his. When the vessel remains in charge of the owners it constitutes a Contract of Affreightment.

Time Charter. The owner hires his ship out for a definite time and usually supplies crew, coal and stores.

Voyage Charter. The owner hires his ship out for a definite trip, as, for example, a single trip between two points or a round trip between two ports with intermediate stops in both or one direction. Owner furnishes Crew, coal and stores.

Tonnage Charter. Charterer pays a certain rate per registered ton, or per ton dead weight capacity.

Bare Boat or Bare Pole Charter. Charterer furnishes crew, coal and stores. Partial bare boat charter sometimes occurs wherein charterer agrees to the owner furnishing the crew, in which case the latter is also responsible for their welfare.

Lump Sum Charters. The Charterer pays a lump sum fixed price for the ship; the owner gets his money whether cargo is put on board or not.

Contract of Affreightment. When a vessel is operated by her owners on their own account, or contracts directly with her shippers.

Lay Days. The days allowed by the Charter party for loading or unloading a vessel. Beyond that time it involves the payment of demurrage.

Demurrage. Is the compensation to be paid for the detention of a vessel beyond the time provided for in the Charter Party, and must be claimed daily. The owner of a vessel has no claim on the cargo for demurrage unless so stated in the bill of lading, and therefore it is important that this clause should be inserted. Where there are both charter party and bill of lading the former should be endorsed as follows: "Paying freight and other charges as per charter party, with all conditions therein." Demurrage claims cease when all the cargo is out of the vessel.

Protest. Or "Writ of Protest" as it is often termed, is a declaration made by the master of a vessel before a Notary, or Consul if in a foreign port, within twenty four hours after the arrival of the vessel in port after the disaster stating that he anticipates that the ship or cargo or both are damaged, and that the same was not due to any fault of the vessel, her officers, or crew, but to the perils of the sea, and protesting against them.

It must be signed by the master and some member of the crew. Afterward it may be extended to show particulars of storms, etc., that caused the damage. The log book should support the statements made in the protest.

After noting a protest, a survey of the ship and cargo must be made before breaking bulk and to begin by opening hatches. Where merchants are acting as surveyors, they should submit some evidence to the Master that they are not in any way interested in the cargo.

To prevent any claim on the ship for damage by water, the Surveyors must certify that the hatches were properly secured, the cargo properly dunnaged; and to make a claim on the underwriters, or enable the Consignor to make such a claim, the surveyors must certify that the cargo is damaged by sea water.

Copy of the protest should be sent to the owners of the vessel.

General Average. Is the principle of law which requires that the parties interested in a marine venture shall contribute to make up the loss of the sufferer when there is a voluntary sacrifice of part of the venture, made by the Master or representative of all concerned, for the benefit of all.

To give the right to claim a general average contribution, the sacrifice

(*a*) Must be voluntary.

(*b*) Must be made by the master or by his authority.

(*c*) Must not be caused by any fault of the party asking the contribution.

(*d*) Must be successful.

(*e*) Must be necessary.

York-Antwerp rules relating to the settlement of cases of general averages are usually adopted, but such must be specifically stated in Bills of Lading or Charter Parties.

It is called General Average because it falls upon the gross amount of ship, cargo and freight at risk and saved by sacrifice.

Some evidence should be produced to show that the sacrifice was necessary and such should be supported by entries in the Log Book.

The ship may hold the cargo until General Average Claim is satisfied but care must be exercised that cargo so held is not of a perishable nature and the ship be later responsible for its destruction through such detention.

Particular Average. Signifies the damage or partial loss happening to the ship, or cargo, or freight in consequence of some fortuitous or unavoidable accident; and it is borne by the individual owners of the articles damaged, or by their insurers.

Petty Averages. A term now seldom heard. Are small sundry charges which occur regularly and are necessarily defrayed by the master in the usual course of the voyage such as port charges, common pilotage and the like which were formerly and in many cases still are borne by the ship and partly by the cargo. In the clause commonly found in a Bill of Lading (primage and average accustomed) average means a kind of composition established by usage for such charges, which were formerly assessed by way of average.

Mortgage. A mortgage is a transaction whereby the ship is given as security for money advanced to the *owner* and he may spend it in any manner he sees fit.

Bottomry Bond. A contract in the nature of a mortgage, by which the owner of a ship or the master, as his agent, hypothecates and binds the ship (and sometimes) freight as security for the repayment of money advanced or lent for the use of the ship, if she terminate her voyage successfully.

If the ship is lost by the perils of the sea, the lender loses the money, but if the ship arrives safe, he is to receive the money lent, with the interest and premium stipulated, although it may be, and usually is, in excess of the legal rates of interest.

Respondentia Bond. When sufficient money cannot be borrowed on the ship and freight the cargo is given as security. This should never be resorted to if it is at all possible to avoid it. The contract is the same as bottomry but has priorty to such in claims.

Freight. The word "Freight" is sometimes used as a term meaning cargo. It is the amount agreed upon in payment for the transportation of cargo and should never be used in any other sense. The freight may be demanded before the cargo is delivered to the consignee. It is generally paid when cargo is on board.

Dead Freight. When the Charterer agrees to give the ship a full cargo and for any reason does not do so, he must also pay the freight on the quantity that will be required to finish the loading. After this payment (which must be collected at the port of loading) is made the ship must not take on any more cargo but proceed to her destination without any unnecessary delay, unless she is so loaded as not to be seaworthy. However, it might be advantageous to the ship to make slight concession to the charterer to free the ship from all responsibility for delay caused by completing the cargo with goods from another party, and even another port.

Pratique. A certificate given after compliance with quarantine regulations permitting a ship to land her passengers and crew.

No member of the crew or any passenger must leave the ship and no person must be allowed to board her, except the pilot; until the health authorities have boarded her and given permission, which they will do if the ship has a clean bill of Health.

In ports that are infected with infectious diseases no member of the crew should be permitted to go ashore and natives should not be allowed on board, except on business concerning the ship. Every reasonable care must be taken to safeguard the crew from infectious or contagious diseases.

Port Charges and General Expenses. Pilotage, tonnage, provisions, water, harbor and hospital dues, cost of labor for discharging and loading, wharfage, cost of coal and other expenses to which a ship is liable to be subjected.

A ship should never be chartered for a port of which the master and owner have no knowledge until further information of the place has been obtained. It is important to know if the port affords a safe harbor, or is an open roadstead, the depth of the water and the harbor regulations.

Where ship must call at two ports in the tropics, whether the first port is to windward or to leeward, should be considered.

Vouchers. All receipts for money expended, should clearly state the purpose for which such expenditures were made.

Marine Insurance is insurance against risks connected with navigation, to which a ship, cargo, freight or other insurable interest in such property may be exposed during a certain voyage or fixed period of time.

The written contract of insurance is called a policy.

Insurable Interest. The party affecting marine insurance must be so situated with regard to the thing insured as to expect pecuniary benefit from its safety of pecuniary loss from its destruction.

Contracts of marine insurance are subject to certain conditions, express or implied, a breach of which voids the contract.

Misrepresentation and concealment of any material fact, or any breach of warranty of any fact, will void the policy.

Seaworthiness. It is an implied condition of marine insurance of a vessel, cargo, freight, that the vessel shall be seaworthy. She must be sufficiently tight, staunch and strong to resist the ordinary attacks of wind and sea during the voyage for which she is insured, and that she must be properly stowed, manned and equipped for the voyage.—This is often slated in a *Seaworthy Certificate* signed by an authorized surveyer. Proper stowage may be attested by a *Loading Certificate.*

Deviation. It is an implied condition of a voyage policy that the vessel will take the course of sailing fixed by commercial custom between two ports, or if none is fixed, that it will take the course that a master of ordinary skill would adopt. Any departure from such course, or unreasonable delay in pursuing the voyage, constitutes what is known as " deviation."

Illegal Traffic. It is an implied condition that a vessel shall not engage in illegal traffic (trade).

Perils of the Seas. Mean all losses or damage which arise from the extraordinary action of the wind and sea, or from extraordinary causes external to the ship, and originating on navigable waters.

Official Log Book. This book is supplied to masters by the U. S. Shipping Commissioners and in it must be recorded all events of importance. The list of the crew, deaths, births, marriages, collisions, offences, fines and punishments, sending a passenger or a member of the crew to the hospital, etc., are important matters and must be recorded.

Certain spaces are arranged in the book for keeping account of any dealing seamen may have with the ship. The book contains full instructions for its use and is to be handed to the U. S. Shipping Commissioner on arrival in port and is used by him in paying off the crew and preparing their discharges.

Precautions. Never sign a receipt for cargo until its condition is known, and, if not in proper condition, state the facts to the person delivering the goods, and, if he wishes to leave them, state the incompleteness, damage, breakage, leakage, shortage or any other fault, on the receipt, in ink, before signing the same.

Never sign any paper or bill until its contents are known and thoroughly understood.

If in doubt about the signing of any paper, postpone it and think it over or consult some reliable person from whom information on your subject may be obtained.

Before signing any paper written in a foreign language, insist on having a true certified copy of the same in some language you understand.

Before starting on a voyage the Master should have a conference with the managing owner, or director, covering all possible points of the voyage. He should receive a letter of voyage instructions with all it contains clearly understood.

Never permit any person to perform any service whatsoever for a ship unless some kind of an understanding or agreement has first been arranged.

In Time of War

A merchantman in time of war must be guided by certain recognized rules of international law. The *right of search* is accorded to a duly commissioned belligerent vessel of war which has the right to stop and search any merchant vessel.

The *right of approach* is the right of any vessel of war to approach a merchant vessel on the high seas for purposes of observation and verification of character and flag. The merchantman need not heave to, and no force is used except where piracy, or slave trade, or other irregularity is suspected. Merchant vessels approached by a man of war should show their colors as a matter of courtesy.

Blockades

A neutral merchantman may be bound for a blockaded port and still not be held liable to violation of blockade if she has no knowledge of the blockade through same not having reached her port of departure before sailing.

CHAPTER XIX

HANDLING A SAILER

I

Foreword

The writer believes that sailing is something to be mastered progressively. Small boat sailing should be part of all sea training. No finer sport exists than boat sailing and as yachts increase in size only the millionaire can enjoy the sport on his own. But even the most wealthy yachtsman falls short of sailing the great craft that merchant seamen take around the world. The sailor with the real salt under his hide never fails to thrill to this greatest of all sports; his business is something more than a mere occupation.

While the art of handling a sailer is simple in the extreme, the amount of experience needed to master it is almost without limit, for new tricks come up every voyage. But all of the gear and the innumerable things that seem to be necessary to the handling of a sailer are based upon common sense. The young seaman, shipped in sail (and every lad who can should go out under canvas), may gain a great deal of valuable experience in a short time by making a study of the work as he goes along. So many men, at sea under sail, drag at braces and halliards, pulling, like the ox, without thought or knowledge of the object of their toil.

The fundamental principles of sailing have been set forth in the chapter on boat sailing, and need not be repeated here. The main evolutions under sail will be given.

A vessel under sail has free movement through an arc of the horizon extending six points each side of the wind, in the case of a square rigger and four points in the case of a fore and after.*

When the course to be made is anywhere within the restricted arc the vessel must sail close hauled, or, where the wind, in the case of a square rigger, is just six points away from the course to be made good, she may make her course by sailing *on the wind*. The terms used at sea for sailing on the wind, are *close*

*Many square rigged craft can only lay $6\frac{1}{2}$ & 7 points to the wind.

hauled, by the wind, full and by, and *on the port* (or starboard) *tack.*

A square rigger on the wind has her yards braced up sharp, the lower yards braced in close against the swifters, and the tacks of the courses are hauled down on the weather side, stretching the foot of the sail forward, the sheets to leeward are hauled aft.

Tacking

A vessel *tacks* when she *goes about* from one tack to another.

Tacking a full-rigged ship is quite an art. The procedure is as follows on a three-masted ship. And here the writer must apologize for quoting from his own book, *Under Sail*, in that way saving effort, and initiating the steamboat sailor into the mysteries of going about on a two thousand five hundred dead weight vessel, flying skysails, and working twenty hands. Most of the textbooks on this subject are men-of-war style with a large crew.

" With livelier weather of the Southern latitudes we were often exercised in tacking and wearing ship, and soon became a very well drilled company, sending the big three-sticker about in record time. The *Fuller* was lively in stays* and with our small crew required the smartest kind of work in handling.

" With all hands, including the ' idlers,' that is, the carpenter, cook and cabin steward, we mustered twenty men forward, hardly a man-o'-war complement, but enough, when driven and directed by superior seamanship, to send the long braces clicking through the sheaves of the patent blocks with a merry chatter.

" ' Hands about ship! ' meant all hands, *and the cook at the fore sheet*, a time-honored station filled by the Celestial with all the importance in the world. It was all the work that Chow ever did on deck and the heathenish glee with which he would ' let go ' at the proper time, added a certain zest to our movements, particularly as we always hoped to have a sea come over and douse him, which often happened.

" At the order, ' Ready! Ready! ' the gear of the main and cro'jik was thrown down from the pins, clear for running. The command ' Ease down the helm! ' and the order ' Spanker boom amidships! ' would quickly follow, the vessel running rapidly into the eye of the wind with everything shaking, and then flat aback.

" ' Rise tacks and sheets! ' and the hands at the clew garnets would sway up on the courses, lifting them clear of the bulwarks.

* A vessel is " in stays " when in the act of going about.

Then all hands would jump like monkeys to the main and cro'jik braces, at the order, 'Weather main, lee cro'jik braces!' the Second Mate, and Chips, standing by to cast off on the other sides. By then, *the wind being a point on the weather bow*, would come the hearty warning, 'Haul taut!' and 'Now, boys, mainsail haul!' and the after yards, aback, with the wind on their weather leeches, would spin about, the gear running through the blocks like snakes afire, the men on deck pawing it in at the pins with feverish haste, belaying as the yards slammed back against the lee swifters on the other tack.

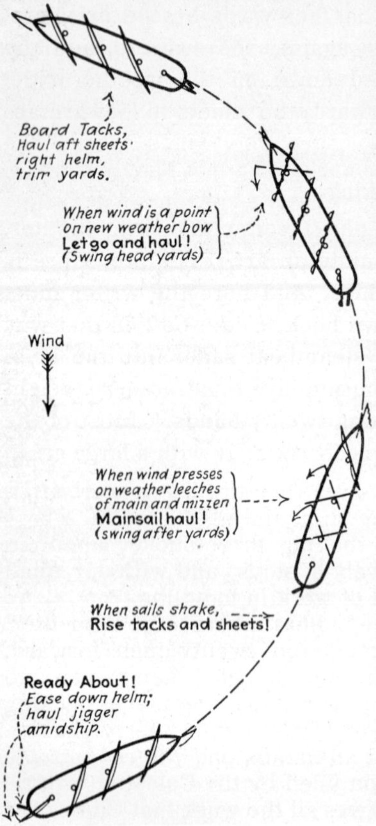

Tacking a fourmast ship.

"By that time the ship would be practically about, with head yards and head sails aiding in the work. As soon as the wind was on the bow, all hands would spring to the lee fore braces. 'Haul taut—*let go and haul!*' thundered the order from aft. Chow would let out a wild yell as he unhitched the fore sheet, and around would go the head yards. Then with jib sheets shifted over and the spanker eased off, as the tacks were boarded and the sheets hauled aft, we would pause to get our breath amid the tangle of gear on deck.

"'Steady out the bowlines—go below, watch below!' and as the watch below would leave the deck, the order 'Lay up the gear clear for running,' was the signal for the crowd on deck to get busy while the good ship raced away on the new tack with the wind six points on the bow, a bone in her teeth, and a half point of leeway showing in the wake."

Careful reading of the above will clarify the following:

Ready about! Crew takes stations for going about.

Spanker sheet is ready to be manned, boom guys slacked off.

Weather head sheets are hauled to windward over the stays.

As ship gets a good way upon her, easing her off a half point or so if necessary, haul the spanker boom amidships slowly and ease down the helm bringing her sharply up into the eye of the wind by the combined action of the rudder and the spanker. At the same time, ease off the head sheets as she runs up. The vessel is now pivoting through the action of the wind and helm.

At the order "ready, ready," the mainsail is hauled up just as it begins to shake. "*Rise tacks and sheets!*"

The head sails lie aback and aid in the turning and as the wind gets hold of the weather leeches of the main and mizzen canvas, the order is "*Mainsail haul!*" sending these yards around very rapidly and further easing the wind pressure aft that, if the yards are not swung at once, would tend to retard her turning into the eye of the wind.

As the after yards spin around, largely by the force of the wind, the vessel is well up with the wind a point on her new weather bow. Then give the order "*Let go and haul!*" The fore sheet and tack are let go, and the men, having jumped to the head braces, swing around the head yards. The wind by that time fills them. *Right the helm.* The spanker is eased off, the head sheets are hauled home. Yards are trimmed, main tack boarded and sheet hauled aft, and she is off on the new tack.

In tacking without the mainsail the order for swinging after yards is "*Main topsail haul!*"

The time to *right the helm* in tacking depends upon how quick a vessel is in stays. If the helm is kept hard over after the wind has shifted on the new weather bow and the ship is swinging fast she may fall off some distance. If she should fall of too rapidly and bring the wind abeam, or even abaft the beam, ease off head sheets, put the helm *a-lee*, and as she comes up ease the helm and haul aft the head sheets.

When a vessel loses way in tacking, *right the helm** at once. In this case the after yards must not be hauled until the wind is directly ahead.

A ship that is slow in stays may be sent about quicker by checking the lee fore brace as she comes up into the wind. If

* Put it amidship.

she gathers sternboard in coming about shift the helm at once, the head yards will then box her about.

The writer has found it a good plan not to haul the head yards until the wind is at least a point on the new weather bow. If a vessel refuses to come around after the head yards have been swung, brail up the spanker and shiver the cross-jack yards (*i.e.*, brace in and spill the wind).

Missing Stays

In this case either let her go around on her heel, that is *wear ship*, or let her fill and try again. In order to fill, it may be necessary to box her back with the head yards. Brace in on the weather braces, and let the head square sails box her off. The ship will have stern-board and the helm will have to be *down*.

A vessel refusing to turn, after yards swung, forward yards on old tack is said to be *in irons*. This is practically the same as missing stays—wear, or box off on old tack.

Before leaving the subject of tacking it may be well to indicate the station of a crew of twenty men on a large three-masted square rigger.

Boatswain and two men on the forecastle head, carpenter and sailmaker at the main tack, one man at the weather cross-jack braces, seven men at the weather main braces, second mate at the lee main braces, three men at the lee cross-jack braces, two men at the main sheet, and one man and cook at the fore sheet.

When it is "*Let go and haul?*"

Three men on the forecastle, all others at the lee fore braces and foresheet. Second mate at the weather fore braces. Those on the forecastle board the fore tack. One man at helm.

Four-masted ships, always bark rigged on the jiggermast, go about like a three master, handling the jigger like a spanker, and hanging the crossjack and mainsail in the gear at the order "*Rise tacks and sheets!*" See diagram, Page 770.

A five master, like the *France*, goes about swinging the three yards on the after square-rigged masts together. The fore yards "*Let go and haul*," as in the case of a three master.

Tacking a Barkentine

Here the evolution is greatly simplified.

Ready about! Stations for stays.

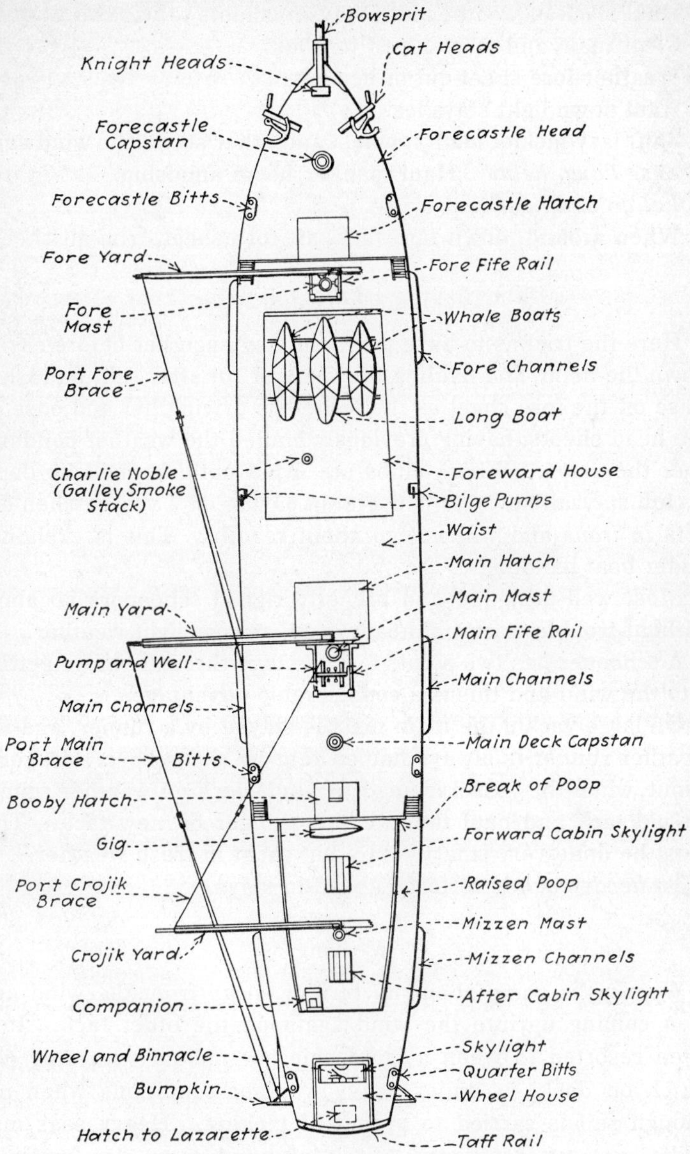

Deck plan of a three mast ship.

Haul slack of weather fore stays'le sheets to windward.
Clear main and mizzen gaff tops'les.
Weather fore sheet out of beckets.
Haul down light stays'les.
Shift lazy tack of main topmast and other stays'le to windward.
Ease down helm! Haul spanker boom amidship.
Let go and haul!
When around, down fore tack, aft fore sheet, trim all sheets.

Tacking a Fore and After

Here the trick is to have plenty of way upon her before easing down the helm, and hauling the spanker (or after sail) amidship. Ease off the fore sheet as the sail stops driving her and ease off the head sheets, having previously hauled the weather pendants over the stays. Where clubs are fitted nothing need be done. A club staysail however is useful in paying off a vessel when she gets *in irons* and will not go about readily. This is explained under boat handling.

Most well-designed and properly rigged schooners go about without trouble except in heavy seas, or very light weather.

A schooner has two points less to move through before getting into the wind and this is a considerable advantage.

On large yachts the main mast is stayed by a runner, and the weather runner is always hauled taut by a purchase. In going about, when the vessel is head to wind, slack off weather runner on old tack and haul taut weather runner on new tack. This must be done very smartly on a big yacht in fresh weather.

To *head-reach* is to forge ahead in stays.

Wearing

Wearing is going about by turning *away* from the wind and then coming up into the wind again on the other tack. It is often resorted to when a large ship goes about with only one watch on deck, or under heavy weather conditions when not enough sail is carried to permit of tacking. Heavy seas may make wearing necessary. Lack of wind may also make it necessary to wear.

Wearing a square rigger is simple. The spanker must be

brailed in, and as she falls off before the wind the after yards are braced in and around on the other tack.

The method of wearing a ship-rigged vessel is as follows—always having in mind the fact that sails should not be put aback, deadening her way.

Haul mainsail up, brail in the spanker, luff ship up until the weather leeches of the topsails shake; then hard up the helm, and brace the after yards in. Keep the sails shaking as she pays off, so that they may be well canted for the other tack by the time the wind is on the quarter. When the wind is abaft the beam, raise fore tack, and shift the head sheets over as soon as they are becalmed. The head yards being nearly becalmed, square them all the weather braces being slacked off roundly as the ship comes-to. Gather in the main and cross-jack braces while the head yards are being braced and fore-tack got down. In wearing under small sail in a ship that answers her weather helm slowly, take care that the maintopsail is not shaken until the ship begins to pay off.

Have in mind the danger of coming to the wind or *flying-to* so rapidly that the fore square sail may be put aback, and if she is lively brace sharp forward as soon as possible after the main and crossjack yards are braced up.

If blowing hard, brace up the fore yards while the vessel is still before the wind.

To Wear Short Round or Box Haul a Ship

Put the helm down, light up head sheets, and slack lee braces, to deaden her way. As she comes to the wind, raise tacks and sheets, and haul up the mainsail and the spanker. As soon as she comes head to the wind, and loses her head-way, square the after yards, brace the head yeards sharp aback, and flatten in the head sheet. The helm being put down to bring her up will now pay her off, as she has stern-way on. As she goes off, keep the after sails lifting, and square in the head yards. As soon as the sails on the foremast give her head-way, shift the helm. When she gets the wind on the other quarter, haul down the jib, haul out the spanker, set the mainsail, and brace the after yards sharp up. As she comes-to on the other tack, brace up the head yards, meet her with the helm, and set the jib.

Wearing a Fore and After

A schooner is put about by wearing when the wind is too light to admit of tacking, or where the sea is so high that she cannot come up to it and go about.

On a large schooner, say a five or six master, the sails go over in wearing in the following order, all booms being carefully steadied by sheets and boom tackles. As she pays off before the wind, haul over the boom next forward from the spanker, and then each succeeding boom forward. When the foresail is over on the new tack, steady the spanker amidship and ease it over with the boom tackle as the wind gybes the sail. The gear is heavy and rubber, or spring, buffers are now fitted to take up the shock on the sheet traveller. Watch out for heads, and mind the helm.

Before wearing the topsails are shifted over the stays.

Wearing is always a losing proposition, for this reason a square rigger often shivers her sails to lose some way before turning on her heel, but when she once starts turning the proper thing is to keep her going around fast. In a schooner the great size and swing of the sails makes the maneuver dangerous unless carried out by experienced seamen.

Square Foresail

Before going into heavy weather with our chapter on sailing, and before leaving the schooner, mention should be made of the square sail generally fitted on large fore and afters. This sail is a fair weather kite and is set from a stationary yard supported by standing lifts and parral, and controlled by braces in the usual way. The square foresail, however, is set by means of *head outhauls* bent to the head earings and leading out to the yardarms. The head of the sail is stopped to hoops that slide along the yard. Amidship from the yard to the deck is a stout wire jackstay (usually four inch wire). The sail, in two parts, port and starboard, is laced to this and brails in and stows against the jackstay.

The sail is only used with the wind well aft, sheets are rove, and use is made of a midship tack.

Sailing with wind aft and booms guyed out to port and starboard, is called going *wing and wing*.

Wearing in Heavy Weather

Ship under lower topsails and fore topmast staysail. Put the helm up, and, as the vessel goes off, square the after-yards, and keep them just lifting. When before the wind, brace round the fore-yard for the other tack, but not sharp up, and put the staysail-sheet over. Brace up the after yards and meet her with the helm. Trim yards and stand on.

Ship under lower main topsail (hove to). Put up the helm and as the vessel goes off square the after yards keeping them lifting. When the wind is aft, brace around the head yards on the new tack, but not sharp up. Shift the staysail sheet, brace up the after yards, and meet her with the helm. Brace up forward, trim yards.

Ship under Bare Poles. Vessels well down by the stern will often wear in this situation by merely pointing the after yards to the wind and filling the head yards; but vessels in good trim will not do this. To assist the vessel around, veer a hawser out of the lee quarter, with a drag attached to the end. As the ship sags off to leeward the drag will be to windward, and will tend to bring the stern round to the wind. When she is before it haul the hawser aboard; be sure to fit a tripping line. If the vessel will not go off, it will be necessary, as a last resort, to cut away the mizzenmast, veer away the hawser, and use the mizzen-topmast as a drag to assist in wearing. Be sure to cut lee rigging first, and attach a second hawser before cutting weather shrouds and stays. These instructions assume your vessel is in a critical situation and *must* wear.

Always, in wearing during very heavy weather, use oil from the quarters and from the closet pipes forward.

When blowing very hard do not attempt to shift over a storm staysail in the usual fashion. Always haul down, shift over the sheet, steady it aft and then hoist, tending the sheet so the sail will not bind on the stay. To shift over as in moderate weather will cost you the sail.

To Club Haul off a Lee Shore

Cock-bill the lee anchor, get a hawser on this for a spring and lead it to the lee quarter; range the cable and unshackle it abaft the windlass. *Helm's a-lee!* and *Raise tacks and sheets!* as for going in stays. The moment she loses head-way, let go the anchor and *Mainsail haul!* As soon as the anchor brings her head to the wind, let the chain cable go, holding on to the spring; and when the after sails take full, cast off or cut the spring, and *Let go and haul!*

This is far more difficult than it reads, but many a fine ship has been saved through club hauling, and many have been lost because, for some reason, the maneuver was not tried.

II

Heavy Weather Sailing

Heaving to

A sailing craft lies best with her bow toward the sea, the wind a point or so forward of the beam. Having no engines to drive her into the sea, she takes an easy position and, if stowed properly and handled in a seamanlike way, will ride out the worst kind of weather. The balance of forward and after sail will effect her helm. A ship usually lies easiest with weather helm. She will gradually come up and fall off as these forces oppose each other. The use of oil is always advisable as shown in the previous chapter.

The trimming of yards is very important in lying to. The forward and after yards should be pointed almost into the wind pressure on after sides. Main yards may be braced up a point higher.

The preparation for heavy weather is as follows:

Preventer topsail sheets on upper topsails.

Preventer braces on crossjack, leading aft to bumpkins, or quarter bitts.

Rolling tackles (heavy watch tackles) from the quarters of yards (hooked to stout end straps) and led to straps about the masts. Set up on these from the deck, belay at fife rails.

To Reef a Course. Haul up and spill the sail as if about to furl. Haul out the reef tackles, and reef. The senior station at sea is at the weather earing. An able seaman always takes this post. As soon as he has called "All out to windward!" the lee earing is hauled taut and the reef points passed.

Then set the sail.

To reef an upper topsail. Lower away on halliards, haul in slack of weather brace until the sail shivers, take in the slack of the reef tackles while the yard comes down, hauling out the weather reef tackle first, pass earing and haul out to leeward. In every heavy weather many seamen prefer to clew up, when going large, and reef with the sail in the gear.

When the fore and main upper topsails are to be reefed, the mizzen topsail is taken in. Put the ship before it and reef the fore topsail first. See page 211.

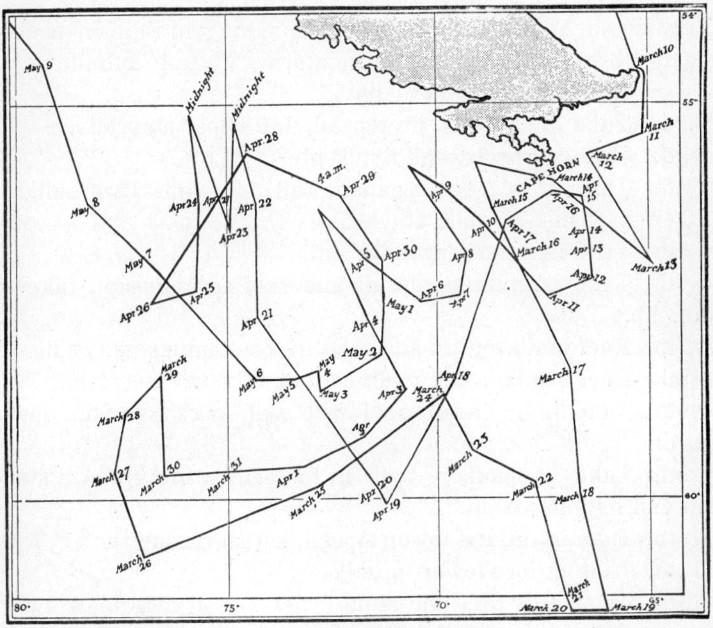

Chart of the course of a ship rounding Cape Horn in a period of adverse gales. Follow each stroke in the zig-zag day by day as the dates are given on the course, from east to west, and you will read the story of a plucky fight lasting weeks, in which the ship "Edward Sewall" was driven back as fast as she advanced while trying to round Cape Horn in 1914.

It took her 67 days to get from latitude 50 south on the east of the continent to the same parallel on the west side. On ten previous voyages the ship had made this portion of the voyage in from 11 to 23 days, the average being 16.4 days. The illustration gives the course in detail between the 54 degree line. The coast line is indicated with no suggestion of the treacherous isles and inlets.

Upper Topsail Splits. The square sails most likely to split are the upper topsails. When such an accident occurs, send the sail down, after stopping it along the yard and cutting robands. Use a strong gantline, and *the weather reef tackle.* This keeps the sail to windward of the stays and it can be got in on deck.

The new sail is sent up by *reefing on the foot.* Pass reef points under the foot. Knot so they can be easily got at. Make up sail with stops, pass robands, and sway aloft with gantline and weather reef tackle. Bend as usual. When bent hook reef tackles and haul out, haul up on all gear, pass reef points, then set sail as usual.

Taking in Sail. The procedure of taking in sail on a ship rigged vessel from all plain sail to storm canvas is as follows:

1st. All plain sail to skysails.

2d. Take in skysails, jib topsail, and upper staysails.

3d. Take in royals, and flying jib.

4th. Take in mizzen topgallant sail, fore topgallant sail, all mizzen staysails, all main staysails.

5th. Take in main topgallant sail.

6th. Take in mizzen topsail and reef fore topsail, take in outer jib.

7th. Reef main topsail and take in fore topmast staysail.

8th. Reef spanker and main course, take in foretopsail.

9th. Take in mainsail, reef fore sail, take in main upper topsail.

10th. Take in spanker, take in foresail, set fore storm staysail, and haul down jib.

11th. Take in mizzen lower topsail, set storm mizzen.

12th. Take in fore lower topsail.

13th. About this time the main lower topsail may blow away. If not *goosewing* it, that is, stow the middle and set one or both clews.

Vessel is now hove-to under fore storm staysail, goosewinged main lower topsail, and storm mizzen. The main lower topsail may blow away and the vessel will ride under her storm mizzen and fore storm staysail, giving her a proper balance and some steerage way. All yards are pointed *almost* into the wind with pressure on after sides. All gear is stopped up where possible, life lines rigged, and oil overboard in bags from the weather cathead, forward closet pipes and from the weather main rigging.

Preventer gear is rove, rolling tackles hooked, and the well is sounded at each bell. An extra hand is at the wheel, and relieving tackles are hooked in after wheelhouse.

Nothing to do but wait for the blow to be over, and to follow the rules for working out of a typhoon or hurricane, if that is the trouble. See page 827.

Seamen may differ some as to this order of taking in the kites, but this was the method practiced on the American Ship *A. J. Fuller*, out of New York, in the early nineties, Captain C. M. Nichols, of Searsport, Me., in command.

If the vessel is hove-to on the wrong tack in order to work clear of the storm center, wear ship as described under that heading. Sometimes a vessel drifting to leeward gets too close to land and she must wear in plenty of time. Always look out for plenty of sea room when hove-to for any length of time.

Scudding

In running before a sea have spanker brailed up and haul up the mainsail. The foresail has a wonderful lifting effect made more noticeable when reefed. Head sails are generally best hauled down. As the weather increases in strength sail is shortened in the usual manner and the fore sail, close-reefed makes a fine sail to run with. In extremely heavy weather it may be difficult to round to and get under control in the usual way. Some of the most expert shipmasters prefer to shorten down to bare poles and keep before it, reducing the speed as much as possible.

A vessel lying so will ship less water than when she is burying her nose through press of sail.

Most American sailing craft are built with substantial after wheelhouses. This is a protection to the helmsman and enables him to steer before the wind without the constant fear of being *pooped*. Where no wheelhouse is provided the helmsman should be securely lashed to the standard of the wheel. Never lash a man to the spindle or the rim of the wheel.

To heave-to when scudding under main lower topsail, reefed foresail and fore staysail.

Haul the foresail up, and if she will run with safety for a short time, under the topsail and staysail, furl the foresail before bringing her to the wind. If, however, there is such a sea running that she cannot keep before it after shortening sail, look out for a smooth, down with the helm, and round short to, in order to avoid exposing her broadside to the sea a moment longer than is absolutely necessary. Use oil as directed.

Broaching-to is the term applied to a vessel scudding in heavy weather when she runs up into the wind and is taken aback. This puts her in the trough and is a situation of great danger. If the vessel is carrying enough canvas to send her over on her beam ends, let fly all sheets and let go halliards. Down helm. This should never occur except through inattention to steering with a heavy quartering sea and squalls. A sudden shift of wind, however, may help broach a vessel to.

Sailing before the wind, fine weather, all plain sail. Vessel is taken aback.

Box off with head yards to tack nearest course. Brace up after yards. When after sails fill, let go and haul head yards.

With wind fair, a vessel is often referred to as *going large*. An old term for this is *rooming*, used in days of bluff bows, square high sterns, spritsails and culverins.

Notes on Handling Sail

In handling sail judgment and quick action must be combined. Under fine weather conditions no special precautions are required. If the wrong piece of gear is let go, it can easily be hauled taut and made fast again, but when the wind is up, at night, and with the ship making way through the water, squalls about, etc., the seaman must thoroughly understand his business. If he does not he will get into a mess of trouble before long. This severity of nature accounts for much of the severity of men to be met with in large sailing ships.

Here it may be well to call attention to the fact that under most conditions stay sails and square sails have a certain *lifting effect*. This is specially true of a reefed fore sail, when scudding.

Sails spread from a gaff have a *downward effect*.

In taking in sail the wind must be spilled from a sail, at the same time the sail must be kept in hand with its gear or it will shake itself to pieces.

Blowing fresh take in a course as follows: Ease off the sheet a little, haul up on the weather buntlines and leechlines, then haul on the lee buntlines and leechlines. Start the tack and haul up on clew garnets, rounding in the gear together. Then haul up the lee clew garnets, keeping command of the sheet.

A topsail is taken in the same way, starting to windward. Of course in fine weather you rise tacks and sheets together with a smart crew.

On any square sail the wind is got out of it by hauling best on the buntlines, slow on the clewlines.

Therefore to *take in a course* in fresh or heavy weather proceed as follows:

Man the weather clew-garnets and buntlines, ease off the main-sheet a fathom or two, and belay, then slack away the main-tack, and haul up the weather clew-garnet and buntlines taking care to have the sail kept full. When the weather-clew is up, and as much of the buntline as can be got, luff the vessel as close to the wind as possible; ease away the main-sheet, and haul the lee clew-garnet and buntlines at the same time.

To *take in a topsail* (upper) proceed as follows:

Slack away the weather-sheet, and haul the weather-clewline close up, and the buntlines as much as possible, then man the weather-brace, let go the lee one. As you start the lee-sheet, *haul in upon the weather-brace*, and haul up the lee-clewline buntline; haul away *downhauls*.

To *take in a topgallant sail*, ease down the halliards, round in on the weather brace, hauling on the clewlines at the same time. This follows the order "*Clew down!*" Then ease off the sheets and "*Clew up!*" the sail, hauling home the buntlines. See p. 213.

Other light sails are taken in in the same way.

Lower topsails are usually allowed to stand except in extreme weather. Sometimes the lee side is taken in, *goosewinging* the sail. Whenever possible send hands aloft to pass the sea gasgets as soon as a sail is up in the gear. Warn men not to pass the gasgets of a course around the lower topsail sheets. All yards should be fitted with *beckets* for the safety of men aloft.

Setting Sail

Sail is usually set under favorable conditions. The method of setting when wind is fresh or blowing hard applies to storm canvas.

Setting a Course

Loose the sail and overhaul the buntlines and leechlines. Let go the clew-garnets and overhaul them, and haul down on the sheets and tacks. If the ship is close-hauled, ease off the lee-braces, *slack the weather-lift* and clew-garnet, and get the tack well down. When the tack is well down, sharpen the yards up again by the brace, *top it well up by the lift*, haul aft the sheet, and then haul out the bowline, if carried. Most modern rigs dispense with this piece of gear.

When bracing up a lower yard man the *lee* brace, and tend the *weather* brace and *lee* lift. Just think over this and it is easy to remember. In the case of the crossjack, man the *weather* brace and tend the *lee* brace, also the *lee* lift, as these braces lead *forward* in a *ship*.

Setting a Lower Topsail, or Lower Topgallant Sail

Man the sheets, let go the buntlines, *ease off* the clewlines as the lower topsail sheets are of chain, the clewlines must not go by the run or the chain will jamb in the shieve at the lower yard arm.

Setting an Upper Topsail

The clews will be sheeted home. Overhaul the *downhauls*, tend the braces, overhaul all buntlines, man the halliards. In large ships the halliards are taken to the winch or deck capstan. *Let go* the topgallant sheets.

Setting a Light Sail

When sheeting home a light sail the lee sheet is brought home first and the clewline is *slacked away*. When the weather sheet is manned the clewline is *let go*. And always when hoisting a yard see the sheets of the next sail above, if any, are let go, and have a hand at the lee brace to tend it. When a sail is set buntlines are overhauled and stopped with cotton twine, this prevents chafe on sail and stops are easily broken when taking in sail. Buntlines are stopped together just under the lead blocks.

Bracing Yards

When going free and the wind shifts *forward* brace *up* the head yards first, then the main, etc.

When wind shifts *aft*, brace *in* the crossjack yards first, then the main, etc.

When close hauled always *hitch* the weather braces on the pins to prevent them coming off. *Hang up* the lee ones in the daytime, and *lay them down clear for running* at night. This is done by taking the end out well clear on the deck, and flaking down toward the pin.

When sweating up braces, give the lower brace another pull after the topsail braces have been hauled taut. Where rope

Close hauled port tack
Note—trim of yards

braces are fitted, put on the strop with the splice under the eye of the hook of the handy billy.*

Many modern ships now reeve wire braces throughout. A small hand winch is used at the pin rail for sweating up.

Have *squaring marks* on all braces. Keep yards square during fine weather in port.

Trimming Yards

When on the wind, brace up lower yards back against the swifters (forward legs of the shrouds), the yards as you go up are braced in a few degrees each one making a slightly smaller angle with the keel. The reason for this is the fact that lower sails are less flat, and as the sails go higher the support becomes less and the leverage greater. This method of trimming is most pronounced when close hauled. When the wind is on the quarter, or aft, yards may be trimmed about the same.

Great judgment is needed in trimming yards and an officer should study his ship and her way through the water. Yards trim much sharper in fine weather than in a rough sea.

Fore and Aft Canvas

Taking in a *jib* when on the wind. Put up the helm and keep the ship off a point or two, let go halliards, man downhaul and *ease off sheet*. The sail will run down easily if this is done. This applies to all staysails. In fresh weather the sheet should be eased just enough to keep the hanks from binding against the stay. With wind free a staysail runs down as a rule without much hauling.

Taking in a *spanker* or *trysail*, man the lee brails best. This spills the wind and helps to bring the sail in snug to the mast.

Large fore and aft sails spread by gaffs and booms require the most careful handling. The gaffs are heavy and cannot be steadied by the vangs when well up, and these spars throw an enormous strain on sails and masts. In reefing, come close to the wind but do not allow the sail to slat heavily. All reef-points must be passed and earing hauled out on boom with equal tension, as the reef points not only supports the sail, but takes a large part of the weight of boom as well, although this is cared for by the weather leg of the topping lift.

**Handy billy*, the small watch tackle used in sweating up lower braces. See p. 141.

The stowing of a gaff topsail and the setting of it is not to be acquired by reading. This is a light weather sail and should be taken in in plenty of time. The sail is hoisted by a halliard to the mast head, the clew is hauled out to the end of the gaff by a sheet, the foot of the sail is hauled down on the weather side of the gaff by a long rope called the *lazy tack*, which must be shifted over after going about. In stowing, man downhaul, and clew-line, gather sail in abaft the doubling, pass gasgets *under* all running gear.

Squalls

An officer in sail must always keep his eye peeled for squalls. At night he must have his sense of wind force keyed up to the working point. Carrying sail at night takes a seaman; almost anyone can *crack-on* during the day.

With a heavy squall coming act quickly. A number of things may be done.

Take in all light sails, letting them hang in their gear. Brail in spanker. Lower upper topsail yards. Brace in lower yards. Raise mainsail. Down jib and set foretopmast staysail.

If the squall looks heavy put up helm and take it over the quarter. Do this before the wind strikes you, and only, of course, if you have the necessary sea room.

If on a schooner, check the sheets and luff.

It will be seen that the two types of craft call for different handling. Square riggers should be put before the squall, and fore-and-afters up into it.

After a squall, or period of heavy weather, make sail slowly but do not force the vessel into a heavy sea. The sea goes down much slower than the wind.

Carrying Away Rigging

Accidents at sea under sail are of common occurrence. Sheets may carry away, gear parts when working sail, braces part, and even stays and shrouds may go in very severe weather. If a fore and aft stay goes, up helm and put ship before it to take off strain, and at once rig preventer gear. If fore stay goes, or foretopmast stay, get up fish tackle and hook at mast head and at gammoning or knight heads and set up on capstan. As these stays take most of the backward thrust of the whole system of masts, this accident occurs most often. The fish tackle should always be handy. A well-regulated ship will always have an abundance of heavy straps, of wire and manila, and plenty of tackles.

If a shroud goes, put ship about at once, by wearing or tacking as may seem best.

Upper Weather Main Topsail Brace Carries Away

Ease lee sheet to spill the sail. Luff into wind and lower on halliards. These directions cover all hoisting square sails.

Lower Weather Main Brace Carries Away

Ease off the sheet, let go the tack and haul up the mainsail, bracing in on the weather lower topsail brace. Take in the lower topsail, starting the weather sheet at once to take the pull off of the main yard. Rig a preventer brace. If yard is swaying about put the main yards aback to steady it.

Parral Carries Away

This is not serious where the braces are standing. Lower the yard, put the sail aback and pass a temporary parral.

Yard Sprung

Fish the yard with suitable spars. These should be shaped properly by the carpenter and hove down close to the yard with wire lashings, and then set these taut with hard wood wedges.*

Cap Carried Away

Pass a *Spanish cap*, that is a chain lashing around the lower-mast head and the topmast, heaving the turns taut with a wire frapping.

Lower Topmast Sprung Just Above the Cap

Lower down till the sprung part is below the cap, wedge and lash. Cut new fid hole and shorten rigging. Set up and hoist sail.

Cutting Away Masts

When this becomes necessary, a vessel being down on her beam ends, always cut *and clear* the lee rigging and stays, before

*See page 150.

cutting or knocking loose the pelican hooks of the weather rigging. Spars smashing alongside to leeward may bilge the vessel.

When hove-to, cut the rigging on both sides except the two forward legs and the stays. Cut these last.

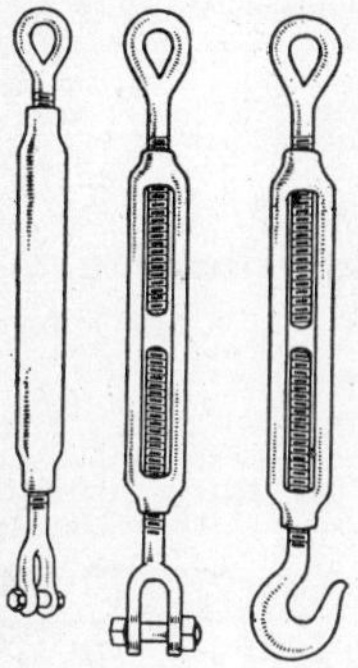

Turn buckles. Handy when rigging must be "set up."

Where a vessel is in an extreme condition, cut away the mizzen and the main masts. Rouse up a bower chain bring it inboard and secure it to the foremast well up. Take a round turn and lash with a hawser. Attach a strong block and three-inch line with plenty of scope for an oil bag. Cut lee rigging and stays, cut weather rigging, and as the mast goes by the board, say a few prayers and veer chain (many have done this), and if all goes well the vessel will bring up on the sea anchor formed by the foremast and gear. Haul out a bag of oil and wait for the storm to blow over.

Jury Rigs

In a case like the one just mentioned, when the weather subsides haul alongside the foremast sea anchor, parbuckle the heavy spars on board and proceed to exercise your seamanship in getting up a jury rig. Work the vessel into the nearest port. Enter a protest before the consul, cable your owners for instructions and generally follow the hints to a master in a port of distress, printed in the chapter ahead.

During all such operations keep sounding the well, look after all tarpaulins—never neglect the cargo.

After this, stand by for a presentation from the underwriters and a newer and more important command.

Man Overboard

On the wind, put down helm, throw over a life ring with water light. Try and sight the man and tell off one hand to watch him. Lower a lee boat. Square the head yards to stop the way. In heavy weather, if the man has the buoy, it may often be possible to work down and pick him up with the vessel.

Before the wind, put the helm down, throw a life, etc. Let fly light sails, brace up the crossjack and head yards and take off the way of the ship. Lower a lee boat.

One of the most important things to do is to keep the man in sight. At night this cannot be done, but assume that he will swim for the water light and keep that in sight and send boat to it. Have a light in the boat.

III

Directions on Nearing another Vessel, your Vessel being under Sail Alone

Close-hauled.—On Starboard Tack.

Hold your course, do not steer wildly, or you may confuse the ship whose duty it is to keep clear of you.

Close-hauled.—On Port Tack.

Take bearing.

Ascertain whether a steamer or not.

If a steamer, keep your course.

If a sailing vessel—

a. If to windward of you, hold your course.

b. If ahead of you, or less than two or three points on the weather bow, hold your course.

c. If to leeward of you, or more than two or three points on the lee bow—

1st. Take bearing again.

2d. If her bearing has altered materially, and continues so to alter, keep your course.

3d. If her bearing has not altered materially, tack, or bear away until it does so.

Wind Aft.

Take bearing.

Ascertain whether a steamer or not.

If a steamer, hold your course.

If a sailing vessel—

a. If right astern, or if overtaking you, hold your course.

b. If in any other direction (except right astern, or overtaking you)—

1st. Take bearing again.

2d. If her bearing has altered materially, and continues so to alter, hold your course.

3d. If her bearing has not altered materially, alter course sufficiently to starboard or to port to assist in altering her bearing.

Running Free.—Wind on Starboard Side.

Take bearing.

Ascertain whether steamer or not.

If a steamer, hold your course.

If a sailing vessel—

a. If to windward of you, or if ahead of you, and going free, or if her Red light only (or her Port side) shows *provided always she is not close-hauled*, keep your course.

b. If ahead of you and close-hauled, or if to leeward of you, or if her Green light (or her Starboard side) shows, or if you are overtaking her—

1st. Take bearing again.

2d. If her bearing has altered materially, and continues so to alter, hold your course.

3d. If her bearing has not altered materially, alter course sufficiently to starboard or port to assist to alter her bearing.

Running Free.—Wind on Port Side.

Take bearing.

Ascertain whether a steamer or not.

If a steamer, hold your course.

If a sailing vessel—

a. If to windward of you, and with the wind on her port side, or right aft, hold your course.

b. Under all circumstances—

1st. Take bearing again.

2d. If her bearing has altered materially, and continues so to alter, hold your course.

c. If she is on your starboard side—

1st. Take bearing again.

2d. If she has altered her bearing materially, hold your course.

3d. If her bearing has not altered materially, alter course sufficiently to starboard or port to assist in altering her bearing.

In all of the above instructions, action depends upon definite knowledge of the course and condition of the other vessel. Never *shave close.* Give way in plenty of time if you are the *burdened vessel.* If you are the *privileged* vessel watch your course and speed. *Know* Rules of Road.

IV

Coming to Anchor with a Sailer

Have the anchors both ready for letting go. Reduce canvas to the lowest working size. As the ship comes to the anchorage luff unto the wind and square the fore and main yards. As soon as the ship gathers sternboard, let go the anchor and veer chain, clewing up and hauling down at the same time.

A fore-and-after has a harder time coming to anchor because of the lack of positive backing force to the sails.

Many conditions of wind and tide and the room available for anchoring must be taken into consideration. In most places ships are taken to their anchorages by tugs, but often it is necessary to manage the business alone.

To come to an anchorage with *the wind and tide in the same direction.* Round up with the after square canvas set. Square the after yards and let go as soon as her way is less than the tide. As she veers chain haul down and clew up.

To come to anchor with *the wind and tide opposed to each other.* Stem the tide, pick out the best anchorage, stow all sail ride with the tide and let go, taking care not to pay out chain too fast. If the wind is strong try and avoid breaking sheer and riding over the anchor so as to foul it.

A fore-and-after working into an anchorage may often gain a desired position by resorting to *half-boards,* that is luffing into the eye of the wind and paying off again before she loses her way. This is often used in making a gain to windward where tacking cannot be resorted to because of shipping or for other reasons. Yachts stop their way by putting helm hard over to port and starboard alternately.

Riding at Single Anchor

A light ship will generally lie best to leeward of her anchor. A deeply laden ship will often lie to windward of it, keeping a good sheer at all times, and seeing that she swings with the tide on a taut cable and always on the same side of the anchor, if possible.

The same precautions are to be observed as in the case of a steamer. Always have sufficient sail bent to take care of her if she trips her anchor. Always have the second bower ready to let go. When the weather makes up veer chain in plenty of time. Keep yards braced up sharp in stiff weather and on the tack that will help hold her sheer. An officer should always stand anchor watch when in an open roadstead.

Casting*

A vessel riding at anchor and getting under way presents many different sets of conditions. In casting to starboard loose lower and upper topsails and jib. Heave to short stay, sheet home and hoist away topsails. Brace up fore yards on starboard tack, main yards on port tack. Crossjack yards square. As she pays off to starboard break out anchor. When main topsails fill, brace around fore yards and crossjack yards, set jib and spanker and proceed. To cast to port brace yards in opposite way.

In casting the seaman must show his judgment and his skill. No rules can be set down covering all conditions. Each time a vessel gets under way new conditions confront the master. Weigh all conditions carefully, the force of wind and tide, the way the vessel is riding, the state of the hawse, the proximity of other craft, or dangers, and the possible courses that can be made out of the anchorage.

Sail and Motor

When close hauled with light wind run the lee engine (if you have twin screws). This will hold her up against leeway and is generally worth while.

Warning

Never approach a coast unless your anchors are bent on in plenty of time and are ready for instant use. Many fine craft have been lost through neglect of this precaution. The shores of Tierra del Fuego have caught many a Cape Horner suddenly driven on the rocks with anchors stowed and cables unbent.

*Casting is the getting under way of a sailing vessel riding at anchor.

The Beaufort Scale of Wind Force

Force of Wind	Conditions	Velocity: Statute Miles per Hour	Velocity: Nautical Miles per Hour	Mean Pressure in Pounds per Square Foot
0.—Calm	Full-rigged ship, all sails set, no headway.	0 to 3	0 to 2.6	0.03
1.—Light air	Just sufficient to give steerage way	8	6.9	0.23
2.—Light breeze	Speed of 1 or 2 knots, "full and by"	13	11.3	0.62
3.—Gentle breeze	Speed of 3 or 4 knots, "full and by"	18	15.6	1.2
4.—Moderate breeze	Speed of 5 or 6 knots, "full and by"	23	20.0	1.9
5.—Fresh breeze	All plain sail, "full and by"	28	24.3	2.9
6.—Strong breeze	Topgallant sails over single-reefed topsails	34	29.5	4.2
7.—Moderate gale	Double-reefed topsails	40	34.7	5.9
8.—Fresh gale	Treble-reefed topsails (or reefed uppertopsails and courses)	48	41.6	8.4
9.—Strong gale	Close-reefed topsails and courses (or lower topsails and courses)	56	48.6	11.5
10.—Whole gale	Close-reefed main topsail and reefed foresail (or lower main topsail and reefed foresail)	65	56.4	15.5
11.—Storm	Storm staysails	75	65.1	20.6
12.—Hurricane	Under bare poles	90 and over.	78.1 and over.	29.6

Note:—Next to knowing a lot about the weather we would advise the seaman to gain a very definite idea of wind velocities. The *Beaufort Scale* of wind forces has come to be generally adopted at sea in vessels of the English-speaking world. It merits careful study. The reader will note that the speed of the wind is also stated in terms of the sail a vessel may carry under various conditions.

Wind Force. The German Meteorological office has issued a Beaufort Scale referring to corresponding sea appearance as follows: 0. Calm—sea like a mirror—smooth. 1. Light Airs—small wavelets with the appearance of scales are formed but without crests. 2. Light Breeze. 3. Gentle Breeze—the waves short and more pronounced; their crests begin to break; the foam is not white, but of glassy appearance. 4. Moderate Breeze—waves become longer; many white horses are formed; the breaking sea produces a short, continuous rustling sound. 5. Fresh Breeze—waves take a more pronounced long form with white foam crests. Sea breaks with a noise like perpetual murmur. 6. Strong Breeze—larger waves begin to form; white foam crests more extensive; sea breaks with a duller rolling noise. 7. Moderate Gale—the sea heaps up and the white foam from the breaking waves begins to be blown in streaks along the direction of the wind; the noise of the breaking sea is audible at greater distance. 8. Fresh Gale. 9. Strong Gale—the height of the waves and their crests increases visibly; the foam is blown in dense streaks along the direction of the wind. The sea begins to "roll." 10. Whole Gale—high waves develop with long overhanging crests; the foam, in great patches, is blown in dense white streaks along the direction of the wind. The whole surface of the sea takes on a white appearance. The rolling of the sea becomes heavy and shock-like. 11. Storm. 12. Hurricane—the waves become so high that ships within sight drop so low in the wave troughs that for a time they are lost to view. The rolling of the sea becomes tumultuous. The sea is covered with white streaky foam lying along the wind direction; the wind blows the edges of the wave crests to froth. Owing to the violence of the wind the air is so filled with foam and spray that distant objects can no longer be seen.

CHAPTER XX

WEATHER AT SEA

I

Foreword

Most people, when they don't know what to talk about, talk about the weather. Authors also seem to follow this system when we glance over the long list of books about the weather. We find a wealth of elaborate maps covered with sinuous curves and many pages of tables. Much of this matter is absolutely worthless to the sailor.

Bowditch contains excellent data on the weather observed at sea, the prevailing winds of the great oceans, and the simple recording instruments in use on board ship; the barometer, thermometer, anemomether, etc. Captain Lecky has a fine chapter on marine meteorology in his *Wrinkles*, and Mr. William Allinghan has written *A Manual of Marine Meteorology* that every ship's officer should study. *The Atmosphere*, by F. J. B. Cordeiro is an excellent book for those who like to get their facts dressed up in mathematics. Here we learn that the cyclone is dynamically a gyroscope. Mr. Cordeiro also prints the letter by Alexander Hamilton, dated at St. Croix, September 6, 1772, in which that distinguished statesman and scholar, then a very young man, records the passing of a cyclone with brilliant vividness. It is said to be his earliest writing.

Professor Milham, of Williams College, records some three hundred titles in the bibliography printed as an appendix to his own very excellent *Meteorology*.

But in a seamanship, a work book in the best sense, the weather must be treated and in a practical way. Sailing craft are absolutely dependent upon it and steamers are largely effected by weather and sea conditions. Several very important things may be called to the attention of the seaman.

On a sailing ship the officer in charge of a watch, and the master, of course, are fully alive to the vast importance, to them, of the weather, especially the wind and its changes. The sea officer, in sail, is constantly keeping his "weather eye" on the clouds, the sky in general and the sea. He becomes of necessity a keen observer of local weather conditions and learns to judge the speed and weight of a squall with remarkable accuracy, even on the darkest night. He soon *feels* the weather. The "glass" and its pumping means volumes to him. Sunset, and sunrise and the high clouds at the zenith, all speak to him with the language of experience. Little jingles sum up a great deal of this ancient lore—

First rise, after low,
Indicates a stronger blow.

Long foretold, long last:
Short notice, soon past.

When the glass falls low,
Prepare for a blow;
When it rises high,
Let all your kites fly.
(Referring to the barometer.)

When the rain's before the wind,
Halyards, sheets, and braces mind.

When the wind's before the rain,
Soon you may make sail again.
(Squalls.)

A red sky in the morning
Is the sailor's warning.
A red sky at night
Is the sailor's delight.

Evening red and morning gray
Are certain signs of a fine day.

A mackerel sky with lamb's tails
Makes tall ships carry low sails.
(Referring to cloud forms.)

June, too soon; July, stand by;
August, look out you must.
September, remember; October,
all over.
(Hurricanes.)

The steamship officer, as stated in the chapter on the Compass, is vitally interested in this question of the speed of sailing craft under different conditions of wind and sea and on the various points of sailing. To accurately judge the above important points he must know the *true force and direction* of the wind, not with relation to his own swiftly moving vessel, but with relation to the sailing craft he is liable to meet.

For instance, a vessel making twenty knots due north with a wind blowing twenty knots due south, would have the wind dead ahead and apparently blowing forty knots, in fact *actually* blowing forty knots *over the steamer*, but only half that fast *over the sea.* If the vessel were steaming south the air would appear to be calm, smoke rising straight up from the stack, and not unlikely showering the bridge with cinders and soot.

Between these two extremes we have an infinite number of variations where the wind blows at an angle to the course of the steamer. In the daytime the direction of the sea waves will often give the true direction of the wind, having in mind the fact that the sea may be running from a previous storm or a distant wind, and may have an appreciably different direction to the wind over head.

The solution to this problem of the true direction and force depends upon the following factors:

Speed of vessel.

Relative direction of wind across vessel (see relative bearings, page 464).

Apparent velocity of wind over vessel. See page 465.

Plotting these three factors to scale and working out a parallelogram of velocities will give the true direction and velocity of the wind over the sea.

Of course no sane person will expect an officer to plot these factors and work out a parallelogram of velocities while on the bridge on a dark night. But by working out problems comfortably on fine afternoons on the bridge he will soon become able to judge correctly just what is the true wind direction and velocity, knowing its apparent direction and velocity and the speed of his ship.

Allingham, in his *Marine Meteorology* gives an excellent table for solving this problem. Still, when these tables are needed most, on a dark wet night, they can not be used. Only judgment and experience are worth while at such times. The late Captain Lecky worked it out by trigonometry using four-place logarithms.

II

Storm Warnings

The seaman who is not equipped with radio, will watch for storm warnings from signal stations along the coast and these warnings should also be heeded by vessels at anchor in exposed harbors where they may drag their moorings.

United States storm warnings by flags are as follows:

Storm Warning Flags.—A red square flag with a black center indicates that a storm of marked violence is expected.

The pennants displayed with the flags indicate the direction of the wind: Red pennant, easterly; white pennant, westerly. The pennant *above* the flag indicates that the wind is expected to blow from the *northerly quadrants; below*, from *southerly quadrants.*

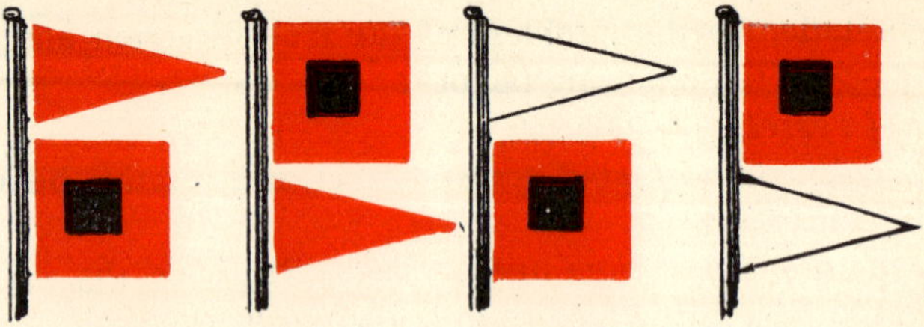

United States Storm Warnings.

By night the approach of storms of marked violence is indicated by: Two red lights, one above the other, for winds beginning from the northeast; a single red light for winds beginning from the southeast; a red light above a white light for winds beginning from the southwest; and a white light above a red light for winds beginning from the northwest.

Hurricane Signal

Hurricane warnings.—Two red flags with black centers, displayed one above the other, indicate the expected approach of tropical hurricanes, and also of those extremely severe and dangerous storms which occasionally move across the Lakes and northern Atlantic coast. These warnings are displayed at all Weather Bureau stations on the Atlantic, Pacific and Gulf coasts of the United States, at Belize, Honduras, and on the following islands of the Atlantic and the Caribbean Sea: Bermuda, Cuba, Jamaica, Haiti, Porto Rico, Turks Island, Virgin Islands of the U. S. A., Dominica, Martinique, St. Lucia, Barbados, St. Vincent, St. Kitts, Trinidad, Grenada, Curaçao, and Swan Island.

By night on the Atlantic, Pacific and Gulf coasts two red lights with a white light between indicate the approach of a hurricane or whole gale.

III

Forecasting the Weather

The following, adapted from an article by Commodore A. B. Bennett, Jr., of the U. S. Power Squadrons, is printed here by permission of the author, and of *Yachting* in which it appeared.*

In order to intelligently predict the weather it is essential to have a working knowledge of the laws that govern its changes.

When reading the *Barometer* we simply read the measure of the weight or pressure of the air at that particular place and elevation. Suppose we go down under water in a submarine bell and in the wall of the bell there is an instrument to indicate the pressure of the water outside. If the water is calm and the bell is moved up and down close to the undulating bottom of the water we would notice a difference in the pressure registered by the instrument being less as we went up and greater as we went down. This is also true of the air for if we climb up and down a mountain the air pressure changes, being lighter on the mountain and heavy in the valleys and at sea level. Again suppose the submarine bell is stationary and a storm comes up and great waves pass over the spot where the bell is located we would notice that as the water rose and fell the pressure would rise and fall. It is the same in the air for there is a constant passing over the earth of waves of atmospheric weight and as these waves pass over, the barometer will show a rise and fall as the crests and troughs of the waves move on.

In the North Temperate Zone the movement of the atmospheric pressure waves is always easterly, the center of the trough or the low points usually passing out over the Gulf of the St.

*The student sailor is advised to consult *Physics of the Air,* by Dr. W. J. Humphreys of the U. S. Weather Bureau, to supplement the reading of this sectio of the seamanship.

Lawrence. This is true with the exception of a few low points which form in the Tropics and either pass up the Mississippi or the Atantic Coast. These waves of atmospheric pressure are not in parallel ridges like the waves of the sea, but they are like a mountain range with peaks of different heights and valleys of different depths passing over the earth, not broadside, but end on; not as a company marching company front, but as in march-ing in column of twos. The speed of their passing varies from one peak and valley a day to one peak and valley in a week.

The high pressure areas are areas where the air is heavy or dense and low pressure areas are areas where the air is light or rare. As air is like fluid in its tendency to flow the direction of its flow is naturally from the high pressure areas to the low pressure areas and this movement of air is wind. The movement of air or wind in its relation to the highs and lows is in obedience to definite meteorological laws. Pull out the stopper of a wash bowl which is full of water and you will notice that the water does not rush to the center, but soon takes on a spiral direction rushing around and around on its way to the low point or opening of the bowl. Air currents or winds behave in the same way about a point of low pressure going spirally and inward and always in a counter clockwise direction. Air currents about a high pressure point flow spirally and outward and always in a clockwise direction. The speed of these air currents, or in other words the force of the wind, is in direct ratio to the slope from the peak to the valley or the amount of difference between and the proximity of the high and low. A high which is not very high and a low which is not very low and considerable distance apart will have hardly any flow of air from one to the other, but a very low point with a high point or high points nearby will result in a very rapid flow of air or a strong wind flowing spirally toward the center of the low as illustrated by a tropical storm or a Western hurricane or cyclone. The areas of low pressure are known as cyclones and the areas of high pressure are known as anticyclones.

The location of the highs and lows is ascertained every day by the Weather Bureau and the easterly advance can be easily watched. The method of ascertaining this is fairly simple. At the same hour every day barometer and thermometer readings are taken at hundreds of stations, ashore and on shipboard. The barometer readings are corrected to sea level, which means making allowances for elevations and temperature. Then the readings are noted upon a map at all the stations and the stations with the same reading are connected by a line. These lines are known as *Isobars*. Also the stations with the same temperature are connected with a dotted line and these lines are known as *Isotherms.* The drawing of the Isobars immediately reveals the highs and lows, their proximity to each other and the steepness of their slopes. The slope is known as the *Barometric Gradient.* Accompanying the report from the stations is a report of the wind, its direction and force and this is shown on the map by an arrow placed in the proper direction.

The barometer is an instrument for the measuring of the weight of the atmosphere and the principles of the instrument were discovered by Torricelli in 1643. He found that when he filled a glass tube (which was closed at one end) with mercury and inverted it in a bowl of mercury that the weight of the air on the mercury in the bowl would support the mercury in the tube to a height of thirty inches. All standard barometers are of the mercury type and *the readings on all barometers represent height of mercury.* The weight of the atmosphere is not measured in pounds or ounces but in height of mercury. For our use the *aneroid** barometer of good make is much better than a mercury type as the aneroid is accurate enough, is compact and easily handled. At least each quarter the aneroid barometer should be compared with a standard barometer. Do not remove from ship. Take set of readings *and time* to W.B. for comparison. In certain parts of the scale the aneroid may rise or fall more or less than the standard and the best way to determine this is to take the reading of the aneroid and compare the range of activity with that of the W.B. standard. This study of relative activity had best be from 29.20 inches to 30.60 inches which is as much range as we will usually need to know about. The best time of the year to make this study is in winter when there are the most active changes and the greatest range of rising and falling atmosphere pressure. The weather words usually found on the face of an aneroid barometer are of small value to the sailor and should be disregarded. The ideal face of an aneroid should be perfectly plain, except for the graduations.

In using a barometer it is important to realize that a single observation of a barometer without reference to the readings at definite intervals preceding is not only useless but liable to be misleading. Therefore it is very necessary to keep a written record of the barometer readings at stated intervals during the twenty-four hours. Another important fact to be considered is that the barometer foretells, as well as indicates weather that is

*The aneroid barometer is a metal box partly exhausted of air, the sides bulge out or in as the air pressure varies. This motion is measured on a scale graduated to inches of mercury, or in millimeters or in centibars. Centibar graduation is being introduced by the British, 100 centibars being the "standard atmosphere" in the C.G.S. (centimetre, gramm, second) system of units. Standard Atmosphere is the pressure of a mercury column of standard gravity, 0° C., 760 millimeters high.

present, foretelling changes as much as twelve to twenty-four hours in advance.*

In forecasting remember that " The possibility is always for a continuance of existing weather unless some phenomenon presents itself which foretells a change."

In regard to the barometer readings, the important points to know are, has the rise or fall been gradual or rapid or if stationary how long has it been so. And in making barometer readings remember that there is a natural change of pressure every day because the principal maximum pressure occurs at 10 a. m. and 10 p. m., and the principal minimum pressure occurs at 4 a. m. and 4 p. m., amounting to .05 of an inch. Therefore, if the barometer shows a fall of .05 between 10 a. m. and 4 p. m. it really means a stationary barometer. This allowance should be made to form an accurate opinion of the barometer change.

A stationary barometer indicates a continuance of existing conditions, but a slight tap on the barometer face will likely move the hand a little indicating the tendency to rise or fall. A rapid rise or a rapid fall indicates that a strong wind is about to blow with a change in the weather, the nature of the change depends upon the direction of the wind. The rapidity of the storm's approach and its intensity will be indicated by the rate and amount of fall in the barometer.

A fall of .01 inch per hour is considered a low rate of fall.

A fall of .03 inch per hour is considered a high rate of fall.

A rate of .10 inch might be reached and a rate of .20 has been recorded.

In the tropics a fall of more than .02 is considered dangerous and the following table shows the distance of the storm center from the vessel by the average rate of fall. See page 826.

Average fall of barometer per hour	Distance from storm center
From .02 to .06 inch	From 250 to 150 miles
From .06 to .08 inch	From 150 to 100 miles
From .08 to .12 inch	From 100 to 80 miles
From .12 to .15 inch	From 80 to 50 miles

When the barometer falls considerably without any particular change of weather a violent storm is raging at a distance. And the barometer falls lower for high winds than for heavy rains.

The barometer falls for southerly winds (including from S. E. by S. westward), for wet weather, stronger wind or for more than one of these changes, except on a few occasions, when moderate wind with rain or snow comes from the northward, If the barometer falls slowly for several days during fine weather.

*The Barograph is a recording aneroid barometer and traces a line of pressure readings on a revolving card moved by a clock.

expect considerable rain. A lowering barometer and rising thermometer indicate heavy rain. A very low barometer is usually attendant upon stormy weather with wind and rain at intervals but the latter not necessarily in any great quantity. Should the barometer continue low when the sky becomes clear, expect more rain in twenty-four hours. If the weather, notwithstanding a very low barometer, is fine and calm it is not to be depended upon as a change may come very suddenly.

For middle latitudes (standard readings):

29.50 and thereabouts is very low.
30.00 inches is an average pressure.
30.50 inches is high.*

The barometer rises for northerly winds (including from N. W. by N. to eastward) for dry or less wet weather, for less wind, or for more than one of these changes except on a few occasions when rain, hail or snow comes from the northward with strong winds. If the barometer continues rising while wet weather continues, the weather after a day or two will probably be fair for some time, and when the barometer and thermometer rise together it is a very sure sign of coming fine weather.

A gradual but steady rise indicates settled weather.

A gradual but steady fall indicates wet or unsettled weather.

A very slow rise from a low point is usually associated with high winds and dry weather.

A rapid rise indicates clear weather with high winds.

A very slow fall from a high point is usually associated with wet and unpleasant weather without much wind.

A sudden fall indicates a sudden shower or high wind or both.

When the air becomes colder and drier with a rising barometer, it is pretty certain that a northeast wind is coming.

* Capt. Arthur H. Mellick, of the United States fisheries ship *Eider*, has submitted the following note, which is interesting in connection with the abnormally high pressure prevailing over Alaska and the Aleutian Islands and the unusually low pressure (barometer 29.64 inches Jan. 17) at Honolulu during January, 1920.

"On the 15th day of January we left Unalaska for the Pribiloff Islands. The barometer then registered 30.62. By midnight it was 30.66 [inches]. On the 16th at midnight it showed 31.00. At noon on the 17th it showed 31.20, at 4.00 p. m. it was above the registered marks, and at midnight it was back to 31.20, where it remained until 4.00 a. m. on the 19th, when it commenced to fall very slowly; and even now, with a northeast gale blowing and heavy snowstorm, it is still 30.68. Such barometer readings I have never seen in this part of Alaska before with all the years that I have been in the country. While at the Pribiloff Islands the sea was very calm and light northeast breeze, but not a particle of ice was to be seen, although it felt as though it was not very far away." *Monthly Weather Review* U. S. W. B.

When the air gets warmer and damper with falling barometer, it is safe to infer that a south-west wind is at hand.

When the wind sets in from points between east and north-east and the barometer falls steadily, a storm is approaching from the south or southwest, its center will pass near or to the south or east of the observer within twelve to twenty-four hours, with wind shifting to northwest by way of north.

When the wind sets in from points between south and south-east and the barometer falls steadily, it indicates a storm approaching from the west or the northwest. Its center will pass near or to the north of the observer within twelve to twenty-four hours, with the wind shifting to northwest by way of south-west and west.

A good aneroid barometer will indicate the height of a table.

The indications afforded by the wind and barometer are the best guide we now have for determining future weather conditions.

Wind is the most important factor in weather and the shifting of the wind is the most trustworthy of weather indications for coming changes though in the warm months the winds are often light and variable and the changes in direction have not quite the same importance as in the colder months.* Wind always takes the name of the point of the compass *from which* it comes.

As a rule winds from the east quadrant with falling barometer indicate foul weather and winds shifting to the west quadrant indicate clearing and fair weather. South winds bring warmth, north winds cold, east winds in middle latitudes indicate the approach of a low from the westward and west winds show that the storm area has passed to the eastward. A rule worth remembering is the following: When the wind comes up with the sun it is likely to go down with it but when the wind rises as the sun sets it is likely to blow all night and probably the next day.

Rain.—In taking up the subject of rain the first thought I wish to convey is that we must think of the air as a mixture of gases holding moisture in the form of water vapor. Like a sponge, it can be anywhere from slightly damp to very wet without dripping and the air can be from slightly humid to very humid without precipitation. The amount of humidity is expressed in per cent., meaning the per cent. of the air's capacity for moisture. A humidity of sixty per cent. is considered good. If the humidity is high and the barometer starts to fall the capacity of the air for moisture is lessened and the moisture will precipitate and fall as rain. It is a fact that from the Mississippi and Missouri valleys to the Atlantic coast and on the Pacific coast rain gen-

* The wind *veers* when it shifts "with the sun"; *right handed* in Northern Hemisphere; *left handed* in Southern Hemisphere. The wind is said to "back" when it shifts "against the sun."

erally begins on a falling barometer. However, in the warmer months summer showers and thunderstorms usually come about the time the barometer turns from falling to rising. Another point that must be borne in mind is that warm air has a much greater capacity for moisture than cold air and that precipitation occurs when moist air is cooled below the dew point as rain, snow, hail or frost.

Rain is preceded from 12 to 24 hours by a rise in atmospheric moisture. Without this increase in moisture the changes in barometer and temperature would not produce rain. A good hygrometer will keep one informed as to the state of humidity and is a great help in forecasting rain. However, there are two natural signs of high humidity which should be remembered. Sound travels easily through moist air so that distant sounds are easily heard which has given rise to the following couplet:

"Sound traveling far and wide
A stormy day will betide."

The other natural sign of rain is excessive refraction of the atmosphere when distant objects as hills are unusually visible or raised, and based on this fact is the old proverb:

"The farther the sight
The nearer the rain."

The signs of falling weather in the colder months are: the formation of a high sheet cloud covering the whole sky, an increase in temperature and moisture of the air and the wind changing to some easterly quarter. The precise direction that the wind takes either N. E. or S. E. varies for different localities and the direction from which the storm is approaching. In New England, the Middle Atlantic States and the Ohio valley, N. E. winds precede storms approaching from the S. W. and S. E. winds precede storms approaching by way of the Great Lakes. Also during the colder months, when the land temperature is below the water temperature of the ocean, precipitation will begin along the seaboard when the wind shifts and blows steadily from the water over the land without regard to the height of the barometer. In such cases the moisture in the warm ocean winds is condensed by the cold of the continental area. During the summer months, on the contrary, the ocean winds are not necessarily rain winds for the reason that they are cooler than the land surfaces and their capacity for moisture is increased by the warmth that is communicated to them by the land surfaces. If, however, the easterly winds of summer increase in force with a falling barometer, the approach of an area of low barometer pressure from the west is indicated and rain will follow in a day or two.

"Rainbow in the morning
Sailor take warning
Rainbow at night
Sailors' delight."

Thunderstorms.—The rain of summer usually occurs with thunder storms which are most frequent from certain directions and the wind in a particular quarter. Beyond the fact that more thunder storms come from a westerly quarter than from any other direction little can be said of value in forecasting their approach by the surface winds only. Their coming can usually be foretold a few hours by the form and movement of the clouds. A thunder storm in summer which does not depress the barometer will be very local and of slight consequence. Thunder storms are rare when the barometer is high and are to be looked for when it is low. About the earliest indication is when the sun in the morning is breaking through clouds and scorching a thunder storm will follow in the afternoon.

Rainbows.—Rainbows are produced by the refraction of the sun's rays in the rain drops in the air, the center of the bow being opposite the sun. A rainbow seen in the morning is to the west and the shower will probably pass over the observer. And if seen in the afternoon the shower is to the east and is passing off.

Fogs.—Fogs are usually produced when a current of warm moist air passes over a body of water of a lower temperature. *Fogs indicate fine weather.* On the Atlantic from 30 to 35 north latitude fogs are almost unknown.

Dew.—When the temperature of the earth's surface falls below the dew point of the air the latter deposits on the cooled surface part of its vapor in dew drops. This is due to the rapid cooling by radiation especially on clear nights when the temperature of the ground and other solid substances becomes colder than the air above and the dew point or frost point is reached by the ground while the air a few feet above may be several degrees warmer. *Dew is an indication of fine weather. Heavy dew in hot weather indicates a continuance of fair weather. No dew, after a hot day, foretells rain.*

Frost suddenly following a heavy rain seldom lasts.

Moon.—A halo or ring around the moon may be caused by ice crystals or water mist in the upper atmosphere and is an indication that bad weather is coming, possibly within twenty-four hours. One of the best forecasts based upon the appearance of the moon is when the moon can be seen quite clearly in the day time fair and cooler weather will follow with winds probably from the northerly quadrant.

"Moon light nights have the heaviest frosts."

Clouds.—Clouds have been poetically called the "Storm signals of the sky." And in every locality there is one direction of cloud motion that betokens bad weather and another which portends fine weather.

"A fog on a mountain is a cloud
And a cloud on earth is a fog."

After fine weather the first signs in the sky of a coming change are usually light streaks, curls, wisps or mottled patches of white distant clouds which increase, and are followed by an overcasting murky vapor that grows into cloudiness—this appearance more or less watery, is an infallible sign, that wind or rain will prevail. Usually the higher and more distant such clouds seem to be the more gradual but more general the change will prove.

One of the important effects of clouds is to prevent the minimum temperature from becoming as low as it would under a clear sky because the radiation from the earth is hindered.

When clouds form over a region where the air is saturated with moisture the globules of water forming the clouds unite and descend through the moist air underneath falling as rain, and the higher the cloud the larger the size of the drops will be. High upper clouds crossing the sun, moon or stars in a direction different from that of the lower clouds or the wind field below, foretell a change of wind toward that direction.

Light scud clouds driving across heavy masses, show wind and rain, but if they are alone they may indicate wind only.

Misty clouds forming or hanging on heights, if they remain, increase or descend, indicate wind and rain, but if they rise or disperse the weather will improve or become fine. Light delicate quiet tints of color with soft undefined form of clouds, indicate and accompany fine weather. Generally the softer the appearance the less wind may be expected and the harder, more greasy, rolled and tufted or ragged the stronger the coming wind will prove.

Unusual gaudy hues with hard definite outlined clouds foretell rain and probably strong wind.

Hard-edged oily-looking clouds indicate wind and small inky-looking clouds foretell rain.

Clouds are different in form and character, and accordingly have been classified as follows:

Cirrus.—Is the most elevated of all, thin and long-drawn looking like carded wool or hair or like curly or fleecy patches. It is the Cat's tail of the sailor, and the Mare's tail of the landsman. Its summer speed averages 67 miles per hour, while in winter it is 78 miles per hour, and has been observed making 182 to 200 miles per hour.

Cumulus.—Is in large masses of hemispherical form above and flat below, one piled above another and often afford rain and thunder gusts. Their tops in summer travel on an average of 34 miles per hour, and in winter 47 miles per hour.

Stratus.—Is in layers or bands extending horizontally, and has an average speed in summer of 13 miles per hour and in winter of 24 miles per hour.

Nimbus.—Has a uniform gray tint and ragged edges, it covers the sky in seasons of continuous rain and is the proper rain cloud.

Cirro-Cumulus.—Like the cirrus of these broken fleece-like clouds, but the parts are more or less rounded and regularly grouped. It is the mackerel sky.

Cirro-Stratus.—The cirrus coalesce in long strata.

Cumulo-Stratus.—Between cumulo and stratus often of a black or bluish tint at the horizon.

> "*Mackerel sky*
> *Twelve hours dry,*
> *The higher the clouds*
> *The finer the weather.*
> *When clouds appear like rocks and towers,*
> *The Earth's refreshed by frequent showers.*"

Thunder and Lightning.—Thunder rolls because lightning is an instant discharge, the sounds reaching us progressively from lower to upper strata of the air. The occurrence of thunder and lightning is practically simultaneous, but an interval elapses before the thunder is heard due to the distance. To calculate the distance approximately allow one mile for every five seconds interval. If lightning is at a distance of or more than fifteen miles thunder will not be heard.

Lightning owing to the different types of flashes has been classified as follows:

Streak: A plain broad smooth streak or flash.

Sinuous: A flash following some general direction, but the line is sinuous, bending from side to side.

Ramified: Part of the flash appears to branch off from the main stem like branches of a tree.

Ball: Wanders without definite course and forms irregular loops.

Beaded: A series of bright beads along streak lightning.

Dark flashes: Not understood, but believed to be a photographic effect within the camera as it is only noted in photographs. *Physics of the Air*, p. 379.

Heat Lightning: Is distant lightning flashes below the horizon, illuminating the higher strata of clouds and too far away for its thunder to be heard.

*Sun and Sky.**—The sun regulates the weather, it gives rise to winter and summer; by evaporation it raises the aqueous vapor into the air and this vapor by cooling causes clouds, rain, snow and hail. The sun is the primary cause of the difference in atmospheric pressure and in this way produces wind.

The following are a few simple indications of the color and appearance of sky at sunset and sunrise and of the sky overhead.

If the sun sets in a sky slightly purple and the atmosphere at the zenith is a bright blue, we may rely upon fine weather.

If the sun is bright at noon it will be red at night.

Whether clear or cloudy, a rosy sky at sunset presages fine weather.

If before sunset the sun appears diffuse and of a brilliant white, it foretells storms.

When after sunset the western sky is of a whitish yellow, extending a great height, it indicates probably rain during the night or next day. Gaudy or unusual hues, with hard definitely outlined clouds, foretell rain and probably wind.

The sun setting after a fine day behind a heavy bank of clouds, with a falling barometer is generally indicative of rain or snow according to the season, either in the night or next morning. Setting in dark clouds expect rain the next day.

A bright yellow sky at sunset indicates wind and a pale yellow sky at sunset indicates rain.

By the prevalence of any kind of red or yellow or other tints, the coming weather may be foretold.

A dark Indian red indicates rain.

A sickly looking greenish hue indicates wind and rain.

A low dawn is when the day breaks on or near the horizon, the first streaks of light being very low down.

A high dawn is when the first indications of daylight are seen above a bank of clouds and indicates wind.

When the sun in the morning is breaking through clouds and scorching, a thunderstorm follows in the afternoon.

A red sky in the morning indicates considerably wind and rain.

A gray sky in the morning indicates fine weather.

A dark gloomy blue sky overhead in the day indicates wind but light.

A bright blue sky indicates fine weather. A solar halo indicates bad weather and when the sun appears to draw water, rain follows soon.

*The character of the day, as determined by the Weather Bureau, is divided into three groups. A day when the sky is three-tenths or less covered with clouds, on the average, is recorded as clear; from four-tenths to seven-tenths as partly cloudy; and eight-tenths or more as cloudy. The degree of cloudiness is determined by a number of eye observations throughout the day.

Radio Weather Forecasts*

The forecasting of weather along the seaboard by the U. S. Weather Bureau has become a service of exceptional value. Seamen of the present day are well informed by radio of the general weather conditions expected over an extensive range of the ocean. The further development of this valuable service is being urged and the ship lanes of the world, with their many observers, may soon be plotted each hour of the day and the weather foretold with scientific accuracy.

Ships with wireless are in a position to gather weather reports from other ships, and with greater meteorological knowledge, to plot weather charts, locate storm centers and forecast the conditions to be expected. Two or more observers in a hurricane, or typhoon, area, exchanging data, would be of great mutual assistance.

IV

Winds

(*Adapted From Bowditch*)

To better understand how the air can be set in motion by differences of pressure it is necessary to have a clear conception of the nature of the air itself.

The atmosphere which completely envelops the earth may be considered as a fluid sea at the bottom of which we live, and which extends upward to a considerable height, probably 200 miles, constantly diminishing in density as the altitude increases.

The air, or material of which this atmosphere is composed, is a transparent gas, which, like all other gases, is perfectly elastic and highly compressible. Although extremely light, it has a perfectly definite weight, a cubic foot of air, at ordinary pressure and temperature, weighing 1.22 ounces, or about one seven hundred and seventieth part of the weight of an equal volume of water. In consequence of this weight it exerts a certain pressure upon the surface of the earth, amounting on the average to 15 pounds for each square inch. To accurately measure this pressure, which is constantly undergoing slight changes, we ordinarily employ a mercurial barometer, an instrument in which the weight of a column of air of given cross section is balanced against that of a column of mercury having an equal cross section; and instead of saying that the pressure of the atmosphere is a certain number of pounds on each square inch, we say that it is a certain number of inches of mercury, meaning thereby

*See W. B. Bulletins of May 16th and May 28th, 1921, and subsequent issues for full instructions as to radio forecasts. Improvement is so rapid instructions are not printed here. Bulletins are free to mariners at W. B. Stations.

rendered them by the pilot charts issued by the Hydrographic Office of the U. S. Navy. Indeed every branch of the vast business of shipping derives incalculable benefit from this service so freely rendered and so ably planned and carried out. It is really the most monumental system of international co-operation in existence today. Thousands of vessels, in all parts of the world are daily adding their fund of standardized observations to the general knowledge of the weather.*

These observations, tabulated and digested by the Weather Bureau of the United States, in conjunction with the systematized observations of this service itself, stretching from the Atlantic to the Pacific, form the basis for the pilot charts issued by the Hydrographic Office. The tidal and current data, and other information sent in by sea observers is worked over by the experts of this office and forms the basis for the vast amount of useful information plotted on these charts. The following notice is printed on the pilot charts:

Reports on Features of Pilot Charts and to Whom Made

That mariners may be fully informed as to the participation of the Hydrographic Office, Navy Department, and the Weather Bureau, Department of Agriculture, in the collection and compilation of data for the several Pilot Charts, and that they may know to which office to send observations, attention is called to the following:

Hydrographic Office.—The Hydrographic Office collects and compiles data on the following features, reports upon which should be made to the nearest of the Branch Hydrographic Offices (in order that no time may be lost in transmission and publication, and that said Branch Hydrographic Offices may keep in touch with all observers arriving in their respective districts) or to the Hydrographic Office in Washington:

Ice, coastwise, field, and berg.
Derelicts.
Wrecks.
Floating wreckage, etc.
Buoys adrift.
Location of fishing banks, whales, and seals.
Currents, ocean and tidal.
Rocks, shoals, and other dangers.
Radio telegraph stations.
Gale and storm signals of foreign countries.
All questions relating to navigation and seamanship.
Maneuvering vessels at sea during storms.

*The British Meteorological Office also issues monthly weather charts, but their information is still behind that of the American charts.

Variation of the compass.
Steam and sail routes.
Discolored water.
Navigational methods, charts, books, and instruments.
Waterspouts.
Great sea waves.
Soundings.
Sailing directions.
Seismic shocks at sea.
Port facilities.
Calming seas with oil.
Changes in aids to navigation.

Weather Bureau.—The Weather Bureau collects and compiles data upon the following features that appear on the Pilot Charts, reports upon which should be made to said Bureau:

Pressure, barometric.
Temperature of air.
Winds, average direction and force of.
Calms, percentage of.
Gales, percentage of.
Trade-wind limits.
Fog, percentage of.
Storm tracks, course of and rate of travel.
Statement of past average conditions of wind and weather.
Rains, equatorial region.

Every person interested in this important branch of human progress should read a pamphlet called "The Marine Meteorological Service of the United States," by W. E. Hurd, sent free of charge by the Government Printing Office, Washington, D. C. upon application.

VI

Data on Cyclonic Storms

Prepared by the Hydrographic Office, U. S. Navy

Early Indications of the Approach of a Storm

The occurrence of tropical cyclonic storms is confined to the summer and autumn months of the respective hemispheres and to the western parts of the several oceans—the North Atlantic, North Pacific, South Pacific, and Indian oceans. They are unknown in the South Atlantic. The Arabian Sea and Bay of Bengal are also visited by cyclonic storms, which occur most frequently in May and October.

In the Atlantic the occurrence of these storms is confined almost exclusively to the period June–November, attaining a maximum frequency in September and October. The number actually occurring is probably somewhat greater than the number recorded. The limited area of the storm within the Tropics (the diameter of the area of violent winds is here frequently less than 100 miles) and the scarcity of observing vessels in the region throughout which the storms manifest their greatest activity make it probable that a considerable percentage escape observation. The occurrence during the eleven-year period, 1890–1900, according to the records of the United States Hydrographic Office, was as follows:

*Occurrence of West India Hurricanes**

	1890	1891	1892	1893	1894	1895	1896	1897	1898	1899	1900	Total
June	0	0	1	0	0	0	0	0	0	0	0	1
July	0	2	0	0	0	0	0	0	0	0	0	2
August	1	1	1	4	0	0	0	0	0	1	0	8
September	2	2	1	0	2	1	3	1	3	2	2	19
October	1	3	4	2	3	1	1	2	0	4	1	22
November	2	0	1	1	0	0	0	0	0	0	0	4

Figure 1 shows in general the path of a storm in the North Atlantic.

In south latitude the storm season is from September to May, February and March being the worst months. It would thus appear that in both hemispheres the storm season corresponds to the time when the sun is approaching the equator on its return from the greatest declination north or south. Fig. 2 shows the general path of a storm in the South Pacific.

During the season of tropical storms whatever interferes with the regularity of the diurnal oscillation of the barometer should be considered an indication of a change of weather. The barometer is by no means an infallible guide for warnings much in advance, but after the beginning of the storm it will more or less accurately indicate the rapidity of approach and distance from the center, and its indications should in no case be disregarded.

One of the earliest indications of the approach of a tropical storm is the appearance of the sky and general clearness of the atmosphere. Tropical cyclonic storms are almost invariably preceded by a day of unusual clearness, when distant objects not usually visible stand out with great distinctness. The temperature at such times is more than usually oppressive.

This is frequently accompanied by an unusually high barometer. Later it may be followed by a restless oscillating or pumping of the mercury caused by the disturbed condition of the

*Over a thirty-five year period West India hurricanes have occurred as follows—May, 1; June, 8; July, 5; August, 23; September, 43; October, 42; November, 2. According to U. S. Weather Bureau Records.

atmosphere. Then the sky becomes overcast and remains so, at first with a delicate cirrus haze, which shows no disposition to clear away at sunset, but which later becomes gradually

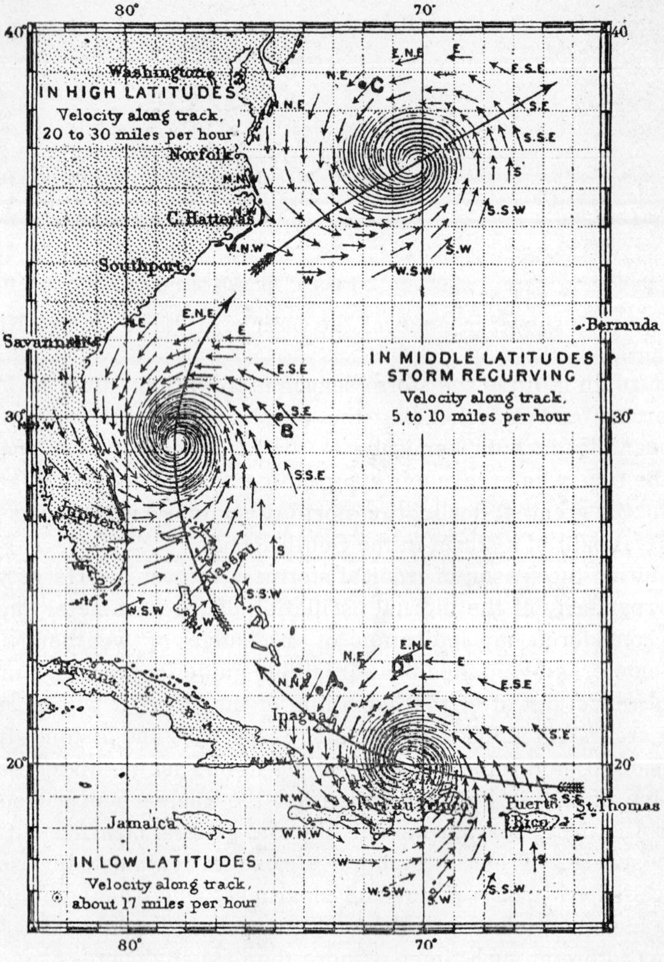

Fig. 1. The Average Path of a Cyclone in the North Atlantic.

more and more dense until the dark mass of the true hurricane cloud appears upon the horizon. From the main body of this cloud portions are detached from time to time and drift across the sky, their progress marked by squalls of rain and wind of increasing force. Rain, indeed, forms one of the most prominent features of the storm. In the outer portions it is fine and mist-

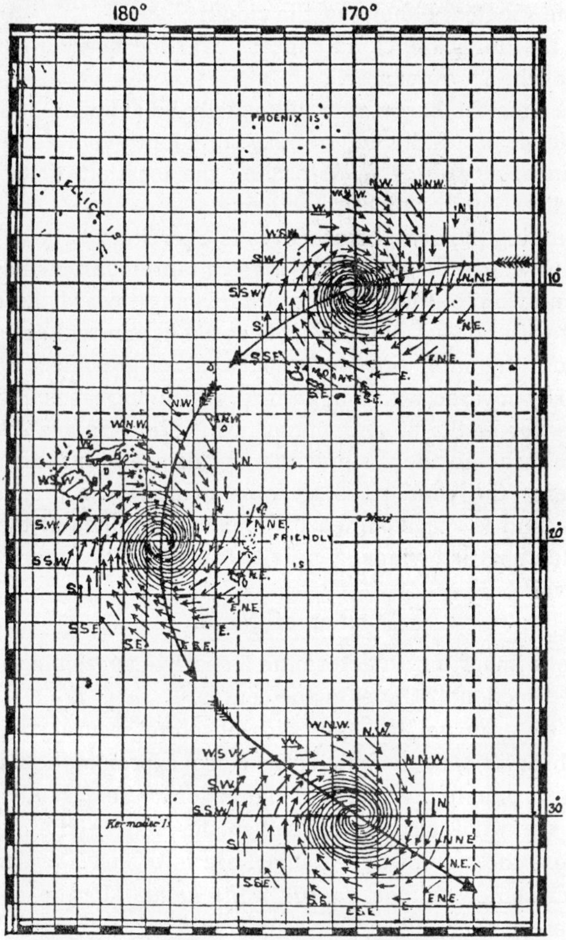

Fig. 2. Average cyclone path South Pacific

like, with occasional showers these latter increasing in frequency and in copiousness. In the neighborhood of the center it falls in torrents. The rain area extends farther in advance of the storm than in the rear.

A long swell from the direction of the storm frequently sets in before any other indications become marked.

When the sky first becomes overcast with the characteristic veil of cirrus the storm center will most probably lie in the direction of the greatest density of the cloud.

When the hurricane cloud appears over the horizon it will be densest at the storm center.

By this time the barometer will usually be showing unmistakable evidence of a fall, and one may confidently look for a storm and begin observations to determine the location of its center and the direction in which it is moving.

Surrounding the actual storm area is a territory of large extent throughout which the barometer reads a tenth of an inch or more below the average, the pressure diminishing toward the central area, but with no such rapidity as is noted within that area itself. Throughout the outer ring unsettled weather prevails. The sky is ordinarily covered with a light haze, which increases in density as the center of the storm approaches. Showers are frequent. Throughout the northern semicircle of this area (in the northern hemisphere) the wind rises to force 6 or 8—the "reinforced trades"—and is accompanied by squalls; throughout the other semicircle unsettled winds, generally from a southeasterly direction, prevail.

Position of Center

It is very important to determine as early as possible the location and direction of travel of the center.

While this can not be done with absolute accuracy with one set of observations, a sufficiently close approximation can be arrived at to enable the vessel to maneuver to the best advantage.

Since the wind circulates against the sun in the northern hemisphere the rule in that hemisphere is to *face the wind* and the storm center will be *on the right hand*. In the southern hemisphere, under the same circumstances, the center is to the *left*. If the wind traveled in exact circles, the center would be eight points to the right when looking directly in the wind's eye. We have seen, however, that the wind follows more or less a spiral path inwards, which brings the center from eight to twelve points to the right of the direction of the wind.

The number of points to the right may vary during the same storm, and as the wind usually shifts in squalls its direction should be taken just after a squall.

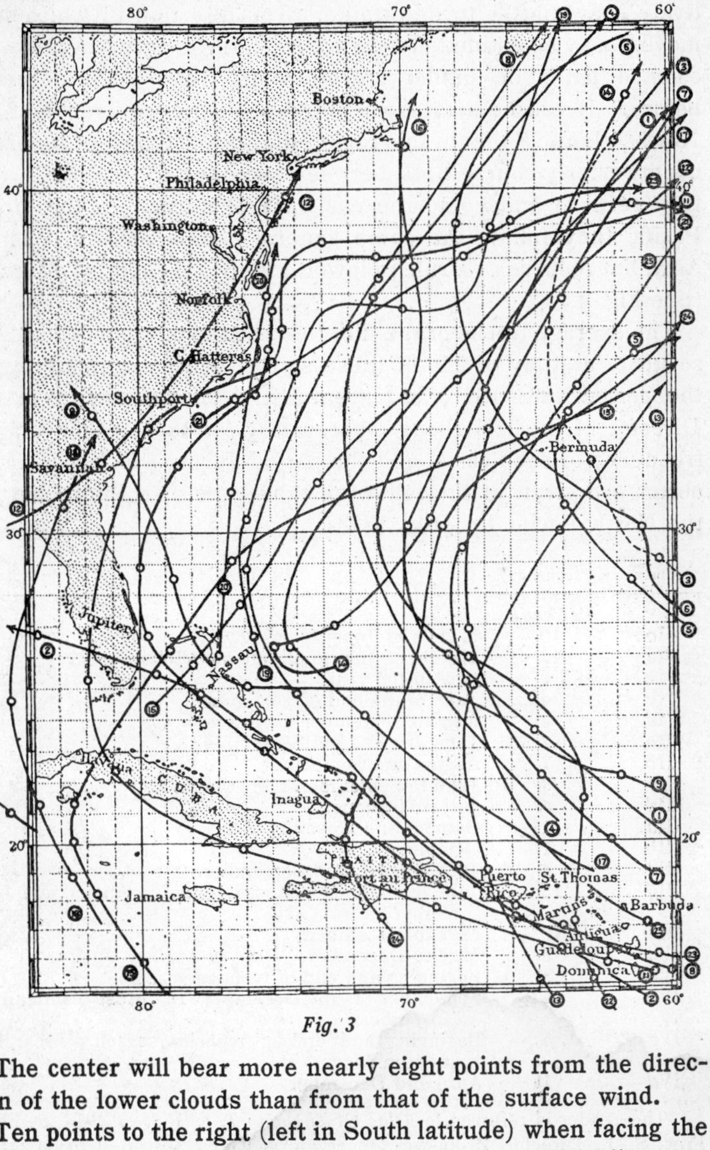

Fig. 3

The center will bear more nearly eight points from the direction of the lower clouds than from that of the surface wind.

Ten points to the right (left in South latitude) when facing the wind is a good average allowance to make, but a larger allowance should be made when in front of the storm center than when in its rear.

The approximate direction of the storm center is a comparatively easy matter to determine. The direction in which it is moving may be estimated with a fair degree of accuracy from the charted paths of similar storms which have been observed before. It will be seen from Fig. 3, "Hurricane Tracks in the North Atlantic," that in this region the storms follow in general a northwesterly course until between latitudes 25° and 30°, when they recurve and go to the eastward of north. In the North Pacific they follow the same general course on the coast of Asia, but recurve as a rule in lower latitudes than in the Atlantic. (See Fig. 4.)

The average tracks of the different classes of typhoons are the result of a study of 244 of these storms which occurred during the period 1884–1897, and are taken from the report of the Director of the Hongkong Observatory for 1897. The relative frequency of each class, and the period during which it is apt to occur, are given in the following table (see also Pilot Chart of the North Pacific for July, 1898):*

Class	Frequency	Period
	Per cent.	
I*aα*	10	Middle of June to end of September.
I*aβ*	12	Middle of July to middle of October.
I*b*	0	Late in the year.
I*c*	4	June to the end of September.
I*d*	2	May to September, inclusive.
II*a*	2	July, August, and September.
II*b*	7	August and September.
II*c*	3	June to September. Maximum in July.
II*d*	4	July and August.
III*a*	1½	October and November.
III*b*	1	October.
III*c*	4	July, August, and September.
III*d*	15	June to October. Most frequent in August and September.
III*e*	12½	May to December.
IV*aα*	8½	May to December. Rare in August.
IV*aβ*	3	Beginning and end of typhoon season.
IV*b*	4½	September 1 to December 1. Most common in November.
IV*c*	4	Beginning and end of typhoon season. Most frequent in May.
IV*d*	1	April and December.

*The reader is referred to *Atlas Of Typhoon Tracks, 1893–1918*, by Louis Froc, S. J., Director, Zi-ka-wei Observatory, China. Printed in *Weather of the Oceans*, Aug., 1920. See page 875.

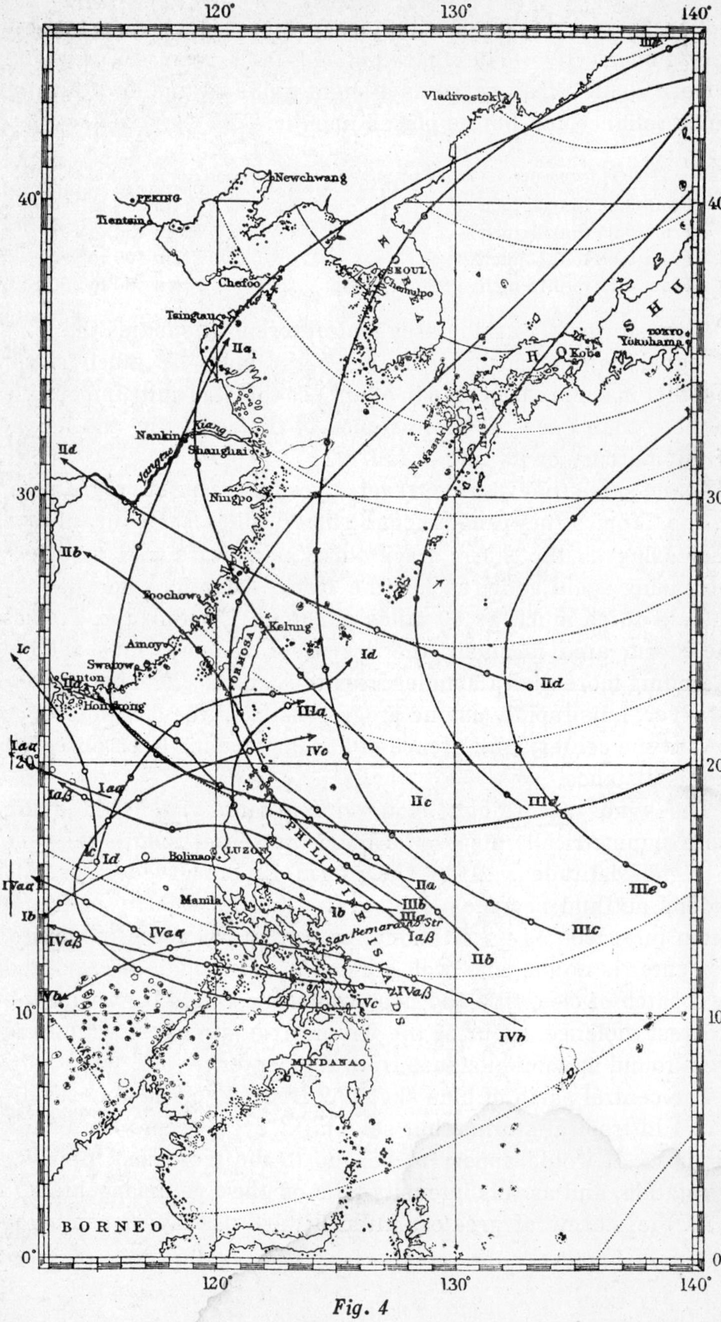

120°
130°
140°
40°
30°
20°
10°
0°
Vladivostok
Newchwang
PEKING
Tientsin
KOREA
SEOUL
Chemulpo
Chefoo
Tsingtau
TOKYO
Yokohama
Kobe
HONSHU
KIUSIU
Nagasaki
Nanking
Kiang
Yangtze
Shanghai
Ningpo
Foochow
Kelung
FORMOSA
Amoy
Swatow
Canton
Hongkong
LUZON
Bolinao
Manila
San Bernardino Str
PHILIPPINE ISLANDS
MINDANAO
BORNEO

Fig. 4

The distance away from the storm center can only be estimated very imperfectly. The following old table from Piddington's "Horn Book" may serve as a slight guide to this end, but too much reliance can not be placed upon it:

Average fall of barometer per hour.	Distance in miles from center.
From 0.02 to 0.06 inch	From 250 to 150.
From 0.06 to 0.08 inch	From 150 to 100.
From 0.08 to 0.12 inch	From 100 to 80.
From 0.12 to 0.15 inch	From 80 to 50.

With storms of varying area and different intensities the lines of equal barometric pressure (isobars) must lie much closer together in some cases than in others, so that it is quite impossible to more than guess at the distance of the center by the height of the mercury or its rate of fall.

At the same time storms travel at varying rates of progression. In the Tropics this ranges from 5 to 20 miles per hour, always decreasing as the storm track turns northward and recurves, increasing again as it reaches the North Atlantic, where it may amount to as much as 50 miles per hour. Within the Tropics the storm area is small, the region of violent winds seldom extending more than 150 miles from the center. The barometer, however, falls rapidly as one progresses from the circumference toward the center, a difference of 2 inches having been observed in this distance.

The winds accordingly blow with greater violence and are more symmetrically disposed around the center than is the case in higher latitudes. After the storm has recurved it usually widens out and becomes less severe, and its velocity of translation increases as its rotational energy grows more moderate. Its center is no longer a well-defined area of small size marked by a patch of clear sky and near which the winds blow with the greatest violence. Out of the Tropics the strongest winds are often found at some distance from the center.

The central patch of blue sky, or "Bull's-Eye," is almost universal in tropical storms, but seldom, if ever, occurs out of the Tropics. It would appear to be due to the increased intensity of rotation, and as this intensity falls off the Eye disappears.

As the storms of greatest intensity are usually of comparatively small area with slow rates of progression it follows that could we have definite and early information of their position and prospective paths it would be an easy matter to avoid the locality of greatest severity.

This, however, is clearly not possible. Even with the advantage of many simultaneous observations at stations some distance apart, such as can be obtained on land by a regularly organized service, it is impossible to foretell with certainty the path of the approaching storm.

The isolated observer on board ship then can do no more than exercise a wise discretion and act according to his best judgment, being guided by such observations as he has at hand. See page 810.

Handling the Ship within Storm Area

If from the weather indications given above, and such others as his experience has taught him, the navigator is led to believe in the approach of a storm, he should at once—

First. Determine the bearing of the center.

Second. Estimate its distance.

Third. Plot its apparent path.

The first two of the above determinations will locate the approximate position of the center, which should be marked on the chart. The relation between the position of the ship and the position and prospective track of the center will indicate the proper course to pursue.

Should the ship be ahead of the storm center it may be assumed that the latter will draw nearer more or less directly It then becomes of the utmost importance to determine its path and so learn whether the vessel is in the right or left semicircle of the storm area.

The right and left semicircles lie on the right and left hands, respectively, of an observer standing on the storm track and facing in the direction the center is moving. Owing to the difference in the direction of rotation of storms north and south of the equator that semicircle which lies between the path and the equator in both the northern and the southern hemispheres prior to the storms recurving (the left-hand semicircle in the northern hemisphere and the right-hand in the southern), is not so liable to the severest winds; and, when in it, it is easier to avoid the storm center. For this reason it is called the *navigable* semicircle, the right semicircle (left in south latitudes) on the other hand is called the *dangerous* semicircle.*

In order to determine the path of the storm and consequently in which semicircle the ship finds herself, it is necessary to wait until the wind shifts.† When this occurs, plot a new position of the center 10 points to the right of the new direction of the wind as before, and the line joining these two positions will be the *probable* path of the storm. If the ship has not been stationary during the time between the two sets of observations (as will indeed never be the case unless at anchor), allowance must be made for the course and distance she has traveled in the interim.

Two bearings of the center with an interval between of from two to three hours will, in general, be sufficient to determine the course of the storm, provided an accurate account is kept of the ship's way, but if the storm be moving slowly a longer interval will be necessary.

Should the wind not shift, but continue to blow steadily with increasing force, and with a falling barometer, it may be assumed that the vessel is on or near the storm track. Owing to the slow advance of storms in the Tropics, a vessel might come within the disturbed area through overtaking the center. In such a case a slight decrease in speed would probably be all that would be necessary, but it should be borne in mind that the storm path is by no means constant either in speed or direction, and that it is particularly liable to recurve away from the equator.

In the cyclones of the Southern Indian ocean the best observers claim that the wind seldom, if ever, blows around the center. Instead of following the usual inward spiral path, the northeasterly and easterly winds of these storms blow almost directly *toward* the center and upward, rather than around it.

Should the position of the vessel lie in advance of the storm center, the procedure to be followed will depend upon whether she is in the dangerous or navigable semicircle. The object in both cases should be to keep as far as possible from the center. Knowing the direction of rotation of storms in both hemispheres,

*Some seamen consider the right hand semicircle safer for steamers. Wind is steadier, sea less confused.

†Not always good. A ship caught in a southeast wind, if storm centre is advancing slowly, might be blown into storm track.

it will be clear that points lying on the right of the storm track (right semicircle) will, as the center approaches and passes, find the wind hauling, in the direction north, east, south, west.

On the left of the track (left semicircle) the wind will shift in the reverse direction. Shifts of the wind usually come in heavy squalls, during which the wind will blow from the new direction, even though it may apparently shift back temporarily during the lull immediately following.

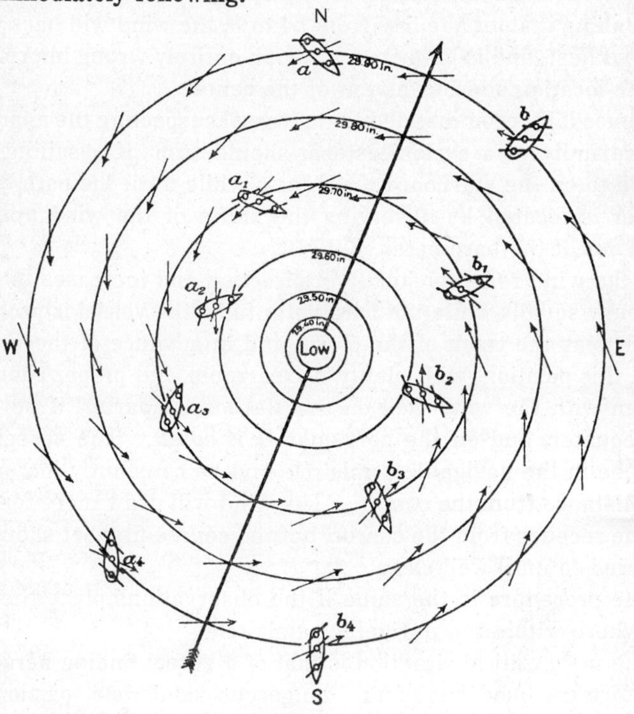

Fig. 5.

It must not be forgotten that the shifts of wind will only occur n the above order when the vessel is stationary. When the course and speed are such as to maintain a constant relative bearing between the ship and storm center, there will be no shift of wind. Should the vessel be outrunning the storm, the wind will indeed shift in the opposite direction to that given, and a navigator in the right semicircle, for instance, and judging only by the shifts of wind without taking into account his own run, might imagine himself on the opposite side. In such a case the barometer must be the guide. If it falls, one is approaching the center; if it rises, one is receding.

An examination of Fig. 5 shows how this is. A vessel hove to at the position marked *b*, and being passed by the storm center, will occupy successive positions in regard to the center from *b* to *b*4, and will experience shifts of wind, as shown by the arrows, from East through South to SW. On the other hand, if the storm center be stationary or moving slowly and a vessel be overtaking it along the line from *b*4 to *b*, the wind will back from SW. to East, and is likely to convey an entirely wrong impression as the location and movement of the center.

Hence it is recommended that a vessel suspecting the approach or proximity of a cyclonic storm should stop (if a sailing ship heave to on the starboard tack) for a while until the path of the center is located by observing the shifts of the wind and the behavior of the barometer.

If the wind remains steady in direction and increases in force in heavy squalls while the barometer falls, the vessel is probably on or near the track of the storm and in advance of the center.

In this position, with plenty of sea room, the proper course is to run with the wind well on the starboard quarter, if north of the equator, and on the port quarter if south. The vessel will thus be in the navigable semicircle and be constantly increasing her distance from the center. The wind will draw more forward as she recedes from the center, but the course first set should be adhered to until well clear.

The procedure is the same if the observations place the ship anywhere within the navigable semicircle.

The most critical situation is that of a vessel finding herself in the forward quadrant of the dangerous semicircle, particularly if at some distance from the center, where the wind shifts but slowly and the barometer indications are undecided.

The general object, however, of putting as much distance as possible between oneself and the storm center should be kept in view. With steamers this may not be difficult, although, should the storm be recurving, the course first set may have to be subsequently altered in order to continue to draw away. A sailing vessel will be set by the wind directly toward the path of the storm and may become involved with the center without being able to avoid it. If so caught in the dangerous semicircle, a sailing vessel should haul by the wind on the starboard tack (on the port tack in south latitude), keep coming up as the wind draws aft, and carry sail as long as the weather permits. If obliged to heave to, do so on the starboard tack in north latitude and on the port tack in south latitude.

This maneuver, while it may not carry a vessel clear of the storm track, will make the best of a bad situation.

A vessel so hove to will find the shifts of wind drawing aft, enabling her to come up to them instead of being headed off, as would be the case on the other tack.

Moreover, since the sea changes its direction less rapidly than the wind, the vessel will come up more nearly head on to the old sea, instead of having it more abeam as on the opposite tack.

A general rule for heaving to is always heave to on whichever tack permits the shifts of wind to draw aft.

If, in spite of all endeavors, the storm center should pass directly over a vessel she will experience a short period of calm, but the seas will be high, confused, and dangerous, being swept in from all directions. After a short interval the wind will burst with hurricane force from a point directly opposite to that from which it was blowing before, and the vessel must be prepared to meet it and to avoid being caught aback.

Should steamers find it necessary to heave to the method of doing so must depend upon the position within the storm area. Many steamers find it preferable to heave to stern to sea, with engines turning over slowly, and drive before it.

Should this course be followed in the dangerous semicircle a steamer would in all probability be running directly into the center of the storm, where the high and confused seas would be more than likely to inflict damage. When obliged to heave to in the dangerous semicircle steamers should keep the wind a little on the starboard bow in north latitude, and on the port bow in south latitude, and make as much headway as the conditions will allow.

The situation is complicated in the southern Indian Ocean by the presence of the belt of intensified southeast trades to the southward of the storm tracks, in which belt the wind may increase in force with a falling barometer, while remaining steady in direction. Under such conditions there are no means of telling whether one is within the storm area proper or merely in the belt of intensified trades.

If, in the latter case, one were to heave to there is a good chance of being caught by the storm recurving or at the best undergoing a needless loss of time. On the other hand, to run off to the northwestward may bring one directly in the path of the storm.

A rule which in practice has been found to meet the situation fairly well is as follows: If well to the eastward of Mauritius and the indications point to being either in the southwest quadrant of a storm or in the intensified trades, with no means of determining which, one should follow the regular rule and heave to, making as much southing as possible. If, however, one is in the neighborhood of Mauritius, one should run to the northwestward and endeavor to get between that island and Madagascar, where usually better weather will be found. The attempt to cross the track ahead of a storm in the Indian Ocean may be made with better chance of success there than elsewhere, since the storms of this region appear to travel more slowly than in other parts of the world.

Figure 5 represents a cyclonic storm in the northern hemisphere after recurving. For simplicity the area of low barometer is made perfectly circular and the center is assumed to be ten points to the right of the direction of the wind at all points within the disturbed area. Let us assume that the center is advancing about NNE., in the direction of the long arrow, shown in heavy full line. The ship *a* has the wind at ENE.; she is to the left of the track, or technically in the navigable semicircle. The ship *b* has the wind at ESE. and is in the dangerous semicircle. As the storm advances these ships, if lying to, *a* upon the port tack, *b* upon the starboard tack, as shown, take with regard to the storm center the successive positions *a a*, etc., *b b*, etc., the wind of ship *a* shifting to the left, of ship *b* to the right, or in both cases drawing aft, and thus diminishing the probability of either ship being struck aback, a danger to which a vessel lying to on the opposite tack (i. e., the starboard tack in the left-hand semicircle or the port tack in the right-hand semicircle) is constantly exposed, the wind in the latter case tending constantly to draw forward. The ship *b* is continually beaten by wind and sea toward the storm track. The ship *a* is drifted away from the track and should she be able to carry sail would soon find better weather by running off to the westward.

Rules for Maneuvering

The rules for maneuvering may be summed up as follows:

Northern Hemisphere

Right or Dangerous Semicircle.—Steamers: Bring the wind on the starboard bow, make as much way as possible, and if obliged to heave to do so head to the sea. Sailing vessels: Keep close hauled on the starboard tack, make as much way as possible, and if obliged to heave to do so on the starboard tack.

Left or Navigable Semicircle.—Steam and sailing vessels: Bring the wind on the starboard quarter, note the course and hold it. If obliged to heave to steamers may do so stern to sea; sailing vessels on the port tack.

On the Storm Track in Front of Center.—Steam and sailing vessels: Run for the left semicircle with wind on starboard quarter, and when in that semicircle maneuver as above.

On the Storm Track in Rear of Center.—Avoid it by the best practicable route, having due regard for the storms recurving to the northward and eastward.

Southern Hemisphere

Left or Dangerous Semicircle.—Steamers: Bring the wind on the port bow, make as much way as possible, and if obliged to heave to do so head to sea. Sailing vessels: Keep close hauled on the port tack, make as much way as possible, and if obliged to heave to do so on the port tack.

Right or Navigable Semicircle.—Steam and sailing vessels: Bring the wind on the port quarter, note the course and hold it. If obliged to heave to, steamers may do so stern to sea; sailing vessels on the starboard tack.

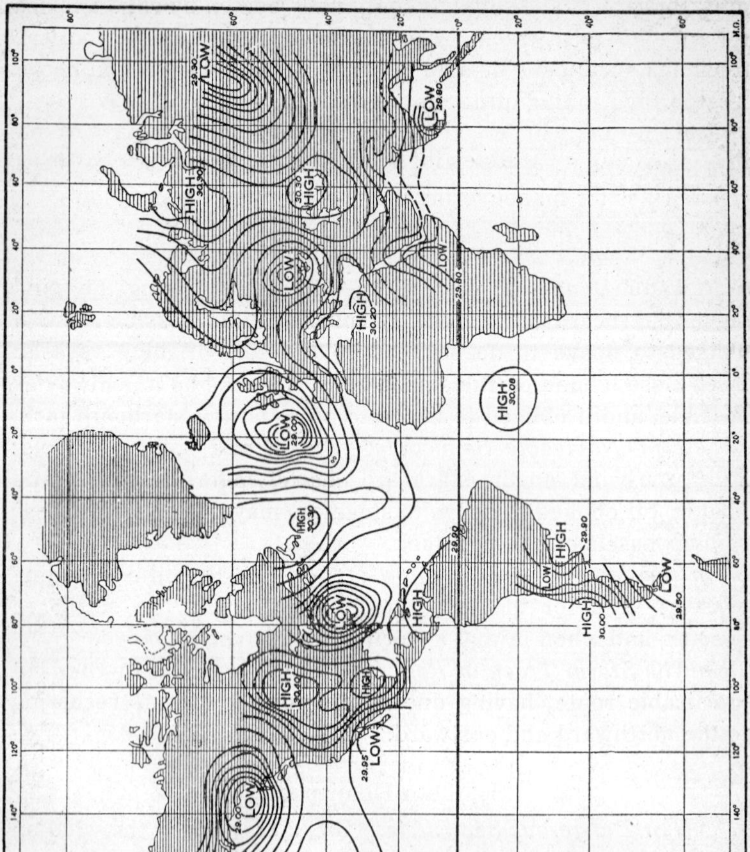

Isobars of World on Nov. 9, 1913. Plotted by F. G. Tingley, U. S. W. B.

VII

Weather on the Oceans of the World

From data compiled by the U. S. Weather Bureau, as published on Pilot Charts issued by the U. S. Hydrographic Office.

From the millions of observations taken since the work of systematic study was founded by Maury, many valuable deductions have been made with regard to the weather at sea.

The monthly forecasts based upon these observations are printed in *Standard Seamanship* with the hope that they will be more useful in this form than when widely scattered on the pilot charts where they are printed for the current month. Here the reader may easily follow changes from month to month by referring to the pilot chart at hand, or to the general ocean chart of any area under investigation.

NORTH ATLANTIC OCEAN

Average Conditions of Wind and Weather

January

Pressure.—The range of pressure is the same as for December. The minimum 29.60 inches, marks the vicinity of the Iceland Low; the maximum, 30.20 inches, appears as two small areas, one east of the 19th meridian between the 29th and 39th parallels, the other in mid-ocean between latitudes 25° and 30° N. A belt of moderately low pressure along the Equator averages 29.90 inches.

Temperature.—The temperature has risen slightly near the British Isles and off the coasts of France and Portugal and ranges over this region between 40° and 55°. Elsewhere it has fallen 3° to 8°. Along the American coast the temperature ranges from 20° at Cape Ray to 67° at Key West. It is 75° to 78° in the Caribbean Sea and 80° or slightly higher over the extreme southern part of the ocean. Along the northern trans-Atlantic routes the mean is from 30° to 50°.

Westerly Winds and Gales.—North of the 40th parallel westerly winds, force 6, predominate from coast to coast. Between the 40th and 35th parallels the westerlies prevail from the American coast to the Azores; between the 30th and 35th parallels they extend eastward to the 45th meridian. Over this region the percentage of southwesterly to northwesterly gales has increased with the approach of midwinter, reaching their greatest development during this month. The highest percentages, 30 to 39, occur west of Scotland. Frequent snow squalls, with winds that sometimes attain hurricane force, accompany the passage of lows along the northern trans-Atlantic routes.

The Trade Winds.—The northeast trades are fairly constant over most of the ocean south of the 26th parallel, but low with greatest steadiness between the 5th and 20th parallels. The southeast trades, force 3 to 4, extend about 2 degrees north of the Equator between 15° and 40° west longitude. Southwesterly winds prevail in the Gulf of Guinea.

Calms.—The highest percentage of calms, 17 to 30, occurs east of the 20th meridian between latitudes 5° and 10° N. The percentage is 11 to 15 south of the 5th parallel between longitudes 35° W. and 0°, and 8 to 11 immediately south of the area of high pressure in mid-ocean. Throughout the West Indies the percentage is 6 to 9.

Northers.—Northers sometimes occur in the Gulf of Mexico and along the coast southward to Colon. These storms are generally preceded by a slight fall in the barometer, but the gale itself is accompanied by a rapid rise.

Fog.—The maximum area, 30 to 35 per cent of days with fog, continues southeast of Newfoundland. An elongated area, percentage 10 to 15, occurs east of the 30th meridian and north of the 41st parallel. South of this parallel, except along the American coast to Hatteras, the ocean is practically free from fog.

February

Pressure.—There has been little change in the pressure distribution since January. The Iceland Low remains unchanged, the isobar of 29.60 inches appearing north of the 55th parallel. The crest of the Azores High, 30.20 inches, occupies an elongated area in middle latitudes south of those islands. A shallow trough of low pressure, 29.90 inches, extends along the Equator.

Temperature.—The temperature along the American coast ranges from 15° at Belle Isle to 70° at Key West, a slight fall having occurred in the Gulf of St. Lawrence and a slight rise off the South Atlantic States. In the Caribbean Sea, it is between 75° and 78°, and about 80° near the Equator. Off the European and African coasts the temperature ranges between 40° and 80°, and along the northern trans-Atlantic routes between 30° and 50°.

Westerly Winds and Gales.—Westerly winds, force 5 to 6, prevail over the ocean north of the 35th parallel. The percentage of gales has fallen north of the 45th parallel and has risen between the 35th and 45th parallels. Frequent snow squalls, with winds that sometimes attain hurricane force, accompany the passage of lows along the northern trans-Atlantic routes.

The Trade Winds.—The northeast trades cover most of the ocean south of the 25th parallel and extend almost to the Equator. Along the African coast they prevail as far north as the 30th parallel.

The southeast trades extend slightly north of the Equator between the 15th and 30th meridians but they are weak and frequently fall to a calm.

Southwesterly winds prevail in the Gulf of Guinea.

Calms.—The highest percentage of calms, 15 to 25, occurs between the northeast and southeast trades east of the 30th meridian. The percentage is also high over most of the region between the 20th and 30th parallels.

Northers.—Northers sometimes occur in the Gulf of Mexico and along the coast southward to Colon. These storms are generally preceded by a slight fall in the barometer but the gale itself is accompanied by a rapid rise.

Fog.—The maximum area, 30 to 35 per cent of days with fog, continues southeast of Newfoundland. An elongated area, percentage 10 to 15 occurs northeast of the Azores. A small area, percentage 10 to 15, is found in mid-ocean north of the 50th parallel. The ocean is practically free from fog along the northern trans-Atlantic routes between the 10th and 40th meridians, and also over the region south of the 40th parallel, except along the American coast to Hatteras.

March

Pressure.—The crest of the high pressure area south of the Azores has decreased from 30.20 to 30.15 inches since February. The high pressure has also decreased in extent; its central area now lies between the 17th and 42d meridians. The Iceland Low is filling in with the approach of spring, and the pressure has increased from 29.60 to 29.70 inches north of the 55th parallel. The trough of low pressure along the Equator has remained practically unchanged since February, ranging about 29.90 inches.

Temperature.—The temperature over the northern trans-Atlantic routes and off the north Atlantic States has risen 3° to 8° since February, the greatest rise occurring in the fog area adjacent to the American coast. The mean temperature over the western part of the ocean ranges from 30° off Nova Scotia to 80° near the Equator. Over the eastern part of the ocean it ranges from 40° off Scotland to 80° south of Freetown, while along the northern trans-Atlantic routes it ranges between 35° and 55°.

Prevailing Westerlies and Gales.—The percentage of westerly winds is high north of the 40th parallel. Westerly winds are also found as far south as the 30th parallel between the 45th and 70th meridians. West of the 70th meridian the winds are north and northwest, with northwesterly gales. The percentage of gales over the region of westerly winds is moderate to high, being 11 to 22 per cent along the northern trans-Atlantic routes, and slightly higher north of the 55th parallel.

There has been a general decrease in the percentage of gales since February over most of the ocean north of the 35th parallel, and a slight increase over most of the region south of it.

The Trade Winds.—The northeast trades occupy most of the ocean south of the 25th parallel. They extend farther north over the Canary Islands, though their development in this region is not so marked. Along the African coast in the latitude of trades the winds are north-northeast, from 3 to 4, but west of longitude 20 they are northeast to east-northeast; force 4 to 5. In the Gulf of Mexico east to southeast trades prevail. Light southeast trades appear 2 or 3 degrees north of the Equator between the 15th and 30th meridians. In the Gulf of Guinea southwest winds of force 2 to 3 prevail.

Calms.—The highest percentage of calms is off the African coast near latitude 7 degrees N. where it is 26. The percentage is also high south of the 5th parallel, between the 10th and 35tn parallels, between the 10th and 35th meridians, where it is 13 to 24. Over the northern Gulf of Mexico the percentage is from 8 to 11, and over the crest of the high pressure, 6 to 11.

Fog.—South of Newfoundland there is a small area of 40 to 45 per cent of days with fog, an increase of 10 per cent over that of February, but the percentage decreases rapidly outward in all directions. From Cape Cod to Cape Henry the percentage is 20, thence southward to Hatteras it is 10. Occasional fogs occur farther south along the Carolina coast. Very little fog is observed between the 20th and 40th meridians. The percentage is low southwest of the British Isles and is only 10 to 15 per cent in the Irish sea.

Ice.—Icebergs may be expected early in the month.

April

Pressure.—The Iceland Low has decreased in intensity since March. The minimum pressure, 29.75 inches, lies between the 55th and 60th parallels. The central area of the Azores High, pressure 30.15, has contracted since March and now lies between latitudes 28° and 36° N. and longitudes 35° and 25° W. In the extreme southern part of the ocean the pressure is 29.90 inches.

Temperature.—The temperature has risen over practically the entire ocean since March. The greatest rise occurred in the Gulf of Mexico and off the New England coast, where the greatest changes amount to 8° to 10° respectively. Along the northern trans-Atlantic routes the change is greater near the American coast and decreases to about 2° in mid-ocean, thence it increases again to about 4° near the British Isles.

The temperature ranges between 35° and 55° along the northern trans-Atlantic routes. Over the northern waters of Newfoundland the temperature is near freezing; southward to latitude 35° there is a rapid rise to 60°; south of this latitude there is a gradual rise to 80° in the Caribbean Sea. In the Gulf of Mexico the temperature ranges between 70° and 80°, and in the eastern part of the ocean it ranges between 45° off Scotland to 80° in the Gulf of Guinea.

Prevailing Westerlies and Gales.—Westerly winds, force 4 to 6, prevail over most of the ocean north of the 35th parallel. The winds become moderate and more variable in the vicinity of the Azores. West of the 45th meridian westerly winds extend as far south as the 30th parallel.

There is a general decrease in the percentage of gales since March over the entire ocean, except along the southern coast of Spain, the northern coast of Africa, and in the Gulf of Mexico, and the vicinity of the West Indies, where there is a slight increase. Along the northern trans-Atlantic routes west of the English Channel the percentage is 7 to 18, being highest in mid-ocean and lowest near the coasts. Comparatively few gales occur outside the region of the westerlies.

The Trade Winds.—The northeast trades, force 4 to 5, lie mainly south of the 26th parallel. East of the 45th meridian the limit trends farther northward and reaches the Madeira Islands. The southern limit of these trades extends to the Equator, west of the 40th meridian; but east of this meridian it recedes gradually from the Equator to about 8° N. on the African coast. The winds of this system vary in direction. East of the 20th meridian they are north and north-northeast; between the 20th and 30th meridians, northeast; west of the 30th meridian to the Gulf of Mexico, northeast to east, except between latitudes 20° and 25° N., where they are east-northeast to east-southeast. In the Gulf of Mexico east to southeast winds prevail.

During April the southeast trades blow feebly and extend above the Equator only to latitude 1° N. between the 15th and 23d meridians. In the Gulf of Guinea the winds are south and south-southwest.

Calms.—The aiea between the southern limit of the northeast trades and the northern limit of the southeast trades is one of light variable winds, with 12 to 30 per cent of calms. Calms average 10 per cent over the crest of the Azores High and in the vicinity of the Madeiras, and throughout most of the West Indian waters.

Fog.—Southeast of Newfoundland, between latitudes 42° and 48° N., and longitudes 48° and 54° W., there is an area of 40 to 45 per cent of days with fog; 20 per cent occurs along the American coast between Nova Scotia and New Jersey; southward, fog decreases and practically disappears below the Carolina coast. Along the northern routes, between the 20th and 40th meridians, the percentage has increased since March. Southwest of the British Isles 10 to 15 per cent occurs over a considerable area extending westward to the 29th meridian, and southward to about the 40th parallel. Another area of 10 to 15 per cent extends from latitude 50° N., northeastward to latitude 55° between longitude 38° and 28° W.

May

Pressure.—During May the pressure gradients become very slight and summer conditions begin on the North Atlantic. The Azores High has increased in area and strength since April and its crest, pressure 30.20 inches, occupies the region; between latitudes 24° and 36° N. and longitudes 29° and 51° W. The pressure diminishes to 29.90 inches along the 55th parallel and over the western portions of the Gulf of Mexico and the Caribbean Sea.

Temperature.—The isotherms are much farther apart than during colder months, except in the neighborhood of Nova Scotia and the Grand Banks. The difference in temperature, due to latitude, is more gradual on the eastern than on the western side of the ocean. Along the American coast the temperature ranges between 45° and 80°, a rise of 5° to 10° since April, the greatest change occurring north of Hatteras. On the eastern side of the ocean the temperature ranges between 50° off Ireland and 80° near Freetown, a rise of 3° to 5° off Europe. South of the 25th parallel the temperature changes have been unimportant. The mean temperature along the northern trans-Atlantic routes is between 55° and 60°.

Prevailing Westerlies and Gales.—North of the 35th parallel westerly winds prevail force 4 to 5. Northerly and southerly winds also occur over this region, and the percentage of easterly winds is very low. East and northeast of the Azores, to the coast of Spain, the prevailing direction is northerly.

Gales have decreased in number since midwinter, although cyclones and anticyclones continue to cross the ocean in succession in northern latitudes. Between the 40th and 50th parallels the highest percentage of gales, 8 to 13, occurs near mid-ocean. Northward the percentage decreases between the 50th and 55th parallels, but increases slightly between the 55th and 60th parallels. Gales are rare south of latitude 30° N.

The Trade Winds.—Over the eastern part of the ocean the northeast trades extend northward slightly beyond the Canary Islands, but west of the 30th meridian the northern limit of these winds is nearly along the 25th parallel. The southern limit is close to the Equator on the American side, but rises to latitude 12° N. at longitude 20° W. The force of the northeast trades is 4 to 5, increasing toward the south. Their direction is northerly off the African coast, but is northeast between the 20th and 30th meridians. Farther westward the direction is more easterly, and north of the Lesser Antilles it is southeasterly, these shifts showing the anticyclonic circulation around the Azores High. The winds are generally east to northeast in the Caribbean Sea and east to southeast in the Gulf of Mexico.

The southeast trades, force 3 to 4, extend from 1° to 30° above the Equator between the 8th and 42d meridians.

Calms—The percentage of calms is 15 to 27 in the region between the northeast and southeast trades. In West Indian waters and over the region between the 25th and 35th parallels the percentage is 10 to 18.

Fog.—The fog area has gradually increased through the winter and the early spring. An area of 40 to 45 per cent of days with fog lies off the east and southeast coasts of Newfoundland, and a smaller area of the same percentage is east of Cape Cod, south of Nova Scotia. Fog decreases east of the 45th meridian. It is 5 per cent west of Ireland, but southward between the 45th and 50th parallels and from the English Channel westward of the 23d meridian it is 10 to 20 per cent.

Hurricanes.—Only one West Indian hurricane has been observed in May during the 40-year period, 1876 to 1915.

June

June is a pleasant month over the North Atlantic. Summer conditions are well established and the weather changes less than during any other month of the year.

Pressure.—The crest of the Azores High has increased from 30.20 to 30.25 inches since May and lies mostly southwest of these islands. The gradients are moderate north and south of this area. The pressure is lowest, 29.80 inches, north of the 57th parallel.

Temperature.—The temperature has risen generally since May and is 8° to 10° higher along the American coast north of the 35th parallel. The temperature along the northern trans-Atlantic routes ranges between 55° and 65°. The lowest temperature shown on the chart is indicated by the 50° isotherm, which extends from slightly north of Scotland to Newfoundland. The temperature ranges between 75° and 80° on the American side of the Atlantic south of the 35th parallel and on the African side south of the 20th parallel. Along the American coast the isotherms are crowded much closer together than along the European and African coasts.

The Westerly Winds.—North of the 35th parallel the largest percentage of the winds is from a westerly direction, except between Spain and the central area of high pressure, where the winds are northerly. Gales have decreased in percentage and occur only 5 to 7 per cent of the time over the stormiest portions of the northern steamship routes. Along the American coast from Sandy Hook to Hatteras southwesterly winds occur one-third of the time.

The Trade Winds.—The northern limit of the northeast trades extends in an easterly direction from the Florida coast and ends slightly northeast of the Madeiras. The southern limit of the northeast trades is within 10° of the Equator at the 20th meridian and within about 6° of the Equator at the 50th meridian. The average force of the trades is 4 to 5. They are north-northeasterly over the extreme eastern part of the trade-wind belt, and northeasterly between the 20th and 30th meridians. Farther westward they are more easterly. West of the 55th meridian and north of the 20th parallel southeasterly winds prevail. The winds are easterly in the Caribbean Sea, and easterly to southeasterly in the Gulf of Mexico.

The southeast trades, force 4, blow as far north as the 5th parallel in mid-ocean. They are 2° to 3° farther north than during May. In the Gulf of Guinea southerly winds prevail, with very little southeasterly tendency.

Calms.—The percentage of calms is highest in the area between the 5th and 10th parallels and east of the 35th meridian, where it ranges between 24 and 37. It is high between the 25th and 35th parallels, especially near the region of high pressure and including the area between longitudes 25° and 50°. The highest percentage in this area is 26.

Fog.—The percentage of fog is highest in June and July. An area of 60 to 65 per cent of days with fog lies east and southeast of Newfoundland. A small area, 40 to 45 per cent, lies south and east of Massachusetts and extends eastward to longitude 64°. This fog area extends from the vicinity of Cape Hatteras in a general northeasterly direction across the ocean to France and the British Isles. In European waters the area of highest percentage, 20 to 25, covers St. Georges Channel and the English Channel and extends westward to longitude 16° W.

Hurricanes.—The hurricane season may be said to begin in June, although only eight hurricanes have occurred this month during the period 1876 to 1916. Most of these storms originated south of Cuba and passed into the eastern part of the Gulf of Mexico.

July

Pressure.—The Azores High occupies its most northern position during July and its central area, pressure 30.25 inches, is of greatest intensity. The Iceland Low has filled up to some extent, the isobar of 29.80 inches no longer existing. This change is due principally to the warming of the adjacent land surfaces with the advance of summer and the northward movement of the Azores High.

There are minor pressure changes in the Gulf of Mexico and Caribbean Sea. The mean over the lower portion of this area is about 29.90 inches.

Temperature.—The temperature has risen over the ocean since June, except in the Gulf of Guinea, where it has fallen slightly. The greatest rise, 4° to 9°, occurs west of the 30th meridian between the 30th and 50th parallels.

The lowest temperature shown on the chart, 60°, occurs over the region northeast of Newfoundland; from this region southward to latitude 33° there is a rapid rise to 75°. In the southwestern part of the ocean the temperature is above 80°. It is from 60° to 70° along the northern trans-Atlantic routes.

The Northeast Trades.—These trades lie mainly between latitude 8° and 28° N., over the western half of the ocean. Over the eastern half they are farther north and the southern and northern limits touch the coast at latitudes 15° and 38° N., respectively. These winds are the typical northeast trades over the eastern part of the ocean and in the Caribbean Sea. They are more easterly over the central part of the ocean and become southeasterly north of the Antilles, showing the anticyclonic circulation around the Azores High.

Calms and Southeast Trades.—With the northward movement of the doldrums and the setting in of the southwest monsoon off the African coast, there has been a change in the percentage of calms south of the 15th parallel, and the greatest percentage, 30, is now found in the 5-degree square immediately south of the Cape Verde Islands. The percentage in this square has increased 16 since June. The greatest decrease, 26 to 32, occurs between the 5th and 10th parallels east of the 25th meridian. There has been a decrease of 10 to 14 per cent in mid-ocean along the northern limits of the northeast trades, though the percentage of calms continued high between the 25th and 35th parallels and over the Azores.

Southeast trades extend above the Equator west of longitude 8° W., reaching latitude 7° N. over the western part of the ocean. South to southwesterly winds continue in the Gulf of Guinea.

The Westerlies.—Westerly winds, force 4, prevail north of the 35th parallel, except east of the Azores High, where northerly winds predominate. The American coast winds north of Florida are mainly from the southwest.

Gales.—There has been a continued decrease in the number of gales and the highest percentage, 4 to 6, occurs in mid-ocean noith of the 45th parallel. Gales seldom occur south of the 35th parallel.

Hurricanes.—Severe storms of the West Indian type have been recorded 10 times in July since 1876, as follows: 1886, 2; 1887, 1; 1901 2; 1908, 1; 1909, 1; 1916, 3. The hurricane season is now at hand, although the full development of conditions favoring the formation of tropical storms in these waters usually is not reached until August.

Fog.—The percentage of days with fog is less than in June, except along the American coast from Cape Cod to Cape Ray, where it is greater. The area of highest percentage, 50 to 55, surrounds Newfoundland and the Grand Banks and, inclosing Nova Scotia to the southwest, touches the New England coast at Cape Ann. Fog seldom occurs this month south of Cape Hatteras. The percentage of days with fog decreases from the Grand Banks eastward, except in the Irish Sea and English Channel, where a slight increase occurs.

August

Pressure.—There has been a slight fall in pressure since July. The present crest of the Azores High, pressure 30.20 inches, appears southwest of those islands. The Iceland Low has deepened and the isobar of 29.80 inches is now found. A small area of moderately low pressure appears off the African coast near Cape Verde. As a result of these changes the pressure gradients remain about the same.

Temperature.—August is the warmest month on the North Atlantic Ocean. The temperature over the western part of the ocean ranges from 50° north of Belle Isle to between 80° and 83° south of the 33d parallel. Sharp contrasts in temperature are experienced off the Grand Banks, the mean temperature rising from 55° at the 47th parallel to 75° at the 40th parallel. Over the eastern part of the ocean the temperature changes are far more gradual, the temperature ranging from 55° at the northern edge of the British Isles to 75° or slightly higher south of the 22d parallel. The temperature along the northern trans-Atlantic routes ranges from 60° to 75°.

The Westerlies.—Westerly winds prevail north of the 35th parallel except east of the Azores, where northerly winds predominate. The westerlies are not so strong as during the colder months when the barometric gradients are steeper.

The Northeast Trades.—These trades lie mainly between latitudes 10° and 28° N. over the western half of the ocean. Over the eastern half they are farther north and the southern and northern limits touch the coast at latitudes 15° and 37° N., respectively. These winds are the typical northeast trades over the eastern part of the ocean and in the Caribbean Sea. They are more easterly over the central part of the ocean and become southeasterly north of the West Indies, showing the anticyclonic circulation around the Azores High.

Calms, the Southwest Monsoon, and the Southeast Trades.—The greatest increase in the percentage of calms, 7 to 10, is found in parts of the Gulf of Guinea and in mid-ocean near the southern limit of the northeast trades. The greatest decrease, 14 to 19, occurs within the area of the southwest monsoon, which reaches its greatest development this month and extends as far westward as the 37th meridian at the 7th parallel. Steady southerly winds continue in the Gulf of Guinea.

The southeast trades extend farthest noith of the Equator in August, the northern limit reaching the 7th parallel over the western part of the ocean.

Gales.—Gales occur least frequently during July and August, as cyclones over the northern part of the ocean are few and feeble. The region of greatest percentage, 4 to 6, lies between the 15th and 40th meridians north ot the 45th parallel. Very few gales occur south of latitude 30° N.

Hurricanes.—About four times as many hurricanes occur in August as in July. These severe storms usually originate west of the 50th meridian between the 10th and 20th parallel. Their direction, at first west-northwesterly, becomes more northerly with their approach to the Florida coast and, unless they head into the Gulf, they ordinarily recurve toward the northeast and pass into the ocean with increased velocity. Forty of these storms occurred in the month of August during the 41-year period, 1876 to 1916.

Fog.—Throughout the fog zone the percentage of days with fog is from 10 to 20 less than during July. The highest percentage, 40 to 45, occurred southeast of Newfoundland. An area of 30 to 35 per cent is found off the New England coast. Fog seldom occurs in August south of Chesapeake Bay. In European waters it averages about 5 per cent in St. Georges Channel.

September

Pressure.—The Azores High has weakened slightly since August and its crest, pressure 30.15 inches, has remained nearly stationary. The Iceland Low has deepened slightly with the beginning of autumn and the area of low pressure over the southern portions of the Gulf of Mexico and the Caribbean Sea is more extensive.

Temperature.—The temperature has fallen over the western and northern parts of the ocean and risen slightly over the eastern part south of the 25th parallel since August. The greatest change occurs along the American coast north of Florida.

Along the new northern trans-Atlantic routes the temperature ranges from 58° to 65°.

The Westerly Winds.—Westerly winds, force 4 to 6, prevail north of the 35th parallel, except east of the crest of the Azores High, where northerly winds predominate.

The Northeast Trades.—These trades lie mainly between latitudes 8° and 28° N., over the western half of the ocean. Over the eastern half they are farther north and the southern and northern limits touch the coast at the 16th and 37th parallels, respectively. These winds are the typical northeast trades over the eastern part of the ocean and in the Caribbean Sea. They are more easterly over the central part of the ocean and become southeasterly north of the West Indies, showing the anticyclonic circulation around the Azores High.

Along the American coast from New York to Jupiter northeast winds prevail.

Calms and Monsoons.—There has been a decided change in the percentage of calms in various parts of the ocean, the greatest decrease, 11 to 16, occurring near the Azores, Bermuda, Florida, and in the northern part of the Gulf of Mexico and the western part of the doldrums. The greatest increase, 11 to 15 per cent, occurs near the Canary Islands, in parts of the Caribbean Sea, and within the area of the southwest monsoon, the influence of which is waning.

Southwesterly winds prevail in the Gulf of Guinea and east of the 30th meridian between the 5th and 10th parallels.

The Southeast Trades.—These trades extend above the Equator to about latitude 5° N. west of the 25th meridian.

Gales.—The percentage of gales has increased over most of the ocean since August and the highest percentage, 9 to 16, occurs in mid-ocean north of the 45th parallel. Gales are seldom recorded south of the 20th parallel.

*Hurricanes.**—West Indian hurricanes are of greatest frequency during the latter part of September and the first part of October. These severe storms occasionally form as far east as the Cape Verde Islands, but they usually originate west of longitude 55°, between the 10th and 20th parallels. They move in a west-northwesterly direction about 250 miles per day, and unless they head into the Gulf of Mexico, generally recurve near the coast between Jupiter and Hatteras, thence pass northeastward with increasing velocity of translation.

Fog.—The percentage of days with fog remains about the same, 30 to 35, off the New England coast and a similar area occurs off Newfoundland—a decrease of 10 per cent since August. An area of 20 to 25 per cent has appeared in mid-ocean north of the Azores. With the exception of an area of 10 to 15 per cent between the Irish Sea and Portugal, very little fog occurs east of the 20th meridian south of the 58th parallel.

October

Pressure.—The Azores High has diminished in intensity and extent since September, and its crest, 30.10 inches, is lower than during any other month. A shallow low has appeared south of the Cape Verde Islands and the low over the Caribbean Sea has contracted in area. The Iceland Low is deepening with the advance of autumn.

Temperature.—The temperature has fallen over the ocean, except in the Gulf of Guinea, where it has risen slightly. The fall is about 3° along the American

* Fifty-five of these storms have been traced in the month of September during the 42-year period 1876 to 1917.

coast south of Hatteras. North of the 37th parallel the fall ranges from 5° to 8°, except over the British Isles, where the change is about 3°.

Along the American coast the temperature ranges from 40° at Belle Isle to 80° south of Key West. Over the eastern part of the ocean it ranges from 50° near the Hebrides to 80° at Cape Verde. Along the new northern trans-Atlantic winter routes the mean is from 55° to 65°.

Westerly Winds.—North of the 40th parallel the winds are fresh, with greatest percentage from westerly quadrants, although they shift considerably with the passage of cyclonic storms.

The Trade Winds.—Over the western half of the ocean the northeast trades lie mainly between the 9th and 26th parallels, but on the eastern slope of the Azores High they continue as far north as the Madeiras. A pronounced type of these trades occurs between the Cape Verde and Canary Islands. In the vicinity of the Madeiras they are occasionally disturbed for days at a time by cyclonic shifts. In mid-ocean the trades are easterly, but again become northeasterly over the West Indies, the Caribbean Sea, and the Gulf of Mexico.

The southeast trades extend 5° to 6° north of the Equator west of the 20th meridian. East of that meridian, in the same latitude, the winds become southerly and in the Gulf of Guinea, south-southwesterly.

American Coast Winds.—Northeasterly winds prevail along the American coast from New York to Jupiter.

Gales and Calms.—With the advance of autumn there has been a decided increase in the percentage of gales; many 5-degree squares north of the 30th parallel have more than twice as many gales as during September.

Calms are of highest percentage over the region between the northeast and southeast trades and over the Caribbean Sea. The percentage is also high over the southern slope of the Azores High as far south as the 20th parallel.

Hurricanes.—More hurricanes form in the neighborhood of the West Indies in October than during any other month of the year; 45 having been traced from 1876 to 1916 inclusive. They move in a west-northwesterly direction about 250 miles a day and unless they head into the Gulf of Mexico generally recurve near the coast between Jupiter and Hatteras, thence pass northeastward with increasing velocity of translation.

Fog.—The percentage of fog remains the same, 30 to 35, as in September over the Grand Banks, but has decreased along the Nova Scotian and New England coasts. There has been a slight increase southwest of the English Channel. Very little fog occurs south of the 38th parallel.

November

Pressure.—The Iceland Low is increasing in energy with the approach of winter, and the isobar of 29.70 inches appears north of the 55th parallel. The pressure has also fallen south of the 10th parallel and a belt of moderately low pressure extends along the Equator. The pressure has risen in the middle latitudes, an area of 30.10 inches appearing off the coast of the United States, and the crest of the Azores High increasing to 30.15 inches.

Temperature.—The temperature has fallen 10° to 18° along the American coast and in the Gulf of Mexico except off central and southern Florida, and 3° to 8° over the British Isles and off western Europe. Elsewhere the changes have been unimportant. Sharp contrasts in temperature appear off the American coast, the temperature ranging from 30° in the Gulf of St. Lawrence to 75° at Key West. Along the northern trans-Atlantic routes the mean is from 45° to 55°. In the greater portion of the Caribbean Sea and east of it, between the 15th parallel and the Equator, the temperature is about 80°.

Westerly Winds.—North of the 35th parallel the winds are fresh, with greatest percentage from the westerly quadrants, although they shift considerably with the passage of cyclonic storms.

Northwesterly winds sweep the American coast from the Gulf of St. Lawrence to Hatteras. South of Hatteras they become northerly to northeasterly merging with the trades south of Jupiter.

The Trade Winds.—West of the 30th meridian the northeast trades lie mainly between the 5th and 26th parallels, but east of that meridian they are farther north, and the southern and northern limits touch the African coast at latitudes 12° and 32° N., respectively. A pronounced type of these trades occurs between the Cape Verde and Canary Islands. In mid-ocean the trades are easterly, but again become northeasterly over the West Indies, the Caribbean Sea, and the Gulf of Mexico.

The southeast trades extend about 4° north of the Equator west of the 15th meridian. East of that meridian, in the same latitude, the winds become southerly, and in the Gulf of Guinea, south-southwesterly.

Gales and Calms.—With the approach of winter, there has been a moderate increase in the percentage of gales north of the 35th parallel, except near the Azores, where it is less than during October.

Gales are infrequent south of latitude 35° N., and only five West India hurricanes have been observed during the 41-year period, 1876 to 1916.

Calms are of highest percentage between the 5th and 10th parallels and northward along the African coast to the Canary Islands.

Fog.—The percentage fog of has diminished generally since October, although the area of highest percentage 30 to 35 per cent of days, continues to the southeast of Newfoundland with little change. A light increase has occurred in the English Channel.

December

Pressure.—The Iceland Low is increasing in energy as winter sets in and the isobar of 29.60 inches appears north of the 55th parallel. A belt of high pressure covers the ocean in middle latitudes and the crest of the Azores High has increased to 30.20 inches. An area of moderately low pressure continues along the Equator.

Temperature.—The temperature has fallen over the entire ocean. North of the 25th parallel the fall is 5° to 10°, except in mid-ocean; south of it, it is 2° to 5°. The temperature along the American coast ranges from below 25° in the Gulf of St. Lawrence to 70° at Key West. It is 75° to 80° in the Caribbean Sea. Along the European and African coasts the temperature ranges from 40° or lower off Scotland to 80° or higher south of the 10th parallel. The mean temperature along the northern trans-Atlantic routes ranges between 40° and 53°.

The Westerly Winds.—Westerly winds predominate north of the 35th parallel over the eastern part of the ocean and north of the 30th parallel west of the 40th meridian. Easterly winds are rare north of the 40th parallel, occurring as a rule only during the passage of cyclonic storms.

Gales.—The percentage of gales has increased as a rule, over the entire ocean, and is high north of the 40th parallel east of the 40th meridian and north of the 35th parallel west of it. The highest percentages, 27 to 33, occur in mid-ocean west of the British Isles. Gales continue rare south of the 30th parallel.

American Coast Winds.—Northwesterly winds sweep the coast from Cape Sable to Hatteras. South of Hatteras they become northerly.

The Trade Winds.—Northeast trade winds prevail between the 5th and 25th parallels. Near Brazil they extend as far south as the Equator and near the African coast as far north as latitude 32° N. These winds are the typical northeast trades over the eastern part of the ocean and in the Caribbean Sea. In the central part of the ocean they become east-northeasterly.

Southeast trade winds extend north of the Equator over the central part of the ocean to the 4th parallel.

Northers.—Northers sometimes occur in the Gulf of Mexico and the western part of the Caribbean Sea at this season. They are generally preceded by a slight fall in the barometer, but are accompanied by a rapid rise.

Calms.—The region of highest percentage of calms is east of the 30th meridian and south of the 10th parallel. Elsewhere calms occur most frequently between the 25th and 30th parallels.

Fog.—The percentage of fog has increased slightly along the immediate American coast from Hatteras to Sidney. The area of maximum percentage of days with a fog, 30 to 35, remains unchanged southeast of Newfoundland, and an area of 5 to 10 per cent has appeared northwest of Ireland. Elsewhere the percentage has decreased.

SOUTH ATLANTIC OCEAN

Average Conditions of Wind and Weather

December, January, and February (the Summer Season)

Pressure.—The permanent area of high pressure, crest 30.15 inches, has moved about 8 degrees to the west and a short distance to the south since the spring, the center now being located near latitude 32° S. and longitude 7° W. It has changed little in area and remains the same in intensity, while the gradients directly south of it are somewhat steeper although this does not hold true of those off the southern coast of South America, where the gradients have changed but little; the isobar of the lowest pressure, 29.30 inches, passes a short distance south of Cape Horn.

Temperature.—There has been a decided southward movement of the isotherms since the spring over the greater part of the ocean, though the general direction of these lines has changed but little, and they still show that the temperatures off the coast of Africa are lower than at the same latitude off the South American coast, the effect of the cool and warm ocean currents remaining nearly constant. The isotherm of 45°, which marks the lowest temperature, has moved slightly to the south, while the spring isotherms of 35° and 40° have disappeared.

Winds.—The southeast trades prevail from the area of high pressure to latitude 5° S. on the eastern part of the ocean and from latitude 15° S. to the Equator on the western. Over the greater part of this area they are well developed, blowing from the southeast from 50 to 60 per cent of the time, with a small percentage of calms and no gales, the average force being about 4. South of the area of high pressure "the brave west winds" prevail. They have increased slightly in intensity since the spring. The winds around the "high" show their anticyclonic movements very plainly, while those within the area are variable in direction and force.

Gales.—There are few gales north of latitude 35° S. on the eastern part of the ocean and 30° S. on the western. On the whole there has been a decided decrease in the number of gales since the spring, although between latitudes 45° and 50° and from the South American coast to longitude 45° W. there has been an increase. South of Cape Horn the percentage has dropped from 26 to 10, which is the greatest change shown on the chart. A number of observations taken in the vicinity of Cape of Good Hope, between south latitudes 30° and 50° and east longitudes 10° and 20° during the month of January, show that north of latitude 38° the percentage of direction and average hours of duration of gales are as follows: NW., 17 per cent, 12 hours; SW., 40 per cent, 20 hours; NE., 7 per cent, 4 hours; SE., 9 per cent, 22 hours; exceptional, or shifting from one direction to another, 27 per cent, 25 hours. South of latitude 38° these figures are as follows: NW., 40 per cent, 32 hours; SW., 21 per cent, 26 hours; NE., 3 per cent, 4 hours; SE., 6 per cent, 53 hours; exceptional, 30 per cent, 25 hours.

March, April, and May (the Autumn Season)

Pressure.—The permanent area of high pressure, crest 30.10 inches, has moved about 10 degrees to the east since summer and now occupies nearly the same position it held during the spring season. It has decreased slightly in intensity and remains practically the same in extent, while the gradients south of this area have changed but little. The isobar of the lowest pressure, 29.30 inches, passes south of Cape Horn near the 59th parallel, having moved a short distance to the south since summer.

Temperature.—The 75° and 80° isotherms show a decided southern movement in the central part of the ocean, while off the coast of South America south of latitude 20° S., and immediately south of Cape of Good Hope the temperature has fallen about 5°; in mid-ocean south of latitude 40° S., the isotherms for the summer and autumn are near together. The 35° and 40° isotherms have reappeared, the former showing the minimum average temperature for the present season.

Winds.—The southeast trades prevail from the area of high pressure to latitude 5° S. on the eastern part of the ocean and from latitude 20° S. to the Equator, on the western. The extent of these winds have changed but little since summer and they remain practically the same in intensity. Over the greater part of this area they are well developed, blowing from the southeast quadrant from 60 to 80 per cent of the time, with a small percentage of calms and gales, the average force being about 4. South of the area of high pressure "the brave west winds" prevail, while along the South American coast between south latitudes 30° and 40° the winds are variable. South of Cape Horn the winds are westerly the greater part of the time with a force of from 5 to 6, having increased slightly in intensity since summer.

Gales.—North of latitude 25° S. there are no gales along the African coast, while in the central and western part of the ocean the percentage ranges from 1 to 2. South of the 30th parallel there is a general increase in the number since the previous season. From a large number of observations taken between south latitudes 30° and 50° and east longitudes 10° and 20°, during the month of April it was shown that in the track of homeward bound vessels, or north of latitude 38°, the percentage of direction and average hours of duration of gales are as follows: NW., 20 per cent, 26 hours; SW., 43 per cent, 22 hours; NE., 15 per cent, 8 hours; SE., 7 per cent, 17 hours; exceptional, or shifting from one direction to another, 15 per cent, 45 hours. In the region covered by outward bound vessels, or south of latitude 38°, these figures are as follows: NW., 40 per cent, 36 hours; SW., 21 per cent, 24 hours; NE., 3 per cent, 23 hours; SE., 9 per cent, 30 hours; exceptional, 27 per cent, 46 hours.

June, July, and August (the Winter Season)

Pressure.—A high-pressure area, crest 30.20 inches, lies between latitudes 25° and 35° S. and longitudes 0° and 22° W. This varies little in extent and intensity from season to season and now occupies its extreme western position, having moved over 10 degrees in longitude since autumn. The pressure diminishes more rapidly to the south than to the north of this high, the 30.00 inch isobar being about 30° north and 15° south of its center, respectively. At latitude 59°, directly south of Cape Horn, the pressure reaches a minimum of 29.30 inches.

Temperature.—Along the southern limit of the southeast trades the temperature ranges between 55° and 75°; along the northern limit it ranges between 75° and 80°. The temperature falls from 45° at latitude 40° S., to 30° at latitude 55° S., the line of freezing temperature running near the 53d parallel. Sudden and marked changes in temperature with rain or snow may be expected while rounding Cape Horn.

Winds.—The southern limit of the southeast trades extends from latitude 30° S. on the African coast to latitude 17° S. off the coast of South America. North of this limit to the Equator the southeast winds are remarkably steady. At the Equator, east of longitude 20° W., the prevailing direction becomes nearly southerly, with force of about 4. The southern and northern limits of the southeast trades draw more to the southward as they approach the African coast. South of the area of high pressure westerly winds prevail; on account of their steady force and comparatively constant direction they are known as the " brave west winds." The winds near the center of the high pressure area are variable as to direction and intermittent in force. Between latitudes 20° and 30° S., along the South American coast, the winds are from north to northeast for a greater portion of the time, and between latitude 30° S., and Cape Horn the prevailing direction is from north to northwest. South to southeast winds, average force 4, prevail along the African coast as far south as latitude 30°; between this parallel and Cape of Good Hope they are variable in direction, with average force of about 4.

Gales.—Tropical cyclones are unknown in the South-Atlantic Ocean, and there are few gales north of latitude 30° S. The largest percentage is 24, found along the " roaring forties " between longitude 40° and 50° W., while it varies from 18 to 20 south of Cape Horn, and is 22 in the square between latitudes 40° and 45° and longitudes 15° to 20° E. From a large number of observations taken between latitudes 30° and 50° S. and longitudes 10° and 20° E. during the month of July it was shown that in the track of homeward bound vessels, or north of latitude 38°, the percentage of direction and average hours of duration of gales are as follows: N.W., 45 per cent, 35 hours; SW., 32 per cent, 22 hours; NE., 4 per cent, 9 hours; SE., 4 per cent, 14 hours; exceptional, or shifting from one direction to another, 15 per cent, 27 hours. In the region covered by outward-bound vessels, or south of latitude 38°, these figures are as follows: NW., 41 per cent, 25 hours; SW., 26 per cent, 21 hours; NE., 1 per cent, 6 hours; SE., 11 per cent, 32 hours; exceptional, 21 per cent, 42 hours.

September, October, and November (the Spring Season)

Pressure.—The semi-permanent area of high pressure, crest 30.15 inches, is now central about 15° west of the South African coast along the 30th parallel of south latitude, having moved about 10° to the east since the previous season. It has contracted somewhat in area and is less in intensity, while there is little change in the gradients, which are much steeper south of the high than toward the north. The isobar of the lowest pressure, 26.30 inches, passes over Cape Horn, having moved about 4° to the north since the winter.

Temperature.—North of latitude 20° S. the temperature over the eastern part of the ocean is much lower than over the western, due to the cooling effects of the Benguela Current off the African coast and the warming effects of the South Equatorial and Brazil Currents off the coast of Brazil. South of latitude 25° S. on the western part of the ocean the fall in temperature is very regular, being about 1° for every degree in latitude, reaching the minimum temperature of 35° near latitude 55° S. There has been a general rise in temperature over the entire ocean since the previous season. This change is small near the Equator, while in the vicinity of Cape Horn the temperature has increased from 30° to 40° and off Cape of Good Hope from 52° to 60°, and at latitude 50° S. and longitude 20° W. it is now 43°, showing an increase of 8° since the winter.

Winds.—The southeast trades prevail from the area of high pressure to latitude 10° S. on the eastern part of the ocean and to the northern limits of the chart on the western. Over the greater part of this area these winds are well developed, blowing from the southeast from 50 to 60 per cent of the time. South of the area of high pressure the " brave west winds " prevail, while the winds around this area show plainly their anticyclonic movement.

Gales.—Few gales occur north of latitude 30° S. on the central and western parts of the ocean and north of latitude 35° S. on the eastern. Along the " roaring forties " the percentage runs as high as 12, while in the winter season the maximum was 24. South of latitude 55° the percentage is from 15 to 26, showing a decided increase in the vicinity of Cape Horn since the winter, while the opposite is true over all other parts of the ocean. From a large number of observations taken between latitudes 30° and 50° S. and longitudes 10° and 20° E., during the month of October, it was shown that in the track of homeward bound vessels, or north of latitude 38°, the percentage of direction and average hours of duration of gales are as follows: NW., 30 per cent, 25 hours; SW., 36 per cent, 23 hours; NE., 2 per cent, 23 hours; SE., 9 per cent, 11 hours; exceptional or shifting from one direction to another, 23 per cent, 36 hours. In the region covered by outward bound vessels, or south of latitude 38°, these figures are as follows: NW., 33 per cent, 21 hours; SW., 35 per cent, 21 hours; NE., 6 per cent, 8 hours; SE., 8 per cent, 35 hours; exceptional 18 per cent, 36 hours.

CENTRAL AMERICAN WATERS

Average Conditions of Wind and Weather

January

Pressure.—The pressure ranges from 30.10 near the 25th parallel to 29.90 below the 10th parallel.

Temperature.—The temperature ranges between 53° in the northern and 70° in the southern portion of the Gulf of Mexico; in the Caribbean Sea it ranges between 70° in the northern and 78° in the southern portion. The temperature is about 75° in the Bay of Panama and adjacent waters.

Winds.—The northeast trades of the Atlantic, force 3 to 5, are fairly constant. In the Gulf the winds are generally easterly. In the Pacific southeasterly winds prevail west of the 85° meridian between the Equator and the 5th parallel; thence northward the prevailing winds are northeasterly.

Gales.—In Atlantic waters, the percentage of days with gales ranges between 8 and 16 immediately north of the 30th parallel; south of this parallel to the 25th between 1 and 5; thence southward and in Pacific waters between 0 and 3.

Calms.—The percentage of days with calms on the Atlantic is about 6 to 9, except along the northern border of South America, where it is decidedly lower; it is very high on the Pacific between the 20th parallel and the Equator being 40 in most of the area between the 10th and 15th parallels.

Northers.—Northers sometimes occur in the Gulf of Mexico and along the coast southward to Colon. These storms are generally preceded by a slight fall in the barometer, but the gale itself is accompanied by a rapid rise.

February

Pressure.—The pressure in Central American waters of the Atlantic ranges from 30.10 inches in the northern to 30.00 inches in the southern portion. It is about 29.90 inches in the Pacific waters of this region.

Temperature.—The temperature ranges between 57° in the northern and 75° in the southern portion of the Gulf of Mexico; in the Caribbean Sea it ranges between 75° in the northern and 78° in the southern portion. The temperature is about 80° in the Central American waters of the Pacific.

Winds.—The northeast trades, force 3 to 5, prevail over the greater portion of the Atlantic. North of the trade wind belt the winds are variable. In the Gulf of Mexico the prevailing winds are southeasterly. In the Pacific the northeast trades, force 3, extend as far south as the 7th parallel; the southeast trades, force 2, extend as far north as the 3d parallel.

Gales.—The percentage of days with gales in Atlantic waters ranges between 9 and 15 immediately north of the 30th parallel; south of this parallel to the 20th between 1 and 4; thence to the 10th between 1 and 2. South of the 10th parallel and in Pacific waters the percentage is 0.

Calms.—The percentage of days with calms is about 6 to 11 on the Atlantic except along the northern border of South America where it ranges between 1 and 3. On the Pacific it is very high, ranging between 20 and 30.

Northers.—Northers sometimes occur in the Gulf of Mexico and along the coast southward to Colon. These storms are generally preceded by a slight fall in the barometer, but the gale itself is accompanied by a rapid rise.

March

Pressure.—The pressure averages about 30.00 inches over the greater portion of the Central American waters of the Atlantic, ranging from 30.05 inches in the extreme northeast portion to 29.95 inches in the extreme southeast portion; in the Pacific waters of this region it ranges between 29.85 and 29.90 inches.

Temperature.—The temperature ranges from 60° in the northern to 75° in the southern portion of the Gulf of Mexico; in the Caribbean Sea it ranges from 75° in the northern to 78° in the southern portion. The temperature is about 80° in the Central American waters of the Pacific.

Winds.—The northeast trades, average force 3 to 5, prevail over the Atlantic portion of the Central American waters south of the 25th parallel. North of this parallel the winds, average force 4, are variable in direction. In the Caribbean Sea the winds are northeasterly, except in the western portion where they are easterly, and easterly to southeasterly in the Gulf of Mexico. In the Central American waters of the Pacific the northeast trades prevail over most of the area north of the 5th parallel; south of this parallel the winds are southeasterly, except near the coast where they are light and variable.

Gales.—The percentage of days with gales in the Central American waters of the Atlantic ranges between 9 and 12 immediately north of the 30th parallel; south of this parallel to the 20th between 1 and 3; south of the 20th parallel to the northern coast of South America and in Pacific waters the percentage averages 1 or less.

Calms.—The percentage of days with calms is about 5 to 10 over Atlantic and Gulf waters, except along the northern coast of South America where it ranges between 1 and 5. On the Pacific the percentage is very high, ranging between 30 and 39 along the coast, but diminishing gradually to the westward.

April

Pressure.—The pressure averages about 30.00 inches over the greater portion of the Central American waters of the Atlantic, ranging from 30.03 inches in the extreme northeastern to 29.95 inches in the extreme southeastern portion; in the Pacific waters of this region it is about 29.85 inches.

Temperature.—The temperature ranges from 68° in the northern to 80° in the southern portion of the Gulf of Mexico; in the Caribbean Sea it ranges from 77° in the northern to 80° in the southern portion; it is about 80° in the Central American waters of the Pacific.

Winds.—The northeast trades, average force 4, prevail over the Central American waters of the Atlantic south of the 26th parallel. North of this parallel the winds, average force 4, are variable in direction. The winds, average force 4, are easterly to southeasterly in the Gulf of Mexico. In the Caribbean Sea the prevailing winds are easterly to northeasterly. In the Central American waters of the Pacific the northeast trades, average force 3, extend over most of the region north of the 5th parallel; the southeast trades, average force 2, extend over most of the region south of the 4th parallel; on the coast immediately north of the 5th parallel the winds are northwesterly and immediately south of it southwesterly.

Gales.—The percentage of days with gales in the Central American waters of the Atlantic ranges between 4 and 13 immediately north of the 30th parallel; south of this parallel to the 20th between 1 and 3; south of the 20th parallel to the northern coast of South America and in Pacific waters the percentage averages 1 or less.

Calms.—The percentage of days with calms is about 5 to 10 in the Central American waters of the Atlantic, except along the northern coast of South America and in the neighborhood of the West Indies and to the eastward where it ranges between 2 and 5. On the Pacific side the percentage is very high, ranging between 27 and 43 along the coast and diminishing gradually to the westward.

May

Pressure.—The average pressure over the Gulf of Mexico and the Caribbean Sea is from 29.90 to 30.00 inches. Toward the open Atlantic the pressure rises, but in the Pacific waters of Central America it falls to about 29.85 inches.

Temperatures.—The mean temperature over most of the region included in the Gulf of Mexico, the Caribbean Sea, and the Pacific coast waters is about 80°, but in the upper Gulf it falls to 75° or slightly lower.

Winds.—The trade wind holds with good steadiness at force 4 over the Atlantic region to the southward of the 27th parallel, as well as in practically the entire Gulf. The inclination of the trade, however, is more nearly easterly than northeasterly, except in the central Caribbean Sea and along the coast of South America to the southeastward of Trinidad. Over much of the Gulf the trade is deflected also into the southeast. In the Central American waters of the Pacific the winds are mostly light and variable, although with approach to the Equator the steadying effect of the southeast trade becomes apparent.

Gales.—Few gales occur over the entire area. In the Pacific region, and up to about the 30th parallel in the Atlantic, the number of days with gales for the month is 1 per cent or less. One West Indian hurricane has been observed in May during the last 40 years.

Calms.—The Pacific in this vicinity is distinguished for its calms, which are of high relative frequency, even as low as the Equator. Over the region to the eastward of the 100th meridian, except where the advance movement of the trade is felt the percentage of days with calms ranges between 20 and 40 per cent. Calms are much less frequent on the Atlantic side, and in the open sweeps of the trades are scarcely to be reckoned with.

June

Pressure.—The average pressure from the Florida Peninsula southeastward along the backbone of the West Indies is about 30.00 inches. A gradual increase occurs to the eastward, but to the westward there is a decrease to 29.85 inches over the Pacific portion.

Temperature.—A mean temperature of 80° or near it prevails over most of the Central American area.

Winds.—Easterly winds of the trades system, with an average force of 4, prevail over the entire Atlantic and Caribbean area south of the 27th parallel. North of the 23d parallel, and over most of the Gulf of Mexico, the winds are slightly the most prevalent from the southeast. On the Pacific side the winds are mostly light and variable except to the southward of the 5th parallel, where winds of the southeast trades system, force 2 to 4, prevail, freshening toward the Equator.

Gales.—Few gales occur on the Atlantic side this month. Off the Pacific coast of Mexico there are occasional squall bursts peculiar to the opening of the rainy season.

Hurricanes.—The hurricane season may be said to begin in June, although only 8 hurricanes have occurred this month during the period 1876 to 1916. Most of these storms originated south of Cuba and passed into the eastern part of the Gulf of Mexico.

Calms.—Over the region dominated by the full sweep of the trades there is a small percentage of calms, but toward the westward in the vicinity of Cuba and the Bahamas, over the extreme southwestern portion of the Caribbean Sea, and throughout the Gulf of Mexico, there are 10 to 17 per cent of calms. Over the Pacific area calms are much more frequent except near the Equator in the trades region.

July

Pressure.—The mean atmospheric pressure over the West Indies is about 30.00 inches, but is higher toward the eastward. In the lower Caribbean Sea, and over most of the Pacific area adjoining southern Mexico and Central America, the pressure is about 29.90 inches.

Temperature.—The temperature over most of the region is about 80°, but in the lower Pacific area, between 5° N. and the Equator, it falls to 75° or slightly lower.

Winds—Over most of the Atlantic and Caribbean area south of the 27th parallel the trade winds persist of average force 4. North of the 25th parallel the force and steadiness decrease and the winds become more variable, though with a southeasterly tendency toward the Florida Peninsula. In the Gulf of Mexico, while diminishing easterly trades are fairly well established south of the 25th parallel, to the northward the winds become increasingly variable. In the Pacific area southerly winds of the southeast trades system carry their influence across the Equator, nearly to the 10th parallel, except toward the coast, along which, as well as to the northward of the 10th parallel generally, northerly winds, force 2 to 3, are in the ascendency.

Gales.—The percentage of days with gales is 1 or less over the Central American and West Indian waters during July.

West Indian Hurricanes.—Ten hurricanes have been observed in these waters in July during the 41-year period, 1876 to 1916, of which 3 occurred in 1916, and are shown on this chart.

Calms.—Calms are few in the unobstructed trades belt of the Atlantic, but they increase in frequency toward the western part of the Caribbean Sea and over the Gulf of Mexico. In the northern part of the Gulf the percentage of days with calms is as high as 20. In the eastern Pacific waters calms are much more frequent than in the Gulf, especially to the northward of the 7th parallel, but they diminish rapidly to less than 10 per cent in the belt of the southeast trades.

August

Pressure.—The pressure is about 30.10 inches over the extreme northeastern part of the Central American waters of the Atlantic, whence it diminishes to the westward and southward, being about 30.00 inches in the vicinity of Florida and the West India Islands. It is slightly below 30.00 inches in the Gulf of Mexico and about 29.90 inches in the southern part of the Caribbean Sea and over the neighboring waters of the Pacific.

Temperature.—The temperature averages about 80° over the waters of both the Atlantic and the Pacific in this region, except between the 6th parallel and the Equator on the Pacific side, where it averages about 75°.

Winds.—Southeasteıly winds prevail over that part of the Atlantic between the 30th and 25th parallels; from the 25th to the 15th parallels they are mostly easterly; thence southward and in the Caribbean Sea they are noıtheasterly or easterly, while in the greater part of the Gulf of Mexico they are southeasterly. The average force of the wind is 3 to 4 on the Atlantic side. Over the waters of the Pacific the winds are northeasterly to easterly between the 15th and the 10th parallels; mostly southerly between the 10th and the 5th parallels, except near the coast, where they are northwesterly; between the 5th parallel and the Equator they are southwesterly near the coast and southerly to southeasterly thence westward. The average force of the wind is 2 to 4 on the Pacific side.

Gales.—The percentage of days with gales is 1 or less over the Central American waters of both the Atlantic and the Pacific.

West India Hurricanes.—Forty of these storms occurred in the month of August within the 41-year period, 1876 to 1916.

Calms.—The percentage of days with calms is 15 to 22 over the Gulf of Mexico, except south of latitude 22° 30′, where it averages about 8; it is 10 to 15 over the Caribbean Sea; also over the Atlantic, except in the region east of longitude 65°, between parallels 25° and 12° 30′, where it averages 3 to 7. On the Pacific side the percentage of calms is very high, ranging from 10 along the Equator, except near the coast, to 30 per cent north of latitude 12° 30′.

September

Pressure.—The average atmospheric pressure during September is about 29.95 inches over the West Indian Islands and 29.90 inches or slightly lower over the southern portions of the Gulf of Mexico and the Caribbean Sea, as well as over the neighboring waters of the Pacific.

Temperature.—The temperature in this region averages about 80° over the waters of both the Atlantic and the Pacific, except between the 5th parallel and the Equator on the Pacific side, where it averages about 75°.

Winds —Southeasterly winds prevail over that part of the Atlantic between the 30th and 20th parallels, except east of Florida to the 70th meridian, wheıe they are northeasterly; from the 20th parallel to the northern coast of South America and in the Caribbean Sea they are easterly to northeasterly, while in the Gulf of Mexico they are easterly. The average force of the wind is 3 to 4 on the Atlantic side. Over the wateıs of the Pacific the winds are mostly northerly, force 2 to 3, from the 10th parallel northward to the coast; between the 10th parallel and the Equator they are southwesterly force 3 to 4 except south of the 5th parallel, west of the 85th meridian where they are southerly to southeasterly.

Gales.—The percentage of days with gales is 1 to 2 over the Gulf of Mexico and 2 to 3 over the Atlantic between the 20th and 30th parallels west of the 55th meridian, while south of the 20th parallel in these waters the percentage in any 5-degree square is not over 2. In the Caribbean Sea and on the Pacific in the neighborhood of Central America the percentage is 1 or less.

West Indian Hurricanes.—Fifty-five of these storms have been traced in the month of September within the 42-year period, 1876 to 1917.

Calms.—The percentage of days with calms is 8 to 15 over the Gulf of Mexico and the Atlantic and 8 to 20 over the Caribbean Sea. On the Pacific side it is very high north of parallel 7° 30′, especially near the coast, where it ranges from 25 to 33; south of parallel 70° 30′ it ranges from 2 to 15.

October

Pressure.—The pressure averages about 30.00 inches over the northern parts of the Gulf of Mexico and the Central American waters of the Atlantic, whence it diminishes southward to about 29.90 inches in the southern parts of this region. It also averages about 29.90 inches over the neighboring waters of the Pacific.

Temperature.—The temperature in this region averages about 80° over the waters of both the Atlantic and the Pacific, except over those bordering on the Equator on the Pacific side, where it averages about 75°.

Winds.—Northeasterly winds prevail over that part of the Atlantic between the 30th and the 20th parallels west of the 70th meridian, while east of this meridian southeasterly winds prevail. From the 20th parallel southward to the northern coast of South America, and in the Caribbean Sea as far west as the 80th meridian the winds are easterly, while in the Caribbean Sea west of the 80th meridian and in the Gulf of Mexico they are northeasterly. The average force of the wind is 3 to 4 on the Atlantic side. Over the waters of the Pacific the winds are mostly northerly, force 2 to 3, between the 10th and 15th parallels, while south of the 10th parallel to the Equator they are southwesterly, force 3 to 4, except south of the 5th parallel west of the 85th meridian, where they are southerly to southeasterly.

Gales.—The percentage of days with gales averages 1 to 2 over the Gulf of Mexico and over the extreme northern part of the Caribbean Sea, 2 to 8 over the Atlantic north of the 25th parallel, and 2 to 3 adjacent to the northern coasts of Cuba and Haiti; elsewhere over the Atlantic south of the 25th parallel; also in the Caribbean Sea south of the 20th parallel, and on the Pacific side the percentage averages 1 or less.

West India Hurricanes.—Forty-five of these storms occurred in the month of October within the 41-year period, 1876 to 1916.

Calms.—The percentage of days with calms averages 5 to 10 over the Gulf of Mexico and the Atlantic waters of this region, while it averages 8 to 20 over the Caribbean Sea. On the Pacific side the percentage is very high north of latitude 7° 30′ ranging from 24 to 48 near the coast; south of that latitude it is also comparatively high near the coast; elsewhere the average is 2 to 12, being lowest along the Equator.

November

Pressure.—The pressure averages about 30.10 inches over the extreme northern part of the Gulf of Mexico and over the Central American waters of the Atlantic from the eastern coast of northern Florida to the 75th meridian. It decreases toward the lower latitudes being about 30.00 inches over the southern part of the Gulf of Mexico and over the West India Islands, and about 29.90 inches over the southern part of the Caribbean Sea and along the northern coast of South America; it also averages about 29.90 inches over the neighboring waters of the Pacific.

Temperature.—The temperature in this region averages about 60° in the northern part of the Gulf of Mexico and in the adjacent waters of the Atlantic, whence it increases to about 80° in the vicinity of the 15th parallel over the Caribbean Sea and the Atlantic. It averages about 80° on the Pacific side, except over the waters bordering on the Equator west of the 90th meridian, where it averages about 75°.

Winds.—Northeasterly winds prevail over the waters on the Atlantic side, force 3 to 4, except between longitudes 52 and 60 north of the 15th parallel, where they are generally easterly. Over the Pacific waters of this region the winds are mostly northerly or northeasterly, force 2 to 3, between the 10th and 15th parallels; also between the 5th and 10th parallels and longitudes 95 and 100; elsewhere south of the 10th parallel to the Equator the winds are southwesterly, force 2 to 3, except between the 5th parallel and the Equator, west of the 85th meridian, where they are southeasterly.

Gales.—The percentage of days with gales averages 2 to 3 over the Gulf of Mexico, and 1 to 2 over the Atlantic waters between the 20th and 30th parallels; elsewhere in this region and in the neighboring waters of the Pacific the percentage is 1 or less.

West India Hurricanes.—Two of these storms occurred in the month of November within the 35-year period, 1876 to 1910.

Calms.—The percentage of days with calms averages 6 to 8 over the Gulf of Mexico and over the Atlantic above latitude 20 as far east as longitude 62° 30′. In other parts of the Atlantic and over the Caribbean Sea it averages 7 to 10, while on the Pacific side it averages 8 to 17 north of latitude 7° 30′, and 2 to 6 south of it.

December

Pressure.—The pressure averages about 30.10 inches over the northern part of the Gulf of Mexico and over the Central American waters of the Atlantic north of the 25th parallel. It decreases toward the lower latitudes, being about 30.00 inches in the vicinity of the 20th parallel, and about 29.90 inches along the coasts of Dutch and French Guiana; it also averages about 29.90 inches over the neighboring waters of the Pacific.

Temperature.—The temperature over the Atlantic waters of this region ranges from about 55° off the northern coast of Florida to about 80° along the northern coast of South America, 55° in the northern to 75° in the southern part of the Gulf of Mexico, and 75° in the northern to 80° in the southern part of the Caribbean Sea.

Winds.—Northeasterly winds prevail over the waters on the Atlantic side, average force 4 except between longitudes 70 and 80 north of parallel 22° 30′ where they are variable, while over the Gulf of Mexico they are northerly to southeasterly. Over the waters on the Pacific side the winds are generally northeasterly, force 2 to 3, between the 5th and 15th parallels, except in the immediate vicinity of the Panama Canal, where they are northwesterly. South of the 5th parallel they are southwesterly east of the 85th meridian, while they are southeasterly thence westward.

Gales.—The percentage of days with gales averages 2 to 3 on the Atlantic side north of the 20th parallel, thence southward and over the neighboring waters of the Pacific it averages 1 or less.

Calms.—The percentage of days with calms averages 3 to 9 over the Atlantic side of this region, while on the Pacific side it averages 30 to 48 north of latitude 7° 30′, thence to the Equator it averages 6 to 25, being lowest near the Equator.

NORTH PACIFIC OCEAN

Average Conditions of Wind and Weather

January

Pressure.—The Aleutian Low has increased in area southward and westward since December. It is central over the middle portion of the Aleutian Islands, and its lowest pressure continues at 29.60 inches. The pressure along the Equator over the western part of the ocean is 29.85 inches, or .05 inch less than in December. The crest of the Asiatic High, still 30.30 inches, extends from the China coast at Shanghai to northern Chosen (Korea). The North Pacific High occupies nearly the same position as in December, and its central pressure remains at 30.20 inches.

Temperature.—There has been a fall of 3° to 5° in temperature in the Gulf of Alaska and along the American coast as far south as Cape San Lucas, and a slight rise in temperature in the area between the 30th and 45th parallels and longitudes 145° W. and 155° E.; elsewhere there has been little change. The line of freezing temperature touches the Asiatic coast at latitude 37° N., passes slightly north of the Kuril Islands, thence over the southernmost of the Aleutian Islands, and reaches the American coast at latitude 56° N. In Asiatic coast and Philippine waters, from the 37th to the 14th parallel, the temperature ranges between 32° and 80°; along the American coast from the 56th to the 11th parallel, it ranges between 32° and 75°. Along the Equator, east of longitude 165° W., the temperature is between 75° and 80°, and west of this meridian it is between 80° and 85°. On the great circle route from San Francisco to Yokohama it ranges between 40° and 50°.

American Coast Winds.—In the most northern part of the Gulf of Alaska the prevailing winds are north and northeasterly; in the neighborhood of Sitka, easterly; from the 55th to the 40th parallel, westerly and southerly; 40th to 20th parallel, northwesterly; 20th to 10th parallel, northerly to northeasterly; 10th to 5th parallel, northwesterly, and thence to the Equator, southerly.

Winds of High Latitudes.—In Bering Sea south of Alaska the winds are northerly, and in the 5-degree square immediately west of the Pribilof Islands, also in the adjacent square to the north, the winds are northeasterly.

Westerly Winds.—The prevailing winds are westerly over the western part of the ocean north of the 25th parallel, except in Asiatic coast waters, due to the cyclonic circulation accompanying the Aleutian Low, and the anticyclonic circulation accompanying the North Pacific and the Asiatic Highs.

Asiatic Coast Winds—The Monsoon.—The winds east of Chosen (Korea) are northeasterly and west of it they are northwesterly. Along the China coast immediately north of Shanghai the winds are northerly; south of Shanghai to the 5th parallel they are northeasterly and are known as the northeast (winter) monsoon.

The monsoon is in full force during January, and blows with greatest strength and constancy off the coast between Macao and Chusan. It shows a marked tendency to follow the coast, and as it weakens at night and the winds become somewhat offshore, northbound sailing vessels may then make fair headway. The thick, rainy weather of the monsoon period renders navigation difficult off the coasts of Taiwan (Formosa) and Luzon. A rising barometer foreruns an increase and a falling barometer a decrease in the strength of the monsoon.

The Northeast Trades.—The northeast trades reach their most northern limit in the eastern part of the ocean at the 29th parallel slightly southeast of the central area of the California High, and are strongest and steadiest south of this region. Between longitudes 145° W. and 155° E. their northern limit is close to the 25th parallel. They extend eastward to within 5° to 8° of the American coast and westward they extend to Asiatic waters, where they merge into the northeast monsoon. They extend as far south as the Equator west of longitude 170° E. East of this longitude their southern limit gradually rises to the 10th parallel at longitude 125° W.

The Southeast Trades.—The southeast trades extend north of the Equator between longitudes 85° W. and 180°. They reach their most northern limit, the 6th parallel, between longitudes 115° and 125° W.

Calms.—The percentage of calms is highest, 40, in the coast waters of Central America; it continues high along the coast to Los Angeles. Calms are frequent east of longitude 155° E. in the belt between the 20th and 25th parallels, also in the vicinity of Japan, and the Philippine, Marianas, and Galapagos Islands, and in the region between the northeast and the southeast trades.

Gales.—The percentage of gales is high over most of the ocean between the 35th and 45th parallels and longitudes 145° E. and 140° W. Over most of the region of the prevailing westerlies the wind system is frequently interrupted by cyclonic storms accompanied by a southeast changing to northwest gales. These gales often sweep the coast from San Francisco northward.

Typhoons and Storm Tracks.—The typhoons of January show a decrease in number over those of December. They originate largely in the vicinity of the Marianas and the Caroline Islands, those of the former recurving before reaching the Philippines, and those of the latter being severely felt in Mindanao and the Pelew Islands. The December and January typhoons reach the mainland in Cochin China or South Anam.

The storm tracks, given in red on the pilot charts, show the paths of important storms and the distance traveled by each in 24 hours. The typhoon tracks are furnished by the Philippine Weather Bureau, and the approximate tracks of storms of middle and higher latitudes are furnished by the Zi-ka-wei Observatory. The number of storms of the higher latitudes is greatest in March and December and least in July.

Fog.—The percentage of days with fog has decreased to 11 along the American coast from Vancouver to Cape San Lucas. Over most of the fog area to the westward as far as longitude 160° W. and in the Gulf of Alaska the percentage is 15 to 20; in Asiatic waters as follows: China coast from Hongkong to Shanghai, 14; north coasts of Taiwan (Formosa) and Luzon, 8; Eastern Sea and Gulf of Pechili, 11; elsewhere, low.

February

Pressure.—The Aleutian Low is central over the western Aleutian Islands with a minimum pressure of 29.60 inches. The pressure is 29.80 inches along the Equator from longitude 120° W. to longitude 120° E. The crest of the Asiatic High, 30.30 inches, covers the Yellow Sea. The crest of the North Pacific High, 30.20 inches, lies within 10° of the California coast between latitudes 28 and 38.

Temperature.—The line of freezing temperature touches the Asiatic coast at slightly below the 37th parallel, crosses the extreme northern portion of Honshu Island, passes south of the Aleutian Islands, and reaches the American coast immediately north of Sitka. In Asiatic coast and Philippine waters from the 38th to the 15th parallel the temperature ranges from 30° to 80°. Along the American coast from the 58th to the 20th parallel it ranges from 30° to 75°. The temperature along the Equator is slightly above 80° west of longitude 150° W.; also over a small area east of the 110th meridian W. On the great circle route from San Francisco to Yokohama it ranges from 35° to 52°.

American Coast Winds.—The winds are northerly west of the Alaska Peninsula; in the neighborhood of Sitka and to the 45th parallel, southeasterly; 45th to 40th parallel, northerly and southerly; 40th to 15th parallel, northwesterly; 15th parallel to Panama, northeasterly; Panama to 5th parallel, northerly; and thence to the Equator, variable with weak southeast trades.

Westerly Winds.—The prevailing winds are northwesterly over the western half of the ocean north of the 25th parallel, except east of Kamchatka, where they are northeasterly. Over the eastern half of the ocean north of the 35th parallel they are westerly, but more variable than over the western half, and frequently are reversed to an easterly direction during the passage of barometric highs and lows.

Asiatic Coast Winds—The Monsoon.—From the Gulf of Pechili to Shanghai the winds are north and northwest, but from Shanghai southward they are northeasterly, and constitute what is known as the winter monsoon. The northeast monsoon is in full force during February and blows with greatest strength and constancy off the coast between Macao and Chusan. It shows a marked tendency to follow the conformation of the coast, but as it weakens slightly at night and the winds become at times somewhat offshore, sailing craft close in to land may make headway against it. The thick, rainy weather off the coasts of Taiwan (Formosa) and Luzon renders navigation difficult in these waters. The Philippine monsoon is much augmented during this season by the prevalence of the northeast trades. A rising barometer foreruns an increase and a falling barometer a decrease in the strength of the monsoon.

The Northeast Trades.—The northeast trades reach their northern limit at the 30th parallel in the eastern part of the ocean; their southern limit is along the 7th parallel from the American coast to longitude 130° W.; it touches the Equator at longitude 170° E. These trades are steadiest, as a rule, between the 5th and 20th parallels.

The Southeast Trades.—The southeast trades extend north of the Equator between Colombia and longitude 165° W. They reach their northern limit along the 5th parallel, between longitudes 115° and 130° W.

Calms.—The percentage of calms is high east of longitude 120° W. between the Equator and the 10th parallel and along the coast from the Equator to San Diego; it is highest, 35 per cent, in Central American waters.

Gales.—The percentage of gales is high over an irregular area occupying the western part of the ocean south and southwest of the Aleutian Low, between the 50th and 30th parallels and longitude 145° E. and 165° W.

Typhoons and Storm Tracks.—The number of typhoons occurring in Asiatic waters during February is less than during any other month of the year. Those that visit the mainland usually enter Anam.

The storm tracks, given in red on the pilot charts, show the paths of important storms and the distance traveled by each in 24 hours. The typhoon tracks are furnished by the Philippine Weather Bureau, and the approximate tracks of storms of middle and higher latitudes are furnished by the Zi-ka-wei Observatory. The number of storms of higher latitudes is greatest in March and December and least in July.

Fog.—The percentage of days with fog averages 20 to 25 along the American coast from the Alaska Peninsula to Cape San Lucas. It decreases toward the west: in Asiatic waters it is 17 on the China coast from Hongkong to Shanghai, and 15 over the Eastern Sea and the Gulf of Pechili.

March

Pressure.—The Aleutian Low fills in with the approach of spring, and now has two centers, each with a pressure of 29.70 inches, one over and mainly east of the Alaskan Peninsula, the other between the Aleutians and Kamchatka. The pressure is moderately low, about 29.85 inches, between the 10th parallel and the Equator. The crest of the Asiatic High has a pressure of 30.10 inches. The California High is a little to the westward of its position in February; the pressure at its crest is 30.20 inches.

Temperature.—The line of freezing temperature touches the Asiatic coast at the 41st parallel, crosses Kokushu Island and the Aleutians, passes south of the Alaska Peninsula, and reaches the American coast at the 59th parallel. In Asiatic coast and Philippine waters, from the 42d to the 15th parallel, the temperature ranges from 30° to 80°, along the American coast from the 60th to the 20th parallel it ranges from 30° to 75°. The temperature is slightly above 80° in an area beginning at the Equator and longitude 140° W., extending westward and increasing in width. It is also slightly above 80° in a small area near the Equator between longitude 110° and 127° W., and in another small area adjacent to Panama. On the great circle sailing route from San Francisco to Yokohama it ranges from 40° to 52°.

American Coast Winds.—Northerly winds prevail north of the 55th parallel from the Alaska Peninsula to longitude 145° W.; thence to 140° W. the winds are northerly and southerly; east of 140° W., easterly. Northwesterly winds sweep the coast from the 55th to the 15th parallel, but are least frequent between the 40th and 50th parallels. From the 15th to the 10th parallel the winds are light north and northeast; 10th to 5th, light northwesterly, and thence to the Equator light southwesterly.

Westerly Winds.—The prevailing winds are westerly over a considerable portion of the ocean between parallels 55 and 30. Over the western half of the ocean, between parallels 50 and 30, northwest winds are most frequent; over the eastern half, between parallels 55 and 35, westerly and southwesterly winds prevail.

Asiatic Coast Winds—The Monsoon.—North of Shanghai northerly and northwesterly winds are prevalent. In the Japan Sea westerly winds prevail over the southwestern and northeastern portions; southerly winds in the northwestern portion and northerly winds in the southeastern portion.

During March the northeast monsoon covers the China and Celebes Seas, the Philippine Islands, and the eastern coast of Asia, as far north as Shanghai. Off the China coast it blows with force 5, but decreases to force 3 to 4 over the waters to the south. The monsoon shows a marked tendency to follow the conformation of the coast, but as it weakens slightly at night and the wind becomes at times somewhat offshore, sailing craft close to land may make headway against it. The thick rainy weather off the coasts of Formosa and Luzon renders navigation difficult in these waters. A rising barometer foreruns an increase and a falling barometer a decrease in the strength of the monsoon.

The Northeast Trades.—The northeast trades, force 4 to 5, reach their most northern limit, the 30th parallel, in the eastern part of the ocean. They are the principal winds in the region between the 25th parallel and the Equator, except in a narrow area along the Equator east of the 180th meridian and in the vicinity of the coasts. They extend to within about 300 miles of the American coast, and in Asiatic waters they merge into the northeast monsoon. In Honolulu they average about 17 days in March.

The Southeast Trades.—The southeast trades extend north of the Equator between longitudes 90° and 170° W., and reach their most northern limit near the 4th parallel, between longitudes 115° and 125° W.

Calms.—The percentage of calms is high, 25 to 45, east of longitude 110° W. from the Gulf of California southward to the Equator; also between the 5th parallel and the Equator, from longitude 110° to 125° W., and from longitude 170° E. to Borneo. The percentage is also high over most of the Philippine waters.

Gales.—The percentage of gales is highest, 11 to 17, in an area between longitudes 145° and 170° E., and latitudes 35 and 40 N., and nearly as high in an area extending thence northeastward to the Aleutian Islands.

Typhoons and Storm Tracks.—Typhoons are infrequent during March, although there is a very slight increase in their number ovei those of February. These occasional typhoons originate in the neighborhood of the Caroline and Pelew Islands, and those that visit the mainland usually enter Anam.

The storm tracks, given in red on the pilot chaits, show the paths of important storms and the distance traveled in each 24 hours. The approximate tracks of storms in middle and higher latitudes are furnished by the Zi-ka-wei Observatory, Pere H. Gauthier, compiler. The number of such storms is greatest in March and December and least in July.

Fog.—The percentage of days with fog is highest, 15 to 20, along the American coast from latitude 55° N. to Cape San Lucas and westward, between the parallels 40 and 55, to longitude 160° W. In Asiatic waters it is 19 along the China coast between Hongkong and Shanghai, and 9 in the Eastern Sea and the Gulf of Pechili.

April

Pressure.—The Aleutian Low continues to fill in. It is central south and east of the Alaska Peninsula with a pressure of 29.75 inches. The pressure between the 10th parallel and the Equator is nearly the same as in March, being about 29.85

inches. The crest of the Asiatic High decreases to 30.00 inches. The North Pacific High increases in extent and pressure. Its center is slightly north and east of its position in March with a pressure of 30.25 inches.

Temperature.—The temperature is 5° to 10° higher than in March over Japanese waters and in adjacent waters to the eastward; elsewhere the changes are slight. The line of freezing temperature continues its northward movement and is now north of the Kuril Islands and the Aleutian Islands and northwest of the Alaska Peninsula, in Asiatic coast and Philippine waters from the 50th to the 20th parallel the temperature ranges from 30° to 80°. It is slightly above 80° south of the 20th parallel to the Equator in Asiatic waters and thence eastward in a diminishing area to about longitude 150° W.; also in a small area touching the American coast between the 9th and 16th parallels, its southern limit being near the Equator and its western limit about longitude 116° W. On the great circle sailing route from San Francisco to Yokohama the temperature ranges from 40° to 57°.

American Coast Winds.—The winds are variable over the northwestern part of the Gulf of Alaska and mostly easterly and southeasterly over the northeastern part; thence southward along the coast to the 45th parallel they are southerly; 45th to the 15th parallel, generally northwesterly; and south of the 15th parallel, light and variable, except southeasterly in the vicinity of Corinto, northwesterly off the Isthmus, and southwesterly near the Equator.

Westerly Winds.—The prevailing winds are westerly over most of the area between the 40th and 55th parallels; they tend to become northwesterly west of longitude 150° W., and to become southwesterly east of this longitude to within about 5° of the coast.

Winds of Bering Sea.—The prevailing winds are northeasterly in Bering Sea north of the 55th parallel, except east of the Pribilofs, where they are westerly. They are westerly south of the 55th parallel.

Asiatic Coast Winds—The Monsoon.—In the Japan Seas the winds are generally variable, but calms occur over the northern portion about one-fourth of the time. In the Yellow Sea the winds are also variable, but tend to blow from northerly and easterly quadrants. In the China Sea the northeast monsoon continues, though with less vigor than during the winter months. Over the Philippines and east of Borneo the monsoon is light and often dies to a calm.

Winds of the High-pressure Area.—Between the 30th and 40th parallels and longitudes 145° E. and 135° W. the winds are mostly variable, although easterly winds, force 3 to 4, predominate over the southern half of the area.

The Northeast Trades.—The northeast trades, force 3 to 5, blow over most of the ocean between the 5th and 30th parallels. Over the western part of the ocean their northern limit gradually inclines southward to the 25th parallel. The southern limit of these trades is slightly north of the 5th parallel over most of the eastern part of the ocean and slightly south of this parallel over most of the western part of the ocean. They average 21 days in April at Honolulu.

The Southeast Trades.—Light southeast trades extend north of the Equator between longitudes 82° and 140° W., and reach their most northern limit near the 5th parallel, between longitudes 95° and 125° W.

Calms.—The percentage of calms is high along the American coast from San Francisco to the Equator, ranging from 20 to 27 between San Francisco and Cape San Lucas; it is higher thence southward along the coast, being 48 at the Isthmus. The percentage is high between the 10th parallel and the Equator from the coast westward to longitude 120° W., and beyond this area south of the 5th parallel to longitude 140° W. It is also high south of the 5th parallel west of longitude 165° E. and in Philippine waters.

Gales.—The percentage of gales is generally high over most of the region of the westerlies, being 11 to 13 between parallels 50 and 55 and longitudes 140° to 160° W., and 10 to 12 in a small area east of the Kuril Islands.

Typhoons and Storm Tracks.—During the 22 years from 1880 to 1901, inclusive, ten tropical cyclones were reported in Asiatic waters in April as against five in March. Many of the April cyclones originate in the Caroline Islands and move in a west-northwest direction. Some cross the Philippines and reach the mainland others recurve at sea toward the Marianas.

The storm tracks, given in red on the pilot charts, show the paths of important storms and the distance traveled by each in 24 hours. The typhoon tracks are furnished by the Philippine Weather Bureau, and the approximate tracks of storms of middle and higher latitudes are furnished by the Zi-ka-wei Observatory, near Shanghai, China. The number of storms of higher latitudes is greatest in March and December and least in July.

Fog.—The percentage of days with fog is 15 to 20 in mid-ocean between latitudes 30° and 50° N. in an area with a northeast-southwest trend, and along the American coast from San Francisco to Cape San Lucas. In Asiatic waters the percentages are as follows: Hongkong to Shanghai, 23; Eastern Sea and Gulf of Pechili, 18; south and west of Japan, 10.

May

Pressure.—The Aleutian Low has continued to fill in and has a pressure of 29.80 inches over two areas, one in the Gulf of Alaska and the other in the southwestern part of Bering Sea. The pressure is also 29.80 inches over Borneo and the Philippine Islands; elsewhere near the Equator it is about 29.85 inches. The Asiatic High has disappeared, owing to the decrease in pressure over the continent with the advance of spring. The North Pacific High occupies about the same position, and has the same pressure at its crest, 30.25 inches, as in April.

Temperature.—The temperature is 5° to 9° higher than in April over Asiatic waters between the 20th and 55th parallels. North of the 40th parallel this rise extends as far eastward as longitude 145° W.; it also includes the western portion of the Gulf of Alaska; elsewhere the changes are slight. The isotherm of 35° extends across Bering Sea from latitude 57° on the Asiatic side to latitude 60° on the American side. Over Asiatic coast waters from the 50th to the 20th parallel the temperature ranges from 40° to 80°; along the American coast, east of longitude 145° W., from the 60th to the 18th parallel it ranges between 45° and 80°. There is a decided dip of the isotherms over the eastern part of the ocean south of the 40th parallel and a subsequent recurve near the coast in a northerly direction. The temperature is slightly above 80° from about the 20th parallel to the Equator in Asiatic waters and thence eastward in a diminishing area to about longitude 150° W.; also in a small area which touches the American coast between the 8th and 18th parallels, and has its southern limit at the 5th parallel and its western limit at longitude 117° W. On the great circle sailing route from San Francisco to Yokohama the temperature ranges from 47° to 63°.

Winds North of Latitude 55° N.—Northerly winds prevail over most of Bering Sea. In the Gulf of Alaska the winds are easterly, except in the neighborhood of Kodiak and the Peninsula of Alaska, where they are variable. Calms occur 20 per cent of the time in the Gulf of Alaska and 8 to 20 per cent in Bering Sea.

American Coast Winds.—South of the 55th parallel westerly winds occur along the coast to Vancouver Island; thence to the 15th parallel the prevailing winds are northwesterly; 15th to the 5th parallel light, variable winds occur, broken by frequent calms. Light southwesterly winds occur near the Equator.

Westerly Winds.—The prevailing winds are westerly, force 4 to 5, between the 40th and 55th parallels except northeasterly immediately east of Kamchatka.

Asiatic Coast Winds.—In the northern part of the Japan Sea, the winds are easterly over the western half and easterly and westerly over the eastern half. In the southern part of the sea they are mostly southerly. Off the west coast of Chosen (Korea) westerly winds prevail. In the vicinity of the lower Japanese Islands the winds are variable; in the neighborhood of Shanghai they are southeasterly.

Between the 30th and 20th parallels the winds, especially during the first half of the month, are northeasterly under the waning influence of the winter monsoon. The southwesterly winds of the summer monsoon are gradually increasing, although in May they are little more than land breezes.

Along the western coast of the Philippine Islands the winds are quite variable, but during the day light southwest winds often occur, changing to southeast at sunset. Along the eastern coast light east and southeast winds prevail.

Winds of the High-pressure Area.—The winds follow a clockwise course around the central area of the North Pacific High; west of this area, so far as longitude 155° E., they are westerly between latitudes 40° and 35° and easterly between latitudes 35° and 30°.

The Northeast Trades.—These trades, force 4 to 5, extend to within about 5° of the American coast between the 25th and 15th parallels. Their northern and southern limits are near the 30th and 4th parallels, respectively. They average 24 days in May over the Hawaiian Islands.

The Southeast Trades.—These trades, force 3 to 4, extend 1° to 5° north of the Equator; they are farthest north between longitudes 150° and 110° W.

Calms.—Calms are frequent along the American coast south of the 25th parallel, except west of lower California. They occur one-half of the time off the coast near Champerico. The percentage is 20 to 35 between latitudes 5° and 10° as far west as longitude 135° W. Around the Philippines calms occur one-fourth and near Borneo and the Celebes one-half of the time.

Gales.—As the spring season advances, the percentage of gales decreases in the region of the westerly winds, the average in May being 6 to 7 per cent over the entire area. The highest percentage, 12, occurs in the 5° square north of the 40th parallel and west of the 180th meridian, also in the square north of the 45th parallel and west of longitude 150° W.

Typhoons and Storm Tracks.—During the 22-year period, 1880–1901, 25 typhoons occurred in Asiatic waters in May, as against 10 in April and 41 in June. They originate near the Pelew Islands and move across the Philippines, then generally recurve to the northeast. The typhoons most likely to prove dangerous to Manila are those of May, September, October, and November.

The storm tracks, given in red on the pilot charts, show the paths of important storms and the distance traveled by each in 24 hours. The typhoon tracks are furnished by the Philippine Weather Bureau, and the approximate tracks of storms of middle and higher latitudes are furnished by the Zi-ka-wei Observatory. The number of storms of higher latitudes is greatest in March and December and least in July.

Fog.—The area of highest percentage of days with fog, 20 to 25, as far as shown by the chart, extends northeastward from northern Japan to the Aleutian Islands. The percentage is between 15 and 20 over the greater portion of the remainder of the area indicated by the blue shading. In Asiatic waters the percentages are as follows: China coast from Hongkong to Shanghai, 12; Eastern Sea and Gulf of Pechili, 21; south and east of Japan, 14.

June

Pressure.—The Aleutian Low very largely loses its identity with the approach of summer, although the pressure continues low, about 29.80 inches, over Bering Sea. Along the Asiatic coast the pressure is 29.75 to 29.80 inches, and in Central American waters it is about 29.85 inches. The North Pacific High continues to occupy nearly the same position and has the same pressure, 30.25 inches, as in April.

Temperature.—The temperature is 5° to 8° higher than in May over Asiatic waters between the 30th and 50th parallels and 5° to 7° higher over the Gulf of Alaska north of the 55th parallel, and in Bering Sea immediately west of the Alaska Peninsula; elsewhere the changes are slight. The temperature is slightly above 40° in Bering Sea near the continents and the Aleutian Islands. In Asiatic coast waters, from the 60th to the 25th parallel, the temperature ranges from 40° to 80°; along the American coast, from the 60th to the 20th parallel, it ranges from 50° to 80°. There is a decided dip of the isotherms over the extreme eastern part of the ocean south of the 40th parallel and a subsequent recurve near the coast in a northerly direction. The temperature is slightly above 80° over Asiatic waters between the 25th parallel and the Equator and thence eastward in a diminishing area to longitude 135° W.; also in a small area which touches the American coast between the 5th and 20th parallels. It is 75° in the vicinity of the Galapagos Islands. On the great circle sailing route from San Francisco to Yokohama the temperature ranges from 46° to 70°.

Winds North of Latitude 55° N.—The winds are generally light and variable north of the 55th parallel, and calms occur 20 per cent or more of the time, except in Bering Sea south of the 60th parallel, between longitudes 170° E. and 170° W.

American Coast Winds.—South of the 55th to the 15th parallel the prevailing winds are northwesterly; thence to the 5th parallel variable; thence to the Equator southwesterly.

Westerly Winds.—The prevailing winds are westerly, force 4 over most of the region between the 40th and 55th parallels, but there is also a high percentage of variable winds over the greater portion of this area. The westerlies are less pronounced in June than during the colder months, owing to decreased barometric gradients and to more settled conditions.

Asiatic Coast Winds.—The Southwest Monsoon.—In June the southwest monsoon is fairly well developed in the China Sea and in the Eastern Sea as far north as Shanghai. It has not the strength and steadiness of the northeast (winter) monsoon, and along most of the China Sea coast it often blows from the south or southeast. The land and sea breezes are well defined during its prevalence, and southbound sailing vessels may easily make headway against it by keeping near the coast. The monsoon affects the winds of the western coast of the Philippine Islands, light southwesterly winds prevailing there during the day, but changing to southeasterly at night.

The Northeast Trades.—These trades, force 3 to 4, extend to within 7° to 10°

of the American coast between the 30th and 15th parallels. Their northern and southern limits are near the 34th parallel and the Equator, respectively. They extend westward as far as longitude 145° E. They are steadiest, force 4, between the 10th and 20th parallels and longitudes 130° and 160° W. East of this area the winds are north-northeast and north as far as the belt of northwest winds along the coast of Lower California. West of the Hawaiian Islands the trades are east-northeast as far as the Marianas. Over the eastern part of the trade belt the northeast winds extend only as far south as latitude 13° N., but the southern limit gradually approaches the Equator toward the west nearly reaching it in east longitude.

The Southeast Trades.—These trades extend farthest north, latitude 8° N., between longitudes 120° and 135° W. They do not extend north of the Equator east of longitude 90° W., and are unimportant west of 170° E.

Calms.—The winds are mostly light and variable with frequent calms in the area between the limits of the northeast and southeast trade winds. Variable winds and calms occur over the region east of longitude 110° W. and north of latitude 5° N. Calms occur 30 to 38 per cent of the time along the American coast between latitudes 5° and 25° N., one-fourth to one-third of the time in the Philippine and East Indian waters, and one-fourth of the time in all of the Japan Sea, except the northeastern portion.

Gales.—The percentage of gales in June is low over the entire ocean. The highest percentage, 3 to 5, is between the 40th and 50th parallels and longitudes 155° E. and 180°.

Typhoons.—June, July, August, and September are the so-called "typhoon months." During these months typhoons occur more frequently and reach higher latitudes than during other months. They originate west of the Caroline Islands and move in a northwesterly direction, often crossing the Philippines or passing to the north of them, thence generally recurving toward the northeast.

The storm tracks, given in red on the pilot charts, show the paths of important storms and the distance traveled by each in 24 hours. The typhoon tracks are furnished by the Philippine Weather Bureau, and the approximate tracks of storms of middle and higher latitudes are furnished by the Zi-ka-wei Observatory. The number of storms of higher latitudes is greatest in March and December and least in July.

Fog.—The area of highest percentage of days with fog, 40 to 50, lies between the western Aleutian Islands and southeastern Kamchatka. Over most of the remainder of the ocean north of the 30th parallel the percentage varies from 10 to 40. Along the American coast the percentage is 30 from Cape San Lucas to San Francisco and 20 to 30 from San Francisco to the 55th parallel. It is about 8 per cent along the Asiatic coast between Hongkong and Shanghai.

July

Pressure.—The pressure is higher than in June over Alaskan waters, but continues low, 29.80 inches, over the western part of Bering Sea. It falls to 29.70 inches along the China coast. The North Pacific High becomes more extensive, but the pressure at its crest remains at 30.25 inches. The pressure increases slightly off the Mexican coast.

Temperature.—The temperature is 5° higher than in June over Bering Sea and 5° to 8° higher generally over Asiatic waters between the 50th and 30th parallels. The latter rise extends between parallels 35 and 50 to longitude 175° W. Thence a rise of 5° extends eastward over a diminishing area to longitude 135° W.; elsewhere the changes are slight.

Over the eastern part of Bering Sea and near Kamchatka the temperature is above 45°. In Asiatic coast waters from the 60th to the 28th parallel it ranges from 45° to 80°; it is slightly above 80° between the 28th parallel and the Equator and thence eastward in a diminishing area to latitude 150° W. Along the American coast from the northern border of the Gulf of Alaska to Cape San Lucas the temperature ranges from 55° to 80°; it is slightly above 80° in an area that touches the coast between Cape San Lucas and Panama. It is about 75° along the Equator from the American coast to longitude 115° W.

The temperature increases quite uniformly over mid-ocean from the 52d to the 30th parallel. Marked differences in temperature occur along the coasts of both continents, as shown by the dip and recurve of the isotherms, and especially by their crowding each other along the California coast. On the great circle sailing route from San Francisco to Yokohama the temperature ranges from 51° to 73°.

Winds North of Latitude 55°.—The winds are generally light and variable north of the 55th parallel. Calms occur in this region about 19 per cent of the time in the Gulf of Alaska and 23 per cent of the time in Bering Sea.

American Coast Winds.—The Southwest Monsoon.—South of the 55th parallel to Cape San Lucas the prevailing winds are northwesterly. Thence to the Equator they are variable with frequent calms. The winds of a light and imperfectly developed monsoon blow over a narrow area that extends from Colombia to longitude 120° W. between the zone of calms and the southeast trades.

Westerly Winds.—Owing to the slight barometric gradient over the northern part of the ocean, resulting from the disappearance of the Aleutian Low, the prevailing westerly winds occupy a small area and are less pronounced than during June.

Asiatic Coast Winds—The Southwest Monsoon.—The summer monsoon manifests its fullest strength and steadiness during July and August in Chinese and Philippine waters as far north as Shanghai and as far east as longitude 130° E., but it is not so strong as the winter monsoon, and the winds occasionally blow from the southeast. The land and sea breezes are so well marked that southbound sailing vessels easily make headway against the monsoon along the lower China coast.

The Northeast Trades.—These winds cover a large area south of latitude 35° N. They are most marked between the Hawaiian Islands and longitude 130° W. They average 29 days in July in Honolulu. West of these islands to the Marianas the trades gradually become more easterly.

The Southeast Trades.—These trades, force 3 to 4, cross the Equator from the South Pacific and extend as far north as the 8th parallel. They are steady between longitudes 100° and 170° W. from the Equator to the 5th parallel, but above this parallel they are intermittent.

Calms.—An extensive area of calms exists on the Asiatic side of the ocean in the vicinity of the Philippines and the East Indies. Another area of calms extends along the American coast from Panama to Cape San Lucas and into the Gulf of California. A narrow belt of calms exists between the limits of the northeast trades and the southeast trades.

Gales.—The percentage of gales is light over the entire ocean; it is greatest, 4 to 5, between Taiwan (Formosa) and longitude 135° E.; it is 2 to 4 in area between longitudes 160° E. and 180° and latitudes 40° and 45° N.

Typhoons and Storm Tracks.—The normal wind direction west of the Philippine Islands is southwesterly by day, changing to southeasterly by night. If the wind blows steadily from the southwest for an entire day, and the daily oscillation of the barometer is absent, it is well to assume the existence of a typhoon northeast of Luzon. Four to six of these storms are likely to occur during any one of the midsummer months.

The storm tracks, given in red on the pilot charts, show the paths of important storms and the distance traveled by each in 24 hours. The typhoon tracks are furnished by the Philippine Weather Bureau, and the approximate tracks of storms in middle and higher latitudes are furnished by the Zi-ka-wei Observatory. The number of storms of the higher latitudes is least in July.

Fog.—An area of 55 to 60 per cent of days with fog covers the ocean between the Kuril and the Aleutian Islands; thence there is a decrease in percentage in all directions, except close off the coast of North America, where there is a local increase to between 30 and 35 per cent from Vancouver Island to the extremity of the California Peninsula. In Asiatic waters the percentage is 15 at Shanghai and 10 over the Japan Sea.

August

Pressure.—The pressure is slightly lower over the northern part of the Gulf of Alaska and slightly higher over the western part of Bering Sea than in July. The pressure continues low, 29.70 inches, along the China coast. The North Pacific High occupies about the same position as in July, but the pressure at its crest increases to 30.30 inches.

Temperature.—The temperature is 5° higher than in July over an area that touches the American coast at Vancouver Island and extends between the Gulf of Alaska, and the crest of the North Pacific High to longitude 165° W.; there is a slight rise elsewhere except in the Equatorial region.

Over Bering Sea the temperature ranges from 45° to 50°. From the 59th parallel in the Sea of Okhotsk along the Asiatic coast to the 33d parallel it ranges from 55° to 80°; it is slightly above 80° between the 33d parallel and the Equator and thence eastward in a diminishing area to longitude 137° W. Along the American coast from the northern part of the Gulf of Alaska to Cape San Lucas it ranges from 55° to 80°; it is slightly above 80° in an area that touches the coast between Cape San Lucas and Panama. It is about 75° along the Equator from the American coast to longitude 130° W.

The temperature increases quite uniformly over mid-ocean from the 52d to the 34th parallel. Marked differences in temperature occur along the American coast from the 35th parallel to San Luis Obispo. The dip of the isotherms over the eastern part of the ocean and their subsequent recurve is not so marked as in July. There is practically no longer a dip of the isotherms over Japan waters. On the great circle sailing route from San Fiancisco to Yokohama the temperature ranges from 55° to 77°.

Westerly Winds.—North of latitude 45° the prevailing winds are not so steadily from the west as during the colder months, and they frequently blow from more northerly and southerly directions.

American Coast Winds.—Northwesterly winds prevail along the American coast from latitude 55° to Cape San Lucas; thence to latitude 10° N. calms, light variable and northeasterly winds prevail; thence to the Equator southwest monsoon winds blow over a narrow area that extends between the zone of calms and the southeast trades from Colombia to longitude 130° W.

The Northeast Trades.—The northeast trades prevail in the area between parallels 10 and 35. This area extends from longitude 117° W. to longitude 140° E. Its widest part is from mid-ocean eastward. The force of the wind is very regular, 3 to 4, over the entire area. The direction is quite northerly in the eastern part, becomes northeasterly at longitude 130° W., and at 170° W. changes to easterly.

The Southeast Trades.—The southeast trades extend across the Equator from the South Pacific between longitudes 145° E. and 90° W. Their most northern limit is the 10th parallel at longitude 130° W. South of latitude 5° N. the winds are from the southeast and steady between longitudes 95° and 155° W.; thence westward they become easterly.

Calms.—There is a narrow area of calms between the northeast and the southeast trades in mid-ocean. It broadens near the continents, especially over the western part of the ocean. The percentage of calms is highest, 43, near Ponape Island.

Asiatic Coast Winds—The Southwest Monsoon.—The monsoon winds are not well defined in the China Sea and are often interrupted by easterly winds. Southwest winds are more pronounced in the Philippine waters, especially during the day; at night they decrease to a calm or become variable, but they may continue from the southwest under the influence of a typhoon northeast of Luzon.

Gales.—The highest percentage of gales, 5 to 7, occurs over an area that extends from Luzon and Formosa eastward to 140° E. The percentage of gales is 4 to 6 in an area lying between latitudes 40° and 45° N. and longitudes 165° E. and 180°.

Typhoons and Storm Tracks.—The typhoon season in Asiatic waters is at its height in August and September, and four to six of these tropical storms are likely to occur during each of these months.

The storm tracks, given in red on the pilot charts, show the paths of important storms and the distance traveled by each in 24 hours. The typhoon tracks are furnished by the Philippine Weather Bureau, and the approximate tracks of storms of middle and higher latitudes are furnished by the Zi-ka-wei Observatory. The number of storms of the higher latitudes is greatest in March and December and least in July.

Fog.—An area of 40 to 45 per cent of days with fog lies south of the Aleutian Islands. The percentage is 20 to 30 in Bering Sea. Along the American coast from Vancouver to San Francisco it is 30 to 49, and 30 to 33 thence to Cape San Lucas. In Asiatic waters the percentage is as follows: Japan Sea, 10; Eastern Sea and Gulf of Pechili, 16; China coast between Hongkong and Shanghai, 4.

September

Pressure.—The pressure decreases over the Gulf of Alaska and Bering Sea, marking the development of the Aleutian Low over Bering Sea, with a central pressure of 29.75 inches. The pressure increases along the China coast, but a low area covers the Philippine Islands and extends as far north as Taiwan (Formosa) and the China coast, and eastward to longitude 138° E. The North Pacific High continues to occupy about the same position as in July and August, but the pressure at its crest decreases to 30.25 inches.

Temperatures.—The seasonal change in temperature begins in September and is marked by a fall of from 5° to 8° in the Sea of Japan and the Yellow Sea and a fall of 5° along the eastern coast of Honshu; elsewhere there is but little change.

Along the Asiatic coast from the 60th parallel, in the Sea of Okhotsk, to the 22d parallel, the temperature ranges from 45° to 80°; it is slightly above 80° from the 22d parallel to the Equator and thence eastward in a diminishing area to longitude 142° W. Along the American coast from the northern part of the Gulf of Alaska to Cape San Lucas the temperature ranges from 50° to 80°; it is slightly above 80° in an area that touches the coast between San Lucas and Panama. It is about 75° along the Equator from the American coast to longitude 130° W.

In mid-ocean a rise in temperature with decreases in latitude is quite uniform between the 52d and 33d parallels. Over the eastern part of the ocean the dip and subsequent recurve of the isotherms for temperatures from 60° to 80° is about the same as in August. On the great circle sailing route from San Francisco to Yokohama the temperature ranges from 56° to 73°.

Winds of High Latitudes.—Northeasterly and southerly winds prevail in Bering Sea west of the southern half of the Aleutian Low; the winds are variable in the western part of the sea and westerly and southerly in the vicinity of the Aleutian Islands. In the Gulf of Alaska, except the extreme northern portion, and over most of the area between the 55th and 45th parallels, the winds are mostly westerly and southerly resulting from the combined influences of the Aleutian Low and the North Pacific High.

American Coast Winds.—South of Alaska the winds, as a rule, are southwesterly. Northwesterly winds prevail along the immediate coast from latitude 55° to Cape San Lucas; south of the point to Colombia the winds are variable with frequent calms. Southwesterly winds occur on the South American coast from the 5th parallel to the Equator.

Asiatic Coast Winds—The Monsoon.—The monsoon blows from the southwest over the China Sea during the first half of September, but it is unsteady in direction, and before the close of the month the winter monsoon from the northeast appears, often suddenly and with storm force, and carries its influence as far south as the 15th parallel. South of this parallel on the western Philippine coasts light westerly and southwesterly winds prevail; these become easterly and northeasterly by the end of the month, or early in October. The winds are northwesterly between the island of Kokushu and the mainland.

The Northeast Trades.—The northeast trades occur in an area between parallels 14° and 27° and longitudes 155° E. and 122° W. In the eastern portion of this area the prevailing direction is nearly north-northeast. These winds are steadiest near the Hawaiian Islands, where they prevail 29 days in September. West of these islands the prevailing direction is about east-northeast.

The Southeast Trades.—The southeast trades extend across the Equator from the South Pacific between longitudes 93° W. and 178° E. Their most northern limit is a little south of the 9th parallel between longitudes 130° and 140° W.

Calms.—The northeast and southeast trades are separated by a narrow belt of calms, the doldrums, which join a considerable area of calms at longitude 123° W. and a larger area of about longitude 160° E. The percentage of calms is high along the American coast between the 5th and 40th parallels. In Asiatic waters it is high off the coasts of northern Borneo and western Mindanao.

Gales.—The percentage of gales is generally high between the 45th and 60th parallels west of longitude 140° W. It is notably high, 11, near Kodiak Island, and highest 12, immediately east of Kamchatka.

Typhoons and Storm Tracks.—The typhoon season is at its height in Asiatic waters during August and September, and from four to six of these tropical storms are likely to occur in each of these months.

The storm tracks, given in red on the pilot charts, show the paths of important storms and the distance traveled by each in 24 hours. The typhoon tracks are furnished by the Philippine Weather Bureau and the approximate tracks of storms of middle and higher latitudes are furnished by the Zi-ka-wei Observatory. The number of storms of the higher latitudes is greatest in March and December and least in July.

Fog.—The percentage of days with fog is 40 to 49 over a narrow belt extending along the American coast from Vancouver to San Francisco and 40 to 30 from San Francisco to Cape San Lucas. It is 40 to 45 in an area that extends from the Kuril Island eastward between the 45th and 51st parallels to longitude 155° W. South of this area the percentage of fog diminishes more rapidly than in any other direction. Elsewhere the percentages are as follows: China coast, from Hongkong to Shanghai, 4; Eastern Sea and Gulf of Pechili, 16; Japan Sea, 10.

October

Pressure.—The Aleutian Low increases in extent and deepens to 29.70 inches with the approach of winter. The pressure is also low, 29.80 inches, in the vicinity of the Philippine Islands.

The pressure continues to increase along the Asiatic coast south of the 50th parallel and is about 30.10 inches over the Yellow Sea. The central pressure of the North Pacific High decreases to 30.20 inches, and the area covered by the crest is slightly less than in August and September.

Temperature.—The seasonal fall in temperature which begins in September over a part of the ocean becomes general in October as far south as the 20th parallel and is considerable over certain areas, being 10° to 15° in Bering Sea, 10° to 20° in the Sea of Okhotsk, and 9° to 13° in the Yellow Sea; it is from 5° to 8° in the Gulf of Alaska, also from Japan and the Kuril Islands eastward between the 50th and 30th parallels to longitude 160° W., and to longitude 145° W., north of the 35th parallel. The change is comparatively slight elsewhere.

Along the Asiatic coast from the 60th parallel in Bering Sea to the 25th parallel the temperature ranges from 25° to 75°. It is slightly above 80° in the western part of the ocean in an area that reaches from the Equator as far north as the 24th parallel between longitudes 145° and 160° E.; thence eastward the 80° area diminishes and extends to longitude 163° W. Along the American coast from the 64th parallel in Bering Sea to the 25th parallel on the Lower California coast the temperature ranges from 30° to 80°; thence to Panama it is slightly above 80°. The isotherm of 75° crosses the Equator at longitudes 85° and 125° W., and reaches latitude 3° N. between longitudes 100° and 115° W.

In mid-ocean the rise in temperature with decrease in latitude is quite uniform between the 54th and the 25th parallels. The dip and the subsequent recurve of the isotherms over the eastern part of the ocean are about the same as in September. On the great circle sailing route from San Francisco to Yokohama the temperature ranges from 48° to 66°.

American Coast Winds.—Over the western part of the Gulf of Alaska the winds are variable; over the eastern portion and southward along the coast to latitude 50° southerly and easterly winds prevail; from latitude 50° to latitude 40° they are mostly variable and calms are frequent; south of the 40th to near the 15th parallel they are northwesterly; thence to the 10th parallel they are light northeasterly; and from the 10th parallel to the Equator, westerly and southwesterly. Calms are frequent between the 25th and 5th parallels.

Asiatic Coast Winds—The Monsoon.—South of latitude 35° N. the northeast monsoon covers the China Sea and extends as far south as the 10th parallel and as far east as longitude 140° E. The change from the southwest to the northeast monsoon is often sudden and accompanied by winds of storm force, usually during the last of September, when the continental summer "low" gives place to the winter "high."

Winds of High Latitudes.—Northerly winds, force 4 to 5, predominate in the eastern part of Bering Sea.

Westerly Winds.—Westerly winds, force 4 to 5, prevail over most of the ocean between parallels 55° and 40°.

The Northeast Trades.—The northeast trades occur between the 28th and 10th parallels. They extend westward from longitude 125° W. and unite with the winds of the northeast monsoon at about longitude 140° E. These winds are mostly north-northeasterly east of longitude 135° W., and northeast and east-northeast west of it. They blow steadily with average force 4, and in Honolulu prevail on an average 29 days in October.

The Southeast Trades.—The southeast trades extend across the Equator from the South Pacific between longitudes 92° and 170° W. They reach their average northern limit, latitude 8° N., between longitudes 125° and 145° W.

Calms.—The percentage of calms is high along the American coast north of the 5th parallel and in the narrow area between the northeast and the southeast trades; also in the vicinity of the islands in the southwestern part of the ocean.

Gales.—The percentage of gales is moderately high north of the 35th parallel. South of this region gales are comparatively few, except in the square bounded by latitudes 30° and 35° N., and longitudes 150° and 155° E., and East of Taiwan (Formosa).

Typhoons and Storm Tracks.—There is an average occurrence of 3 typhoons in October. Their region of formation extends from latitude 6° to 17° N., and from longitudes 129° to 142° E. The typhoons likely to prove most dangerous to Manila are those which occur during May, September, October, and November.

Along the western coasts of the Philippine Islands the winds are easterly and northeasterly, becoming light at sunset. If a steady breeze blows from any one quarter during an entire day, it is an indication of a typhoon having its center two to four points to the left of the point toward which the wind is blowing.

The storm tracks, given in red on the pilot charts, show the paths of important storms and the distance traveled by each in 24 hours. The typhoon tracks are furnished by the Philippine Weather Bureau, and the approximate tracks of storms of middle and higher latitudes are furnished by the Zi-ka-wei Observatory. The number of storms of the higher latitudes is greatest in March and December and least in July.

Fog.—The percentage of days with fog is much less in October than in September, but it continues comparatively high off the American coast, being 30 from Vancouver to San Francisco and 30 to 20 thence southward to Cape San Lucas. Fog diminishes rapidly in other directions, except over an area between latitudes 40° and 51° N., and longitudes 148° E. and 180°. The percentage is from 5 to 7 over the China Sea and northward along the China coast to and including the Gulf of Pechili.

November

Pressure.—The Aleutian Low is deeper than in October, the lowest pressure being about 29.60 inches. The pressure is moderately low along the Equator. It increases in Asiatic waters, by reason of the eastward extension of the continental high central over Mongolia. The North Pacific High moves nearer to the coast, and its central pressure decreases to 30.15 inches.

Temperature.—The temperature falls about 10° to 15° since October over the Japan and Yellow Seas and east of southern Japan to about longitude 150° E., also east of Hokushu and the Kuril Islands to about longitude 170° E. To the eastward of these areas to longitude 180° the temperature falls about 5° to 8°. It also falls about 5° to 8° in the Gulf of Alaska. The changes elsewhere are slight.

Over Bering Sea the temperature is below freezing. Along the immediate Asiatic coast from Vladivostok to Hongkong the temperature ranges from 35° to 73°. It is slightly above 80° in the western part of the ocean in an area that reaches from the Equator as far north as the 18th parallel between longitudes 130° and 170° E.; thence eastward this area diminishes in width and extends to longitude 155° W. at the Equator. Along the immediate American coast from latitude 59°, on the eastern border of the Gulf of Alaska, to latitude 20° N. the temperature ranges from 35° to 80°. It is slightly above 80° in an area that touches the coast between the 20th and 10th parallels. It is about 75° along the Equator between longitudes 88° and 130° W.

Over mid-ocean the temperature is 35° at latitude 51° N. and 75° at latitude 25° N. The rise in temperature with decrease in latitude is quite uniform. On the great circle sailing route from San Francisco to Yokohama the temperature ranges from 42° to 60°.

American Coast Winds.—Easterly winds prevail along the American coast in the eastern portion of the Gulf of Alaska; thence to the 40th parallel they are mostly from southerly quadrants; between the 40th and 15th parallels northwesterly winds prevail; and between the 15th and 10th parallels they are northerly and northeasterly.

Asiatic Coast Winds.—The northeast (winter) monsoon, under the influence of the Asiatic High, covers the Philippine Islands, the China Sea, and the waters of the China coast as far north as Shanghai. Along the China coast the force of the monsoon is offset to some extent by land breezes at night, and vessels can make headway against it by hugging the shore. A rise in the barometer foreruns an increase in the strength of the monsoon and a fall a decrease.

Westerly Winds.—The prevailing winds are westerly over the greater part of the ocean between the 35th and 55th parallels, owing to the cyclonic circulation accompanying the Aleutian Low and the anticyclonic circulation accompanying the high pressure belt of the middle latitudes.

The Northeast Trades.—The northeast trades occur between the 12th and 25th parallels, except near their eastern limit, where they are found as far north as the 30th parallel. They are northeasterly to east-northeasterly from longitude 120° W. to 180°. They prevail about 18 days in Honolulu in November. In Asiatic waters they unite with the winds of the monsoon.

The Southeast Trades.—The southeast trades extend across the Equator from the South Pacific between longitudes 80° W. and 175° W. to slightly above the 7th parallel at their most northern limit.

Calms.—The percentage of calms is high along the greater part of the American and Asiatic coasts; also over the region west of longitude 175° E. and south of the 10th parallel.

Gales.—Southeast to northwest gales occur frequently north of the 35th parallel but their number decreases along the coast. The prevailing direction is northwesterly west of longitude 165° W. between the 35th and 50th parallels.

Typhoons and Storm Tracks.—The region of the formation of the October and November typhoons is between the 6th and 17th parallels and longitudes 123° and 155° E. There is an average occurrence of two over the entire region in November. Typhoons occur most frequently in September and least frequently in February. They are likely to prove most dangerous to Manila during May, September, October and November.

The storm tracks, given in red on the pilot charts, show the paths of important storms and the distance traveled by each in 24 hours. The typhoon tracks are furnished by the Philippine Weather Bureau, and the approximate tracks of storms of middle and higher latitudes are furnished by the Zi-ka-wei Observatory. The number of storms of the higher latitudes is greatest in March and December and least in July.

Fog.—The percentage of days with fog is generally less than in October. The area of maximum percentage, 20, is along the American coast from Vancouver to Cape San Lucas. The percentage is low across the ocean; it is 9 on the China coast from Hongkong to Shanghai, and 8 in the Eastern Sea and the Gulf of Pechili.

December

Pressure.—The Aleutian Low lies to the northward and westward of its position in November, being central southwest of the Pribilof Islands, slightly below the 55th parallel. Its lowest pressure continues at 29.60 inches. The pressure is moderately low along the Equator. The pressure of the Asiatic High increases. Its crest, 30.30 inches, extends beyond the coast of northern Chosen (Korea). The California High occupies a position slightly more to the southwest than in November, and its central pressure, 30.20 inches, is .05 inch more than in November.

Temperature.—The temperature falls 5° to 7° in Asiatic waters adjacent to the mainland between the 40th and 20th parallels and 5° to 8° in an irregular area that extends along the American coast between the 50th and 35th parallels. The latter area becomes narrower as it approaches its western limit, the 180th meridian, where it extends only between the 45th and 40th parallels. The changes elsewhere within the range of observations are slight.

The line of freezing temperature touches the Asiatic mainland in the Gulf of Pechili at latitude 37°, crosses the central portion of the Kuril Islands and the western extremity of the Aleutians, passing thence slightly to the north of the latter and reaching the American coast on the eastern border of the Gulf of Alaska. Along the immediate Asiatic coast from latitude 37° in the Gulf of Pechili to Hongkong the temperature ranges from 32° to 65°; thence southward over the China Sea to latitude 10° it ranges from 65° to 80°. Along the American coast from latitude 57° on the eastern border of the Gulf of Alaska to latitude 20° it ranges from 32° to 75°; thence to the Equator the temperature is slightly above 75°. It is slightly above 80° in the western part of an area that extends along the Equator as far east as longitude 150° W. and reaches its most northern limit, the 18th parallel, between longitudes 140° and 156° E.

Over mid-ocean the temperature is 39° at latitude 50° N.; it is 75° at latitude 20° N. The rise in temperature with decrease in latitude is quite uniform. On the great circle sailing route from San Francisco to Yokohama the temperature ranges from 40° to 55°.

American Coast Winds.—The winds are easterly in the Gulf of Alaska in the neighborhood of Sitka, and southerly and westerly north of Vancouver Island. They are southeasterly between the Strait of Juan de Fuca and San Francisco, thence to the 20th parallel northwesterly; from the 20th to the 10th north to northeast; from the 10th to the 5th north to northwest; and from the 5th to the Equator southwesterly.

Winds of High Latitudes.—In Bering Sea the winds are easterly and northeasterly in the eastern portion north of the 60th parallel, and northerly and northwesterly between the 60th and 55th parallels. Between the 55th and 50th parallels they are from westerly quadrants east of longitude 175° E., and immediately west of this meridian they are mostly southerly.

Asiatic Coast Winds—The Monsoon.—West to northwest winds prevail along the Asiatic coast between the 45th and 30th parallels; they tend to become northeasterly between the 30th and 25th parallels. South of the 25th to the 5th parallel the northeast monsoon exerts its full force. Near the mainland the monsoon tends to follow the coast, and as it weakens slightly by night with an offshore breeze, northbound coasting vessels may then make fair headway against it. The thick, rainy weather of the monsoon period makes navigation difficult on the northern and eastern coasts of Taiwan (Formosa) and Luzon. A rising barometer foreruns an increase and a falling barometer a decrease in the strength of the monsoon.

The Northeast Trades.—Over the eastern half of the ocean the northeast trades extend northward almost to the 30th parallel; over the western half, to near the 25th parallel. They extend eastward to within 5 or 6 degrees of the American coast and westward to the northeast monsoon region off the Asiatic coast. Over the eastern and western parts of the ocean they are northeasterly in direction, but more easterly over the central part. These winds extend to the Equator between longitudes 150° and 175° E. In Honolulu they prevail 18 days during the month.

The Southeast Trades.—The southeast trades extend north of the Equator between longitudes 85° and 155° W. They reach their most northern limit about the 6th parallel, between longitudes 110° and 120° W. Between longitudes 100° and 85° W. these equatorial winds blow steadily from the south.

Calms.—The percentage of calms is high along the American coast south of the 40th parallel, particularly between the 20th and 5th parallels; also over the regions west of Japan and Chosen (Korea), over most of the Philippine waters, and in the vicinity of the Hawaiian Islands.

Gales.—The percentage of gales is high over most of the ocean between the 35th and 55th parallels, except in the vicinity of San Francisco and the Farallon Islands. Gales are also frequent over the 5-degree square southeast of Yokohama.

Typhoons and Storm Tracks.—The average number of December typhoons is one as against two for November. The continental storms this month are more frequent than are those of tropical origin.

The storm tracks given in red on the pilot charts, show the paths of important storms and the distance traveled in each 24 hours. The approximate tracks of storms in the middle and higher latitudes are furnished by the Zi-ka-wei Observatory, Pere H. Gauthier, compiler. The number of such storms is greatest in March and December and least in July.

Fog.—The percentage of days with fog, 15, in the area of maximum percentage off the American coast between Vancouver and Cape San Lucas is less than in November. It continues low across the ocean and increases slightly in Asiatic waters, where the percentages are as follows: China coast from Hongkong to Shanghai, 14; Eastern Sea and Gulf of Pechili, 11; Japan Sea, 23.

SOUTH PACIFIC OCEAN

Average Conditions of Wind and Weather

December, January, and February (the Summer Season)

Pressure.—The permanent area of high pressure, crest 30.20 inches, has moved about 5 degrees farther to the west and 2 degrees farther to the south since the spring; the center is now located at latitude 32° S. and longitude 102° W., having increased in extent and remains the same in intensity. Directly south of this area the gradients are steeper than to the north and there has been little change in their positions since the spring. Over the western part of the ocean the gradients are not so regular and the area of high pressure that in spring extended to the eastward from the Australian coast has disappeared. The isobar of the lowest pressure shown on the chart, 29.30 inches, has changed little in position and runs in an easterly direction from the intersection of the 59th parallel of south latitude and the 90th meridian of west longitude.

Temperature.—The area inclosed by the isotherm of 80° has moved somewhat to the south and west since the spring. Over the western and central part of the ocean the isotherms have moved southward from 3 to 8 degrees. On the 150th meridian of west longitude this movement is remarkably uniform, as all the isotherms with the exception of that of 75° have moved from 5 to 6 degrees in latitude. On the eastern part of the ocean the isotherms of 60° to 75° curve to the south as they strike the coast, while these same lines for the previous season have a northerly trend, recurving slightly to the south at the end.

Winds.—The southeast trades that extend from 5° to 30° south latitude have moved 5 degrees to the south since the previous season. Directly south of the trade wind limits the winds are variable, while westerly winds prevail south of the 40th parallel over the greater part of the ocean.

Gales.—Gales are now at their minimum, and as a rule the decrease in the number since spring is marked. In the 5-degree square from latitude 55° to 60° S. and longitude 70° to 75° W. the percentage has fallen from 26 to 8, while in only a few localities has there been even a slight increase. The "Southerly Burster" that prevails off the southeast coast of Australia is frequently met with during this season. It forms after an extremely hot period of weather and is often of a violent character, although the most severe portion of the storm is apt to be of short duration.

March, April, and May (the Autumn Season)

Pressure.—The permanent area of high pressure, crest 30.15 inches, has moved about 8 degrees to the east since the summer, the center now being near latitude 32° S. and longitude 92° W.; it has decreased somewhat in intensity and contracted in extent, having assumed an elliptical form. There has been little change in the gradients either north or south of this area, and the isobar of the lowest pressure shown on the chart, 29.30 inches, has changed its position but little. There is a secondary area of high pressure, crest 30.10 inches, off the south coast of Australia, the western portion extending into the Indian Ocean.

Temperature.—The 80° isotherm has moved to the eastward and now extends to the 130th meridian, west longitude, enclosing a much larger area than in the summer season, although the western end has moved about 8 degrees to the north. Over the central part of the ocean there has been a general southward movement of the isotherms, while south of latitude 20° S., off the coasts of Australia and South America, the movement has been to the north, although in the latter case the isotherms for the two seasons cross near the coast.

Winds.—The southeast trades now extend from latitude 10° to 25° S. on the western part of the ocean and from the Equator to latitude 25° S. on the eastern. Directly south of the trade wind limits the winds are for the most part variable, while south of latitude 40° S. westerly winds prevail over the greater part of the ocean.

Gales.—There is a marked increase in the number of gales since summer; it is greatest in the square between latitudes 55° to 60° S. and longitudes 75° to 80° W., where the percentage has risen from 12° to 30°. Storms of cyclonic origin occur only in the western part of the ocean, but as 90 per cent of them have been reported between the months of December and March, they are not likely to be encountered during the autumn season. This also holds true in regard to tornadoes and "Southerly Bursters" that prevail during the summer months off the southeast coast of Australia.

June, July, and August (the Winter Season)

Pressure.—The principal area of high pressure, crest 30.20 inches, extends between latitudes 27° and 35° S. and longitudes 87° and 111° W. It varies little in either extent or intensity, the total movement of its center during the year being about 10 degrees in longitude along the 30th parallel of south latitude. South of this area the isobars are much closer together than to the north, the effects of the steep gradients being shown in the increased force of the wind and the greater number of gales toward the south. A second area of high pressure, crest 30.10 inches, extends east from the coast of Australia to longitude 167° E.

Temperature.—The highest temperature over the ocean, 80°, is found west of longitude 140° W., between the Equator and latitude 10° S., while the lowest temperature shown, 40°, is located between latitudes 50° and 55° S. The temperature on the east coast of Australia ranges from 75° in the north to 50° in the south, the distance between the isotherms being nearly uniform, while on the other hand, as these lines approach the South American coast, the distance between them becomes very irregular. North of the 25th parallel the temperature on the South American coast is much lower than at the same latitude on the Australian coast, this being due to the effects of the cold Peru Current on the one hand and the warm East Australian Current on the other.

Winds.—Between latitude 20° S., the southern limit of the southeast trades, and latitude 5° N., the northern limit, the winds are remarkably constant in direction and force, the percentage of both gales and calms, as a rule, being low. Near the northwestern coast of South America the prevailing direction of the trades is about south, there being a tendency for the winds to blow parallel with the coast. The winds are variable over the greater part of the ocean south of latitude 25° S., though they blow from westerly quadrants a greater portion of the time with an average force of 4 to 6.

Gales.—There are few storms of cyclonic character during the winter season as nearly 90 per cent of them occur between December and March. The southerly "Burster" that prevails in the vicinity of southeast Australia during a large portion of the year is also rare at this season. There are few gales above latitude 20° S., while between the 20th and 30th parallels the percentage is about 3 for the western and central portions of the ocean and between 1 and 2 east of longitude 95° W. South of latitude 30° gales increase rapidly in number, the maximum percentage, 28, being found between latitudes 55° and 60° S. and longitudes 90° and 95° W.

September, October, and November (the Spring Season)

Pressure.—The semi-permanent area of high pressure, crest 30.20 inches, central at latitude 30° S. and longitude 97° W., is practically the same in intensity and position as during the winter months, while it has increased slightly in area. South of this area the gradients are much steeper than to the north, and there has been little change in the position of the isobars since the previous season. A second area of high pressure, crest 30.00 inches, extends eastward from Australia to longitude 163° W. The isobar of the lowest pressure shown, 29.30 inches, extends from Cape Horn in a southwesterly direction, and its eastern end has moved slightly to the north since winter.

Temperature.—The highest temperature shown, 80° is found west of longitude 147° W. and between the Equator and latitude 13° S., while the isotherm of the lowest temperature, 40°, extends in a westerly direction from latitude 57° S. and longitude 70° W., its position having changed but little since winter. The distances between the isotherms off the Australian coast are remarkably uniform, while off the South American coast just the opposite is true, the irregularities being due to the effect of the Peru Current, which varies much more in intensity and temperature than the Australian Current. The average southerly movement of the isotherms since winter is about 5° in latitude, though this movement is not altogether uniform, and in mid-ocean the temperature has changed but little.

Winds.—The southeast trades prevail between the 5th and 20th parallels of south latitude, and are remarkably constant in both direction and force, while near the northwest coast of South America the tendency is for them to draw along the coast, becoming southerly. South of the trade-wind limits the winds are variable over the greater part of the ocean, although they prevail from the westerly quadrants in the vicinity of Cape Horn and south of Australia.

Gales.—There has been a decided decrease in the number of gales over the greater part of the ocean since the winter, except in the square southwest of Cape Horn where the percentage has increased from 20 to 26, while the average percentage for the four squares to the westward of this square has fallen from 25 to 21. The "Southerly Burster" that prevails off the coast of southeast Australia during certain portions of the year, as well as storms of cyclonic character, first make their appearance in November, although they are not common until summer.

INDIAN OCEAN

Average Conditions of Wind and Weather

January

Pressure.—The pressure is highest over the southern Indian Ocean with two crests of 30.15 inches each between the 30th and 36th parallels, one being between longitudes 62° and 76° E. and the other between longitudes 88° and 100° E.; it is comparatively high, 30 to 30.05 inches, over the Indian Seas. The pressure is low near the Equator with a central pressure of 29.80 inches between latitudes 3° and 10° S. and longitudes 75° and 90° E. Another low-pressure area is central between Borneo and Australia. The lowest pressure shown on the chart, 29.60 inches, is south of the 45th parallel.

Temperature.—The temperature is about 83° at the Equator, thence northward it becomes gradually lower and is slightly below 75° at the extreme northern portions of the Indian Seas. From the Equator southward the temperature becomes quite uniformly lower with increase in latitude and is slightly below 45° at the 50th parallel.

The Monsoon Winds.—The northeast monsoon, force 2 to 5, prevails over the northern Indian Ocean and below the Equator along the African coast to about latitude 10° S. The northwest monsoon is more unsteady and of lighter force, often sinking to a calm. It prevails over an area that borders on the southern limit of the northeast monsoon, touches the African coast between latitudes 10°

and 15° S., and extends across the ocean to and along the western coasts of Sumatra and Java.

In the Persian Gulf and the southern part of the Red Sea the winds are southeasterly and northwesterly, and in the northern part of the Red Sea, northwesterly.

Winds of the Trades Region.—The southeast trades are steadiest, force 3 to 5, to the eastward of the 70th meridian between the 10th and 30th parallels. West of 70° E. the trades are more easterly, and the winds become more variable toward the coast of Madagascar. The winds are northerly at the northern entrance of the Mozambique Channel, and southerly at the southern entrance. Easterly winds prevail between 30° and 35° S. and the 30th and 70th meridians.

The Prevailing Westerlies.—South of the 35th parallel the prevailing winds are westerly, except that between Australia and 40° S. they are variable. South of 40° S. the average force of the westerlies is 6, with frequent gales.

Cyclones.—These severe storms seldom occur in the Bay of Bengal, and never in the Arabian Sea during January, although squally weather is occasionally experienced in the Persian Gulf and along the Mekran coast. Cyclones originate more frequently in the southern ocean between Madagascar and the 90th meridian than during any other month. They first move in a southwesterly direction, then recurve to the southeast; their tracks are most numerous in the neighborhood of Mauritius and Reunion.

Fog.—Little or no fog occurs north of latitude 30° S. The highest percentage of days with fog, 20 to 35, occurs along the 50th parallels between longitudes 40° and 60° E.

February

Pressure.—The pressure is highest over the southern Indian Ocean with two crests of 30.15 inches each between the 27th and 30th parallels, one being between longitudes 58° and 69° E. and the other between longitudes 81° and 92° E. Pressure is lowest over the southern portion near latitude 50° S. where it deepens to 29.70 inches It is also low in the eastern equatorial region, between Borneo and Australia, 29.80 inches, and comparatively low over the western equatorial portion.

Temperature.—The temperature is about 83° over most of the region along the Equator, thence northward it becomes gradually lower and is slightly below 70° at the head of the Arabian Sea. The temperature south of the region along the Equator becomes quite uniformly lower with increase in latitude and is slightly below 40° at the 50th parallel.

The Monsoon Winds.—The northeast monsoon, force 2 to 4, continues north of the Equator and down the African coast as far as Zanzibar. It is more northerly in the eastern portions of the Indian Seas and more easterly in the western portions. Between latitudes 0° and 10° S. and longitudes 60° and 80° E. northerly to northwesterly monsoons prevail; east of the 80th meridian, between the same latitudes, the winds are westerly, with frequent calms.

The winds over the northern part of the Bay of Bengal are variable; over the northern part of the Arabian Sea, northerly to northwesterly; in the southern part of the Red Sea, southeasterly and northwesterly; and in the northern part, northwesterly.

Region of the Southeast Trades.—This region is included between latitudes 10° and 30° S., except west of longitude 75°, where the area is much contracted. Off the west coast of Australia southerly trades prevail; thence to the 70th meridian they are southeasterly; thence to Madagascar, easterly. Along the African coast between latitudes 10° and 20° S. northerly winds prevail. In the southern part of the Mozambique Channel the winds are southerly; thence to Port Elizabeth, northeasterly, and along the south coast of Africa to the Cape, westerly to southerly.

The Prevailing Westerlies.—South of the 40th parallel westerly winds predominate. The percentage of gales is highest in this region, but is lower in February and March than during other months.

Storms.—Severe storms do not occur over the Indian Seas during February, although there are occasional squalls over Sokotra and off the Mekran coast. In the Bay of Bengal the monsoon sometimes attains the force of a gale. Cyclones are most frequent in the Southern Ocean between Madagascar and the 90th meridian during January and February. These storms on the average first move in a southwesterly direction, then recurve toward the southeast.

Fog.—The highest percentage of days with fog, 20 to 25 occurs south of the 45th parallel in two areas, one between longitudes 42° and 60° E., the other between 80° and 110° E. The percentage decreases northward, and above the 30th parallel little or no fog occurs.

March

Pressure.—The high over the western part of the Arabian Sea has moved northward, and its crest is now only 30.00 inches. The Equatorial low has filled in, its lowest pressure being 29.85 inches, over the East Indies. The pressure is highest, 30.15 inches, west of Australia, between latitudes 29° and 35° S., comparatively high, 30.10 inches, immediately south of Australia, and lowest, 29.70 inches, south of latitude 45° S.

Temperature.—Over most of the Equatorial region, including the Bay of Bengal and most of the Arabian Sea, the temperature is from 80° to 85°. It decreases gradually from 80° at latitude 20° S. to below 45° south of the 46th parallel.

Winds North of the Equator.—The northeast monsoon, force 3, prevails over most of this region. The winds are from westerly quadrants at the heads of the Indian Seas, and become easterly in the Gulf of Aden. Winds of force 4 obtain in the Red Sea, being southeast and northwest over the southern part and northwest over the northern part.

Winds between 0° and 10° S.—Between the Equator and 5° S. easterly winds prevail from the African coast to the 55th parallel, thence to the 75th parallel the winds are northerly, thence to Sumatra, mostly northerly and northwesterly. Over the rest of the region the winds are light and variable.

Calms.—Calms occur most frequently around Sumatra, also over the lower portions of the Bay of Bengal and the Red Sea, and in the Mozambique Channel. The percentage is highest, 32, near Singapore.

The Southeast Trades.—The southeast trades, force 4 to 5, blow generally between latitudes 10° and 30°. In the Mozambique Channel the winds are variable in the northern part and southerly between the 15th and 25th parallels. North of Australia they are easterly, southwesterly, and westerly. The African coast winds between parallels 25 and 30 are northeasterly. Between the 75th meridian and Madagascar the trades become east to east-southeast.

The Prevailing Westerlies.—Between parallels 30 and 35 the winds are variable; south of this region the westerlies, force 4 to 6, predominate. Gales average about 10; the percentage is highest, 15 to 19, between latitudes 40° and 45° S. and longitudes 15° and 30° E.

Storms.—Occasional squalls occur over the Indian Seas. South of the Equator cyclones are frequent. They form in the doldrums, near the limit of the trades, and move in a southwesterly direction, then generally recurve to the southeast.

Fog.—The highest percentage of days with fog, 10 to 15, occurs between latitudes 44° and 48° S. and longitudes 52° and 92° E. Elsewhere there is little fog.

April

Pressure.—The pressure is highest, 30.15 inches, west of Australia, between the 28th and 37th parallels, and lowest, 29.60 inches, near the 50th parallel. It increases to 29.90 inches at the head of the Arabian Sea, and decreases to 29.80 inches in a narrow belt extending 10° on each side of the Equator.

Temperature.—Over most of the area extending from the heads of the Indian Seas to latitude 15° S. the temperature is comparatively high, ranging from 80° to 85°. It is 65° at latitude 35° S., thence falls rapidly to 40° at the 50th parallel.

Winds North of the Equator.—The northeasterly winds of the winter monsoon are modified by the increasing continental warmth during April and May, and tend to become light and variable. Calms increase over the entire region, except the extreme northern waters of the Indian Seas. The winds are easterly in the Gulf of Aden; thence along the coast to the head of the Bay of Bengal they follow the general contour of the land. In the center of the seas there is a tendency to blow from the north or east, but southwesterly winds increase over the entire bay.

Winds between 0° and 5° S.—The percentage of calms continues high over this region, being highest, 29, near Sumatra. Easterly winds prevail west of longitude 50° E., and westerly winds between longitudes 50° and 100° E.

The Southeast Trades.—The southeast trades, force 2 to 5, blow between latitudes 5° and 30° S. South of the 10th parallel they possess considerable steadiness; north of it they tend to become variable. Southeast to south winds occur west of Madagascar.

The Prevailing Westerlies.—Between latitudes 30° and 40° S. the winds are variable, force 4 to 6, with the westerly component increasing toward the south. South of the 40th parallel strong westerly winds predominate, with an average of about 15 per cent of days with gales west of the 125th meridian.

Cyclones.—During the first half of April the weather at the heads of the Indian Seas is as quiet as in March. Occasional storms form in the second half of the month over the center or the southeastern part of the Arabian Sea, and move northeastward or northwestward. The infrequent storms of the Bay of Bengal form in the central or eastern part in connection with the southwest monsoon, and move northeastward. In the South Indian Ocean cyclones are less frequent than in March. They usually form 8° or 10° south of the Equator, move southwestward, and later recurve to the southeast.

Fog.—Fog is rare north of latitude 35° S., and the percentage is low south of it. The highest percentage of days with fog, 10 to 20, occurs in a small area south of the 43d parallel between longitudes 43° and 56° E.

May

Pressure.—North of 5° south latitude the pressure is 29.75 to 29.80 inches, being lowest at the heads of the Indian Seas, where the warm weather low is advancing from southern Asia. South of 5° S. the pressure increases to the crest of high pressure, 30.20 inches, that lies between latitudes 23° and 31° S. and longitudes 44° and 88° E. South of the high the pressure decreases more rapidly than north of it, and is about 29.50 inches near the 50th parallel.

Temperature.—The temperature is 85° over the southern portion of the Red Sea, the greater portion of the Indian Seas, and southward, west of the 75th meridian, to the Equator. Below the Equator it is 80° as far as latitude 12° on the eastern and 22° on the western side of the ocean. In general the temperatures are higher in the same latitude on the western than on the eastern side, as far as latitude 45° S. The temperature decreases to about 40° in mid-ocean near latitude 50° S.

Winds North of the Equator.—Westerly winds prevail north of the Equator over most of the region west of the 100th meridian. The southwest (summer) monsoon gradually develops over the entire area during May, but the attainment of its full strength occurs in June and is usually accompanied by severe squalls. Easterly winds prevail in the Gulf of Aden, and northwesterly winds, force 3 to 4, over most of the Red Sea. Calms occur 10 to 20 per cent of the time over most of the region between the Equator and 15° north.

The Southeast Trades.—These trade winds, force 3 to 4, prevail over the area between the Equator and latitude 30° S. Over the extreme northern and southern portions of this area the trades are broken by variable winds, and calms are frequent between the Equator and 10° S. The trades are steadiest between latitudes 10° and 25° S. Along the African coast near the Equator they follow the contour of the land and merge into the southwest monsoon.

The Prevailing Westerlies.—Between latitudes 30° and 35° S. the winds are strong and variable, with a tendency to become westerly. Farther south the prevailing direction is westerly, force 5 to 6.

Gales.—Gales are confined mainly to the southern part of the ocean over the area dominated by the westerly winds. As autumn advances the percentage of days with gales increases. In May it averages about 15 per cent between the 35th and 40th parallels and 20 per cent near the 50th parallel. The percentage decreases toward the Equatoı.

Cyclones.—These storms occur with increasing frequency over the Indian Seas as spring advances. They may form at any time during May, but in the Aıabian Sea are most likely to appear during the second half of the month. They are usually severe and move in a direction between west and north-northeast. In the South Indian Ocean cyclones decrease in number. They originate in the northern part of the trade-wind area, move first in a southwesterly direction, then usually recurve to the southeast. The storm of May 24–28, 1916, is the only one of record in the annals of the Royal Alfred Observatory, Mauritius, which traveled to the west of Rodriguez after the 29th of April.

Fog.—An area of 20 to 30 per cent of days with fog occurs near the 50th parallel between the 30th and 70th meridians. The percentage decreases slowly east and west of this area, and rapidly north of it. There is practically no fog north of latitude 30° S.

June

Pressure.—The continental summer low, pressure 29.55 to 29.60 inches, is well established over the heads of the Indian Seas. There is an increase northward to 29.70 inches over the Red Sea. A belt of high pressure lies between Australia and Southern Africa with its crest, 30.15 inches, off the African coast between Madagascar and latitude 30° S. South of this belt the barometer falls 29.60 inches near latitude 50° S.

Temperature.—The temperature is 80° to 90° north of latitude 10° S. The highest temperature for the month, 90°, occurs over the western part of the Gulf of Aden and the southern part of the Red Sea. Over most of the Arabian Sea and the western part of the Bay of Bengal, the temperature is 85° to 88°. South of latitude 10° S. the temperature falls quite uniformly to 45° or 40° between the 45th and 50th parallels.

The Southwest Monsoon.—Except for northwest winds over the Red Sea and the Persian Gulf, the southwest monsoon, force 3 to 5, dominates the ocean north of the Equator. It overspreads the Arabian Sea early in June, and by the third week is in full force over the Bay of Bengal. Severe thundeɪstorms, thick, cloudy weather, and gales, with occasional dangerous cyclones, occur during the period immediately preceding the full force of the monsoon.

The Southeast Trades.—The southeast trades, force 3 to 5, occupy most of the region between the Equator and latitude 25° S., except between 0° and 5° S., east of the 75th meridian, where the winds are variable with about 10 per cent of calms. West of the 65th meridian, between 0° and 5° S., the trades become merged with the southwest monsoon.

The Prevailing Westerlies.—Between latitudes 25° and 30° S. light variable winds prevail, though west of longitude 65° easterly winds predominate. Over most of the area south of 30° S. winds from the westerly quadrant prevail, average force 6. The percentage of gales in this region is high, increasing toward the south. The average is about 20 per cent, except in the region immediately south of Australia, where the percentage is much less.

Cyclones.—Cyclonic storms are rare this month in the South Indian Ocean. They have increased in number over the Indian Seas, where most of them form during the early half of the month in advance of the monsoon. In the Arabian Sea they are usually severe; they originate off the upper cost of India, and move slowly in a northwesterly direction, passing into the Persian Gulf, or entering the Arabian Desert. The cyclones of the Bay of Bengal are less severe than those of the Arabian Sea.

Fog.—The area of highest percentage of days with fog, 15 to 20, lies between latitudes 43° and 48° S. and longitudes 38° and 58° E. From this area fog decreases in all directions and practically disappears north of the 35th parallel.

July

Pressure.—The areas of highest and lowest pressure present much the same appearance as in June, except that they are slightly intensified—the low pressure in Indian waters having decreased to 29.50 inches over the northern part of the Arabian Sea and the high pressure in latitudes 25°–30° S. having increased to 30.30 inches and moving toward mid-ocean. The pressure at 50° S. is about 29.60 inches.

Temperature.—In the Indian Sea area the temperature has fallen slightly over the June average, owing to the cloudy skies of the monsoon but the mean is 80° to 85° over most of the region north of 10° S. latitude except for 8° or 10° east of the coast of Africa south of Cape Guardafui, where the temperature is 78° or 79°. The temperature at 30° S. is 64° to 70° and at the 50th parallel about 40°.

Winds—The Monsoon.—The southwest monsoon is a settled wind north of the Equator and blows strongly force 5 to 6 as during the last days of June. It penetrates into the Gulf of Aden, but in the Red Sea the winds are northwesterly force 4.

Variables.—The winds are moderately light and variable over a narrow belt east of the 70th meridian between 0° and 5° S. where the monsoon is separated from the southeast trade winds. West of the 70th meridian the line of demarcation narrows until the trade merges almost directly into the monsoon.

Trades.—The force of the trade winds is 3 to 5. Their southern limit is about the 25th parallel south although they continue somewhat into the belt of variables lying between them and the westerlies. South-southeasterly winds predominate in the Mozambique Channel and easterly winds west of 65° E. between parallels 25° and 30° S.

Westerlies.—South of the 35th parallel across the ocean and south of the 30th parallel over the eastern half of the ocean the prevailing winds are westerly. The percentage of westerly gales is slightly higher than in June and between 40° and 50° S. gales occur about one-fourth of the time.

Cyclones.—The cyclones of July are usually of slight intensity and are rare except over the northwestern angle of the Bay of Bengal where two or three are likely to occur each July. The cyclone of 1871 southwest of Sumatra is the only whirling storm of consequence recorded this month in the South Indian Ocean.

Fog.—The fog area has changed only slightly as a whole over the Southern Ocean. East of the 90th meridian the area has narrowed. Between the 40th and 60th meridians, south of the 43d parallel, the occurrence of fog is more frequent than in June, having increased to 20 to 30 per cent of days with fog.

August

Pressure.—The pressure distribution is the same in August as in July, except for slight modifications. Over the Bay of Bengal and the Arabian Sea the summer area of low pressure shows a slight increase over the northern portion now averaging 29.60 inches. Along the Equator the average pressure is about 29.85 inches. The area of high pressure 30.30 inches at its crest has moved westward from mid-ocean and is central along the 30th parallel of south latitude. At 50° S. the low pressure is permanent; in August it is from 29.65 to 29.70 inches.

Temperature.—In African coast waters the temperature averages from 63° south of Cape Agulhas to 80° at Cape Guardafui and from 80° to 90° in the Gulf of Aden and the Red Sea. North of the Equator the lowest temperature slightly below 80° is over the western part of the Arabian Sea but the whole Indian area is cooler than during May and early June, owing to the heavy monsoon clouds. The temperature is near 40° along the 50th parallel.

Winds—The Monsoon.—The southwest monsoon is the prevailing wind, force 3 to 5, north of the Equator, but has decreased in force since July. The skies continue generally cloudy, and gales are prevalent, especially over the western part of the Arabian Sea over and to the eastward of Socotra. The winds are mainly northwesterly in the Red Sea.

The Southeast Trades.—From the Equator to about 3° south latitude the winds are light and variable, but show a tendency to become affected, more or less, by the monsoon to the north and the trades to the south. The southeast trades, though rarely attaining force 5, are comparatively steady between 5° and 25° S.

Between 25° and 35° S. winds from all quadrants often occur, although over the eastern half of the belt the tendency is to become westerly and southerly, and over the western half to become easterly and northerly, following the normal circulation around the "high."

The Westerlies.—South of the variables over the belt of high pressure the winds are mainly westerly, force 4 to 6, although interrupted by passing cyclones peculiar to the middle latitudes. Gales occur from a sixth to a third of a time between 35° and 50° S.

Tropical Cyclones.—Few of these dangerous storms occur in August. These few are confined to the northern part of the Bay of Bengal, and are never as severe as during the spring and autumn months.

Fog.—The percentage of days with fog is low over the southern ocean. The highest percentage is only 10 to 15, and occurs between 42° and 50° S. and 20° and 50° E.

September

Pressure.—The pressure over the Arabian Sea and the Bay of Bengal is about a tenth of an inch higher in September than in August; the minimum at the heads of the seas is about 29.70 inches. The equatorial pressure is 29.85 to 29.90 inches. The highest pressure occurs between 20° and 30° south latitude, with the crest, 30.20 inches, over the western part of the ocean southeast of Madagascar. Near the 50th parallel the pressure, as in August, is about 29.70 inches.

Temperature.—The changes in temperature, as a rule, are slight since August. Owing to the decreased cloudiness over the western part of the Arabian Sea, that region is somewhat warmer than in the previous month. Most of the ocean north of 10° S. has a temperature of about 80°. A maximum of 85° to 90° occurs over the Gulf of Aden and the Red Sea. From 10° S. to 30° N. there is little more than a range of 12° in temperature, but over a similar extent from 10° S. to 50° S. there is a range of more than 40° in temperature.

The Southwest Monsoon.—The southwest monsoon continues north of the Equator, and is strongest, force 4 to 5, over the center of the Bay of Bengal and the southwestern part of the Arabian Sea, but it is weaker than in August and is gradually being replaced by the variable winds which precede the winter monsoon. Northwesterly winds prevail over most of the Red Sea and the Persian Gulf.

Southeast Trades and Doldrums.—The average southern limit of the southeast trades is about 25° S. The northern limit is between 5° S. and the Equator, and in this region the doldrums occupy a width of about 5° of latitude over the eastern half of the ocean, thence diminish in width westward. The average force of the trades is 3 to 4.

"Horse Latitude" Winds and Westerlies.—South of the trades over the ridge of high pressure between 25° and 35° S., the more or less variable winds of the "horse latitudes" occur. On the north they show the influence of the trades and on the south the influence of the westerlies.

Between 35° and 50° S. the winds are mostly westerly, with average force of nearly 6. In this region gales are frequent, averaging 20 to 27 per cent of the winds over half of the area.

Cyclones.—Tropical storms are confined principally to the Bay of Bengal. Here occur in September the undeveloped cyclones peculiar to August, and in addition the more dangerous whirls of autumn. The earlier the northeasterly winds set in that much earlier is there a predisposition to storms of a severe type.

Fog.—The region of fog shows little change from that of August. The percentage of days with fog is light over even the most frequented areas, the maximum being 10 to 15 per cent over an extent roughly defined within latitudes 42° and 48° S. and longitudes 15° and 47° E.

October

Pressure.—The seasonal change in pressure over the Indian Ocean for October is most important over the north equatorial region. The increasing pressure over Asia is spreading to the Bay of Bengal and the Arabian Sea, and the central area of lowest pressure for these seas, now 29.80 inches, has moved southward and covers most of the region between latitudes 15° N. and 5° S. The permanent ridge of high pressure lies between Australia and southern Africa. Its crest fluctuates in position from month to month and sometimes divides, as in October, when one crest (30.15 inches) appears southeast of Madagascar and the other (30.20 inches) over the eastern half of the ocean. The lowest pressure on the chart (29.60 inches) is near the 50th parallel of south latitude.

Temperature.—Over most of the Red Sea the temperature is 85° to 88°. Over most of the Indian Sea region and thence southward to latitude 10° or 13° S. the temperature is between 80° and 83°. Between 20° and 35° south latitude, off the west Australian coast, the temperatureis 58° to 70°,or 5° to 10 ° lower than in the same latitudes off the east African coast. The temperature falls to about 40° near the 50th parallel.

Winds North of the Equator—The Monsoon.—As the pressure changes the winds also change over the region north of the Equator. The southwest monsoon is weakening and disappearing and the northeast monsoon is gaining strength toward the last of the season. In consequence, the winds are variable with frequent calms over the northern seas. There is a considerable northerly component of the winds however, over the Arabian Sea. Between 10° N. and the Equator the winds are westerly, except near the coast of Africa, where they are mostly southerly. In the Red Sea calms are frequent; the predominating winds are southeasterly in the southern part and northwesterly in the northern part.

The Southeast Trades.—The trades have changed very little since September and occupy practically the same area, between parallels 5° and 25° S., blowing with force 2 to 4. They blow across the Equator in African coast waters. These winds prevail to some extent in the Mozambique Channel, with local modifications, which give a northerly turn to the winds at the northern entrance and a southerly turn at the southern entrance.

Winds from 25° to 50° S.—Between latitudes 25° and 35° S. are the calms and variable winds of the "horse latitudes." The winds, however, are inclined to become southerly over the eastern end of the belt and northerly over the western end. Over the southern part of the belt gales are increasing in frequency, and south of the 35th parallel, over the region where westerly winds prevail, an average of about one-fifth of the winds are of gale force.

Tropical Cyclones.—Tropical cyclones begin to occur at rare intervals in the South Indian Ocean this month. In the seas north of the Equator, particularly in the Bay of Bengal, the fall season of severe cyclones is at its height. These storms may form over any part of the bay, not being limited to the northern part, as during midsummer. They are likely to occur following a considerable period of fine weather, and October is, therefore, considered to be the most treacherous month of the year in these waters.

Fog.—Little fog occurs north of the 30th parallel of south latitude, and the percentage of days with fog is low south of it. The area of most frequent occurrence, 10 to 20 per cent of days with fog, is west of the 40th meridian, south of the 48th parallel.

November

Pressure.—The southward movement of the continental high has caused a considerable increase in the pressure over the northern waters of the Arabian Sea and the Bay of Bengal, the pressure being 30 inches at the head of the Arabian Sea. Two centers of low pressure, 29.80 inches each, appear, one over the eastern part of the Arabian Sea and the other south of the Bay of Bengal. High pressure continues between Australia and southern Africa with the crest, 30.20 inches, near Australia. The pressure decreases thence southward and is 29.50 inches over a part of the ocean near latitude 50° S.

Temperature.—The autumnal fall in temperature is being felt over the northern portions of the Red Sea the Arabian Sea, and the Bay of Bengal, but over most of the ocean north of 10° south latitude the temperature continues to average about 80°. The southern limit of the isotherm of 80° is in the Mozambique Channel near 23° south latitude. Between 15° and 35° S. the western part of the ocean is considerably warmer than the eastern part. The isotherm of 70°, for instance, while it rises from mid-ocean and reaches Australia near 21° S., falls as it approaches the African coast, which it touches near latitude 34° S. There is little difference in temperature across the ocean near the 50th parallel, the mean being approximately 40°.

Winds of the Monsoon Region.—The northeast monsoon prevails over most of the Arabian Sea and the Bay of Bengal, although traces of the summer monsoon linger in the southern part of the Bay. Between 5° N. and the Equator, except near the African coast, where the northeast monsoon and the southeast trades converge, the westerly monsoon is the prevailing wind. Over most of the Gulf of Aden the prevailing winds are easterly, but they are southeasterly at the entrance to the Red Sea and continue southeasterly as far north as the 20th parallel, above which northwesterly winds are general.

Calms.—Calms occur most frequently over the northern and southern portions of the Indian Seas and throughout the neighborhood of the East Indies.

The Southeast Trades.—The average northern and southern limits of these winds are nearly along latitudes 5° and 27° S., respectively. The trades blow with greater steadiness, force 3 to 4, between latitudes 10° and 20° S. In the vicinity of Madagascar the winds are mostly southeasterly to northeasterly on the eastern side; in the Mozambique Channel they are easterly to northerly at the northern entrance and easterly to southerly at the southern entrance.

The Westerlies.—Between latitudes 30° and 50° S. the prevailing winds are westerly. They generally increase in force toward the south, and south of the 40th parallel from 11 to 22 per cent of the winds are gales, the highest percentages being toward mid-ocean.

Tropical Cyclones.—The tropical cyclones of the Bay of Bengal are fewer and less intense than during October. Their average occurrence in the Arabian Sea is one during November. A few of the cyclones of the Arabian Sea have crossed India from the bay. The storm movement is usually in a west-northwesterly direction at first, later recurving through north into northeast.

Hurricanes are increasing in strength and number in the south Indian Ocean. They originate over that belt of the ocean lying between Sumatra and Madagascar. They usually move first in a southwesterly direction, later often recurving through south into southeast.

Fog.—Little or no fog occurs north of 30° S. and the percentage is low south of that parallel. There is a moderate local increase to 15 to 20 per cent of days with fog near the 50th parallel to the west of the 50th meridian.

December

Pressure.—The Equatorial depression of December is marked by three fairly well-defined lows, pressure 29.80 inches each—one south of the Arabian Sea; another west of Sumatra; and a third between Australia and Borneo. Moderately high pressure prevails over the northern portions of the Indian Seas and the Red Sea, and high pressure, with a crest of 30.20 inches, continues between Australia and southern Africa. Near the 50th parallel the pressure is 29.60 inches.

Temperature.—The temperature is about 75° at the heads of the Indian Seas; but between about 10° or 15° north and south of the Equator it is 80° to 82°. South of this region of high temperature there is a gradual fall to 45° between the 45th and 50th parallels.

The Northeast Monsoon.—The northeast (winter) monsoon, force 3 to 4, prevails over the Indian waters and extends down the African coast to latitude 10° S.

Northwesterly winds prevail in the Persian Gulf and the Gulf of Oman, and easterly winds in the Gulf of Aden. In the southern part of the Red Sea the winds are southeasterly and in the northern part northwesterly.

Equatorial Winds and Calms.—Between 5° N. and 10° S., except along the coast of Africa, light winds with frequent calms, prevail. Over the northern part of the area northerly winds are most numerous; between 0° and 5° S. the winds are westerly; and between 5° and 10° S., westerly and southeasterly. The percentage of calms near Sumatra is about 20.

The Southeast Trades.—These winds occur between 10° and 30° S. east of the 50th meridian. Their average force is 3 to 4. West of Madagascar the winds are mostly northeasterly and southeasterly; south of Madagascar, easterly.

Winds South of 30° S.—Between 30° and 35° S. from Africa to the 60th meridian the winds are easterly. Elsewhere generally south of the 30th parallel westerly winds prevail. The westerlies blow with force 5 to 6 south of 35° S., and over most of the region gales are frequent.

Cyclones.—Cyclones are rare in the Arabian Sea in December, and seldom form in the Bay of Bengal after the middle of the month. Cyclonic storms increase in number in the South Indian Ocean where their tracks are embraced between 5° and 35° S.—They move at first toward the southwest, then recurve toward the southeast.

Fog.—The northern limit of fog is irregular, but in general is south of the 30th parallel. The percentage is low, as a rule, but there is a maximum area of 15 to 20 per cent of days with fog south of the 45th parallel to the west of the 70th meridian.

Explanation

The writer wishes to say here that the foregoing summation of the weather to be expected all over the world is not intended for regular reading.

When voyages are being planned, or are in progress, these valuable summaries, prepared by the U. S. Weather Bureau, are here for the use of the seaman.

Active cooperation of seamen of all nations in the work of collecting weather data has made these forecasts possible. The writer, on many a voyage, has marveled at their accuracy. But the seaman must remember that only average conditions are set down. At sea the unexpected and the unusual must always be reckoned with.

Note:—Marine observers and all shipmasters should make application for "Weather of the Oceans," issued monthly by the U. S. Weather Bureau. It will be sent to them free of charge.

CHAPTER XXI

SAFETY ON BOARD SHIP

I

General

Buoy and water light

The crew of a vessel are unlike almost any other group of workers. They live with their work, their home, for the time they are on a voyage, is the ship. The work is extremely hazardous if carried on by men who are not thoroughly trained. But even with the best training and under the best possible conditions casualties at sea will average higher than on land.

Loss of life at sea in the merchant service was so abnormal during the World War that figures for this period are of no value in computing averages. In the *Bulletin* of The American Museum of Safety, of October, 1917, Dr. Frederick L. Hoffman, statistician for the Prudential Insurance Company, published a paper on the accident hazard at sea covering the decade before 1914. The following extract is taken from this paper by permission.

" Loss of life in the American merchant marine may be conservatively based upon the assumption of a fatality rate of three per 1,000, which, in all probability, is rather below than above the facts of actual experience. In the British merchant marine the corresponding fatality rate is five per 1,000.

" . . . A clear distinction requires to be made between navigation hazards proper, or such as are directly attributable to weather and other agencies resulting in maritime disasters, and accidents more or less inherent or incidental to maritime employment, such as directly concern the men employed in navigation and occupations pertinent thereto, as separate and distinct from accidents to passengers or other persons on board, in consequence of maritime casualties more or less extraneous to the management of the vessel as such.

" Primarily, the causes of maritime disasters are foundering, stranding and collisions, which in the American experience for recent years account for 62 per cent of the disasters attributable to all causes. Of the total, 7.5 per cent were attributable to foundering, 24.4 per cent to stranding and 29.9 per cent to collisions. In the case of vessels on the Great Lakes, however, foundering accounts for only 4.3 per cent of the disasters, while stranding accounts for 27.8 per cent and collisions for 34.3 per cent.

" There are no trustworthy statistics for the United States regarding the loss of life in navigation, and practically no statistics whatever regarding the injuries sustained in connection with the labor on ships or in the loading and unloading, or in the handling of freight, or other duties of 'longshoremen, etc. Since the inherent risk of all maritime occupations is the danger of drowning, it is but in conformity to the anticipated results, as disclosed by the industrial experience of the Prudential Insurance Company, that in contrast to a proportion of 1.3 per cent of deaths by drowning in the mortality from all causes for all occupied males, the proportion was 11.0 per cent for persons employed in navigation.

" According to the medico-acturial experience, the general mortality of men employed in navigation is considerably above the average of employments without exposure to navigation hazards. In the experience of the British merchant marine the accident fatality rate was 5.0 per 1,000 for all maritime occupations during the period 1909–1913, or, specifically, 4.8 per 1,000 for masters, 4.6 for sailors and 4.2 for engineers. As regards the fatality hazard at sea, there would, therefore, appear to be no very material difference in the accident liability of the most specific occupations.

" Since the most important difference in navigation relates to the motive power employed, it is extremely significant that according to British experience, the accident liability in the navigation of sailing vessels should be very decidedly in excess of the corresponding accident liability of steam vessels. During the period 1909–1913 the general mortality rate (including diseases) was 12.7 per 1,000 for men on sailing vessels, against 3.8 per 1,000 for men on steam vessels. The accident mortality due to wrecks and casualties was 8.1 per 1,000 for men on sailing vessels, against 1.5 per 1,000 for men on steam vessels. The mortality due to other accidents was 2.6 per 1,000 for sailing vessels and 0.6 per 1,000 for steam vessels. The mortality from diseases, excluding suicides and homicides, was 2.0 per 1,000 for sailing vessels and 1.7 per 1,000 for steam vessels. It is, therefore, self-evident that the replacement of sailing vessels has very materially reduced the hazards to life in navigation and, in all probability, in a measure an improvement has also resulted in the general health of the men, largely, no doubt, because of better sanitary conditions, more commodious sleeping quarters, better ventilation, etc.

" Further reduction in the accident rate has resulted from the ever-increasing average size of the vessels employed. For illustration, according to the American experience for recent years for vessels under 100 tons, in distress, 47.8 were lost against a loss of only two per cent in the case of vessels of a size of 6,000 tons and over."

From the foregoing it will be noted that steamers are safer than sailers, and that large vessels are safer than small ones, all of which seems reasonable. On the other hand, the losses at sea are out of all proportion. Too little thought is given to safety work, sanitation, and morale.

The regular operations of seamanship call for precautions at every turn and these should be emphasized as a matter of course. The *slinging of scaffold planks* is often slovenly done by means of a marling hitch. Scaffold planks should be specially fitted with suitable cross bars and strong rope bridles.

Marling spikes should all be fitted with long lanyards so that when working aloft a man may sling the lanyard around his neck and keep it there while working. Always carry a spike, point up, with a half hitch of the lanyard about the point.

Rope off all hatch openings when not working.

Cover all hatches, especially at night.

Rope off 'tween deck hatches in the trunks and wells where passageways open alongside of them.

See that all *gangways* are fitted with efficient hand rails. See that the top of hand rails comes to the rail of the vessel, or is connected with it by a suitable rope. Have gangways *properly lighted.*

Do not send men into *tanks* or *peaks* until certain that these are *gas free.* Always send men into such places with a French bowline (see page 86).

At sea always have efficient *life lines* fitted across the well decks.

Be certain that all *heavy weights* on deck, and in the 'tween decks and holds are *securely lashed.*

In going aloft *grab hold of the shrouds.* Never grab ratlines.

Never permit men to *drop gear* or *blocks* from aloft.

Examine all gantlines, bo's'n's chairs, etc., before sending men aloft. Never use worn gantlines.

Do not allow smoking near the paint or oil lockers.

Do not allow smoking in or near the holds.

Never use *worn or doubtful cargo gear* or other ship's gear.

When in the stream avoid the use of *shore boats*, especially at night. The writer lost two men who started back to the ship at night in a skiff. When clear of a breakwater, which gave them a false sense of security, they were swamped and drowned.

Always keep an eye on the *possible accidents that are looking for a chance to happen.*

An officer who is alive to his job will feel the responsibility resting upon him. Men who have this feeling generally go about their business in a business-like way. There is very little *monkey work* going on when they are on the job. Seamen recognize such officers and attend strictly to business. The officer who is too inexperienced to look after certain things, who gets out of the way of trouble, generally finds it waiting for him just around the corner of the Old Man's cabin door.

II

Drowning

Many seamen are indifferent swimmers. Living so near the water they gain a certain contempt for it. In merchant vessels where not too much attention is given to the crew after working hours, many men go along for years without learning to swim. It would be a good plan to make all hands go overboard at least once a week when in waters where this can be done. If the Chief Mate sends all hands over the side for a half hour during the Sunday morning washdown, it would do a lot of good. The Humane Society of the Commonwealth of Massachusetts has published an excellent set of rules for rescuing and restoring the apparently drowned which are here given.

How to Effect a Rescue

A. The Best Method when there is No Struggling

Provided the drowning person does not struggle, turn him on his back, place your hands on either side of his face. Then turn on your back, hold him in front of you, and swim with the back stroke, taking care to keep his face above the surface of the water.

Remember that it is most important to keep the face of the drowning person above the surface of the water. Avoid all jerking, struggling or tugging, but swim with a regular, well-timed kick of the legs, husbanding the strength for continued effort.

B. The Best Method for One Who Struggles

When the drowning person is struggling, and difficult to manage, turn him on his back, and take a firm hold of his arms just above the elbows. Draw the arms upwards at right angles to the body and swim with the back stroke. This hold will put the drowning person under the control of the rescuer, who can prevent him from turning round or clutching.

When carrying a struggling person on the surface of the water it will be of advantage to keep the elbows well out from the sides, as this expands the chest, inflates the lungs and adds to his buoyancy. The legs should be kept well up to the surface, the body being as horizontal as possible.

C. The Best Method for One Who Struggles Violently

If the arms be difficult to grasp or the struggling so violent as to prevent a firm hold, slip your hands under the armpits of the drowning person and place them on his chest or round his arms.

Raise them at right angles to the body, thus placing the drowning person completely in your power. Then turn on your back and swim with the back stroke.

Rescuers should at all times be governed by circumstances, using their judgment which method to adopt in conveying the drowning person to shore, taking care to avoid wasting their strength hopelessly against tide or stream —always float or swim with it and gradually make for shore, or wait until a boat or other help arrives.

D. If Clutched by the Wrists

If the rescuer be held by the wrists, turn both arms simultaneously against the drowning person's thumbs, outwards, and bring the arms at right angles to the body, thus dislocating the thumbs of the drowning person if he does not leave go.

E. If Clutched Round the Neck

If clutched round the neck, take a deep breath, lean well over the drowning person, immediately place one hand in the small of his back and pass the other over on to his face; with the thumb and forefinger pinch the nostrils close, at the same time place the palm of the hand on the chin and push away with all force possible.

F. Easy Method of Assisting Tired Swimmer

An easy method of assisting a tired swimmer or one attacked by cramp, as well as others who may be quiet. The person being assisted must place both hands on the shoulders of the rescuer with the arms at full stretch, and lie upon the back. The rescuer being uppermost, and having arms and legs free, swims with the breast stroke.

Enter of—*Royal Life Saving Society.*

Restoring the Apparently Drowned

Rule 1. Unless in extreme cold weather, when there may be danger of freezing, do not move the patient, but instantly expose the face to a current of cold air, wipe dry the mouth and nostrils, rip the clothing so as to expose the chest and waist, and give two or three quick smarting slaps on the stomach and chest with the open hand. If the patient does not revive, proceed at once as follows:

G

Rule 2. To Draw Off the Water from the Stomach and Lungs.—Turn the patient on his face, place a large roll of clothing beneath the stomach and press heavily on the back and spine over it for half a minute, or so long as fluids flow freely from the mouth (Fig. G).

Rule 3. To Produce Respiration. — If no assistance is at hand and you must work alone, place the patient on his back with the shoulders slightly raised on a folded article of clothing. Draw forward the tongue and keep it projecting beyond the lips. If the lower jaw be raised, the teeth may be made to hold the tongue in place; it may be necessary to retain the tongue by tying a handkerchief under the chin and over the head. Grasp the arms just below the elbows, and draw them steadily upwards until they nearly meet above the head. (This enlarges the capacity of the chest and induces inspiration.) (Fig. H.) Next, lower the arms to the side, and press firmly downward and inward and backward on the sides and front of the chest, over lower ribs and sternum. (This produces expiration.) (Fig. I.)

H

I

Repeat these measures deliberately and perseveringly twelve to fifteen times in every minute. Occasionally rub the limbs upward from the extremities toward the heart, and dash cold water in the face.

Rule 4. If an assistant is at hand, and two can work together, have one kneel at the patient's head and one astride the hips of the patient facing the patient's face. (Fig. J.) Proceed as given above, save that when the operator at the head lowers the arms to the sides, the second operator presses on the sides and front of the chest backwards and downwards, throwing all his weight into it. (Fig. K.) The method followed by two workers is the same as that by one, save that the second operator applies the pressure on the chest, and in the time when the arms are being raised applies friction and warmth to the body.

J

K

Rule 5. Send for medical aid, stimulants and warm blankets and clothes as soon as possible.

Rule 6. Keep up the efforts for fully two hours, or until the patient breathes.

Rule 7. Practice drying and rubbing from the beginning in so far as possible without interfering with the movements of artificial respiration.

Rule 8. *After-Treatment.*—As soon as the breathing is established, let the patient be stripped of all wet clothing, wrapped in blankets only, put to bed comfortably warm, but with a free circulation of fresh air, and left to perfect rest. Internally give a little brandy or hot water or other stimulant at hand every ten or fifteen minutes for the first hour, and as often after as necessary.

III

U. S. Coast Guard Lifesaving Stations

Lifesaving stations are located at frequent intervals along the coast. Foreign lifesaving stations and rescue huts are marked on charts and are designated in the sailing directions.

The recognized answer to the distress signals (see page 596) is a pyrotechnic signal, a rocket, or a flare of some kind. Or a gun in the daytime. The shore station will attempt to put a line over your rigging if you are fast ashore and the sea is too high to get a boat out to you.

Instructions for the Use of the Gun and Rocket Apparatus for Saving Life from Shipwreck as Practiced by the United States Coast Guard

If your vessel is stranded and a shot with a small line is fired over it, get hold of the line and haul on board until you get a tail-block with an endless line rove through it; make the tailblock fast to the lower mast, well up, or in the event the masts are gone, to the best place to be found; cast off small shot line, see that rope in block runs free, and make a signal to shore. (Figure A.) This is the whip.

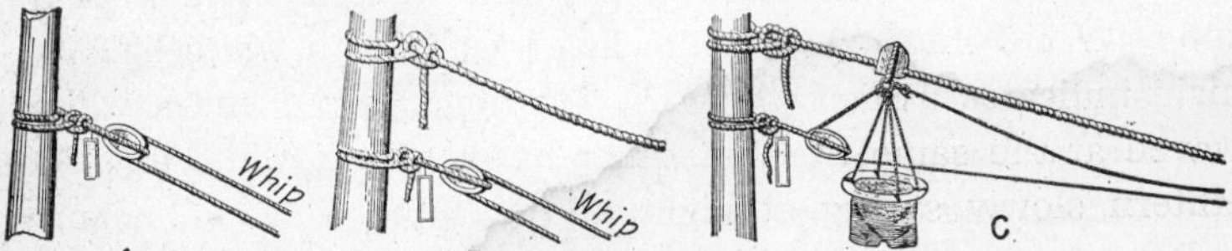

A B C

A hawser will be bent to the endless line on shore and hauled off to your ship by the life-saving crew. Make hawser fast about two feet above the tailblock and unbend hawser from endless line. See that rope in block runs free and show signal to shore. (Figure B.)

Life-savers on shore will then set hawser taut and by means of the whip will haul off to your ship a breeches buoy. (Figure C.)

Let one man get clear into breeches buoy, thrusting his legs through the breeches; make signal to shore as before, and he will be hauled ashore by the life-savers and the empty buoy returned to the ship.

There should be on board every vessel a copy of detailed Instructions to Mariners in Case of Shipwreck, including wreck signals, etc., issued by the United States Coast Guard. A copy of the instructions may be secured by masters of vessels upon request addressed to the Captain Commandant, United States Coast Guard, Washington, D. C.

The business of handling the line shot over a vessel is largely a matter of intelligence. In hauling out the tail block a small tag will be found on the block containing the above instructions in several languages.

Getting a Line Ashore

This can be done in a number of ways. If on a lee shore a line can be floated in, or the line may be shot across to the beach by the line-throwing gun. An ordinary rocket may also be used and will carry a cod line about two hundred feet against the wind, and of course somewhat further with the wind.

The newer types of line-throwing guns have a longer range and should easily put a line against a stiff breeze for a distance of fifteen hundred feet.

When a line has been put across between the ship and the shore certain recognized signals are employed.

A red flag waved on shore by day or a red light by night indicates "*Haul Away.*" A white flag by day or a white light by night indicates "*Slack Away.*" Two flags, a red and a white, waved at the same time on shore by day, or a white and red lantern slowly swung at night at the same time will signify "*Do not attempt to land in your own boats. It is impossible.*" A man on shore beckoning by day or two torches burning near together by night will signify "*This is the best place to land.*"

Answering signals from the ship may be made by waving a flag, handkerchief, hat or the hand and arm. At night by using a lantern or rocket or if working with the whip by jerking on either the hawser or the whip.

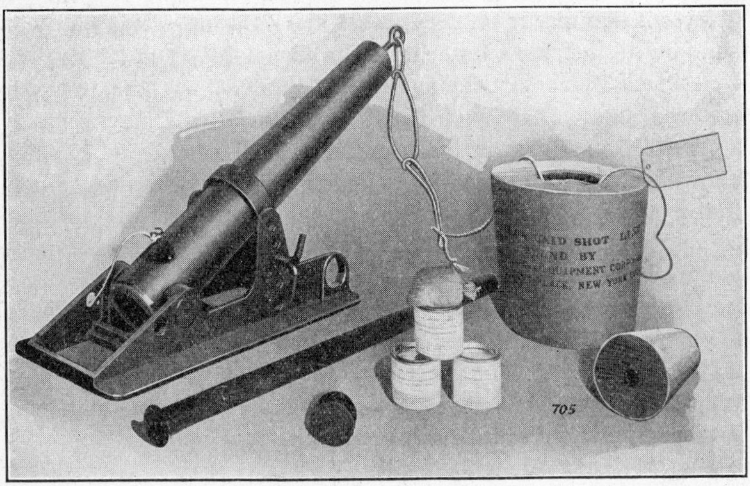

The Steward Line-Throwing Gun.

Caution: Keep cool. Don't get excited and try to calm your passengers and crew as much as possible. You may have to wait several hours after you are discovered, but help will surely come.

Summary of Instructions

When the Coast Guard crew arrive at a point opposite your vessel they will immediately proceed to shoot a line over her. Get hold of this line as soon as you can and if possible reeve the end of it, cutting away the projectile, through a block well up your rigging on the mast nearest shore is best. If this cannot be done reeve it through the ratlines or over something so that several persons can help haul on it. By this shot line, as it is called, you will haul on board a tail block through which is rove a whip. Attached to this tail block will be a tally board giving directions in French and English as to how to proceed.

Make the tail block fast as high up on your mast, or if the mast is gone then up as high as you can on your vessel and signal to shore that they should haul away. When you determine which is the hauling part give all the assistance possible and get the three inch hawser, which you will find attached to the whip line, on board. Make this line fast to the mast about two feet above the tail block and signal to shore that they should haul away. They will tighten up on the hawser and as soon as it is taut will send out to the ship a breeches buoy suspended from the hawser by a specially constructed block and hauled back and forth by the whip line. Place your passengers in the buoy making them stick their legs through the breeches. Children should be sent ashore in care of an adult placing the child in such a position that it will free its protector and thereby be in a better position to hold on. The same procedure should be followed with cripples. Women should be sent ashore in pairs facing each other. Send a young strong man with an old woman or man. Unless too heavy, men can be sent ashore easiest by having each place a leg in the breeches and straddling the buoy. If the weather is very cold, wrap children, old people and cripples in blankets. Women can stand more cold than men.

IV

Cleanliness

The smart appearance of a vessel is the best indication of the quality of her crew. Insist upon a regular routine of cleaning every day in the week, no matter what the weather. Crew's quarters should be inspected daily by the Chief Mate; water closets, galleys, store rooms, all should be ready for inspection at some appointed hour. It is a good plan for the Master to make a weekly inspection of the entire vessel from stem to stern with all store rooms opened and the men responsible standing by, dressed clean and neat.

The condition of some forecastles is a reflection on everyone on board. If owners came on board frequently and just took a quiet walk around many mates would get very busy.

The preparation of food should only be permitted under sanitary conditions. Kids, dishes, and all mess rooms, lockers, etc., should be carefully inspected and kept scrupulously clean. It takes some effort to start such a system where the contrary prevails, but when once under way the men themselves insist upon the standard established.

A wise marine superintendent will look into the forecastle, the moment a vessel returns to port.

Vessels that are not clean carry with them an odor of neglect that is reflected in the slovenly and careless way in which everything is done. Dirt shows poor seamanship, and costs someone a lot of money, generally the owner and the underwriter, in the end.

Living Quarters

Greater care is being taken in the design of living accommodation for the crew. The vessel should be looked upon as a home, and with a small amount of care improvements in light, ventilation, and arrangement can easily be made. Many naval architects are doing valuable work in studying this question of housing the crew.

Bath rooms should all be showers, placed in a light and roomy situation where they can be kept clean and can be scrubbed out each day. A shower under the break of the poop or the forecastle with large openings for sunlight and air would be ideal. Usually these things are placed in some out-of-the-way corner and smell to the skies, never seeing sunlight or air. The deck crew should wash out on deck in mild weather under the deck hose. They generally do this.

Mess rooms should be provided for the various divisions in a vessel. The principal officers should mess in the cabin with the Master. The junior officers should have their own mess room. It is a good plan to have the watch officers and the assistant engineers mess together with the chief steward and the wireless operators. Keep mess rooms a decent distance from W. C.'s.

Quartermasters, oilers, watertenders, etc., should have a separate mess. The boatswain and deck engineer and carpenter should be in this mess.

Seamen and firemen and coal passers should have their separate messes.

This duplication of messes is not so difficult. It calls for arrangement in design and helps in the better working of the vessel. All messes should have a recognized head who should be held responsible for the condition and behavior of the mess.

The Master should actively concern himself with the quality, cleanliness and quantity of the food in the ship and should visit the various messes whenever he feels like seeing how well his command is getting on, this should be quite often.

Clean living quarters and wholesome, well-cooked food go a long way toward working efficiency. Mess rooms should be well ventilated.

Drinking Water

The supply of drinking water should be carefully guarded. Drinking water tanks should be so connected that nothing can be put into them without some safeguard. The writer recalls a case where water from the Schuylkill River was run into a drinking tank. The Master died of typhoid and the Chief Engineer nearly lost his life through the same sickness, caused by this water, served on the cabin table before the mistake was discovered.

In taking drinking water aboard be certain that it is pure and fit for use.

Where *scuttle butts* are used clean them thoroughly every Saturday morning.

Where water cannot be evaporated on board, and the shore supply is suspicious, filter this and boil. Bedford in *The Sailor's Pocket Book*, gives these instructions:*

"In all localities where the quality of the water is suspicious, condensed water should, if possible, be used for drinking and cooking purposes. When this is not feasible, the water should be carefully filtered and boiled.

"Two barrels, one inside the other, having a space of four to six inches clear all round between them, filled with layers of sand, gravel, and charcoal, form an excellent filter. The inside one, without a bottom, rests on three stones placed in layers of sand, charcoal, and coarse gravel; the water, flowing or being poured into the space between the two barrels, and having thus to force its way through the substances into the inner barrel, becomes purified.

"The water should be drawn off by means of a pipe, running through the outer into the inner barrel. Animal charcoal is the best. When, after a time, it ceases to act, it should be removed and well dried. It can then be used again with advantage. It is impossible to use too much of it."

Bedding

All mattresses, blankets, etc., should be got up at least once

* An old, but very useful book.

a week and kept on deck in the sun all day. Make this day a *field day* for the crew and tell off a few men to thoroughly clean out the living quarters. Inspect the bedding and condemn it or have it scrubbed if not sanitary. All mattresses should have covers which can be washed. Thorough *fumigation* of all living quarters is advised at least once a year or more often if necessary. *Before battening down be sure all hands are out of spaces to be purified.*

The Master in most cargo vessels is charged with the duty of doctoring the crew. Some Masters dislike this and have the steward, or some smart youngster, prescribe the usual doses of black draft, etc. However, many of the old-school shipmasters, old sailing ship men, looked upon this as one of their real responsibilities. In fact it is a grave responsibility and should be so considered. Masters should have the benefit of simple instruction ashore in first aid and in prescribing the medicines carried in the ship's chest. This is so essential, that with all of our "reforms" no one seems to have considered it as being necessary.*

One of the best handbooks is the "Medical Handbook of the U. S. Lighthouse Service." This may be had from the Superintendent of Documents, Government Printing Office, Washington, D. C. The price is fifty cents.

V

Morale

The vessel takes her tone from the Master, who, in turn, gets his inspiration from the owners. It pays very handsomely to have a clean, well-organized and contented vessel. There is less loss from damage to ship and cargo. Less of the ship's stores are wasted. Crew changes are cut down and the accident risk from new men is lessened. Cargo is better looked after, holds are policed better, and a feeling of good will prevails that is missing in the "grouchy" vessel where everyone goes about with a chip on his shoulder.

This is of course very desirable, and the question is, "How can it be done?"

In the first place the Master and his officers both on deck and below, must work together. In ships where the "Old Man"

*Medical advice is now often available by radio.

and the "Chief" work together for the best interests of the owners, and are supported by competent and level-headed executives in the persons of the Chief Mate and the First Assistant, a "home ship" can easily be organized.

Organizing ability is simply applied common sense. Without it a crew may be on the verge of mutiny in a few days. The mates stand upon their *rights*, the men invoke all of their *rights*, and the result is a mess of discomfort, ill will, and loss to all.

As a general rule men never do any thinking for themselves. The mate who gets up awnings, lays out work in a rational way, demands that it be done properly, and who is just as insistent for the comfort of his men as he is for the work they are to do, soon makes a home ship. When a man finds he is under skilled direction, and actually has more time to himself while doing first-class work for his employers, and finds himself in clean and orderly surroundings, he bucks up and takes new interest.

On so many vessels the men, after their little trick of duty, are thrown into a dirty forecastle, fed atrocious food, and allowed to exist at the standard set by the dirtiest members of the crew. When these conditions are reversed, the scudgy members are soon eliminated and a clean self-respecting crowd comes in.

Expensive near-cabin food, poorly prepared and served, seems to be the rule on many ships. Waste of any kind always brings with it a sense of neglect higher up.

Seamen prefer clean well cooked wholesome food properly served on a clean mess table.

The writer lived for a year in a clean well-kept forecastle and knows what he is talking about. A seaman, in the old days, and let us hope in the new, carried a few books to sea with him, had a few belongings, and his bag or chest was the essence of neatness. Now that pay is better, crooks ashore are less dangerous, and advancement is more easily attained, young men should find the forecastle a fit place to enter in the first steps toward command, and they should bring something with them from this association that will make them more tolerant and better men as they advance to higher stations.

CHAPTER XXII

SHIP MAINTENANCE

I

Painting

Nowhere in the world is there such constant wearing away and rusting out as on board ship. A house may get along for years without paint or attention, but a ship will fall apart from neglect if she is not attended to almost every day. Steel is especially subject to rust under sea conditions and the nature of the structure, the wide temperature ranges and stresses under which it operates, tends to help corrosion and decay.

A newly built ship is allowed to rust in order that the mill scale can be brushed off. This scale itself will not rust, but if allowed to remain it sets up a galvanic couple with the steel and gradually pits the surface.

Rust, forming under the mill scale, loosens it and it is then removed by wire brushes, or by some mechanical method, either a sand blast or a mechanical scraper or brush.

Rust itself is not generally understood by seamen and the following is of interest. It is from a pamphlet by the *Bitucoat* Company.

" When iron or steel is exposed to the action of air, moisture, and a limited degree of warmth—RUST—a hydrated oxide of iron of no exact chemical formula—is formed, and this compound has the peculiar faculty of giving up part of its oxygen to the neighboring molecules of iron, thus oxidizing or rusting them, and this new rust then re-absorbs fresh oxygen from the air and again distributes it; so, once formed, its action is continuous, ever increasing, ever growing.

" Oxygen is necessary to the formation of rust. Therefore the longer you exclude this element, the longer do you ward off corrosion."

On board ship the time-honored method of cleaning away rust was the *chipping hammer*. The *scraper* was also employed and, after chipping for a day or so, the *wire brush* was brought into play.

With the increase in size of vessels and the comparative increase in the cost of labor, mechanical scraping and cleaning tools seem in a fair way of coming into general use. These may be either pneumatic or electrical. Current is always available, and an air compressor is almost a necessity; in the Diesel ships it is part of the main propelling plant.

Scaling and chipping by hand seem to be doomed, and no one will regret their passing away. Chipping all day over the side on a scaffold plank in the burning sun, knowing that you were getting nowhere and never would, was soul destroying labor.

The *Rotary Scraper* has shown that one man can do as much work as ten to fifteen men working by hand, furthermore he knows he is getting a dirty job done quickly.

In the *Porterite* apparatus a sand blast is used in cleaning off old paint and rust. This operates by air pressure.

Air pressure is also used by this system to apply the paint or other coating. In fact paint spraying is in general use where large surfaces must be covered.

The largest surfaces in a ship are the stretches of the outside shell plating. Here the hull is conveniently divided as follows. The *bottom*, or *underbody*, from keel to light load line—the *boot-top* between light and a foot or so above deep load line—the *topside* above this and to the rail.

Paint guns are used to apply paint under air pressure, and care has to be taken to use them according to instructions. The following instructions for the use of a paint gun apply to the *Spraco* pneumatic painting equipment.

To Use Paint Gun

First: Fill material container with coating material, being careful to strain out all paint skins or foreign matter. The material may be poured into the container through the filler plug in the top of the container, after *bleeder valve* on control head has been screwed all the way *in*. Refill in same way.

Second: Screw filler plug back in place and make hose connections from air and paint outlets on control head to air and paint inlets on the gun. Two kinds of hose are furnished, and it is important that the *rubber hose* be used on the *air line*, and the *special material hose* on the *paint line.*

Third: Blow out *your* air supply line to remove all moisture and dirt, then connect same to the control had at point marked " Line."

Fourth: Screw bleeder valve *out* to the limit and open paint shutoff cock in paint line.

Fifth: Turn on air supply and adjust reducing valves so as to obtain the proper pressures on both air and material, as specified in the following table.

The *air pressure* is indicated on the gauge marked " Air," and is adjusted by means of the reducing valve to right of the gauge. The *paint pressure* is indicated on the gauge marked " Paint," and is adjusted by means of reducing valve to right of gauge.

Approximate Operating Pressures

Kind of Material	Approx. Air Pressure	Approx. Paint Pressure
Lacquers, Shellacs, Light Varnishes, Fillers, and Light Primers	15 to 30 lbs.	5 to 15 lbs.
Light Mill Whites, Steel Primers, etc.	30 to 45 lbs.	15 to 30 lbs.
18 lbs. Red Lead, Structural Paints, and Light Copper Oxide and Graphite Paints	40 to 55 lbs.	30 to 45 lbs.
25 lbs. Red Lead, Heavy Copper Oxides, Anti-corrosives, and similar paints	60 to 80 lbs.	50 to 60 lbs.
30 lbs. Red Lead, Norfolk Special Anti-fouling Paint, etc.	100 to 125 lbs.	75 to 90 lbs.
Freight Car Paints, Heavy Mill Whites, etc., for rapid work	55 to 70 lbs.	40 to 60 lbs.
Asphaltum and similar paints	50 to 80 lbs.	20 to 60 lbs.
Varnishes (varying according to make up)	15 to 45 lbs.	5 to 35 lbs.

When starting up the equipment, the operator should be guided by the above schedule of operating pressures. It is to be noted that these pressures are only approximate, and the pressure should be varied up or down until the desired fineness of spray and speed of application are secured. If more than one length of hose is used, or the gun is operated at a considerable height above the material container, higher gauge pressures will be required.

In general, the higher the air pressure, the finer the spray produced, and the higher the material pressure, the greater speed of application. It is not advisable, however, to use higher pressures than are necessary to produce satisfactory results.

Sixth: Pull back the gun trigger as far as possible and, holding it in this position, adjust needle valve PG-15 and cap PG-11 until the desired character of spray is produced. The flow of air is regulated by screwing the needle valve *in* or *out*, and the flow of material by screwing the cap PG-11 *on* or *off*. When the needle valve has been set at the desired position, it should be clamped by means of lock-nut G-16, and the equipment is ready for operation.

To " Blow Back " Gun

When using the gun continuously it may be necessary periodically to " blow back " the gun to dislodge any solids in the paint, which may have collected in the body of the gun or material hose, also to agitate the paint in the container. This may be done in the following manner:

First: Turn spreader attachment on gun to position marked " Off."

Second: Screw *in* bleeder valve to the limit, which will relieve pressure on material container.

Third: Block opening in cap with finger and pull the trigger. The air will drive any material in the gun or paint hose back into the container, and the air bubbling up through the material will agitate same.

Fourth: Screw bleeder valve *out* to the limit and proceed with the work.

Continuous Agitation

If it is necessary that the material be continuously agitated so as to keep the heavier parts in suspension, the agitating attachment, shown in the accompanying illustration, should be used. This attachment is screwed into the main air port in the bottom of the control head. To agitate the material it is necessary only to screw bleeder valve *part way in*. This will allow air, which has passed through the agitator attachment and bubbled up through the paint, to blow out through the opening around the bleeder valve stem. The farther in the bleeder valve is screwed, the greater will be the agitation. The bleeder valve should not be screwed in too far, however, as this will hold the check ball on its seat, and thus prevent any air passing through the agitator pipe. The proper place to set the bleeder valve to agitate sufficiently any particular kind of paint can be easily determined by a little experimentation. It is advisable, however, not to agitate the paint any more than necessary.

Shutting Down and Cleaning

When shutting down the equipment for a short period, such as overnight, proceed as follows:

First: "Blow back" gun as described above and close paint shutoff cock in paint line.

Second: Shut off main air supply.

Third: Dip nose of gun is can of paint solvent suitable for use with the particular material handled.

If the equipment is to be shut down for a long period, proceed as follows:

First: "Blow back" gun as heretofore described and leave bleeder valve screwed *in* to the limit.

Second: Remove cover of material container. Empty out all paint and clean interior of container.

Third: Put a small amount of paint solvent into the container and replace cover.

Fourth: Screw bleeder valve *out* to the limit.

Fifth: Screw needle valve on gun *in* to the limit, and unscrew cap *part way*.

Sixth: Pull the trigger and discharge the solvent a sufficient length of time entirely to clear control head, hose, and gun of paint.

Seventh: Screw *out* needle valve and screw *in* bleeder valve to the limit and "blow back" gun.

Eighth: Turn off main air supply and empty out any paint solvent remaining in the material container.

The equipment may now be left for any length of time and will be ready for use again without further cleaning.

Paints in General

Much of the following information is adapted from The Sailor's Manual of Paints and Painting and General Instructions for Painting and Cementing Vessels, issued by the U. S. Navy.

Definitions

Paint is a mixture of pigment with vehicle, intended to be spread in thin coats for decoration or protection, or both.

According to this definition, a mixture of pigment and varnish is a paint and on the other hand, a solution of stains in oil or varnish, no pigment being present, is not a paint.

* *Pigment.* The fine solid particles used in the preparation of paint and substantially insoluble in the vehicle.

Asphaltic materials are not pigments except when they contain substances substantially insoluble in the vehicle in which they are used.

The pigments used in paint manufacture may be divided into (*a*) white bases, (*b*) extenders, (*c*) natural earth colors, (*d*) chemical colors, (*e*) pigment lakes, etc.

* *Vehicle.* The liquid portion of a paint.

Here anything that is dissolved in the liquid portion of a paint is a part of the vehicle.

The vehicles used in paints may be divided into (*a*) linseed oil, (*b*) poppy-seed oil, (*c*) perilla oil, (*d*) China-wood oil, (*e*) sunflower oil, (*f*) menhaden fish oil, (*g*) cottonseed oil, (*h*) corn oil, (*i*) soya-bean oil, turpentine, mineral substitute turpentines, varnishes, and driers.

Pigments

Principal White Pigments

The most important white pigments are white lead, zinc oxide, basic sulphate of lead, lithopone, and certain inert pigments, such as barytes, asbestine, silica, etc.

White Lead

White lead (basic carbonate) is a compound of metallic lead with carbonic acid gas, oxygen, and water. It is manufactured by a number of processes, the two most important of which are the well-known " old Dutch process " and the more modern " cylinder " or " quick process." White lead made by either process is acceptable to the Navy Department under the standard specifications for white lead.

In the " old Dutch process " metallic lead is melted and cast into perforated disks, called buckles. These buckles, which are about 6 inches in diameter, are placed into pots containing about one pint of dilute acetic acid (vinegar). The pots are placed in rooms, in tiers or layers, 600 to 1,000 pots to each tier. They are covered with boards and layers of tan bark are placed between tiers. The rooms, kown as " stacks," are kept closed for three or four months, during which period the heat and carbonic acid gas generated by formentation of the tan bark, together with the acid vapors, combine to crrode the lead more or less completely into a white flaky substances (basic lead carbonate).

Note. Definitions marked with the asterisk (*) are quoted from " Standard definitions of terms relating to paint specifications," *American Society for Testing Materials*—1916.

This white substance after it is crushed, screened, floated, ground in water, and dried forms the white lead of commerce, and is either sold in the dry state to paint and color manufacturers or ground in linseed oil and sold in this form for general painting purposes. In the " Cylinder " or " Quick process " method lead is blown into fine granules by means of a jet of superheated steam. This powdered lead is charged into large slowly revolving wooden cylinders or drums, moistened with dilute acetic acid, and subjected for several days to the action of air and carbonic acid derived from burning coke. The subsequent procedure resembles closely the methods of the old Dutch process.

While a useful and valuable pigment on account of its opacity and working qualities, it is subject to somewhat rapid disintegration.

The durability of good white lead may be about three years, but in the meanwhile the paint will disintegrate on the surface and begin to wear off in the form of a fine powder (" chalking ") or to come off in flakes (" scaling ").

White-lead paint seldom retains its original color; it is generally darkened by the action of sulphur contained in the atmosphere.

Sublimed White Lead or Basic Sulphate White Lead.

This product is so named because it is obtained from Galena, a lead sulphide ore, by a sublimation process. The ore as it is mined is roasted. The fumes arising from the roasted ore unite with the oxygen in the air and form a white powder, which does not require grinding. Sublimed white lead differs from (basic carbonate) white lead in that it is a basic sulphate of lead.

It exceeds in the fineness of the particles the ordinary grades of (basic carbonate) white lead, and is considered equal to them in whiteness, body, covering power, and wearing qualities. It differs from basic carbonate white lead in that it is practically non-poisonous and resists to a much greater degree the blackening action of the sulphur compounds of sewer gas and of fuel gas.

Zinc Oxide.

Zinc oxide, as its name implies, is a compound of zinc and oxygen.

Zinc oxide is the finest and nearest white of all so-called white pigments. French process zinc oxide is more nearly pure white than the American process pigments. It costs more, however, and should be used only in white enamels. It is unaffected in color by any gases present in the atmosphere, has no effect upon any pigment with which it may be mixed, and is non-poisonous. Owing to its extreme hardness, it is less resistant to temperature changes than is white lead. It is used to advantage in white

Note: Attention is called to the growing use of Aluminum paint both aboard ship and ashore; in the latter use it is proving superior in the protection of steel structures, tanks, bridges, etc. Aboard ship it is finding a place as a protective and light reflecting coating in engine rooms and compartments.

enamels and in combination with white lead and various other pigments.

In consequence of the extreme fineness of the zinc oxide pigment, it requires more oil in mixing than any other white pigment. In 100 pounds of zinc oxide paint, ready for use, there are about 46 pounds of oil and 54 pounds of pigment, while the proportions in corroded white lead of similar consistency are about 36 pounds of oil to 76 pounds of pigments.

Lithopone.

Lithopone is essentially a combination of zinc sulphide and barium sulphate (blanc fixe or " permanent white "). It is very fine, white, and amorphous, and, if properly made, has excellent body and valuable properties as a pigment. Most varieties of lithopone should not be used with white lead pigments or with oils containing a lead drier, because of the tendency of the mixture to darken. Lithopone has the peculiar property of darkening in sunlight and recovering its color in the dark. As a paint pigment lithopone is best suited for interior use in wall finishes and enamels.

Extenders.

An extender is a white or colorless substance added to white or colored paints. It is sometimes used to form the solid base in which staining colors or dyes are precipitated to decrease the preponderance of chemically active pigments in the paint film.

Barytes or silica is sometimes added to basic carbonate white lead to limit the excessive spreading power of a paint and thus to increase the thickness of the paint film.

Some of the extenders in common use are:

Barium sulphate (barytes, blanc fixe, permanent white).
Silica (silex, silicious earth).
Magnesium silicate (asbestus, asbestine, pulp talc).
Aluminum silicate (china clay, kaolin).
Calcium sulphate (gypsum, terra alba).
Calcium carbonate (white mineral primer, Paris white, whiting, etc.).

These extenders are inert in the sense that they are chemically stable; that is, they neither act upon nor are acted upon by any other constituent in the paints. They therefore do not affect color nor destroy the life of the vehicle.

Principal Color Pigments.

Color pigments are used in conjunction with white base pigments, to produce any desired shade of color. They are also used alone with the necessary vehicles. They may be divided into the following classes, based on the methods of manufacture, viz:

Natural earth colors. These are found as deposits in the earth and utilized as pigments either in their natural state, after grinding and purification, or after further treatment, such as oxidation by burning, calcination, etc. Some of the colors are: Indian red, ochre, metallic brown, siennas, umbers, mineral blacks.

Chemical colors. Chemical colors are pigments produced by chemical action of one substance, usually in solution, upon another substance, resulting in the formation of a colored compound. Some of the chemical colors are: Prussian and Chinese blue, lead chromate, chrome green, ultramarine blue, cobalt blue, vermilion, red lead, orange mineral, and litharge.

Carbon blacks. The carbon blacks are practically pure carbon. They comprise (*a*) lampblack, which is a specially prepared soot from oil lamps; (*b*) gas blacks, from natural gas; (*c*) graphite, which was originally a natural product, but which now may also be produced by means of the electric furnace; (*d*) bone black, ivory black, drip black, vine black, etc., made by carbonizing animal and vegetable substances.

With the exception of those named under (*d*), the above blacks are practically pure carbons. They are therefore chemically inert, but are not classed among the " inert or reinforcing pigments " because they are not used to obtain the results for which inert pigments are used.

The carbon blacks have enormous covering capacity in proportion to their weight. Their durability and tinting power is good. They are seldom used alone as a pure color; it is better to grind with them such a proportion of colorless inert pigment as will measurably increase the thickness of the plant film without impairing its quality.

Vehicles

A *vehicle* is a liquid carrier which is mixed with a pigment to permit the application of the pigment by brush or other suitable means, and which acts as a binder for the pigment.

Vehicles may be subdivided as follows:

Oils:

Drying oils—
- Linseed oil.
- Poppy-seed oil.
- China-wood oil.
- Sunflower-seed oil.
- Menhaden or fish oil.

Semidrying and nondrying oils—
- Cottonseed oil.
- Corn oil.
- Soya-bean oil.

Volatile oils or thinners:
- Turpentine (pure gum spirits).
- Wood turpentine
- Mineral spirits (turpentine substitute).
- Benzol.
- Toluol.
- Coal-tar naphtha.
- Alcohol.

Driers:

Oil driers: Compounds such as lead oxide, manganese oxides, lead-manganese oxides, cobalt acetate, dissolved in linseed oil.

Liquid driers: Oil driers which also contain turpentine, benzine, or both.

Japan driers: Liquid driers which also contain gums or gum resins.

Oils.

Oils are divided into "drying," "semidrying," and "non-drying" oils. Drying oils have the property of absorbing oxygen and forming a tough elastic film. Semidrying oils possess this property in a less degree, and for this reason are not used as extensively as the drying oils. Oils are used in paint to give it the necessary fluidity, to insure the uniform distribution of pigment on the painted surface, to form a firmly adherent and coherent film, and to impart to the paint the desire ldluster.

Linseed oil. Linseed oil is generally used to form the non-volatile part of the vehicle. It is extracted from the seed of the flax plant. The seed is first ground, then subjected to steam heat, and the oil extracted by means of a hydraulic press. The oil after this treatment contains various foreign substances called "foots." These "foots" are removed by settling or filtration. As storage has the effect of settling the "foots," linseed oil should not be unnecessarily shaken up just prior to its introduction into the paint.

China wood oil. China wood oil, or tung oil, as it is sometimes called, is the oil obtained by heating and crushing the nuts of tung trees, which grow in China and Japan. This oil, when properly treated, will dry to a clear waterproof elastic film.

Menhaden or fish oil. This oil is obtained by steaming and pressing menhaden or "piogey" fish, which are caught in large quantities off the Atlantic coast. There are several grades, the most satisfactory of which is the grade known as "light winter pressed." This oil is of pale straw color and dries quickly.

Cottonseed oil. This oil is pressed from the seed of the cotton plant. It is little used in paint manufacture.

Corn oil. This oil is a by-product in the manufacture of starch and alcoholic liquids. It dries slower than cottonseed oil and is used principally in color grinding.

Soya-bean oil. This oil is obtained by crushing, steaming, and pressing the seed of soya-bean plant. When mixed in proper proportions with linseed oil it gives fairly good service in some paints. It is a semidrying oil, but can be made to dry quickly by mixing it with lead manganese driers.

Volatile Oils or Thinners.

Of all the volatile oils or thinners mentioned in the classification given above, the two turpentines evaporate the most slowly. The turpentines differ from the other thinners listed, in that they are oxidizers; that is, they assist the oils used in the paint to absorb oxygen from the air and become dry. The other thinners are not oxidizers. All the thinners, however, are used only for their mechanical effect on the oil. They thin or "cut" the oil to facilitate the spreading, to reduce excessive proportions of oil, and to hasten the "setting" of the paint. They also assist the penetration of the priming coat on wood, reduce the gloss of undercoatings, thereby improving the adhesion of subsequent coats, and destroy gloss entirely in the case of flat finishes.

Thinners, however, *should not be used in excess*, as they will then seriously impair the durability of the paint by reducing the proportion of oil. As the oil in the paint is the "binder" or life of the paint, the thinning of the binder results in lessened durability.

This result is very apparent in what is known as "flat" paint, where the proportion of oil is reduced by the addition of thinners to such an extent that the paint dries without gloss.

Gum spirits of turpentine. Gum spirits of turpentine is obtained from pine trees by cutting pockets in the bark of the trees and collecting the sap drippings. When this sap is distilled, either by direct fire or steam, it yields turpentine.

Wood turpentine. Wood turpentine is produced by destructively distilling or steam distilling pine wood. High grade refined wood turpentine has a sweet smell, is transparent, and equal to gum spirits as a solvent. It is accepted for use on a par with pure gum spirits of turpentine.

Mineral spirits (*turpentine substitute*). Turpentine substitute is a light volatile product collected in the distillation of crude oil. Where this product has the proper evaporating value, high flash point, and freedom from sulphur, it is very suitable as a paint thinner. It differs from the two turpentines in that it completely evaporates as the paint dries, and therefore serves only to dilute the oil. Turpentine, on the other hand, acts on the oil somewhat as a drier; it also leaves on the surface of the paint a small percentage of glossy material, which, in a slight degree, acts as a "binder" for the pigments.

Turpentine substitute is sometimes used as a thinner in varnishes. Varnishes thinned with turpentine can not be further reduced with substitute, because of the tendency of an excess substitute to separate the gums in the varnish from the oil; it is therefore imperative that Navy varnishes should never be thinned with turpentine substitute.

If varnishes on board ship become too thick for proper application they should be thinned with turpentine.

Benzol. Benzol is a product obtained from the distillation of coal tar. A small portion of benzol is a valuable constituent of paint.

Toluol. Toluol or toluene is a light oil distillate from coal tar. It has a higher boiling point than benzol. It is produced in commercial grades suitable for paint trade. It is not used by the Navy Department.

Coal tar naphtha. Coal tar naphtha is not used much in above-water paints, but is used in bottom paints and in varnishes. It is one of the products obtained in the distillation of coal tar.

Driers—In General.

To expedite the drying of a paint driers are used. It has been found that certain metallic compounds, when mixed with oil, add to their drying properties. When raw linseed oil is treated in this way and heated to a certain temperature for a definite length of time it becomes " boiled oil." It is for this reason that boiled oil dries more quickly than raw oil.

If a strongly concentrated mixture of oil and metallic oxides is thinned with a volatile thinner, it becomes an " oil or paint " drier. If a gum or resin is used in the manufacture of the drier, it is sometimes called a " Japan " drier.

A drier acts on the oil in a paint and does not affect the pigment. The drier aids the drying of the oil because of a change which takes place in the oil due to the chemical action of drier. This chemical action is known as catalysis.

Mixed Paints

White Paint.

A white paint consists of a base, usually white lead or white zinc, or both, an oil, thinners, and driers. All of these ingredients have been described in the preceding pages.

Settling of Pigments.

A paint is a mixture in which the solid and liquid ingredients do not combine chemically. The pigments can separate from the vehicle and settle to the bottom of the container.

A separation of this kind takes place in practically all paints where heavy pigments are used. This settling of heavy pigments, in red lead and white lead paints, very often results in the pigments forming a hard, solid mass on the bottom of the container.

The caking of the pigment is due to the affinity between particles of pigment. As soon as they come into contact they unite and gradually form a solid mass.

Prevention of Settling.

The settling and caking can be greatly reduced by incorporating in the paint an inert pigment of the type already described. These inert pigments get in between the particles of pigment, prevent the uniting of the latter, and thereby reduce settling and almost entirely obviate caking.

Value of Thorough Mixing.

Experience and good judgment are required to know when a paint has been properly mixed. In general, however, paint should be mixed about fifteen minutes.

Preparation of Surfaces to be Painted

Next in importance to a properly compounded, well-mixed paint is the careful cleaning of the surface. The old biblical adage, " A house founded on the sand will fall," holds true in paint work. The most expensive paint will be of little value as a protective or decorative coating if it is applied on an insecure foundation. The paint secures its hold on the surface by the penetration of part of the vehicles in the pores of the surface. If loose old paint, rust, dirt, dust, moisture, or grease exists on the surface, it will prevent the new paint from entering the surface pores.

When painting ironwork it is very important to remove all scales, grease, rust, and moisture. Rust has the property of spreading and extending from a center if there is the slightest chance to do so. Deep-seated rust spots may be removed by applying heat from a painter's torch. The heat converts the rust into another form, which is harmless and can be easily dusted off.

Application of Paint

As painting on board ship is mostly done by brush, only this method of application will be considered. The following advice will be of value if properly followed:

First. Hold the brush by the handle and not by the stock. If the brush is held by the stock the hands become covered with paint, which may cause blood poisoning, especially if small cuts are exposed and lead paints are used.

Second. Hold the brush at right angles to the surface, with the ends of the brush alone touching, and lift it clear of the surface when starting the return stroke. If the brush is held obliquely to the surface and not lifted the painted surface will be uneven, showing laps and spots and a general dauby appearance.

Third. Do not completely fill the brush with paint. Dip only the ends of the brush into the paint. Do not charge the brush with paint until the preceding charge has become sufficiently exhausted.

Fourth. Apply the paint with long strokes parallel to the grain of the wood. When painting along smooth surfaces draw the brush along the whole surface if convenient, so that there will be fewer breaks in the lines.

Fifth. Cross the work by laying off the paint over a small section with parallel strokes and then crossing the first application with parallel strokes at right angles to the first ones. A medium pressure should be applied during the crossing and a light pressure during the final laying off. All final laying off should be in the length direction of the work.

Sixth. When painting overhead surfaces, the ceiling panels should, as far as possible, be laid off fore and aft, and the beams athwartship. Where panels contain a great many pipes running parallel with the beams it would be difficult to lay off the ceiling panel fore and aft. In such cases better results will be obtained by laying off parallel with the beams.

Seventh. When painting vertical surfaces, bulkheads, etc., the work should be laid off vertically. In all cases each succeeding coat of paint should be laid off in the same direction.

Eighth. Keep the paint in the pot well mixed while the work is proceeding.

Ninth. Remember that paint applied in a too heavy coat will show brush marks and will give an uneven finish. Better results will be obtained by applying two coats of thin or medium body paint than one coat of heavy paint.

Tenth. Do not apply a succeeding coat of paint before a previous coat is sufficiently dry. A paint dries because of its contact with the air, and the drying of the first coat will be retarded if the second coat is applied too soon.

Care of Paint

After a container of paint has been opened and the paint partly used it should be covered and kept as air-tight as possible to prevent a paint scum from forming on the surface.

When scums or foreign substances become mixed in with the paint it should, before being used, be strained through fine-gauge wire or cheesecloth.

Do not expose shellac unnecessarily to the air, as the alcohol evaporates quickly from the shellac, thereby producing a thick stringy mass.

Do not allow nails or other iron substances to fall into shellac, as iron will discolor the shellac sufficiently to render it useless. Shellac should not be applied on a damp day, as moisture has a tendency to turn it white. Always pour unused paint back into the stock container and wipe out the empty pot with a brush. This will prevent skin forming on the sides of the pot and will keep the pot in good condition for the subsequent use.

Brushes and How to Care for Them

For general work on board ship the following brushes have been found to be most suitable. Sizes are generally specified by number in manufacturers' catalogues.

Type of Brush	Suitable for Use on—
Flat paint brush	Large surfaces.
Sash tool brush	Small surfaces.
Fitch brush	Do.
Do	Very small surfaces.
Oval varnish brush	Rough work.
Flat varnish brush	Medium work.
Ox-hair varnish brush	High-grade work.
Camel's-hair lettering brush	Small surfaces.
Do. larger	Large work.
Painter's dusters	Cleaning work.

How to Prevent Bristles from Falling Out.

Steps should be taken to tighten the bristles of all brushes before they are put in use, since paint and varnish brushes which are in every way satisfactory at the time of inspection when delivered by contractors, may when issued from store be defective in that they shed bristles to a very objectionable extent. This shedding of bristles has been ascertained to be due to the drying out of handles while in store. The bristles may be tightened by holding the brush in a vertical position with the bristles pointing up and wetting the end of the wooden handle inside the bristles with about a teaspoonful of water, then allowing about half an hour for the handle to swell, thus restoring the original pressure of handle and ferrule on the bristles; or it is still better to immerse the brush for 24 hours in water to top of ferrule.

How to Properly Clean a Brush.

No matter how good a brush may be it will be ruined very quickly if not properly treated when not in use. A paint brush after use should be thoroughly cleaned out in turpentine substitute or soap and water. If left in water for any length of time, the bristles are liable to twist and lose their elasticity. After cleaning, the brush should be kept in a trough containing a sufficient quantity of raw linseed oil to cover about one-half the bristle. Large brushes should have a small hole bored through the handle well up toward the stock. A wire can be inserted so that the brush can be suspended in the trough of oil. Brushes should never be stowed standing in buckets with the weight of the brush on the bristles. If large brushes are allowed to stand on the point they soon lose their shape and become useless.

(*Note.* Should a paint brush become quite hard with paint, it should be soaked for 24 hours in raw linseed oil and then in hot turpentine. This treatment will generally loosen up the bristle.)

Varnish brushes should be suspended in the same kind of varnish with which they are used. If this method is not possible, boiled oil may be used instead. If a varnish brush has been thoroughly cleaned in turpentine substitute, gasoline, or soap and hot water it may be kept lying flat on its side in a suitable box.

Lettering brushes should be washed in turpentine substitute or gasoline until clean. If they are not to be used for some time they should be dipped in olive oil and smoothed from heel to point.

Shellac brushes should be kept in a small amount of mixed shellac or alcohol. Never put them in water. If the brush is not required for use in the near future, clean it in alcohol.

Binding of Brushes.

To prevent the bristle in a round brush from spreading, it is good practice to bind the heel end of the bristles at the ferrule with cotton line. The effect of the serving or binding is to make the brush stiffer and to hold the bristles together. As the bristles become shorter, due to wear, the binding can be removed. Flat brushes need not be bound.

Varnish

A varnish is a solution or fluid, usually transparent or translucent, though occasionally opaque, which when spread upon a surface in a thin film dries by the evaporation of its volatile constituents, by the oxidation of other constituents, or partly by evaporation and partly by oxidation, to a continuous, protective coating which improves or better displays the surface over which it is spread, and to a considerable degree protects it from dirt and injury. Varnish is usually made by melting resin or varnish resins in pots, after which it is mixed with heated linseed oil or a mixture of linseed and china wood oils. This compound is further heated until the desired consistency has been obtained, after which it is thinned with turpentine, mineral spirits, or a mixture thereof. The drier is usually added in the form of lead manganese oxides.

Application. After the surface to be varnished has been thoroughly cleaned, filled, and rubbed off, the varnish is applied with a brush in the form of a uniform coat by crossing the work and allowing the varnish to flow in a smooth coating. It is essential that the surfaces be thoroughly cleaned from all dust particles, as these show plainly in the varnish.

Three days should be allowed to intervene between coats. Three coats should be applied on all new work.

For a dull finish, rub with pumice stone and water, then wash off and dry the surface with damp chamois skin.

For a gloss finish, rub with pumice stone and crude oil, wipe and rub surface with rotten stone, then clean with crude oil (8 parts), mineral spirits (1 part), finishing with cheesecloth or clean waste.

Do not apply the varnish too thick as it will not dry underneath. The outer surface will dry first, forming a skin which will prevent the varnish underneath from coming in contact with the air and drying.

Bituminous Compositions

Efficiency. Experience extending over a number of years has indicated that the most efficient coating for metal work when applied on clean or new surfaces in double bottoms, inner bottoms, machinery spaces, fresh-water tanks, and similar spaces is a material usually made from coal tar, pitch, or asphalt.

Nature of material. Bituminous composition is generally considered to consist of a bituminous solution, which is applied cold as a priming coat, and a bituminous enamel, which is applied hot over the solution. The solution consists of bituminous material thinned with a suitable solvent to a brushing consistency. The enamel consists of bituminous material of relatively high melting point, with or without the addition of mineral matter.

Notes on the Use of Bituminous Compositions

(1) The solution will not adhere to a dirty surface and, as the solution forms a bond between the metal and the enamel, it is essential that, prior to applying the solution, the metal surface be absolutely free from oil, grease, or rust. Many of the failures of bituminous compositions have been due to the applications of the material over dirty surfaces rather than to any inherent defect in the bituminous material itself.

(2) Care must be exercised in heating the enamel previous to application. As this material has a tendency to boil over, the pot must be only partly filled. The mineral matter tends to settle out from the hot enamel, and hence the material must be kept well stirred.

(3) The enamel should be applied to a uniform thickness of 1/16 to 1/8 inch. Care must be taken to see that the enamel completely covers the solution, as the solution itself affords but little protection. As the solution and enamel are both black it may be difficult to see where the enamel has been applied, but with care and proper supervision this difficulty can be avoided.

Bottom Paints

Kinds used. Although in the past a number of proprietary bottom paints were used, the only bottom paints now used as standard are the anticorrosive and antifouling paints as manufactured at navy yards. The formulas for such paints are given in the following table.

Object of anticorrosive bottom paint. To prevent the destruction of the steel plating an insulating coating is first applied to the steel vessel's bottom. This insulates the metals in the antifouling coating from the steel. This first coating is known as the anticorrosive coating because of the fact that it prevents the corrosion of the plating.

Object of antifouling bottom paint. As is well known, the object of applying a bottom paint is to prevent the fouling of the ship's bottom. The ingredient used in antifouling paint to destroy marine growth is oxide of mercury. The antifouling paint should not come in contact with the steel plating of a ship's bottom, since it may cause pitting and the consequent destruction of the steel.

Preparation of surface. It has been stated in the preceding section on the preparation of surfaces to be painted, that all surfaces must be carefully cleaned. This statement is particularly true in the case of ship bottom paints because of the service conditions to which these paints are subjected. Oil and grease frequently found at the water line must be cleaned off with gasoline or some other solvent of grease.

Even though all loose paint has been scraped and chipped off, the anticorrosive paint will flake off almost as soon as it has been applied if the oil and grease have not been removed.

Application of anticorrosive paint. Before applying any paint stir each drum until the paint has reached a uniform consistency. As the paint contains heavy pigments which settle rapidly it must be frequently stirred during its application.

The anticorrosive paint dries very quickly because of the quick evaporating properties of its vehicle, and for this reason an operator must take care not to unconsciously keep painting over one spot and thereby build up a thick coating, with resultant waste of paint.

The paint should be applied with short rapid strokes, while the operator progresses steadily over the area to be painted.

Application of antifouling paint. The antifouling paint can be applied almost immediately over the anticorrosive paint, two hours being generally considered a sufficient interval of time between the two coats. As in the case of the anticorrosive, the antifouling contains heavy metallic pigments. These impart to the paint its antifouling properties and must not be allowed to settle. Stir the paint frequently. Apply the antifouling paint only over the anticorrosive paint and not over bare metal, for if this is done pitting of the steel will surely follow.

Outside Paints

Material	Weight per Gallon	Covering Power, Sq. Yds.	Ingredients	Quantities Required for 1 Gallon	Quantities Required for 10 Gallons
Red lead....	25 lbs. 4 ozs.	56	Red lead, dry..	20 lbs.......	200 lbs.
			Raw linseed oil	5 pts........	6 gals. 1 qt.
			Petroleum spirits.......	2 gills.......	2 qts. 1 pt.
			Drier........	2 gills.......	2 qts. 1 pt.
Boot-topping red.	9 lbs. 10 ozs.	45	Venetian red, dry.........	2 lbs. 14½ ozs.	29 lbs. 1 oz.
			Mixing varnish	4 pts. 1 gill..	5 gals. 2½ pts.
			Drier........	8¾ gills.....	2 gals. 5 pts.
			Petroleum spirits.......	3⅓ gills.....	1 gal.
Boot-topping black.	9 lbs. 5 ozs.	76	Mixing varnish	2 pts........	2 gals. 2 qts.
			Drier........	2 pts........	2 gals. 2 qts.
			Petroleum spirits.......	2 pts. 1½ gills	3 gals.
			Drop black, in oil..........	2 lbs.......	19 lbs. 11 ozs.
			White zinc, dry, American process..	1 lb. 14 ozs..	18 lbs. 12 ozs.
Boot-topping slate color.	9 lbs. 12 ozs.	76	White zinc, dry	3 lbs.......	30 lbs.
			Lampblack, in oil.........	3 ozs.......	1 lb. 14 ozs.
			Mixing varnish	3 pts. 2 gills.	4 gals. 3 pts.
			Petroleum spirits.......	2 pts........	2 gals. 2 qts.
			Drier........	2 pts........	2 gals. 2 qts.
Slate color..	15 lbs. 8 ozs.	53	Neutral blanc fixe.........	3 lbs. 5 ozs..	33 lbs.
			Zinc oxide, dry	3 lbs. 7 ozs..	34 lbs. 6 ozs.
			Acheson graphite.....	10½ ozs.....	6 lbs. 8 ozs.
			Lampblack, dry	3/10 oz......	3 ozs.
			Linseed oil, raw.........	5 pts. 1 gill..	6 gals. 5 pts.
			Drier........	5 gills......	1 gal. 2 qts.
			Petroleum spirits.......	½ gill......	1 pt. 1 gill
Outside white.	17 lbs. 4 ozs.	54	White lead, in oil..........	5 lbs.......	50 lbs.
			White zinc, in oil..........	9 lbs.......	90 lbs.
			Raw linseed oil..........	3 pts.......	3 gals. 3 qts.

Outside Paints—Continued

Material	Weight per Gallon	Covering Power, Sq. Yds.	Ingredients	Quantities Required for 1 Gallon	Quantities Required for 10 Gallons
Outside white.	17 lbs. 4 ozs.	54	Petroleum spirits.......	3 gills.......	3 qts. 1½ pts.
			Drier........	2 gills.......	2 qts. 1 pt.
			Ultramarine blue........	1/12 oz......	4/5 oz.
Spar color...	18 lbs. 11 ozs.	55	White lead, in oil..........	14 lbs.......	140 lbs.
			Yellow ocher, in oil.......	1 lb. 6 ozs...	14 lbs.
			Venetian red, in oil........	9/10 oz......	9 ozs.
			Raw linseed oil..........	3 pts. 1 gill..	3 gals. 3 qts.
			Petroleum spirits.......	3⅔ gills.....	1 gal. 1 pt.
			Drier........	1½ gills.....	1 qt. 7 gills
Spar color for smoke-stacks (silica paint).	20 lbs. 10 ozs.	37	Silica, dry.....	2 lbs........	20 lbs.
			White lead, in oil..........	6 lbs........	60 lbs.
			White lead, dry	6 lbs........	60 lbs.
			Yellow ocher, in oil.......	1 lb. 4 ozs...	12 lbs. 8 ozs.
			Litharge......	1 lbs. 4 ozs..	12 lbs. 8 ozs.
			Boiled oil.....	10 gills......	3 gals. 1 pt.
			Petroleum spirits.......	8 gills.......	2 gals. 2 qts.
			Venetian red, dry........	1 oz.........	10 ozs.
Spar color for smoke-stacks.	12 lbs.	40	Spanish whiting......	4 lbs........	40 lbs.
			Portland cement......	13 ozs.......	8 lbs.
			Yellow ocher, in oil.......	1 lb. 3 ozs...	12 lbs.
			Venetian red, in oil.......	1 oz.........	10 ozs.
			Kerosene oil..	6 pts. 2 gills..	8 gals.
Slate color for smoke-stacks.	13 lbs.	53	White lead, dry	4 lbs. 13 ozs..	48 lbs. 2 ozs.
			White zinc, dry	1 lb. 14 ozs...	18 lbs. 12 ozs.
			Lampblack, dry	5¾ ozs......	3 lbs. 9½ ozs.
			Litharge......	5⅜ ozs......	3 lbs. 5¾ ozs.
			Mineral oil (kerosene)...	2 qts........	5 gals.
			Drier.........	2½ gills.....	3 qts.
			Damar varnish	1 qt.........	2 gals. 2 qts.

Outside Paints—Continued

Material	Weight per Gallon	Covering Power, Sq. Yds.	Ingredients	Quantities Required for	
				1 Gallon	10 Gallons
Outside brown.	17 lbs. 4 ozs.	50	White lead, in oil	10 lbs.	100 lbs.
			Burnt sienna, in oil	3 lbs.	30 lbs.
			Burnt umber, in oil	8 ozs.	5 lbs.
			Indian red, in oil	4 ozs.	2 lbs. 8 ozs.
			Raw linseed oil	3 pts.	3 gals. 3 qts.
			Petroleum spirits	3 gills	3 qts. 1½ pts.
			Drier	2 gills	2 qts. 1 pt.
Hospital ship green.	11 lbs. 8 ozs.	..	Chrome green, in oil	7 lbs. 9½ ozs.	76 lbs.
			Raw linseed oil	5 pts. 2 gills	3 gals. 2⅔ pts.
			Petroleum spirits	3 3/10 gills	1 gal.
			Drier	2 gills	2 qts. 1¾ pts.
			Spar varnish	½ gill	1 pt.
Outside black.	8 lbs. 4 ozs.	53	Lampblack, in oil	3 lbs. 12 ozs.	37 lbs. 8 ozs.
			Raw linseed oil	3 pts. 1 gill	4 gals. ½ pt.
			Petroleum spirits	3 gills	3 qts. 1½ pts.
			Drier	3½ gills	1 gal. 1 gill.
Anticorrosive ship-bottom paint (Norfolk No. 17).	11 lbs. 8 ozs.	30	Grain alcohol	3 qts.	7 gals. 1 qt.
			Gum shellac, grade A	13 ozs.	7 lbs. 14 ozs.
			Turpentine	2 gills	4 pts. 3 1/5 gills.
			Pine-tar oil	2 gills	4 pts. 3 1/5 gills.
			Metallic zinc, dry	1 lb.	9 lbs. 8 ozs.
			White zinc oxide, dry	3 lbs.	28 lbs. 8 ozs.
Antifouling ship-bottom paint (Norfolk No. 19).	10 lbs. 8 ozs.	27	Grain alcohol	4 pts. 3 gills	6 gals.
			Gum shellac, grade A	1 lb. 8 ozs.	13 lbs. 12 ozs.
			Pine-tar oil	3 gills	1 gal.
			Turpentine	3 gills	1 gal.
			White zinc oxide, dry	1 lb. 8 ozs.	13 lbs. 12 ozs.
			Indian red	1 lb. 8 ozs.	13 lbs. 12 ozs.
			Red oxide of mercury, dry	8 ozs.	4 lbs. 12 ozs.

Inside Paints

Material	Weight per Gallon	Covering Power, Sq. Yds.	Ingredients	Quantities Required for 1 Gallon	Quantities Required for 10 Gallons
Red lead for confined spaces.	26 lbs. 14 ozs.	40	Red lead, dry	20 lbs. 10½ ozs.	206 lbs. 9 ozs.
			Boiled linseed oil	6 pts. 1 gill	8 gals.
Inside white	18 lbs.	48	White lead, in oil	7 lbs.	70 lbs.
			White zinc, in oil (American)	7 lbs.	70 lbs.
			Raw linseed oil	7⅔ gills	2 gals. 3 pts.
			Petroleum spirits	8⅙ gills	2 gals. 2 qts.
			Drier	1½ gills	3 pts. 3 gills
			Ultramarine blue, in oil	1/12 ozs.	4/5 oz.
Inside white for confined spaces.	18 lbs. 10 ozs.	40	White lead, in oil	14 lbs. 9½ ozs.	146 lbs.
			Boiled linseed oil	5 pts.	6 gals. 1 qt.
Flat white	17 lbs. 8 ozs.	60	White zinc, French, in oil	15 lbs. 4 ozs.	152 lbs. 8 ozs
			Petroleum spirits	3 pts.	3 gals. 3 qts.
			Damar varnish	½ gill	5 gills.
			Drier	¼ gill	2½ gills.
			Ultramarine blue in oil	2/25 oz.	8/10 oz.
White enamel.	11 lbs. 1 oz.	60	White zinc, French, in oil	4 lbs.	40 lbs.
			Damar varnish	7 qts.	8 gals. 3 qts.
			Ultramarine blue, in oil	1/25 oz.	4/10 oz.
Priming green.	18 lbs. 14 ozs.	60	White lead, basic sulphate, in oil	7 lbs.	70 lbs.
			White zinc, in oil (American)	8 lbs.	80 lbs.
			Petroleum spirits	2 pts.	2 gals. 2 qts.
			Raw linseed oil	2 pts.	2 gals. 2 qts.
			Drier	1½ gills	1 qt. 7 gills.
			Chrome green, in oil	½ oz.	5 ozs.

Striping Paints—Continued

Material	Weight per Gallon	Covering Power, Sq. Yds.	Ingredients	Quantities Required for 1 Gallon	Quantities Required for 10 Gallons
Black........	10 lbs. 11 ozs.	48	Lampblack, in oil..........	9 lbs.........	90 lbs.
			spirits.......	1 pt.........	1 gal. 1 qt.
			Drier.........	1 pt.........	1 gal. 1 qt.
Green......	13 lbs. 10 ozs.	50	Chrome green, in oil........	10 lbs. 8 ozs	105 lbs.
			Raw linseed oil	9¼ gills.....	2 gals. 7 pts.
			Drier.........	2 gills.......	2 qts. 1 pt.
			Petroleum spirits.......	4¾ gills.....	1 gal. 2 qts.
Red.........	15 lbs. 7 ozs.	53	Vermilion, in oil..........	13 lbs.......	130 lbs.
			Raw linseed oil	2 qts.........	5 gals.
			Petroleum spirits.......	1 pt.........	1 gal. 1 qt.
			Drier.........	2 gills.......	2 qts. 1 pt.
Lead color...	21 lbs. 7 ozs.	70	White lead, in oil..........	17 lbs.......	170 lbs.
			Lampblack, in oil..........	1 lb.........	10 lbs.
			Raw linseed oil	7 gills.......	2 gals. 1 qt.
			Petroleum spirits.......	7 gills.......	2 gals. 1 qt.
			Drier.........	1 gill.......	2 pts. 2 gills.
[illegible]..	13 lbs. 12 ozs.	48	Chrome yellow, in oil........	11 lbs.......	110 lbs.
			Raw linseed oil	2 pts........	2 gals. 2 qts.
			Petroleum spirits.......	1 pt.........	1 gal. 1 qt.
			Drier.........	1 gill.......	2 pts. 2 gills.
[illegible]e.......	16 lbs. 4 ozs.	48	Ultramarine blue, in oil...	2 lbs. 10 ozs..	26 lbs. 4 ozs.
			White lead, in oil..........	10 lbs. 10 ozs.	106 lbs. 4 ozs.
			Raw linseed oil	2 pts. 1 gill ..	2 gals. 3 qts.
			Petroleum spirits.......	1 pt.........	1 gal. 1 qt.
			Drier.........	2 gills.......	2 qts. 1 pt.

Miscellaneous Formula

Material	Weight per Gallon	Covering Power, Sq. Yds.	Ingredients	1 Gallon	10 Gallons
Under cork..	12 lbs. 5 ozs.	15	Spanish whiting......	7 lbs. 5½ ozs.	73 lbs. 8 ozs.
			Interior varnish......	5 pts. 1 gill...	6 gals. 2 qts.
			Raw linseed oil	1 gill........	10 4/5 gills.
			Drier.........	1 gill........	10 4/5 gills.

Asphalt Cement

Paving asphalt	pounds	90
Trinidad asphalt	do..	25
Val de Travers asphalt	do..	25
Powdered English resin	do..	2
Powdered slack lime	do..	3½
Portland cement	do..	30

This is boiled four hours and kept working during boiling. The metal is first coated with formula No. 58.

Linoleum Cement

Spanish whiting	pounds	120
Gum shellac, grade B	do..	32
Alcohol (grain)	gallons	7½
Gasoline	do..	1
Crude rubber	ounces	2

The rubber is cut in the gasoline and is then added to the mixture of the other three ingredients and the whole is then ground to an intimate mixture. The price of this cement is approximately 8 cents per pound, and since there are about 10½ pounds of cement in 1 gallon, the price per gallon is approximately 84 cents. Pre-war prices.

Slate Color Smoothing Cement

(For 100 pounds.)

Spanish whiting	pounds	10
White lead, dry	do..	32
White zinc, American, dry	do..	16
Litharge	do..	16
Lampblack, American, dry	do..	16
Raw linseed oil	gall[illegible]	1½
Turpentine	d[illegible]	[illegible]
Drier	[illegible]	[illegible]

Red Smoothing Cement

(For 100 pounds.)

Venetian red, dry	poun[illegible]	[illegible]
Spanish whiting	do..	[illegible]
White lead, dry	do..	[illegible]
White zinc, American, dry	do..	[illegible]
Litharge	do..	1[illegible]
Raw linseed oil	gallons	1[illegible]
Turpentine	do..	¾
Japan drier	do..	⅜

*Oil and Water Stop**

(Weight per gallon, 19 pounds.)

Clear shellac	3 quarts 2 gills.
Red lead, dry	12½ pounds.

* The above will give a mixture about the consistency of thick paste. For light plating, stops will be made by soaking 10-ounce canvas for one-half day in clear shellac, then coated with the above mixture. For heavy plating, ball lamp wick will be treated in the same way.

Cementing

The use of cement wash in tanks and in other parts of the ship is increasing. This makes a very good protective cover and can be used where moisture would prevent the adhesion of other materials.

Have the surfaces clean and use sharp sand. Sea sand, tumbled about by the waves with the small sharp edges worn off is not the best. Sharp sand is the sand dug from the side of a bank. Sometimes this also is worn.

Portland cement takes its initial set in about a half hour, possibly sooner. Do not mix cement mortar until ready to use it at once. When cement mortar takes its initial set some men *re-temper* it, that is they soften it up with a trowel. This makes it less strong.

As portland cement will harden best under water it is an ideal material for use in tanks. Salt water does not materially effect its strength.

Where hot water is run into tanks the asphaltic compounds soften and cement should be used.

Drinking tanks coated with cement wash, and allowed to season, are very satisfactory. After the cement has hardened fill and empty them, or wash them down with a fresh water hose before filling.

Where deep pockets have to be cemented use clean sharp cinders as an *aggregate*. Work the spaces between them full of cement mortar.

Mortar is generally best with one part of cement to two of sand. This coats each grain of sand and also fills the spaces in between.

This is called a 1–2 mixture.

II

Docking

The American Bureau of Shipping recommends that all vessels be docked within six months of launching.

Periodical docking thereafter is necessary and should be a regular part of the maintenance program.

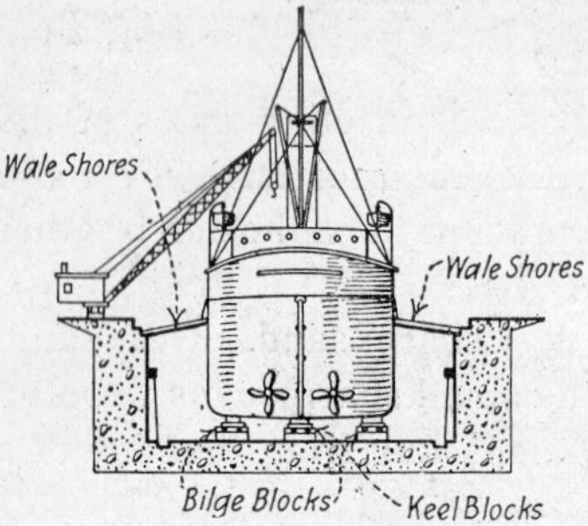

Graving Dock

When necessary to get at a vessel's bottom she may be put into the following kinds of docks:

Graving, or dry dock. This is an excavation that fills at high water. The vessel is floated in, a gate is closed and the dock is pumped out, the vessel resting on keel and bilge blocks and held by wale shores.

Floating dock. This consists of a series of pontoons with bottom and sides. Sea cocks are opened and the dock sinks, the bottom pontoons lying below the level of the vessel's keel. The vessel is then floated into the submerged dock, placed over the blocks and the dock is pumped out, rising under the vessel on the blocks, and lifting her. No wale shores are used.

A Floating Dock.

The Marine Railway is limited to lifting vessels of moderate tonnage. This is simply a reversal of the process of launching. A vessel is hauled up an inclined railway, riding in a cradle running on tracks that extend under water beneath the vessel to be hauled out. A heavy winch or engine is connected to the cradle by means of chains or wire purchases.

In former times, before the use of docks and when craft were smaller, *heaving down*, and *careening* was resorted to.

A Marine Railway.

Strictly speaking a vessel was *hove down* in deep water, her bottom being exposed by the simple expedient of attaching tackles from her mast heads to another vessel, or a hulk, and heeling her over. Suitable preventer shrouds were rigged.

Where a propeller wheel is damaged, and no dock available, this method, applied longitudinally, is often used. See next page.

Careening consists in running a vessel on a sloping beach at high tide and letting the drop of the tide heel her over and expose her bottom for examination or repair.

These two ancient practices are practical for small craft and are still employed where other facilities are not available.

Breaming is the term used when grass and other marine growth is burned off of a vessel's bottom.

The repairs to be made on an average vessel when in dry dock are summed up in the following note from *Marine Engineering:*

"The length of time between dry-dockings depends upon many factors, such as the port repair facilities, time available, the practice of the operating company, etc. Some companies make it a custom to dry dock a vessel every six months, others at a much longer interval. The United States Shipping Board has tried to average about eight months between dockings. It is wise to dry dock a new vessel within six months of launching.

"Besides the managing company's shore representative, a surveyor from the registration society, and possibly an inspector from the United States Steamboat Inspection Service, who have been notified in advance of the docking, will make an inspection of the vessel and require or suggest various repairs, some of which are noted here. If the shell plating is indented perceptibly, these plates should be located, and if not faired at this time a record should be kept of same so as to place the responsibility.

"If it be a new vessel it will be advisable to remove the *propeller fair water cone* and harden up the *propeller nuts* (which may take up a quarter of a turn in the case of a new wheel). If time permits, find the pitch of the propeller, doing this for all blades. Examine and harden up *blade nuts* of separable blade propeller, if necessary. Measure the amount of clearance in the stern bearing (i. e., the amount the shaft is down). The lignum vitae is bored for a clearance of about 1/16 inch and the classification societies require that this bearing be re-wooded when this clearance as shown by a tapered wooden wedge has increased to about 5/16 inch.

"Tail Shaft and Rudder Gudgeon Bearings

"If the tail shaft has two separate *bronze liners*, or one at the stern bearing near the propeller and one in way of the *stuffing*

Exposing a damaged propeller by shifting weights forward.

box at the aft peak bulkhead, the classification societies will require that the shaft be drawn clear of the stern tube for survey every two years. This consists in tapping the liners lightly to see whether they are loose, also to examine the shaft between the liners for cracks or undue corrosion. The fit of the propeller on the tail shaft should also be examined. This must bear at the large end of the taper; the small end of the shaft's taper can be .005 inch smaller in diameter than the hole in the hub for a large propeller. The fit and bearing of the key should also be checked, as, if local, the tail shaft may crack; looseness will, of course, cause vibration. Some firms, with the separate liner type of tail shaft, red lead the shaft between liners and cover it with canvas and a layer of rope marline coated with red lead. If the bronze liners are continuous, i. e., in separate pieces but soldered to each other at the joints, the societies call for the tail shaft survey every three years.

"Further repairs directly under the engineering department would be to examine and grind in, if necessary, all sea valves, clear their strainers and repack the tail shaft gland.

"The rudder *gudgeon pin* or *pintle bearings* should be examined for proper bearing and clearance; when new, the latter may be about 3/32 inch on the diameter of the pin for a fair sized cargo vessel. The gudgeon pin bearings are either lignum vitae or bronze, although of late soft steel has been used.

"Riveting, Scraping and Painting

"It is advisable where possible when docking to have all ballast tanks full, as any leaks will then readily show up. Any tanks that require cleaning or rivet driving may be drained, although with steam up they can be more quickly pumped out, and the writer would advise that steam be kept up, as the ship can be listed or trimmed, if desired, and is under control. All leaky rivets will be calked,

The propeller unshipped by use of chain hoists. This and above photo show work on S. S. Nesco, Capt. E. R. Bergh. Done at Fayal, Azores.

hardened up or re-driven as required by the classification society surveyor and the work when completed passed by him.

"Before coming off the dry dock it is customary to wire-brush or scrape the shell plating and apply one coat of anti-corrosive, together with a coat of anti-fouling, below the light waterline and one of boot-topping above.

"If the important repairs, condition of the hull, condition and clearance of tail shaft and rudder gudgeon bearings and any other important data are noted in the log books, much money will be saved in the operation of the vessel by avoiding the needless repetition of certain repairs, and a better report can be turned into the managing company." *See Maintenance book.*

In addition to the above a great deal of work is done by the deck department. Cables are ranged on the floor of the dock and all shackle pins knocked out and examined. Markings are overhauled and the chain tested. This work may not be done every time the vessel docks but it should be attended to at every second docking at least. Then too, the absence of water on deck makes it a good time to do a lot of deck painting in waterways, etc.

On entering a dock the Chief Mate or Master should consult the dock master and get the rules and regulations of the dock. The Dock Master will call for the docking plan, and this should be ready for him.

Where there is no docking plan, on a large vessel the dock master will get certain dimensions, draft, dead rise, etc., from the regular blue prints.

It is generally best to enter a dock light, tanks pumped out, etc. The vessel should be on an even keel and a good method of putting her exactly even is to hang a hand lead over the stem, where the vessel has a straight stem.

Assistance should be given in every way to the dock master and his crew.

While in dock examine carefully and note the location of all under-water valves. See the condition of the bottom, the location and state of the zinc plates near bronze valves and propeller. The condition and actual construction of the rudder. Keep in mind the possibility of some day having to use a jury rig. Make careful notes of everything that pertains to the maintenance of the vessel and enter it in the *maintenance book* under the heading of "docking." Each docking should be given a serial number with date, place, condition of hull and fittings, also repairs effected, time in dock, and remarks.

When docking, after grounding, examine cement in double bottoms also "sight" all outside bilge strakes to note any deflection.

An interesting article on the corrosion of steel vessels appeared in *Yachting* of November, 1918, and we quote from it here.

"It is significant that when examining a vessel's bottom after several months at sea it is seldom, if ever, that corrosion is found to have taken place equally over any considerable area; it is invariably found in 'spots,' as exemplified by the familiar 'rust-cones.' This is exactly what one would expect from galvanic as distinct from chemical action, and seems to support the theory that even the commencement of corrosion is attributable to electrical action.

"Zinc protectors are, of course, a valuable preventative of corrosion, but their action is distinctly local. In way of valves through the ship's bottom, propellers of gun metal or other alloys, etc., they divert the electrolytic action to themselves, but their radius of influence is not great. In order to render any effectual help in combating corrosion of the vessel's structure, it would be necessary to fit thousands of them, an obviously impractical arrangement.

"An interesting feature about the corrosion of vessels' bottoms is that it is enormously greater nearer the waterline than at the bottom portions of the structure, more particularly in the case of deep-draught vessels. Thus, in one special case of a vessel of 26 or 28 feet draught, experience showed that the corrosion was small in those portions deeper than about 20 feet; it then increased rapidly up to a depth of about 6 or 8 feet, above which it was more or less constant and greater than the remainder. This phenomenon is probably due to the fact that in those portions of the surrounding water which were constantly aerated by the disturbing motion of the sea, fresh active corrosive elements are continually added. Hence, the especial care which is bestowed upon the 'between wind and water' portions of a vessel's hull, which is frequently coated with a special 'boot-topping.'"

When in some foreign docks be careful about little things like having the zinc plates stripped off at night just before flooding the dock. This has been done.

Also, before flooding be satisfied that *all* bottom plugs, removed for drainage, have been properly replaced. The Chief Mate and First Assistant should look after this themselves.

On leaving a dock a large vessel may be riding very light. The unfortunate case of the *St. Paul*, capsizing shortly after leaving dry dock, where it is said some sea cocks were left open by workmen, should be kept in mind. Also always close all lower coal ports. Take every precaution against capsizing. A vessel once out of the dock should at once fill enough of her ballast tanks to insure stability.

The dry dock and the repair yard are an excellent place for the seaman to gain knowledge of the structure of his ship. The repairs that go on, the opening up of vessels, afford a fine opportunity to study naval construction at first hand and to see the effects of collisions and other accidents.

It is a very useful thing for the ship's officer to know just *what* repairs can be made. Some of the recent Thermit welds almost surpass belief. Nowadays nothing seems to be broken beyond complete repair.

III

Decks

The ship's deck, where planking is laid, deserves better care than is given it on the average vessel today. Once the deck was almost holy and a shipmaster looked upon a spot on the deck as a direct personal grievance. Chief mates were constantly looking after the condition of the deck. Tar spots on deck brought down the wrath of the mate as nothing else. In fact a snow white deck has a wonderful effect upon all hands. On passenger vessels and on the bridge about the wheelhouse and wherever plank decking is to be found the same care should be taken as in the past.

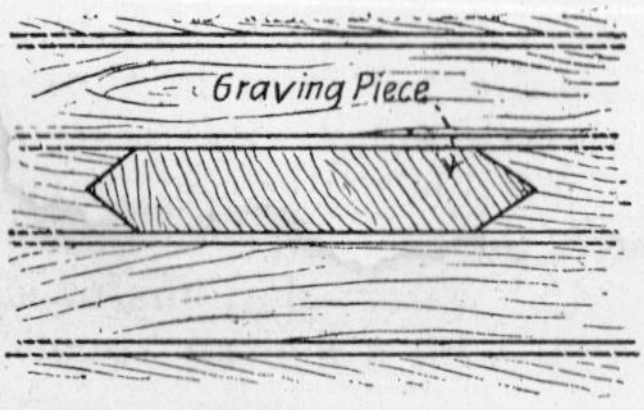

How to fit a Graving Piece.

Deck plugs are often set with the grain running at an angle with the planking and *graving pieces* are put in without regard to finish. Best deck plugs are made of white pine or poplar. Always use graving pieces, do not run *strakes* full of pitch or glue. Most American decks are of long leaf yellow pine. Margin plank is often made of teak, a brownish wood that is not discolored by rust. Teak is a very durable wood excellent for decking and boat construction. It is said to resist decay for two thousand years when properly handled. Teak may therefore be considered durable enough for any part of a modern steel vessel.

Deck seams are caulked with oakum and *pitched* or filled with *marine glue*. For fine promenade decks *white* marine glue is sometimes used and makes a very smart-looking deck.

The directions below are given with Jeffrie's Marine Glue:

14 lbs. of marine glue will run from 200 to 250 ft. of seam $3/4$ in. deep by $1/4$ in. wide. If properly used and not over heated, it will last 4 to 6 years in a seam, and has been known to last 10 to 12 years. When carefully applied to a dry deck it will never leave the sides of the seam.

Caulking Decks

The oakum to be laid well down in the seam, hard, leaving the seam three-quarters of an inch deep after caulking, for the glue, the seam as usual, to be payed promptly.

Water, cold naptha, or coal oil to be used in dipping the caulking irons, as linseed oil or grease prevents the glue from adhering to the edge of the planks.

Paying Decks

In paying decks the glue should be poured from the ladle into the seams, holding the nose of the ladle an inch from the deck.

Note.—If the ladle is drawn on the seams, as is frequently done when pitch is used, a quantity of atmosphere is enveloped, and has not time to escape before the glue becomes set; this will cause air bubbles in hot weather and leave the seams hollow and unsound.

The workmen in all cases paying from them, that is walking backwards.

Paying Seams of Deck.

When old caulking is to be broken out a rase knife is used to clear the seams, in order that the glue may adhere to the edge of the plank; the seams may be afterwards caulked or hardened down, as may be required, to the depth before described, viz., three-quarters of an inch, if the thickness of the timber will allow of it; and if the weather be sufficiently fine to allow the decks to be payed with pitch, it will do also for the glue.

Cleaning Off

The deck to be cleaned off on the following day if the ship be required for immediate service, otherwise it is best to clean off when she goes to sea. No inconvenience from its uncleanliness will be found as with pitch.

Caulking

The caulking of a ship's seams and the caulking of decks, is of such ancient origin that no one can say with certainty when the art was first practiced. Undoubtedly it was an old method of making a vessel watertight, even in the days of Noah.

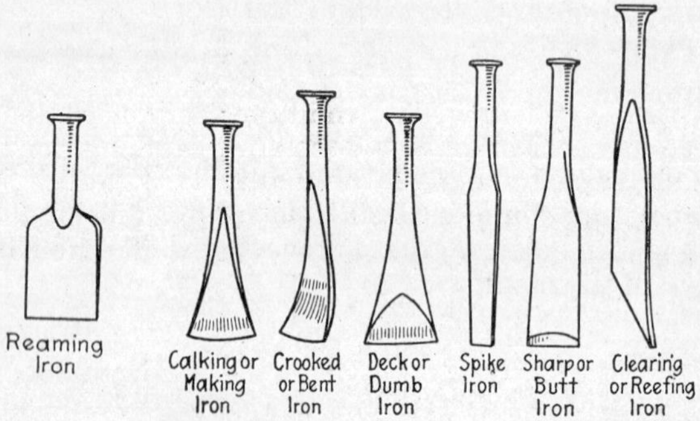

The tools used by caulkers carry with them the slow changes of this ancient art. Caulkers, as a body of men, are slow to talk, and long on thinking and thoroughness. And in speaking of " caulkers " we refer to the men who have grown up in the craft.

The tools of the caulker are his special pride. Caulking and golf have much in common. The right " iron " must be used, and it must be used in just the right way. The oakum must be rolled just so, the seam must be *reamed* open, if too close, the *hawsing iron* may have to be employed, driven in by the *hawsing beetle*, a large long-handled maul with *soft* steel rings, mind you, and not the tempered steel rings of the *caulking mallet*.

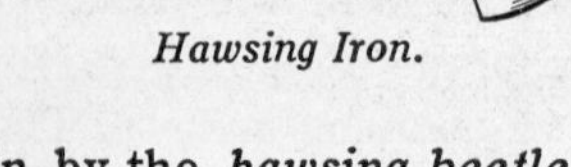

Hawsing Iron.

In fact the whole business, or I should say, " art " of caulking is hedged in with technicalities.

Like so many things connected with ships and the sea, the question of caulking has many sides. The *reaming iron* is really a broad sharp-edged chisel. The *hawsing iron* is held by a loose iron handle, giving the helper a chance to stand clear of the long handled *hawsing beetle.* The *hawsing iron* may be sharp like the reaming iron, or it may have a square edge like the *caulking iron.*

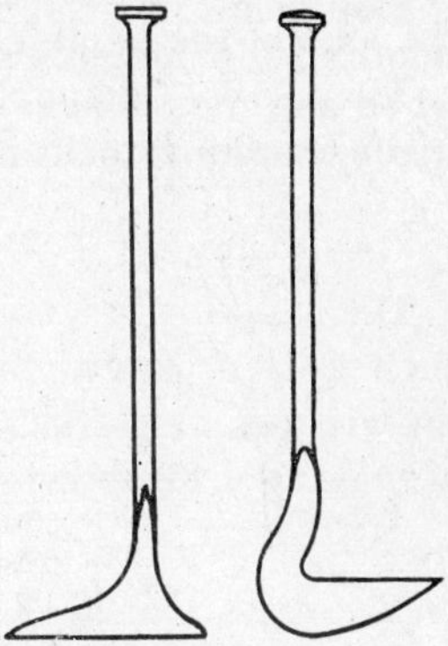

Reef Hook *Boot Iron*

Caulking irons are of various shapes and kinds, as shown in the illustrations. The *making iron* has a sharp edge; the deck or *dumb iron*, a broad edge. The edge of irons may be sharp, or squared off or have one, two, or three *creases.*

When old oakum is to be cleared out of a seam a *reef hook* is used, also a *rase knife* or *reefing iron* may be used. The *boot iron* is a long-handled caulking tool used to get the oakum into places not easily reached by the ordinary irons.

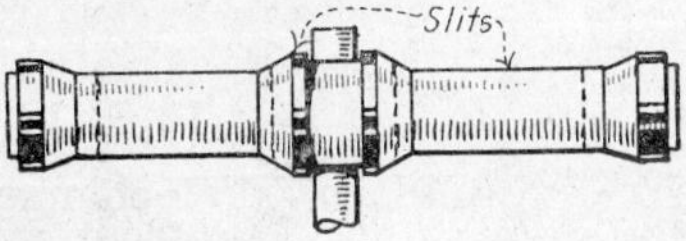

Head of Caulking Mallet.

While the irons are important, the old caulker places a great deal of store by his *mallet.* In the first place a real mallet *must* be of specially seasoned *live oak.* Nothing else will do as well. *Black mesquite* and *red wood*, have been used, and during the war thousands of *white oak* mallets were made, but the real caulking mallet must be of live oak, otherwise it has no virtue. A caulker, when selecting his mallet will try the " ring " of every mallet in the shop, working them down one against another until his choice falls between two. Then for a half hour or so he will try them, striking the ends of the mallet with a caulking iron. Have you ever heard the peculiar musical ring of a caulking mallet? This is simply the outward evidence of the perfect rebound of a fine mallet.

A first-rate caulking mallet will spring back into position for the next stroke without effort on the part of the experienced caulker. This effect is largely due to the " slits " to be found in the best mallets. The slits are in line with the hole for the handle and are placed with the greatest care, directly through the axis of the hammer.

Mr. G. W. Campbell, of 253, Broadway, New York, who has made caulking tools for the past thirty-five years, is authority for much of the lore here given.

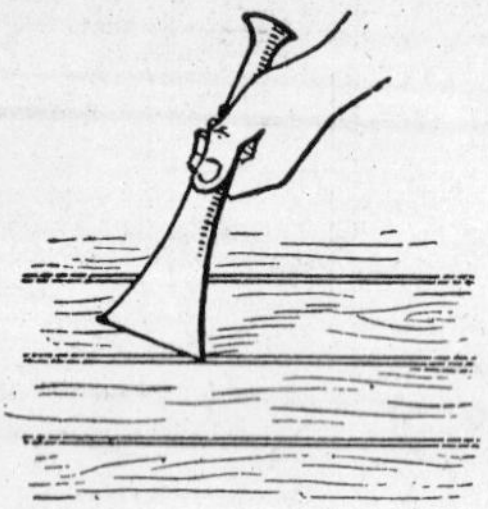

How to hold a Caulking Iron.

The caulker is a conscientious man; the safety of the ship and its lives depend upon the honesty and thoroughness of his work; perhaps he feels this; it is a part of the business, and he is very touchy about his tools.

Of course we all know that a caulking iron is held as shown in the drawing, and worked along a seam in the deck with a rocking motion.

Many a fine deck has been ruined by poor caulking. Now that the war is over we are getting back to the old smart ways at sea.

IV

Washing Down

Washing down is a daily rite on every well-conducted vessel and usually takes place in the morning watch just after coffee around the fore hatch. Where wooden decks are to be kept in condition it is very necessary. Where coal is burned it clears away the cinders, freshens up the wooden fittings on deck and generally puts a morning shine on things fore and aft. *Wash deck gear* should be kept in special chests near the hose reels. *Wash deck hose* should be small, fitting to the *deck plugs* with suitable *reducers.* $1\frac{1}{2}$ inch hose is very handy.

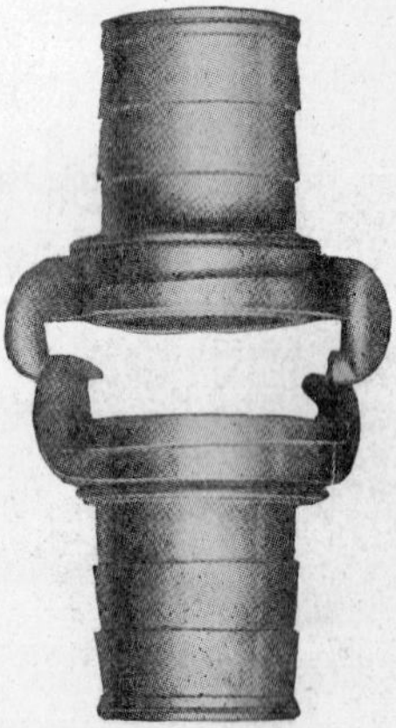

McNab-Kitsell hose coupling—open.

Coir brooms are best for decks, and long-handled *holystones* should be used on the white decks at least once a week with plenty of sand. Where plain ladders and hand rails are used, *sand* and *canvas* with plenty of *elbow grease* is all that is necessary to make the ship look like a Dutch kitchen of a Sunday morning.

Gratings should always be left in the natural wood and scrubbed with sand and canvas.

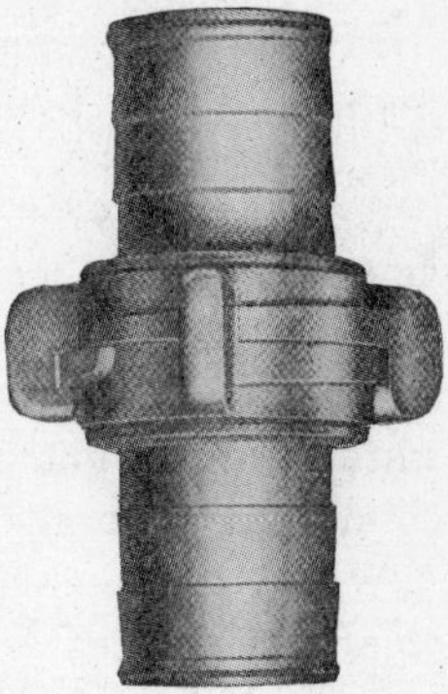

McNab-Kitsell coupling —closed.

A very handy hose coupling has been devised, doing away with threads. The coupling has no "male" or "female" parts and can be attached anywhere. This is the McNab-Kitsell coupling.

Swabs have gone out of fashion but may come back again. It is a nice sailor job to make hand and deck swabs, and all paint work and varnish work wet with salt water should be swabbed off before it dries. Only lubbers use waste for this purpose. Swabs are economical. *Waste* is well named.

Squeegees should be used on the deck before swabbing.

In many liners the promenade deck is washed down and holystoned at night, winding up at the end of the mid-watch.

Brass work is going out of fashion as an evidence of smartness. Very little goes a long way. A shiny door handle with a rim of grease about the base of it, smearing the white paint, is a left-handed sort of smartness.

The *gangway* should be washed and wiped down each morning when in port.

Wherever *canvas screens* are fitted have them *clean*, and always in good repair.

Do not attempt anything that cannot be kept up. Have everything simple but *clean*. *Wheel covers, binnacle covers, telegraph covers,* all should be kept clean, and should be scrubbed when at sea and stowed away clean and dry for use when in port.

The routine of washing down should be carefully worked out by the Chief Mate, the men told off for certain duties until the work is reduced to a system eliminating all wasted effort. Follow this principle throughout. If you save a half hour by this give it to the men to clean up for breakfast.

V

Laying Up

A modern vessel deteriorates rapidly when out of active service unless the greatest care is taken to protect all exposed metal parts, to keep water out of boats, to open up all scuppers and drains, and to keep the tanks and bilges free from stagnant water. Deck machinery is specially subject to neglect under conditions generally prevailing when a craft lies idle.

White lead and tallow, should be applied to all exposed wearing surfaces and cylinders and valves should be oiled internally before draining off steam.

Decks are liable to rapid deterioration. This is specially so of planked decks in warm weather ports. The daily wetting down is a necessity that should be provided for when a vessel is out of active service.

The safety of a vessel itself, whether at a wharf or lying in the stream, is of the greatest importance. Where craft are moored close together damage is certain to follow with heavy weather. The placing of lines and laying out of anchors under these conditions is of the utmost importance. Lines may chafe through, anchors may foul and loose their holding power.

Vessels moored in shallow water may rest on the bottom at low tide. On the face of it this may not seem harmful, but boulders have a habit of getting under ships, and vessels have been known to ride over their own or other vessel's anchors and settle down with the tide, the anchor flukes punching up against their bottom plates.

Vessels covered with salt water marine growths are best taken care of when anchored or tied up in fresh water.

The fire risk is great on idle vessels. Nothing but careful policing and constant attention to the ship by selected ship keepers can lessen this risk.

Where a vessel is laid up under proper supervision and a skeleton crew is kept at regular work, the ship may come into active service in good condition and with much valuable work done. A vessel laid up should be surveyed and a plan of maintenance work provided. This should be done each day by the stand-by crew, no matter how small. Washing, cleaning and painting should go on constantly during working hours. Night watches should be strictly kept and all lines and ground tackle tended, riding and gangway lights kept lit.

The log book should be written up each day, and signed by the responsible ship keeper. Stores received, issued and expended should be entered in the log, or stores ledger, and every detail of the business of keeping ship should be recorded.

A vessel out of service represents a heavy charge against the owners, and the owners should insist upon proper care and an authentic record of such care.

VI

The Maintenance Book

This is an important record and should remain with the ship from voyage to voyage, being turned over from one Chief Mate to another, by the Master, who should inspect it from time to time and initial his approval, or disapproval.

The Maintenance Book should be divided into the various parts of the ship.

Fore peak.
Chain locker—Ground tackle.
Forecastle under deck.
Forecastle upper deck.
No. 1 lower hold.
    lower 'tween deck.
    upper 'tween deck.

And so on, taking in the bridge deck, boats and all parts coming under the jurisdiction of the Chief Mate.

All repair work, alterations, painting, etc., should be entered with the date, the time employed, the number of men, and a brief description of what was done, material used, etc.

A separate section for dockings will, as indicated previously, be of great value later on.

The Chief Mate may tell off a smart youngster, who writes a good hand, to keep the book posted up to date, using the Boatswain's Order Book, and his own notes to compile the data. Most mates, where a Maintenance Book is kept, write it up themselves as a record of their personal care of the vessel.

The Maintenance Book should also have a column for repair notes, giving the parts in need of repair, when and how broken. This forms a constant record of repairs needed, of repairs made at sea, and of repairs made in port, or by shore labor. A wide awake owner will require an abstract from the ship's Maintenance Book to be deposited at the office after each voyage, same to be certified as correct by the Master, Chief Engineer and Chief Mate.

In closing the author wishes to leave a final word with his readers. Seamanship can only be acquired at sea. The professional seaman, after a long apprenticeship, develops a special aptitude and sea habit unknown to those who live ashore. The great size of vessels and the modern complication of their gear, calls for constant study and practice. Wherever possible practice the art of seamanship. Learn all you can and instruct others, this is specially the duty of an officer—he must be a leader and an instructor in all things pertaining to his work.

When seamanship is neglected the world at large has no great respect for seamen. Strandings, collisions, fires, foundering and numerous minor accidents leave an appalling loss of life and property in their wake. Bad luck always follows close behind the lubberly seafarer. The sooner owners, underwriters, examiners and seafaring men themselves come to realize this the better for safe and profitable commerce on the sea.

When seamanship is diligently practiced it attains its just importance, and the thorough seaman takes on a personal dignity in keeping with his great responsibilities.

INDEX.